Precalculus

MATH 1060

Ron Larson

CENGAGE
Learning·

Australia • Brazil • Japan • Korea • Mexico • Singapore • Spain • United Kingdom • United States

Precalculus: MATH 1060, Ninth Edition

Precalculus, Ninth Edition
Ron Larson

© 2014 Cengage Learning. All rights reserved.

For product information and technology assistance, contact us at
Cengage Learning Customer & Sales Support, 1-800-354-9706

For permission to use material from this text or product,
submit all requests online at **cengage.com/permissions**
Further permissions questions can be emailed to
permissionrequest@cengage.com

This book contains select works from existing Cengage Learning resources and was produced by Cengage Learning Custom Solutions for collegiate use. As such, those adopting and/or contributing to this work are responsible for editorial content accuracy, continuity and completeness.

Compilation © 2015 Cengage Learning

ISBN: 978-1-337-04825-5

WCN: 01-100-101

Cengage Learning
20 Channel Center Street
Boston, MA 02210
USA

Cengage Learning is a leading provider of customized learning solutions with office locations around the globe, including Singapore, the United Kingdom, Australia, Mexico, Brazil, and Japan. Locate your local office at:
www.international.cengage.com/region.

Cengage Learning products are represented in Canada by Nelson Education, Ltd.

For your lifelong learning solutions, visit **www.cengage.com/custom.**

Visit our corporate website at **www.cengage.com.**

Brief Contents

Chapter 1   Functions and Their Graphs 1

Chapter 2   Polynomial and Rational Functions 113

Chapter 3   Exponential and Logarithmic Functions 199

Chapter 4   Trigonometry 261

Chapter 5   Analytic Trigonometry 349

Appendix A: Review of Fundamental Concepts of Algebra A1

Answers to Odd-Numbered Exercises and Tests A75

Index A171

1 Functions and Their Graphs

1.1 Rectangular Coordinates
1.2 Graphs of Equations
1.3 Linear Equations in Two Variables
1.4 Functions
1.5 Analyzing Graphs of Functions
1.6 A Library of Parent Functions
1.7 Transformations of Functions
1.8 Combinations of Functions: Composite Functions
1.9 Inverse Functions
1.10 Mathematical Modeling and Variation

Snowstorm *(Exercise 47, page 66)*

Bacteria *(Example 8, page 80)*

Average Speed *(Example 7, page 54)*

Alternative-Fueled Vehicles
(Example 10, page 42)

Americans with Disabilities Act *(page 28)*

1

1.1   Rectangular Coordinates

The Cartesian plane can help you visualize relationships between two variables. For instance, in Exercise 37 on page 9, given how far north and west one city is from another, plotting points to represent the cities can help you visualize these distances and determine the flying distance between the cities.

- ◾ Plot points in the Cartesian plane.
- ◾ Use the Distance Formula to find the distance between two points.
- ◾ Use the Midpoint Formula to find the midpoint of a line segment.
- ◾ Use a coordinate plane to model and solve real-life problems.

The Cartesian Plane

Just as you can represent real numbers by points on a real number line, you can represent ordered pairs of real numbers by points in a plane called the **rectangular coordinate system,** or the **Cartesian plane,** named after the French mathematician René Descartes (1596–1650).

    Two real number lines intersecting at right angles form the Cartesian plane, as shown in Figure 1.1. The horizontal real number line is usually called the **x-axis,** and the vertical real number line is usually called the **y-axis.** The point of intersection of these two axes is the **origin,** and the two axes divide the plane into four parts called **quadrants.**

Figure 1.1

Figure 1.2

    Each point in the plane corresponds to an **ordered pair** (x, y) of real numbers x and y, called **coordinates** of the point. The **x-coordinate** represents the directed distance from the y-axis to the point, and the **y-coordinate** represents the directed distance from the x-axis to the point, as shown in Figure 1.2.

Directed distance from y-axis (x, y) Directed distance from x-axis

    The notation (x, y) denotes both a point in the plane and an open interval on the real number line. The context will tell you which meaning is intended.

EXAMPLE 1   **Plotting Points in the Cartesian Plane**

Plot the points $(-1, 2)$, $(3, 4)$, $(0, 0)$, $(3, 0)$, and $(-2, -3)$.

Solution   To plot the point $(-1, 2)$, imagine a vertical line through -1 on the x-axis and a horizontal line through 2 on the y-axis. The intersection of these two lines is the point $(-1, 2)$. Plot the other four points in a similar way, as shown in Figure 1.3.

Figure 1.3

✓ **Checkpoint** ◀))) Audio-video solution in English & Spanish at LarsonPrecalculus.com.

Plot the points $(-3, 2)$, $(4, -2)$, $(3, 1)$, $(0, -2)$, and $(-1, -2)$.

The beauty of a rectangular coordinate system is that it allows you to *see* relationships between two variables. It would be difficult to overestimate the importance of Descartes's introduction of coordinates in the plane. Today, his ideas are in common use in virtually every scientific and business-related field.

EXAMPLE 2   **Sketching a Scatter Plot**

The table shows the numbers N (in millions) of subscribers to a cellular telecommunication service in the United States from 2001 through 2010, where t represents the year. Sketch a scatter plot of the data.   *(Source: CTIA-The Wireless Association)*

Solution   To sketch a *scatter plot* of the data shown in the table, represent each pair of values by an ordered pair (t, N) and plot the resulting points, as shown below. For instance, the ordered pair (2001, 128.4) represents the first pair of values. Note that the break in the t-axis indicates omission of the years before 2001.

Year, t	Subscribers, N
2001	128.4
2002	140.8
2003	158.7
2004	182.1
2005	207.9
2006	233.0
2007	255.4
2008	270.3
2009	290.9
2010	311.0

DATA — Spreadsheet at LarsonPrecalculus.com

Subscribers to a Cellular Telecommunication Service

Checkpoint ◄))) *Audio-video solution in English & Spanish at LarsonPrecalculus.com.*

The table shows the numbers N (in thousands) of cellular telecommunication service employees in the United States from 2001 through 2010, where t represents the year. Sketch a scatter plot of the data.   *(Source: CTIA-The Wireless Association)*

t	N
2001	203.6
2002	192.4
2003	205.6
2004	226.0
2005	233.1
2006	253.8
2007	266.8
2008	268.5
2009	249.2
2010	250.4

DATA — Spreadsheet at LarsonPrecalculus.com

▷ **TECHNOLOGY** The scatter plot in Example 2 is only one way to represent the data graphically. You could also represent the data using a bar graph or a line graph. Try using a graphing utility to represent the data given in Example 2 graphically.

In Example 2, you could have let $t = 1$ represent the year 2001. In that case, there would not have been a break in the horizontal axis, and the labels 1 through 10 (instead of 2001 through 2010) would have been on the tick marks.

The Pythagorean Theorem and the Distance Formula

The following famous theorem is used extensively throughout this course.

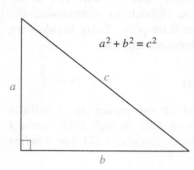

$$a^2 + b^2 = c^2$$

Figure 1.4

> ### Pythagorean Theorem
>
> For a right triangle with hypotenuse of length c and sides of lengths a and b, you have $a^2 + b^2 = c^2$, as shown in Figure 1.4. (The converse is also true. That is, if $a^2 + b^2 = c^2$, then the triangle is a right triangle.)

Suppose you want to determine the distance d between two points (x_1, y_1) and (x_2, y_2) in the plane. These two points can form a right triangle, as shown in Figure 1.5. The length of the vertical side of the triangle is $|y_2 - y_1|$ and the length of the horizontal side is $|x_2 - x_1|$.

By the Pythagorean Theorem,

$$d^2 = |x_2 - x_1|^2 + |y_2 - y_1|^2$$
$$d = \sqrt{|x_2 - x_1|^2 + |y_2 - y_1|^2} = \sqrt{(x_2 - x_1)^2 + (y_2 - y_1)^2}.$$

This result is the **Distance Formula.**

Figure 1.5

> ### The Distance Formula
>
> The distance d between the points (x_1, y_1) and (x_2, y_2) in the plane is
> $$d = \sqrt{(x_2 - x_1)^2 + (y_2 - y_1)^2}.$$

EXAMPLE 3   **Finding a Distance**

Find the distance between the points $(-2, 1)$ and $(3, 4)$.

Algebraic Solution

Let
$$(x_1, y_1) = (-2, 1) \quad \text{and} \quad (x_2, y_2) = (3, 4).$$

Then apply the Distance Formula.

$$d = \sqrt{(x_2 - x_1)^2 + (y_2 - y_1)^2} \quad \text{Distance Formula}$$
$$= \sqrt{[3 - (-2)]^2 + (4 - 1)^2} \quad \text{Substitute for } x_1, y_1, x_2, \text{ and } y_2.$$
$$= \sqrt{(5)^2 + (3)^2} \quad \text{Simplify.}$$
$$= \sqrt{34} \quad \text{Simplify.}$$
$$\approx 5.83 \quad \text{Use a calculator.}$$

So, the distance between the points is about 5.83 units. Use the Pythagorean Theorem to check that the distance is correct.

$$d^2 \stackrel{?}{=} 5^2 + 3^2 \quad \text{Pythagorean Theorem}$$
$$\left(\sqrt{34}\right)^2 \stackrel{?}{=} 5^2 + 3^2 \quad \text{Substitute for } d.$$
$$34 = 34 \quad \text{Distance checks. } \checkmark$$

Graphical Solution

Use centimeter graph paper to plot the points $A(-2, 1)$ and $B(3, 4)$. Carefully sketch the line segment from A to B. Then use a centimeter ruler to measure the length of the segment.

The line segment measures about 5.8 centimeters. So, the distance between the points is about 5.8 units.

✓ **Checkpoint** ◀))) Audio-video solution in English & Spanish at LarsonPrecalculus.com.

Find the distance between the points $(3, 1)$ and $(-3, 0)$.

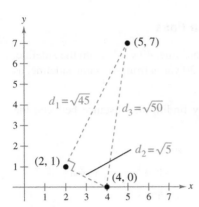

Figure 1.6

▷ **ALGEBRA HELP**   You
can review the techniques
for evaluating a radical in
Appendix A.2.

EXAMPLE 4   **Verifying a Right Triangle**

Show that the points

$$(2, 1), \quad (4, 0), \quad \text{and} \quad (5, 7)$$

are vertices of a right triangle.

Solution   The three points are plotted in Figure 1.6. Using the Distance Formula, the lengths of the three sides are as follows.

$$d_1 = \sqrt{(5 - 2)^2 + (7 - 1)^2} = \sqrt{9 + 36} = \sqrt{45}$$

$$d_2 = \sqrt{(4 - 2)^2 + (0 - 1)^2} = \sqrt{4 + 1} = \sqrt{5}$$

$$d_3 = \sqrt{(5 - 4)^2 + (7 - 0)^2} = \sqrt{1 + 49} = \sqrt{50}$$

Because $(d_1)^2 + (d_2)^2 = 45 + 5 = 50 = (d_3)^2$, you can conclude by the Pythagorean Theorem that the triangle must be a right triangle.

✓ *Checkpoint* *Audio-video solution in English & Spanish at LarsonPrecalculus.com.*

Show that the points $(2, -1)$, $(5, 5)$, and $(6, -3)$ are vertices of a right triangle.

The Midpoint Formula

To find the **midpoint** of the line segment that joins two points in a coordinate plane, you can find the average values of the respective coordinates of the two endpoints using the **Midpoint Formula.**

The Midpoint Formula

The midpoint of the line segment joining the points (x_1, y_1) and (x_2, y_2) is given by the Midpoint Formula

$$\text{Midpoint} = \left(\frac{x_1 + x_2}{2}, \frac{y_1 + y_2}{2} \right).$$

For a proof of the Midpoint Formula, see Proofs in Mathematics on page 110.

EXAMPLE 5   **Finding a Line Segment's Midpoint**

Find the midpoint of the line segment joining the points

$$(-5, -3) \quad \text{and} \quad (9, 3).$$

Solution   Let $(x_1, y_1) = (-5, -3)$ and $(x_2, y_2) = (9, 3)$.

$$\text{Midpoint} = \left(\frac{x_1 + x_2}{2}, \frac{y_1 + y_2}{2} \right) \qquad \text{Midpoint Formula}$$

$$= \left(\frac{-5 + 9}{2}, \frac{-3 + 3}{2} \right) \qquad \text{Substitute for } x_1, y_1, x_2, \text{ and } y_2.$$

$$= (2, 0) \qquad \text{Simplify.}$$

The midpoint of the line segment is $(2, 0)$, as shown in Figure 1.7.

Figure 1.7

✓ *Checkpoint* *Audio-video solution in English & Spanish at LarsonPrecalculus.com.*

Find the midpoint of the line segment joining the points $(-2, 8)$ and $(4, -10)$.

Applications

EXAMPLE 6   **Finding the Length of a Pass**

A football quarterback throws a pass from the 28-yard line, 40 yards from the sideline. A wide receiver catches the pass on the 5-yard line, 20 yards from the same sideline, as shown in Figure 1.8. How long is the pass?

Solution   You can find the length of the pass by finding the distance between the points $(40, 28)$ and $(20, 5)$.

$$d = \sqrt{(x_2 - x_1)^2 + (y_2 - y_1)^2} \qquad \text{Distance Formula}$$
$$= \sqrt{(40 - 20)^2 + (28 - 5)^2} \qquad \text{Substitute for } x_1, y_1, x_2, \text{ and } y_2.$$
$$= \sqrt{20^2 + 23^2} \qquad \text{Simplify.}$$
$$= \sqrt{400 + 529} \qquad \text{Simplify.}$$
$$= \sqrt{929} \qquad \text{Simplify.}$$
$$\approx 30 \qquad \text{Use a calculator.}$$

So, the pass is about 30 yards long.

✓ **Checkpoint** ◄))) *Audio-video solution in English & Spanish at LarsonPrecalculus.com.*

A football quarterback throws a pass from the 10-yard line, 10 yards from the sideline. A wide receiver catches the pass on the 32-yard line, 25 yards from the same sideline. How long is the pass?

In Example 6, the scale along the goal line does not normally appear on a football field. However, when you use coordinate geometry to solve real-life problems, you are free to place the coordinate system in any way that is convenient for the solution of the problem.

EXAMPLE 7   **Estimating Annual Sales**

Starbucks Corporation had annual sales of approximately $9.8 billion in 2009 and $11.7 billion in 2011. Without knowing any additional information, what would you estimate the 2010 sales to have been?   *(Source: Starbucks Corporation)*

Solution   One solution to the problem is to assume that sales followed a linear pattern. With this assumption, you can estimate the 2010 sales by finding the midpoint of the line segment connecting the points $(2009, 9.8)$ and $(2011, 11.7)$.

$$\text{Midpoint} = \left(\frac{x_1 + x_2}{2}, \frac{y_1 + y_2}{2}\right) \qquad \text{Midpoint Formula}$$
$$= \left(\frac{2009 + 2011}{2}, \frac{9.8 + 11.7}{2}\right) \qquad \text{Substitute for } x_1, x_2, y_1, \text{ and } y_2.$$
$$= (2010, 10.75) \qquad \text{Simplify.}$$

So, you would estimate the 2010 sales to have been about $10.75 billion, as shown in Figure 1.9. (The actual 2010 sales were about $10.71 billion.)

✓ **Checkpoint** ◄))) *Audio-video solution in English & Spanish at LarsonPrecalculus.com.*

Yahoo! Inc. had annual revenues of approximately $7.2 billon in 2008 and $6.3 billion in 2010. Without knowing any additional information, what would you estimate the 2009 revenue to have been?   *(Source: Yahoo! Inc.)*

Football Pass

Figure 1.8

Starbucks Corporation Sales

Figure 1.9

Much of computer graphics, including this computer-generated tessellation, consists of transformations of points in a coordinate plane. Example 8 illustrates one type of transformation called a translation. Other types include reflections, rotations, and stretches.

EXAMPLE 8   **Translating Points in the Plane**

The triangle in Figure 1.10 has vertices at the points $(-1, 2)$, $(1, -4)$, and $(2, 3)$. Shift the triangle three units to the right and two units up and find the vertices of the shifted triangle, as shown in Figure 1.11.

Figure 1.10

Figure 1.11

Solution   To shift the vertices three units to the right, add 3 to each of the x-coordinates. To shift the vertices two units up, add 2 to each of the y-coordinates.

Original Point	Translated Point
$(-1, 2)$	$(-1 + 3, 2 + 2) = (2, 4)$
$(1, -4)$	$(1 + 3, -4 + 2) = (4, -2)$
$(2, 3)$	$(2 + 3, 3 + 2) = (5, 5)$

✓ *Checkpoint* *Audio-video solution in English & Spanish at LarsonPrecalculus.com.*

Find the vertices of the parallelogram shown after translating it two units to the left and four units down.

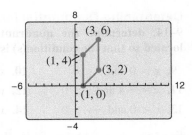

The figures in Example 8 were not really essential to the solution. Nevertheless, it is strongly recommended that you develop the habit of including sketches with your solutions—even when they are not required.

Summarize   (Section 1.1)

1. Describe the Cartesian plane *(page 2)*. For an example of plotting points in the Cartesian plane, see Example 1.

2. State the Distance Formula *(page 4)*. For examples of using the Distance Formula to find the distance between two points, see Examples 3 and 4.

3. State the Midpoint Formula *(page 5)*. For an example of using the Midpoint Formula to find the midpoint of a line segment, see Example 5.

4. Describe examples of how to use a coordinate plane to model and solve real-life problems *(pages 6 and 7, Examples 6–8)*.

1.1   Exercises

See CalcChat.com for tutorial help and worked-out solutions to odd-numbered exercises.

Vocabulary: Fill in the blanks.

1. An ordered pair of real numbers can be represented in a plane called the rectangular coordinate system or the _____ plane.
2. The point of intersection of the *x*- and *y*-axes is the _____, and the two axes divide the coordinate plane into four parts called _____.
3. The _____ _____ is a result derived from the Pythagorean Theorem.
4. Finding the average values of the representative coordinates of the two endpoints of a line segment in a coordinate plane is also known as using the _____ _____.

Skills and Applications

Plotting Points in the Cartesian Plane In Exercises 5 and 6, plot the points in the Cartesian plane.

5. $(-4, 2), (-3, -6), (0, 5), (1, -4), (0, 0), (3, 1)$
6. $\left(1, -\frac{1}{3}\right), (0.5, -1), \left(\frac{3}{7}, 3\right), \left(-\frac{4}{3}, -\frac{3}{7}\right), (-2, 2.5)$

Finding the Coordinates of a Point In Exercises 7 and 8, find the coordinates of the point.

7. The point is located three units to the left of the *y*-axis and four units above the *x*-axis.
8. The point is on the *x*-axis and 12 units to the left of the *y*-axis.

Determining Quadrant(s) for a Point In Exercises 9–14, determine the quadrant(s) in which (x, y) is located so that the condition(s) is (are) satisfied.

9. $x > 0$ and $y < 0$
10. $x < 0$ and $y < 0$
11. $x = -4$ and $y > 0$
12. $y < -5$
13. $x < 0$ and $-y > 0$
14. $xy > 0$

Sketching a Scatter Plot In Exercises 15 and 16, sketch a scatter plot of the data shown in the table.

15. The table shows the number *y* of Wal-Mart stores for each year *x* from 2003 through 2010. *(Source: Wal-Mart Stores, Inc.)*

DATA	Year, x	Number of Stores, y
	2003	4906
	2004	5289
	2005	6141
	2006	6779
	2007	7262
	2008	7720
	2009	8416
	2010	8970

Spreadsheet at LarsonPrecalculus.com

16. The table shows the lowest temperature on record *y* (in degrees Fahrenheit) in Duluth, Minnesota, for each month *x*, where *x* = 1 represents January. *(Source: NOAA)*

DATA	Month, x	Temperature, y
	1	−39
	2	−39
	3	−29
	4	−5
	5	17
	6	27
	7	35
	8	32
	9	22
	10	8
	11	−23
	12	−34

Spreadsheet at LarsonPrecalculus.com

Finding a Distance In Exercises 17–22, find the distance between the points.

17. $(-2, 6), (3, -6)$
18. $(8, 5), (0, 20)$
19. $(1, 4), (-5, -1)$
20. $(1, 3), (3, -2)$
21. $\left(\frac{1}{2}, \frac{4}{3}\right), (2, -1)$
22. $(9.5, -2.6), (-3.9, 8.2)$

Verifying a Right Triangle In Exercises 23 and 24, (a) find the length of each side of the right triangle, and (b) show that these lengths satisfy the Pythagorean Theorem.

23.

24.

Verifying a Polygon In Exercises 25–28, show that the points form the vertices of the indicated polygon.

25. Right triangle: $(4, 0), (2, 1), (-1, -5)$
26. Right triangle: $(-1, 3), (3, 5), (5, 1)$
27. Isosceles triangle: $(1, -3), (3, 2), (-2, 4)$
28. Isosceles triangle: $(2, 3), (4, 9), (-2, 7)$

Plotting, Distance, and Midpoint In Exercises 29–36, (a) plot the points, (b) find the distance between the points, and (c) find the midpoint of the line segment joining the points.

29. $(6, -3), (6, 5)$
30. $(1, 4), (8, 4)$
31. $(1, 1), (9, 7)$
32. $(1, 12), (6, 0)$
33. $(-1, 2), (5, 4)$
34. $(2, 10), (10, 2)$
35. $(-16.8, 12.3), (5.6, 4.9)$
36. $\left(\frac{1}{2}, 1\right), \left(-\frac{5}{2}, \frac{4}{3}\right)$

37. Flying Distance

An airplane flies from Naples, Italy, in a straight line to Rome, Italy, which is 120 kilometers north and 150 kilometers west of Naples. How far does the plane fly?

38. Sports A soccer player passes the ball from a point that is 18 yards from the endline and 12 yards from the sideline. A teammate who is 42 yards from the same endline and 50 yards from the same sideline receives the pass. (See figure.) How long is the pass?

39. Sales The Coca-Cola Company had sales of $19,564 million in 2002 and $35,123 million in 2010. Use the Midpoint Formula to estimate the sales in 2006. Assume that the sales followed a linear pattern. *(Source: The Coca-Cola Company)*

40. Earnings per Share The earnings per share for Big Lots, Inc. were $1.89 in 2008 and $2.83 in 2010. Use the Midpoint Formula to estimate the earnings per share in 2009. Assume that the earnings per share followed a linear pattern. *(Source: Big Lots, Inc.)*

Translating Points in the Plane In Exercises 41–44, find the coordinates of the vertices of the polygon after the indicated translation to a new position in the plane.

41.

42.

43. Original coordinates of vertices: $(-7, -2), (-2, 2),$ $(-2, -4), (-7, -4)$

   Shift: eight units up, four units to the right

44. Original coordinates of vertices: $(5, 8), (3, 6), (7, 6)$

   Shift: 6 units down, 10 units to the left

45. Minimum Wage Use the graph below, which shows the minimum wages in the United States (in dollars) from 1950 through 2011. *(Source: U.S. Department of Labor)*

(a) Which decade shows the greatest increase in minimum wage?

(b) Approximate the percent increases in the minimum wage from 1990 to 1995 and from 1995 to 2011.

(c) Use the percent increase from 1995 to 2011 to predict the minimum wage in 2016.

(d) Do you believe that your prediction in part (c) is reasonable? Explain.

46. Data Analysis: Exam Scores The table shows the mathematics entrance test scores x and the final examination scores y in an algebra course for a sample of 10 students.

x	22	29	35	40	44	48	53	58	65	76
y	53	74	57	66	79	90	76	93	83	99

(a) Sketch a scatter plot of the data.

(b) Find the entrance test score of any student with a final exam score in the 80s.

(c) Does a higher entrance test score imply a higher final exam score? Explain.

Exploration

47. Using the Midpoint Formula   A line segment has (x_1, y_1) as one endpoint and (x_m, y_m) as its midpoint. Find the other endpoint (x_2, y_2) of the line segment in terms of x_1, y_1, x_m, and y_m.

48. Using the Midpoint Formula   Use the result of Exercise 47 to find the coordinates of the endpoint of a line segment when the coordinates of the other endpoint and midpoint are, respectively,

(a) $(1, -2), (4, -1)$ and (b) $(-5, 11), (2, 4)$.

49. Using the Midpoint Formula   Use the Midpoint Formula three times to find the three points that divide the line segment joining (x_1, y_1) and (x_2, y_2) into four parts.

50. Using the Midpoint Formula   Use the result of Exercise 49 to find the points that divide the line segment joining the given points into four equal parts.

(a) $(1, -2), (4, -1)$ (b) $(-2, -3), (0, 0)$

51. Make a Conjecture   Plot the points $(2, 1)$, $(-3, 5)$, and $(7, -3)$ on a rectangular coordinate system. Then change the signs of the indicated coordinates of each point and plot the three new points on the same rectangular coordinate system. Make a conjecture about the location of a point when each of the following occurs.

(a) The sign of the x-coordinate is changed.

(b) The sign of the y-coordinate is changed.

(c) The signs of both the x- and y-coordinates are changed.

52. Collinear Points   Three or more points are *collinear* when they all lie on the same line. Use the steps following to determine whether the set of points $\{A(2, 3), B(2, 6), C(6, 3)\}$ and the set of points $\{A(8, 3), B(5, 2), C(2, 1)\}$ are collinear.

(a) For each set of points, use the Distance Formula to find the distances from A to B, from B to C, and from A to C. What relationship exists among these distances for each set of points?

(b) Plot each set of points in the Cartesian plane. Do all the points of either set appear to lie on the same line?

(c) Compare your conclusions from part (a) with the conclusions you made from the graphs in part (b). Make a general statement about how to use the Distance Formula to determine collinearity.

53. Think About It   When plotting points on the rectangular coordinate system, is it true that the scales on the x- and y-axes must be the same? Explain.

54. Think About It   What is the y-coordinate of any point on the x-axis? What is the x-coordinate of any point on the y-axis?

True or False?   **In Exercises 55–57, determine whether the statement is true or false. Justify your answer.**

55. In order to divide a line segment into 16 equal parts, you would have to use the Midpoint Formula 16 times.

56. The points $(-8, 4)$, $(2, 11)$, and $(-5, 1)$ represent the vertices of an isosceles triangle.

57. If four points represent the vertices of a polygon, and the four sides are equal, then the polygon must be a square.

58. HOW DO YOU SEE IT?   Use the plot of the point (x_0, y_0) in the figure. Match the transformation of the point with the correct plot. Explain your reasoning. [The plots are labeled (i), (ii), (iii), and (iv).]

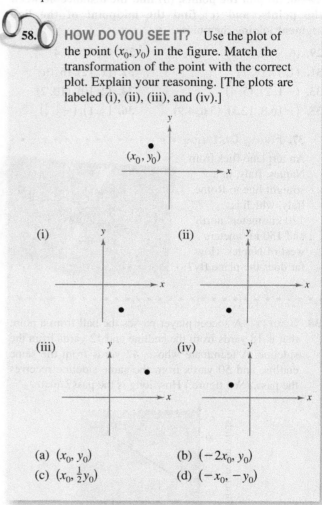

(a) (x_0, y_0) (b) $(-2x_0, y_0)$

(c) $(x_0, \frac{1}{2}y_0)$ (d) $(-x_0, -y_0)$

59. Proof   Prove that the diagonals of the parallelogram in the figure intersect at their midpoints.

1.2 Graphs of Equations

- Sketch graphs of equations.
- Identify *x*- and *y*-intercepts of graphs of equations.
- Use symmetry to sketch graphs of equations.
- Write equations of and sketch graphs of circles.
- Use graphs of equations in solving real-life problems.

The Graph of an Equation

In Section 1.1, you used a coordinate system to graphically represent the relationship between two quantities. There, the graphical picture consisted of a collection of points in a coordinate plane.

Frequently, a relationship between two quantities is expressed as an **equation in two variables.** For instance, $y = 7 - 3x$ is an equation in x and y. An ordered pair (a, b) is a **solution** or **solution point** of an equation in x and y when the substitutions $x = a$ and $y = b$ result in a true statement. For instance, $(1, 4)$ is a solution of $y = 7 - 3x$ because $4 = 7 - 3(1)$ is a true statement.

In this section, you will review some basic procedures for sketching the graph of an equation in two variables. The **graph of an equation** is the set of all points that are solutions of the equation.

The graph of an equation can help you see relationships between real-life quantities. For example, in Exercise 87 on page 21, you will use a graph to predict the life expectancy of a child born in 2015.

▷ **ALGEBRA HELP** When evaluating an expression or an equation, remember to follow the Basic Rules of Algebra. To review these rules, see Appendix A.1.

EXAMPLE 1 Determining Solution Points

Determine whether (a) $(2, 13)$ and (b) $(-1, -3)$ lie on the graph of $y = 10x - 7$.

Solution

a.

$y = 10x - 7$ Write original equation.

$13 \overset{?}{=} 10(2) - 7$ Substitute 2 for x and 13 for y.

$13 = 13$ $(2, 13)$ is a solution. ✔

The point $(2, 13)$ *does* lie on the graph of $y = 10x - 7$ because it is a solution point of the equation.

b.

$y = 10x - 7$ Write original equation.

$-3 \overset{?}{=} 10(-1) - 7$ Substitute -1 for x and -3 for y.

$-3 \neq -17$ $(-1, -3)$ is not a solution.

The point $(-1, -3)$ *does not* lie on the graph of $y = 10x - 7$ because it is *not* a solution point of the equation.

✔ **Checkpoint** 🔊))) *Audio-video solution in English & Spanish at LarsonPrecalculus.com.*

Determine whether (a) $(3, -5)$ and (b) $(-2, 26)$ lie on the graph of $y = 14 - 6x$. ■

The basic technique used for sketching the graph of an equation is the **point-plotting method.**

The Point-Plotting Method of Graphing

1. When possible, isolate one of the variables.
2. Construct a table of values showing several solution points.
3. Plot these points in a rectangular coordinate system.
4. Connect the points with a smooth curve or line.

It is important to use negative values, zero, and positive values for x when constructing a table.

EXAMPLE 2   Sketching the Graph of an Equation

Sketch the graph of

$y = -3x + 7.$

Solution

Because the equation is already solved for y, construct a table of values that consists of several solution points of the equation. For instance, when $x = -1$,

$y = -3(-1) + 7$

$\quad = 10$

which implies that

$(-1, 10)$

is a solution point of the equation.

x	$y = -3x + 7$	(x, y)
-1	10	$(-1, 10)$
0	7	$(0, 7)$
1	4	$(1, 4)$
2	1	$(2, 1)$
3	-2	$(3, -2)$
4	-5	$(4, -5)$

From the table, it follows that

$(-1, 10), (0, 7), (1, 4), (2, 1), (3, -2), \quad$ and $\quad (4, -5)$

are solution points of the equation. After plotting these points and connecting them, you can see that they appear to lie on a line, as shown below.

✓ *Checkpoint* ◀))) *Audio-video solution in English & Spanish at LarsonPrecalculus.com.*

Sketch the graph of each equation.

a. $y = -3x + 2$

b. $y = 2x + 1$

EXAMPLE 3   **Sketching the Graph of an Equation**

Sketch the graph of

$$y = x^2 - 2.$$

Solution

Because the equation is already solved for y, begin by constructing a table of values.

x	-2	-1	0	1	2	3
$y = x^2 - 2$	2	-1	-2	-1	2	7
(x, y)	$(-2, 2)$	$(-1, -1)$	$(0, -2)$	$(1, -1)$	$(2, 2)$	$(3, 7)$

> **• • REMARK** One of your goals
> in this course is to learn to
> classify the basic shape of a
> graph from its equation. For
> instance, you will learn that the
> *linear equation* in Example 2
> has the form
>
> $$y = mx + b$$
>
> and its graph is a line. Similarly,
> the *quadratic equation* in
> Example 3 has the form
>
> $$y = ax^2 + bx + c$$
>
> and its graph is a parabola.

Next, plot the points given in the table, as shown in Figure 1.12. Finally, connect the points with a smooth curve, as shown in Figure 1.13.

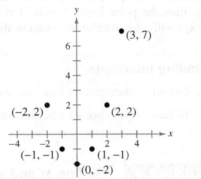

Figure 1.12   **Figure 1.13**

✓ *Checkpoint* ◄))) *Audio-video solution in English & Spanish at LarsonPrecalculus.com.*

Sketch the graph of each equation.

a. $y = x^2 + 3$

b. $y = 1 - x^2$

The point-plotting method demonstrated in Examples 2 and 3 is easy to use, but it has some shortcomings. With too few solution points, you can misrepresent the graph of an equation. For instance, when you only plot the four points

$$(-2, 2), (-1, -1), (1, -1), \quad \text{and} \quad (2, 2)$$

in Figure 1.12, any one of the three graphs below is reasonable.

No x-intercepts; one y-intercept

Three x-intercepts; one y-intercept

One x-intercept; two y-intercepts

No intercepts
Figure 1.14

▷TECHNOLOGY To graph an equation involving x and y on a graphing utility, use the following procedure.

1. Rewrite the equation so that y is isolated on the left side.

2. Enter the equation into the graphing utility.

3. Determine a *viewing window* that shows all important features of the graph.

4. Graph the equation.

Intercepts of a Graph

It is often easy to determine the solution points that have zero as either the x-coordinate or the y-coordinate. These points are called **intercepts** because they are the points at which the graph intersects or touches the x- or y-axis. It is possible for a graph to have no intercepts, one intercept, or several intercepts, as shown in Figure 1.14.

Note that an x-intercept can be written as the ordered pair $(a, 0)$ and a y-intercept can be written as the ordered pair $(0, b)$. Some texts denote the x-intercept as the x-coordinate of the point $(a, 0)$ [and the y-intercept as the y-coordinate of the point $(0, b)$] rather than the point itself. Unless it is necessary to make a distinction, the term *intercept* will refer to either the point or the coordinate.

Finding Intercepts

1. To find x-intercepts, let y be zero and solve the equation for x.

2. To find y-intercepts, let x be zero and solve the equation for y.

EXAMPLE 4   **Finding *x*- and *y*-Intercepts**

To find the x-intercepts of the graph of $y = x^3 - 4x$, let $y = 0$. Then $0 = x^3 - 4x = x(x^2 - 4)$ has solutions $x = 0$ and $x = \pm 2$.

x-intercepts: $(0, 0), (2, 0), (-2, 0)$ See figure.

To find the y-intercept of the graph of $y = x^3 - 4x$, let $x = 0$. Then $y = (0)^3 - 4(0)$ has one solution, $y = 0$.

y-intercept: $(0, 0)$ See figure.

✓ *Checkpoint* ◀))) *Audio-video solution in English & Spanish at LarsonPrecalculus.com.*

Find the x- and y-intercepts of the graph of $y = -x^2 - 5x$ shown in the figure below.

Symmetry

Graphs of equations can have **symmetry** with respect to one of the coordinate axes or with respect to the origin. Symmetry with respect to the x-axis means that when the Cartesian plane is folded along the x-axis, the portion of the graph above the x-axis coincides with the portion below the x-axis. Symmetry with respect to the y-axis or the origin can be described in a similar manner, as shown below.

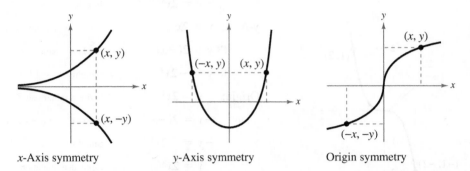

x-Axis symmetry y-Axis symmetry   Origin symmetry

Knowing the symmetry of a graph *before* attempting to sketch it is helpful, because then you need only half as many solution points to sketch the graph. There are three basic types of symmetry, described as follows.

Graphical Tests for Symmetry

1. A graph is **symmetric with respect to the x-axis** if, whenever (x, y) is on the graph, $(x, -y)$ is also on the graph.

2. A graph is **symmetric with respect to the y-axis** if, whenever (x, y) is on the graph, $(-x, y)$ is also on the graph.

3. A graph is **symmetric with respect to the origin** if, whenever (x, y) is on the graph, $(-x, -y)$ is also on the graph.

You can conclude that the graph of $y = x^2 - 2$ is symmetric with respect to the y-axis because the point $(-x, y)$ is also on the graph of $y = x^2 - 2$. (See the table below and Figure 1.15.)

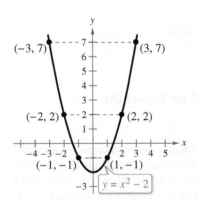

y-Axis symmetry
Figure 1.15

x	-3	-2	-1	1	2	3
y	7	2	-1	-1	2	7
(x, y)	$(-3, 7)$	$(-2, 2)$	$(-1, -1)$	$(1, -1)$	$(2, 2)$	$(3, 7)$

Algebraic Tests for Symmetry

1. The graph of an equation is symmetric with respect to the x-axis when replacing y with $-y$ yields an equivalent equation.

2. The graph of an equation is symmetric with respect to the y-axis when replacing x with $-x$ yields an equivalent equation.

3. The graph of an equation is symmetric with respect to the origin when replacing x with $-x$ and y with $-y$ yields an equivalent equation.

EXAMPLE 5 **Testing for Symmetry**

Test $y = 2x^3$ for symmetry with respect to both axes and the origin.

Solution

x-Axis: $y = 2x^3$ Write original equation.

$-y = 2x^3$ Replace y with $-y$. Result is *not* an equivalent equation.

y-Axis: $y = 2x^3$ Write original equation.

$y = 2(-x)^3$ Replace x with $-x$.

$y = -2x^3$ Simplify. Result is *not* an equivalent equation.

Origin: $y = 2x^3$ Write original equation.

$-y = 2(-x)^3$ Replace y with $-y$ and x with $-x$.

$-y = -2x^3$ Simplify.

$y = 2x^3$ Equivalent equation

Of the three tests for symmetry, the only one that is satisfied is the test for origin symmetry (see Figure 1.16).

Figure 1.16

✓ *Checkpoint* *Audio-video solution in English & Spanish at LarsonPrecalculus.com.*

Test $y^2 = 6 - x$ for symmetry with respect to both axes and the origin.

EXAMPLE 6   **Using Symmetry as a Sketching Aid**

Use symmetry to sketch the graph of $x - y^2 = 1$.

Solution   Of the three tests for symmetry, the only one that is satisfied is the test for x-axis symmetry because $x - (-y)^2 = 1$ is equivalent to $x - y^2 = 1$. So, the graph is symmetric with respect to the x-axis. Using symmetry, you only need to find the solution points above the x-axis and then reflect them to obtain the graph, as shown in Figure 1.17.

Figure 1.17

✓ *Checkpoint* *Audio-video solution in English & Spanish at LarsonPrecalculus.com.*

Use symmetry to sketch the graph of $y = x^2 - 4$.

▷ **ALGEBRA HELP** In Example 7, $|x - 1|$ is an absolute value expression. You can review the techniques for evaluating an absolute value expression in Appendix A.1.

EXAMPLE 7   **Sketching the Graph of an Equation**

Sketch the graph of $y = |x - 1|$.

Solution   This equation fails all three tests for symmetry, and consequently its graph is not symmetric with respect to either axis or to the origin. The absolute value bars indicate that y is always nonnegative. Construct a table of values. Then plot and connect the points, as shown in Figure 1.18. From the table, you can see that $x = 0$ when $y = 1$. So, the y-intercept is $(0, 1)$. Similarly, $y = 0$ when $x = 1$. So, the x-intercept is $(1, 0)$.

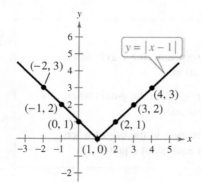

Figure 1.18

x	-2	-1	0	1	2	3	4
$y = |x - 1|$	3	2	1	0	1	2	3
(x, y)	$(-2, 3)$	$(-1, 2)$	$(0, 1)$	$(1, 0)$	$(2, 1)$	$(3, 2)$	$(4, 3)$

✓ *Checkpoint* *Audio-video solution in English & Spanish at LarsonPrecalculus.com.*

Sketch the graph of $y = |x - 2|$.

Circles

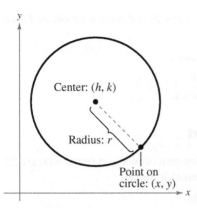

Figure 1.19

Throughout this course, you will learn to recognize several types of graphs from their equations. For instance, you will learn to recognize that the graph of a second-degree equation of the form

$$y = ax^2 + bx + c$$

is a parabola (see Example 3). The graph of a **circle** is also easy to recognize.

Consider the circle shown in Figure 1.19. A point (x, y) lies on the circle if and only if its distance from the center (h, k) is r. By the Distance Formula,

$$\sqrt{(x - h)^2 + (y - k)^2} = r.$$

By squaring each side of this equation, you obtain the **standard form of the equation of a circle.** For example, a circle with its center at $(h, k) = (1, 3)$ and radius $r = 4$ is given by

$$\sqrt{(x - 1)^2 + (y - 3)^2} = 4 \qquad \text{Substitute for } h, k, \text{ and } r.$$
$$(x - 1)^2 + (y - 3)^2 = 16. \qquad \text{Square each side.}$$

Standard Form of the Equation of a Circle

A point (x, y) lies on the circle of **radius** r and **center** (h, k) if and only if

$$(x - h)^2 + (y - k)^2 = r^2.$$

> **REMARK** Be careful when you are finding h and k from the standard form of the equation of a circle. For instance, to find h and k from the equation of the circle in Example 8, rewrite the quantities $(x + 1)^2$ and $(y - 2)^2$ using subtraction.
>
> $$(x + 1)^2 = [x - (-1)]^2,$$
> $$(y - 2)^2 = [y - (2)]^2$$
>
> So, $h = -1$ and $k = 2$.

From this result, you can see that the standard form of the equation of a circle *with its center at the origin*, $(h, k) = (0, 0)$, is simply

$$x^2 + y^2 = r^2. \qquad \text{Circle with center at origin}$$

EXAMPLE 8 Writing the Equation of a Circle

The point $(3, 4)$ lies on a circle whose center is at $(-1, 2)$, as shown in Figure 1.20. Write the standard form of the equation of this circle.

Solution

The radius of the circle is the distance between $(-1, 2)$ and $(3, 4)$.

$$r = \sqrt{(x - h)^2 + (y - k)^2} \qquad \text{Distance Formula}$$
$$= \sqrt{[3 - (-1)]^2 + (4 - 2)^2} \qquad \text{Substitute for } x, y, h, \text{ and } k.$$
$$= \sqrt{4^2 + 2^2} \qquad \text{Simplify.}$$
$$= \sqrt{16 + 4} \qquad \text{Simplify.}$$
$$= \sqrt{20} \qquad \text{Radius}$$

Using $(h, k) = (-1, 2)$ and $r = \sqrt{20}$, the equation of the circle is

$$(x - h)^2 + (y - k)^2 = r^2 \qquad \text{Equation of circle}$$
$$[x - (-1)]^2 + (y - 2)^2 = \left(\sqrt{20}\right)^2 \qquad \text{Substitute for } h, k, \text{ and } r.$$
$$(x + 1)^2 + (y - 2)^2 = 20. \qquad \text{Standard form}$$

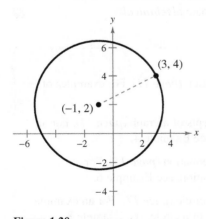

Figure 1.20

✓ **Checkpoint** 🔊 Audio-video solution in English & Spanish at LarsonPrecalculus.com.

The point $(1, -2)$ lies on a circle whose center is at $(-3, -5)$. Write the standard form of the equation of this circle.

Application

In this course, you will learn that there are many ways to approach a problem. Three common approaches are illustrated in Example 9.

A Numerical Approach: Construct and use a table.

A Graphical Approach: Draw and use a graph.

An Algebraic Approach: Use the rules of algebra.

EXAMPLE 9   **Recommended Weight**

The median recommended weights y (in pounds) for men of medium frame who are 25 to 59 years old can be approximated by the mathematical model

$$y = 0.073x^2 - 6.99x + 289.0, \quad 62 \le x \le 76$$

where x is a man's height (in inches).   *(Source: Metropolitan Life Insurance Company)*

a. Construct a table of values that shows the median recommended weights for men with heights of 62, 64, 66, 68, 70, 72, 74, and 76 inches.

b. Use the table of values to sketch a graph of the model. Then use the graph to estimate *graphically* the median recommended weight for a man whose height is 71 inches.

c. Use the model to confirm *algebraically* the estimate you found in part (b).

Solution

a. You can use a calculator to construct the table, as shown on the left.

b. The table of values can be used to sketch the graph of the equation, as shown in Figure 1.21. From the graph, you can estimate that a height of 71 inches corresponds to a weight of about 161 pounds.

c. To confirm algebraically the estimate found in part (b), you can substitute 71 for x in the model.

$$y = 0.073(71)^2 - 6.99(71) + 289.0 \approx 160.70$$

So, the graphical estimate of 161 pounds is fairly good.

 Checkpoint ◀))) *Audio-video solution in English & Spanish at LarsonPrecalculus.com.*

Use Figure 1.21 to estimate *graphically* the median recommended weight for a man whose height is 75 inches. Then confirm the estimate *algebraically.*   ▪

DATA	Height, x	Weight, y
	62	136.2
	64	140.6
	66	145.6
	68	151.2
	70	157.4
	72	164.2
	74	171.5
	76	179.4

Spreadsheet at LarsonPrecalculus.com

Recommended Weight

Figure 1.21

Summarize *(Section 1.2)*

1. Describe how to sketch the graph of an equation *(page 11)*. For examples of graphing equations, see Examples 1–3.

2. Describe how to identify the x- and y-intercepts of a graph *(page 14)*. For an example of identifying x- and y-intercepts, see Example 4.

3. Describe how to use symmetry to graph an equation *(page 15)*. For an example of using symmetry to graph an equation, see Example 6.

4. State the standard form of the equation of a circle *(page 17)*. For an example of writing the standard form of the equation of a circle, see Example 8.

5. Describe how to use the graph of an equation to solve a real-life problem *(page 18, Example 9)*.

1.2 Exercises

See CalcChat.com for tutorial help and worked-out solutions to odd-numbered exercises.

Vocabulary: Fill in the blanks.

1. An ordered pair (a, b) is a _____ of an equation in x and y when the substitutions $x = a$ and $y = b$ result in a true statement.

2. The set of all solution points of an equation is the _____ of the equation.

3. The points at which a graph intersects or touches an axis are called the _____ of the graph.

4. A graph is symmetric with respect to the _____ if, whenever (x, y) is on the graph, $(-x, y)$ is also on the graph.

5. The equation $(x - h)^2 + (y - k)^2 = r^2$ is the standard form of the equation of a _____ with center _____ and radius _____.

6. When you construct and use a table to solve a problem, you are using a _____ approach.

Skills and Applications

Determining Solution Points In Exercises 7–14, determine whether each point lies on the graph of the equation.

Equation	Points	
7. $y = \sqrt{x + 4}$	(a) $(0, 2)$	(b) $(5, 3)$
8. $y = \sqrt{5 - x}$	(a) $(1, 2)$	(b) $(5, 0)$
9. $y = x^2 - 3x + 2$	(a) $(2, 0)$	(b) $(-2, 8)$
10. $y = 4 - |x - 2|$	(a) $(1, 5)$	(b) $(6, 0)$
11. $y = |x - 1| + 2$	(a) $(2, 3)$	(b) $(-1, 0)$
12. $2x - y - 3 = 0$	(a) $(1, 2)$	(b) $(1, -1)$
13. $x^2 + y^2 = 20$	(a) $(3, -2)$	(b) $(-4, 2)$
14. $y = \frac{1}{3}x^3 - 2x^2$	(a) $\left(2, -\frac{16}{3}\right)$	(b) $(-3, 9)$

Sketching the Graph of an Equation In Exercises 15–18, complete the table. Use the resulting solution points to sketch the graph of the equation.

15. $y = -2x + 5$

x	-1	0	1	2	$\frac{5}{2}$
y					
(x, y)					

16. $y = \frac{3}{4}x - 1$

x	-2	0	1	$\frac{4}{3}$	2
y					
(x, y)					

17. $y = x^2 - 3x$

x	-1	0	1	2	3
y					
(x, y)					

18. $y = 5 - x^2$

x	-2	-1	0	1	2
y					
(x, y)					

Identifying x- and y-Intercepts In Exercises 19–22, identify the x- and y-intercepts of the graph. Verify your results algebraically.

19. $y = (x - 3)^2$

20. $y = 16 - 4x^2$

21. $y = |x + 2|$

22. $y^2 = 4 - x$

Finding x- and y-Intercepts In Exercises 23–32, find the x- and y-intercepts of the graph of the equation.

23. $y = 5x - 6$	24. $y = 8 - 3x$
25. $y = \sqrt{x + 4}$	26. $y = \sqrt{2x - 1}$
27. $y = |3x - 7|$	28. $y = -|x + 10|$
29. $y = 2x^3 - 4x^2$	30. $y = x^4 - 25$
31. $y^2 = 6 - x$	32. $y^2 = x + 1$

Testing for Symmetry In Exercises 33–40, use the algebraic tests to check for symmetry with respect to both axes and the origin.

33. $x^2 - y = 0$

34. $x - y^2 = 0$

35. $y = x^3$

36. $y = x^4 - x^2 + 3$

37. $y = \dfrac{x}{x^2 + 1}$

38. $y = \dfrac{1}{x^2 + 1}$

39. $xy^2 + 10 = 0$

40. $xy = 4$

Using Symmetry as a Sketching Aid In Exercises 41–44, assume that the graph has the indicated type of symmetry. Sketch the complete graph of the equation. To print an enlarged copy of the graph, go to *MathGraphs.com*.

41.

y-Axis symmetry

42.

x-Axis symmetry

43.

Origin symmetry

44.

y-Axis symmetry

Sketching the Graph of an Equation In Exercises 45–56, identify any intercepts and test for symmetry. Then sketch the graph of the equation.

45. $y = -3x + 1$

46. $y = 2x - 3$

47. $y = x^2 - 2x$

48. $y = -x^2 - 2x$

49. $y = x^3 + 3$

50. $y = x^3 - 1$

51. $y = \sqrt{x - 3}$

52. $y = \sqrt{1 - x}$

53. $y = |x - 6|$

54. $y = 1 - |x|$

55. $x = y^2 - 1$

56. $x = y^2 - 5$

Graphical Analysis In Exercises 57–68, use a graphing utility to graph the equation. Use a standard setting. Approximate any intercepts.

57. $y = 3 - \frac{1}{2}x$

58. $y = \frac{2}{3}x - 1$

59. $y = x^2 - 4x + 3$

60. $y = x^2 + x - 2$

61. $y = \dfrac{2x}{x - 1}$

62. $y = \dfrac{4}{x^2 + 1}$

63. $y = \sqrt[3]{x} + 2$

64. $y = \sqrt[3]{x + 1}$

65. $y = x\sqrt{x + 6}$

66. $y = (6 - x)\sqrt{x}$

67. $y = |x + 3|$

68. $y = 2 - |x|$

Writing the Equation of a Circle In Exercises 69–76, write the standard form of the equation of the circle with the given characteristics.

69. Center: $(0, 0)$; Radius: 4

70. Center: $(0, 0)$; Radius: 5

71. Center: $(2, -1)$; Radius: 4

72. Center: $(-7, -4)$; Radius: 7

73. Center: $(-1, 2)$; Solution point: $(0, 0)$

74. Center: $(3, -2)$; Solution point: $(-1, 1)$

75. Endpoints of a diameter: $(0, 0)$, $(6, 8)$

76. Endpoints of a diameter: $(-4, -1)$, $(4, 1)$

Sketching the Graph of a Circle In Exercises 77–82, find the center and radius of the circle. Then sketch the graph of the circle.

77. $x^2 + y^2 = 25$

78. $x^2 + y^2 = 16$

79. $(x - 1)^2 + (y + 3)^2 = 9$

80. $x^2 + (y - 1)^2 = 1$

81. $\left(x - \frac{1}{2}\right)^2 + \left(y - \frac{1}{2}\right)^2 = \frac{9}{4}$

82. $(x - 2)^2 + (y + 3)^2 = \frac{16}{9}$

83. Depreciation A hospital purchases a new magnetic resonance imaging (MRI) machine for \$500,000. The depreciated value y (reduced value) after t years is given by $y = 500{,}000 - 40{,}000t$, $0 \le t \le 8$. Sketch the graph of the equation.

84. Consumerism You purchase an all-terrain vehicle (ATV) for \$8000. The depreciated value y after t years is given by $y = 8000 - 900t$, $0 \le t \le 6$. Sketch the graph of the equation.

85. Geometry A regulation NFL playing field (including the end zones) of length x and width y has a perimeter of $346\frac{2}{3}$ or $\frac{1040}{3}$ yards.

(a) Draw a rectangle that gives a visual representation of the problem. Use the specified variables to label the sides of the rectangle.

(b) Show that the width of the rectangle is $y = \frac{520}{3} - x$ and its area is $A = x\left(\frac{520}{3} - x\right)$.

(c) Use a graphing utility to graph the area equation. Be sure to adjust your window settings.

(d) From the graph in part (c), estimate the dimensions of the rectangle that yield a maximum area.

(e) Use your school's library, the Internet, or some other reference source to find the actual dimensions and area of a regulation NFL playing field and compare your findings with the results of part (d).

The symbol ⊹ indicates an exercise or a part of an exercise in which you are instructed to use a graphing utility.

86. Geometry   A soccer playing field of length x and width y has a perimeter of 360 meters.

(a) Draw a rectangle that gives a visual representation of the problem. Use the specified variables to label the sides of the rectangle.

(b) Show that the width of the rectangle is $y = 180 - x$ and its area is $A = x(180 - x)$.

(c) Use a graphing utility to graph the area equation. Be sure to adjust your window settings.

(d) From the graph in part (c), estimate the dimensions of the rectangle that yield a maximum area.

(e) Use your school's library, the Internet, or some other reference source to find the actual dimensions and area of a regulation Major League Soccer field and compare your findings with the results of part (d).

87. Population Statistics

The table shows the life expectancies of a child (at birth) in the United States for selected years from 1930 through 2000.   *(Source: U.S. National Center for Health Statistics)*

DATA	Year	Life Expectancy, y
	1930	59.7
	1940	62.9
	1950	68.2
	1960	69.7
	1970	70.8
	1980	73.7
	1990	75.4
	2000	76.8

Spreadsheet at LarsonPrecalculus.com

A model for the life expectancy during this period is

$$y = -0.002t^2 + 0.50t + 46.6, \quad 30 \le t \le 100$$

where y represents the life expectancy and t is the time in years, with $t = 30$ corresponding to 1930.

(a) Use a graphing utility to graph the data from the table and the model in the same viewing window. How well does the model fit the data? Explain.

(b) Determine the life expectancy in 1990 both graphically and algebraically.

87. Population Statistics (continued)

(c) Use the graph to determine the year when life expectancy was approximately 76.0. Verify your answer algebraically.

(d) One projection for the life expectancy of a child born in 2015 is 78.9. How does this compare with the projection given by the model?

(e) Do you think this model can be used to predict the life expectancy of a child 50 years from now? Explain.

88. Electronics   The resistance y (in ohms) of 1000 feet of solid copper wire at 68 degrees Fahrenheit is

$$y = \frac{10{,}370}{x^2}$$

where x is the diameter of the wire in mils (0.001 inch).

(a) Complete the table.

x	5	10	20	30	40	50
y						

x	60	70	80	90	100
y					

(b) Use the table of values in part (a) to sketch a graph of the model. Then use your graph to estimate the resistance when $x = 85.5$.

(c) Use the model to confirm algebraically the estimate you found in part (b).

(d) What can you conclude in general about the relationship between the diameter of the copper wire and the resistance?

Exploration

89. Think About It   Find a and b if the graph of $y = ax^2 + bx^3$ is symmetric with respect to (a) the y-axis and (b) the origin. (There are many correct answers.)

90. HOW DO YOU SEE IT?   The graph of the circle with equation $x^2 + y^2 = 1$ is shown below. Describe the types of symmetry that you observe.

1.3 Linear Equations in Two Variables

Linear equations in two variables can help you model and solve real-life problems. For instance, in Exercise 90 on page 33, you will use a surveyor's measurements to find a linear equation that models a mountain road.

- Use slope to graph linear equations in two variables.
- Find the slope of a line given two points on the line.
- Write linear equations in two variables.
- Use slope to identify parallel and perpendicular lines.
- Use slope and linear equations in two variables to model and solve real-life problems.

Using Slope

The simplest mathematical model for relating two variables is the **linear equation in two variables** $y = mx + b$. The equation is called *linear* because its graph is a line. (In mathematics, the term *line* means *straight line*.) By letting $x = 0$, you obtain

$$y = m(0) + b = b.$$

So, the line crosses the y-axis at $y = b$, as shown in the figures below. In other words, the y-intercept is $(0, b)$. The steepness or slope of the line is m.

$$y = mx + b$$

Slope ⤴ ⤴ y-Intercept

The **slope** of a nonvertical line is the number of units the line rises (or falls) vertically for each unit of horizontal change from left to right, as shown below.

Positive slope, line rises.

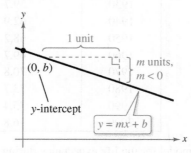

Negative slope, line falls.

A linear equation written in **slope-intercept form** has the form $y = mx + b$.

The Slope-Intercept Form of the Equation of a Line

The graph of the equation

$$y = mx + b$$

is a line whose slope is m and whose y-intercept is $(0, b)$.

Once you have determined the slope and the y-intercept of a line, it is a relatively simple matter to sketch its graph. In the next example, note that none of the lines is vertical. A vertical line has an equation of the form

$$x = a. \qquad \text{Vertical line}$$

The equation of a vertical line cannot be written in the form $y = mx + b$ because the slope of a vertical line is undefined, as indicated in Figure 1.22.

Slope is undefined.
Figure 1.22

EXAMPLE 1   **Graphing a Linear Equation**

Sketch the graph of each linear equation.

a. $y = 2x + 1$

b. $y = 2$

c. $x + y = 2$

Solution

a. Because $b = 1$, the y-intercept is $(0, 1)$. Moreover, because the slope is $m = 2$, the line *rises* two units for each unit the line moves to the right.

When m is positive, the line rises.

b. By writing this equation in the form $y = (0)x + 2$, you can see that the y-intercept is $(0, 2)$ and the slope is zero. A zero slope implies that the line is horizontal—that is, it does not rise *or* fall.

When m is 0, the line is horizontal.

c. By writing this equation in slope-intercept form

$$x + y = 2 \qquad \text{Write original equation.}$$
$$y = -x + 2 \qquad \text{Subtract } x \text{ from each side.}$$
$$y = (-1)x + 2 \qquad \text{Write in slope-intercept form.}$$

you can see that the y-intercept is $(0, 2)$. Moreover, because the slope is $m = -1$, the line *falls* one unit for each unit the line moves to the right.

When m is negative, the line falls.

✓ **Checkpoint** ◀))) *Audio-video solution in English & Spanish at LarsonPrecalculus.com.*

Sketch the graph of each linear equation.

a. $y = -3x + 2$

b. $y = -3$

c. $4x + y = 5$

Finding the Slope of a Line

Given an equation of a line, you can find its slope by writing the equation in slope-intercept form. If you are not given an equation, then you can still find the slope of a line. For instance, suppose you want to find the slope of the line passing through the points (x_1, y_1) and (x_2, y_2), as shown below.

As you move from left to right along this line, a change of $(y_2 - y_1)$ units in the vertical direction corresponds to a change of $(x_2 - x_1)$ units in the horizontal direction.

$$y_2 - y_1 = \text{the change in } y = \text{rise}$$

and

$$x_2 - x_1 = \text{the change in } x = \text{run}$$

The ratio of $(y_2 - y_1)$ to $(x_2 - x_1)$ represents the slope of the line that passes through the points (x_1, y_1) and (x_2, y_2).

$$\text{Slope} = \frac{\text{change in } y}{\text{change in } x} = \frac{\text{rise}}{\text{run}} = \frac{y_2 - y_1}{x_2 - x_1}$$

The Slope of a Line Passing Through Two Points

The **slope** m of the nonvertical line through (x_1, y_1) and (x_2, y_2) is

$$m = \frac{y_2 - y_1}{x_2 - x_1}$$

where $x_1 \neq x_2$.

When using the formula for slope, the *order of subtraction* is important. Given two points on a line, you are free to label either one of them as (x_1, y_1) and the other as (x_2, y_2). However, once you have done this, you must form the numerator and denominator using the same order of subtraction.

$$m = \frac{y_2 - y_1}{x_2 - x_1} \qquad m = \frac{y_1 - y_2}{x_1 - x_2} \qquad m = \frac{y_2 - y_1}{x_1 - x_2}$$

Correct   Correct   Incorrect

For instance, the slope of the line passing through the points $(3, 4)$ and $(5, 7)$ can be calculated as

$$m = \frac{7 - 4}{5 - 3} = \frac{3}{2}$$

or, reversing the subtraction order in both the numerator and denominator, as

$$m = \frac{4 - 7}{3 - 5} = \frac{-3}{-2} = \frac{3}{2}.$$

EXAMPLE 2   **Finding the Slope of a Line Through Two Points**

Find the slope of the line passing through each pair of points.

a. $(-2, 0)$ and $(3, 1)$ **b.** $(-1, 2)$ and $(2, 2)$

c. $(0, 4)$ and $(1, -1)$ **d.** $(3, 4)$ and $(3, 1)$

Solution

a. Letting $(x_1, y_1) = (-2, 0)$ and $(x_2, y_2) = (3, 1)$, you obtain a slope of

$$m = \frac{y_2 - y_1}{x_2 - x_1} = \frac{1 - 0}{3 - (-2)} = \frac{1}{5}.$$ See Figure 1.23.

b. The slope of the line passing through $(-1, 2)$ and $(2, 2)$ is

$$m = \frac{2 - 2}{2 - (-1)} = \frac{0}{3} = 0.$$ See Figure 1.24.

c. The slope of the line passing through $(0, 4)$ and $(1, -1)$ is

$$m = \frac{-1 - 4}{1 - 0} = \frac{-5}{1} = -5.$$ See Figure 1.25.

d. The slope of the line passing through $(3, 4)$ and $(3, 1)$ is

$$m = \frac{1 - 4}{3 - 3} = \frac{-3}{0}.$$ See Figure 1.26.

Because division by 0 is undefined, the slope is undefined and the line is vertical.

• • **REMARK** In Figures 1.23
• through 1.26, note the
• relationships between slope
• and the orientation of the line.
•
• **a.** Positive slope: line rises
•   from left to right
•
• **b.** Zero slope: line is horizontal
•
• **c.** Negative slope: line falls
•   from left to right
•
• **d.** Undefined slope: line is
•   vertical
• • • • • • • • • • • • • • • • • • ▷

Figure 1.23

Figure 1.24

Figure 1.25

Figure 1.26

✓ *Checkpoint*   *Audio-video solution in English & Spanish at LarsonPrecalculus.com.*

Find the slope of the line passing through each pair of points.

a. $(-5, -6)$ and $(2, 8)$ **b.** $(4, 2)$ and $(2, 5)$

c. $(0, 0)$ and $(0, -6)$ **d.** $(0, -1)$ and $(3, -1)$

Writing Linear Equations in Two Variables

If (x_1, y_1) is a point on a line of slope m and (x, y) is *any other* point on the line, then

$$\frac{y - y_1}{x - x_1} = m.$$

This equation involving the variables x and y, rewritten in the form

$$y - y_1 = m(x - x_1)$$

is the **point-slope form** of the equation of a line.

Point-Slope Form of the Equation of a Line

The equation of the line with slope m passing through the point (x_1, y_1) is

$$y - y_1 = m(x - x_1).$$

The point-slope form is most useful for *finding* the equation of a line. You should remember this form.

EXAMPLE 3   Using the Point-Slope Form

Find the slope-intercept form of the equation of the line that has a slope of 3 and passes through the point $(1, -2)$.

Solution   Use the point-slope form with $m = 3$ and $(x_1, y_1) = (1, -2)$.

$$y - y_1 = m(x - x_1) \qquad \text{Point-slope form}$$
$$y - (-2) = 3(x - 1) \qquad \text{Substitute for } m, x_1, \text{ and } y_1.$$
$$y + 2 = 3x - 3 \qquad \text{Simplify.}$$
$$y = 3x - 5 \qquad \text{Write in slope-intercept form.}$$

The slope-intercept form of the equation of the line is $y = 3x - 5$. Figure 1.27 shows the graph of this equation.

Figure 1.27

✓ *Checkpoint* ◄))) Audio-video solution in English & Spanish at LarsonPrecalculus.com.

Find the slope-intercept form of the equation of the line that has the given slope and passes through the given point.

a. $m = 2$, $(3, -7)$

b. $m = -\frac{2}{3}$, $(1, 1)$

c. $m = 0$, $(1, 1)$

•• **REMARK** When you find an equation of the line that passes through two given points, you only need to substitute the coordinates of one of the points in the point-slope form. It does not matter which point you choose because both points will yield the same result.

The point-slope form can be used to find an equation of the line passing through two points (x_1, y_1) and (x_2, y_2). To do this, first find the slope of the line

$$m = \frac{y_2 - y_1}{x_2 - x_1}, \quad x_1 \neq x_2$$

and then use the point-slope form to obtain the equation

$$y - y_1 = \frac{y_2 - y_1}{x_2 - x_1}(x - x_1). \qquad \text{Two-point form}$$

This is sometimes called the **two-point form** of the equation of a line.

Parallel and Perpendicular Lines

Slope can tell you whether two nonvertical lines in a plane are parallel, perpendicular, or neither.

Parallel and Perpendicular Lines

1. Two distinct nonvertical lines are **parallel** if and only if their slopes are equal. That is,

$$m_1 = m_2.$$

2. Two nonvertical lines are **perpendicular** if and only if their slopes are negative reciprocals of each other. That is,

$$m_1 = \frac{-1}{m_2}.$$

EXAMPLE 4 **Finding Parallel and Perpendicular Lines**

Find the slope-intercept form of the equations of the lines that pass through the point $(2, -1)$ and are (a) parallel to and (b) perpendicular to the line $2x - 3y = 5$.

Solution By writing the equation of the given line in slope-intercept form

$2x - 3y = 5$	Write original equation.
$-3y = -2x + 5$	Subtract $2x$ from each side.
$y = \frac{2}{3}x - \frac{5}{3}$	Write in slope-intercept form.

you can see that it has a slope of $m = \frac{2}{3}$, as shown in Figure 1.28.

a. Any line parallel to the given line must also have a slope of $\frac{2}{3}$. So, the line through $(2, -1)$ that is parallel to the given line has the following equation.

$y - (-1) = \frac{2}{3}(x - 2)$	Write in point-slope form.
$3(y + 1) = 2(x - 2)$	Multiply each side by 3.
$3y + 3 = 2x - 4$	Distributive Property
$y = \frac{2}{3}x - \frac{7}{3}$	Write in slope-intercept form.

b. Any line perpendicular to the given line must have a slope of $-\frac{3}{2}$ (because $-\frac{3}{2}$ is the negative reciprocal of $\frac{2}{3}$). So, the line through $(2, -1)$ that is perpendicular to the given line has the following equation.

$y - (-1) = -\frac{3}{2}(x - 2)$	Write in point-slope form.
$2(y + 1) = -3(x - 2)$	Multiply each side by 2.
$2y + 2 = -3x + 6$	Distributive Property
$y = -\frac{3}{2}x + 2$	Write in slope-intercept form.

✓ **Checkpoint** ◀))) *Audio-video solution in English & Spanish at LarsonPrecalculus.com.*

Find the slope-intercept form of the equations of the lines that pass through the point $(-4, 1)$ and are (a) parallel to and (b) perpendicular to the line $5x - 3y = 8$. ■

Notice in Example 4 how the slope-intercept form is used to obtain information about the graph of a line, whereas the point-slope form is used to write the equation of a line.

Figure 1.28

▷ **TECHNOLOGY** On a graphing utility, lines will not appear to have the correct slope unless you use a viewing window that has a square setting. For instance, try graphing the lines in Example 4 using the standard setting $-10 \leq x \leq 10$ and $-10 \leq y \leq 10$. Then reset the viewing window with the square setting $-9 \leq x \leq 9$ and $-6 \leq y \leq 6$. On which setting do the lines $y = \frac{2}{3}x - \frac{5}{3}$ and $y = -\frac{3}{2}x + 2$ appear to be perpendicular?

Applications

In real-life problems, the slope of a line can be interpreted as either a *ratio* or a *rate*. If the *x*-axis and *y*-axis have the same unit of measure, then the slope has no units and is a **ratio.** If the *x*-axis and *y*-axis have different units of measure, then the slope is a **rate** or **rate of change.**

EXAMPLE 5 Using Slope as a Ratio

The maximum recommended slope of a wheelchair ramp is $\frac{1}{12}$. A business is installing a wheelchair ramp that rises 22 inches over a horizontal length of 24 feet. Is the ramp steeper than recommended? *(Source: ADA Standards for Accessible Design)*

Solution The horizontal length of the ramp is 24 feet or $12(24) = 288$ inches, as shown below. So, the slope of the ramp is

$$\text{Slope} = \frac{\text{vertical change}}{\text{horizontal change}} = \frac{22 \text{ in.}}{288 \text{ in.}} \approx 0.076.$$

Because $\frac{1}{12} \approx 0.083$, the slope of the ramp is not steeper than recommended.

22 in.
24 ft

✓ Checkpoint ◀))) *Audio-video solution in English & Spanish at LarsonPrecalculus.com.*

The business in Example 5 installs a second ramp that rises 36 inches over a horizontal length of 32 feet. Is the ramp steeper than recommended?

EXAMPLE 6 Using Slope as a Rate of Change

A kitchen appliance manufacturing company determines that the total cost C (in dollars) of producing x units of a blender is

$$C = 25x + 3500. \qquad \text{Cost equation}$$

Describe the practical significance of the *y*-intercept and slope of this line.

Solution The *y*-intercept $(0, 3500)$ tells you that the cost of producing zero units is $3500. This is the *fixed cost* of production—it includes costs that must be paid regardless of the number of units produced. The slope of $m = 25$ tells you that the cost of producing each unit is $25, as shown in Figure 1.29. Economists call the cost per unit the *marginal cost*. If the production increases by one unit, then the "margin," or extra amount of cost, is $25. So, the cost increases at a rate of $25 per unit.

✓ Checkpoint ◀))) *Audio-video solution in English & Spanish at LarsonPrecalculus.com.*

An accounting firm determines that the value V (in dollars) of a copier t years after its purchase is

$$V = -300t + 1500.$$

Describe the practical significance of the *y*-intercept and slope of this line.

The Americans with Disabilities Act (ADA) became law on July 26, 1990. It is the most comprehensive formulation of rights for persons with disabilities in U.S. (and world) history.

Manufacturing

$C = 25x + 3500$

Marginal cost: $m = \$25$

Fixed cost: 3500

Cost (in dollars)

Number of units

Production cost
Figure 1.29

Businesses can deduct most of their expenses in the same year they occur. One exception is the cost of property that has a useful life of more than 1 year. Such costs must be *depreciated* (decreased in value) over the useful life of the property. Depreciating the *same amount* each year is called *linear* or *straight-line depreciation*. The *book value* is the difference between the original value and the total amount of depreciation accumulated to date.

EXAMPLE 7 **Straight-Line Depreciation**

A college purchased exercise equipment worth $12,000 for the new campus fitness center. The equipment has a useful life of 8 years. The salvage value at the end of 8 years is $2000. Write a linear equation that describes the book value of the equipment each year.

Solution Let V represent the value of the equipment at the end of year t. Represent the initial value of the equipment by the data point $(0, 12{,}000)$ and the salvage value of the equipment by the data point $(8, 2000)$. The slope of the line is

$$m = \frac{2000 - 12{,}000}{8 - 0}$$

$$= -\$1250$$

which represents the annual depreciation in *dollars per year*. Using the point-slope form, you can write the equation of the line as follows.

$$V - 12{,}000 = -1250(t - 0) \qquad \text{Write in point-slope form.}$$

$$V = -1250t + 12{,}000 \qquad \text{Write in slope-intercept form.}$$

The table shows the book value at the end of each year, and Figure 1.30 shows the graph of the equation.

Useful Life of Equipment

$V = -1250t + 12{,}000$

Straight-line depreciation
Figure 1.30

Year, t	Value, V
0	12,000
1	10,750
2	9500
3	8250
4	7000
5	5750
6	4500
7	3250
8	2000

✓ *Checkpoint* ◄))) Audio-video solution in English & Spanish at LarsonPrecalculus.com.

A manufacturing firm purchased a machine worth $24,750. The machine has a useful life of 6 years. After 6 years, the machine will have to be discarded and replaced. That is, it will have no salvage value. Write a linear equation that describes the book value of the machine each year.

In many real-life applications, the two data points that determine the line are often given in a disguised form. Note how the data points are described in Example 7.

Best Buy

Figure 1.31

$EXAMPLE 8$ **Predicting Sales**

The sales for Best Buy were approximately \$49.7 billion in 2009 and \$50.3 billion in 2010. Using only this information, write a linear equation that gives the sales in terms of the year. Then predict the sales in 2013.   *(Source: Best Buy Company, Inc.)*

Solution   Let $t = 9$ represent 2009. Then the two given values are represented by the data points $(9, 49.7)$ and $(10, 50.3)$. The slope of the line through these points is

$$m = \frac{50.3 - 49.7}{10 - 9} = 0.6.$$

You can find the equation that relates the sales y and the year t to be

$$y - 49.7 = 0.6(t - 9)$$ Write in point-slope form.

$$y = 0.6t + 44.3.$$ Write in slope-intercept form.

According to this equation, the sales in 2013 will be

$$y = 0.6(13) + 44.3 = 7.8 + 44.3 = \$52.1 \text{ billion. (See Figure 1.31.)}$$

✓ **Checkpoint** ◄))) *Audio-video solution in English & Spanish at LarsonPrecalculus.com.*

The sales for Nokia were approximately \$58.6 billion in 2009 and \$56.6 billion in 2010. Repeat Example 8 using this information.   *(Source: Nokia Corporation)*

The prediction method illustrated in Example 8 is called **linear extrapolation.** Note in Figure 1.32 that an extrapolated point does not lie between the given points. When the estimated point lies between two given points, as shown in Figure 1.33, the procedure is called **linear interpolation.**

Because the slope of a vertical line is not defined, its equation cannot be written in slope-intercept form. However, every line has an equation that can be written in the **general form** $Ax + By + C = 0$, where A and B are not both zero.

Linear extrapolation
Figure 1.32

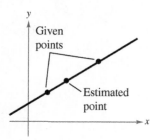

Linear interpolation
Figure 1.33

Summary of Equations of Lines

1. General form: $Ax + By + C = 0$

2. Vertical line: $x = a$

3. Horizontal line: $y = b$

4. Slope-intercept form: $y = mx + b$

5. Point-slope form: $y - y_1 = m(x - x_1)$

6. Two-point form: $y - y_1 = \dfrac{y_2 - y_1}{x_2 - x_1}(x - x_1)$

Summarize   (Section 1.3)

1. Explain how to use slope to graph a linear equation in two variables *(page 22)* and how to find the slope of a line passing through two points *(page 24)*. For examples of using and finding slopes, see Examples 1 and 2.

2. State the point-slope form of the equation of a line *(page 26)*. For an example of using point-slope form, see Example 3.

3. Explain how to use slope to identify parallel and perpendicular lines *(page 27)*. For an example of finding parallel and perpendicular lines, see Example 4.

4. Describe examples of how to use slope and linear equations in two variables to model and solve real-life problems *(pages 28–30, Examples 5–8)*.

1.3 Exercises

See **CalcChat.com** for tutorial help and worked-out solutions to odd-numbered exercises.

Vocabulary: Fill in the blanks.

1. The simplest mathematical model for relating two variables is the _____ equation in two variables $y = mx + b$.

2. For a line, the ratio of the change in y to the change in x is called the _____ of the line.

3. The _____-_____ form of the equation of a line with slope m passing through (x_1, y_1) is $y - y_1 = m(x - x_1)$.

4. Two lines are _____ if and only if their slopes are equal.

5. Two lines are _____ if and only if their slopes are negative reciprocals of each other.

6. When the x-axis and y-axis have different units of measure, the slope can be interpreted as a _____.

7. The prediction method _____ _____ is the method used to estimate a point on a line when the point does not lie between the given points.

8. Every line has an equation that can be written in _____ form.

Skills and Applications

Identifying Lines **In Exercises 9 and 10, identify the line that has each slope.**

9. (a) $m = \frac{2}{3}$
   (b) m is undefined.
   (c) $m = -2$

10. (a) $m = 0$
    (b) $m = -\frac{3}{4}$
    (c) $m = 1$

Sketching Lines **In Exercises 11 and 12, sketch the lines through the point with the indicated slopes on the same set of coordinate axes.**

Point	Slopes
11. $(2, 3)$	(a) 0 (b) 1
	(c) 2 (d) -3
12. $(-4, 1)$	(a) 3 (b) -3
	(c) $\frac{1}{2}$ (d) Undefined

Estimating the Slope of a Line **In Exercises 13 and 14, estimate the slope of the line.**

13.

14.

Graphing a Linear Equation **In Exercises 15–24, find the slope and y-intercept (if possible) of the equation of the line. Sketch the line.**

15. $y = 5x + 3$
16. $y = -x - 10$
17. $y = -\frac{1}{2}x + 4$
18. $y = \frac{3}{2}x + 6$
19. $y - 3 = 0$
20. $x + 5 = 0$
21. $5x - 2 = 0$
22. $3y + 5 = 0$
23. $7x - 6y = 30$
24. $2x + 3y = 9$

Finding the Slope of a Line Through Two Points **In Exercises 25–34, plot the points and find the slope of the line passing through the pair of points.**

25. $(0, 9), (6, 0)$
26. $(12, 0), (0, -8)$
27. $(-3, -2), (1, 6)$
28. $(2, 4), (4, -4)$
29. $(5, -7), (8, -7)$
30. $(-2, 1), (-4, -5)$
31. $(-6, -1), (-6, 4)$
32. $(0, -10), (-4, 0)$
33. $(4.8, 3.1), (-5.2, 1.6)$
34. $\left(\frac{11}{2}, -\frac{4}{3}\right), \left(-\frac{3}{2}, -\frac{1}{3}\right)$

Using a Point and Slope **In Exercises 35–42, use the point on the line and the slope m of the line to find three additional points through which the line passes. (There are many correct answers.)**

35. $(2, 1), \quad m = 0$
36. $(3, -2), \quad m = 0$
37. $(-8, 1), \quad m$ is undefined.
38. $(1, 5), \quad m$ is undefined.
39. $(-5, 4), \quad m = 2$
40. $(0, -9), \quad m = -2$
41. $(-1, -6), \quad m = -\frac{1}{2}$
42. $(7, -2), \quad m = \frac{1}{2}$

Finding an Equation of a Line In Exercises 43–54, find an equation of the line that passes through the given point and has the indicated slope m. Sketch the line.

43. $(0, -2)$, $m = 3$

44. $(0, 10)$, $m = -1$

45. $(-3, 6)$, $m = -2$

46. $(0, 0)$, $m = 4$

47. $(4, 0)$, $m = -\frac{1}{3}$

48. $(8, 2)$, $m = \frac{1}{4}$

49. $(2, -3)$, $m = -\frac{1}{2}$

50. $(-2, -5)$, $m = \frac{3}{4}$

51. $(6, -1)$, m is undefined.

52. $(-10, 4)$, m is undefined.

53. $\left(4, \frac{5}{2}\right)$, $m = 0$

54. $(-5.1, 1.8)$, $m = 5$

Finding an Equation of a Line In Exercises 55–64, find an equation of the line passing through the points. Sketch the line.

55. $(5, -1), (-5, 5)$

56. $(4, 3), (-4, -4)$

57. $(-8, 1), (-8, 7)$

58. $(-1, 4), (6, 4)$

59. $\left(2, \frac{1}{2}\right), \left(\frac{1}{2}, \frac{5}{4}\right)$

60. $(1, 1), \left(6, -\frac{2}{3}\right)$

61. $(1, 0.6), (-2, -0.6)$

62. $(-8, 0.6), (2, -2.4)$

63. $(2, -1), \left(\frac{1}{3}, -1\right)$

64. $\left(\frac{7}{3}, -8\right), \left(\frac{7}{3}, 1\right)$

Parallel and Perpendicular Lines In Exercises 65–68, determine whether the lines are parallel, perpendicular, or neither.

65. L_1: $y = \frac{1}{3}x - 2$
    L_2: $y = \frac{1}{3}x + 3$

66. L_1: $y = 4x - 1$
    L_2: $y = 4x + 7$

67. L_1: $y = \frac{1}{2}x - 3$
    L_2: $y = -\frac{1}{2}x + 1$

68. L_1: $y = -\frac{4}{5}x - 5$
    L_2: $y = \frac{5}{4}x + 1$

Parallel and Perpendicular Lines In Exercises 69–72, determine whether the lines L_1 and L_2 passing through the pairs of points are parallel, perpendicular, or neither.

69. L_1: $(0, -1), (5, 9)$
    L_2: $(0, 3), (4, 1)$

70. L_1: $(-2, -1), (1, 5)$
    L_2: $(1, 3), (5, -5)$

71. L_1: $(3, 6), (-6, 0)$
    L_2: $(0, -1), \left(5, \frac{7}{3}\right)$

72. L_1: $(4, 8), (-4, 2)$
    L_2: $(3, -5), \left(-1, \frac{1}{3}\right)$

Finding Parallel and Perpendicular Lines In Exercises 73–80, write equations of the lines through the given point (a) parallel to and (b) perpendicular to the given line.

73. $4x - 2y = 3$, $(2, 1)$

74. $x + y = 7$, $(-3, 2)$

75. $3x + 4y = 7$, $\left(-\frac{2}{3}, \frac{7}{8}\right)$

76. $5x + 3y = 0$, $\left(\frac{7}{8}, \frac{3}{4}\right)$

77. $y + 3 = 0$, $(-1, 0)$

78. $x - 4 = 0$, $(3, -2)$

79. $x - y = 4$, $(2.5, 6.8)$

80. $6x + 2y = 9$, $(-3.9, -1.4)$

Intercept Form of the Equation of a Line In Exercises 81–86, use the *intercept form* to find the equation of the line with the given intercepts. The intercept form of the equation of a line with intercepts $(a, 0)$ and $(0, b)$ is

$$\frac{x}{a} + \frac{y}{b} = 1, \ a \neq 0, \ b \neq 0.$$

81. x-intercept: $(2, 0)$
    y-intercept: $(0, 3)$

82. x-intercept: $(-3, 0)$
    y-intercept: $(0, 4)$

83. x-intercept: $\left(-\frac{1}{6}, 0\right)$
    y-intercept: $\left(0, -\frac{2}{3}\right)$

84. x-intercept: $\left(\frac{2}{3}, 0\right)$
    y-intercept: $(0, -2)$

85. Point on line: $(1, 2)$
    x-intercept: $(c, 0)$
    y-intercept: $(0, c)$, $c \neq 0$

86. Point on line: $(-3, 4)$
    x-intercept: $(d, 0)$
    y-intercept: $(0, d)$, $d \neq 0$

87. **Sales** The following are the slopes of lines representing annual sales y in terms of time x in years. Use the slopes to interpret any change in annual sales for a one-year increase in time.

    (a) The line has a slope of $m = 135$.

    (b) The line has a slope of $m = 0$.

    (c) The line has a slope of $m = -40$.

88. **Sales** The graph shows the sales (in billions of dollars) for Apple Inc. in the years 2004 through 2010. (*Source: Apple Inc.*)

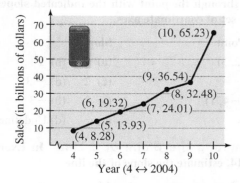

    (a) Use the slopes of the line segments to determine the years in which the sales showed the greatest increase and the least increase.

    (b) Find the slope of the line segment connecting the points for the years 2004 and 2010.

    (c) Interpret the meaning of the slope in part (b) in the context of the problem.

89. Road Grade You are driving on a road that has a 6% uphill grade. This means that the slope of the road is $\frac{6}{100}$. Approximate the amount of vertical change in your position when you drive 200 feet.

90. Road Grade

From the top of a mountain road, a surveyor takes several horizontal measurements x and several vertical measurements y, as shown in the table (x and y are measured in feet).

x	300	600	900	1200
y	-25	-50	-75	-100

x	1500	1800	2100
y	-125	-150	-175

(a) Sketch a scatter plot of the data.

(b) Use a straightedge to sketch the line that you think best fits the data.

(c) Find an equation for the line you sketched in part (b).

(d) Interpret the meaning of the slope of the line in part (c) in the context of the problem.

(e) The surveyor needs to put up a road sign that indicates the steepness of the road. For instance, a surveyor would put up a sign that states "8% grade" on a road with a downhill grade that has a slope of $-\frac{8}{100}$. What should the sign state for the road in this problem?

Rate of Change In Exercises 91 and 92, you are given the dollar value of a product in 2013 and the rate at which the value of the product is expected to change during the next 5 years. Use this information to write a linear equation that gives the dollar value V of the product in terms of the year t. (Let $t = 13$ represent 2013.)

	2013 Value	Rate
91.	$2540	$125 decrease per year
92.	$156	$4.50 increase per year

93. Cost The cost C of producing n computer laptop bags is given by

$$C = 1.25n + 15{,}750, \quad 0 < n.$$

Explain what the C-intercept and the slope measure.

94. Monthly Salary A pharmaceutical salesperson receives a monthly salary of $2500 plus a commission of 7% of sales. Write a linear equation for the salesperson's monthly wage W in terms of monthly sales S.

95. Depreciation A sub shop purchases a used pizza oven for $875. After 5 years, the oven will have to be discarded and replaced. Write a linear equation giving the value V of the equipment during the 5 years it will be in use.

96. Depreciation A school district purchases a high-volume printer, copier, and scanner for $24,000. After 10 years, the equipment will have to be replaced. Its value at that time is expected to be $2000. Write a linear equation giving the value V of the equipment during the 10 years it will be in use.

97. Temperature Conversion Write a linear equation that expresses the relationship between the temperature in degrees Celsius C and degrees Fahrenheit F. Use the fact that water freezes at 0°C (32°F) and boils at 100°C (212°F).

98. Brain Weight The average weight of a male child's brain is 970 grams at age 1 and 1270 grams at age 3. (*Source: American Neurological Association*)

(a) Assuming that the relationship between brain weight y and age t is linear, write a linear model for the data.

(b) What is the slope and what does it tell you about brain weight?

(c) Use your model to estimate the average brain weight at age 2.

(d) Use your school's library, the Internet, or some other reference source to find the actual average brain weight at age 2. How close was your estimate?

(e) Do you think your model could be used to determine the average brain weight of an adult? Explain.

99. Cost, Revenue, and Profit A roofing contractor purchases a shingle delivery truck with a shingle elevator for $42,000. The vehicle requires an average expenditure of $9.50 per hour for fuel and maintenance, and the operator is paid $11.50 per hour.

(a) Write a linear equation giving the total cost C of operating this equipment for t hours. (Include the purchase cost of the equipment.)

(b) Assuming that customers are charged $45 per hour of machine use, write an equation for the revenue R derived from t hours of use.

(c) Use the formula for profit $P = R - C$ to write an equation for the profit derived from t hours of use.

(d) Use the result of part (c) to find the break-even point—that is, the number of hours this equipment must be used to yield a profit of 0 dollars.

100. Geometry The length and width of a rectangular garden are 15 meters and 10 meters, respectively. A walkway of width x surrounds the garden.

(a) Draw a diagram that gives a visual representation of the problem.

(b) Write the equation for the perimeter y of the walkway in terms of x.

(c) Use a graphing utility to graph the equation for the perimeter.

(d) Determine the slope of the graph in part (c). For each additional one-meter increase in the width of the walkway, determine the increase in its perimeter.

Exploration

True or False? In Exercises 101 and 102, determine whether the statement is true or false. Justify your answer.

101. A line with a slope of $-\frac{5}{7}$ is steeper than a line with a slope of $-\frac{6}{7}$.

102. The line through $(-8, 2)$ and $(-1, 4)$ and the line through $(0, -4)$ and $(-7, 7)$ are parallel.

103. Right Triangle Explain how you could use slope to show that the points $A(-1, 5)$, $B(3, 7)$, and $C(5, 3)$ are the vertices of a right triangle.

104. Vertical Line Explain why the slope of a vertical line is said to be undefined.

105. Think About It With the information shown in the graphs, is it possible to determine the slope of each line? Is it possible that the lines could have the same slope? Explain.

(a)   (b)

106. Perpendicular Segments Find d_1 and d_2 in terms of m_1 and m_2, respectively (see figure). Then use the Pythagorean Theorem to find a relationship between m_1 and m_2.

107. Think About It Is it possible for two lines with positive slopes to be perpendicular? Explain.

108. Slope and Steepness The slopes of two lines are -4 and $\frac{5}{2}$. Which is steeper? Explain.

109. Comparing Slopes Use a graphing utility to compare the slopes of the lines $y = mx$, where $m = 0.5, 1, 2,$ and 4. Which line rises most quickly? Now, let $m = -0.5, -1, -2,$ and -4. Which line falls most quickly? Use a square setting to obtain a true geometric perspective. What can you conclude about the slope and the "rate" at which the line rises or falls?

110. HOW DO YOU SEE IT? Match the description of the situation with its graph. Also determine the slope and y-intercept of each graph and interpret the slope and y-intercept in the context of the situation. [The graphs are labeled (i), (ii), (iii), and (iv).]

(i)   (ii)

(iii)   (iv)

(a) A person is paying \$20 per week to a friend to repay a \$200 loan.

(b) An employee receives \$12.50 per hour plus \$2 for each unit produced per hour.

(c) A sales representative receives \$30 per day for food plus \$0.32 for each mile traveled.

(d) A computer that was purchased for \$750 depreciates \$100 per year.

Finding a Relationship for Equidistance In Exercises 111–114, find a relationship between x and y such that (x, y) is equidistant (the same distance) from the two points.

111. $(4, -1), (-2, 3)$ **112.** $(6, 5), (1, -8)$

113. $\left(3, \frac{5}{2}\right), (-7, 1)$ **114.** $\left(-\frac{1}{2}, -4\right), \left(\frac{7}{2}, \frac{5}{4}\right)$

Project: Bachelor's Degrees To work an extended application analyzing the numbers of bachelor's degrees earned by women in the United States from 1998 through 2009, visit this text's website at *LarsonPrecalculus.com*. (*Source: National Center for Education Statistics*)

1.4   Functions

Functions can help you model and solve real-life problems. For instance, in Exercise 74 on page 47, you will use a function to model the force of water against the face of a dam.

■ Determine whether relations between two variables are functions, and use function notation.
■ Find the domains of functions.
■ Use functions to model and solve real-life problems.
■ Evaluate difference quotients.

Introduction to Functions and Function Notation

Many everyday phenomena involve two quantities that are related to each other by some rule of correspondence. The mathematical term for such a rule of correspondence is a **relation.** In mathematics, equations and formulas often represent relations. For instance, the simple interest I earned on $1000 for 1 year is related to the annual interest rate r by the formula $I = 1000r$.

The formula $I = 1000r$ represents a special kind of relation that matches each item from one set with *exactly one* item from a different set. Such a relation is called a **function.**

Definition of Function

A **function** f from a set A to a set B is a relation that assigns to each element x in the set A exactly one element y in the set B. The set A is the **domain** (or set of inputs) of the function f, and the set B contains the **range** (or set of outputs).

To help understand this definition, look at the function below, which relates the time of day to the temperature.

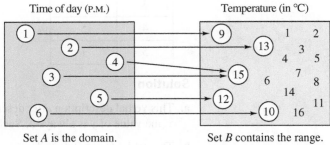

Time of day (P.M.)   Temperature (in °C)

Set A is the domain.   Set B contains the range.
Inputs: 1, 2, 3, 4, 5, 6   Outputs: 9, 10, 12, 13, 15

The following ordered pairs can represent this function. The first coordinate (x-value) is the input and the second coordinate (y-value) is the output.

$$\{(1, 9), (2, 13), (3, 15), (4, 15), (5, 12), (6, 10)\}$$

Characteristics of a Function from Set _A_ to Set _B_

1. Each element in A must be matched with an element in B.

2. Some elements in B may not be matched with any element in A.

3. Two or more elements in A may be matched with the same element in B.

4. An element in A (the domain) cannot be matched with two different elements in B.

Four common ways to represent functions are as follows.

Four Ways to Represent a Function

1. *Verbally* by a sentence that describes how the input variable is related to the output variable

2. *Numerically* by a table or a list of ordered pairs that matches input values with output values

3. *Graphically* by points on a graph in a coordinate plane in which the horizontal axis represents the input values and the vertical axis represents the output values

4. *Algebraically* by an equation in two variables

To determine whether a relation is a function, you must decide whether each input value is matched with exactly one output value. When any input value is matched with two or more output values, the relation is not a function.

EXAMPLE 1 Testing for Functions

Determine whether the relation represents y as a function of x.

a. The input value x is the number of representatives from a state, and the output value y is the number of senators.

b.

Input, x	Output, y
2	11
2	10
3	8
4	5
5	1

c.
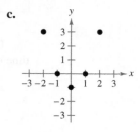

Solution

a. This verbal description *does* describe y as a function of x. Regardless of the value of x, the value of y is always 2. Such functions are called *constant functions*.

b. This table *does not* describe y as a function of x. The input value 2 is matched with two different y-values.

c. The graph *does* describe y as a function of x. Each input value is matched with exactly one output value.

✓ *Checkpoint* ◄))) Audio-video solution in English & Spanish at LarsonPrecalculus.com.

Determine whether the relation represents y as a function of x.

a. *Domain, x   Range, y*

b.

Input, x	0	1	2	3	4
Output, y	-4	-2	0	2	4

Representing functions by sets of ordered pairs is common in *discrete mathematics*. In algebra, however, it is more common to represent functions by equations or formulas involving two variables. For instance, the equation

$$y = x^2 \qquad\qquad \text{\small y is a function of x.}$$

represents the variable y as a function of the variable x. In this equation, x is the **independent variable** and y is the **dependent variable.** The domain of the function is the set of all values taken on by the independent variable x, and the range of the function is the set of all values taken on by the dependent variable y.

HISTORICAL NOTE

Many consider Leonhard Euler
(1707–1783), a Swiss
mathematician, the most prolific
and productive mathematician
in history. One of his greatest
influences on mathematics was
his use of symbols, or notation.
Euler introduced the function
notation $y = f(x)$.

EXAMPLE 2   **Testing for Functions Represented Algebraically**

Which of the equations represent(s) y as a function of x?

a. $x^2 + y = 1$

b. $-x + y^2 = 1$

Solution   To determine whether y is a function of x, try to solve for y in terms of x.

a. Solving for y yields

$$x^2 + y = 1 \qquad\qquad \text{\small Write original equation.}$$
$$y = 1 - x^2. \qquad\qquad \text{\small Solve for y.}$$

To each value of x there corresponds exactly one value of y. So, y is a function of x.

b. Solving for y yields

$$-x + y^2 = 1 \qquad\qquad \text{\small Write original equation.}$$
$$y^2 = 1 + x \qquad\qquad \text{\small Add x to each side.}$$
$$y = \pm\sqrt{1 + x}. \qquad\qquad \text{\small Solve for y.}$$

The $\pm$ indicates that to a given value of x there correspond two values of y. So, y is not a function of x.

✓ *Checkpoint* *Audio-video solution in English & Spanish at LarsonPrecalculus.com.*

Which of the equations represent(s) y as a function of x?

a. $x^2 + y^2 = 8$ **b.** $y - 4x^2 = 36$

When using an equation to represent a function, it is convenient to name the function for easy reference. For example, you know that the equation $y = 1 - x^2$ describes y as a function of x. Suppose you give this function the name "f." Then you can use the following **function notation.**

Input	Output	Equation
x	$f(x)$	$f(x) = 1 - x^2$

The symbol $f(x)$ is read as *the value of f at x* or simply *f of x*. The symbol $f(x)$ corresponds to the y-value for a given x. So, you can write $y = f(x)$. Keep in mind that f is the *name* of the function, whereas $f(x)$ is the *value* of the function at x. For instance, the function $f(x) = 3 - 2x$ has *function values* denoted by $f(-1), f(0), f(2)$, and so on. To find these values, substitute the specified input values into the given equation.

For $x = -1$, $f(-1) = 3 - 2(-1) = 3 + 2 = 5.$

For $x = 0$, $f(0) = 3 - 2(0) = 3 - 0 = 3.$

For $x = 2$, $f(2) = 3 - 2(2) = 3 - 4 = -1.$

Although f is often used as a convenient function name and x is often used as the independent variable, you can use other letters. For instance,

$$f(x) = x^2 - 4x + 7, \quad f(t) = t^2 - 4t + 7, \quad \text{and} \quad g(s) = s^2 - 4s + 7$$

all define the same function. In fact, the role of the independent variable is that of a "placeholder." Consequently, the function could be described by

$$f(\;\rule{1em}{0.8em}\;) = (\;\rule{1em}{0.8em}\;)^2 - 4(\;\rule{1em}{0.8em}\;) + 7.$$

EXAMPLE 3   Evaluating a Function

Let $g(x) = -x^2 + 4x + 1$. Find each function value.

a. $g(2)$ **b.** $g(t)$ **c.** $g(x + 2)$

Solution

a. Replacing x with 2 in $g(x) = -x^2 + 4x + 1$ yields the following.

$$\begin{aligned} g(2) &= -(2)^2 + 4(2) + 1 \\ &= -4 + 8 + 1 \\ &= 5 \end{aligned}$$

b. Replacing x with t yields the following.

$$\begin{aligned} g(t) &= -(t)^2 + 4(t) + 1 \\ &= -t^2 + 4t + 1 \end{aligned}$$

c. Replacing x with $x + 2$ yields the following.

$$\begin{aligned} g(x + 2) &= -(x + 2)^2 + 4(x + 2) + 1 \\ &= -(x^2 + 4x + 4) + 4x + 8 + 1 \\ &= -x^2 - 4x - 4 + 4x + 8 + 1 \\ &= -x^2 + 5 \end{aligned}$$

• • REMARK   In Example 3(c), note that $g(x + 2)$ is not equal to $g(x) + g(2)$. In general, $g(u + v) \neq g(u) + g(v)$.

✓ **Checkpoint** ◀))) *Audio-video solution in English & Spanish at LarsonPrecalculus.com.*

Let $f(x) = 10 - 3x^2$. Find each function value.

a. $f(2)$ **b.** $f(-4)$ **c.** $f(x - 1)$ ◼

A function defined by two or more equations over a specified domain is called a **piecewise-defined function.**

EXAMPLE 4   A Piecewise-Defined Function

Evaluate the function when $x = -1, 0$, and 1.

$$f(x) = \begin{cases} x^2 + 1, & x < 0 \\ x - 1, & x \geq 0 \end{cases}$$

Solution   Because $x = -1$ is less than 0, use $f(x) = x^2 + 1$ to obtain $f(-1) = (-1)^2 + 1 = 2$. For $x = 0$, use $f(x) = x - 1$ to obtain $f(0) = (0) - 1 = -1$. For $x = 1$, use $f(x) = x - 1$ to obtain $f(1) = (1) - 1 = 0$.

✓ **Checkpoint** ◀))) *Audio-video solution in English & Spanish at LarsonPrecalculus.com.*

Evaluate the function given in Example 4 when $x = -2, 2$, and 3.   ◼

EXAMPLE 5 **Finding Values for Which f(x) = 0**

Find all real values of x such that $f(x) = 0$.

a. $f(x) = -2x + 10$ **b.** $f(x) = x^2 - 5x + 6$

Solution For each function, set $f(x) = 0$ and solve for x.

a. $-2x + 10 = 0$ Set $f(x)$ equal to 0.

         $-2x = -10$ Subtract 10 from each side.

            $x = 5$ Divide each side by -2.

    So, $f(x) = 0$ when $x = 5$.

b. $x^2 - 5x + 6 = 0$ Set $f(x)$ equal to 0.

   $(x - 2)(x - 3) = 0$ Factor.

       $x - 2 = 0$ ⟹ $x = 2$ Set 1st factor equal to 0.

       $x - 3 = 0$ ⟹ $x = 3$ Set 2nd factor equal to 0.

    So, $f(x) = 0$ when $x = 2$ or $x = 3$.

✓ *Checkpoint* *Audio-video solution in English & Spanish at LarsonPrecalculus.com.*

Find all real values of x such that $f(x) = 0$, where $f(x) = x^2 - 16$.

EXAMPLE 6 **Finding Values for Which f(x) = g(x)**

Find the values of x for which $f(x) = g(x)$.

a. $f(x) = x^2 + 1$ and $g(x) = 3x - x^2$

b. $f(x) = x^2 - 1$ and $g(x) = -x^2 + x + 2$

Solution

a. $x^2 + 1 = 3x - x^2$ Set $f(x)$ equal to $g(x)$.

    $2x^2 - 3x + 1 = 0$ Write in general form.

  $(2x - 1)(x - 1) = 0$ Factor.

        $2x - 1 = 0$ ⟹ $x = \frac{1}{2}$ Set 1st factor equal to 0.

        $x - 1 = 0$ ⟹ $x = 1$ Set 2nd factor equal to 0.

    So, $f(x) = g(x)$ when $x = \dfrac{1}{2}$ or $x = 1$.

b. $x^2 - 1 = -x^2 + x + 2$ Set $f(x)$ equal to $g(x)$.

     $2x^2 - x - 3 = 0$ Write in general form.

  $(2x - 3)(x + 1) = 0$ Factor.

        $2x - 3 = 0$ ⟹ $x = \frac{3}{2}$ Set 1st factor equal to 0.

        $x + 1 = 0$ ⟹ $x = -1$ Set 2nd factor equal to 0.

    So, $f(x) = g(x)$ when $x = \dfrac{3}{2}$ or $x = -1$.

✓ *Checkpoint* *Audio-video solution in English & Spanish at LarsonPrecalculus.com.*

Find the values of x for which $f(x) = g(x)$, where $f(x) = x^2 + 6x - 24$ and $g(x) = 4x - x^2$.

The Domain of a Function

▷ **TECHNOLOGY** Use a
graphing utility to graph the
functions $y = \sqrt{4 - x^2}$ and
$y = \sqrt{x^2 - 4}$. What is the
domain of each function?
Do the domains of these two
functions overlap? If so, for
what values do the domains
overlap?

The domain of a function can be described explicitly or it can be *implied* by the
expression used to define the function. The **implied domain** is the set of all real
numbers for which the expression is defined. For instance, the function

$$f(x) = \frac{1}{x^2 - 4} \qquad \text{Domain excludes } x\text{-values that result in division by zero.}$$

has an implied domain consisting of all real x other than $x = \pm 2$. These two values are
excluded from the domain because division by zero is undefined. Another common type
of implied domain is that used to avoid even roots of negative numbers. For example,
the function

$$f(x) = \sqrt{x} \qquad \text{Domain excludes } x\text{-values that result in even roots of negative numbers.}$$

is defined only for $x \geq 0$. So, its implied domain is the interval $[0, \infty)$. In general, the
domain of a function *excludes* values that would cause division by zero *or* that would
result in the even root of a negative number.

EXAMPLE 7   **Finding the Domain of a Function**

Find the domain of each function.

a. $f: \{(-3, 0), (-1, 4), (0, 2), (2, 2), (4, -1)\}$ **b.** $g(x) = \dfrac{1}{x + 5}$

c. Volume of a sphere: $V = \frac{4}{3}\pi r^3$ **d.** $h(x) = \sqrt{4 - 3x}$

Solution

a. The domain of f consists of all first coordinates in the set of ordered pairs.

   Domain $= \{-3, -1, 0, 2, 4\}$

b. Excluding x-values that yield zero in the denominator, the domain of g is the set of
all real numbers x except $x = -5$.

c. Because this function represents the volume of a sphere, the values of the radius r
must be positive. So, the domain is the set of all real numbers r such that $r > 0$.

d. This function is defined only for x-values for which

   $4 - 3x \geq 0$.

By solving this inequality, you can conclude that $x \leq \frac{4}{3}$. So, the domain is the interval
$\left(-\infty, \frac{4}{3}\right]$.

✓ *Checkpoint* Audio-video solution in English & Spanish at LarsonPrecalculus.com.

Find the domain of each function.

a. $f: \{(-2, 2), (-1, 1), (0, 3), (1, 1), (2, 2)\}$ **b.** $g(x) = \dfrac{1}{3 - x}$

c. Circumference of a circle: $C = 2\pi r$ **d.** $h(x) = \sqrt{x - 16}$

In Example 7(c), note that the domain of a function may be implied by the
physical context. For instance, from the equation

$$V = \frac{4}{3}\pi r^3$$

you would have no reason to restrict r to positive values, but the physical context
implies that a sphere cannot have a negative or zero radius.

Applications

EXAMPLE 8 **The Dimensions of a Container**

You work in the marketing department of a soft-drink company and are experimenting with a new can for iced tea that is slightly narrower and taller than a standard can. For your experimental can, the ratio of the height to the radius is 4.

a. Write the volume of the can as a function of the radius r.

b. Write the volume of the can as a function of the height h.

$\frac{h}{r} = 4$

Solution

a. $V(r) = \pi r^2 h = \pi r^2(4r) = 4\pi r^3$ Write V as a function of r.

b. $V(h) = \pi r^2 h = \pi \left(\dfrac{h}{4}\right)^2 h = \dfrac{\pi h^3}{16}$ Write V as a function of h.

✓ Checkpoint *Audio-video solution in English & Spanish at LarsonPrecalculus.com.*

For the experimental can described in Example 8, write the *surface area* as a function of (a) the radius r and (b) the height h.

EXAMPLE 9 **The Path of a Baseball**

A batter hits a baseball at a point 3 feet above ground at a velocity of 100 feet per second and an angle of 45°. The path of the baseball is given by the function

$$f(x) = -0.0032x^2 + x + 3$$

where $f(x)$ is the height of the baseball (in feet) and x is the horizontal distance from home plate (in feet). Will the baseball clear a 10-foot fence located 300 feet from home plate?

Algebraic Solution

When $x = 300$, you can find the height of the baseball as follows.

$f(x) = -0.0032x^2 + x + 3$ Write original function.

$f(300) = -0.0032(300)^2 + 300 + 3$ Substitute 300 for x.

$= 15$ Simplify.

When $x = 300$, the height of the baseball is 15 feet. So, the baseball will clear a 10-foot fence.

Graphical Solution

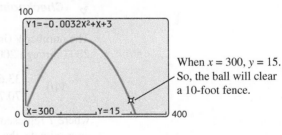

When $x = 300$, $y = 15$. So, the ball will clear a 10-foot fence.

✓ Checkpoint *Audio-video solution in English & Spanish at LarsonPrecalculus.com.*

A second baseman throws a baseball toward the first baseman 60 feet away. The path of the baseball is given by

$$f(x) = -0.004x^2 + 0.3x + 6$$

where $f(x)$ is the height of the baseball (in feet) and x is the horizontal distance from the second baseman (in feet). The first baseman can reach 8 feet high. Can the first baseman catch the baseball without jumping?

Alternative fuels for vehicles include electricity, ethanol, hydrogen, compressed natural gas, liquefied natural gas, and liquefied petroleum gas.

EXAMPLE 10 **Alternative-Fueled Vehicles**

The number V (in thousands) of alternative-fueled vehicles in the United States increased in a linear pattern from 2003 through 2005, and then increased in a different linear pattern from 2006 through 2009, as shown in the bar graph. These two patterns can be approximated by the function

$$V(t) = \begin{cases} 29.05t + 447.7, & 3 \le t \le 5 \\ 65.50t + 241.9, & 6 \le t \le 9 \end{cases}$$

where t represents the year, with $t = 3$ corresponding to 2003. Use this function to approximate the number of alternative-fueled vehicles for each year from 2003 through 2009. *(Source: U.S. Energy Information Administration)*

Number of Alternative-Fueled Vehicles in the U.S.

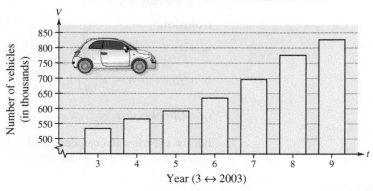

Year (3 ↔ 2003)

Solution From 2003 through 2005, use $V(t) = 29.05t + 447.7$.

534.9	563.9	593.0
2003	2004	2005

From 2006 to 2009, use $V(t) = 65.50t + 241.9$.

634.9	700.4	765.9	831.4
2006	2007	2008	2009

✓ *Checkpoint* *Audio-video solution in English & Spanish at LarsonPrecalculus.com.*

The number V (in thousands) of 85%-ethanol-fueled vehicles in the United States from 2003 through 2009 can be approximated by the function

$$V(t) = \begin{cases} 33.65t + 77.8, & 3 \le t \le 5 \\ 70.75t - 126.6, & 6 \le t \le 9 \end{cases}$$

where t represents the year, with $t = 3$ corresponding to 2003. Use this function to approximate the number of 85%-ethanol-fueled vehicles for each year from 2003 through 2009. *(Source: U.S. Energy Information Administration)*

Difference Quotients

One of the basic definitions in calculus employs the ratio

$$\frac{f(x + h) - f(x)}{h}, \quad h \ne 0.$$

This ratio is called a **difference quotient,** as illustrated in Example 11.

EXAMPLE 11   **Evaluating a Difference Quotient**

·· REMARK You may find it easier to calculate the difference quotient in Example 11 by first finding $f(x + h)$, and then substituting the resulting expression into the difference quotient

$$\frac{f(x + h) - f(x)}{h}.$$

For $f(x) = x^2 - 4x + 7$, find $\dfrac{f(x + h) - f(x)}{h}$.

Solution

$$\frac{f(x + h) - f(x)}{h} = \frac{[(x + h)^2 - 4(x + h) + 7] - (x^2 - 4x + 7)}{h}$$

$$= \frac{x^2 + 2xh + h^2 - 4x - 4h + 7 - x^2 + 4x - 7}{h}$$

$$= \frac{2xh + h^2 - 4h}{h} = \frac{h(2x + h - 4)}{h} = 2x + h - 4, \quad h \neq 0$$

✓ Checkpoint ◀))) *Audio-video solution in English & Spanish at LarsonPrecalculus.com.*

For $f(x) = x^2 + 2x - 3$, find $\dfrac{f(x + h) - f(x)}{h}$. ∎

Summary of Function Terminology

Function: A **function** is a relationship between two variables such that to each value of the independent variable there corresponds exactly one value of the dependent variable.

Function Notation: $y = f(x)$

     f is the *name* of the function.

     y is the **dependent variable.**

     x is the **independent variable.**

     $f(x)$ is the *value of the function at x.*

Domain: The **domain** of a function is the set of all values (inputs) of the independent variable for which the function is defined. If x is in the domain of f, then f is said to be *defined* at x. If x is not in the domain of f, then f is said to be *undefined* at x.

Range: The **range** of a function is the set of all values (outputs) assumed by the dependent variable (that is, the set of all function values).

Implied Domain: If f is defined by an algebraic expression and the domain is not specified, then the **implied domain** consists of all real numbers for which the expression is defined.

Summarize (Section 1.4)

1. State the definition of a function and describe function notation *(pages 35–38)*. For examples of determining functions and using function notation, see Examples 1–6.

2. State the definition of the implied domain of a function *(page 40)*. For an example of finding the domains of functions, see Example 7.

3. Describe examples of how functions can model real-life problems *(pages 41 and 42, Examples 8–10)*.

4. State the definition of a difference quotient *(page 42)*. For an example of evaluating a difference quotient, see Example 11.

1.4 Exercises

See CalcChat.com for tutorial help and worked-out solutions to odd-numbered exercises.

Vocabulary: Fill in the blanks.

1. A relation that assigns to each element x from a set of inputs, or _____, exactly one element y in a set of outputs, or _____, is called a _____.

2. For an equation that represents y as a function of x, the set of all values taken on by the _____ variable x is the domain, and the set of all values taken on by the _____ variable y is the range.

3. If the domain of the function f is not given, then the set of values of the independent variable for which the expression is defined is called the _____ _____.

4. In calculus, one of the basic definitions is that of a _____ _____, given by $\dfrac{f(x+h)-f(x)}{h}$, $h \neq 0$.

Skills and Applications

Testing for Functions In Exercises 5–8, determine whether the relation represents y as a function of x.

5. Domain, x   Range, y

6. Domain, x   Range, y

7.

Input, x	10	7	4	7	10
Output, y	3	6	9	12	15

8.

Input, x	0	3	9	12	15
Output, y	3	3	3	3	3

Testing for Functions In Exercises 9 and 10, which sets of ordered pairs represent functions from A to B? Explain.

9. $A = \{0, 1, 2, 3\}$ and $B = \{-2, -1, 0, 1, 2\}$
    (a) $\{(0, 1), (1, -2), (2, 0), (3, 2)\}$
    (b) $\{(0, -1), (2, 2), (1, -2), (3, 0), (1, 1)\}$
    (c) $\{(0, 0), (1, 0), (2, 0), (3, 0)\}$
    (d) $\{(0, 2), (3, 0), (1, 1)\}$

10. $A = \{a, b, c\}$ and $B = \{0, 1, 2, 3\}$
    (a) $\{(a, 1), (c, 2), (c, 3), (b, 3)\}$
    (b) $\{(a, 1), (b, 2), (c, 3)\}$
    (c) $\{(1, a), (0, a), (2, c), (3, b)\}$
    (d) $\{(c, 0), (b, 0), (a, 3)\}$

Testing for Functions Represented Algebraically
In Exercises 11–20, determine whether the equation represents y as a function of x.

11. $x^2 + y^2 = 4$
12. $x^2 + y = 4$
13. $2x + 3y = 4$
14. $(x - 2)^2 + y^2 = 4$
15. $y = \sqrt{16 - x^2}$
16. $y = \sqrt{x + 5}$
17. $y = |4 - x|$
18. $|y| = 4 - x$
19. $y = -75$
20. $x - 1 = 0$

Evaluating a Function In Exercises 21–32, evaluate (if possible) the function at each specified value of the independent variable and simplify.

21. $f(x) = 2x - 3$
    (a) $f(1)$ (b) $f(-3)$ (c) $f(x - 1)$

22. $V(r) = \frac{4}{3}\pi r^3$
    (a) $V(3)$ (b) $V\left(\frac{3}{2}\right)$ (c) $V(2r)$

23. $g(t) = 4t^2 - 3t + 5$
    (a) $g(2)$ (b) $g(t - 2)$ (c) $g(t) - g(2)$

24. $h(t) = t^2 - 2t$
    (a) $h(2)$ (b) $h(1.5)$ (c) $h(x + 2)$

25. $f(y) = 3 - \sqrt{y}$
    (a) $f(4)$ (b) $f(0.25)$ (c) $f(4x^2)$

26. $f(x) = \sqrt{x + 8} + 2$
    (a) $f(-8)$ (b) $f(1)$ (c) $f(x - 8)$

27. $q(x) = 1/(x^2 - 9)$
    (a) $q(0)$ (b) $q(3)$ (c) $q(y + 3)$

28. $q(t) = (2t^2 + 3)/t^2$
    (a) $q(2)$ (b) $q(0)$ (c) $q(-x)$

29. $f(x) = |x|/x$
    (a) $f(2)$ (b) $f(-2)$ (c) $f(x - 1)$

30. $f(x) = |x| + 4$
    (a) $f(2)$ (b) $f(-2)$ (c) $f(x^2)$

31. $f(x) = \begin{cases} 2x + 1, & x < 0 \\ 2x + 2, & x \geq 0 \end{cases}$
    (a) $f(-1)$ (b) $f(0)$ (c) $f(2)$

32. $f(x) = \begin{cases} 4 - 5x, & x \leq -2 \\ 0, & -2 < x < 2 \\ x^2 + 1, & x \geq 2 \end{cases}$
    (a) $f(-3)$ (b) $f(4)$ (c) $f(-1)$

Evaluating a Function In Exercises 33–36, complete the table.

33. $f(x) = x^2 - 3$

x	-2	-1	0	1	2
$f(x)$					

34. $h(t) = \frac{1}{2}|t + 3|$

t	-5	-4	-3	-2	-1
$h(t)$					

35. $f(x) = \begin{cases} -\frac{1}{2}x + 4, & x \le 0 \\ (x - 2)^2, & x > 0 \end{cases}$

x	-2	-1	0	1	2
$f(x)$					

36. $f(x) = \begin{cases} 9 - x^2, & x < 3 \\ x - 3, & x \ge 3 \end{cases}$

x	1	2	3	4	5
$f(x)$					

Finding Values for Which $f(x) = 0$ **In Exercises 37–44, find all real values of** x **such that** $f(x) = 0$.

37. $f(x) = 15 - 3x$

38. $f(x) = 5x + 1$

39. $f(x) = \dfrac{3x - 4}{5}$

40. $f(x) = \dfrac{12 - x^2}{5}$

41. $f(x) = x^2 - 9$

42. $f(x) = x^2 - 8x + 15$

43. $f(x) = x^3 - x$

44. $f(x) = x^3 - x^2 - 4x + 4$

Finding Values for Which $f(x) = g(x)$ **In Exercises 45–48, find the value(s) of** x **for which** $f(x) = g(x)$.

45. $f(x) = x^2, \quad g(x) = x + 2$

46. $f(x) = x^2 + 2x + 1, \quad g(x) = 7x - 5$

47. $f(x) = x^4 - 2x^2, \quad g(x) = 2x^2$

48. $f(x) = \sqrt{x} - 4, \quad g(x) = 2 - x$

Finding the Domain of a Function In Exercises 49–60, find the domain of the function.

49. $f(x) = 5x^2 + 2x - 1$

50. $g(x) = 1 - 2x^2$

51. $h(t) = \dfrac{4}{t}$

52. $s(y) = \dfrac{3y}{y + 5}$

53. $g(y) = \sqrt{y - 10}$

54. $f(t) = \sqrt[3]{t + 4}$

55. $g(x) = \dfrac{1}{x} - \dfrac{3}{x + 2}$

56. $h(x) = \dfrac{10}{x^2 - 2x}$

57. $f(s) = \dfrac{\sqrt{s - 1}}{s - 4}$

58. $f(x) = \dfrac{\sqrt{x + 6}}{6 + x}$

59. $f(x) = \dfrac{x - 4}{\sqrt{x}}$

60. $f(x) = \dfrac{x + 2}{\sqrt{x - 10}}$

61. Maximum Volume An open box of maximum volume is to be made from a square piece of material 24 centimeters on a side by cutting equal squares from the corners and turning up the sides (see figure).

(a) The table shows the volumes V (in cubic centimeters) of the box for various heights x (in centimeters). Use the table to estimate the maximum volume.

Height, x	1	2	3	4	5	6
Volume, V	484	800	972	1024	980	864

(b) Plot the points (x, V) from the table in part (a). Does the relation defined by the ordered pairs represent V as a function of x?

(c) Given that V is a function of x, write the function and determine its domain.

62. Maximum Profit The cost per unit in the production of an MP3 player is \$60. The manufacturer charges \$90 per unit for orders of 100 or less. To encourage large orders, the manufacturer reduces the charge by \$0.15 per MP3 player for each unit ordered in excess of 100 (for example, there would be a charge of \$87 per MP3 player for an order size of 120).

(a) The table shows the profits P (in dollars) for various numbers of units ordered, x. Use the table to estimate the maximum profit.

Units, x	130	140	150	160	170
Profit, P	3315	3360	3375	3360	3315

(b) Plot the points (x, P) from the table in part (a). Does the relation defined by the ordered pairs represent P as a function of x?

(c) Given that P is a function of x, write the function and determine its domain. (*Note:* $P = R - C$, where R is revenue and C is cost.)

63. Geometry Write the area A of a square as a function of its perimeter P.

64. Geometry Write the area A of a circle as a function of its circumference C.

65. Path of a Ball The height y (in feet) of a baseball thrown by a child is

$$y = -\frac{1}{10}x^2 + 3x + 6$$

where x is the horizontal distance (in feet) from where the ball was thrown. Will the ball fly over the head of another child 30 feet away trying to catch the ball? (Assume that the child who is trying to catch the ball holds a baseball glove at a height of 5 feet.)

66. Postal Regulations A rectangular package to be sent by the U.S. Postal Service can have a maximum combined length and girth (perimeter of a cross section) of 108 inches (see figure).

(a) Write the volume V of the package as a function of x. What is the domain of the function?

(b) Use a graphing utility to graph the function. Be sure to use an appropriate window setting.

(c) What dimensions will maximize the volume of the package? Explain your answer.

67. Geometry A right triangle is formed in the first quadrant by the x- and y-axes and a line through the point $(2, 1)$ (see figure). Write the area A of the triangle as a function of x, and determine the domain of the function.

Figure for 67   Figure for 68

68. Geometry A rectangle is bounded by the x-axis and the semicircle $y = \sqrt{36 - x^2}$ (see figure). Write the area A of the rectangle as a function of x, and graphically determine the domain of the function.

69. Prescription Drugs The percents p of prescriptions filled with generic drugs in the United States from 2004 through 2010 (see figure) can be approximated by the model

$$p(t) = \begin{cases} 4.57t + 27.3, & 4 \le t \le 7 \\ 3.35t + 37.6, & 8 \le t \le 10 \end{cases}$$

where t represents the year, with $t = 4$ corresponding to 2004. Use this model to find the percent of prescriptions filled with generic drugs in each year from 2004 through 2010. (*Source: National Association of Chain Drug Stores*)

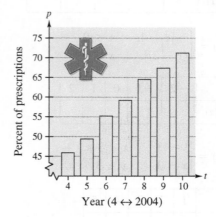

Year (4 ↔ 2004)

70. Median Sale Price The median sale prices p (in thousands of dollars) of an existing one-family home in the United States from 2000 through 2010 (see figure) can be approximated by the model

$$p(t) = \begin{cases} 0.438t^2 + 10.81t + 145.9, & 0 \le t \le 6 \\ 5.575t^2 - 110.67t + 720.8, & 7 \le t \le 10 \end{cases}$$

where t represents the year, with $t = 0$ corresponding to 2000. Use this model to find the median sale price of an existing one-family home in each year from 2000 through 2010. (*Source: National Association of Realtors*)

Year (0 ↔ 2000)

71. Cost, Revenue, and Profit A company produces a product for which the variable cost is $12.30 per unit and the fixed costs are $98,000. The product sells for $17.98. Let x be the number of units produced and sold.

(a) The total cost for a business is the sum of the variable cost and the fixed costs. Write the total cost C as a function of the number of units produced.

(b) Write the revenue R as a function of the number of units sold.

(c) Write the profit P as a function of the number of units sold. (*Note: $P = R - C$*)

72. Average Cost The inventor of a new game believes that the variable cost for producing the game is $0.95 per unit and the fixed costs are $6000. The inventor sells each game for $1.69. Let x be the number of games sold.

(a) The total cost for a business is the sum of the variable cost and the fixed costs. Write the total cost C as a function of the number of games sold.

(b) Write the average cost per unit $\overline{C} = C/x$ as a function of x.

73. Height of a Balloon A balloon carrying a transmitter ascends vertically from a point 3000 feet from the receiving station.

(a) Draw a diagram that gives a visual representation of the problem. Let h represent the height of the balloon and let d represent the distance between the balloon and the receiving station.

(b) Write the height of the balloon as a function of d. What is the domain of the function?

• • **74. Physics** • • • • • • • • • • • • • • • • •

The function $F(y) = 149.76\sqrt{10}\,y^{5/2}$ estimates the force F (in tons) of water against the face of a dam, where y is the depth of the water (in feet).

(a) Complete the table. What can you conclude from the table?

y	5	10	20	30	40
$F(y)$					

(b) Use the table to approximate the depth at which the force against the dam is 1,000,000 tons.

(c) Find the depth at which the force against the dam is 1,000,000 tons algebraically.

75. Transportation For groups of 80 or more people, a charter bus company determines the rate per person according to the formula

$$\text{Rate} = 8 - 0.05(n - 80), \quad n \geq 80$$

where the rate is given in dollars and n is the number of people.

(a) Write the revenue R for the bus company as a function of n.

(b) Use the function in part (a) to complete the table. What can you conclude?

n	90	100	110	120	130	140	150
$R(n)$							

76. E-Filing The table shows the numbers of tax returns (in millions) made through e-file from 2003 through 2010. Let $f(t)$ represent the number of tax returns made through e-file in the year t. (*Source: Internal Revenue Service*)

DATA	Year	Number of Tax Returns Made Through E-File
	2003	52.9
	2004	61.5
	2005	68.5
	2006	73.3
	2007	80.0
	2008	89.9
	2009	95.0
	2010	98.7

Spreadsheet at LarsonPrecalculus.com

(a) Find $\dfrac{f(2010) - f(2003)}{2010 - 2003}$ and interpret the result in the context of the problem.

(b) Make a scatter plot of the data.

(c) Find a linear model for the data algebraically. Let N represent the number of tax returns made through e-file and let $t = 3$ correspond to 2003.

(d) Use the model found in part (c) to complete the table.

t	3	4	5	6	7	8	9	10
N								

(e) Compare your results from part (d) with the actual data.

(f) Use a graphing utility to find a linear model for the data. Let $x = 3$ correspond to 2003. How does the model you found in part (c) compare with the model given by the graphing utility?

f **Evaluating a Difference Quotient** **In Exercises 77–84, find the difference quotient and simplify your answer.**

77. $f(x) = x^2 - x + 1$, $\dfrac{f(2 + h) - f(2)}{h}$, $h \neq 0$

78. $f(x) = 5x - x^2$, $\dfrac{f(5 + h) - f(5)}{h}$, $h \neq 0$

79. $f(x) = x^3 + 3x$, $\dfrac{f(x + h) - f(x)}{h}$, $h \neq 0$

80. $f(x) = 4x^2 - 2x$, $\dfrac{f(x + h) - f(x)}{h}$, $h \neq 0$

81. $g(x) = \dfrac{1}{x^2}$, $\dfrac{g(x) - g(3)}{x - 3}$, $x \neq 3$

82. $f(t) = \dfrac{1}{t - 2}$, $\dfrac{f(t) - f(1)}{t - 1}$, $t \neq 1$

83. $f(x) = \sqrt{5x}$, $\dfrac{f(x) - f(5)}{x - 5}$, $x \neq 5$

84. $f(x) = x^{2/3} + 1$, $\dfrac{f(x) - f(8)}{x - 8}$, $x \neq 8$

Matching and Determining Constants **In Exercises 85–88, match the data with one of the following functions**

$$f(x) = cx, \; g(x) = cx^2, \; h(x) = c\sqrt{|x|}, \; \text{and} \; r(x) = \dfrac{c}{x}$$

and determine the value of the constant c that will make the function fit the data in the table.

85.

x	-4	-1	0	1	4
y	-32	-2	0	-2	-32

86.

x	-4	-1	0	1	4
y	-1	$-\frac{1}{4}$	0	$\frac{1}{4}$	1

87.

x	-4	-1	0	1	4
y	-8	-32	Undefined	32	8

88.

x	-4	-1	0	1	4
y	6	3	0	3	6

Exploration

True or False? **In Exercises 89–92, determine whether the statement is true or false. Justify your answer.**

89. Every relation is a function.

90. Every function is a relation.

91. For the function

$$f(x) = x^4 - 1$$

the domain is $(-\infty, \infty)$ and the range is $(0, \infty)$.

92. The set of ordered pairs $\{(-8, -2), (-6, 0), (-4, 0), (-2, 2), (0, 4), (2, -2)\}$ represents a function.

93. **Think About It**   Consider

$$f(x) = \sqrt{x - 1} \quad \text{and} \quad g(x) = \dfrac{1}{\sqrt{x - 1}}.$$

Why are the domains of f and g different?

94. **Think About It**   Consider

$$f(x) = \sqrt{x - 2} \text{ and } g(x) = \sqrt[3]{x - 2}.$$

Why are the domains of f and g different?

95. **Think About It**   Given

$$f(x) = x^2$$

is f the independent variable? Why or why not?

96. **HOW DO YOU SEE IT?**   The graph represents the height h of a projectile after t seconds.

(a) Explain why h is a function of t.

(b) Approximate the height of the projectile after 0.5 second and after 1.25 seconds.

(c) Approximate the domain of h.

(d) Is t a function of h? Explain.

Think About It   **In Exercises 97 and 98, determine whether the statements use the word *function* in ways that are mathematically correct. Explain your reasoning.**

97. (a) The sales tax on a purchased item is a function of the selling price.

   (b) Your score on the next algebra exam is a function of the number of hours you study the night before the exam.

98. (a) The amount in your savings account is a function of your salary.

   (b) The speed at which a free-falling baseball strikes the ground is a function of the height from which it was dropped.

1.5 Analyzing Graphs of Functions

Graphs of functions can help you visualize relationships between variables in real life. For instance, in Exercise 90 on page 59, you will use the graph of a function to visually represent the temperature of a city over a 24-hour period.

■ Use the Vertical Line Test for functions.
■ Find the zeros of functions.
■ Determine intervals on which functions are increasing or decreasing and determine relative maximum and relative minimum values of functions.
■ Determine the average rate of change of a function.
■ Identify even and odd functions.

The Graph of a Function

In Section 1.4, you studied functions from an algebraic point of view. In this section, you will study functions from a graphical perspective.

The **graph of a function** f is the collection of ordered pairs $(x, f(x))$ such that x is in the domain of f. As you study this section, remember that

x = the directed distance from the y-axis

$y = f(x)$ = the directed distance from the x-axis

as shown in the figure at the right.

EXAMPLE 1   Finding the Domain and Range of a Function

Use the graph of the function f, shown in Figure 1.34, to find (a) the domain of f, (b) the function values $f(-1)$ and $f(2)$, and (c) the range of f.

Solution

a. The closed dot at $(-1, 1)$ indicates that $x = -1$ is in the domain of f, whereas the open dot at $(5, 2)$ indicates that $x = 5$ is not in the domain. So, the domain of f is all x in the interval $[-1, 5)$.

b. Because $(-1, 1)$ is a point on the graph of f, it follows that $f(-1) = 1$. Similarly, because $(2, -3)$ is a point on the graph of f, it follows that $f(2) = -3$.

c. Because the graph does not extend below $f(2) = -3$ or above $f(0) = 3$, the range of f is the interval $[-3, 3]$.

Figure 1.34

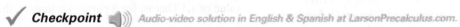

• •REMARK The use of dots (open or closed) at the extreme left and right points of a graph indicates that the graph does not extend beyond these points. If such dots are not on the graph, then assume that the graph extends beyond these points.

✓ **Checkpoint** 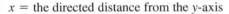 *Audio-video solution in English & Spanish at LarsonPrecalculus.com.*

Use the graph of the function f to find (a) the domain of f, (b) the function values $f(0)$ and $f(3)$, and (c) the range of f.

By the definition of a function, at most one y-value corresponds to a given x-value. This means that the graph of a function cannot have two or more different points with the same x-coordinate, and no two points on the graph of a function can be vertically above or below each other. It follows, then, that a vertical line can intersect the graph of a function at most once. This observation provides a convenient visual test called the **Vertical Line Test** for functions.

Vertical Line Test for Functions

A set of points in a coordinate plane is the graph of y as a function of x if and only if no *vertical* line intersects the graph at more than one point.

EXAMPLE 2   **Vertical Line Test for Functions**

Use the Vertical Line Test to decide whether each of the following graphs represents y as a function of x.

(a)

(b)

(c)

Solution

a. This *is not* a graph of y as a function of x, because there are vertical lines that intersect the graph twice. That is, for a particular input x, there is more than one output y.

b. This *is* a graph of y as a function of x, because every vertical line intersects the graph at most once. That is, for a particular input x, there is at most one output y.

c. This *is* a graph of y as a function of x. (Note that when a vertical line does not intersect the graph, it simply means that the function is undefined for that particular value of x.) That is, for a particular input x, there is at most one output y.

✓ **Checkpoint** ◀))) *Audio-video solution in English & Spanish at LarsonPrecalculus.com.*

Use the Vertical Line Test to decide whether the graph represents y as a function of x.

▷ **TECHNOLOGY** Most graphing utilities graph functions of x more easily than other types of equations. For instance, the graph shown in (a) above represents the equation $x - (y - 1)^2 = 0$. To use a graphing utility to duplicate this graph, you must first solve the equation for y to obtain $y = 1 \pm \sqrt{x}$, and then graph the two equations $y_1 = 1 + \sqrt{x}$ and $y_2 = 1 - \sqrt{x}$ in the same viewing window.

Zeros of a Function

▷ **ALGEBRA HELP** To do
Example 3, you need to be able
to solve equations. You can
review the techniques for solving
equations in Appendix A.5.

If the graph of a function of x has an x-intercept at $(a, 0)$, then a is a **zero** of the function.

Zeros of a Function

The **zeros of a function** f of x are the x-values for which $f(x) = 0$.

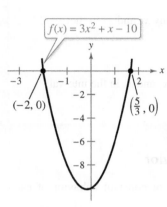

Zeros of f: $x = -2$, $x = \frac{5}{3}$
Figure 1.35

EXAMPLE 3   **Finding the Zeros of a Function**

Find the zeros of each function.

a. $f(x) = 3x^2 + x - 10$

b. $g(x) = \sqrt{10 - x^2}$

c. $h(t) = \dfrac{2t - 3}{t + 5}$

Solution   To find the zeros of a function, set the function equal to zero and solve for the independent variable.

a. $3x^2 + x - 10 = 0$ Set $f(x)$ equal to 0.

$\qquad (3x - 5)(x + 2) = 0$ Factor.

$\qquad\qquad 3x - 5 = 0 \implies x = \frac{5}{3}$ Set 1st factor equal to 0.

$\qquad\qquad x + 2 = 0 \implies x = -2$ Set 2nd factor equal to 0.

The zeros of f are $x = \frac{5}{3}$ and $x = -2$. In Figure 1.35, note that the graph of f has $\left(\frac{5}{3}, 0\right)$ and $(-2, 0)$ as its x-intercepts.

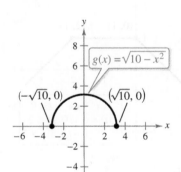

Zeros of g: $x = \pm\sqrt{10}$
Figure 1.36

b. $\sqrt{10 - x^2} = 0$ Set $g(x)$ equal to 0.

$\qquad 10 - x^2 = 0$ Square each side.

$\qquad\qquad 10 = x^2$ Add x^2 to each side.

$\qquad\quad \pm\sqrt{10} = x$ Extract square roots.

The zeros of g are $x = -\sqrt{10}$ and $x = \sqrt{10}$. In Figure 1.36, note that the graph of g has $\left(-\sqrt{10}, 0\right)$ and $\left(\sqrt{10}, 0\right)$ as its x-intercepts.

c. $\dfrac{2t - 3}{t + 5} = 0$ Set $h(t)$ equal to 0.

$\qquad 2t - 3 = 0$ Multiply each side by $t + 5$.

$\qquad\qquad 2t = 3$ Add 3 to each side.

$\qquad\qquad t = \dfrac{3}{2}$ Divide each side by 2.

The zero of h is $t = \frac{3}{2}$. In Figure 1.37, note that the graph of h has $\left(\frac{3}{2}, 0\right)$ as its t-intercept.

✓ **Checkpoint**))) Audio-video solution in English & Spanish at LarsonPrecalculus.com.

Find the zeros of each function.

a. $f(x) = 2x^2 + 13x - 24$ **b.** $g(t) = \sqrt{t - 25}$ **c.** $h(x) = \dfrac{x^2 - 2}{x - 1}$

Zero of h: $t = \frac{3}{2}$
Figure 1.37

Increasing and Decreasing Functions

The more you know about the graph of a function, the more you know about the function itself. Consider the graph shown in Figure 1.38. As you move from *left to right*, this graph falls from $x = -2$ to $x = 0$, is constant from $x = 0$ to $x = 2$, and rises from $x = 2$ to $x = 4$.

Increasing, Decreasing, and Constant Functions

A function f is **increasing** on an interval when, for any x_1 and x_2 in the interval,

$$x_1 < x_2 \quad \text{implies} \quad f(x_1) < f(x_2).$$

A function f is **decreasing** on an interval when, for any x_1 and x_2 in the interval,

$$x_1 < x_2 \quad \text{implies} \quad f(x_1) > f(x_2).$$

A function f is **constant** on an interval when, for any x_1 and x_2 in the interval,

$$f(x_1) = f(x_2).$$

Figure 1.38

EXAMPLE 4   **Describing Function Behavior**

Use the graphs to describe the increasing, decreasing, or constant behavior of each function.

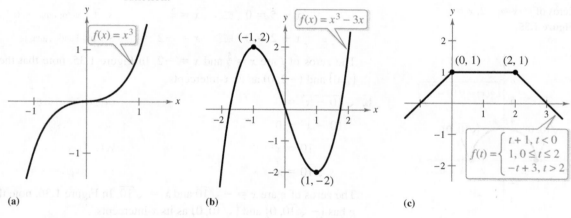

(a)   (b)   (c)

Solution

a. This function is increasing over the entire real line.

b. This function is increasing on the interval $(-\infty, -1)$, decreasing on the interval $(-1, 1)$, and increasing on the interval $(1, \infty)$.

c. This function is increasing on the interval $(-\infty, 0)$, constant on the interval $(0, 2)$, and decreasing on the interval $(2, \infty)$.

✓ **Checkpoint** ◀))) Audio-video solution in English & Spanish at LarsonPrecalculus.com.

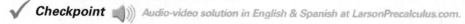

Graph the function

$$f(x) = x^3 + 3x^2 - 1.$$

Then use the graph to describe the increasing and decreasing behavior of the function.

To help you decide whether a function is increasing, decreasing, or constant on an interval, you can evaluate the function for several values of x. However, you need calculus to determine, for certain, all intervals on which a function is increasing, decreasing, or constant.

The points at which a function changes its increasing, decreasing, or constant behavior are helpful in determining the **relative minimum** or **relative maximum** values of the function.

REMARK A relative minimum or relative maximum is also referred to as a local minimum or local maximum.

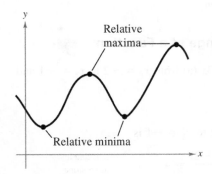

Relative maxima

Relative minima

Figure 1.39

Definitions of Relative Minimum and Relative Maximum

A function value $f(a)$ is called a **relative minimum** of f when there exists an interval (x_1, x_2) that contains a such that

$$x_1 < x < x_2 \quad \text{implies} \quad f(a) \le f(x).$$

A function value $f(a)$ is called a **relative maximum** of f when there exists an interval (x_1, x_2) that contains a such that

$$x_1 < x < x_2 \quad \text{implies} \quad f(a) \ge f(x).$$

Figure 1.39 shows several different examples of relative minima and relative maxima. In Section 2.1, you will study a technique for finding the *exact point* at which a second-degree polynomial function has a relative minimum or relative maximum. For the time being, however, you can use a graphing utility to find reasonable approximations of these points.

EXAMPLE 5   **Approximating a Relative Minimum**

Use a graphing utility to approximate the relative minimum of the function

$$f(x) = 3x^2 - 4x - 2.$$

Solution   The graph of f is shown in Figure 1.40. By using the *zoom* and *trace* features or the *minimum* feature of a graphing utility, you can estimate that the function has a relative minimum at the point

$$(0.67, -3.33). \qquad \text{Relative minimum}$$

Later, in Section 2.1, you will be able to determine that the exact point at which the relative minimum occurs is $\left(\frac{2}{3}, -\frac{10}{3}\right)$.

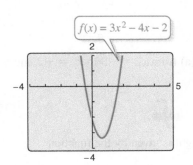

$f(x) = 3x^2 - 4x - 2$

Figure 1.40

✔ *Checkpoint* 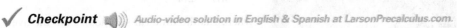 Audio-video solution in English & Spanish at LarsonPrecalculus.com.

Use a graphing utility to approximate the relative maximum of the function

$$f(x) = -4x^2 - 7x + 3.$$

You can also use the *table* feature of a graphing utility to numerically approximate the relative minimum of the function in Example 5. Using a table that begins at 0.6 and increments the value of x by 0.01, you can approximate that the minimum of $f(x) = 3x^2 - 4x - 2$ occurs at the point $(0.67, -3.33)$.

▷ **TECHNOLOGY** When you use a graphing utility to estimate the x- and y-values of a relative minimum or relative maximum, the *zoom* feature will often produce graphs that are nearly flat. To overcome this problem, you can manually change the vertical setting of the viewing window. The graph will stretch vertically when the values of Ymin and Ymax are closer together.

Average Rate of Change

In Section 1.3, you learned that the slope of a line can be interpreted as a *rate of change*. For a nonlinear graph whose slope changes at each point, the **average rate of change** between any two points $(x_1, f(x_1))$ and $(x_2, f(x_2))$ is the slope of the line through the two points (see Figure 1.41). The line through the two points is called the **secant line,** and the slope of this line is denoted as m_{sec}.

$$\text{Average rate of change of } f \text{ from } x_1 \text{ to } x_2 = \frac{f(x_2) - f(x_1)}{x_2 - x_1}$$

$$= \frac{\text{change in } y}{\text{change in } x}$$

$$= m_{sec}$$

Figure 1.41

 EXAMPLE 6   **Average Rate of Change of a Function**

Find the average rates of change of $f(x) = x^3 - 3x$ (a) from $x_1 = -2$ to $x_2 = -1$ and (b) from $x_1 = 0$ to $x_2 = 1$ (see Figure 1.42).

Solution

a. The average rate of change of f from $x_1 = -2$ to $x_2 = -1$ is

$$\frac{f(x_2) - f(x_1)}{x_2 - x_1} = \frac{f(-1) - f(-2)}{-1 - (-2)} = \frac{2 - (-2)}{1} = 4. \qquad \text{Secant line has positive slope.}$$

b. The average rate of change of f from $x_1 = 0$ to $x_2 = 1$ is

$$\frac{f(x_2) - f(x_1)}{x_2 - x_1} = \frac{f(1) - f(0)}{1 - 0} = \frac{-2 - 0}{1} = -2. \qquad \text{Secant line has negative slope.}$$

 ✓ *Checkpoint* ◄))) *Audio-video solution in English & Spanish at LarsonPrecalculus.com.*

Find the average rates of change of $f(x) = x^2 + 2x$ (a) from $x_1 = -3$ to $x_2 = -2$ and (b) from $x_1 = -2$ to $x_2 = 0$.

Figure 1.42

Average speed is an average rate of change.

EXAMPLE 7   **Finding Average Speed** 𝑓

The distance s (in feet) a moving car is from a stoplight is given by the function

$$s(t) = 20t^{3/2}$$

where t is the time (in seconds). Find the average speed of the car (a) from $t_1 = 0$ to $t_2 = 4$ seconds and (b) from $t_1 = 4$ to $t_2 = 9$ seconds.

Solution

a. The average speed of the car from $t_1 = 0$ to $t_2 = 4$ seconds is

$$\frac{s(t_2) - s(t_1)}{t_2 - t_1} = \frac{s(4) - s(0)}{4 - 0} = \frac{160 - 0}{4} = 40 \text{ feet per second.}$$

b. The average speed of the car from $t_1 = 4$ to $t_2 = 9$ seconds is

$$\frac{s(t_2) - s(t_1)}{t_2 - t_1} = \frac{s(9) - s(4)}{9 - 4} = \frac{540 - 160}{5} = 76 \text{ feet per second.}$$

✓ *Checkpoint* ◄))) *Audio-video solution in English & Spanish at LarsonPrecalculus.com.*

In Example 7, find the average speed of the car (a) from $t_1 = 0$ to $t_2 = 1$ second and (b) from $t_1 = 1$ second to $t_2 = 4$ seconds. ■

Even and Odd Functions

In Section 1.2, you studied different types of symmetry of a graph. In the terminology of functions, a function is said to be **even** when its graph is symmetric with respect to the *y*-axis and **odd** when its graph is symmetric with respect to the origin. The symmetry tests in Section 1.2 yield the following tests for even and odd functions.

Tests for Even and Odd Functions

A function $y = f(x)$ is **even** when, for each x in the domain of f, $f(-x) = f(x)$.

A function $y = f(x)$ is **odd** when, for each x in the domain of f, $f(-x) = -f(x)$.

EXAMPLE 8 **Even and Odd Functions**

a. The function $g(x) = x^3 - x$ is odd because $g(-x) = -g(x)$, as follows.

$$g(-x) = (-x)^3 - (-x) \qquad \text{Substitute } -x \text{ for } x.$$

$$= -x^3 + x \qquad \text{Simplify.}$$

$$= -(x^3 - x) \qquad \text{Distributive Property}$$

$$= -g(x) \qquad \text{Test for odd function}$$

b. The function $h(x) = x^2 + 1$ is even because $h(-x) = h(x)$, as follows.

$$h(-x) = (-x)^2 + 1 \qquad \text{Substitute } -x \text{ for } x.$$

$$= x^2 + 1 \qquad \text{Simplify.}$$

$$= h(x) \qquad \text{Test for even function}$$

Figure 1.43 shows the graphs and symmetry of these two functions.

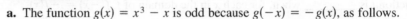

✓ **Checkpoint** ◀))) *Audio-video solution in English & Spanish at LarsonPrecalculus.com.*

Determine whether the function is even, odd, or neither. Then describe the symmetry.

a. $f(x) = 5 - 3x$ **b.** $g(x) = x^4 - x^2 - 1$ **c.** $h(x) = 2x^3 + 3x$

(a) Symmetric to origin: Odd Function

(b) Symmetric to *y*-axis: Even Function

Figure 1.43

Summarize (Section 1.5)

1. State the Vertical Line Test for functions *(page 50)*. For an example of using the Vertical Line Test, see Example 2.

2. Explain how to find the zeros of a function *(page 51)*. For an example of finding the zeros of functions, see Example 3.

3. Explain how to determine intervals on which functions are increasing or decreasing *(page 52)* and how to determine relative maximum and relative minimum values of functions *(page 53)*. For an example of describing function behavior, see Example 4. For an example of approximating a relative minimum, see Example 5.

4. Explain how to determine the average rate of change of a function *(page 54)*. For examples of determining average rates of change, see Examples 6 and 7.

5. State the definitions of an even function and an odd function *(page 55)*. For an example of identifying even and odd functions, see Example 8.

1.5 Exercises

See **CalcChat.com** for tutorial help and worked-out solutions to odd-numbered exercises.

Vocabulary: Fill in the blanks.

1. The _____ _____ _____ is used to determine whether the graph of an equation is a function of y in terms of x.

2. The _____ of a function f are the values of x for which $f(x) = 0$.

3. A function f is _____ on an interval when, for any x_1 and x_2 in the interval, $x_1 < x_2$ implies $f(x_1) > f(x_2)$.

4. A function value $f(a)$ is a relative _____ of f when there exists an interval (x_1, x_2) containing a such that $x_1 < x < x_2$ implies $f(a) \geq f(x)$.

5. The _____ _____ _____ _____ between any two points $(x_1, f(x_1))$ and $(x_2, f(x_2))$ is the slope of the line through the two points, and this line is called the _____ line.

6. A function f is _____ when, for each x in the domain of f, $f(-x) = -f(x)$.

Skills and Applications

Domain, Range, and Values of a Function In Exercises 7–10, use the graph of the function to find the domain and range of f and the indicated function values.

7. (a) $f(-2)$ (b) $f(-1)$ 8. (a) $f(-1)$ (b) $f(2)$
    (c) $f\left(\frac{1}{2}\right)$ (d) $f(1)$ (c) $f(0)$ (d) $f(1)$

9. (a) $f(2)$ (b) $f(1)$ 10. (a) $f(-2)$ (b) $f(1)$
    (c) $f(3)$ (d) $f(-1)$ (c) $f(0)$ (d) $f(2)$

Vertical Line Test for Functions In Exercises 11–14, use the Vertical Line Test to determine whether y is a function of x. To print an enlarged copy of the graph, go to *MathGraphs.com*.

11. $y = \frac{1}{4}x^3$ 12. $x - y^2 = 1$

13. $x^2 + y^2 = 25$ 14. $x^2 = 2xy - 1$

Finding the Zeros of a Function In Exercises 15–24, find the zeros of the function algebraically.

15. $f(x) = 2x^2 - 7x - 30$

16. $f(x) = 3x^2 + 22x - 16$

17. $f(x) = \dfrac{x}{9x^2 - 4}$

18. $f(x) = \dfrac{x^2 - 9x + 14}{4x}$

19. $f(x) = \frac{1}{2}x^3 - x$

20. $f(x) = 9x^4 - 25x^2$

21. $f(x) = x^3 - 4x^2 - 9x + 36$

22. $f(x) = 4x^3 - 24x^2 - x + 6$

23. $f(x) = \sqrt{2x} - 1$

24. $f(x) = \sqrt{3x + 2}$

Graphing and Finding Zeros In Exercises 25–30, (a) use a graphing utility to graph the function and find the zeros of the function and (b) verify your results from part (a) algebraically.

25. $f(x) = 3 + \dfrac{5}{x}$ 26. $f(x) = x(x - 7)$

27. $f(x) = \sqrt{2x + 11}$ 28. $f(x) = \sqrt{3x - 14} - 8$

29. $f(x) = \dfrac{3x - 1}{x - 6}$ 30. $f(x) = \dfrac{2x^2 - 9}{3 - x}$

Describing Function Behavior In Exercises 31–38, determine the intervals on which the function is increasing, decreasing, or constant.

31. $f(x) = \frac{3}{2}x$

32. $f(x) = x^2 - 4x$

33. $f(x) = x^3 - 3x^2 + 2$

34. $f(x) = \sqrt{x^2 - 1}$

35. $f(x) = |x + 1| + |x - 1|$

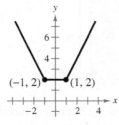

36. $f(x) = \frac{x^2 + x + 1}{x + 1}$

37. $f(x) = \begin{cases} x + 3, & x \le 0 \\ 3, & 0 < x \le 2 \\ 2x + 1, & x > 2 \end{cases}$

38. $f(x) = \begin{cases} 2x + 1, & x \le -1 \\ x^2 - 2, & x > -1 \end{cases}$

Describing Function Behavior In Exercises 39–46, (a) use a graphing utility to graph the function and visually determine the intervals on which the function is increasing, decreasing, or constant, and (b) make a table of values to verify whether the function is increasing, decreasing, or constant on the intervals you identified in part (a).

39. $f(x) = 3$

40. $g(x) = x$

41. $g(s) = \frac{s^2}{4}$

42. $f(x) = 3x^4 - 6x^2$

43. $f(x) = \sqrt{1 - x}$

44. $f(x) = x\sqrt{x + 3}$

45. $f(x) = x^{3/2}$

46. $f(x) = x^{2/3}$

Approximating Relative Minima or Maxima In Exercises 47–54, use a graphing utility to graph the function and approximate (to two decimal places) any relative minima or maxima.

47. $f(x) = 3x^2 - 2x - 5$

48. $f(x) = -x^2 + 3x - 2$

49. $f(x) = -2x^2 + 9x$

50. $f(x) = x(x - 2)(x + 3)$

51. $f(x) = x^3 - 3x^2 - x + 1$

52. $h(x) = x^3 - 6x^2 + 15$

53. $h(x) = (x - 1)\sqrt{x}$

54. $g(x) = x\sqrt{4 - x}$

Graphical Analysis In Exercises 55–60, graph the function and determine the interval(s) for which $f(x) \ge 0$.

55. $f(x) = 4 - x$

56. $f(x) = 4x + 2$

57. $f(x) = 9 - x^2$

58. $f(x) = x^2 - 4x$

59. $f(x) = \sqrt{x - 1}$

60. $f(x) = -(1 + |x|)$

Average Rate of Change of a Function In Exercises 61–64, find the average rate of change of the function from x_1 to x_2.

Function	x-Values
61. $f(x) = -2x + 15$	$x_1 = 0, x_2 = 3$
62. $f(x) = x^2 - 2x + 8$	$x_1 = 1, x_2 = 5$
63. $f(x) = x^3 - 3x^2 - x$	$x_1 = 1, x_2 = 3$
64. $f(x) = -x^3 + 6x^2 + x$	$x_1 = 1, x_2 = 6$

65. Research and Development The amounts y (in millions of dollars) the U.S. Department of Energy spent for research and development from 2005 through 2010 can be approximated by the model

$$y = 56.77t^2 - 366.8t + 8916, \quad 5 \le t \le 10$$

where t represents the year, with $t = 5$ corresponding to 2005. (*Source: American Association for the Advancement of Science*)

(a) Use a graphing utility to graph the model.

(b) Find the average rate of change of the model from 2005 to 2010. Interpret your answer in the context of the problem.

66. Finding Average Speed Use the information in Example 7 to find the average speed of the car from $t_1 = 0$ to $t_2 = 9$ seconds. Explain why the result is less than the value obtained in part (b) of Example 7.

Physics In Exercises 67–70, (a) use the position equation $s = -16t^2 + v_0 t + s_0$ to write a function that represents the situation, (b) use a graphing utility to graph the function, (c) find the average rate of change of the function from t_1 to t_2, (d) describe the slope of the secant line through t_1 and t_2, (e) find the equation of the secant line through t_1 and t_2, and (f) graph the secant line in the same viewing window as your position function.

67. An object is thrown upward from a height of 6 feet at a velocity of 64 feet per second.

$t_1 = 0, t_2 = 3$

68. An object is thrown upward from a height of 6.5 feet at a velocity of 72 feet per second.

$t_1 = 0, t_2 = 4$

69. An object is thrown upward from ground level at a velocity of 120 feet per second.

$t_1 = 3, t_2 = 5$

70. An object is dropped from a height of 80 feet.

$t_1 = 1, t_2 = 2$

Even, Odd, or Neither? In Exercises 71–76, determine whether the function is even, odd, or neither. Then describe the symmetry.

71. $f(x) = x^6 - 2x^2 + 3$ **72.** $g(x) = x^3 - 5x$

73. $f(x) = x\sqrt{1 - x^2}$ **74.** $h(x) = x\sqrt{x + 5}$

75. $f(s) = 4s^{3/2}$ **76.** $g(s) = 4s^{2/3}$

Even, Odd, or Neither? In Exercises 77–82, sketch a graph of the function and determine whether it is even, odd, or neither. Verify your answer algebraically.

77. $f(x) = -9$ **78.** $f(x) = 5 - 3x$

79. $f(x) = -|x - 5|$ **80.** $h(x) = x^2 - 4$

81. $f(x) = \sqrt{1 - x}$ **82.** $g(t) = \sqrt[3]{t - 1}$

Height of a Rectangle In Exercises 83 and 84, write the height h of the rectangle as a function of x.

83.

84.

Length of a Rectangle In Exercises 85 and 86, write the length L of the rectangle as a function of y.

85.

86.

87. Lumens The number of lumens (time rate of flow of light) L from a fluorescent lamp can be approximated by the model

$$L = -0.294x^2 + 97.744x - 664.875, \quad 20 \le x \le 90$$

where x is the wattage of the lamp.

(a) Use a graphing utility to graph the function.

(b) Use the graph from part (a) to estimate the wattage necessary to obtain 2000 lumens.

88. Geometry Corners of equal size are cut from a square with sides of length 8 meters (see figure).

(a) Write the area A of the resulting figure as a function of x. Determine the domain of the function.

(b) Use a graphing utility to graph the area function over its domain. Use the graph to find the range of the function.

(c) Identify the figure that results when x is the maximum value in the domain of the function. What would be the length of each side of the figure?

89. Coordinate Axis Scale Each function described below models the specified data for the years 2003 through 2013, with $t = 3$ corresponding to 2003. Estimate a reasonable scale for the vertical axis (e.g., hundreds, thousands, millions, etc.) of the graph and justify your answer. (There are many correct answers.)

(a) $f(t)$ represents the average salary of college professors.

(b) $f(t)$ represents the U.S. population.

(c) $f(t)$ represents the percent of the civilian work force that is unemployed.

90. Data Analysis: Temperature

The table shows the temperatures y (in degrees Fahrenheit) in a city over a 24-hour period. Let x represent the time of day, where $x = 0$ corresponds to 6 A.M.

Time, x	Temperature, y
0	34
2	50
4	60
6	64
8	63
10	59
12	53
14	46
16	40
18	36
20	34
22	37
24	45

DATA
Spreadsheet at LarsonPrecalculus.com

A model that represents these data is given by

$$y = 0.026x^3 - 1.03x^2 + 10.2x + 34, \quad 0 \le x \le 24.$$

(a) Use a graphing utility to create a scatter plot of the data. Then graph the model in the same viewing window.

(b) How well does the model fit the data?

(c) Use the graph to approximate the times when the temperature was increasing and decreasing.

(d) Use the graph to approximate the maximum and minimum temperatures during this 24-hour period.

(e) Could this model predict the temperatures in the city during the next 24-hour period? Why or why not?

91. Writing   Use a graphing utility to graph each function. Write a paragraph describing any similarities and differences you observe among the graphs.

(a) $y = x$

(b) $y = x^2$

(c) $y = x^3$

(d) $y = x^4$

(e) $y = x^5$

(f) $y = x^6$

92. HOW DO YOU SEE IT?   Use the graph of the function to answer (a)–(e).

(a) Find the domain and range of f.

(b) Find the zero(s) of f.

(c) Determine the intervals over which f is increasing, decreasing, or constant.

(d) Approximate any relative minimum or relative maximum values of f.

(e) Is f even, odd, or neither?

Exploration

True or False? In Exercises 93 and 94, determine whether the statement is true or false. Justify your answer.

93. A function with a square root cannot have a domain that is the set of real numbers.

94. It is possible for an odd function to have the interval $[0, \infty)$ as its domain.

Think About It   In Exercises 95 and 96, find the coordinates of a second point on the graph of a function f when the given point is on the graph and the function is (a) even and (b) odd.

95. $\left(-\frac{5}{3}, -7\right)$

96. $(2a, 2c)$

97. Graphical Reasoning   Graph each of the functions with a graphing utility. Determine whether the function is even, odd, or neither.

$f(x) = x^2 - x^4$ $g(x) = 2x^3 + 1$

$h(x) = x^5 - 2x^3 + x$ $j(x) = 2 - x^6 - x^8$

$k(x) = x^5 - 2x^4 + x - 2$ $p(x) = x^9 + 3x^5 - x^3 + x$

What do you notice about the equations of functions that are odd? What do you notice about the equations of functions that are even? Can you describe a way to identify a function as odd or even by inspecting the equation? Can you describe a way to identify a function as neither odd nor even by inspecting the equation?

98. Even, Odd, or Neither?   If f is an even function, determine whether g is even, odd, or neither. Explain.

(a) $g(x) = -f(x)$ (b) $g(x) = f(-x)$

(c) $g(x) = f(x) - 2$ (d) $g(x) = f(x - 2)$

1.6   A Library of Parent Functions

- Identify and graph linear and squaring functions.
- Identify and graph cubic, square root, and reciprocal functions.
- Identify and graph step and other piecewise-defined functions.
- Recognize graphs of parent functions.

Linear and Squaring Functions

One of the goals of this text is to enable you to recognize the basic shapes of the graphs of different types of functions. For instance, you know that the graph of the **linear function** $f(x) = ax + b$ is a line with slope $m = a$ and y-intercept at $(0, b)$. The graph of the linear function has the following characteristics.

- The domain of the function is the set of all real numbers.
- When $m \neq 0$, the range of the function is the set of all real numbers.
- The graph has an x-intercept at $(-b/m, 0)$ and a y-intercept at $(0, b)$.
- The graph is increasing when $m > 0$, decreasing when $m < 0$, and constant when $m = 0$.

Piecewise-defined functions can help you model real-life situations. For instance, in Exercise 47 on page 66, you will write a piecewise-defined function to model the depth of snow during a snowstorm.

EXAMPLE 1   **Writing a Linear Function**

Write the linear function f for which $f(1) = 3$ and $f(4) = 0$.

Solution   To find the equation of the line that passes through $(x_1, y_1) = (1, 3)$ and $(x_2, y_2) = (4, 0)$, first find the slope of the line.

$$m = \frac{y_2 - y_1}{x_2 - x_1} = \frac{0 - 3}{4 - 1} = \frac{-3}{3} = -1$$

Next, use the point-slope form of the equation of a line.

$$y - y_1 = m(x - x_1) \qquad \text{Point-slope form}$$
$$y - 3 = -1(x - 1) \qquad \text{Substitute for } x_1, y_1, \text{ and } m.$$
$$y = -x + 4 \qquad \text{Simplify.}$$
$$f(x) = -x + 4 \qquad \text{Function notation}$$

The figure below shows the graph of this function.

$f(x) = -x + 4$

✓ **Checkpoint**   ◄))) Audio-video solution in English & Spanish at LarsonPrecalculus.com.

Write the linear function f for which $f(-2) = 6$ and $f(4) = -9$.

nulinukas/Shutterstock.com

There are two special types of linear functions, the **constant function** and the **identity function.** A constant function has the form

$$f(x) = c$$

and has the domain of all real numbers with a range consisting of a single real number c. The graph of a constant function is a horizontal line, as shown in Figure 1.44. The identity function has the form

$$f(x) = x.$$

Its domain and range are the set of all real numbers. The identity function has a slope of $m = 1$ and a y-intercept at $(0, 0)$. The graph of the identity function is a line for which each x-coordinate equals the corresponding y-coordinate. The graph is always increasing, as shown in Figure 1.45.

Figure 1.44

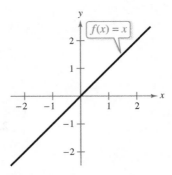

Figure 1.45

The graph of the **squaring function**

$$f(x) = x^2$$

is a U-shaped curve with the following characteristics.

- The domain of the function is the set of all real numbers.
- The range of the function is the set of all nonnegative real numbers.
- The function is even.
- The graph has an intercept at $(0, 0)$.
- The graph is decreasing on the interval $(-\infty, 0)$ and increasing on the interval $(0, \infty)$.
- The graph is symmetric with respect to the y-axis.
- The graph has a relative minimum at $(0, 0)$.

The figure below shows the graph of the squaring function.

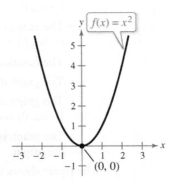

Cubic, Square Root, and Reciprocal Functions

The following summarizes the basic characteristics of the graphs of the **cubic, square root,** and **reciprocal functions.**

1. The graph of the *cubic* function

$$f(x) = x^3$$

has the following characteristics.

- The domain of the function is the set of all real numbers.
- The range of the function is the set of all real numbers.
- The function is odd.
- The graph has an intercept at $(0, 0)$.
- The graph is increasing on the interval $(-\infty, \infty)$.
- The graph is symmetric with respect to the origin.

The figure shows the graph of the cubic function.

Cubic function

2. The graph of the *square root* function

$$f(x) = \sqrt{x}$$

has the following characteristics.

- The domain of the function is the set of all nonnegative real numbers.
- The range of the function is the set of all nonnegative real numbers.
- The graph has an intercept at $(0, 0)$.
- The graph is increasing on the interval $(0, \infty)$.

The figure shows the graph of the square root function.

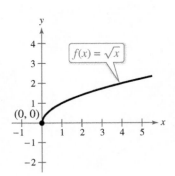

Square root function

3. The graph of the *reciprocal* function

$$f(x) = \frac{1}{x}$$

has the following characteristics.

- The domain of the function is $(-\infty, 0) \cup (0, \infty)$.
- The range of the function is $(-\infty, 0) \cup (0, \infty)$.
- The function is odd.
- The graph does not have any intercepts.
- The graph is decreasing on the intervals $(-\infty, 0)$ and $(0, \infty)$.
- The graph is symmetric with respect to the origin.

The figure shows the graph of the reciprocal function.

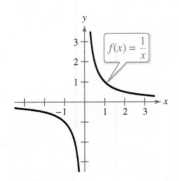

Reciprocal function

Step and Piecewise-Defined Functions

Functions whose graphs resemble sets of stairsteps are known as **step functions.** The most famous of the step functions is the **greatest integer function,** denoted by $[\![x]\!]$ and defined as

$$f(x) = [\![x]\!] = \textit{the greatest integer less than or equal to } x.$$

Some values of the greatest integer function are as follows.

$$[\![-1]\!] = (\text{greatest integer} \le -1) = -1$$

$$\left[\!\!\left[-\tfrac{1}{2}\right]\!\!\right] = \left(\text{greatest integer} \le -\tfrac{1}{2}\right) = -1$$

$$\left[\!\!\left[\tfrac{1}{10}\right]\!\!\right] = \left(\text{greatest integer} \le \tfrac{1}{10}\right) = 0$$

$$[\![1.5]\!] = (\text{greatest integer} \le 1.5) = 1$$

$$[\![1.9]\!] = (\text{greatest integer} \le 1.9) = 1$$

Figure 1.46

The graph of the greatest integer function

$$f(x) = [\![x]\!]$$

has the following characteristics, as shown in Figure 1.46.

- The domain of the function is the set of all real numbers.
- The range of the function is the set of all integers.
- The graph has a y-intercept at $(0, 0)$ and x-intercepts in the interval $[0, 1)$.
- The graph is constant between each pair of consecutive integer values of x.
- The graph jumps vertically one unit at each integer value of x.

▷ **TECHNOLOGY** When using your graphing utility to graph a step function, you should set your graphing utility to *dot* mode.

EXAMPLE 2 **Evaluating a Step Function**

Evaluate the function when $x = -1, 2,$ and $\tfrac{3}{2}$.

$$f(x) = [\![x]\!] + 1$$

Solution For $x = -1$, the greatest integer ≤ -1 is -1, so

$$f(-1) = [\![-1]\!] + 1 = -1 + 1 = 0.$$

For $x = 2$, the greatest integer ≤ 2 is 2, so

$$f(2) = [\![2]\!] + 1 = 2 + 1 = 3.$$

For $x = \tfrac{3}{2}$, the greatest integer $\le \tfrac{3}{2}$ is 1, so

$$f\left(\tfrac{3}{2}\right) = \left[\!\!\left[\tfrac{3}{2}\right]\!\!\right] + 1 = 1 + 1 = 2.$$

Verify your answers by examining the graph of $f(x) = [\![x]\!] + 1$ shown in Figure 1.47.

Figure 1.47

✓ **Checkpoint** ◀))) *Audio-video solution in English & Spanish at LarsonPrecalculus.com.*

Evaluate the function when $x = -\tfrac{3}{2}, 1,$ and $-\tfrac{5}{2}$.

$$f(x) = [\![x + 2]\!]$$

Recall from Section 1.4 that a piecewise-defined function is defined by two or more equations over a specified domain. To graph a piecewise-defined function, graph each equation separately over the specified domain, as shown in Example 3.

Figure 1.48

EXAMPLE 3   **Graphing a Piecewise-Defined Function**

Sketch the graph of $f(x) = \begin{cases} 2x + 3, & x \le 1 \\ -x + 4, & x > 1 \end{cases}$.

Solution   This piecewise-defined function consists of two linear functions. At $x = 1$ and to the left of $x = 1$, the graph is the line $y = 2x + 3$, and to the right of $x = 1$ the graph is the line $y = -x + 4$, as shown in Figure 1.48. Notice that the point $(1, 5)$ is a solid dot and the point $(1, 3)$ is an open dot. This is because $f(1) = 2(1) + 3 = 5$.

✔ **Checkpoint** ◀))) *Audio-video solution in English & Spanish at LarsonPrecalculus.com.*

Sketch the graph of $f(x) = \begin{cases} -\frac{1}{2}x - 6, & x \le -4 \\ x + 5, & x > -4 \end{cases}$.

Parent Functions

The eight graphs shown below represent the most commonly used functions in algebra. Familiarity with the basic characteristics of these simple graphs will help you analyze the shapes of more complicated graphs—in particular, graphs obtained from these graphs by the rigid and nonrigid transformations studied in the next section.

(a) Constant Function

(b) Identity Function

(c) Absolute Value Function

(d) Square Root Function

(e) Quadratic Function

(f) Cubic Function

(g) Reciprocal Function

(h) Greatest Integer Function

Summarize   (Section 1.6)

1. Explain how to identify and graph linear and squaring functions (*pages 60 and 61*). For an example involving a linear function, see Example 1.

2. Explain how to identify and graph cubic, square root, and reciprocal functions (*page 62*).

3. Explain how to identify and graph step and other piecewise-defined functions (*page 63*). For an example involving a step function, see Example 2. For an example of graphing a piecewise-defined function, see Example 3.

4. State and sketch the graphs of parent functions (*page 64*).

Vocabulary

In Exercises 1–9, match each function with its name.

1. $f(x) = [\![x]\!]$ **2.** $f(x) = x$ **3.** $f(x) = 1/x$

4. $f(x) = x^2$ **5.** $f(x) = \sqrt{x}$ **6.** $f(x) = c$

7. $f(x) = |x|$ **8.** $f(x) = x^3$ **9.** $f(x) = ax + b$

  (a) squaring function   (b) square root function   (c) cubic function

  (d) linear function   (e) constant function   (f) absolute value function

  (g) greatest integer function   (h) reciprocal function   (i) identity function

10. Fill in the blank: The constant function and the identity function are two special types of _____ functions.

Skills and Applications

Writing a Linear Function In Exercises 11–14, (a) write the linear function f such that it has the indicated function values and (b) sketch the graph of the function.

11. $f(1) = 4$, $f(0) = 6$ **12.** $f(-3) = -8$, $f(1) = 2$

13. $f(-5) = -1$, $f(5) = -1$

14. $f\left(\frac{2}{3}\right) = -\frac{15}{2}$, $f(-4) = -11$

Graphing a Function In Exercises 15–26, use a graphing utility to graph the function. Be sure to choose an appropriate viewing window.

15. $f(x) = 2.5x - 4.25$ **16.** $f(x) = \frac{5}{6} - \frac{2}{3}x$

17. $g(x) = -2x^2$ **18.** $f(x) = 3x^2 - 1.75$

19. $f(x) = x^3 - 1$ **20.** $f(x) = (x-1)^3 + 2$

21. $f(x) = 4 - 2\sqrt{x}$ **22.** $h(x) = \sqrt{x+2} + 3$

23. $f(x) = 4 + (1/x)$ **24.** $k(x) = 1/(x-3)$

25. $g(x) = |x| - 5$ **26.** $f(x) = |x-1|$

Evaluating a Step Function In Exercises 27–30, evaluate the function for the indicated values.

27. $f(x) = [\![x]\!]$

  (a) $f(2.1)$ (b) $f(2.9)$ (c) $f(-3.1)$ (d) $f\left(\frac{7}{2}\right)$

28. $h(x) = [\![x+3]\!]$

  (a) $h(-2)$ (b) $h\left(\frac{1}{2}\right)$ (c) $h(4.2)$ (d) $h(-21.6)$

29. $k(x) = [\![\frac{1}{2}x + 6]\!]$

  (a) $k(5)$ (b) $k(-6.1)$ (c) $k(0.1)$ (d) $k(15)$

30. $g(x) = -7[\![x+4]\!] + 6$

  (a) $g\left(\frac{1}{8}\right)$ (b) $g(9)$ (c) $g(-4)$ (d) $g\left(\frac{3}{2}\right)$

Graphing a Step Function In Exercises 31–34, sketch the graph of the function.

31. $g(x) = -[\![x]\!]$ **32.** $g(x) = 4[\![x]\!]$

33. $g(x) = [\![x]\!] - 1$ **34.** $g(x) = [\![x-3]\!]$

Graphing a Piecewise-Defined Function In Exercises 35–40, sketch the graph of the function.

35. $g(x) = \begin{cases} x+6, & x \le -4 \\ \frac{1}{2}x - 4, & x > -4 \end{cases}$

36. $f(x) = \begin{cases} \sqrt{4+x}, & x < 0 \\ \sqrt{4-x}, & x \ge 0 \end{cases}$

37. $f(x) = \begin{cases} 1-(x-1)^2, & x \le 2 \\ \sqrt{x-2}, & x > 2 \end{cases}$

38. $f(x) = \begin{cases} x^2 + 5, & x \le 1 \\ -x^2 + 4x + 3, & x > 1 \end{cases}$

39. $h(x) = \begin{cases} 4 - x^2, & x < -2 \\ 3 + x, & -2 \le x < 0 \\ x^2 + 1, & x \ge 0 \end{cases}$

40. $k(x) = \begin{cases} 2x + 1, & x \le -1 \\ 2x^2 - 1, & -1 < x \le 1 \\ 1 - x^2, & x > 1 \end{cases}$

Graphing a Function In Exercises 41 and 42, (a) use a graphing utility to graph the function and (b) state the domain and range of the function.

41. $s(x) = 2\left(\frac{1}{4}x - [\![\frac{1}{4}x]\!]\right)$

42. $k(x) = 4\left(\frac{1}{2}x - [\![\frac{1}{2}x]\!]\right)^2$

43. Wages A mechanic's pay is $14.00 per hour for regular time and time-and-a-half for overtime. The weekly wage function is

$$W(h) = \begin{cases} 14h, & 0 < h \le 40 \\ 21(h-40) + 560, & h > 40 \end{cases}$$

where h is the number of hours worked in a week.

(a) Evaluate $W(30)$, $W(40)$, $W(45)$, and $W(50)$.

(b) The company increased the regular work week to 45 hours. What is the new weekly wage function?

44. Revenue The table shows the monthly revenue y (in thousands of dollars) of a landscaping business for each month of the year 2013, with $x = 1$ representing January.

Month, x	Revenue, y
1	5.2
2	5.6
3	6.6
4	8.3
5	11.5
6	15.8
7	12.8
8	10.1
9	8.6
10	6.9
11	4.5
12	2.7

Spreadsheet at LarsonPrecalculus.com

A mathematical model that represents these data is

$$f(x) = \begin{cases} -1.97x + 26.3 \\ 0.505x^2 - 1.47x + 6.3. \end{cases}$$

(a) Use a graphing utility to graph the model. What is the domain of each part of the piecewise-defined function? How can you tell? Explain your reasoning.

(b) Find $f(5)$ and $f(11)$, and interpret your results in the context of the problem.

(c) How do the values obtained from the model in part (a) compare with the actual data values?

45. Fluid Flow The intake pipe of a 100-gallon tank has a flow rate of 10 gallons per minute, and two drainpipes have flow rates of 5 gallons per minute each. The figure shows the volume V of fluid in the tank as a function of time t. Determine the combination of the input pipe and drain pipes in which the fluid is flowing in specific subintervals of the 1 hour of time shown on the graph. (There are many correct answers.)

Volume (in gallons)

(60, 100)
(10, 75) (20, 75)
(45, 50)
(5, 50)
(50, 50)
(30, 25) (40, 25)
(0, 0)

Time (in minutes)

nulinukas/Shutterstock.com

46. Delivery Charges The cost of sending an overnight package from New York to Atlanta is $26.10 for a package weighing up to, but not including, 1 pound and $4.35 for each additional pound or portion of a pound.

(a) Use the greatest integer function to create a model for the cost C of overnight delivery of a package weighing x pounds, $x > 0$.

(b) Sketch the graph of the function.

• • **47. Snowstorm** • • • • • • • • • • •

During a nine-hour snowstorm, it snows at a rate of 1 inch per hour for the first 2 hours, at a rate of 2 inches per hour for the next 6 hours, and at a rate of 0.5 inch per hour for the final hour. Write and graph a piecewise-defined function that gives the depth of the snow during the snowstorm. How many inches of snow accumulated from the storm?

Exploration

48. **HOW DO YOU SEE IT?** For each graph of f shown below, answer (a)–(d).

$f(x) = x^2$

$f(x) = x^3$

(a) Find the domain and range of f.

(b) Find the x- and y-intercepts of the graph of f.

(c) Determine the intervals on which f is increasing, decreasing, or constant.

(d) Determine whether f is even, odd, or neither. Then describe the symmetry.

True or False? In Exercises 49 and 50, determine whether the statement is true or false. Justify your answer.

49. A piecewise-defined function will always have at least one x-intercept or at least one y-intercept.

50. A linear equation will always have an x-intercept and a y-intercept.

1.7 Transformations of Functions

Transformations of functions can help you model real-life applications. For instance, Exercise 69 on page 74 shows how a transformation of a function can model the number of horsepower required to overcome wind drag on an automobile.

■ Use vertical and horizontal shifts to sketch graphs of functions.
■ Use reflections to sketch graphs of functions.
■ Use nonrigid transformations to sketch graphs of functions.

Shifting Graphs

Many functions have graphs that are transformations of the parent graphs summarized in Section 1.6. For example, you can obtain the graph of

$$h(x) = x^2 + 2$$

by shifting the graph of $f(x) = x^2$ *up* two units, as shown in Figure 1.49. In function notation, h and f are related as follows.

$$h(x) = x^2 + 2 = f(x) + 2 \qquad \text{Upward shift of two units}$$

Similarly, you can obtain the graph of

$$g(x) = (x - 2)^2$$

by shifting the graph of $f(x) = x^2$ to the *right* two units, as shown in Figure 1.50. In this case, the functions g and f have the following relationship.

$$g(x) = (x - 2)^2 = f(x - 2) \qquad \text{Right shift of two units}$$

Figure 1.49

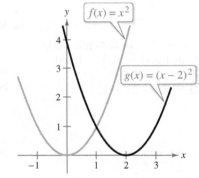

Figure 1.50

The following list summarizes this discussion about horizontal and vertical shifts.

• • REMARK In items 3 and 4, be sure you see that $h(x) = f(x - c)$ corresponds to a *right* shift and $h(x) = f(x + c)$ corresponds to a *left* shift for $c > 0$.

▷

Vertical and Horizontal Shifts

Let c be a positive real number. **Vertical and horizontal shifts** in the graph of $y = f(x)$ are represented as follows.

1. Vertical shift c units *up:* $\qquad h(x) = f(x) + c$

2. Vertical shift c units *down:* $\qquad h(x) = f(x) - c$

3. Horizontal shift c units to the *right:* $\;h(x) = f(x - c)$

4. Horizontal shift c units to the *left:* $\quad h(x) = f(x + c)$

Some graphs can be obtained from combinations of vertical and horizontal shifts, as demonstrated in Example 1(b). Vertical and horizontal shifts generate a *family of functions,* each with the same shape but at a different location in the plane.

Robert Young/Shutterstock.com

| EXAMPLE 1 | **Shifts in the Graph of a Function** |

Use the graph of $f(x) = x^3$ to sketch the graph of each function.

a. $g(x) = x^3 - 1$

b. $h(x) = (x + 2)^3 + 1$

Solution

a. Relative to the graph of $f(x) = x^3$, the graph of

$$g(x) = x^3 - 1$$

is a downward shift of one unit, as shown below.

REMARK   In Example 1(a),
note that $g(x) = f(x) - 1$ and
in Example 1(b),
$h(x) = f(x + 2) + 1$.

b. Relative to the graph of $f(x) = x^3$, the graph of

$$h(x) = (x + 2)^3 + 1$$

involves a left shift of two units and an upward shift of one unit, as shown below.

✓ *Checkpoint* 🔊)) Audio-video solution in English & Spanish at LarsonPrecalculus.com.

Use the graph of $f(x) = x^3$ to sketch the graph of each function.

a. $h(x) = x^3 + 5$

b. $g(x) = (x - 3)^3 + 2$

In Example 1(b), you obtain the same result when the vertical shift precedes the horizontal shift *or* when the horizontal shift precedes the vertical shift.

Reflecting Graphs

Another common type of transformation is a **reflection.** For instance, if you consider the *x*-axis to be a mirror, then the graph of $h(x) = -x^2$ is the mirror image (or reflection) of the graph of $f(x) = x^2$, as shown in Figure 1.51.

Figure 1.51

Reflections in the Coordinate Axes

Reflections in the coordinate axes of the graph of $y = f(x)$ are represented as follows.

1. Reflection in the *x*-axis: $h(x) = -f(x)$

2. Reflection in the *y*-axis: $h(x) = f(-x)$

Figure 1.52

EXAMPLE 2   **Writing Equations from Graphs**

The graph of the function

$$f(x) = x^4$$

is shown in Figure 1.52. Each of the graphs below is a transformation of the graph of *f*. Write an equation for each of these functions.

(a)

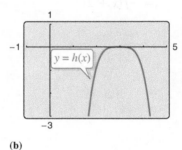

(b)

Solution

a. The graph of *g* is a reflection in the *x*-axis *followed by* an upward shift of two units of the graph of $f(x) = x^4$. So, the equation for *g* is

$$g(x) = -x^4 + 2.$$

b. The graph of *h* is a horizontal shift of three units to the right *followed by* a reflection in the *x*-axis of the graph of $f(x) = x^4$. So, the equation for *h* is

$$h(x) = -(x - 3)^4.$$

✓ **Checkpoint** ◄))) *Audio-video solution in English & Spanish at LarsonPrecalculus.com.*

The graph is a transformation of the graph of $f(x) = x^4$. Write an equation for the function.

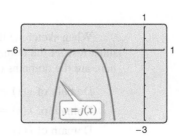

| EXAMPLE 3 | **Reflections and Shifts**

Compare the graph of each function with the graph of $f(x) = \sqrt{x}$.

a. $g(x) = -\sqrt{x}$ **b.** $h(x) = \sqrt{-x}$ **c.** $k(x) = -\sqrt{x+2}$

Algebraic Solution

a. The graph of g is a reflection of the graph of f in the x-axis because

$$g(x) = -\sqrt{x}$$
$$= -f(x).$$

b. The graph of h is a reflection of the graph of f in the y-axis because

$$h(x) = \sqrt{-x}$$
$$= f(-x).$$

c. The graph of k is a left shift of two units followed by a reflection in the x-axis because

$$k(x) = -\sqrt{x+2}$$
$$= -f(x+2).$$

Graphical Solution

a. Graph f and g on the same set of coordinate axes. From the graph, you can see that the graph of g is a reflection of the graph of f in the x-axis.

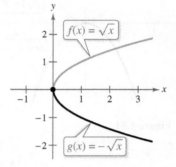

b. Graph f and h on the same set of coordinate axes. From the graph, you can see that the graph of h is a reflection of the graph of f in the y-axis.

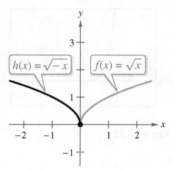

c. Graph f and k on the same set of coordinate axes. From the graph, you can see that the graph of k is a left shift of two units of the graph of f, followed by a reflection in the x-axis.

 Checkpoint Audio-video solution in English & Spanish at LarsonPrecalculus.com.

Compare the graph of each function with the graph of

$$f(x) = \sqrt{x-1}.$$

a. $g(x) = -\sqrt{x-1}$ **b.** $h(x) = \sqrt{-x-1}$

When sketching the graphs of functions involving square roots, remember that you must restrict the domain to exclude negative numbers inside the radical. For instance, here are the domains of the functions in Example 3.

Domain of $g(x) = -\sqrt{x}$: $x \geq 0$

Domain of $h(x) = \sqrt{-x}$: $x \leq 0$

Domain of $k(x) = -\sqrt{x+2}$: $x \geq -2$

Figure 1.53

Figure 1.54

Figure 1.55

Figure 1.56

Nonrigid Transformations

Horizontal shifts, vertical shifts, and reflections are **rigid transformations** because the basic shape of the graph is unchanged. These transformations change only the *position* of the graph in the coordinate plane. **Nonrigid transformations** are those that cause a *distortion*—a change in the shape of the original graph. For instance, a nonrigid transformation of the graph of $y = f(x)$ is represented by $g(x) = cf(x)$, where the transformation is a **vertical stretch** when $c > 1$ and a **vertical shrink** when $0 < c < 1$. Another nonrigid transformation of the graph of $y = f(x)$ is represented by $h(x) = f(cx)$, where the transformation is a **horizontal shrink** when $c > 1$ and a **horizontal stretch** when $0 < c < 1$.

EXAMPLE 4   **Nonrigid Transformations**

Compare the graph of each function with the graph of $f(x) = |x|$.

a. $h(x) = 3|x|$ **b.** $g(x) = \frac{1}{3}|x|$

Solution

a. Relative to the graph of $f(x) = |x|$, the graph of $h(x) = 3|x| = 3f(x)$ is a vertical stretch (each y-value is multiplied by 3) of the graph of f. (See Figure 1.53.)

b. Similarly, the graph of $g(x) = \frac{1}{3}|x| = \frac{1}{3}f(x)$ is a vertical shrink $\left(\text{each } y\text{-value is multiplied by } \frac{1}{3}\right)$ of the graph of f. (See Figure 1.54.)

✓ *Checkpoint* Audio-video solution in English & Spanish at LarsonPrecalculus.com.

Compare the graph of each function with the graph of $f(x) = x^2$.

a. $g(x) = 4x^2$ **b.** $h(x) = \frac{1}{4}x^2$

EXAMPLE 5   **Nonrigid Transformations**

Compare the graph of each function with the graph of $f(x) = 2 - x^3$.

a. $g(x) = f(2x)$ **b.** $h(x) = f\left(\frac{1}{2}x\right)$

Solution

a. Relative to the graph of $f(x) = 2 - x^3$, the graph of $g(x) = f(2x) = 2 - (2x)^3 = 2 - 8x^3$ is a horizontal shrink $(c > 1)$ of the graph of f. (See Figure 1.55.)

b. Similarly, the graph of $h(x) = f\left(\frac{1}{2}x\right) = 2 - \left(\frac{1}{2}x\right)^3 = 2 - \frac{1}{8}x^3$ is a horizontal stretch $(0 < c < 1)$ of the graph of f. (See Figure 1.56.)

✓ *Checkpoint* Audio-video solution in English & Spanish at LarsonPrecalculus.com.

Compare the graph of each function with the graph of $f(x) = x^2 + 3$.

a. $g(x) = f(2x)$ **b.** $h(x) = f\left(\frac{1}{2}x\right)$

Summarize   (Section 1.7)

1. Describe how to shift the graph of a function vertically and horizontally *(page 67)*. For an example of shifting the graph of a function, see Example 1.

2. Describe how to reflect the graph of a function in the x-axis and in the y-axis *(page 69)*. For examples of reflecting graphs of functions, see Examples 2 and 3.

3. Describe nonrigid transformations of the graph of a function *(page 71)*. For examples of nonrigid transformations, see Examples 4 and 5.

1.7   Exercises

See **CalcChat.com** for tutorial help and worked-out solutions to odd-numbered exercises.

Vocabulary

In Exercises 1–3, fill in the blanks.

1. Horizontal shifts, vertical shifts, and reflections are called _____ transformations.

2. A reflection in the x-axis of $y = f(x)$ is represented by $h(x) =$ _____, while a reflection in the y-axis of $y = f(x)$ is represented by $h(x) =$ _____.

3. A nonrigid transformation of $y = f(x)$ represented by $g(x) = cf(x)$ is a _____ _____ when $c > 1$ and a _____ _____ when $0 < c < 1$.

4. Match the rigid transformation of $y = f(x)$ with the correct representation of the graph of h, where $c > 0$.

   (a) $h(x) = f(x) + c$ (i) A horizontal shift of f, c units to the right
   (b) $h(x) = f(x) - c$ (ii) A vertical shift of f, c units down
   (c) $h(x) = f(x + c)$ (iii) A horizontal shift of f, c units to the left
   (d) $h(x) = f(x - c)$ (iv) A vertical shift of f, c units up

Skills and Applications

5. **Shifts in the Graph of a Function** For each function, sketch (on the same set of coordinate axes) a graph of each function for $c = -1, 1$, and 3.

   (a) $f(x) = |x| + c$ (b) $f(x) = |x - c|$

6. **Shifts in the Graph of a Function** For each function, sketch (on the same set of coordinate axes) a graph of each function for $c = -3, -1, 1$, and 3.

   (a) $f(x) = \sqrt{x} + c$ (b) $f(x) = \sqrt{x - c}$

7. **Shifts in the Graph of a Function** For each function, sketch (on the same set of coordinate axes) a graph of each function for $c = -2, 0$, and 2.

   (a) $f(x) = [\![x]\!] + c$ (b) $f(x) = [\![x + c]\!]$

8. **Shifts in the Graph of a Function** For each function, sketch (on the same set of coordinate axes) a graph of each function for $c = -3, -1, 1$, and 3.

   (a) $f(x) = \begin{cases} x^2 + c, & x < 0 \\ -x^2 + c, & x \geq 0 \end{cases}$

   (b) $f(x) = \begin{cases} (x + c)^2, & x < 0 \\ -(x + c)^2, & x \geq 0 \end{cases}$

Sketching Transformations   In Exercises 9 and 10, use the graph of f to sketch each graph. To print an enlarged copy of the graph, go to *MathGraphs.com*.

9. (a) $y = f(-x)$
   (b) $y = f(x) + 4$
   (c) $y = 2f(x)$
   (d) $y = -f(x - 4)$
   (e) $y = f(x) - 3$
   (f) $y = -f(x) - 1$
   (g) $y = f(2x)$

10. (a) $y = f(x - 5)$
    (b) $y = -f(x) + 3$
    (c) $y = \frac{1}{3}f(x)$
    (d) $y = -f(x + 1)$
    (e) $y = f(-x)$
    (f) $y = f(x) - 10$
    (g) $y = f(\frac{1}{3}x)$

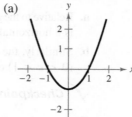

11. **Writing Equations from Graphs** Use the graph of $f(x) = x^2$ to write an equation for each function whose graph is shown.

    (a)   (b)

12. **Writing Equations from Graphs** Use the graph of $f(x) = x^3$ to write an equation for each function whose graph is shown.

    (a)   (b)

13. **Writing Equations from Graphs** Use the graph of $f(x) = |x|$ to write an equation for each function whose graph is shown.

(a)

(b)

14. **Writing Equations from Graphs** Use the graph of $f(x) = \sqrt{x}$ to write an equation for each function whose graph is shown.

(a)

(b)

Identifying a Parent Function In Exercises 15–20, identify the parent function and the transformation shown in the graph. Write an equation for the function shown in the graph.

15.

16.

17.

18.

19.

20.

Identifying a Parent Function In Exercises 21–46, g is related to one of the parent functions described in Section 1.6. (a) Identify the parent function f. (b) Describe the sequence of transformations from f to g. (c) Sketch the graph of g. (d) Use function notation to write g in terms of f.

21. $g(x) = 12 - x^2$

22. $g(x) = (x - 8)^2$

23. $g(x) = x^3 + 7$

24. $g(x) = -x^3 - 1$

25. $g(x) = \frac{2}{3}x^2 + 4$

26. $g(x) = 2(x - 7)^2$

27. $g(x) = 2 - (x + 5)^2$

28. $g(x) = -\frac{1}{4}(x + 2)^2 - 2$

29. $g(x) = \sqrt{3x}$

30. $g(x) = \sqrt{\frac{1}{4}x}$

31. $g(x) = (x - 1)^3 + 2$

32. $g(x) = (x + 3)^3 - 10$

33. $g(x) = 3(x - 2)^3$

34. $g(x) = -\frac{1}{2}(x + 1)^3$

35. $g(x) = -|x| - 2$

36. $g(x) = 6 - |x + 5|$

37. $g(x) = -|x + 4| + 8$

38. $g(x) = |-x + 3| + 9$

39. $g(x) = -2|x - 1| - 4$

40. $g(x) = \frac{1}{2}|x - 2| - 3$

41. $g(x) = 3 - [\![x]\!]$

42. $g(x) = 2[\![x + 5]\!]$

43. $g(x) = \sqrt{x - 9}$

44. $g(x) = \sqrt{x + 4} + 8$

45. $g(x) = \sqrt{7 - x} - 2$

46. $g(x) = \sqrt{3x} + 1$

Writing an Equation from a Description In Exercises 47–54, write an equation for the function described by the given characteristics.

47. The shape of $f(x) = x^2$, but shifted three units to the right and seven units down

48. The shape of $f(x) = x^2$, but shifted two units to the left, nine units up, and then reflected in the x-axis

49. The shape of $f(x) = x^3$, but shifted 13 units to the right

50. The shape of $f(x) = x^3$, but shifted six units to the left, six units down, and then reflected in the y-axis

51. The shape of $f(x) = |x|$, but shifted 12 units up and then reflected in the x-axis

52. The shape of $f(x) = |x|$, but shifted four units to the left and eight units down

53. The shape of $f(x) = \sqrt{x}$, but shifted six units to the left and then reflected in both the x-axis and the y-axis

54. The shape of $f(x) = \sqrt{x}$, but shifted nine units down and then reflected in both the x-axis and the y-axis

55. **Writing Equations from Graphs** Use the graph of $f(x) = x^2$ to write an equation for each function whose graph is shown.

(a)

(b)

56. Writing Equations from Graphs Use the graph of

$$f(x) = x^3$$

to write an equation for each function whose graph is shown.

(a)

(b)

(2, 2)

(1, −2)

57. Writing Equations from Graphs Use the graph of

$$f(x) = |x|$$

to write an equation for each function whose graph is shown.

(a)

(4, −2)

(b)

(−2, 3)

58. Writing Equations from Graphs Use the graph of

$$f(x) = \sqrt{x}$$

to write an equation for each function whose graph is shown.

(a)

(4, 16)

(b)

$\left(4, -\frac{1}{2}\right)$

Identifying a Parent Function **In Exercises 59–64, identify the parent function and the transformation shown in the graph. Write an equation for the function shown in the graph. Then use a graphing utility to verify your answer.**

59.

60.

61.

62.

63.

64.

Graphical Analysis **In Exercises 65–68, use the viewing window shown to write a possible equation for the transformation of the parent function.**

65.

66.

67.

68.

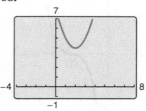

69. Automobile Aerodynamics

The number of horsepower H required to overcome wind drag on an automobile is approximated by

$$H(x) = 0.002x^2 + 0.005x - 0.029, \quad 10 \le x \le 100$$

where x is the speed of the car (in miles per hour).

(a) Use a graphing utility to graph the function.

(b) Rewrite the horsepower function so that x represents the speed in kilometers per hour. [Find $H(x/1.6)$.] Identify the type of transformation applied to the graph of the horsepower function.

70. Households The numbers N (in millions) of households in the United States from 2003 through 2010 can be approximated by

$$N = -0.068(x - 13.68)^2 + 119, \quad 3 \le t \le 10$$

where t represents the year, with $t = 3$ corresponding to 2003. *(Source: U.S. Census Bureau)*

(a) Describe the transformation of the parent function $f(x) = x^2$. Then use a graphing utility to graph the function over the specified domain.

(b) Find the average rate of change of the function from 2003 to 2010. Interpret your answer in the context of the problem.

(c) Use the model to predict the number of households in the United States in 2018. Does your answer seem reasonable? Explain.

Exploration

True or False? **In Exercises 71–74, determine whether the statement is true or false. Justify your answer.**

71. The graph of $y = f(-x)$ is a reflection of the graph of $y = f(x)$ in the x-axis.

72. The graph of $y = -f(x)$ is a reflection of the graph of $y = f(x)$ in the y-axis.

73. The graphs of $f(x) = |x| + 6$ and $f(x) = |-x| + 6$ are identical.

74. If the graph of the parent function $f(x) = x^2$ is shifted six units to the right, three units up, and reflected in the x-axis, then the point $(-2, 19)$ will lie on the graph of the transformation.

75. Finding Points on a Graph The graph of $y = f(x)$ passes through the points $(0, 1)$, $(1, 2)$, and $(2, 3)$. Find the corresponding points on the graph of $y = f(x + 2) - 1$.

76. Think About It You can use either of two methods to graph a function: plotting points or translating a parent function as shown in this section. Which method of graphing do you prefer to use for each function? Explain.

(a) $f(x) = 3x^2 - 4x + 1$

(b) $f(x) = 2(x - 1)^2 - 6$

77. Predicting Graphical Relationships Use a graphing utility to graph f, g, and h in the same viewing window. Before looking at the graphs, try to predict how the graphs of g and h relate to the graph of f.

(a) $f(x) = x^2$, $g(x) = (x - 4)^2$,
$h(x) = (x - 4)^2 + 3$

(b) $f(x) = x^2$, $g(x) = (x + 1)^2$,
$h(x) = (x + 1)^2 - 2$

(c) $f(x) = x^2$, $g(x) = (x + 4)^2$,
$h(x) = (x + 4)^2 + 2$

78. HOW DO YOU SEE IT? Use the graph of $y = f(x)$ to find the intervals on which each of the graphs in (a)–(e) is increasing and decreasing. If not possible, then state the reason.

(a) $y = f(-x)$ (b) $y = -f(x)$ (c) $y = \frac{1}{2}f(x)$

(d) $y = -f(x - 1)$ (e) $y = f(x - 2) + 1$

79. Describing Profits Management originally predicted that the profits from the sales of a new product would be approximated by the graph of the function f shown. The actual profits are shown by the function g along with a verbal description. Use the concepts of transformations of graphs to write g in terms of f.

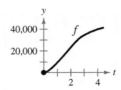

(a) The profits were only three-fourths as large as expected.

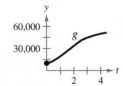

(b) The profits were consistently $10,000 greater than predicted.

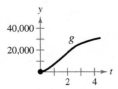

(c) There was a two-year delay in the introduction of the product. After sales began, profits grew as expected.

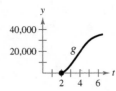

80. Reversing the Order of Transformations Reverse the order of transformations in Example 2(a). Do you obtain the same graph? Do the same for Example 2(b). Do you obtain the same graph? Explain.

1.8 Combinations of Functions: Composite Functions

Arithmetic combinations of functions can help you model and solve real-life problems. For instance, in Exercise 57 on page 82, you will use arithmetic combinations of functions to analyze numbers of pets in the United States.

■ Add, subtract, multiply, and divide functions.
■ Find the composition of one function with another function.
■ Use combinations and compositions of functions to model and solve real-life problems.

Arithmetic Combinations of Functions

Just as two real numbers can be combined by the operations of addition, subtraction, multiplication, and division to form other real numbers, two *functions* can be combined to create new functions. For example, the functions $f(x) = 2x - 3$ and $g(x) = x^2 - 1$ can be combined to form the sum, difference, product, and quotient of f and g.

$$f(x) + g(x) = (2x - 3) + (x^2 - 1) = x^2 + 2x - 4 \qquad \text{Sum}$$

$$f(x) - g(x) = (2x - 3) - (x^2 - 1) = -x^2 + 2x - 2 \qquad \text{Difference}$$

$$f(x)g(x) = (2x - 3)(x^2 - 1) = 2x^3 - 3x^2 - 2x + 3 \qquad \text{Product}$$

$$\frac{f(x)}{g(x)} = \frac{2x - 3}{x^2 - 1}, \quad x \neq \pm 1 \qquad \text{Quotient}$$

The domain of an **arithmetic combination** of functions f and g consists of all real numbers that are common to the domains of f and g. In the case of the quotient $f(x)/g(x)$, there is the further restriction that $g(x) \neq 0$.

Sum, Difference, Product, and Quotient of Functions

Let f and g be two functions with overlapping domains. Then, for all x common to both domains, the *sum, difference, product,* and *quotient* of f and g are defined as follows.

1. Sum: $\qquad (f + g)(x) = f(x) + g(x)$

2. Difference: $(f - g)(x) = f(x) - g(x)$

3. Product: $\qquad (fg)(x) = f(x) \cdot g(x)$

4. Quotient: $\left(\dfrac{f}{g}\right)(x) = \dfrac{f(x)}{g(x)}, \quad g(x) \neq 0$

EXAMPLE 1 **Finding the Sum of Two Functions**

Given $f(x) = 2x + 1$ and $g(x) = x^2 + 2x - 1$, find $(f + g)(x)$. Then evaluate the sum when $x = 3$.

Solution The sum of f and g is

$$(f + g)(x) = f(x) + g(x) = (2x + 1) + (x^2 + 2x - 1) = x^2 + 4x.$$

When $x = 3$, the value of this sum is

$$(f + g)(3) = 3^2 + 4(3) = 21.$$

✓ *Checkpoint* ◀))) *Audio-video solution in English & Spanish at LarsonPrecalculus.com.*

Given $f(x) = x^2$ and $g(x) = 1 - x$, find $(f + g)(x)$. Then evaluate the sum when $x = 2$.

Michael Pettigrew/Shutterstock.com

EXAMPLE 2 **Finding the Difference of Two Functions**

Given $f(x) = 2x + 1$ and $g(x) = x^2 + 2x - 1$, find $(f - g)(x)$. Then evaluate the difference when $x = 2$.

Solution The difference of f and g is

$$(f - g)(x) = f(x) - g(x) = (2x + 1) - (x^2 + 2x - 1) = -x^2 + 2.$$

When $x = 2$, the value of this difference is

$$(f - g)(2) = -(2)^2 + 2 = -2.$$

✓ **Checkpoint** ◀))) Audio-video solution in English & Spanish at LarsonPrecalculus.com.

Given $f(x) = x^2$ and $g(x) = 1 - x$, find $(f - g)(x)$. Then evaluate the difference when $x = 3$.

EXAMPLE 3 **Finding the Product of Two Functions**

Given $f(x) = x^2$ and $g(x) = x - 3$, find $(fg)(x)$. Then evaluate the product when $x = 4$.

Solution The product of f and g is

$$(fg)(x) = f(x)g(x) = (x^2)(x - 3) = x^3 - 3x^2.$$

When $x = 4$, the value of this product is

$$(fg)(4) = 4^3 - 3(4)^2 = 16.$$

✓ **Checkpoint** ◀))) Audio-video solution in English & Spanish at LarsonPrecalculus.com.

Given $f(x) = x^2$ and $g(x) = 1 - x$, find $(fg)(x)$. Then evaluate the product when $x = 3$.

In Examples 1–3, both f and g have domains that consist of all real numbers. So, the domains of $f + g, f - g$, and fg are also the set of all real numbers. Remember to consider any restrictions on the domains of f and g when forming the sum, difference, product, or quotient of f and g.

EXAMPLE 4 **Finding the Quotients of Two Functions**

Find $(f/g)(x)$ and $(g/f)(x)$ for the functions $f(x) = \sqrt{x}$ and $g(x) = \sqrt{4 - x^2}$. Then find the domains of f/g and g/f.

Solution The quotient of f and g is

$$\left(\frac{f}{g}\right)(x) = \frac{f(x)}{g(x)} = \frac{\sqrt{x}}{\sqrt{4 - x^2}}$$

and the quotient of g and f is

$$\left(\frac{g}{f}\right)(x) = \frac{g(x)}{f(x)} = \frac{\sqrt{4 - x^2}}{\sqrt{x}}.$$

• • **REMARK** Note that the domain of f/g includes $x = 0$, but not $x = 2$, because $x = 2$ yields a zero in the denominator, whereas the domain of g/f includes $x = 2$, but not $x = 0$, because $x = 0$ yields a zero in the denominator. • • • • • • • • • • • • • • • ▷

The domain of f is $[0, \infty)$ and the domain of g is $[-2, 2]$. The intersection of these domains is $[0, 2]$. So, the domains of f/g and g/f are as follows.

Domain of f/g: $[0, 2)$ Domain of g/f: $(0, 2]$

✓ **Checkpoint** ◀))) Audio-video solution in English & Spanish at LarsonPrecalculus.com.

Find $(f/g)(x)$ and $(g/f)(x)$ for the functions $f(x) = \sqrt{x - 3}$ and $g(x) = \sqrt{16 - x^2}$. Then find the domains of f/g and g/f.

Composition of Functions

Another way of combining two functions is to form the **composition** of one with the other. For instance, if $f(x) = x^2$ and $g(x) = x + 1,$ then the composition of f with g is

$$f(g(x)) = f(x + 1)$$
$$= (x + 1)^2.$$

This composition is denoted as $f \circ g$ and reads as "f composed with g."

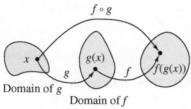

$f \circ g$

x g $g(x)$ f $f(g(x))$

Domain of g

Domain of f

Figure 1.57

Definition of Composition of Two Functions

The **composition** of the function f with the function g is

$$(f \circ g)(x) = f(g(x)).$$

The domain of $f \circ g$ is the set of all x in the domain of g such that $g(x)$ is in the domain of f. (See Figure 1.57.)

EXAMPLE 5   **Composition of Functions**

Given $f(x) = x + 2$ and $g(x) = 4 - x^2,$ find the following.

a. $(f \circ g)(x)$

b. $(g \circ f)(x)$

c. $(g \circ f)(-2)$

Solution

a. The composition of f with g is as follows.

$$(f \circ g)(x) = f(g(x)) \qquad \text{Definition of } f \circ g$$
$$= f(4 - x^2) \qquad \text{Definition of } g(x)$$
$$= (4 - x^2) + 2 \qquad \text{Definition of } f(x)$$
$$= -x^2 + 6 \qquad \text{Simplify.}$$

b. The composition of g with f is as follows.

$$(g \circ f)(x) = g(f(x)) \qquad \text{Definition of } g \circ f$$
$$= g(x + 2) \qquad \text{Definition of } f(x)$$
$$= 4 - (x + 2)^2 \qquad \text{Definition of } g(x)$$
$$= 4 - (x^2 + 4x + 4) \qquad \text{Expand.}$$
$$= -x^2 - 4x \qquad \text{Simplify.}$$

Note that, in this case, $(f \circ g)(x) \neq (g \circ f)(x).$

c. Using the result of part (b), write the following.

$$(g \circ f)(-2) = -(-2)^2 - 4(-2) \qquad \text{Substitute.}$$
$$= -4 + 8 \qquad \text{Simplify.}$$
$$= 4 \qquad \text{Simplify.}$$

⋯⋯⋯⋯⋯⋯⋯⋯⋯▷

REMARK The following tables of values help illustrate the composition $(f \circ g)(x)$ in Example 5(a).

x	0	1	2	3
$g(x)$	4	3	0	-5

$g(x)$	4	3	0	-5
$f(g(x))$	6	5	2	-3

x	0	1	2	3
$f(g(x))$	6	5	2	-3

Note that the first two tables can be combined (or "composed") to produce the values in the third table.

✓ **Checkpoint** ◀))) *Audio-video solution in English & Spanish at LarsonPrecalculus.com.*

Given $f(x) = 2x + 5$ and $g(x) = 4x^2 + 1,$ find the following.

a. $(f \circ g)(x)$ **b.** $(g \circ f)(x)$ **c.** $(f \circ g)\left(-\frac{1}{2}\right)$

■

EXAMPLE 6   **Finding the Domain of a Composite Function**

Find the domain of $(f \circ g)(x)$ for the functions

$$f(x) = x^2 - 9 \quad \text{and} \quad g(x) = \sqrt{9 - x^2}.$$

Algebraic Solution

The composition of the functions is as follows.

$$\begin{aligned}
(f \circ g)(x) &= f(g(x)) \\
&= f\left(\sqrt{9 - x^2}\right) \\
&= \left(\sqrt{9 - x^2}\right)^2 - 9 \\
&= 9 - x^2 - 9 \\
&= -x^2
\end{aligned}$$

From this, it might appear that the domain of the composition is the set of all real numbers. This, however, is not true. Because the domain of f is the set of all real numbers and the domain of g is $[-3, 3]$, the domain of $f \circ g$ is $[-3, 3]$.

Graphical Solution

The x-coordinates of the points on the graph extend from -3 to 3. So, the domain of $f \circ g$ is $[-3, 3]$.

✓ *Checkpoint* ◀))) *Audio-video solution in English & Spanish at LarsonPrecalculus.com.*

Find the domain of $(f \circ g)(x)$ for the functions $f(x) = \sqrt{x}$ and $g(x) = x^2 + 4$.   ■

In Examples 5 and 6, you formed the composition of two given functions. In calculus, it is also important to be able to identify two functions that make up a given composite function. For instance, the function $h(x) = (3x - 5)^3$ is the composition of $f(x) = x^3$ and $g(x) = 3x - 5$. That is,

$$h(x) = (3x - 5)^3 = [g(x)]^3 = f(g(x)).$$

Basically, to "decompose" a composite function, look for an "inner" function and an "outer" function. In the function h above, $g(x) = 3x - 5$ is the inner function and $f(x) = x^3$ is the outer function.

EXAMPLE 7   **Decomposing a Composite Function**

Write the function $h(x) = \dfrac{1}{(x - 2)^2}$ as a composition of two functions.

Solution   One way to write h as a composition of two functions is to take the inner function to be $g(x) = x - 2$ and the outer function to be

$$f(x) = \frac{1}{x^2} = x^{-2}.$$

Then write

$$\begin{aligned}
h(x) &= \frac{1}{(x - 2)^2} \\
&= (x - 2)^{-2} \\
&= f(x - 2) \\
&= f(g(x)).
\end{aligned}$$

✓ *Checkpoint* ◀))) *Audio-video solution in English & Spanish at LarsonPrecalculus.com.*

Write the function $h(x) = \dfrac{\sqrt[3]{8 - x}}{5}$ as a composition of two functions.   ■

Application

EXAMPLE 8   **Bacteria Count**

Refrigerated foods can have two types of bacteria: pathogenic bacteria, which can cause foodborne illness, and spoilage bacteria, which give foods an unpleasant look, smell, taste, or texture.

The number N of bacteria in a refrigerated food is given by

$$N(T) = 20T^2 - 80T + 500, \quad 2 \le T \le 14$$

where T is the temperature of the food in degrees Celsius. When the food is removed from refrigeration, the temperature of the food is given by

$$T(t) = 4t + 2, \quad 0 \le t \le 3$$

where t is the time in hours.

a. Find the composition $(N \circ T)(t)$ and interpret its meaning in context.

b. Find the time when the bacteria count reaches 2000.

Solution

a. $(N \circ T)(t) = N(T(t))$

$$= 20(4t + 2)^2 - 80(4t + 2) + 500$$

$$= 20(16t^2 + 16t + 4) - 320t - 160 + 500$$

$$= 320t^2 + 320t + 80 - 320t - 160 + 500$$

$$= 320t^2 + 420$$

The composite function $(N \circ T)(t)$ represents the number of bacteria in the food as a function of the amount of time the food has been out of refrigeration.

b. The bacteria count will reach 2000 when $320t^2 + 420 = 2000$. Solve this equation to find that the count will reach 2000 when $t \approx 2.2$ hours. Note that when you solve this equation, you reject the negative value because it is not in the domain of the composite function.

✓ *Checkpoint* *Audio-video solution in English & Spanish at LarsonPrecalculus.com.*

The number N of bacteria in a refrigerated food is given by

$$N(T) = 8T^2 - 14T + 200, \quad 2 \le T \le 12$$

where T is the temperature of the food in degrees Celsius. When the food is removed from refrigeration, the temperature of the food is given by

$$T(t) = 2t + 2, \quad 0 \le t \le 5$$

where t is the time in hours.

a. Find the composition $(N \circ T)(t)$.

b. Find the time when the bacteria count reaches 1000.

Summarize   (Section 1.8)

1. Explain how to add, subtract, multiply, and divide functions *(page 76)*. For examples of finding arithmetic combinations of functions, see Examples 1–4.

2. Explain how to find the composition of one function with another function *(page 78)*. For examples that use compositions of functions, see Examples 5–7.

3. Describe a real-life example that uses a composition of functions *(page 80, Example 8)*.

1.8 Exercises

See **CalcChat.com** for tutorial help and worked-out solutions to odd-numbered exercises.

Vocabulary: Fill in the blanks.

1. Two functions f and g can be combined by the arithmetic operations of _____, _____, _____, and _____ to create new functions.

2. The _____ of the function f with g is $(f \circ g)(x) = f(g(x))$.

Skills and Applications

Graphing the Sum of Two Functions In Exercises 3 and 4, use the graphs of f and g to graph $h(x) = (f + g)(x)$. To print an enlarged copy of the graph, go to *MathGraphs.com*.

3.

4.

Finding Arithmetic Combinations of Functions In Exercises 5–12, find (a) $(f + g)(x)$, (b) $(f - g)(x)$, (c) $(fg)(x)$, and (d) $(f/g)(x)$. What is the domain of f/g?

5. $f(x) = x + 2$, $g(x) = x - 2$
6. $f(x) = 2x - 5$, $g(x) = 2 - x$
7. $f(x) = x^2$, $g(x) = 4x - 5$
8. $f(x) = 3x + 1$, $g(x) = 5x - 4$
9. $f(x) = x^2 + 6$, $g(x) = \sqrt{1 - x}$
10. $f(x) = \sqrt{x^2 - 4}$, $g(x) = \dfrac{x^2}{x^2 + 1}$
11. $f(x) = \dfrac{1}{x}$, $g(x) = \dfrac{1}{x^2}$
12. $f(x) = \dfrac{x}{x + 1}$, $g(x) = x^3$

Evaluating an Arithmetic Combination of Functions In Exercises 13–24, evaluate the indicated function for $f(x) = x^2 + 1$ and $g(x) = x - 4$.

13. $(f + g)(2)$
14. $(f - g)(-1)$
15. $(f - g)(0)$
16. $(f + g)(1)$
17. $(f - g)(3t)$
18. $(f + g)(t - 2)$
19. $(fg)(6)$
20. $(fg)(-6)$
21. $(f/g)(5)$
22. $(f/g)(0)$
23. $(f/g)(-1) - g(3)$
24. $(fg)(5) + f(4)$

Graphing Two Functions and Their Sum In Exercises 25 and 26, graph the functions f, g, and $f + g$ on the same set of coordinate axes.

25. $f(x) = \frac{1}{2}x$, $g(x) = x - 1$
26. $f(x) = 4 - x^2$, $g(x) = x$

Graphical Reasoning In Exercises 27–30, use a graphing utility to graph f, g, and $f + g$ in the same viewing window. Which function contributes most to the magnitude of the sum when $0 \le x \le 2$? Which function contributes most to the magnitude of the sum when $x > 6$?

27. $f(x) = 3x$, $g(x) = -\dfrac{x^3}{10}$
28. $f(x) = \dfrac{x}{2}$, $g(x) = \sqrt{x}$
29. $f(x) = 3x + 2$, $g(x) = -\sqrt{x + 5}$
30. $f(x) = x^2 - \frac{1}{2}$, $g(x) = -3x^2 - 1$

Finding Compositions of Functions In Exercises 31–34, find (a) $f \circ g$, (b) $g \circ f$, and (c) $g \circ g$.

31. $f(x) = x^2$, $g(x) = x - 1$
32. $f(x) = 3x + 5$, $g(x) = 5 - x$
33. $f(x) = \sqrt[3]{x - 1}$, $g(x) = x^3 + 1$
34. $f(x) = x^3$, $g(x) = \dfrac{1}{x}$

Finding Domains of Functions and Composite Functions In Exercises 35–42, find (a) $f \circ g$ and (b) $g \circ f$. Find the domain of each function and each composite function.

35. $f(x) = \sqrt{x + 4}$, $g(x) = x^2$
36. $f(x) = \sqrt[3]{x - 5}$, $g(x) = x^3 + 1$
37. $f(x) = x^2 + 1$, $g(x) = \sqrt{x}$
38. $f(x) = x^{2/3}$, $g(x) = x^6$
39. $f(x) = |x|$, $g(x) = x + 6$
40. $f(x) = |x - 4|$, $g(x) = 3 - x$
41. $f(x) = \dfrac{1}{x}$, $g(x) = x + 3$
42. $f(x) = \dfrac{3}{x^2 - 1}$, $g(x) = x + 1$

Evaluating Combinations of Functions In Exercises 43–46, use the graphs of f and g to evaluate the functions.

43. (a) $(f + g)(3)$ (b) $(f/g)(2)$
44. (a) $(f - g)(1)$ (b) $(fg)(4)$
45. (a) $(f \circ g)(2)$ (b) $(g \circ f)(2)$
46. (a) $(f \circ g)(1)$ (b) $(g \circ f)(3)$

Decomposing a Composite Function In Exercises 47–54, find two functions f and g such that $(f \circ g)(x) = h(x)$. **(There are many correct answers.)**

47. $h(x) = (2x + 1)^2$ 48. $h(x) = (1 - x)^3$
49. $h(x) = \sqrt[3]{x^2 - 4}$ 50. $h(x) = \sqrt{9 - x}$
51. $h(x) = \dfrac{1}{x + 2}$ 52. $h(x) = \dfrac{4}{(5x + 2)^2}$
53. $h(x) = \dfrac{-x^2 + 3}{4 - x^2}$
54. $h(x) = \dfrac{27x^3 + 6x}{10 - 27x^3}$

55. **Stopping Distance**   The research and development department of an automobile manufacturer has determined that when a driver is required to stop quickly to avoid an accident, the distance (in feet) the car travels during the driver's reaction time is given by $R(x) = \frac{3}{4}x$, where x is the speed of the car in miles per hour. The distance (in feet) traveled while the driver is braking is given by $B(x) = \frac{1}{15}x^2$.

(a) Find the function that represents the total stopping distance T.

(b) Graph the functions R, B, and T on the same set of coordinate axes for $0 \le x \le 60$.

(c) Which function contributes most to the magnitude of the sum at higher speeds? Explain.

56. **Vital Statistics**   Let $b(t)$ be the number of births in the United States in year t, and let $d(t)$ represent the number of deaths in the United States in year t, where $t = 10$ corresponds to 2010.

(a) If $p(t)$ is the population of the United States in year t, then find the function $c(t)$ that represents the percent change in the population of the United States.

(b) Interpret the value of $c(13)$.

• • 57. **Pets** •

Let $d(t)$ be the number of dogs in the United States in year t, and let $c(t)$ be the number of cats in the United States in year t, where $t = 10$ corresponds to 2010.

(a) Find the function $p(t)$ that represents the total number of dogs and cats in the United States.

(b) Interpret the value of $p(13)$.

(c) Let $n(t)$ represent the population of the United States in year t, where $t = 10$ corresponds to 2010. Find and interpret

$$h(t) = \frac{p(t)}{n(t)}.$$

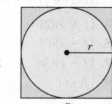

58. **Graphical Reasoning**   An electronically controlled thermostat in a home lowers the temperature automatically during the night. The temperature in the house T (in degrees Fahrenheit) is given in terms of t, the time in hours on a 24-hour clock (see figure).

(a) Explain why T is a function of t.

(b) Approximate $T(4)$ and $T(15)$.

(c) The thermostat is reprogrammed to produce a temperature H for which $H(t) = T(t - 1)$. How does this change the temperature?

(d) The thermostat is reprogrammed to produce a temperature H for which $H(t) = T(t) - 1$. How does this change the temperature?

(e) Write a piecewise-defined function that represents the graph.

59. **Geometry**   A square concrete foundation is a base for a cylindrical tank (see figure).

(a) Write the radius r of the tank as a function of the length x of the sides of the square.

(b) Write the area A of the circular base of the tank as a function of the radius r.

(c) Find and interpret $(A \circ r)(x)$.

60. Bacteria Count The number N of bacteria in a refrigerated food is given by

$$N(T) = 10T^2 - 20T + 600, \quad 2 \le T \le 20$$

where T is the temperature of the food in degrees Celsius. When the food is removed from refrigeration, the temperature of the food is given by

$$T(t) = 3t + 2, \quad 0 \le t \le 6$$

where t is the time in hours.

(a) Find the composition $(N \circ T)(t)$ and interpret its meaning in context.

(b) Find the bacteria count after 0.5 hour.

(c) Find the time when the bacteria count reaches 1500.

61. Salary You are a sales representative for a clothing manufacturer. You are paid an annual salary, plus a bonus of 3% of your sales over \$500,000. Consider the two functions $f(x) = x - 500,000$ and $g(x) = 0.03x$. When x is greater than \$500,000, which of the following represents your bonus? Explain your reasoning.

(a) $f(g(x))$

(b) $g(f(x))$

62. Consumer Awareness The suggested retail price of a new hybrid car is p dollars. The dealership advertises a factory rebate of \$2000 and a 10% discount.

(a) Write a function R in terms of p giving the cost of the hybrid car after receiving the rebate from the factory.

(b) Write a function S in terms of p giving the cost of the hybrid car after receiving the dealership discount.

(c) Form the composite functions $(R \circ S)(p)$ and $(S \circ R)(p)$ and interpret each.

(d) Find $(R \circ S)(25,795)$ and $(S \circ R)(25,795)$. Which yields the lower cost for the hybrid car? Explain.

Exploration

Siblings **In Exercises 63 and 64, three siblings are three different ages. The oldest is twice the age of the middle sibling, and the middle sibling is six years older than one-half the age of the youngest.**

63. (a) Write a composite function that gives the oldest sibling's age in terms of the youngest. Explain how you arrived at your answer.

(b) If the oldest sibling is 16 years old, then find the ages of the other two siblings.

64. (a) Write a composite function that gives the youngest sibling's age in terms of the oldest. Explain how you arrived at your answer.

(b) If the youngest sibling is two years old, then find the ages of the other two siblings.

True or False? **In Exercises 65 and 66, determine whether the statement is true or false. Justify your answer.**

65. If $f(x) = x + 1$ and $g(x) = 6x$, then

$$(f \circ g)(x) = (g \circ f)(x).$$

66. When you are given two functions $f(x)$ and $g(x)$, you can calculate $(f \circ g)(x)$ if and only if the range of g is a subset of the domain of f.

67. Proof Prove that the product of two odd functions is an even function, and that the product of two even functions is an even function.

68. **HOW DO YOU SEE IT?** The graphs labeled L_1, L_2, L_3, and L_4 represent four different pricing discounts, where p is the original price (in dollars) and S is the sale price (in dollars). Match each function with its graph. Describe the situations in parts (c) and (d).

(a) $f(p)$: A 50% discount is applied.

(b) $g(p)$: A \$5 discount is applied.

(c) $(g \circ f)(p)$

(d) $(f \circ g)(p)$

69. Conjecture Use examples to hypothesize whether the product of an odd function and an even function is even or odd. Then prove your hypothesis.

70. Proof

(a) Given a function f, prove that $g(x)$ is even and $h(x)$ is odd, where $g(x) = \frac{1}{2}[f(x) + f(-x)]$ and

$$h(x) = \frac{1}{2}[f(x) - f(-x)].$$

(b) Use the result of part (a) to prove that any function can be written as a sum of even and odd functions. [*Hint:* Add the two equations in part (a).]

(c) Use the result of part (b) to write each function as a sum of even and odd functions.

$$f(x) = x^2 - 2x + 1, \quad k(x) = \frac{1}{x+1}$$

1.9 Inverse Functions

Inverse functions can help you model and solve real-life problems. For instance, in Exercise 94 on page 92, an inverse function can help you determine the percent load interval for a diesel engine.

■ Find inverse functions informally and verify that two functions are inverse functions of each other.
■ Use graphs of functions to determine whether functions have inverse functions.
■ Use the Horizontal Line Test to determine whether functions are one-to-one.
■ Find inverse functions algebraically.

Inverse Functions

Recall from Section 1.4 that a set of ordered pairs can represent a function. For instance, the function $f(x) = x + 4$ from the set $A = \{1, 2, 3, 4\}$ to the set $B = \{5, 6, 7, 8\}$ can be written as follows.

$$f(x) = x + 4: \ \{(1, 5), (2, 6), (3, 7), (4, 8)\}$$

In this case, by interchanging the first and second coordinates of each of these ordered pairs, you can form the **inverse function** of f, which is denoted by f^{-1}. It is a function from the set B to the set A, and can be written as follows.

$$f^{-1}(x) = x - 4: \ \{(5, 1), (6, 2), (7, 3), (8, 4)\}$$

Note that the domain of f is equal to the range of f^{-1}, and vice versa, as shown in the figure below. Also note that the functions f and f^{-1} have the effect of "undoing" each other. In other words, when you form the composition of f with f^{-1} or the composition of f^{-1} with f, you obtain the identity function.

$$f(f^{-1}(x)) = f(x - 4) = (x - 4) + 4 = x$$
$$f^{-1}(f(x)) = f^{-1}(x + 4) = (x + 4) - 4 = x$$

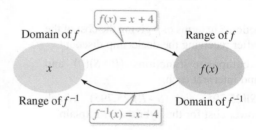

Domain of f $\boxed{f(x) = x + 4}$ Range of f

x $f(x)$

Range of f^{-1} Domain of f^{-1}
$\boxed{f^{-1}(x) = x - 4}$

EXAMPLE 1 **Finding an Inverse Function Informally**

Find the inverse function of $f(x) = 4x$. Then verify that both $f(f^{-1}(x))$ and $f^{-1}(f(x))$ are equal to the identity function.

Solution The function f *multiplies* each input by 4. To "undo" this function, you need to *divide* each input by 4. So, the inverse function of $f(x) = 4x$ is

$$f^{-1}(x) = \frac{x}{4}.$$

Verify that $f(f^{-1}(x)) = x$ and $f^{-1}(f(x)) = x$ as follows.

$$f(f^{-1}(x)) = f\!\left(\frac{x}{4}\right) = 4\!\left(\frac{x}{4}\right) = x \qquad f^{-1}(f(x)) = f^{-1}(4x) = \frac{4x}{4} = x$$

✓ *Checkpoint* ◀))) *Audio-video solution in English & Spanish at LarsonPrecalculus.com.*

Find the inverse function of $f(x) = \frac{1}{5}x$. Then verify that both $f(f^{-1}(x))$ and $f^{-1}(f(x))$ are equal to the identity function.

Definition of Inverse Function

Let f and g be two functions such that

$$f(g(x)) = x \qquad \text{for every } x \text{ in the domain of } g$$

and

$$g(f(x)) = x \qquad \text{for every } x \text{ in the domain of } f.$$

Under these conditions, the function g is the **inverse function** of the function f. The function g is denoted by f^{-1} (read "f-inverse"). So,

$$f(f^{-1}(x)) = x \quad \text{and} \quad f^{-1}(f(x)) = x.$$

The domain of f must be equal to the range of f^{-1}, and the range of f must be equal to the domain of f^{-1}.

Do not be confused by the use of -1 to denote the inverse function f^{-1}. In this text, whenever f^{-1} is written, it *always* refers to the inverse function of the function f and *not* to the reciprocal of $f(x)$.

If the function g is the inverse function of the function f, then it must also be true that the function f is the inverse function of the function g. For this reason, you can say that the functions f and g are *inverse functions of each other.*

EXAMPLE 2 **Verifying Inverse Functions**

Which of the functions is the inverse function of $f(x) = \dfrac{5}{x - 2}$?

$$g(x) = \frac{x - 2}{5} \qquad h(x) = \frac{5}{x} + 2$$

Solution By forming the composition of f with g, you have

$$f(g(x)) = f\left(\frac{x - 2}{5}\right) = \frac{5}{\left(\dfrac{x - 2}{5}\right) - 2} = \frac{25}{x - 12} \neq x.$$

Because this composition is not equal to the identity function x, it follows that g *is not* the inverse function of f. By forming the composition of f with h, you have

$$f(h(x)) = f\left(\frac{5}{x} + 2\right) = \frac{5}{\left(\dfrac{5}{x} + 2\right) - 2} = \frac{5}{\left(\dfrac{5}{x}\right)} = x.$$

So, it appears that h *is* the inverse function of f. Confirm this by showing that the composition of h with f is also equal to the identity function, as follows.

$$h(f(x)) = h\left(\frac{5}{x - 2}\right) = \frac{5}{\left(\dfrac{5}{x - 2}\right)} + 2 = x - 2 + 2 = x$$

✓ *Checkpoint* ◉))) Audio-video solution in English & Spanish at LarsonPrecalculus.com.

Which of the functions is the inverse function of $f(x) = \dfrac{x - 4}{7}$?

$$g(x) = 7x + 4 \qquad h(x) = \frac{7}{x - 4}$$

■

The Graph of an Inverse Function

The graphs of a function f and its inverse function f^{-1} are related to each other in the following way. If the point (a, b) lies on the graph of f, then the point (b, a) must lie on the graph of f^{-1}, and vice versa. This means that the graph of f^{-1} is a *reflection* of the graph of f in the line $y = x$, as shown in Figure 1.58.

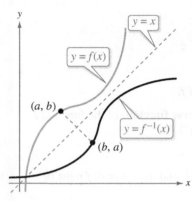

Figure 1.58

EXAMPLE 3 Verifying Inverse Functions Graphically

Sketch the graphs of the inverse functions $f(x) = 2x - 3$ and $f^{-1}(x) = \frac{1}{2}(x + 3)$ on the same rectangular coordinate system and show that the graphs are reflections of each other in the line $y = x$.

Solution The graphs of f and f^{-1} are shown in Figure 1.59. It appears that the graphs are reflections of each other in the line $y = x$. You can further verify this reflective property by testing a few points on each graph. Note in the following list that if the point (a, b) is on the graph of f, then the point (b, a) is on the graph of f^{-1}.

Graph of $f(x) = 2x - 3$	Graph of $f^{-1}(x) = \frac{1}{2}(x + 3)$
$(-1, -5)$	$(-5, -1)$
$(0, -3)$	$(-3, 0)$
$(1, -1)$	$(-1, 1)$
$(2, 1)$	$(1, 2)$
$(3, 3)$	$(3, 3)$

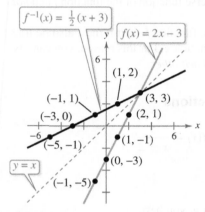

Figure 1.59

✓ **Checkpoint** ◀))) *Audio-video solution in English & Spanish at LarsonPrecalculus.com.*

Sketch the graphs of the inverse functions $f(x) = 4x - 1$ and $f^{-1}(x) = \frac{1}{4}(x + 1)$ on the same rectangular coordinate system and show that the graphs are reflections of each other in the line $y = x$.

EXAMPLE 4 Verifying Inverse Functions Graphically

Sketch the graphs of the inverse functions $f(x) = x^2$ $(x \geq 0)$ and $f^{-1}(x) = \sqrt{x}$ on the same rectangular coordinate system and show that the graphs are reflections of each other in the line $y = x$.

Solution The graphs of f and f^{-1} are shown in Figure 1.60. It appears that the graphs are reflections of each other in the line $y = x$. You can further verify this reflective property by testing a few points on each graph. Note in the following list that if the point (a, b) is on the graph of f, then the point (b, a) is on the graph of f^{-1}.

Graph of $f(x) = x^2$, $x \geq 0$	Graph of $f^{-1}(x) = \sqrt{x}$
$(0, 0)$	$(0, 0)$
$(1, 1)$	$(1, 1)$
$(2, 4)$	$(4, 2)$
$(3, 9)$	$(9, 3)$

Figure 1.60

Try showing that $f(f^{-1}(x)) = x$ and $f^{-1}(f(x)) = x$.

✓ **Checkpoint** ◀))) *Audio-video solution in English & Spanish at LarsonPrecalculus.com.*

Sketch the graphs of the inverse functions $f(x) = x^2 + 1$ $(x \geq 0)$ and $f^{-1}(x) = \sqrt{x - 1}$ on the same rectangular coordinate system and show that the graphs are reflections of each other in the line $y = x$.

One-to-One Functions

The reflective property of the graphs of inverse functions gives you a *geometric* test for determining whether a function has an inverse function. This test is called the **Horizontal Line Test** for inverse functions.

Horizontal Line Test for Inverse Functions

A function f has an inverse function if and only if no *horizontal* line intersects the graph of f at more than one point.

If no horizontal line intersects the graph of f at more than one point, then no y-value matches with more than one x-value. This is the essential characteristic of what are called **one-to-one functions.**

One-to-One Functions

A function f is **one-to-one** when each value of the dependent variable corresponds to exactly one value of the independent variable. A function f has an inverse function if and only if f is one-to-one.

Consider the function $f(x) = x^2$. The table on the left is a table of values for $f(x) = x^2$. The table on the right is the same as the table on the left but with the values in the columns interchanged. The table on the right does not represent a function because the input $x = 4$, for instance, matches with two different outputs: $y = -2$ and $y = 2$. So, $f(x) = x^2$ is not one-to-one and does not have an inverse function.

x	$f(x) = x^2$
-2	4
-1	1
0	0
1	1
2	4
3	9

x	y
4	-2
1	-1
0	0
1	1
4	2
9	3

Figure 1.61

Figure 1.62

EXAMPLE 5 **Applying the Horizontal Line Test**

a. The graph of the function $f(x) = x^3 - 1$ is shown in Figure 1.61. Because no horizontal line intersects the graph of f at more than one point, f *is* a one-to-one function and *does* have an inverse function.

b. The graph of the function $f(x) = x^2 - 1$ is shown in Figure 1.62. Because it is possible to find a horizontal line that intersects the graph of f at more than one point, f *is not* a one-to-one function and *does not* have an inverse function.

✓ *Checkpoint* ◀))) *Audio-video solution in English & Spanish at LarsonPrecalculus.com.*

Use the graph of f to determine whether the function has an inverse function.

a. $f(x) = \frac{1}{2}(3 - x)$

b. $f(x) = |x|$

Finding Inverse Functions Algebraically

For relatively simple functions (such as the one in Example 1), you can find inverse functions by inspection. For more complicated functions, however, it is best to use the following guidelines. The key step in these guidelines is Step 3—interchanging the roles of x and y. This step corresponds to the fact that inverse functions have ordered pairs with the coordinates reversed.

• • **REMARK**   Note what happens when you try to find the inverse function of a function that is not one-to-one.

$$f(x) = x^2 + 1 \qquad \text{Original function}$$

$$y = x^2 + 1 \qquad \text{Replace } f(x) \text{ with } y.$$

$$x = y^2 + 1 \qquad \text{Interchange } x \text{ and } y.$$

$$x - 1 = y^2 \qquad \text{Isolate } y\text{-term.}$$

$$y = \pm\sqrt{x - 1} \qquad \text{Solve for } y.$$

You obtain two y-values for each x.

▷

Finding an Inverse Function

1. Use the Horizontal Line Test to decide whether f has an inverse function.

2. In the equation for $f(x)$, replace $f(x)$ with y.

3. Interchange the roles of x and y, and solve for y.

4. Replace y with $f^{-1}(x)$ in the new equation.

5. Verify that f and f^{-1} are inverse functions of each other by showing that the domain of f is equal to the range of f^{-1}, the range of f is equal to the domain of f^{-1}, and $f(f^{-1}(x)) = x$ and $f^{-1}(f(x)) = x$.

EXAMPLE 6   **Finding an Inverse Function Algebraically**

Find the inverse function of

$$f(x) = \frac{5 - x}{3x + 2}.$$

Solution   The graph of f is shown in Figure 1.63. This graph passes the Horizontal Line Test. So, you know that f is one-to-one and has an inverse function.

$$f(x) = \frac{5 - x}{3x + 2}$$

Figure 1.63

$$f(x) = \frac{5 - x}{3x + 2} \qquad \text{Write original function.}$$

$$y = \frac{5 - x}{3x + 2} \qquad \text{Replace } f(x) \text{ with } y.$$

$$x = \frac{5 - y}{3y + 2} \qquad \text{Interchange } x \text{ and } y.$$

$$x(3y + 2) = 5 - y \qquad \text{Multiply each side by } 3y + 2.$$

$$3xy + 2x = 5 - y \qquad \text{Distributive Property}$$

$$3xy + y = 5 - 2x \qquad \text{Collect terms with } y.$$

$$y(3x + 1) = 5 - 2x \qquad \text{Factor.}$$

$$y = \frac{5 - 2x}{3x + 1} \qquad \text{Solve for } y.$$

$$f^{-1}(x) = \frac{5 - 2x}{3x + 1} \qquad \text{Replace } y \text{ with } f^{-1}(x).$$

Check that $f(f^{-1}(x)) = x$ and $f^{-1}(f(x)) = x$.

✓ **Checkpoint**   Audio-video solution in English & Spanish at LarsonPrecalculus.com.

Find the inverse function of

$$f(x) = \frac{5 - 3x}{x + 2}.$$

∎

EXAMPLE 7 **Finding an Inverse Function Algebraically**

Find the inverse function of

$$f(x) = \sqrt{2x - 3}.$$

Solution The graph of f is a curve, as shown in the figure below. Because this graph passes the Horizontal Line Test, you know that f is one-to-one and has an inverse function.

$f(x) = \sqrt{2x - 3}$	Write original function.
$y = \sqrt{2x - 3}$	Replace $f(x)$ with y.
$x = \sqrt{2y - 3}$	Interchange x and y.
$x^2 = 2y - 3$	Square each side.
$2y = x^2 + 3$	Isolate y-term.
$y = \dfrac{x^2 + 3}{2}$	Solve for y.
$f^{-1}(x) = \dfrac{x^2 + 3}{2}, \quad x \geq 0$	Replace y with $f^{-1}(x)$.

The graph of f^{-1} in the figure is the reflection of the graph of f in the line $y = x$. Note that the range of f is the interval $[0, \infty)$, which implies that the domain of f^{-1} is the interval $[0, \infty)$. Moreover, the domain of f is the interval $\left[\frac{3}{2}, \infty\right)$, which implies that the range of f^{-1} is the interval $\left[\frac{3}{2}, \infty\right)$. Verify that $f(f^{-1}(x)) = x$ and $f^{-1}(f(x)) = x$.

$$f^{-1}(x) = \frac{x^2 + 3}{2}, x \geq 0$$

$y = x$

$\left(0, \frac{3}{2}\right)$

$f(x) = \sqrt{2x - 3}$

$\left(\frac{3}{2}, 0\right)$

 Checkpoint Audio-video solution in English & Spanish at LarsonPrecalculus.com.

Find the inverse function of

$$f(x) = \sqrt[3]{10 + x}.$$

Summarize (Section 1.9)

1. State the definition of an inverse function *(page 85)*. For examples of finding inverse functions informally and verifying inverse functions, see Examples 1 and 2.

2. Explain how to use the graph of a function to determine whether the function has an inverse function *(page 86)*. For examples of verifying inverse functions graphically, see Examples 3 and 4.

3. Explain how to use the Horizontal Line Test to determine whether a function is one-to-one *(page 87)*. For an example of applying the Horizontal Line Test, see Example 5.

4. Explain how to find an inverse function algebraically *(page 88)*. For examples of finding inverse functions algebraically, see Examples 6 and 7.

1.9 Exercises

See CalcChat.com for tutorial help and worked-out solutions to odd-numbered exercises.

Vocabulary: Fill in the blanks.

1. If the composite functions $f(g(x))$ and $g(f(x))$ both equal x, then the function g is the _____ function of f.
2. The inverse function of f is denoted by _____.
3. The domain of f is the _____ of f^{-1}, and the _____ of f^{-1} is the range of f.
4. The graphs of f and f^{-1} are reflections of each other in the line _____.
5. A function f is _____ when each value of the dependent variable corresponds to exactly one value of the independent variable.
6. A graphical test for the existence of an inverse function of f is called the _____ Line Test.

Skills and Applications

Finding an Inverse Function Informally In Exercises 7–12, find the inverse function of f informally. Verify that $f(f^{-1}(x)) = x$ and $f^{-1}(f(x)) = x$.

7. $f(x) = 6x$
8. $f(x) = \frac{1}{3}x$
9. $f(x) = 3x + 1$
10. $f(x) = \frac{x-1}{5}$
11. $f(x) = \sqrt[3]{x}$
12. $f(x) = x^5$

Verifying Inverse Functions In Exercises 13–16, verify that f and g are inverse functions.

13. $f(x) = -\frac{7}{2}x - 3$, $g(x) = -\frac{2x+6}{7}$
14. $f(x) = \frac{x-9}{4}$, $g(x) = 4x + 9$
15. $f(x) = x^3 + 5$, $g(x) = \sqrt[3]{x-5}$
16. $f(x) = \frac{x^3}{2}$, $g(x) = \sqrt[3]{2x}$

Sketching the Graph of an Inverse Function In Exercises 17–20, use the graph of the function to sketch the graph of its inverse function $y = f^{-1}(x)$.

17.

18.

19.

20.

Verifying Inverse Functions In Exercises 21–32, verify that f and g are inverse functions (a) algebraically and (b) graphically.

21. $f(x) = 2x$, $g(x) = \frac{x}{2}$
22. $f(x) = x - 5$, $g(x) = x + 5$
23. $f(x) = 7x + 1$, $g(x) = \frac{x-1}{7}$
24. $f(x) = 3 - 4x$, $g(x) = \frac{3-x}{4}$
25. $f(x) = \frac{x^3}{8}$, $g(x) = \sqrt[3]{8x}$
26. $f(x) = \frac{1}{x}$, $g(x) = \frac{1}{x}$
27. $f(x) = \sqrt{x-4}$, $g(x) = x^2 + 4$, $x \geq 0$
28. $f(x) = 1 - x^3$, $g(x) = \sqrt[3]{1-x}$
29. $f(x) = 9 - x^2$, $x \geq 0$, $g(x) = \sqrt{9-x}$, $x \leq 9$
30. $f(x) = \frac{1}{1+x}$, $x \geq 0$, $g(x) = \frac{1-x}{x}$, $0 < x \leq 1$
31. $f(x) = \frac{x-1}{x+5}$, $g(x) = -\frac{5x+1}{x-1}$
32. $f(x) = \frac{x+3}{x-2}$, $g(x) = \frac{2x+3}{x-1}$

Using a Table to Determine an Inverse Function In Exercises 33 and 34, does the function have an inverse function?

33.

x	−1	0	1	2	3	4
$f(x)$	−2	1	2	1	−2	−6

34.

x	−3	−2	−1	0	2	3
$f(x)$	10	6	4	1	−3	−10

Using a Table to Find an Inverse Function In Exercises 35 and 36, use the table of values for $y = f(x)$ to complete a table for $y = f^{-1}(x)$.

35.

x	-2	-1	0	1	2	3
$f(x)$	-2	0	2	4	6	8

36.

x	-3	-2	-1	0	1	2
$f(x)$	-10	-7	-4	-1	2	5

Applying the Horizontal Line Test In Exercises 37–40, does the function have an inverse function?

37.

38.

39.

40.

Applying the Horizontal Line Test In Exercises 41–44, use a graphing utility to graph the function, and use the Horizontal Line Test to determine whether the function has an inverse function.

41. $g(x) = (x + 5)^3$
42. $f(x) = \frac{1}{8}(x + 2)^2 - 1$
43. $f(x) = -2x\sqrt{16 - x^2}$
44. $h(x) = |x + 4| - |x - 4|$

Finding and Analyzing Inverse Functions In Exercises 45–56, (a) find the inverse function of f, (b) graph both f and f^{-1} on the same set of coordinate axes, (c) describe the relationship between the graphs of f and f^{-1}, and (d) state the domains and ranges of f and f^{-1}.

45. $f(x) = 2x - 3$
46. $f(x) = 3x + 1$
47. $f(x) = x^5 - 2$
48. $f(x) = x^3 + 1$
49. $f(x) = \sqrt{4 - x^2}$, $0 \le x \le 2$
50. $f(x) = x^2 - 2$, $x \le 0$
51. $f(x) = \frac{4}{x}$
52. $f(x) = -\frac{2}{x}$
53. $f(x) = \frac{x + 1}{x - 2}$
54. $f(x) = \frac{x - 3}{x + 2}$
55. $f(x) = \sqrt[3]{x - 1}$
56. $f(x) = x^{3/5}$

Finding an Inverse Function In Exercises 57–72, determine whether the function has an inverse function. If it does, then find the inverse function.

57. $f(x) = x^4$
58. $f(x) = \frac{1}{x^2}$
59. $g(x) = \frac{x}{8}$
60. $f(x) = 3x + 5$
61. $p(x) = -4$
62. $f(x) = \frac{3x + 4}{5}$
63. $f(x) = (x + 3)^2$, $x \ge -3$
64. $q(x) = (x - 5)^2$
65. $f(x) = \begin{cases} x + 3, & x < 0 \\ 6 - x, & x \ge 0 \end{cases}$
66. $f(x) = \begin{cases} -x, & x \le 0 \\ x^2 - 3x, & x > 0 \end{cases}$
67. $h(x) = -\frac{4}{x^2}$
68. $f(x) = |x - 2|$, $x \le 2$
69. $f(x) = \sqrt{2x + 3}$
70. $f(x) = \sqrt{x - 2}$
71. $f(x) = \frac{6x + 4}{4x + 5}$
72. $f(x) = \frac{5x - 3}{2x + 5}$

Restricting the Domain In Exercises 73–82, restrict the domain of the function f so that the function is one-to-one and has an inverse function. Then find the inverse function f^{-1}. State the domains and ranges of f and f^{-1}. Explain your results. (There are many correct answers.)

73. $f(x) = (x - 2)^2$
74. $f(x) = 1 - x^4$
75. $f(x) = |x + 2|$
76. $f(x) = |x - 5|$
77. $f(x) = (x + 6)^2$
78. $f(x) = (x - 4)^2$
79. $f(x) = -2x^2 + 5$
80. $f(x) = \frac{1}{2}x^2 - 1$
81. $f(x) = |x - 4| + 1$
82. $f(x) = -|x - 1| - 2$

Composition with Inverses In Exercises 83–88, use the functions $f(x) = \frac{1}{8}x - 3$ and $g(x) = x^3$ to find the indicated value or function.

83. $(f^{-1} \circ g^{-1})(1)$
84. $(g^{-1} \circ f^{-1})(-3)$
85. $(f^{-1} \circ f^{-1})(6)$
86. $(g^{-1} \circ g^{-1})(-4)$
87. $(f \circ g)^{-1}$
88. $g^{-1} \circ f^{-1}$

Composition with Inverses In Exercises 89–92, use the functions $f(x) = x + 4$ and $g(x) = 2x - 5$ to find the specified function.

89. $g^{-1} \circ f^{-1}$
90. $f^{-1} \circ g^{-1}$
91. $(f \circ g)^{-1}$
92. $(g \circ f)^{-1}$

93. Hourly Wage   Your wage is $10.00 per hour plus $0.75 for each unit produced per hour. So, your hourly wage y in terms of the number of units produced x is $y = 10 + 0.75x$.

(a) Find the inverse function. What does each variable represent in the inverse function?

(b) Determine the number of units produced when your hourly wage is $24.25.

94. Diesel Mechanics

The function

$y = 0.03x^2 + 245.50, \quad 0 < x < 100$

approximates the exhaust temperature y in degrees Fahrenheit, where x is the percent load for a diesel engine.

(a) Find the inverse function. What does each variable represent in the inverse function?

(b) Use a graphing utility to graph the inverse function.

(c) The exhaust temperature of the engine must not exceed 500 degrees Fahrenheit. What is the percent load interval?

Exploration

True or False?   **In Exercises 95 and 96, determine whether the statement is true or false. Justify your answer.**

95. If f is an even function, then f^{-1} exists.

96. If the inverse function of f exists and the graph of f has a y-intercept, then the y-intercept of f is an x-intercept of f^{-1}.

Graphical Analysis   **In Exercises 97 and 98, use the graph of the function f to create a table of values for the given points. Then create a second table that can be used to find f^{-1}, and sketch the graph of f^{-1} if possible.**

97.

98.

99. Proof   Prove that if f and g are one-to-one functions, then $(f \circ g)^{-1}(x) = (g^{-1} \circ f^{-1})(x)$.

100. Proof   Prove that if f is a one-to-one odd function, then f^{-1} is an odd function.

101. Think About It   The function $f(x) = k(2 - x - x^3)$ has an inverse function, and $f^{-1}(3) = -2$. Find k.

102. Think About It   Consider the functions $f(x) = x + 2$ and $f^{-1}(x) = x - 2$. Evaluate $f(f^{-1}(x))$ and $f^{-1}(f(x))$ for the indicated values of x. What can you conclude about the functions?

x	-10	0	7	45
$f(f^{-1}(x))$				
$f^{-1}(f(x))$				

103. Think About It   Restrict the domain of $f(x) = x^2 + 1$ to $x \geq 0$. Use a graphing utility to graph the function. Does the restricted function have an inverse function? Explain.

104. **HOW DO YOU SEE IT?**   The cost C for a business to make personalized T-shirts is given by

$C(x) = 7.50x + 1500$

where x represents the number of T-shirts.

(a) The graphs of C and C^{-1} are shown below. Match each function with its graph.

(b) Explain what $C(x)$ and $C^{-1}(x)$ represent in the context of the problem.

One-to-One Function Representation   **In Exercises 105 and 106, determine whether the situation could be represented by a one-to-one function. If so, then write a statement that best describes the inverse function.**

105. The number of miles n a marathon runner has completed in terms of the time t in hours

106. The depth of the tide d at a beach in terms of the time t over a 24-hour period

1.10 Mathematical Modeling and Variation

- Use mathematical models to approximate sets of data points.
- Use the *regression* feature of a graphing utility to find the equation of a least squares regression line.
- Write mathematical models for direct variation, direct variation as an *n*th power, inverse variation, combined variation, and joint variation.

Introduction

In this section, you will study the following techniques for fitting models to data: *least squares regression* and *direct and inverse variation.*

You can use functions as models to represent a wide variety of real-life data sets. For instance, in Exercise 75 on page 103, a variation model can be used to model the water temperatures of the ocean at various depths.

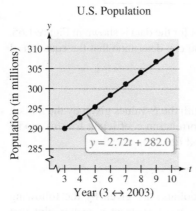

Figure 1.64

U.S. Population

REMARK   Note that the linear model in Example 1 was found using the *regression* feature of a graphing utility and is the line that *best* fits the data. This concept of a "best-fitting" line is discussed on the next page.

> **EXAMPLE 1**   **A Mathematical Model**

The populations *y* (in millions) of the United States from 2003 through 2010 are shown in the table.   *(Source: U.S. Census Bureau)*

Year, *t*	2003	2004	2005	2006	2007	2008	2009	2010
Population, *y*	290.1	292.8	295.5	298.4	301.2	304.1	306.8	308.7

Spreadsheet at LarsonPrecalculus.com

A linear model that approximates the data is

$$y = 2.72t + 282.0, \quad 3 \le t \le 10$$

where *t* represents the year, with *t* = 3 corresponding to 2003. Plot the actual data *and* the model on the same set of coordinate axes. How closely does the model represent the data?

Solution   The actual data are plotted in Figure 1.64, along with the graph of the linear model. From the graph, it appears that the model is a "good fit" for the actual data. You can see how well the model fits by comparing the actual values of *y* with the values of *y* given by the model. The values given by the model are labeled *y** in the table below.

t	3	4	5	6	7	8	9	10
y	290.1	292.8	295.5	298.4	301.2	304.1	306.8	308.7
*y**	290.2	292.9	295.6	298.3	301.0	303.8	306.5	309.2

✓ **Checkpoint**   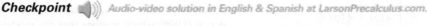 Audio-video solution in English & Spanish at LarsonPrecalculus.com.

The median sales prices *y* (in thousands of dollars) of new homes sold in a neighborhood from 2003 through 2010 are given by the following ordered pairs. *(Spreadsheet at LarsonPrecalculus.com)*

DATA
(2003, 179.4)   (2005, 191.0)   (2007, 202.6)   (2009, 214.9)
(2004, 185.4)   (2006, 196.7)   (2008, 208.7)   (2010, 221.4)

A linear model that approximates the data is

$$y = 5.96t + 161.3, \quad 3 \le t \le 10$$

where *t* represents the year, with *t* = 3 corresponding to 2003. Plot the actual data *and* the model on the same set of coordinate axes. How closely does the model represent the data?

Least Squares Regression and Graphing Utilities

So far in this text, you have worked with many different types of mathematical models that approximate real-life data. In some instances the model was given (as in Example 1), whereas in other instances you were asked to find the model using simple algebraic techniques or a graphing utility.

To find a model that approximates a set of data most accurately, statisticians use a measure called the **sum of square differences,** which is the sum of the squares of the differences between actual data values and model values. The "best-fitting" linear model, called the **least squares regression line,** is the one with the least sum of square differences.

Recall that you can approximate this line visually by plotting the data points and drawing the line that appears to best fit the data—or you can enter the data points into a calculator or computer and use the *linear regression* feature of the calculator or computer.

When you use the *regression* feature of a graphing calculator or computer program, you will notice that the program may also output an "*r*-value." This *r*-value is the **correlation coefficient** of the data and gives a measure of how well the model fits the data. The closer the value of $|r|$ is to 1, the better the fit.

EXAMPLE 2 **Finding a Least Squares Regression Line**

The data in the table show the numbers E (in millions) of Medicare enrollees from 2003 through 2010. Construct a scatter plot that represents the data and find the least squares regression line for the data. *(Source: U.S. Centers for Medicare and Medicaid Services)*

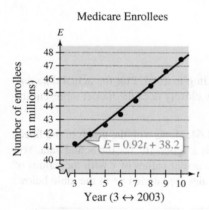

Medicare Enrollees

$E = 0.92t + 38.2$

Year (3 ↔ 2003)

Figure 1.65

	Year	Medicare Enrollees, *E*
DATA	2003	41.2
	2004	41.9
	2005	42.6
	2006	43.4
	2007	44.4
	2008	45.5
	2009	46.6
	2010	47.5

Spreadsheet at LarsonPrecalculus.com

Solution Let $t = 3$ represent 2003. The scatter plot for the data is shown in Figure 1.65. Using the *regression* feature of a graphing utility, you can determine that the equation of the least squares regression line is

$$E = 0.92t + 38.2$$

To check this model, compare the actual *E*-values with the *E*-values given by the model, which are labeled *E*∗ in the table at the left. The correlation coefficient for this model is $r \approx 0.996$, which implies that the model is a good fit.

t	*E*	*E*∗
3	41.2	41.0
4	41.9	41.9
5	42.6	42.8
6	43.4	43.7
7	44.4	44.6
8	45.5	45.6
9	46.6	46.5
10	47.5	47.4

✓ *Checkpoint* *Audio-video solution in English & Spanish at LarsonPrecalculus.com.*

The total Medicare disbursements (in billions of dollars) are given by the following ordered pairs. *(Spreadsheet at LarsonPrecalculus.com)* Construct a scatter plot that represents the data and find the least squares regression line for the data. *(Source: U.S. Centers for Medicare and Medicaid Services)*

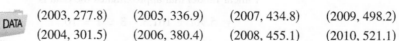

DATA
(2003, 277.8) (2005, 336.9) (2007, 434.8) (2009, 498.2)
(2004, 301.5) (2006, 380.4) (2008, 455.1) (2010, 521.1)

Direct Variation

There are two basic types of linear models. The more general model has a *y*-intercept that is nonzero.

$$y = mx + b, \quad b \neq 0$$

The simpler model

$$y = kx$$

has a *y*-intercept that is zero. In the simpler model, *y* is said to **vary directly** as *x*, or to be **directly proportional** to *x*.

Direct Variation

The following statements are equivalent.

1. *y* **varies directly** as *x*.
2. *y* is **directly proportional** to *x*.
3. $y = kx$ for some nonzero constant *k*.

k is the **constant of variation** or the **constant of proportionality**.

EXAMPLE 3 **Direct Variation**

In Pennsylvania, the state income tax is directly proportional to *gross income*. You are working in Pennsylvania and your state income tax deduction is $46.05 for a gross monthly income of $1500. Find a mathematical model that gives the Pennsylvania state income tax in terms of gross income.

Solution

Verbal Model: | State income tax | = | *k* | · | Gross income |

Labels: State income tax = *y* (dollars)
Gross income = *x* (dollars)
Income tax rate = *k* (percent in decimal form)

Equation: $y = kx$

To solve for *k*, substitute the given information into the equation $y = kx$, and then solve for *k*.

$$y = kx$$ Write direct variation model.

$$46.05 = k(1500)$$ Substitute 46.05 for *y* and 1500 for *x*.

$$0.0307 = k$$ Simplify.

So, the equation (or model) for state income tax in Pennsylvania is

$$y = 0.0307x.$$

In other words, Pennsylvania has a state income tax rate of 3.07% of gross income. The graph of this equation is shown in Figure 1.66.

 ✓ **Checkpoint** ◀))) *Audio-video solution in English & Spanish at LarsonPrecalculus.com.*

The simple interest on an investment is directly proportional to the amount of the investment. For instance, an investment of $2500 will earn $187.50 after 1 year. Find a mathematical model that gives the interest *I* after 1 year in terms of the amount invested *P*.

Pennsylvania Taxes

$y = 0.0307x$

(1500, 46.05)

State income tax (in dollars)

Gross income (in dollars)

Figure 1.66

Direct Variation as an *n*th Power

Another type of direct variation relates one variable to a *power* of another variable. For example, in the formula for the area of a circle

$$A = \pi r^2$$

the area A is directly proportional to the square of the radius r. Note that for this formula, π is the constant of proportionality.

⋯⋯⋯⋯⋯⋯⋯⋯⋯▷

$\vdots$•**REMARK**   Note that the direct variation model $y = kx$ is a special case of $y = kx^n$ with $n = 1$.

> ### Direct Variation as an *n*th Power
>
> The following statements are equivalent.
> 1. y **varies directly as the *n*th power** of x.
> 2. y is **directly proportional to the *n*th power** of x.
> 3. $y = kx^n$ for some nonzero constant k.

EXAMPLE 4   **Direct Variation as an *n*th Power**

The distance a ball rolls down an inclined plane is directly proportional to the square of the time it rolls. During the first second, the ball rolls 8 feet. (See Figure 1.67.)

a. Write an equation relating the distance traveled to the time.

b. How far will the ball roll during the first 3 seconds?

Solution

$t = 0$ sec
$t = 1$ sec
10
20
30
40   $t = 3$ sec
50
60
70

Figure 1.67

a. Letting d be the distance (in feet) the ball rolls and letting t be the time (in seconds), you have

$$d = kt^2.$$

Now, because $d = 8$ when $t = 1$, you can see that $k = 8$, as follows.

$d = kt^2$	Write direct variation model.
$8 = k(1)^2$	Substitute 8 for d and 1 for t.
$8 = k$	Simplify.

So, the equation relating distance to time is

$$d = 8t^2.$$

b. When $t = 3$, the distance traveled is

$d = 8(3)^2$	Substitute 3 for t.
$= 8(9)$	Simplify.
$= 72$ feet.	Simplify.

So, the ball will roll 72 feet during the first 3 seconds.

✓ *Checkpoint* 🔊 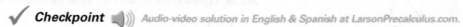 *Audio-video solution in English & Spanish at LarsonPrecalculus.com.*

Neglecting air resistance, the distance s an object falls varies directly as the square of the duration t of the fall. An object falls a distance of 144 feet in 3 seconds. How far will it fall in 6 seconds?

In Examples 3 and 4, the direct variations are such that an *increase* in one variable corresponds to an *increase* in the other variable. This is also true in the model $d = \frac{1}{5}F$, $F > 0$, where an increase in F results in an increase in d. You should not, however, assume that this always occurs with direct variation. For example, in the model $y = -3x$, an increase in x results in a *decrease* in y, and yet y is said to vary directly as x.

Inverse Variation

> **Inverse Variation**
>
> The following statements are equivalent.
>
> **1.** y **varies inversely** as x.
>
> **2.** y is **inversely proportional** to x.
>
> **3.** $y = \dfrac{k}{x}$ for some nonzero constant k.

If x and y are related by an equation of the form $y = k/x^n$, then y varies inversely as the nth power of x (or y is inversely proportional to the nth power of x).

EXAMPLE 5   **Inverse Variation**

A company has found that the demand for one of its products varies inversely as the price of the product. When the price is \$6.25, the demand is 400 units. Approximate the demand when the price is \$5.75.

Solution

Let p be the price and let x be the demand. Because x varies inversely as p, you have

$$x = \frac{k}{p}.$$

Now, because $x = 400$ when $p = 6.25$, you have

$$x = \frac{k}{p} \qquad \text{Write inverse variation model.}$$

$$400 = \frac{k}{6.25} \qquad \text{Substitute 400 for } x \text{ and 6.25 for } p.$$

$$(400)(6.25) = k \qquad \text{Multiply each side by 6.25.}$$

$$2500 = k. \qquad \text{Simplify.}$$

So, the equation relating price and demand is

$$x = \frac{2500}{p}.$$

When $p = 5.75$, the demand is

$$x = \frac{2500}{p} \qquad \text{Write inverse variation model.}$$

$$= \frac{2500}{5.75} \qquad \text{Substitute 5.75 for } p.$$

$$\approx 435 \text{ units.} \qquad \text{Simplify.}$$

So, the demand for the product is 435 units when the price of the product is \$5.75.

 ✓ Checkpoint *Audio-video solution in English & Spanish at LarsonPrecalculus.com.*

The company in Example 5 has found that the demand for another of its products varies inversely as the price of the product. When the price is \$2.75, the demand is 600 units. Approximate the demand when the price is \$3.25.

According to the National Association of Manufacturers, "manufacturing supports an estimated 17 million jobs in the U.S.—about one in six private sector jobs."

Combined Variation

Some applications of variation involve problems with *both* direct and inverse variations in the same model. These types of models are said to have **combined variation.**

If $P_2 > P_1$, then $V_2 < V_1$.

If the temperature is held constant and pressure increases, then the volume decreases.

Figure 1.68

EXAMPLE 6   **Combined Variation**

A gas law states that the volume of an enclosed gas varies directly as the temperature *and* inversely as the pressure, as shown in Figure 1.68. The pressure of a gas is 0.75 kilogram per square centimeter when the temperature is 294 K and the volume is 8000 cubic centimeters.

a. Write an equation relating pressure, temperature, and volume.

b. Find the pressure when the temperature is 300 K and the volume is 7000 cubic centimeters.

Solution

a. Let V be volume (in cubic centimeters), let P be pressure (in kilograms per square centimeter), and let T be temperature (in Kelvin). Because V varies directly as T and inversely as P, you have

$$V = \frac{kT}{P}.$$

Now, because $P = 0.75$ when $T = 294$ and $V = 8000$, you have

$$V = \frac{kT}{P}$$ Write combined variation model.

$$8000 = \frac{k(294)}{0.75}$$ Substitute 8000 for V, 294 for T, and 0.75 for P.

$$\frac{6000}{294} = k$$ Simplify.

$$\frac{1000}{49} = k.$$ Simplify.

So, the equation relating pressure, temperature, and volume is

$$V = \frac{1000}{49}\left(\frac{T}{P}\right).$$

b. Isolate P on one side of the equation by multiplying each side by P and dividing each side by V to obtain $P = \frac{1000}{49}\left(\frac{T}{V}\right)$. When $T = 300$ and $V = 7000$, the pressure is

$$P = \frac{1000}{49}\left(\frac{T}{V}\right)$$ Combined variation model solved for P.

$$= \frac{1000}{49}\left(\frac{300}{7000}\right)$$ Substitute 300 for T and 7000 for V.

$$= \frac{300}{343}$$ Simplify.

$$\approx 0.87 \text{ kilogram per square centimeter.}$$ Simplify.

So, the pressure is about 0.87 kilogram per square centimeter when the temperature is 300 K and the volume is 7000 cubic centimeters.

✓ **Checkpoint** ◄))) *Audio-video solution in English & Spanish at LarsonPrecalculus.com.*

The resistance of a copper wire carrying an electrical current is directly proportional to its length and inversely proportional to its cross-sectional area. Given that #28 copper wire (which has a diameter of 0.0126 inch) has a resistance of 66.17 ohms per thousand feet, what length of #28 copper wire will produce a resistance of 33.5 ohms? ∎

Joint Variation

> ### Joint Variation
>
> The following statements are equivalent.
>
> **1.** z **varies jointly** as x and y.   **2.** z is **jointly proportional** to x and y.
>
> **3.** $z = kxy$ for some nonzero constant k.

If x, y, and z are related by an equation of the form $z = kx^n y^m$, then z varies jointly as the nth power of x and the mth power of y.

EXAMPLE 7   Joint Variation

The *simple* interest for a certain savings account is jointly proportional to the time and the principal. After one quarter (3 months), the interest on a principal of $5000 is $43.75. (a) Write an equation relating the interest, principal, and time. (b) Find the interest after three quarters.

Solution

a. Let I = interest (in dollars), P = principal (in dollars), and t = time (in years). Because I is jointly proportional to P and t, you have

$$I = kPt.$$

For $I = 43.75$, $P = 5000$, and $t = \frac{1}{4}$, you have

$$43.75 = k(5000)\left(\frac{1}{4}\right)$$

which implies that $k = 4(43.75)/5000 = 0.035$. So, the equation relating interest, principal, and time is

$$I = 0.035Pt$$

which is the familiar equation for simple interest where the constant of proportionality, 0.035, represents an annual interest rate of 3.5%.

b. When $P = \$5000$ and $t = \frac{3}{4}$, the interest is

$$I = (0.035)(5000)\left(\frac{3}{4}\right) = \$131.25.$$

✓ *Checkpoint* *Audio-video solution in English & Spanish at LarsonPrecalculus.com.*

The kinetic energy E of an object varies jointly with the object's mass m and the square of the object's velocity v. An object with a mass of 50 kilograms traveling at 16 meters per second has a kinetic energy of 6400 joules. What is the kinetic energy of an object with mass of 70 kilograms traveling at 20 meters per second?   ◼

> ### Summarize   (Section 1.10)
>
> **1.** Give an example of how you can use a mathematical model to approximate a set of data points (*page 93, Example 1*).
>
> **2.** Describe how you can use the *regression* feature of a graphing utility to find the equation of a least squares regression line (*page 94, Example 2*).
>
> **3.** Describe direct variation, direct variation as an nth power, inverse variation, combined variation, and joint variation (*pages 95–99, Examples 3–7*).

1.10 Exercises

See **CalcChat.com** for tutorial help and worked-out solutions to odd-numbered exercises.

Vocabulary: Fill in the blanks.

1. Two techniques for fitting models to data are called direct and inverse _____ and least squares _____.
2. Statisticians use a measure called the _____ of _____ _____ to find a model that approximates a set of data most accurately.
3. The linear model with the least sum of square differences is called the _____ _____ _____ line.
4. An *r*-value of a set of data, also called a _____ _____, gives a measure of how well a model fits a set of data.
5. Direct variation models can be described as "*y* varies directly as *x*," or "*y* is _____ _____ to *x*."
6. In direct variation models of the form $y = kx$, *k* is called the _____ of _____.
7. The direct variation model $y = kx^n$ can be described as "*y* varies directly as the *n*th power of *x*," or "*y* is _____ _____ to the *n*th power of *x*."
8. The mathematical model $y = \dfrac{k}{x}$ is an example of _____ variation.
9. Mathematical models that involve both direct and inverse variation are said to have _____ variation.
10. The joint variation model $z = kxy$ can be described as "*z* varies jointly as *x* and *y*," or "*z* is _____ _____ to *x* and *y*."

Skills and Applications

11. **Labor Force** The total numbers of people 16 years of age and over (in thousands) not in the U.S. civilian labor force from 1998 through 2010 are given by the following ordered pairs. *(Spreadsheet at LarsonPrecalculus.com)*

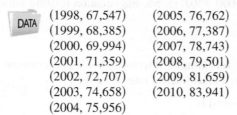

(1998, 67,547)	(2005, 76,762)
(1999, 68,385)	(2006, 77,387)
(2000, 69,994)	(2007, 78,743)
(2001, 71,359)	(2008, 79,501)
(2002, 72,707)	(2009, 81,659)
(2003, 74,658)	(2010, 83,941)
(2004, 75,956)	

A linear model that approximates the data is $y = 1298.8t + 57{,}094$, $8 \le t \le 20$, where *y* represents the total number of people 16 years of age and over (in thousands) not in the U.S. civilian labor force and $t = 8$ represents 1998. Plot the actual data and the model on the same set of coordinate axes. How closely does the model represent the data? *(Source: U.S. Bureau of Labor Statistics)*

12. **Sports** The winning times (in minutes) in the women's 400-meter freestyle swimming event in the Olympics from 1948 through 2008 are given by the following ordered pairs. *(Spreadsheet at LarsonPrecalculus.com)*

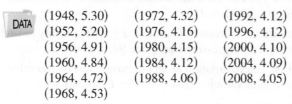

(1948, 5.30)	(1972, 4.32)	(1992, 4.12)
(1952, 5.20)	(1976, 4.16)	(1996, 4.12)
(1956, 4.91)	(1980, 4.15)	(2000, 4.10)
(1960, 4.84)	(1984, 4.12)	(2004, 4.09)
(1964, 4.72)	(1988, 4.06)	(2008, 4.05)
(1968, 4.53)		

A linear model that approximates the data is $y = -0.020t + 5.00$, $-2 \le t \le 58$, where *y* represents the winning time (in minutes) and $t = -2$ represents 1948. Plot the actual data and the model on the same set of coordinate axes. How closely does the model represent the data? Does it appear that another type of model may be a better fit? Explain. *(Source: International Olympic Committee)*

Sketching a Line **In Exercises 13–16, sketch the line that you think best approximates the data in the scatter plot. Then find an equation of the line. To print an enlarged copy of the graph, go to *MathGraphs.com*.**

13.

14.

15.

16.

17. Sports The lengths (in feet) of the winning men's discus throws in the Olympics from 1920 through 2008 are given by the following ordered pairs. *(Spreadsheet at LarsonPrecalculus.com)* *(Source: International Olympic Committee)*

DATA
(1920, 146.6)	(1956, 184.9)	(1984, 218.5)
(1924, 151.3)	(1960, 194.2)	(1988, 225.8)
(1928, 155.3)	(1964, 200.1)	(1992, 213.7)
(1932, 162.3)	(1968, 212.5)	(1996, 227.7)
(1936, 165.6)	(1972, 211.3)	(2000, 227.3)
(1948, 173.2)	(1976, 221.5)	(2004, 229.3)
(1952, 180.5)	(1980, 218.7)	(2008, 225.8)

(a) Sketch a scatter plot of the data. Let y represent the length of the winning discus throw (in feet) and let $t = 20$ represent 1920.

(b) Use a straightedge to sketch the best-fitting line through the points and find an equation of the line.

(c) Use the *regression* feature of a graphing utility to find the least squares regression line that fits the data.

(d) Compare the linear model you found in part (b) with the linear model given by the graphing utility in part (c).

18. Data Analysis: Broadway Shows The annual gross ticket sales S (in millions of dollars) for Broadway shows in New York City from 1995 through 2011 are given by the following ordered pairs. *(Spreadsheet at LarsonPrecalculus.com)* *(Source: The Broadway League)*

DATA
(1995, 406)	(2004, 771)
(1996, 436)	(2005, 769)
(1997, 499)	(2006, 862)
(1998, 558)	(2007, 939)
(1999, 588)	(2008, 938)
(2000, 603)	(2009, 943)
(2001, 666)	(2010, 1020)
(2002, 643)	(2011, 1080)
(2003, 721)	

(a) Use a graphing utility to create a scatter plot of the data. Let $t = 5$ represent 1995.

(b) Use the *regression* feature of the graphing utility to find the equation of the least squares regression line that fits the data.

(c) Use the graphing utility to graph the scatter plot you created in part (a) and the model you found in part (b) in the same viewing window. How closely does the model represent the data?

(d) Use the model to predict the annual gross ticket sales in 2017.

(e) Interpret the meaning of the slope of the linear model in the context of the problem.

Direct Variation In Exercises 19–26, assume that y is directly proportional to x. Use the given x-value and y-value to find a linear model that relates y and x.

19. $x = 2, y = 14$ **20.** $x = 5, y = 12$

21. $x = 10, y = 2050$ **22.** $x = 6, y = 580$

23. $x = 5, y = 1$ **24.** $x = -24, y = 3$

25. $x = 4, y = 8\pi$ **26.** $x = \pi, y = -1$

Direct Variation as an nth Power In Exercises 27–30, use the given values of k and n to complete the table for the direct variation model $y = kx^n$. Plot the points in a rectangular coordinate system.

x	2	4	6	8	10
$y = kx^n$					

27. $k = 1, n = 2$ **28.** $k = 2, n = 2$

29. $k = \frac{1}{2}, n = 3$ **30.** $k = \frac{1}{4}, n = 3$

Inverse Variation as an nth Power In Exercises 31–34, use the given values of k and n to complete the table for the inverse variation model $y = k/x^n$. Plot the points in a rectangular coordinate system.

x	2	4	6	8	10
$y = k/x^n$					

31. $k = 2, n = 1$

32. $k = 5, n = 1$

33. $k = 10, n = 2$

34. $k = 20, n = 2$

Think About It In Exercises 35 and 36, use the graph to determine whether y varies directly as some power of x or inversely as some power of x. Explain.

35.   36.

Determining Variation In Exercises 37–40, determine whether the variation model represented by the ordered pairs (x, y) is of the form $y = kx$ or $y = k/x$, and find k. Then write a model that relates y and x.

37. $(5, 1), \left(10, \frac{1}{2}\right), \left(15, \frac{1}{3}\right), \left(20, \frac{1}{4}\right), \left(25, \frac{1}{5}\right)$

38. $(5, 2), (10, 4), (15, 6), (20, 8), (25, 10)$

39. $(5, -3.5), (10, -7), (15, -10.5), (20, -14), (25, -17.5)$

40. $(5, 24), (10, 12), (15, 8), (20, 6), \left(25, \frac{24}{5}\right)$

Finding a Mathematical Model In Exercises 41–50, find a mathematical model for the verbal statement.

41. A varies directly as the square of r.

42. V varies directly as the cube of e.

43. y varies inversely as the square of x.

44. h varies inversely as the square root of s.

45. F varies directly as g and inversely as r^2.

46. z varies jointly as the square of x and the cube of y.

47. *Newton's Law of Cooling:* The rate of change R of the temperature of an object is directly proportional to the difference between the temperature T of the object and the temperature T_e of the environment in which the object is placed.

48. *Boyle's Law:* For a constant temperature, the pressure P of a gas is inversely proportional to the volume V of the gas.

49. *Logistic Growth:* The rate of growth R of a population is jointly proportional to the size S of the population and the difference between S and the maximum population size L that the environment can support.

50. *Newton's Law of Universal Gravitation:* The gravitational attraction F between two objects of masses m_1 and m_2 is jointly proportional to the masses and inversely proportional to the square of the distance r between the objects.

Describing a Formula In Exercises 51–54, write a sentence using the variation terminology of this section to describe the formula.

51. *Surface area of a sphere:*

$S = 4\pi r^2$

52. *Average speed:*

$r = d/t$

53. *Area of a triangle:*

$A = \frac{1}{2}bh$

54. *Volume of a right circular cylinder:*

$V = \pi r^2 h$

Finding a Mathematical Model In Exercises 55–62, find a mathematical model that represents the statement. (Determine the constant of proportionality.)

55. A varies directly as r^2. ($A = 9\pi$ when $r = 3$.)

56. y varies inversely as x. ($y = 3$ when $x = 25$.)

57. y is inversely proportional to x. ($y = 7$ when $x = 4$.)

58. z varies jointly as x and y. ($z = 64$ when $x = 4$ and $y = 8$.)

59. F is jointly proportional to r and the third power of s. ($F = 4158$ when $r = 11$ and $s = 3$.)

60. P varies directly as x and inversely as the square of y. $\left(P = \frac{28}{3} \text{ when } x = 42 \text{ and } y = 9.\right)$

61. z varies directly as the square of x and inversely as y. ($z = 6$ when $x = 6$ and $y = 4$.)

62. v varies jointly as p and q and inversely as the square of s. ($v = 1.5$ when $p = 4.1$, $q = 6.3$, and $s = 1.2$.)

63. Simple Interest The simple interest on an investment is directly proportional to the amount of the investment. An investment of \$3250 will earn \$113.75 after 1 year. Find a mathematical model that gives the interest I after 1 year in terms of the amount invested P.

64. Simple Interest The simple interest on an investment is directly proportional to the amount of the investment. An investment of \$6500 will earn \$211.25 after 1 year. Find a mathematical model that gives the interest I after 1 year in terms of the amount invested P.

65. Measurement Use the fact that 13 inches is approximately the same length as 33 centimeters to find a mathematical model that relates centimeters y to inches x. Then use the model to find the numbers of centimeters in 10 inches and 20 inches.

66. Measurement Use the fact that 14 gallons is approximately the same amount as 53 liters to find a mathematical model that relates liters y to gallons x. Then use the model to find the numbers of liters in 5 gallons and 25 gallons.

Hooke's Law In Exercises 67–70, use Hooke's Law for springs, which states that the distance a spring is stretched (or compressed) varies directly as the force on the spring.

67. A force of 220 newtons stretches a spring 0.12 meter. What force is required to stretch the spring 0.16 meter?

68. A force of 265 newtons stretches a spring 0.15 meter.

(a) What force is required to stretch the spring 0.1 meter?

(b) How far will a force of 90 newtons stretch the spring?

69. The coiled spring of a toy supports the weight of a child. The spring is compressed a distance of 1.9 inches by the weight of a 25-pound child. The toy will not work properly if its spring is compressed more than 3 inches. What is the maximum weight for which the toy will work properly?

70. An overhead garage door has two springs, one on each side of the door. A force of 15 pounds is required to stretch each spring 1 foot. Because of a pulley system, the springs stretch only one-half the distance the door travels. The door moves a total of 8 feet, and the springs are at their natural lengths when the door is open. Find the combined lifting force applied to the door by the springs when the door is closed.

71. Ecology   The diameter of the largest particle that can be moved by a stream varies approximately directly as the square of the velocity of the stream. A stream with a velocity of $\frac{1}{4}$ mile per hour can move coarse sand particles about 0.02 inch in diameter. Approximate the velocity required to carry particles 0.12 inch in diameter.

72. Music   The frequency of vibrations of a piano string varies directly as the square root of the tension on the string and inversely as the length of the string. The middle A string has a frequency of 440 vibrations per second. Find the frequency of a string that has 1.25 times as much tension and is 1.2 times as long.

73. Work   The work W done when lifting an object varies jointly with the object's mass m and the height h that the object is lifted. The work done when a 120-kilogram object is lifted 1.8 meters is 2116.8 joules. How much work is done when lifting a 100-kilogram object 1.5 meters?

74. Beam Load   The maximum load that can be safely supported by a horizontal beam varies jointly as the width of the beam and the square of its depth and inversely as the length of the beam. Determine the changes in the maximum safe load under the following conditions.

(a) The width and length of the beam are doubled.

(b) The width and depth of the beam are doubled.

75. Data Analysis: Ocean Temperatures

An oceanographer took readings of the water temperatures C (in degrees Celsius) at several depths d (in meters). The data collected are shown as ordered pairs (d, C). *(Spreadsheet at LarsonPrecalculus.com)*

 (1000, 4.2)   (4000, 1.2)
(2000, 1.9)   (5000, 0.9)
(3000, 1.4)

(a) Sketch a scatter plot of the data.

(b) Does it appear that the data can be modeled by the inverse variation model $C = k/d$? If so, find k for each pair of coordinates.

(c) Determine the mean value of k from part (b) to find the inverse variation model $C = k/d$.

(d) Use a graphing utility to plot the data points and the inverse model from part (c).

(e) Use the model to approximate the depth at which the water temperature is $3°C$.

76. Data Analysis: Light Intensity   A light probe is located x centimeters from a light source, and the intensity y (in microwatts per square centimeter) of the light is measured. The results are shown as ordered pairs (x, y). *(Spreadsheet at LarsonPrecalculus.com)*

DATA   (30, 0.1881)   (34, 0.1543)   (38, 0.1172)
(42, 0.0998)   (46, 0.0775)   (50, 0.0645)

A model for the data is $y = 262.76/x^{2.12}$.

(a) Use a graphing utility to plot the data points and the model in the same viewing window.

(b) Use the model to approximate the light intensity 25 centimeters from the light source.

Exploration

True or False?   **In Exercises 77 and 78, decide whether the statement is true or false. Justify your answer.**

77. In the equation for the area of a circle, $A = \pi r^2$, the area A varies jointly with π and the square of the radius r.

78. If the correlation coefficient for a least squares regression line is close to -1, then the regression line cannot be used to describe the data.

79. Writing

(a) Given that y varies directly as the square of x and x is doubled, how will y change? Explain.

(b) Given that y varies inversely as the square of x and x is doubled, how will y change? Explain.

80. HOW DO YOU SEE IT?   Discuss how well the data shown in each scatter plot can be approximated by a linear model.

Project: Fraud and Identity Theft   To work an extended application analyzing the numbers of fraud complaints and identity theft victims in the United States in 2010, visit this text's website at *LarsonPrecalculus.com*. *(Source: U.S. Federal Trade Commission)*

Chapter Summary

	What Did You Learn?	Explanation/Examples	Review Exercises
Section 1.1	Plot points in the Cartesian plane (p. 2), use the Distance Formula (p. 4) and the Midpoint Formula (p. 5), and use a coordinate plane to model and solve real-life problems (p. 6).	For an ordered pair (x, y), the x-coordinate is the directed distance from the y-axis to the point, and the y-coordinate is the directed distance from the x-axis to the point. The coordinate plane can help you find the length of a football pass. (See Example 6.)	1–6
Section 1.2	Sketch graphs of equations (p. 11), identify intercepts (p. 14), and use symmetry to sketch graphs of equations (p. 15).	To find x-intercepts, let y be zero and solve for x. To find y-intercepts, let x be zero and solve for y. Graphs can have symmetry with respect to one of the coordinate axes or with respect to the origin.	7–22
	Write equations of and sketch graphs of circles (p. 17).	A point (x, y) lies on the circle of radius r and center (h, k) if and only if $(x - h)^2 + (y - k)^2 = r^2$.	23–27
	Use graphs of equations in solving real-life problems (p. 18).	The graph of an equation can help you estimate the recommended weight for a man. (See Example 9.)	28
Section 1.3	Use slope to graph linear equations in two variables (p. 22).	The graph of the equation $y = mx + b$ is a line whose slope is m and whose y-intercept is $(0, b)$.	29–32
	Find the slope of a line given two points on the line (p. 24).	The slope m of the nonvertical line through (x_1, y_1) and (x_2, y_2) is $m = (y_2 - y_1)/(x_2 - x_1)$, where $x_1 \neq x_2$.	33, 34
	Write linear equations in two variables (p. 26), and identify parallel and perpendicular lines (p. 27).	The equation of the line with slope m passing through the point (x_1, y_1) is $y - y_1 = m(x - x_1)$. **Parallel lines:** $m_1 = m_2$ **Perpendicular lines:** $m_1 = -1/m_2$	35–40
	Use slope and linear equations in two variables to model and solve real-life problems (p. 28).	A linear equation in two variables can help you describe the book value of exercise equipment in a given year. (See Example 7.)	41, 42
Section 1.4	Determine whether relations between two variables are functions and use function notation (p. 35), and find the domains of functions (p. 40).	A function f from a set A (domain) to a set B (range) is a relation that assigns to each element x in the set A exactly one element y in the set B. **Equation:** $f(x) = 5 - x^2$ $f(2)$: $f(2) = 5 - 2^2 = 1$ **Domain of $f(x) = 5 - x^2$:** All real numbers	43–50
	Use functions to model and solve real-life problems (p. 41).	A function can model the number of alternative-fueled vehicles in the United States. (See Example 10.)	51, 52
	Evaluate difference quotients (p. 42).	Difference quotient: $[f(x + h) - f(x)]/h, h \neq 0$	53, 54
Section 1.5	Use the Vertical Line Test for functions (p. 50).	A set of points in a coordinate plane is the graph of y as a function of x if and only if no *vertical* line intersects the graph at more than one point.	55, 56
	Find the zeros of functions (p. 51).	**Zeros of $f(x)$:** x-values for which $f(x) = 0$	57–60

	What Did You Learn?	**Explanation/Examples**	**Review Exercises**
Section 1.5	Determine intervals on which functions are increasing or decreasing *(p. 52)*, relative minimum and maximum values of functions *(p. 53)*, and the average rates of change of functions *(p. 54)*.	To determine whether a function is increasing, decreasing, or constant on an interval, evaluate the function for several values of x. The points at which the behavior of a function changes can help determine a relative minimum or relative maximum. The average rate of change between any two points is the slope of the line (secant line) through the two points.	61–66
	Identify even and odd functions *(p. 55)*.	**Even:** For each x in the domain of f, $f(-x) = f(x)$. **Odd:** For each x in the domain of f, $f(-x) = -f(x)$.	67, 68
Section 1.6	Identify and graph different types of functions *(p. 60)*, and recognize graphs of parent functions *(p. 64)*.	**Linear:** $f(x) = ax + b$; **Squaring:** $f(x) = x^2$; **Cubic:** $f(x) = x^3$; **Square Root:** $f(x) = \sqrt{x}$; **Reciprocal:** $f(x) = 1/x$ Eight of the most commonly used functions in algebra are shown on page 64.	69–74
Section 1.7	Use vertical and horizontal shifts *(p. 67)*, reflections *(p. 69)*, and nonrigid transformations *(p. 71)* to sketch graphs of functions.	**Vertical shifts:** $h(x) = f(x) + c$ or $h(x) = f(x) - c$ **Horizontal shifts:** $h(x) = f(x - c)$ or $h(x) = f(x + c)$ **Reflection in x-axis:** $h(x) = -f(x)$ **Reflection in y-axis:** $h(x) = f(-x)$ **Nonrigid transformations:** $h(x) = cf(x)$ or $h(x) = f(cx)$	75–84
Section 1.8	Add, subtract, multiply, and divide functions *(p. 76)*, find compositions of functions *(p. 78)*, and use combinations and compositions of functions to model and solve real-life problems *(p. 80)*.	$(f + g)(x) = f(x) + g(x)$ $(f - g)(x) = f(x) - g(x)$ $(fg)(x) = f(x) \cdot g(x)$ $(f/g)(x) = f(x)/g(x), g(x) \neq 0$ The composition of the function f with the function g is $(f \circ g)(x) = f(g(x))$. A composite function can represent the number of bacteria in food as a function of the amount of time the food has been out of refrigeration. (See Example 8.)	85–90
Section 1.9	Find inverse functions informally and verify that two functions are inverse functions of each other *(p. 84)*.	Let f and g be two functions such that $f(g(x)) = x$ for every x in the domain of g and $g(f(x)) = x$ for every x in the domain of f. Under these conditions, the function g is the inverse function of the function f.	91, 92
	Use graphs to find inverse functions *(p. 86)*, use the Horizontal Line Test *(p. 87)*, and find inverse functions algebraically *(p. 88)*.	If the point (a, b) lies on the graph of f, then the point (b, a) must lie on the graph of f^{-1}, and vice versa. In short, the graph of f^{-1} is a reflection of the graph of f in the line $y = x$. To find an inverse function, replace $f(x)$ with y, interchange the roles of x and y, solve for y, and then replace y with $f^{-1}(x)$.	93–98
Section 1.10	Use mathematical models to approximate sets of data points *(p. 93)*, and use the *regression* feature of a graphing utility to find the equation of a least squares regression line *(p. 94)*.	To see how well a model fits a set of data, compare the actual values and model values of y. (See Example 1.) The sum of square differences is the sum of the squares of the differences between actual data values and model values. The least squares regression line is the linear model with the least sum of square differences.	99
	Write mathematical models for direct variation, direct variation as an *n*th power, inverse variation, combined variation, and joint variation *(pp. 95–99)*.	**Direct variation:** $y = kx$ for some nonzero constant k. **Direct variation as an *n*th power:** $y = kx^n$ for some nonzero constant k. **Inverse variation:** $y = k/x$ for some nonzero constant k. **Joint variation:** $z = kxy$ for some nonzero constant k.	100, 101

Review Exercises
See CalcChat.com for tutorial help and worked-out solutions to odd-numbered exercises.

1.1 **Plotting Points in the Cartesian Plane** In Exercises 1 and 2, plot the points in the Cartesian plane.

1. $(5, 5), (-2, 0), (-3, 6), (-1, -7)$

2. $(0, 6), (8, 1), (5, -4), (-3, -3)$

Determining Quadrant(s) for a Point In Exercises 3 and 4, determine the quadrant(s) in which (x, y) is located so that the condition(s) is (are) satisfied.

3. $x > 0$ and $y = -2$ **4.** $xy = 4$

5. **Plotting, Distance, and Midpoint** Plot the points $(-2, 6)$ and $(4, -3)$. Then find the distance between the points and the midpoint of the line segment joining the points.

6. **Sales** Barnes & Noble had annual sales of $5.1 billion in 2008 and $7.0 billion in 2010. Use the Midpoint Formula to estimate the sales in 2009. Assume that the annual sales followed a linear pattern. (*Source: Barnes & Noble, Inc.*)

1.2 **Sketching the Graph of an Equation** In Exercises 7–10, construct a table of values. Use the resulting solution points to sketch the graph of the equation.

7. $y = 3x - 5$ **8.** $y = -\frac{1}{2}x + 2$

9. $y = x^2 - 3x$ **10.** $y = 2x^2 - x - 9$

Finding x- and y-Intercepts In Exercises 11–14, find the x- and y-intercepts of the graph of the equation.

11. $y = 2x + 7$ **12.** $y = |x + 1| - 3$

13. $y = (x - 3)^2 - 4$ **14.** $y = x\sqrt{4 - x^2}$

Intercepts, Symmetry, and Graphing In Exercises 15–22, identify any intercepts and test for symmetry. Then sketch the graph of the equation.

15. $y = -4x + 1$ **16.** $y = 5x - 6$

17. $y = 5 - x^2$ **18.** $y = x^2 - 10$

19. $y = x^3 + 3$ **20.** $y = -6 - x^3$

21. $y = \sqrt{x + 5}$ **22.** $y = |x| + 9$

Sketching the Graph of a Circle In Exercises 23–26, find the center and radius of the circle. Then sketch the graph of the circle.

23. $x^2 + y^2 = 9$ **24.** $x^2 + y^2 = 4$

25. $(x + 2)^2 + y^2 = 16$ **26.** $x^2 + (y - 8)^2 = 81$

27. **Writing the Equation of a Circle** Write the standard form of the equation of the circle for which the endpoints of a diameter are $(0, 0)$ and $(4, -6)$.

28. **Physics** The force F (in pounds) required to stretch a spring x inches from its natural length (see figure) is

$$F = \frac{5}{4}x, \ 0 \le x \le 20.$$

Natural length

x in.

F

(a) Use the model to complete the table.

x	0	4	8	12	16	20
Force, F						

(b) Sketch a graph of the model.

(c) Use the graph to estimate the force necessary to stretch the spring 10 inches.

1.3 **Graphing a Linear Equation** In Exercises 29–32, find the slope and y-intercept (if possible) of the equation of the line. Sketch the line.

29. $y = 3x + 13$ **30.** $y = -10x + 9$

31. $y = 6$ **32.** $x = -3$

Finding the Slope of a Line Through Two Points In Exercises 33 and 34, plot the points and find the slope of the line passing through the pair of points.

33. $(6, 4), (-3, -4)$ **34.** $(-3, 2), (8, 2)$

Finding an Equation of a Line In Exercises 35 and 36, find an equation of the line that passes through the given point and has the indicated slope m. Sketch the line.

35. $(10, -3), \ m = -\frac{1}{2}$ **36.** $(-8, 5), \ m = 0$

Finding an Equation of a Line In Exercises 37 and 38, find an equation of the line passing through the points.

37. $(-1, 0), (6, 2)$ **38.** $(11, -2), (6, -1)$

Finding Parallel and Perpendicular Lines In Exercises 39 and 40, write the slope-intercept form of the equations of the lines through the given point (a) parallel to and (b) perpendicular to the given line.

39. $5x - 4y = 8, \ (3, -2)$ **40.** $2x + 3y = 5, \ (-8, 3)$

41. Sales A discount outlet is offering a 20% discount on all items. Write a linear equation giving the sale price S for an item with a list price L.

42. Hourly Wage A microchip manufacturer pays its assembly line workers $12.25 per hour. In addition, workers receive a piecework rate of $0.75 per unit produced. Write a linear equation for the hourly wage W in terms of the number of units x produced per hour.

1.4 Testing for Functions Represented Algebraically In Exercises 43–46, determine whether the equation represents y as a function of x.

43. $16x - y^4 = 0$ **44.** $2x - y - 3 = 0$

45. $y = \sqrt{1 - x}$ **46.** $|y| = x + 2$

Evaluating a Function In Exercises 47 and 48, evaluate the function at each specified value of the independent variable and simplify.

47. $f(x) = x^2 + 1$

  (a) $f(2)$ (b) $f(-4)$ (c) $f(t^2)$ (d) $f(t + 1)$

48. $h(x) = \begin{cases} 2x + 1, & x \le -1 \\ x^2 + 2, & x > -1 \end{cases}$

  (a) $h(-2)$ (b) $h(-1)$ (c) $h(0)$ (d) $h(2)$

Finding the Domain of a Function In Exercises 49 and 50, find the domain of the function. Verify your result with a graph.

49. $f(x) = \sqrt{25 - x^2}$ **50.** $h(x) = \dfrac{x}{x^2 - x - 6}$

Physics In Exercises 51 and 52, the velocity of a ball projected upward from ground level is given by $v(t) = -32t + 48$, where t is the time in seconds and v is the velocity in feet per second.

51. Find the velocity when $t = 1$.

52. Find the time when the ball reaches its maximum height. [*Hint:* Find the time when $v(t) = 0$.]

Evaluating a Difference Quotient In Exercises 53 and 54, find the difference quotient and simplify your answer.

53. $f(x) = 2x^2 + 3x - 1$, $\dfrac{f(x + h) - f(x)}{h}$, $h \ne 0$

54. $f(x) = x^3 - 5x^2 + x$, $\dfrac{f(x + h) - f(x)}{h}$, $h \ne 0$

1.5 Vertical Line Test for Functions In Exercises 55 and 56, use the Vertical Line Test to determine whether y is a function of x. To print an enlarged copy of the graph, go to *MathGraphs.com*.

55. $y = (x - 3)^2$ **56.** $x = -|4 - y|$

Figure for 55

Figure for 56

Finding the Zeros of a Function In Exercises 57–60, find the zeros of the function algebraically.

57. $f(x) = 3x^2 - 16x + 21$ **58.** $f(x) = 5x^2 + 4x - 1$

59. $f(x) = \dfrac{8x + 3}{11 - x}$ **60.** $f(x) = x^3 - x^2$

Describing Function Behavior In Exercises 61 and 62, use a graphing utility to graph the function and visually determine the intervals on which the function is increasing, decreasing, or constant.

61. $f(x) = |x| + |x + 1|$ **62.** $f(x) = (x^2 - 4)^2$

Approximating Relative Minima or Maxima In Exercises 63 and 64, use a graphing utility to graph the function and approximate (to two decimal places) any relative minima or maxima.

63. $f(x) = -x^2 + 2x + 1$ **64.** $f(x) = x^3 - 4x^2 - 1$

Average Rate of Change of a Function In Exercises 65 and 66, find the average rate of change of the function from x_1 to x_2.

65. $f(x) = -x^2 + 8x - 4$, $x_1 = 0, x_2 = 4$

66. $f(x) = 2 - \sqrt{x + 1}$, $x_1 = 3, x_2 = 7$

Even, Odd, or Neither? In Exercises 67–68, determine whether the function is even, odd, or neither. Then describe the symmetry.

67. $f(x) = x^4 - 20x^2$ **68.** $f(x) = 2x\sqrt{x^2 + 3}$

1.6 Writing a Linear Function In Exercises 69 and 70, (a) write the linear function f such that it has the indicated function values, and (b) sketch the graph of the function.

69. $f(2) = -6$, $f(-1) = 3$

70. $f(0) = -5$, $f(4) = -8$

Graphing a Function In Exercises 71–74, sketch the graph of the function.

71. $f(x) = 3 - x^2$ **72.** $f(x) = \sqrt{x + 1}$

73. $g(x) = \dfrac{1}{x + 5}$

74. $f(x) = \begin{cases} 5x - 3, & x \ge -1 \\ -4x + 5, & x < -1 \end{cases}$

1.7 **Identifying a Parent Function** In Exercises 75–84, h is related to one of the parent functions described in this chapter. (a) Identify the parent function f. (b) Describe the sequence of transformations from f to h. (c) Sketch the graph of h. (d) Use function notation to write h in terms of f.

75. $h(x) = x^2 - 9$

76. $h(x) = (x - 2)^3 + 2$

77. $h(x) = -\sqrt{x} + 4$

78. $h(x) = |x + 3| - 5$

79. $h(x) = -(x + 2)^2 + 3$

80. $h(x) = \frac{1}{2}(x - 1)^2 - 2$

81. $h(x) = -[\![x]\!] + 6$

82. $h(x) = -\sqrt{x + 1} + 9$

83. $h(x) = 5[\![x - 9]\!]$

84. $h(x) = -\frac{1}{3}x^3$

1.8 **Finding Arithmetic Combinations of Functions** In Exercises 85 and 86, find (a) $(f + g)(x)$, (b) $(f - g)(x)$, (c) $(fg)(x)$ and (d) $(f/g)(x)$. What is the domain of f/g?

85. $f(x) = x^2 + 3$, $g(x) = 2x - 1$

86. $f(x) = x^2 - 4$, $g(x) = \sqrt{3 - x}$

Finding Domains of Functions and Composite Functions In Exercises 87 and 88, find (a) $f \circ g$ and (b) $g \circ f$. Find the domain of each function and each composite function.

87. $f(x) = \frac{1}{3}x - 3$, $g(x) = 3x + 1$

88. $f(x) = x^3 - 4$, $g(x) = \sqrt[3]{x + 7}$

Bacteria Count In Exercises 89 and 90, the number N of bacteria in a refrigerated food is given by $N(T) = 25T^2 - 50T + 300$, $1 \leq T \leq 19$, where T is the temperature of the food in degrees Celsius. When the food is removed from refrigeration, the temperature of the food is given by $T(t) = 2t + 1$, $0 \leq t \leq 9$, where t is the time in hours.

89. Find the composition $(N \circ T)(t)$ and interpret its meaning in context.

90. Find the time when the bacteria count reaches 750.

1.9 **Finding an Inverse Function Informally** In Exercises 91 and 92, find the inverse function of f informally. Verify that $f(f^{-1}(x)) = x$ and $f^{-1}(f(x)) = x$.

91. $f(x) = 3x + 8$

92. $f(x) = \dfrac{x - 4}{5}$

Applying the Horizontal Line Test In Exercises 93 and 94, use a graphing utility to graph the function, and use the Horizontal Line Test to determine whether the function has an inverse function.

93. $f(x) = (x - 1)^2$

94. $h(t) = \dfrac{2}{t - 3}$

Finding and Analyzing Inverse Functions In Exercises 95 and 96, (a) find the inverse function of f, (b) graph both f and f^{-1} on the same set of coordinate axes, (c) describe the relationship between the graphs of f and f^{-1}, and (d) state the domains and ranges of f and f^{-1}.

95. $f(x) = \frac{1}{2}x - 3$

96. $f(x) = \sqrt{x + 1}$

Restricting the Domain In Exercises 97 and 98, restrict the domain of the function f to an interval on which the function is increasing, and determine f^{-1} on that interval.

97. $f(x) = 2(x - 4)^2$

98. $f(x) = |x - 2|$

1.10

99. Compact Discs The values V (in billions of dollars) of shipments of compact discs in the United States from 2004 through 2010 are given by the following ordered pairs. *(Spreadsheet at LarsonPrecalculus.com)* *(Source: Recording Industry Association of America)*

DATA
(2004, 11.45) (2005, 10.52) (2006, 9.37)
(2007, 7.45)   (2008, 5.47)   (2009, 4.27)
(2010, 3.36)

(a) Use a graphing utility to create a scatter plot of the data. Let t represent the year, with $t = 4$ corresponding to 2004.

(b) Use the *regression* feature of the graphing utility to find the equation of the least squares regression line that fits the data. Then graph the model and the scatter plot you found in part (a) in the same viewing window. How closely does the model represent the data?

100. Travel Time The travel time between two cities is inversely proportional to the average speed. A train travels between the cities in 3 hours at an average speed of 65 miles per hour. How long would it take to travel between the cities at an average speed of 80 miles per hour?

101. Cost The cost of constructing a wooden box with a square base varies jointly as the height of the box and the square of the width of the box. A box of height 16 inches and width 6 inches costs $28.80. How much would a box of height 14 inches and width 8 inches cost?

Exploration

True or False? In Exercises 102 and 103, determine whether the statement is true or false. Justify your answer.

102. Relative to the graph of $f(x) = \sqrt{x}$, the function $h(x) = -\sqrt{x + 9} - 13$ is shifted 9 units to the left and 13 units down, then reflected in the x-axis.

103. If f and g are two inverse functions, then the domain of g is equal to the range of f.

Chapter Test

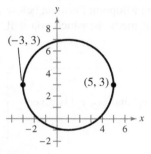

Figure for 6

Take this test as you would take a test in class. When you are finished, check your work against the answers given in the back of the book.

1. Plot the points $(-2, 5)$ and $(6, 0)$. Then find the distance between the points and the midpoint of the line segment joining the points.

2. A cylindrical can has a radius of 4 centimeters. Write the volume V of the can as a function of the height h.

In Exercises 3–5, use intercepts and symmetry to sketch the graph of the equation.

3. $y = 3 - 5x$ 4. $y = 4 - |x|$ 5. $y = x^2 - 1$

6. Write the standard form of the equation of the circle shown at the left.

In Exercises 7 and 8, find an equation of the line passing through the points.

7. $(2, -3), (-4, 9)$ 8. $(3, 0.8), (7, -6)$

9. Write equations of the lines that pass through the point $(0, 4)$ and are (a) parallel to and (b) perpendicular to the line $5x + 2y = 3$.

10. Evaluate $f(x) = \dfrac{\sqrt{x + 9}}{x^2 - 81}$ at each value and simplify: (a) $f(7)$ (b) $f(-5)$ (c) $f(x - 9)$.

11. Find the domain of $f(x) = 10 - \sqrt{3 - x}$.

In Exercises 12–14, (a) find the zeros of the function, (b) use a graphing utility to graph the function, (c) approximate the intervals on which the function is increasing, decreasing, or constant, and (d) determine whether the function is even, odd, or neither.

12. $f(x) = 2x^6 + 5x^4 - x^2$ 13. $f(x) = 4x\sqrt{3 - x}$ 14. $f(x) = |x + 5|$

15. Sketch the graph of $f(x) = \begin{cases} 3x + 7, & x \le -3 \\ 4x^2 - 1, & x > -3 \end{cases}$.

In Exercises 16–18, identify the parent function in the transformation. Then sketch a graph of the function.

16. $h(x) = -[\![x]\!]$ 17. $h(x) = -\sqrt{x + 5} + 8$ 18. $h(x) = -2(x - 5)^3 + 3$

In Exercises 19 and 20, find (a) $(f + g)(x)$, (b) $(f - g)(x)$, (c) $(fg)(x)$, (d) $(f/g)(x)$, (e) $(f \circ g)(x)$, and (f) $(g \circ f)(x)$.

19. $f(x) = 3x^2 - 7, \quad g(x) = -x^2 - 4x + 5$ 20. $f(x) = 1/x, \quad g(x) = 2\sqrt{x}$

In Exercises 21–23, determine whether the function has an inverse function. If so, find the inverse function.

21. $f(x) = x^3 + 8$ 22. $f(x) = |x^2 - 3| + 6$ 23. $f(x) = 3x\sqrt{x}$

In Exercises 24–26, find a mathematical model that represents the statement. (Determine the constant of proportionality.)

24. v varies directly as the square root of s. ($v = 24$ when $s = 16$.)

25. A varies jointly as x and y. ($A = 500$ when $x = 15$ and $y = 8$.)

26. b varies inversely as a. ($b = 32$ when $a = 1.5$.)

Proofs in Mathematics ■ ■ ■ ■ ■ ■ ■ ■ ■ ■ ■ ■ ■ ■ ■

What does the word *proof* mean to you? In mathematics, the word *proof* means a valid argument. When you are proving a statement or theorem, you must use facts, definitions, and accepted properties in a logical order. You can also use previously proved theorems in your proof. For instance, the proof of the Midpoint Formula below uses the Distance Formula. There are several different proof methods, which you will see in later chapters.

The Midpoint Formula *(p. 5)*

The midpoint of the line segment joining the points (x_1, y_1) and (x_2, y_2) is given by the Midpoint Formula

$$\text{Midpoint} = \left(\frac{x_1 + x_2}{2}, \frac{y_1 + y_2}{2} \right).$$

Proof

Using the figure, you must show that $d_1 = d_2$ and $d_1 + d_2 = d_3$.

By the Distance Formula, you obtain

$$d_1 = \sqrt{\left(\frac{x_1 + x_2}{2} - x_1 \right)^2 + \left(\frac{y_1 + y_2}{2} - y_1 \right)^2}$$

$$= \frac{1}{2} \sqrt{(x_2 - x_1)^2 + (y_2 - y_1)^2}$$

$$d_2 = \sqrt{\left(x_2 - \frac{x_1 + x_2}{2} \right)^2 + \left(y_2 - \frac{y_1 + y_2}{2} \right)^2}$$

$$= \frac{1}{2} \sqrt{(x_2 - x_1)^2 + (y_2 - y_1)^2}$$

$$d_3 = \sqrt{(x_2 - x_1)^2 + (y_2 - y_1)^2}$$

So, it follows that $d_1 = d_2$ and $d_1 + d_2 = d_3$. ■

P.S. Problem Solving ▪ ▪ ▪ ▪ ▪ ▪ ▪ ▪ ▪ ▪ ▪ ▪ ▪

1. **Monthly Wages** As a salesperson, you receive a monthly salary of $2000, plus a commission of 7% of sales. You receive an offer for a new job at $2300 per month, plus a commission of 5% of sales.

   (a) Write a linear equation for your current monthly wage W_1 in terms of your monthly sales S.

   (b) Write a linear equation for the monthly wage W_2 of your new job offer in terms of the monthly sales S.

   (c) Use a graphing utility to graph both equations in the same viewing window. Find the point of intersection. What does it signify?

   (d) You think you can sell $20,000 per month. Should you change jobs? Explain.

2. **Telephone Keypad** For the numbers 2 through 9 on a telephone keypad (see figure), create two relations: one mapping numbers onto letters, and the other mapping letters onto numbers. Are both relations functions? Explain.

3. **Sums and Differences of Functions** What can be said about the sum and difference of each of the following?

   (a) Two even functions

   (b) Two odd functions

   (c) An odd function and an even function

4. **Inverse Functions** The two functions

   $$f(x) = x \quad \text{and} \quad g(x) = -x$$

   are their own inverse functions. Graph each function and explain why this is true. Graph other linear functions that are their own inverse functions. Find a general formula for a family of linear functions that are their own inverse functions.

5. **Proof** Prove that a function of the following form is even.

   $$y = a_{2n}x^{2n} + a_{2n-2}x^{2n-2} + \cdots + a_2x^2 + a_0$$

6. **Miniature Golf** A miniature golf professional is trying to make a hole-in-one on the miniature golf green shown. The golf ball is at the point $(2.5, 2)$ and the hole is at the point $(9.5, 2)$. The professional wants to bank the ball off the side wall of the green at the point (x, y). Find the coordinates of the point (x, y). Then write an equation for the path of the ball.

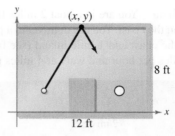

Figure for 6

7. **Titanic** At 2:00 P.M. on April 11, 1912, the *Titanic* left Cobh, Ireland, on her voyage to New York City. At 11:40 P.M. on April 14, the *Titanic* struck an iceberg and sank, having covered only about 2100 miles of the approximately 3400-mile trip.

   (a) What was the total duration of the voyage in hours?

   (b) What was the average speed in miles per hour?

   (c) Write a function relating the distance of the *Titanic* from New York City and the number of hours traveled. Find the domain and range of the function.

   (d) Graph the function from part (c).

8. **Average Rate of Change** Consider the function $f(x) = -x^2 + 4x - 3$. Find the average rate of change of the function from x_1 to x_2.

   (a) $x_1 = 1, x_2 = 2$

   (b) $x_1 = 1, x_2 = 1.5$

   (c) $x_1 = 1, x_2 = 1.25$

   (d) $x_1 = 1, x_2 = 1.125$

   (e) $x_1 = 1, x_2 = 1.0625$

   (f) Does the average rate of change seem to be approaching one value? If so, then state the value.

   (g) Find the equations of the secant lines through the points $(x_1, f(x_1))$ and $(x_2, f(x_2))$ for parts (a)–(e).

   (h) Find the equation of the line through the point $(1, f(1))$ using your answer from part (f) as the slope of the line.

9. **Inverse of a Composition** Consider the functions $f(x) = 4x$ and $g(x) = x + 6$.

   (a) Find $(f \circ g)(x)$.

   (b) Find $(f \circ g)^{-1}(x)$.

   (c) Find $f^{-1}(x)$ and $g^{-1}(x)$.

   (d) Find $(g^{-1} \circ f^{-1})(x)$ and compare the result with that of part (b).

   (e) Repeat parts (a) through (d) for $f(x) = x^3 + 1$ and $g(x) = 2x$.

   (f) Write two one-to-one functions f and g, and repeat parts (a) through (d) for these functions.

   (g) Make a conjecture about $(f \circ g)^{-1}(x)$ and $(g^{-1} \circ f^{-1})(x)$.

111

10. Trip Time You are in a boat 2 miles from the nearest point on the coast. You are to travel to a point Q, 3 miles down the coast and 1 mile inland (see figure). You row at 2 miles per hour and walk at 4 miles per hour.

Not drawn to scale.

(a) Write the total time T of the trip as a function of x.

(b) Determine the domain of the function.

(c) Use a graphing utility to graph the function. Be sure to choose an appropriate viewing window.

(d) Find the value of x that minimizes T.

(e) Write a brief paragraph interpreting these values.

11. Heaviside Function The **Heaviside function** $H(x)$ is widely used in engineering applications. (See figure.) To print an enlarged copy of the graph, go to *MathGraphs.com*.

$$H(x) = \begin{cases} 1, & x \geq 0 \\ 0, & x < 0 \end{cases}$$

Sketch the graph of each function by hand.

(a) $H(x) - 2$

(b) $H(x - 2)$

(c) $-H(x)$

(d) $H(-x)$

(e) $\frac{1}{2}H(x)$

(f) $-H(x - 2) + 2$

12. Repeated Composition Let $f(x) = \dfrac{1}{1 - x}$.

(a) What are the domain and range of f?

(b) Find $f(f(x))$. What is the domain of this function?

(c) Find $f(f(f(x)))$. Is the graph a line? Why or why not?

13. Associative Property with Compositions Show that the Associative Property holds for compositions of functions—that is,

$$(f \circ (g \circ h))(x) = ((f \circ g) \circ h)(x).$$

14. Graphical Analysis Consider the graph of the function f shown in the figure. Use this graph to sketch the graph of each function. To print an enlarged copy of the graph, go to *MathGraphs.com*.

(a) $f(x + 1)$

(b) $f(x) + 1$

(c) $2f(x)$

(d) $f(-x)$

(e) $-f(x)$

(f) $|f(x)|$

(g) $f(|x|)$

15. Graphical Analysis Use the graphs of f and f^{-1} to complete each table of function values.

(a)

x	-4	-2	0	4
$(f(f^{-1}(x)))$				

(b)

x	-3	-2	0	1
$(f + f^{-1})(x)$				

(c)

x	-3	-2	0	1
$(f \cdot f^{-1})(x)$				

(d)

x	-4	-3	0	4
$|f^{-1}(x)|$				

2 Polynomial and Rational Functions

- 2.1   Quadratic Functions and Models
- 2.2   Polynomial Functions of Higher Degree
- 2.3   Polynomial and Synthetic Division
- 2.4   Complex Numbers
- 2.5   Zeros of Polynomial Functions
- 2.6   Rational Functions
- 2.7   Nonlinear Inequalities

Candle Making *(Example 11, page 163)*

Impedance
(Exercise 91, page 153)

Lyme Disease *(Exercise 86, page 146)*

Tree Growth
(Exercise 104, page 136)

Path of a Diver *(Exercise 75, page 121)*

2.1 Quadratic Functions and Models

You can use quadratic functions to model the path of an object or person. For instance, in Exercise 75 on page 121, you will use a quadratic function to model the path of a diver.

- Analyze graphs of quadratic functions.
- Write quadratic functions in standard form and use the results to sketch graphs of functions.
- Find minimum and maximum values of quadratic functions in real-life applications.

The Graph of a Quadratic Function

In this and the next section, you will study the graphs of polynomial functions. In Section 1.6, you were introduced to the following basic functions.

$$f(x) = ax + b \qquad \text{Linear function}$$

$$f(x) = c \qquad \text{Constant function}$$

$$f(x) = x^2 \qquad \text{Squaring function}$$

These functions are examples of **polynomial functions.**

Definition of Polynomial Function

Let n be a nonnegative integer and let $a_n, a_{n-1}, \ldots, a_2, a_1, a_0$ be real numbers with $a_n \neq 0$. The function

$$f(x) = a_n x^n + a_{n-1} x^{n-1} + \cdots + a_2 x^2 + a_1 x + a_0$$

is called a **polynomial function of x with degree n.**

Polynomial functions are classified by degree. For instance, a constant function $f(x) = c$ with $c \neq 0$ has degree 0, and a linear function $f(x) = ax + b$ with $a \neq 0$ has degree 1. In this section, you will study second-degree polynomial functions, which are called **quadratic functions.**

For instance, each of the following functions is a quadratic function.

$$f(x) = x^2 + 6x + 2$$

$$g(x) = 2(x + 1)^2 - 3$$

$$h(x) = 9 + \frac{1}{4}x^2$$

$$k(x) = -3x^2 + 4$$

$$m(x) = (x - 2)(x + 1)$$

Note that the squaring function is a simple quadratic function that has degree 2.

Definition of Quadratic Function

Let a, b, and c be real numbers with $a \neq 0$. The function

$$f(x) = ax^2 + bx + c \qquad \text{Quadratic function}$$

is called a **quadratic function.**

The graph of a quadratic function is a special type of "U"-shaped curve called a **parabola.** Parabolas occur in many real-life applications—especially those involving reflective properties of satellite dishes and flashlight reflectors. You will study these properties in Section 10.2.

All parabolas are symmetric with respect to a line called the **axis of symmetry,** or simply the **axis** of the parabola. The point where the axis intersects the parabola is the **vertex** of the parabola, as shown below. When the leading coefficient is positive, the graph of

$$f(x) = ax^2 + bx + c$$

is a parabola that opens upward. When the leading coefficient is negative, the graph of

$$f(x) = ax^2 + bx + c$$

is a parabola that opens downward.

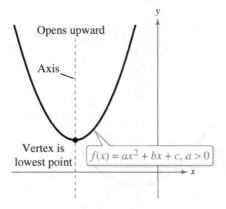

Leading coefficient is positive. Leading coefficient is negative.

The simplest type of quadratic function is

$$f(x) = ax^2.$$

Its graph is a parabola whose vertex is $(0, 0)$. When $a > 0$, the vertex is the point with the *minimum* y-value on the graph, and when $a < 0$, the vertex is the point with the *maximum* y-value on the graph, as shown below.

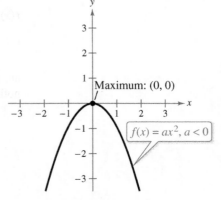

Leading coefficient is positive. Leading coefficient is negative.

When sketching the graph of

$$f(x) = ax^2$$

it is helpful to use the graph of $y = x^2$ as a reference, as discussed in Section 1.7. There you learned that when $a > 1$, the graph of $y = af(x)$ is a vertical stretch of the graph of $y = f(x)$. When $0 < a < 1$, the graph of $y = af(x)$ is a vertical shrink of the graph of $y = f(x)$. This is demonstrated again in Example 1.

EXAMPLE 1   **Sketching Graphs of Quadratic Functions**

Sketch the graph of each quadratic function and compare it with the graph of $y = x^2$.

a. $f(x) = \frac{1}{3}x^2$ **b.** $g(x) = 2x^2$

▷ **ALGEBRA HELP**   You can review the techniques for shifting, reflecting, and stretching graphs in Section 1.7.

Solution

a. Compared with $y = x^2$, each output of $f(x) = \frac{1}{3}x^2$ "shrinks" by a factor of $\frac{1}{3}$, creating the broader parabola shown in Figure 2.1.

b. Compared with $y = x^2$, each output of $g(x) = 2x^2$ "stretches" by a factor of 2, creating the narrower parabola shown in Figure 2.2.

Figure 2.1

Figure 2.2

 Checkpoint ◄))) *Audio-video solution in English & Spanish at LarsonPrecalculus.com.*

Sketch the graph of each quadratic function and compare it with the graph of $y = x^2$.

a. $f(x) = \frac{1}{4}x^2$ **b.** $g(x) = -\frac{1}{6}x^2$

c. $h(x) = \frac{5}{2}x^2$ **d.** $k(x) = -4x^2$

In Example 1, note that the coefficient a determines how wide the parabola $f(x) = ax^2$ opens. When $|a|$ is small, the parabola opens wider than when $|a|$ is large. Recall from Section 1.7 that the graphs of

$$y = f(x \pm c), \quad y = f(x) \pm c, \quad y = f(-x), \quad \text{and} \quad y = -f(x)$$

are rigid transformations of the graph of $y = f(x)$. For instance, in the figures below, notice how the graph of $y = x^2$ can be transformed to produce the graphs of

$$f(x) = -x^2 + 1 \quad \text{and} \quad g(x) = (x + 2)^2 - 3.$$

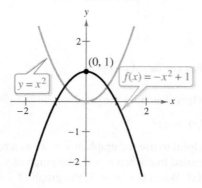

Reflection in x-axis followed by an upward shift of one unit

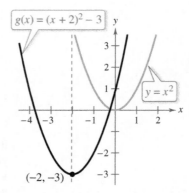

Left shift of two units followed by a downward shift of three units

The Standard Form of a Quadratic Function

The **standard form** of a quadratic function is $f(x) = a(x - h)^2 + k$. This form is especially convenient for sketching a parabola because it identifies the vertex of the parabola as (h, k).

• • REMARK The standard form of a quadratic function identifies four basic transformations of the graph of $y = x^2$.

a. The factor a produces a vertical stretch or shrink.

b. When $a < 0$, the graph is reflected in the x-axis.

c. The factor $(x - h)^2$ represents a horizontal shift of h units.

d. The term k represents a vertical shift of k units.

> ### Standard Form of a Quadratic Function
>
> The quadratic function
>
> $$f(x) = a(x - h)^2 + k, \quad a \neq 0$$
>
> is in **standard form**. The graph of f is a parabola whose axis is the vertical line $x = h$ and whose vertex is the point (h, k). When $a > 0$, the parabola opens upward, and when $a < 0$, the parabola opens downward.

To graph a parabola, it is helpful to begin by writing the quadratic function in standard form using the process of completing the square, as illustrated in Example 2. In this example, notice that when completing the square, you *add and subtract* the square of half the coefficient of x within the parentheses instead of adding the value to each side of the equation as is done in Appendix A.5.

EXAMPLE 2	**Using Standard Form to Graph a Parabola**

Sketch the graph of

$$f(x) = 2x^2 + 8x + 7.$$

Identify the vertex and the axis of the parabola.

▷ **ALGEBRA HELP** You can review the techniques for completing the square in Appendix A.5.

Solution Begin by writing the quadratic function in standard form. Notice that the first step in completing the square is to factor out any coefficient of x^2 that is not 1.

$$f(x) = 2x^2 + 8x + 7 \qquad \text{Write original function.}$$
$$= 2(x^2 + 4x) + 7 \qquad \text{Factor 2 out of } x\text{-terms.}$$
$$= 2(x^2 + 4x + 4 - 4) + 7 \qquad \text{Add and subtract 4 within parentheses.}$$

$$\underset{(4/2)^2}{\underline{\hspace{1cm}}\uparrow}$$

After adding and subtracting 4 within the parentheses, you must now regroup the terms to form a perfect square trinomial. The -4 can be removed from inside the parentheses; however, because of the 2 outside of the parentheses, you must multiply -4 by 2, as shown below.

$$f(x) = 2(x^2 + 4x + 4) - 2(4) + 7 \qquad \text{Regroup terms.}$$
$$= 2(x^2 + 4x + 4) - 8 + 7 \qquad \text{Simplify.}$$
$$= 2(x + 2)^2 - 1 \qquad \text{Write in standard form.}$$

From this form, you can see that the graph of f is a parabola that opens upward and has its vertex at $(-2, -1)$. This corresponds to a left shift of two units and a downward shift of one unit relative to the graph of $y = 2x^2$, as shown in Figure 2.3. In the figure, you can see that the axis of the parabola is the vertical line through the vertex, $x = -2$.

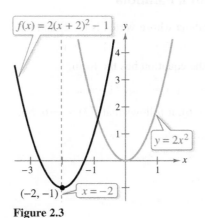

$f(x) = 2(x + 2)^2 - 1$

$y = 2x^2$

$(-2, -1)$ $x = -2$

Figure 2.3

✓ *Checkpoint* *Audio-video solution in English & Spanish at LarsonPrecalculus.com.*

Sketch the graph of

$$f(x) = 3x^2 - 6x + 4.$$

Identify the vertex and the axis of the parabola.

▷ **ALGEBRA HELP** You can review the techniques for using the Quadratic Formula in Appendix A.5.

To find the x-intercepts of the graph of $f(x) = ax^2 + bx + c$, you must solve the equation $ax^2 + bx + c = 0$. When $ax^2 + bx + c$ does not factor, you can use the Quadratic Formula to find the x-intercepts. Remember, however, that a parabola may not have x-intercepts.

EXAMPLE 3   **Finding the Vertex and x-Intercepts of a Parabola**

Sketch the graph of $f(x) = -x^2 + 6x - 8$. Identify the vertex and x-intercepts.

Solution

$f(x) = -x^2 + 6x - 8$	Write original function.
$= -(x^2 - 6x) - 8$	Factor -1 out of x-terms.
$= -(x^2 - 6x + 9 - 9) - 8$	Add and subtract 9 within parentheses.
$= -(x^2 - 6x + 9) - (-9) - 8$	Regroup terms.
$= -(x - 3)^2 + 1$	Write in standard form.

$(-6/2)^2$

From this form, you can see that f is a parabola that opens downward with vertex $(3, 1)$. The x-intercepts of the graph are determined as follows.

$-(x^2 - 6x + 8) = 0$	Factor out -1.
$-(x - 2)(x - 4) = 0$	Factor.
$x - 2 = 0 \implies x = 2$	Set 1st factor equal to 0.
$x - 4 = 0 \implies x = 4$	Set 2nd factor equal to 0.

So, the x-intercepts are $(2, 0)$ and $(4, 0)$, as shown in Figure 2.4.

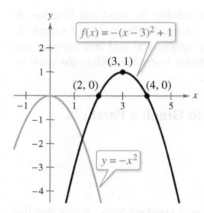

$f(x) = -(x - 3)^2 + 1$

$(3, 1)$

$(2, 0)$ $(4, 0)$

$y = -x^2$

Figure 2.4

✓ *Checkpoint* ◀))) *Audio-video solution in English & Spanish at LarsonPrecalculus.com.*

Sketch the graph of $f(x) = x^2 - 4x + 3$. Identify the vertex and x-intercepts.

EXAMPLE 4   **Writing the Equation of a Parabola**

Write the standard form of the equation of the parabola whose vertex is $(1, 2)$ and that passes through the point $(3, -6)$.

Solution   Because the vertex is $(h, k) = (1, 2)$, the equation has the form

$$f(x) = a(x - 1)^2 + 2. \qquad \text{Substitute for } h \text{ and } k \text{ in standard form.}$$

Because the parabola passes through the point $(3, -6)$, it follows that $f(3) = -6$. So,

$f(x) = a(x - 1)^2 + 2$	Write in standard form.
$-6 = a(3 - 1)^2 + 2$	Substitute 3 for x and -6 for $f(x)$.
$-6 = 4a + 2$	Simplify.
$-8 = 4a$	Subtract 2 from each side.
$-2 = a.$	Divide each side by 4.

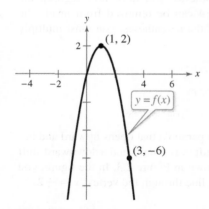

$(1, 2)$

$y = f(x)$

$(3, -6)$

Figure 2.5

The equation in standard form is $f(x) = -2(x - 1)^2 + 2$. The graph of f is shown in Figure 2.5.

✓ *Checkpoint* ◀))) *Audio-video solution in English & Spanish at LarsonPrecalculus.com.*

Write the standard form of the equation of the parabola whose vertex is $(-4, 11)$ and that passes through the point $(-6, 15)$.

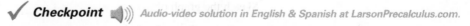

Finding Minimum and Maximum Values

Many applications involve finding the maximum or minimum value of a quadratic function. By completing the square of the quadratic function $f(x) = ax^2 + bx + c$, you can rewrite the function in standard form (see Exercise 93).

$$f(x) = a\left(x + \frac{b}{2a}\right)^2 + \left(c - \frac{b^2}{4a}\right) \qquad \text{Standard form}$$

So, the vertex of the graph of f is $\left(-\dfrac{b}{2a}, f\left(-\dfrac{b}{2a}\right)\right)$, which implies the following.

Minimum and Maximum Values of Quadratic Functions

Consider the function $f(x) = ax^2 + bx + c$ with vertex $\left(-\dfrac{b}{2a}, f\left(-\dfrac{b}{2a}\right)\right)$.

1. When $a > 0$, f has a *minimum* at $x = -\dfrac{b}{2a}$. The minimum value is $f\left(-\dfrac{b}{2a}\right)$.

2. When $a < 0$, f has a *maximum* at $x = -\dfrac{b}{2a}$. The maximum value is $f\left(-\dfrac{b}{2a}\right)$.

EXAMPLE 5 **The Maximum Height of a Baseball**

The path of a baseball after being hit is given by the function $f(x) = -0.0032x^2 + x + 3$, where $f(x)$ is the height of the baseball (in feet) and x is the horizontal distance from home plate (in feet). What is the maximum height of the baseball?

Algebraic Solution

For this quadratic function, you have

$$f(x) = ax^2 + bx + c = -0.0032x^2 + x + 3$$

which implies that $a = -0.0032$ and $b = 1$. Because $a < 0$, the function has a maximum at $x = -b/(2a)$. So, the baseball reaches its maximum height when it is

$$x = -\frac{b}{2a} = -\frac{1}{2(-0.0032)} = 156.25 \text{ feet from home plate.}$$

At this distance, the maximum height is

$$f(156.25) = -0.0032(156.25)^2 + 156.25 + 3 = 81.125 \text{ feet.}$$

Graphical Solution

The maximum height is $y = 81.125$ feet at $x = 156.25$ feet.

✓ **Checkpoint** ◄))) *Audio-video solution in English & Spanish at LarsonPrecalculus.com.*

Rework Example 5 when the path of the baseball is given by the function

$$f(x) = -0.007x^2 + x + 4.$$

Summarize (Section 2.1)

1. State the definition of a quadratic function and describe its graph *(pages 114–116)*. For an example of sketching the graphs of quadratic functions, see Example 1.

2. State the standard form of a quadratic function *(page 117)*. For examples that use the standard form of a quadratic function, see Examples 2–4.

3. Describe how to find the minimum or maximum value of a quadratic function *(page 119)*. For a real-life example that involves finding the maximum height of a baseball, see Example 5.

2.1 Exercises

See CalcChat.com for tutorial help and worked-out solutions to odd-numbered exercises.

Vocabulary: Fill in the blanks.

1. Linear, constant, and squaring functions are examples of _____ functions.

2. A polynomial function of x with degree n has the form $f(x) = a_n x^n + a_{n-1} x^{n-1} + \cdots + a_1 x + a_0$ ($a_n \neq 0$), where n is a _____ _____ and $a_n, a_{n-1}, \ldots, a_1, a_0$ are _____ numbers.

3. A _____ function is a second-degree polynomial function, and its graph is called a _____.

4. The graph of a quadratic function is symmetric about its _____.

5. When the graph of a quadratic function opens upward, its leading coefficient is _____ and the vertex of the graph is a _____.

6. When the graph of a quadratic function opens downward, its leading coefficient is _____ and the vertex of the graph is a _____.

Skills and Applications

Matching In Exercises 7–12, match the quadratic function with its graph. [The graphs are labeled (a), (b), (c), (d), (e), and (f).]

(a)

(b)

(c)

(d)

(e)

(f)

7. $f(x) = (x - 2)^2$

8. $f(x) = (x + 4)^2$

9. $f(x) = x^2 - 2$

10. $f(x) = (x + 1)^2 - 2$

11. $f(x) = 4 - (x - 2)^2$

12. $f(x) = -(x - 4)^2$

Sketching Graphs of Quadratic Functions In Exercises 13–16, sketch the graph of each quadratic function and compare it with the graph of $y = x^2$.

13. (a) $f(x) = \frac{1}{2}x^2$ (b) $g(x) = -\frac{1}{8}x^2$
    (c) $h(x) = \frac{3}{2}x^2$ (d) $k(x) = -3x^2$

14. (a) $f(x) = x^2 + 1$ (b) $g(x) = x^2 - 1$
    (c) $h(x) = x^2 + 3$ (d) $k(x) = x^2 - 3$

15. (a) $f(x) = (x - 1)^2$ (b) $g(x) = (3x)^2 + 1$
    (c) $h(x) = \left(\frac{1}{3}x\right)^2 - 3$ (d) $k(x) = (x + 3)^2$

16. (a) $f(x) = -\frac{1}{2}(x - 2)^2 + 1$
    (b) $g(x) = \left[\frac{1}{2}(x - 1)\right]^2 - 3$
    (c) $h(x) = -\frac{1}{2}(x + 2)^2 - 1$
    (d) $k(x) = [2(x + 1)]^2 + 4$

Using Standard Form to Graph a Parabola In Exercises 17–34, write the quadratic function in standard form and sketch its graph. Identify the vertex, axis of symmetry, and x-intercept(s).

17. $f(x) = x^2 - 6x$

18. $g(x) = x^2 - 8x$

19. $h(x) = x^2 - 8x + 16$

20. $g(x) = x^2 + 2x + 1$

21. $f(x) = x^2 + 8x + 13$

22. $f(x) = x^2 - 12x + 44$

23. $f(x) = x^2 - 14x + 54$

24. $h(x) = x^2 + 16x - 17$

25. $f(x) = x^2 + 34x + 289$

26. $f(x) = x^2 - 30x + 225$

27. $f(x) = x^2 - x + \frac{5}{4}$

28. $f(x) = x^2 + 3x + \frac{1}{4}$

29. $f(x) = -x^2 + 2x + 5$

30. $f(x) = -x^2 - 4x + 1$

31. $h(x) = 4x^2 - 4x + 21$

32. $f(x) = 2x^2 - x + 1$

33. $f(x) = \frac{1}{4}x^2 - 2x - 12$

34. $f(x) = -\frac{1}{3}x^2 + 3x - 6$

Graphical Analysis In Exercises 35–42, use a graphing utility to graph the quadratic function. Identify the vertex, axis of symmetry, and x-intercept(s). Then check your results algebraically by writing the quadratic function in standard form.

35. $f(x) = -(x^2 + 2x - 3)$ 36. $f(x) = -(x^2 + x - 30)$

37. $g(x) = x^2 + 8x + 11$ 38. $f(x) = x^2 + 10x + 14$

39. $f(x) = 2x^2 - 16x + 32$

40. $f(x) = -4x^2 + 24x - 41$

41. $g(x) = \frac{1}{2}(x^2 + 4x - 2)$ 42. $f(x) = \frac{3}{5}(x^2 + 6x - 5)$

Writing the Equation of a Parabola In Exercises 43–46, write an equation for the parabola in standard form.

43.

44.

45.

46.

Writing the Equation of a Parabola In Exercises 47–56, write the standard form of the equation of the parabola that has the indicated vertex and passes through the given point.

47. Vertex: $(-2, 5)$; point: $(0, 9)$

48. Vertex: $(4, -1)$; point: $(2, 3)$

49. Vertex: $(1, -2)$; point: $(-1, 14)$

50. Vertex: $(2, 3)$; point: $(0, 2)$

51. Vertex: $(5, 12)$; point: $(7, 15)$

52. Vertex: $(-2, -2)$; point: $(-1, 0)$

53. Vertex: $\left(-\frac{1}{4}, \frac{3}{2}\right)$; point: $(-2, 0)$

54. Vertex: $\left(\frac{5}{2}, -\frac{3}{4}\right)$; point: $(-2, 4)$

55. Vertex: $\left(-\frac{5}{2}, 0\right)$; point: $\left(-\frac{7}{2}, -\frac{16}{3}\right)$

56. Vertex: $(6, 6)$; point: $\left(\frac{61}{10}, \frac{3}{2}\right)$

Graphical Reasoning In Exercises 57 and 58, determine the x-intercept(s) of the graph visually. Then find the x-intercept(s) algebraically to confirm your results.

57. $y = x^2 - 4x - 5$

58. $y = 2x^2 + 5x - 3$

Graphical Analysis In Exercises 59–64, use a graphing utility to graph the quadratic function. Find the x-intercept(s) of the graph and compare them with the solutions of the corresponding quadratic equation when $f(x) = 0$.

59. $f(x) = x^2 - 4x$

60. $f(x) = -2x^2 + 10x$

61. $f(x) = x^2 - 9x + 18$

62. $f(x) = x^2 - 8x - 20$

63. $f(x) = 2x^2 - 7x - 30$

64. $f(x) = \frac{7}{10}(x^2 + 12x - 45)$

Finding Quadratic Functions In Exercises 65–70, find two quadratic functions, one that opens upward and one that opens downward, whose graphs have the given x-intercepts. (There are many correct answers.)

65. $(-1, 0), (3, 0)$

66. $(-5, 0), (5, 0)$

67. $(0, 0), (10, 0)$

68. $(4, 0), (8, 0)$

69. $(-3, 0), \left(-\frac{1}{2}, 0\right)$

70. $\left(-\frac{5}{2}, 0\right), (2, 0)$

Number Problems In Exercises 71–74, find two positive real numbers whose product is a maximum.

71. The sum is 110.

72. The sum is S.

73. The sum of the first and twice the second is 24.

74. The sum of the first and three times the second is 42.

75. Path of a Diver

The path of a diver is given by the function

$$f(x) = -\frac{4}{9}x^2 + \frac{24}{9}x + 12$$

where $f(x)$ is the height (in feet) and x is the horizontal distance from the end of the diving board (in feet). What is the maximum height of the diver?

76. Height of a Ball The path of a punted football is given by the function

$$f(x) = -\frac{16}{2025}x^2 + \frac{9}{5}x + 1.5$$

where $f(x)$ is the height (in feet) and x is the horizontal distance (in feet) from the point at which the ball is punted.

(a) How high is the ball when it is punted?

(b) What is the maximum height of the punt?

(c) How long is the punt?

77. Minimum Cost A manufacturer of lighting fixtures has daily production costs of $C = 800 - 10x + 0.25x^2$, where C is the total cost (in dollars) and x is the number of units produced. How many fixtures should be produced each day to yield a minimum cost?

78. Maximum Profit The profit P (in hundreds of dollars) that a company makes depends on the amount x (in hundreds of dollars) the company spends on advertising according to the model $P = 230 + 20x - 0.5x^2$. What expenditure for advertising will yield a maximum profit?

79. Maximum Revenue The total revenue R earned (in thousands of dollars) from manufacturing handheld video games is given by

$$R(p) = -25p^2 + 1200p$$

where p is the price per unit (in dollars).

(a) Find the revenues when the prices per unit are $20, $25, and $30.

(b) Find the unit price that will yield a maximum revenue. What is the maximum revenue? Explain your results.

80. Maximum Revenue The total revenue R earned per day (in dollars) from a pet-sitting service is given by $R(p) = -12p^2 + 150p$, where p is the price charged per pet (in dollars).

(a) Find the revenues when the prices per pet are $4, $6, and $8.

(b) Find the unit price that will yield a maximum revenue. What is the maximum revenue? Explain your results.

81. Numerical, Graphical, and Analytical Analysis A rancher has 200 feet of fencing to enclose two adjacent rectangular corrals (see figure).

(a) Write the area A of the corrals as a function of x.

(b) Construct a table showing possible values of x and the corresponding areas of the corral. Use the table to estimate the dimensions that will produce the maximum enclosed area.

(c) Use a graphing utility to graph the area function. Use the graph to approximate the dimensions that will produce the maximum enclosed area.

(d) Write the area function in standard form to find analytically the dimensions that will produce the maximum area.

(e) Compare your results from parts (b), (c), and (d).

82. Geometry An indoor physical fitness room consists of a rectangular region with a semicircle on each end. The perimeter of the room is to be a 200-meter single-lane running track.

(a) Draw a diagram that gives a visual representation of the problem. Let x and y represent the length and width of the rectangular region, respectively.

(b) Determine the radius of each semicircular end of the room. Determine the distance, in terms of y, around the inside edge of each semicircular part of the track.

(c) Use the result of part (b) to write an equation, in terms of x and y, for the distance traveled in one lap around the track. Solve for y.

(d) Use the result of part (c) to write the area A of the rectangular region as a function of x. What dimensions will produce a rectangle of maximum area?

83. Maximum Revenue A small theater has a seating capacity of 2000. When the ticket price is $20, attendance is 1500. For each $1 decrease in price, attendance increases by 100.

(a) Write the revenue R of the theater as a function of ticket price x.

(b) What ticket price will yield a maximum revenue? What is the maximum revenue?

84. Maximum Area A Norman window is constructed by adjoining a semicircle to the top of an ordinary rectangular window (see figure). The perimeter of the window is 16 feet.

(a) Write the area A of the window as a function of x.

(b) What dimensions will produce a window of maximum area?

85. Graphical Analysis From 1950 through 2005, the per capita consumption C of cigarettes by Americans (age 18 and older) can be modeled by $C = 3565.0 + 60.30t - 1.783t^2$, $0 \le t \le 55$, where t is the year, with $t = 0$ corresponding to 1950. (*Source: Tobacco Outlook Report*)

(a) Use a graphing utility to graph the model.

(b) Use the graph of the model to approximate the maximum average annual consumption. Beginning in 1966, all cigarette packages were required by law to carry a health warning. Do you think the warning had any effect? Explain.

(c) In 2005, the U.S. population (age 18 and over) was 296,329,000. Of those, about 59,858,458 were smokers. What was the average annual cigarette consumption *per smoker* in 2005? What was the average daily cigarette consumption *per smoker*?

86. Data Analysis: Sales The sales y (in billions of dollars) for Harley-Davidson from 2000 through 2010 are shown in the table. *(Source: U.S. Harley-Davidson, Inc.)*

Year	Sales, y
2000	2.91
2001	3.36
2002	4.09
2003	4.62
2004	5.02
2005	5.34
2006	5.80
2007	5.73
2008	5.59
2009	4.78
2010	4.86

Spreadsheet at LarsonPrecalculus.com

(a) Use a graphing utility to create a scatter plot of the data. Let x represent the year, with $x = 0$ corresponding to 2000.

(b) Use the *regression* feature of the graphing utility to find a quadratic model for the data.

(c) Use the graphing utility to graph the model in the same viewing window as the scatter plot. How well does the model fit the data?

(d) Use the *trace* feature of the graphing utility to approximate the year in which the sales for Harley-Davidson were the greatest.

(e) Verify your answer to part (d) algebraically.

(f) Use the model to predict the sales for Harley-Davidson in 2013.

Exploration

True or False? **In Exercises 87 and 88, determine whether the statement is true or false. Justify your answer.**

87. The graph of $f(x) = -12x^2 - 1$ has no x-intercepts.

88. The graphs of

$$f(x) = -4x^2 - 10x + 7$$

and

$$g(x) = 12x^2 + 30x + 1$$

have the same axis of symmetry.

Think About It **In Exercises 89–92, find the values of b such that the function has the given maximum or minimum value.**

89. $f(x) = -x^2 + bx - 75$; Maximum value: 25

90. $f(x) = -x^2 + bx - 16$; Maximum value: 48

91. $f(x) = x^2 + bx + 26$; Minimum value: 10

92. $f(x) = x^2 + bx - 25$; Minimum value: -50

93. Verifying the Vertex Write the quadratic function

$$f(x) = ax^2 + bx + c$$

in standard form to verify that the vertex occurs at

$$\left(-\frac{b}{2a},\ f\left(-\frac{b}{2a}\right)\right).$$

94. 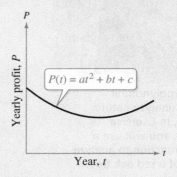 **HOW DO YOU SEE IT?** The graph shows a quadratic function of the form

$$P(t) = at^2 + bt + c$$

which represents the yearly profits for a company, where $P(t)$ is the profit in year t.

(a) Is the value of a positive, negative, or zero? Explain.

(b) Write an expression in terms of a and b that represents the year t when the company made the least profit.

(c) The company made the same yearly profits in 2004 and 2012. Estimate the year in which the company made the least profit.

(d) Assume that the model is still valid today. Are the yearly profits currently increasing, decreasing, or constant? Explain.

95. Proof Assume that the function

$$f(x) = ax^2 + bx + c, \quad a \neq 0$$

has two real zeros. Prove that the x-coordinate of the vertex of the graph is the average of the zeros of f. (*Hint:* Use the Quadratic Formula.)

Project: Height of a Basketball To work an extended application analyzing the height of a basketball after it has been dropped, visit this text's website at *LarsonPrecalculus.com*.

2.2 Polynomial Functions of Higher Degree

■ Use transformations to sketch graphs of polynomial functions.
■ Use the Leading Coefficient Test to determine the end behaviors of graphs of polynomial functions.
■ Find and use the real zeros of polynomial functions as sketching aids.
■ Use the Intermediate Value Theorem to help locate the real zeros of polynomial functions.

Graphs of Polynomial Functions

In this section, you will study basic features of the graphs of polynomial functions. The first feature is that the graph of a polynomial function is **continuous.** Essentially, this means that the graph of a polynomial function has no breaks, holes, or gaps, as shown in Figure 2.6(a). The graph shown in Figure 2.6(b) is an example of a piecewise-defined function that is not continuous.

You can use polynomial functions to analyze nature. For instance, in Exercise 104 on page 136, you will use a polynomial function to analyze the growth of a red oak tree.

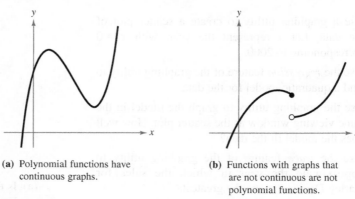

(a) Polynomial functions have continuous graphs.

(b) Functions with graphs that are not continuous are not polynomial functions.

Figure 2.6

The second feature is that the graph of a polynomial function has only smooth, rounded turns, as shown in Figure 2.7. A polynomial function cannot have a sharp turn. For instance, the function $f(x) = |x|$, the graph of which has a sharp turn at the point $(0, 0)$, as shown in Figure 2.8, is not a polynomial function.

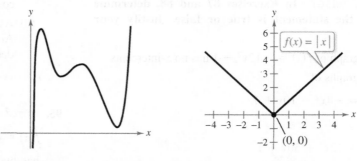

Polynomial functions have graphs with smooth, rounded turns.
Figure 2.7

Graphs of polynomial functions cannot have sharp turns.
Figure 2.8

The graphs of polynomial functions of degree greater than 2 are more difficult to analyze than the graphs of polynomial functions of degree 0, 1, or 2. However, using the features presented in this section, coupled with your knowledge of point plotting, intercepts, and symmetry, you should be able to make reasonably accurate sketches *by hand*.

The polynomial functions that have the simplest graphs are monomial functions of the form $f(x) = x^n$, where n is an integer greater than zero. From Figure 2.9, you can see that when n is *even*, the graph is similar to the graph of $f(x) = x^2$, and when n is *odd*, the graph is similar to the graph of $f(x) = x^3$. Moreover, the greater the value of n, the flatter the graph near the origin.

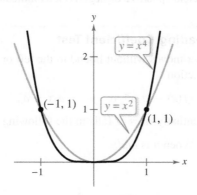

(a) When n is even, the graph of $y = x^n$ touches the axis at the x-intercept.

(b) When n is odd, the graph of $y = x^n$ crosses the axis at the x-intercept.

Figure 2.9

REMARK For functions given by $f(x) = x^n$, when n is even, the graph of the function is symmetric with respect to the y-axis, and when n is odd, the graph of the function is symmetric with respect to the origin.

EXAMPLE 1 **Sketching Transformations of Monomial Functions**

Sketch the graph of each function.

a. $f(x) = -x^5$ **b.** $h(x) = (x + 1)^4$

Solution

a. Because the degree of $f(x) = -x^5$ is odd, its graph is similar to the graph of $y = x^3$. In Figure 2.10, note that the negative coefficient has the effect of reflecting the graph in the x-axis.

b. The graph of $h(x) = (x + 1)^4$, as shown in Figure 2.11, is a left shift by one unit of the graph of $y = x^4$.

▷ **ALGEBRA HELP** You can review the techniques for shifting, reflecting, and stretching graphs in Section 1.7.

Figure 2.10

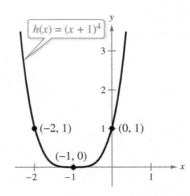

Figure 2.11

✓ *Checkpoint* ◄))) *Audio-video solution in English & Spanish at LarsonPrecalculus.com.*

Sketch the graph of each function.

a. $f(x) = (x + 5)^4$

b. $g(x) = x^4 - 7$

c. $h(x) = 7 - x^4$

d. $k(x) = \frac{1}{4}(x - 3)^4$

The Leading Coefficient Test

In Example 1, note that both graphs eventually rise or fall without bound as x moves to the left or to the right. Whether the graph of a polynomial function eventually rises or falls can be determined by the function's degree (even or odd) and by its leading coefficient (positive or negative), as indicated in the **Leading Coefficient Test.**

Leading Coefficient Test

As x moves without bound to the left or to the right, the graph of the polynomial function

$$f(x) = a_n x^n + \cdots + a_1 x + a_0$$

eventually rises or falls in the following manner.

1. When n is *odd:*

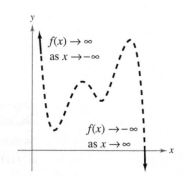

If the leading coefficient is positive ($a_n > 0$), then the graph falls to the left and rises to the right.

If the leading coefficient is negative ($a_n < 0$), then the graph rises to the left and falls to the right.

2. When n is *even:*

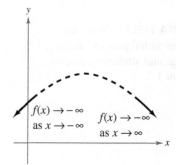

If the leading coefficient is positive ($a_n > 0$), then the graph rises to the left and to the right.

If the leading coefficient is negative ($a_n < 0$), then the graph falls to the left and to the right.

The dashed portions of the graphs indicate that the test determines *only* the right-hand and left-hand behavior of the graph.

▷

REMARK The notation "$f(x) \to -\infty$ as $x \to -\infty$" indicates that the graph falls to the left. The notation "$f(x) \to \infty$ as $x \to \infty$" indicates that the graph rises to the right.

As you continue to study polynomial functions and their graphs, you will notice that the degree of a polynomial plays an important role in determining other characteristics of the polynomial function and its graph.

EXAMPLE 2 **Applying the Leading Coefficient Test**

Describe the right-hand and left-hand behavior of the graph of each function.

a. $f(x) = -x^3 + 4x$ **b.** $f(x) = x^4 - 5x^2 + 4$ **c.** $f(x) = x^5 - x$

Solution

a. Because the degree is odd and the leading coefficient is negative, the graph rises to the left and falls to the right, as shown below.

$f(x) = -x^3 + 4x$

b. Because the degree is even and the leading coefficient is positive, the graph rises to the left and to the right, as shown below.

$f(x) = x^4 - 5x^2 + 4$

c. Because the degree is odd and the leading coefficient is positive, the graph falls to the left and rises to the right, as shown below.

$f(x) = x^5 - x$

✓ **Checkpoint** ◀))) *Audio-video solution in English & Spanish at LarsonPrecalculus.com.*

Describe the right-hand and left-hand behavior of the graph of each function.

a. $f(x) = \frac{1}{4}x^3 - 2x$ **b.** $f(x) = -3.6x^5 + 5x^3 - 1$

In Example 2, note that the Leading Coefficient Test tells you only whether the graph *eventually* rises or falls to the right or to the left. Other characteristics of the graph, such as intercepts and minimum and maximum points, must be determined by other tests.

Real Zeros of Polynomial Functions

It can be shown that for a polynomial function f of degree n, the following statements are true.

1. The function f has, at most, n real zeros. (You will study this result in detail in the discussion of the Fundamental Theorem of Algebra in Section 2.5.)

2. The graph of f has, at most, $n - 1$ turning points. (Turning points, also called relative minima or relative maxima, are points at which the graph changes from increasing to decreasing or vice versa.)

Finding the zeros of a polynomial function is one of the most important problems in algebra. There is a strong interplay between graphical and algebraic approaches to this problem.

REMARK Remember that the *zeros* of a function of x are the x-values for which the function is zero.

▷ **ALGEBRA HELP** To do Example 3 algebraically, you need to be able to completely factor polynomials. You can review the techniques for factoring in Appendix A.3.

Real Zeros of Polynomial Functions

When f is a polynomial function and a is a real number, the following statements are equivalent.

1. $x = a$ is a *zero* of the function f.

2. $x = a$ is a *solution* of the polynomial equation $f(x) = 0$.

3. $(x - a)$ is a *factor* of the polynomial $f(x)$.

4. $(a, 0)$ is an *x-intercept* of the graph of f.

EXAMPLE 3   **Finding Real Zeros of a Polynomial Function**

Find all real zeros of $f(x) = -2x^4 + 2x^2$. Then determine the maximum possible number of turning points of the graph of the function.

Solution   To find the real zeros of the function, set $f(x)$ equal to zero and solve for x.

$$-2x^4 + 2x^2 = 0 \qquad \text{Set } f(x) \text{ equal to 0.}$$

$$-2x^2(x^2 - 1) = 0 \qquad \text{Remove common monomial factor.}$$

$$-2x^2(x - 1)(x + 1) = 0 \qquad \text{Factor completely.}$$

So, the real zeros are $x = 0$, $x = 1$, and $x = -1$. Because the function is a fourth-degree polynomial, the graph of f can have at most $4 - 1 = 3$ turning points. In this case, the graph of f has three turning points, as shown in Figure 2.12.

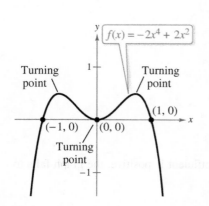

Turning point

Turning point

$(1, 0)$

$(-1, 0)$ $(0, 0)$

Turning point

$f(x) = -2x^4 + 2x^2$

Figure 2.12

 Checkpoint ◀))) *Audio-video solution in English & Spanish at LarsonPrecalculus.com.*

Find all real zeros of $f(x) = x^3 - 12x^2 + 36x$. Then determine the maximum possible number of turning points of the graph of the function.

In Example 3, note that because the exponent is greater than 1, the factor $-2x^2$ yields the *repeated* zero $x = 0$.

Repeated Zeros

A factor $(x - a)^k$, $k > 1$, yields a **repeated zero** $x = a$ of **multiplicity** k.

1. When k is odd, the graph *crosses* the x-axis at $x = a$.

2. When k is even, the graph *touches* the x-axis (but does not cross the x-axis) at $x = a$.

To graph polynomial functions, use the fact that a polynomial function can change signs only at its zeros. Between two consecutive zeros, a polynomial must be entirely positive or entirely negative. (This follows from the Intermediate Value Theorem, which you will study later in this section.) This means that when you put the real zeros of a polynomial function in order, they divide the real number line into intervals in which the function has no sign changes. These resulting intervals are **test intervals** in which you choose a representative x-value to determine whether the value of the polynomial function is positive (the graph lies above the x-axis) or negative (the graph lies below the x-axis).

▷ **TECHNOLOGY** Example 4 uses an *algebraic approach* to describe the graph of the function. A graphing utility can complement this approach. Remember to find a viewing window that shows all significant features of the graph. For instance, viewing window (a) illustrates all of the significant features of the function in Example 4 while viewing window (b) does not.

(a)

(b)

EXAMPLE 4 Sketching the Graph of a Polynomial Function

Sketch the graph of $f(x) = 3x^4 - 4x^3$.

Solution

1. *Apply the Leading Coefficient Test.* Because the leading coefficient is positive and the degree is even, you know that the graph eventually rises to the left and to the right (see Figure 2.13).

2. *Find the Real Zeros of the Polynomial.* By factoring $f(x) = 3x^4 - 4x^3$ as $f(x) = x^3(3x - 4)$, you can see that the real zeros of f are $x = 0$ and $x = \frac{4}{3}$ (both of odd multiplicity). So, the x-intercepts occur at $(0, 0)$ and $\left(\frac{4}{3}, 0\right)$. Add these points to your graph, as shown in Figure 2.13.

3. *Plot a Few Additional Points.* Use the zeros of the polynomial to find the test intervals. In each test interval, choose a representative x-value and evaluate the polynomial function, as shown in the table.

Test Interval	Representative x-Value	Value of f	Sign	Point on Graph
$(-\infty, 0)$	-1	$f(-1) = 7$	Positive	$(-1, 7)$
$\left(0, \frac{4}{3}\right)$	1	$f(1) = -1$	Negative	$(1, -1)$
$\left(\frac{4}{3}, \infty\right)$	1.5	$f(1.5) = 1.6875$	Positive	$(1.5, 1.6875)$

4. *Draw the Graph.* Draw a continuous curve through the points, as shown in Figure 2.14. Because both zeros are of odd multiplicity, you know that the graph should cross the x-axis at $x = 0$ and $x = \frac{4}{3}$.

▷ • **REMARK** If you are unsure of the shape of a portion of the graph of a polynomial function, then plot some additional points, such as the point $(0.5, -0.3125)$, as shown in Figure 2.14.

Figure 2.13

Figure 2.14

✓ *Checkpoint* ◄))) Audio-video solution in English & Spanish at LarsonPrecalculus.com.

Sketch the graph of $f(x) = 2x^3 - 6x^2$.

A polynomial function is in **standard form** when its terms are in descending order of exponents from left to right. Before applying the Leading Coefficient Test to a polynomial function, it is a good idea to make sure that the polynomial function is in standard form.

EXAMPLE 5   Sketching the Graph of a Polynomial Function

Sketch the graph of $f(x) = -2x^3 + 6x^2 - \frac{9}{2}x$.

Solution

1. *Apply the Leading Coefficient Test.*   Because the leading coefficient is negative and the degree is odd, you know that the graph eventually rises to the left and falls to the right (see Figure 2.15).

2. *Find the Real Zeros of the Polynomial.*   By factoring

$$f(x) = -2x^3 + 6x^2 - \frac{9}{2}x$$
$$= -\frac{1}{2}x(4x^2 - 12x + 9)$$
$$= -\frac{1}{2}x(2x - 3)^2$$

you can see that the real zeros of f are $x = 0$ (odd multiplicity) and $x = \frac{3}{2}$ (even multiplicity). So, the x-intercepts occur at $(0, 0)$ and $\left(\frac{3}{2}, 0\right)$. Add these points to your graph, as shown in Figure 2.15.

3. *Plot a Few Additional Points.*   Use the zeros of the polynomial to find the test intervals. In each test interval, choose a representative x-value and evaluate the polynomial function, as shown in the table.

Test Interval	Representative x-Value	Value of f	Sign	Point on Graph
$(-\infty, 0)$	-0.5	$f(-0.5) = 4$	Positive	$(-0.5, 4)$
$\left(0, \frac{3}{2}\right)$	0.5	$f(0.5) = -1$	Negative	$(0.5, -1)$
$\left(\frac{3}{2}, \infty\right)$	2	$f(2) = -1$	Negative	$(2, -1)$

• • • • • • • • • • • • • • • ▷
•
•• **REMARK** Observe in Example 5 that the sign of $f(x)$ is positive to the left of and negative to the right of the zero $x = 0$. Similarly, the sign of $f(x)$ is negative to the left and to the right of the zero $x = \frac{3}{2}$. This suggests that if the zero of a polynomial function is of *odd* multiplicity, then the sign of $f(x)$ changes from one side to the other side of the zero. If the zero is of *even* multiplicity, then the sign of $f(x)$ does not change from one side to the other side of the zero.

4. *Draw the Graph.*   Draw a continuous curve through the points, as shown in Figure 2.16. As indicated by the multiplicities of the zeros, the graph crosses the x-axis at $(0, 0)$ but does not cross the x-axis at $\left(\frac{3}{2}, 0\right)$.

Figure 2.15   **Figure 2.16**

✓ *Checkpoint* ◄))) *Audio-video solution in English & Spanish at LarsonPrecalculus.com.*

Sketch the graph of $f(x) = -\frac{1}{4}x^4 + \frac{3}{2}x^3 - \frac{9}{4}x^2$.

The Intermediate Value Theorem

The **Intermediate Value Theorem** implies that if

$$(a, f(a)) \quad \text{and} \quad (b, f(b))$$

are two points on the graph of a polynomial function such that $f(a) \neq f(b)$, then for any number d between $f(a)$ and $f(b)$ there must be a number c between a and b such that $f(c) = d$. (See figure.)

Intermediate Value Theorem

Let a and b be real numbers such that $a < b$. If f is a polynomial function such that $f(a) \neq f(b)$, then, in the interval $[a, b]$, f takes on every value between $f(a)$ and $f(b)$.

The Intermediate Value Theorem helps you locate the real zeros of a polynomial function in the following way. If you can find a value $x = a$ at which a polynomial function is positive, and another value $x = b$ at which it is negative, then you can conclude that the function has at least one real zero between these two values. For example, the function

$$f(x) = x^3 + x^2 + 1$$

is negative when $x = -2$ and positive when $x = -1$. So, it follows from the Intermediate Value Theorem that f must have a real zero somewhere between -2 and -1, as shown below.

The function f must have a real zero
somewhere between -2 and -1.

By continuing this line of reasoning, you can approximate any real zeros of a polynomial function to any desired accuracy. This concept is further demonstrated in Example 6.

▷ TECHNOLOGY You can use
the *table* feature of a graphing
utility to approximate the real
zero of the polynomial function
in Example 6. Construct a table
that shows function values for
$-2 \le x \le 4$, as shown below.

X	Y1
-2	-11
-1	-1
0	1
1	1
2	5
3	19
4	49
X=0	

Scroll through the table looking
for consecutive values that differ
in sign. From the table, you can
see that $f(-1)$ and $f(0)$ differ
in sign. So, you can conclude
from the Intermediate Value
Theorem that the function has
a real zero between -1 and 0.
You can adjust your table to
show function values for
$-1 \le x \le 0$ using increments
of 0.1, as shown below.

X	Y1
-1	-1
-.9	-.539
-.8	-.152
-.7	.167
-.6	.424
-.5	.625
-.4	.776
X=-.7	

By scrolling through the table,
you can see that $f(-0.8)$ and
$f(-0.7)$ differ in sign. So, the
function has a real zero between
-0.8 and -0.7. Repeating this
process several times, you should
obtain $x \approx -0.755$ as the real
zero of the function. Use the
zero or *root* feature of the
graphing utility to confirm
this result.

EXAMPLE 6 Using the Intermediate Value Theorem

Use the Intermediate Value Theorem to approximate the real zero of

$$f(x) = x^3 - x^2 + 1.$$

Solution Begin by computing a few function values, as follows.

x	-2	-1	0	1
$f(x)$	-11	-1	1	1

Because $f(-1)$ is negative and $f(0)$ is positive, you can apply the Intermediate Value
Theorem to conclude that the function has a real zero between -1 and 0. To pinpoint
this zero more closely, divide the interval $[-1, 0]$ into tenths and evaluate the function
at each point. When you do this, you will find that

$$f(-0.8) = -0.152 \quad \text{and} \quad f(-0.7) = 0.167.$$

So, f must have a real zero between -0.8 and -0.7, as shown below.

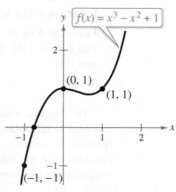

The function f has a real zero between
-0.8 and -0.7.

For a more accurate approximation, compute function values between $f(-0.8)$ and
$f(-0.7)$ and apply the Intermediate Value Theorem again. By continuing this process,
you can approximate this zero to any desired accuracy.

✓ *Checkpoint*   Audio-video solution in English & Spanish at LarsonPrecalculus.com.

Use the Intermediate Value Theorem to approximate the real zero of

$$f(x) = x^3 - 3x^2 - 2.$$

Summarize (Section 2.2)

1. Describe the graphs of monomial functions of the form $f(x) = x^n$ *(page 125)*. For
   an example of sketching transformations of monomial functions, see Example 1.

2. Describe the Leading Coefficient Test *(page 126)*. For an example of
   applying the Leading Coefficient Test, see Example 2.

3. Describe the real zeros of polynomial functions *(page 128)*. For examples
   involving the real zeros of polynomial functions, see Examples 3–5.

4. State the Intermediate Value Theorem *(page 131)*. For an example of using
   the Intermediate Value Theorem, see Example 6.

2.2 Exercises

Vocabulary: Fill in the blanks.

1. The graphs of all polynomial functions are _____, which means that the graphs have no breaks, holes, or gaps.

2. The _____ _____ _____ is used to determine the left-hand and right-hand behavior of the graph of a polynomial function.

3. A polynomial function of degree n has at most _____ real zeros and at most _____ turning points.

4. When $x = a$ is a zero of a polynomial function f, the following three statements are true.
   (a) $x = a$ is a _____ of the polynomial equation $f(x) = 0$.
   (b) _____ is a factor of the polynomial $f(x)$.
   (c) $(a, 0)$ is an _____ of the graph of f.

5. When a real zero of a polynomial function is of even multiplicity, the graph of f _____ the x-axis at $x = a$, and when it is of odd multiplicity, the graph of f _____ the x-axis at $x = a$.

6. A factor $(x - a)^k$, $k > 1$, yields a _____ _____ $x = a$ of _____ k.

7. A polynomial function is written in _____ form when its terms are written in descending order of exponents from left to right.

8. The _____ _____ Theorem states that if f is a polynomial function such that $f(a) \neq f(b)$, then, in the interval $[a, b]$, f takes on every value between $f(a)$ and $f(b)$.

Skills and Applications

Matching In Exercises 9–14, match the polynomial function with its graph. [The graphs are labeled (a), (b), (c), (d), (e), and (f).]

9. $f(x) = -2x^2 - 5x$
10. $f(x) = 2x^3 - 3x + 1$
11. $f(x) = -\frac{1}{4}x^4 + 3x^2$
12. $f(x) = -\frac{1}{3}x^3 + x^2 - \frac{4}{3}$
13. $f(x) = x^4 + 2x^3$
14. $f(x) = \frac{1}{5}x^5 - 2x^3 + \frac{9}{5}x$

(a)

(b)

(c)

(d)

(e)

(f)

Sketching Transformations of Monomial Functions In Exercises 15–18, sketch the graph of $y = x^n$ and each transformation.

15. $y = x^3$
   (a) $f(x) = (x - 4)^3$ (b) $f(x) = x^3 - 4$
   (c) $f(x) = -\frac{1}{4}x^3$ (d) $f(x) = (x - 4)^3 - 4$

16. $y = x^5$
   (a) $f(x) = (x + 1)^5$ (b) $f(x) = x^5 + 1$
   (c) $f(x) = 1 - \frac{1}{2}x^5$ (d) $f(x) = -\frac{1}{2}(x + 1)^5$

17. $y = x^4$
   (a) $f(x) = (x + 3)^4$ (b) $f(x) = x^4 - 3$
   (c) $f(x) = 4 - x^4$ (d) $f(x) = \frac{1}{2}(x - 1)^4$
   (e) $f(x) = (2x)^4 + 1$ (f) $f(x) = \left(\frac{1}{2}x\right)^4 - 2$

18. $y = x^6$
   (a) $f(x) = -\frac{1}{8}x^6$ (b) $f(x) = (x + 2)^6 - 4$
   (c) $f(x) = x^6 - 5$ (d) $f(x) = -\frac{1}{4}x^6 + 1$
   (e) $f(x) = \left(\frac{1}{4}x\right)^6 - 2$ (f) $f(x) = (2x)^6 - 1$

Apply the Leading Coefficient Test In Exercises 19–30, describe the right-hand and left-hand behavior of the graph of the polynomial function.

19. $f(x) = \frac{1}{5}x^3 + 4x$

20. $f(x) = 2x^2 - 3x + 1$

21. $g(x) = 5 - \frac{7}{2}x - 3x^2$

22. $h(x) = 1 - x^6$

23. $g(x) = -x^3 + 3x^2$

24. $g(x) = -x^4 + 4x - 6$

25. $f(x) = -2.1x^5 + 4x^3 - 2$

26. $f(x) = 4x^5 - 7x + 6.5$

27. $f(x) = 6 - 2x + 4x^2 - 5x^7$

28. $f(x) = (3x^4 - 2x + 5)/4$

29. $h(t) = -\frac{3}{4}(t^2 - 3t + 6)$

30. $f(s) = -\frac{7}{8}(s^3 + 5s^2 - 7s + 1)$

Graphical Analysis In Exercises 31–34, use a graphing utility to graph the functions f and g in the same viewing window. Zoom out sufficiently far to show that the right-hand and left-hand behaviors of f and g appear identical.

31. $f(x) = 3x^3 - 9x + 1, \quad g(x) = 3x^3$

32. $f(x) = -\frac{1}{3}(x^3 - 3x + 2), \quad g(x) = -\frac{1}{3}x^3$

33. $f(x) = -(x^4 - 4x^3 + 16x), \quad g(x) = -x^4$

34. $f(x) = 3x^4 - 6x^2, \quad g(x) = 3x^4$

Finding Real Zeros of a Polynomial Function In Exercises 35–50, (a) find all real zeros of the polynomial function, (b) determine the multiplicity of each zero, (c) determine the maximum possible number of turning points of the graph of the function, and (d) use a graphing utility to graph the function and verify your answers.

35. $f(x) = x^2 - 36$

36. $f(x) = 81 - x^2$

37. $h(t) = t^2 - 6t + 9$

38. $f(x) = x^2 + 10x + 25$

39. $f(x) = \frac{1}{3}x^2 + \frac{1}{3}x - \frac{2}{3}$

40. $f(x) = \frac{1}{2}x^2 + \frac{5}{2}x - \frac{3}{2}$

41. $f(x) = 3x^3 - 12x^2 + 3x$

42. $g(x) = 5x(x^2 - 2x - 1)$

43. $f(t) = t^3 - 8t^2 + 16t$

44. $f(x) = x^4 - x^3 - 30x^2$

45. $g(t) = t^5 - 6t^3 + 9t$

46. $f(x) = x^5 + x^3 - 6x$

47. $f(x) = 3x^4 + 9x^2 + 6$

48. $f(x) = 2x^4 - 2x^2 - 40$

49. $g(x) = x^3 + 3x^2 - 4x - 12$

50. $f(x) = x^3 - 4x^2 - 25x + 100$

Graphical Analysis In Exercises 51–54, (a) use a graphing utility to graph the function, (b) use the graph to approximate any x-intercepts of the graph, (c) set $y = 0$ and solve the resulting equation, and (d) compare the results of part (c) with any x-intercepts of the graph.

51. $y = 4x^3 - 20x^2 + 25x$

52. $y = 4x^3 + 4x^2 - 8x - 8$

53. $y = x^5 - 5x^3 + 4x$

54. $y = \frac{1}{4}x^3(x^2 - 9)$

Finding a Polynomial Function In Exercises 55–64, find a polynomial function that has the given zeros. (There are many correct answers.)

55. $0, 8$

56. $0, -7$

57. $2, -6$

58. $-4, 5$

59. $0, -4, -5$

60. $0, 1, 10$

61. $4, -3, 3, 0$

62. $-2, -1, 0, 1, 2$

63. $1 + \sqrt{3}, 1 - \sqrt{3}$

64. $2, 4 + \sqrt{5}, 4 - \sqrt{5}$

Finding a Polynomial Function In Exercises 65–74, find a polynomial of degree n that has the given zero(s). (There are many correct answers.)

Zero(s)	Degree
65. $x = -3$	$n = 2$
66. $x = -12, -6$	$n = 2$
67. $x = -5, 0, 1$	$n = 3$
68. $x = -2, 4, 7$	$n = 3$
69. $x = 0, \sqrt{3}, -\sqrt{3}$	$n = 3$
70. $x = 9$	$n = 3$
71. $x = -5, 1, 2$	$n = 4$
72. $x = -4, -1, 3, 6$	$n = 4$
73. $x = 0, -4$	$n = 5$
74. $x = -1, 4, 7, 8$	$n = 5$

Sketching the Graph of a Polynomial Function In Exercises 75–88, sketch the graph of the function by (a) applying the Leading Coefficient Test, (b) finding the real zeros of the polynomial, (c) plotting sufficient solution points, and (d) drawing a continuous curve through the points.

75. $f(x) = x^3 - 25x$

76. $g(x) = x^4 - 9x^2$

77. $f(t) = \frac{1}{4}(t^2 - 2t + 15)$

78. $g(x) = -x^2 + 10x - 16$

79. $f(x) = x^3 - 2x^2$

80. $f(x) = 8 - x^3$

81. $f(x) = 3x^3 - 15x^2 + 18x$

82. $f(x) = -4x^3 + 4x^2 + 15x$

83. $f(x) = -5x^2 - x^3$

84. $f(x) = -48x^2 + 3x^4$

85. $f(x) = x^2(x - 4)$

86. $h(x) = \frac{1}{3}x^3(x - 4)^2$

87. $g(t) = -\frac{1}{4}(t - 2)^2(t + 2)^2$

88. $g(x) = \frac{1}{10}(x + 1)^2(x - 3)^3$

Graphical Analysis In Exercises 89–92, use a graphing utility to graph the function. Use the *zero* or *root* feature to approximate the real zeros of the function. Then determine the multiplicity of each zero.

89. $f(x) = x^3 - 16x$

90. $f(x) = \frac{1}{4}x^4 - 2x^2$

91. $g(x) = \frac{1}{5}(x + 1)^2(x - 3)(2x - 9)$

92. $h(x) = \frac{1}{5}(x + 2)^2(3x - 5)^2$

Using the Intermediate Value Theorem In Exercises 93–96, (a) use the Intermediate Value Theorem and the *table* feature of a graphing utility to find intervals one unit in length in which the polynomial function is guaranteed to have a zero. (b) Adjust the table to approximate the zeros of the function. Use the *zero* or *root* feature of the graphing utility to verify your results.

93. $f(x) = x^3 - 3x^2 + 3$

94. $f(x) = 0.11x^3 - 2.07x^2 + 9.81x - 6.88$

95. $g(x) = 3x^4 + 4x^3 - 3$

96. $h(x) = x^4 - 10x^2 + 3$

97. Numerical and Graphical Analysis You plan to construct an open box from a square piece of material, 36 inches on a side, by cutting equal squares with sides of length x from the corners and turning up the sides (see figure).

(a) Write a function V that represents the volume of the box.

(b) Determine the domain of the function V.

(c) Use a graphing utility to construct a table that shows the box heights x and the corresponding volumes $V(x)$. Use the table to estimate the dimensions that will produce a maximum volume.

(d) Use the graphing utility to graph V and use the graph to estimate the value of x for which $V(x)$ is a maximum. Compare your result with that of part (c).

98. Maximum Volume You plan to construct an open box with locking tabs from a square piece of material 24 inches on a side by cutting equal squares from the corners and folding along the dashed lines (see figure).

(a) Write a function V that represents the volume of the box.

(b) Determine the domain of the function V.

(c) Sketch a graph of the function and estimate the value of x for which $V(x)$ is a maximum.

99. Construction A roofing contractor is fabricating gutters from 12-inch aluminum sheeting. The contractor plans to use an aluminum siding folding press to create the gutter by creasing equal lengths for the sidewalls (see figure).

(a) Let x represent the height of the sidewall of the gutter. Write a function A that represents the cross-sectional area of the gutter.

(b) The length of the aluminum sheeting is 16 feet. Write a function V that represents the volume of one run of gutter in terms of x.

(c) Determine the domain of the function V.

(d) Use a graphing utility to construct a table that shows the sidewall heights x and the corresponding volumes $V(x)$. Use the table to estimate the dimensions that will produce a maximum volume.

(e) Use the graphing utility to graph V. Use the graph to estimate the value of x for which $V(x)$ is a maximum. Compare your result with that of part (d).

(f) Would changing the length of the aluminum sheet affect the value of x for which $V(x)$ is a maximum? Explain.

100. Construction An industrial propane tank is formed by adjoining two hemispheres to the ends of a right circular cylinder. The length of the cylindrical portion of the tank is four times the radius of the hemispherical components (see figure).

(a) Write a function V that represents the total volume of the tank in terms of r.

(b) Find the domain of the function V.

(c) Use a graphing utility to graph the function.

(d) Use the graph from part (c) to estimate the radius and length of the cylindrical portion of the tank when the total volume of the tank is 120 cubic feet.

101. Revenue The revenues R (in millions of dollars) for a company from 2003 through 2010 can be modeled by

$$R = 6.212t^3 - 132.87t^2 + 863.2t - 1115, \; 3 \le t \le 10$$

where t represents the year, with $t = 3$ corresponding to 2003.

(a) Use a graphing utility to approximate any relative extrema of the model over its domain.

(b) Use the graphing utility to approximate the intervals on which the revenue for the company is increasing and decreasing over its domain.

(c) Use the results of parts (a) and (b) to describe the company's revenue during this time period.

102. Revenue The revenues R (in millions of dollars) for a company from 2003 through 2010 can be modeled by

$$R = -0.1685t^4 + 4.298t^3 - 39.044t^2 + 149.9t - 185,$$

$$3 \le t \le 10$$

where t represents the year, with $t = 3$ corresponding to 2003.

(a) Use a graphing utility to approximate any relative extrema of the model over its domain.

(b) Use the graphing utility to approximate the intervals on which the revenue for the company is increasing and decreasing over its domain.

(c) Use the results of parts (a) and (b) to describe the company's revenue during this time period.

103. Revenue The revenue R (in millions of dollars) for a company is related to its advertising expense by the function

$$R = \frac{1}{100,000}(-x^3 + 600x^2), \quad 0 \le x \le 400$$

where x is the amount spent on advertising (in tens of thousands of dollars). Use the graph of this function to estimate the point on the graph at which the function is increasing most rapidly. This point is called the *point of diminishing returns* because any expense above this amount will yield less return per dollar invested in advertising.

Advertising expense
(in tens of thousands of dollars)

104. Tree Growth

The growth of a red oak tree is approximated by the function

$$G = -0.003t^3 + 0.137t^2 + 0.458t - 0.839,$$

$$2 \le t \le 34$$

where G is the height of the tree (in feet) and t is its age (in years).

(a) Use a graphing utility to graph the function.

(b) Estimate the age of the tree when it is growing most rapidly. This point is called the *point of diminishing returns* because the increase in size will be less with each additional year.

(c) Using calculus, the point of diminishing returns can be found by finding the vertex of the parabola

$$y = -0.009t^2 + 0.274t + 0.458.$$

Find the vertex of this parabola.

(d) Compare your results from parts (b) and (c).

Exploration

True or False? In Exercises 105–111, determine whether the statement is true or false. Justify your answer.

105. A fifth-degree polynomial function can have five turning points in its graph.

106. If f is a polynomial function of x such that $f(2) = -6$ and $f(6) = 6$, then f has at most one real zero between $x = 2$ and $x = 6$.

107. A polynomial function cannot have more real zeros than it has turning points.

108. If the graph of a polynomial function falls to the right, then its leading coefficient is negative.

109. If the graph of a polynomial function rises to the left, then its leading coefficient is positive.

110. The graph of the function

$$f(x) = x^4 - 6x^3 - 3x - 8$$

falls to the left and to the right.

111. The graph of the function

$$f(x) = 2 + x - x^2 + x^3 - x^4 + x^5 + x^6 - x^7$$

rises to the left and falls to the right.

112. HOW DO YOU SEE IT? For each graph, describe a polynomial function that could represent the graph. (Indicate the degree of the function and the sign of its leading coefficient.)

(a)

(b)

(c)

(d)

113. Modeling Polynomials Sketch the graph of a polynomial function that is of fourth degree, has a zero of multiplicity 2, and has a negative leading coefficient. Sketch the graph of another polynomial function with the same characteristics except that the leading coefficient is positive.

114. Modeling Polynomials Sketch the graph of a polynomial function that is of fifth degree, has a zero of multiplicity 2, and has a negative leading coefficient. Sketch the graph of another polynomial function with the same characteristics except that the leading coefficient is positive.

115. Graphical Reasoning Sketch a graph of the function $f(x) = x^4$. Explain how the graph of each function g differs (if it does) from the graph of f. Determine whether g is even, odd, or neither.

(a) $g(x) = f(x) + 2$

(b) $g(x) = f(x + 2)$

(c) $g(x) = f(-x)$

(d) $g(x) = -f(x)$

(e) $g(x) = f\left(\frac{1}{2}x\right)$

(f) $g(x) = \frac{1}{2}f(x)$

(g) $g(x) = f(x^{3/4})$

(h) $g(x) = (f \circ f)(x)$

116. Think About It For each function, identify the degree of the function and whether the degree of the function is even or odd. Identify the leading coefficient and whether the leading coefficient is positive or negative. Use a graphing utility to graph each function. Describe the relationship between the degree of the function and the sign of the leading coefficient of the function and the right-hand and left-hand behavior of the graph of the function.

(a) $f(x) = x^3 - 2x^2 - x + 1$

(b) $f(x) = 2x^5 + 2x^2 - 5x + 1$

(c) $f(x) = -2x^5 - x^2 + 5x + 3$

(d) $f(x) = -x^3 + 5x - 2$

(e) $f(x) = 2x^2 + 3x - 4$

(f) $f(x) = x^4 - 3x^2 + 2x - 1$

(g) $f(x) = x^2 + 3x + 2$

117. Think About It Sketch the graph of each polynomial function. Then count the number of real zeros of the function and the numbers of relative minima and relative maxima. Compare these numbers with the degree of the polynomial. What do you observe?

(a) $f(x) = -x^3 + 9x$

(b) $f(x) = x^4 - 10x^2 + 9$

(c) $f(x) = x^5 - 16x$

118. Think About It Explore transformations of the form

$$g(x) = a(x - h)^5 + k.$$

(a) Use a graphing utility to graph the functions

$$y_1 = -\frac{1}{3}(x - 2)^5 + 1$$

and

$$y_2 = \frac{3}{5}(x + 2)^5 - 3.$$

Determine whether the graphs are increasing or decreasing. Explain.

(b) Will the graph of g always be increasing or decreasing? If so, then is this behavior determined by a, h, or k? Explain.

(c) Use the graphing utility to graph the function

$$H(x) = x^5 - 3x^3 + 2x + 1.$$

Use the graph and the result of part (b) to determine whether H can be written in the form

$$H(x) = a(x - h)^5 + k.$$

Explain.

2.3   Polynomial and Synthetic Division

Synthetic division can help you evaluate polynomial functions. For instance, in Exercise 86 on page 146, you will use synthetic division to evaluate a model for the number of confirmed cases of Lyme disease in Maine.

- Use long division to divide polynomials by other polynomials.
- Use synthetic division to divide polynomials by binomials of the form $(x - k)$.
- Use the Remainder Theorem and the Factor Theorem.

Long Division of Polynomials

Suppose you are given the graph of

$$f(x) = 6x^3 - 19x^2 + 16x - 4.$$

Notice that a zero of f occurs at $x = 2$, as shown at the right. Because $x = 2$ is a zero of f, you know that $(x - 2)$ is a factor of $f(x)$. This means that there exists a second-degree polynomial $q(x)$ such that

$$f(x) = (x - 2) \cdot q(x).$$

To find $q(x)$, you can use **long division,** as illustrated in Example 1.

$f(x) = 6x^3 - 19x^2 + 16x - 4$

EXAMPLE 1   **Long Division of Polynomials**

Divide the polynomial $6x^3 - 19x^2 + 16x - 4$ by $x - 2$, and use the result to factor the polynomial completely.

Solution

Think $\dfrac{6x^3}{x} = 6x^2$.

Think $\dfrac{-7x^2}{x} = -7x$.

Think $\dfrac{2x}{x} = 2$.

$$
\begin{array}{r}
6x^2 - 7x + 2 \\
x - 2 \overline{)\, 6x^3 - 19x^2 + 16x - 4} \\
\underline{6x^3 - 12x^2} \\
-7x^2 + 16x \\
\underline{-7x^2 + 14x} \\
2x - 4 \\
\underline{2x - 4} \\
0
\end{array}
$$

Multiply: $6x^2(x - 2)$.
Subtract.
Multiply: $-7x(x - 2)$.
Subtract.
Multiply: $2(x - 2)$.
Subtract.

From this division, you can conclude that

$$6x^3 - 19x^2 + 16x - 4 = (x - 2)(6x^2 - 7x + 2)$$

and by factoring the quadratic $6x^2 - 7x + 2$, you have

$$6x^3 - 19x^2 + 16x - 4 = (x - 2)(2x - 1)(3x - 2).$$

✓ **Checkpoint** ◀))) *Audio-video solution in English & Spanish at LarsonPrecalculus.com.*

Divide the polynomial $3x^2 + 19x + 28$ by $x + 4$, and use the result to factor the polynomial completely.

In Example 1, $x - 2$ is a factor of the polynomial

$$6x^3 - 19x^2 + 16x - 4$$

and the long division process produces a remainder of zero. Often, long division will produce a nonzero remainder. For instance, when you divide $x^2 + 3x + 5$ by $x + 1$, you obtain the following.

$$
\begin{array}{r}
x + 2 \quad \longleftarrow \text{ Quotient} \\
\text{Divisor} \longrightarrow x + 1 \overline{)\, x^2 + 3x + 5} \quad \longleftarrow \text{ Dividend} \\
\underline{x^2 + x} \\
2x + 5 \\
\underline{2x + 2} \\
3 \quad \longleftarrow \text{ Remainder}
\end{array}
$$

In fractional form, you can write this result as follows.

$$
\underbrace{\frac{\overbrace{x^2 + 3x + 5}^{\text{Dividend}}}{\underbrace{x + 1}_{\text{Divisor}}}}_{} = \overbrace{x + 2}^{\text{Quotient}} + \frac{\overset{\text{Remainder}}{\downarrow}{3}}{\underbrace{x + 1}_{\text{Divisor}}}
$$

This implies that

$$x^2 + 3x + 5 = (x + 1)(x + 2) + 3 \qquad \text{Multiply each side by } (x + 1).$$

which illustrates the following theorem, called the **Division Algorithm.**

The Division Algorithm

If $f(x)$ and $d(x)$ are polynomials such that $d(x) \neq 0$, and the degree of $d(x)$ is less than or equal to the degree of $f(x)$, then there exist unique polynomials $q(x)$ and $r(x)$ such that

$$f(x) = d(x)q(x) + r(x)$$

$$
\underset{\text{Dividend}}{\uparrow} \quad \underset{\substack{\text{Quotient} \\ \text{Divisor}}}{\uparrow} \quad \underset{\text{Remainder}}{\uparrow}
$$

where $r(x) = 0$ or the degree of $r(x)$ is less than the degree of $d(x)$. If the remainder $r(x)$ is zero, $d(x)$ *divides evenly* into $f(x)$.

The Division Algorithm can also be written as

$$\frac{f(x)}{d(x)} = q(x) + \frac{r(x)}{d(x)}.$$

In the Division Algorithm, the rational expression $f(x)/d(x)$ is **improper** because the degree of $f(x)$ is greater than or equal to the degree of $d(x)$. On the other hand, the rational expression $r(x)/d(x)$ is **proper** because the degree of $r(x)$ is less than the degree of $d(x)$.

Before you apply the Division Algorithm, follow these steps.

1. Write the dividend and divisor in descending powers of the variable.

2. Insert placeholders with zero coefficients for missing powers of the variable.

Note how these steps are applied in the next example.

EXAMPLE 2   **Long Division of Polynomials**

Divide $x^3 - 1$ by $x - 1$.

Solution   Because there is no x^2-term or x-term in the dividend $x^3 - 1$, you need to rewrite the dividend as $x^3 + 0x^2 + 0x - 1$ before you apply the Division Algorithm.

$$
\begin{array}{r}
x^2 + x + 1 \\
x - 1 \overline{)\, x^3 + 0x^2 + 0x - 1} \\
\end{array}
$$

$$
\begin{array}{rl}
\underline{x^3 - x^2} & \text{Multiply } x^2 \text{ by } x - 1. \\
x^2 + 0x & \text{Subtract and bring down } 0x. \\
\underline{x^2 - x} & \text{Multiply } x \text{ by } x - 1. \\
x - 1 & \text{Subtract and bring down } -1. \\
\underline{x - 1} & \text{Multiply } 1 \text{ by } x - 1. \\
0 & \text{Subtract.}
\end{array}
$$

So, $x - 1$ divides evenly into $x^3 - 1$, and you can write

$$\frac{x^3 - 1}{x - 1} = x^2 + x + 1, \quad x \neq 1.$$

You can check this result by multiplying.

$$(x - 1)(x^2 + x + 1) = x^3 + x^2 + x - x^2 - x - 1$$
$$= x^3 - 1$$

✓ *Checkpoint* Audio-video solution in English & Spanish at LarsonPrecalculus.com.

Divide $x^3 - 2x^2 - 9$ by $x - 3$.

Note that the condition $x \neq 1$ in Example 1 is equivalent to the condition in the Division Algorithm that $d(x) \neq 0$. Statement of this condition will be omitted for the remainder of this section, but you should be aware that the results of polynomial division are only valid when the divisor does not equal zero.

EXAMPLE 3   **Long Division of Polynomials**

Divide $-5x^2 - 2 + 3x + 2x^4 + 4x^3$ by $2x - 3 + x^2$.

Solution   Begin by writing the dividend and divisor in descending powers of x.

$$
\begin{array}{r}
2x^2 \qquad\quad + 1 \\
x^2 + 2x - 3 \overline{)\, 2x^4 + 4x^3 - 5x^2 + 3x - 2} \\
\end{array}
$$

$$
\begin{array}{rl}
\underline{2x^4 + 4x^3 - 6x^2} & \text{Multiply } 2x^2 \text{ by } x^2 + 2x - 3. \\
x^2 + 3x - 2 & \text{Subtract and bring down } 3x - 2. \\
\underline{x^2 + 2x - 3} & \text{Multiply } 1 \text{ by } x^2 + 2x - 3. \\
x + 1 & \text{Subtract.}
\end{array}
$$

Note that the first subtraction eliminated two terms from the dividend. When this happens, the quotient skips a term. You can write the result as

$$\frac{2x^4 + 4x^3 - 5x^2 + 3x - 2}{x^2 + 2x - 3} = 2x^2 + 1 + \frac{x + 1}{x^2 + 2x - 3}.$$

✓ *Checkpoint* Audio-video solution in English & Spanish at LarsonPrecalculus.com.

Divide $-x^3 + 9x + 6x^4 - x^2 - 3$ by $1 + 3x$.

Synthetic Division

There is a nice shortcut for long division of polynomials by divisors of the form $x - k$. This shortcut is called **synthetic division.** The pattern for synthetic division of a cubic polynomial is summarized as follows. (The pattern for higher-degree polynomials is similar.)

Synthetic Division (for a Cubic Polynomial)

To divide $ax^3 + bx^2 + cx + d$ by $x - k$, use the following pattern.

k $\;a\quad b\quad c\quad d$ ← Coefficients of dividend

ka

$a\qquad\qquad r$ ← Remainder

Coefficients of quotient

Vertical pattern: Add terms in columns.
Diagonal pattern: Multiply results by k.

This algorithm for synthetic division works only for divisors of the form $x - k$. Remember that $x + k = x - (-k)$.

EXAMPLE 4   **Using Synthetic Division**

Use synthetic division to divide $x^4 - 10x^2 - 2x + 4$ by $x + 3$.

Solution   You should set up the array as follows. Note that a zero is included for the missing x^3-term in the dividend.

$$-3 \;\Big|\; 1 \quad 0 \quad -10 \quad -2 \quad 4$$

Then, use the synthetic division pattern by adding terms in columns and multiplying the results by -3.

Divisor: $x + 3$ Dividend: $x^4 - 10x^2 - 2x + 4$

$$
\begin{array}{r|rrrrr}
-3 & 1 & 0 & -10 & -2 & 4 \\
   &   & -3 & 9 & 3 & -3 \\
\hline
   & 1 & -3 & -1 & 1 & \boxed{1}
\end{array}
$$
← Remainder: 1

Quotient: $x^3 - 3x^2 - x + 1$

So, you have

$$\frac{x^4 - 10x^2 - 2x + 4}{x + 3} = x^3 - 3x^2 - x + 1 + \frac{1}{x + 3}.$$

✓ *Checkpoint* Audio-video solution in English & Spanish at LarsonPrecalculus.com.

Use synthetic division to divide $5x^3 + 8x^2 - x + 6$ by $x + 2$.

The Remainder and Factor Theorems

The remainder obtained in the synthetic division process has an important interpretation, as described in the **Remainder Theorem.**

The Remainder Theorem

If a polynomial $f(x)$ is divided by $x - k$, then the remainder is

$$r = f(k).$$

For a proof of the Remainder Theorem, see Proofs in Mathematics on page 195.

The Remainder Theorem tells you that synthetic division can be used to evaluate a polynomial function. That is, to evaluate a polynomial function $f(x)$ when $x = k$, divide $f(x)$ by $x - k$. The remainder will be $f(k)$, as illustrated in Example 5.

EXAMPLE 5   **Using the Remainder Theorem**

Use the Remainder Theorem to evaluate

$$f(x) = 3x^3 + 8x^2 + 5x - 7$$

when $x = -2$.

Solution   Using synthetic division, you obtain the following.

$$
\begin{array}{r|rrrr}
-2 & 3 & 8 & 5 & -7 \\
   &   & -6 & -4 & -2 \\
\hline
   & 3 & 2 & 1 & -9
\end{array}
$$

Because the remainder is $r = -9$, you can conclude that

$$f(-2) = -9. \qquad r = f(k)$$

This means that $(-2, -9)$ is a point on the graph of f. You can check this by substituting $x = -2$ in the original function.

Check

$$f(-2) = 3(-2)^3 + 8(-2)^2 + 5(-2) - 7$$

$$= 3(-8) + 8(4) - 10 - 7$$

$$= -24 + 32 - 10 - 7$$

$$= -9$$

✓ *Checkpoint* ◄))) *Audio-video solution in English & Spanish at LarsonPrecalculus.com.*

Use the Remainder Theorem to find each function value given

$$f(x) = 4x^3 + 10x^2 - 3x - 8.$$

a. $f(-1)$ **b.** $f(4)$

c. $f\left(\frac{1}{2}\right)$ **d.** $f(-3)$ ◼

▷ TECHNOLOGY You can evaluate a function with your graphing utility by entering the function in the equation editor and using the *table* feature in *ask* mode. When the table is set to *ask* mode, you can enter values in the X column and the corresponding function values will be displayed in the function column.

Another important theorem is the **Factor Theorem,** which is stated below.

The Factor Theorem

A polynomial $f(x)$ has a factor $(x - k)$ if and only if $f(k) = 0$.

For a proof of the Factor Theorem, see Proofs in Mathematics on page 195.

Using the Factor Theorem, you can test whether a polynomial has $(x - k)$ as a factor by evaluating the polynomial at $x = k$. If the result is 0, then $(x - k)$ is a factor.

EXAMPLE 6   Factoring a Polynomial: Repeated Division

Show that $(x - 2)$ and $(x + 3)$ are factors of $f(x) = 2x^4 + 7x^3 - 4x^2 - 27x - 18$. Then find the remaining factors of $f(x)$.

Algebraic Solution

Using synthetic division with the factor $(x - 2)$, you obtain the following.

$$
\begin{array}{r|rrrrr}
2 & 2 & 7 & -4 & -27 & -18 \\
  &   & 4 & 22 & 36 & 18 \\
\hline
  & 2 & 11 & 18 & 9 & 0
\end{array}
$$

0 remainder, so $f(2) = 0$ and $(x - 2)$ is a factor.

Take the result of this division and perform synthetic division again using the factor $(x + 3)$.

$$
\begin{array}{r|rrrr}
-3 & 2 & 11 & 18 & 9 \\
   &   & -6 & -15 & -9 \\
\hline
   & 2 & 5 & 3 & 0
\end{array}
$$

$$\underbrace{\qquad\qquad}_{2x^2 + 5x + 3}$$

0 remainder, so $f(-3) = 0$ and $(x + 3)$ is a factor.

Because the resulting quadratic expression factors as

$$2x^2 + 5x + 3 = (2x + 3)(x + 1)$$

the complete factorization of $f(x)$ is

$$f(x) = (x - 2)(x + 3)(2x + 3)(x + 1).$$

Graphical Solution

From the graph of $f(x) = 2x^4 + 7x^3 - 4x^2 - 27x - 18$, you can see that there are four x-intercepts (see figure below). These occur at $x = -3$, $x = -\frac{3}{2}$, $x = -1$, and $x = 2$. (Check this algebraically.) This implies that $(x + 3)$, $\left(x + \frac{3}{2}\right)$, $(x + 1)$, and $(x - 2)$ are factors of $f(x)$. $\left[\text{Note that } \left(x + \frac{3}{2}\right) \text{ and } (2x + 3) \text{ are equivalent factors because they both yield the same zero, } x = -\frac{3}{2}.\right]$

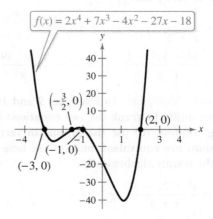

$f(x) = 2x^4 + 7x^3 - 4x^2 - 27x - 18$

✓ ***Checkpoint*** 🔊)) *Audio-video solution in English & Spanish at LarsonPrecalculus.com.*

Show that $(x + 3)$ is a factor of $f(x) = x^3 - 19x - 30$. Then find the remaining factors of $f(x)$.

Summarize   (Section 2.3)

1. Describe how to divide one polynomial by another polynomial using long division *(pages 138 and 139)*. For examples of long division of polynomials, see Examples 1–3.

2. Describe the algorithm for synthetic division *(page 141)*. For an example of using synthetic division, see Example 4.

3. State the Remainder Theorem and the Factor Theorem *(pages 142 and 143)*. For an example of using the Remainder Theorem, see Example 5. For an example of using the Factor Theorem, see Example 6.

2.3   Exercises

See CalcChat.com for tutorial help and worked-out solutions to odd-numbered exercises.

Vocabulary

1. Two forms of the Division Algorithm are shown below. Identify and label each term or function.

$$f(x) = d(x)q(x) + r(x) \qquad \frac{f(x)}{d(x)} = q(x) + \frac{r(x)}{d(x)}$$

In Exercises 2–6, fill in the blanks.

2. In the Division Algorithm, the rational expression $r(x)/d(x)$ is _____ because the degree of $r(x)$ is less than the degree of $d(x)$.

3. In the Division Algorithm, the rational expression $f(x)/d(x)$ is _____ because the degree of $f(x)$ is greater than or equal to the degree of $d(x)$.

4. An alternative method to long division of polynomials is called _____ _____, in which the divisor must be of the form $x - k$.

5. The _____ Theorem states that a polynomial $f(x)$ has a factor $(x - k)$ if and only if $f(k) = 0$.

6. The _____ Theorem states that if a polynomial $f(x)$ is divided by $x - k$, then the remainder is $r = f(k)$.

Skills and Applications

Analytical Analysis   In Exercises 7 and 8, use long division to verify that $y_1 = y_2$.

7. $y_1 = \dfrac{x^2}{x + 2}, \quad y_2 = x - 2 + \dfrac{4}{x + 2}$

8. $y_1 = \dfrac{x^4 - 3x^2 - 1}{x^2 + 5}, \quad y_2 = x^2 - 8 + \dfrac{39}{x^2 + 5}$

Graphical Analysis   In Exercises 9 and 10, (a) use a graphing utility to graph the two equations in the same viewing window, (b) use the graphs to verify that the expressions are equivalent, and (c) use long division to verify the results algebraically.

9. $y_1 = \dfrac{x^2 + 2x - 1}{x + 3}, \quad y_2 = x - 1 + \dfrac{2}{x + 3}$

10. $y_1 = \dfrac{x^4 + x^2 - 1}{x^2 + 1}, \quad y_2 = x^2 - \dfrac{1}{x^2 + 1}$

Long Division of Polynomials   In Exercises 11–26, use long division to divide.

11. $(2x^2 + 10x + 12) \div (x + 3)$

12. $(5x^2 - 17x - 12) \div (x - 4)$

13. $(4x^3 - 7x^2 - 11x + 5) \div (4x + 5)$

14. $(6x^3 - 16x^2 + 17x - 6) \div (3x - 2)$

15. $(x^4 + 5x^3 + 6x^2 - x - 2) \div (x + 2)$

16. $(x^3 + 4x^2 - 3x - 12) \div (x - 3)$

17. $(x^3 - 27) \div (x - 3)$ 18. $(x^3 + 125) \div (x + 5)$

19. $(7x + 3) \div (x + 2)$ 20. $(8x - 5) \div (2x + 1)$

21. $(x^3 - 9) \div (x^2 + 1)$ 22. $(x^5 + 7) \div (x^3 - 1)$

23. $(3x + 2x^3 - 9 - 8x^2) \div (x^2 + 1)$

24. $(5x^3 - 16 - 20x + x^4) \div (x^2 - x - 3)$

25. $\dfrac{x^4}{(x - 1)^3}$ 26. $\dfrac{2x^3 - 4x^2 - 15x + 5}{(x - 1)^2}$

Using Synthetic Division   In Exercises 27–46, use synthetic division to divide.

27. $(3x^3 - 17x^2 + 15x - 25) \div (x - 5)$

28. $(5x^3 + 18x^2 + 7x - 6) \div (x + 3)$

29. $(6x^3 + 7x^2 - x + 26) \div (x - 3)$

30. $(2x^3 + 14x^2 - 20x + 7) \div (x + 6)$

31. $(4x^3 - 9x + 8x^2 - 18) \div (x + 2)$

32. $(9x^3 - 16x - 18x^2 + 32) \div (x - 2)$

33. $(-x^3 + 75x - 250) \div (x + 10)$

34. $(3x^3 - 16x^2 - 72) \div (x - 6)$

35. $(5x^3 - 6x^2 + 8) \div (x - 4)$

36. $(5x^3 + 6x + 8) \div (x + 2)$

37. $\dfrac{10x^4 - 50x^3 - 800}{x - 6}$ 38. $\dfrac{x^5 - 13x^4 - 120x + 80}{x + 3}$

39. $\dfrac{x^3 + 512}{x + 8}$ 40. $\dfrac{x^3 - 729}{x - 9}$

41. $\dfrac{-3x^4}{x - 2}$ 42. $\dfrac{-3x^4}{x + 2}$

43. $\dfrac{180x - x^4}{x - 6}$ 44. $\dfrac{5 - 3x + 2x^2 - x^3}{x + 1}$

45. $\dfrac{4x^3 + 16x^2 - 23x - 15}{x + \frac{1}{2}}$ 46. $\dfrac{3x^3 - 4x^2 + 5}{x - \frac{3}{2}}$

Using the Remainder Theorem In Exercises 47–54, write the function in the form $f(x) = (x - k)q(x) + r$ for the given value of k, and demonstrate that $f(k) = r$.

47. $f(x) = x^3 - x^2 - 14x + 11, \quad k = 4$

48. $f(x) = x^3 - 5x^2 - 11x + 8, \quad k = -2$

49. $f(x) = 15x^4 + 10x^3 - 6x^2 + 14, \quad k = -\frac{2}{3}$

50. $f(x) = 10x^3 - 22x^2 - 3x + 4, \quad k = \frac{1}{5}$

51. $f(x) = x^3 + 3x^2 - 2x - 14, \quad k = \sqrt{2}$

52. $f(x) = x^3 + 2x^2 - 5x - 4, \quad k = -\sqrt{5}$

53. $f(x) = -4x^3 + 6x^2 + 12x + 4, \quad k = 1 - \sqrt{3}$

54. $f(x) = -3x^3 + 8x^2 + 10x - 8, \quad k = 2 + \sqrt{2}$

Using the Remainder Theorem In Exercises 55–58, use the Remainder Theorem and synthetic division to find each function value. Verify your answers using another method.

55. $f(x) = 2x^3 - 7x + 3$

    (a) $f(1)$ (b) $f(-2)$ (c) $f\left(\frac{1}{2}\right)$ (d) $f(2)$

56. $g(x) = 2x^6 + 3x^4 - x^2 + 3$

    (a) $g(2)$ (b) $g(1)$ (c) $g(3)$ (d) $g(-1)$

57. $h(x) = x^3 - 5x^2 - 7x + 4$

    (a) $h(3)$ (b) $h(2)$ (c) $h(-2)$ (d) $h(-5)$

58. $f(x) = 4x^4 - 16x^3 + 7x^2 + 20$

    (a) $f(1)$ (b) $f(-2)$ (c) $f(5)$ (d) $f(-10)$

Using the Factor Theorem In Exercises 59–66, use synthetic division to show that x is a solution of the third-degree polynomial equation, and use the result to factor the polynomial completely. List all real solutions of the equation.

59. $x^3 - 7x + 6 = 0, \quad x = 2$

60. $x^3 - 28x - 48 = 0, \quad x = -4$

61. $2x^3 - 15x^2 + 27x - 10 = 0, \quad x = \frac{1}{2}$

62. $48x^3 - 80x^2 + 41x - 6 = 0, \quad x = \frac{2}{3}$

63. $x^3 + 2x^2 - 3x - 6 = 0, \quad x = \sqrt{3}$

64. $x^3 + 2x^2 - 2x - 4 = 0, \quad x = \sqrt{2}$

65. $x^3 - 3x^2 + 2 = 0, \quad x = 1 + \sqrt{3}$

66. $x^3 - x^2 - 13x - 3 = 0, \quad x = 2 - \sqrt{5}$

Factoring a Polynomial In Exercises 67–74, (a) verify the given factors of $f(x)$, (b) find the remaining factor(s) of $f(x)$, (c) use your results to write the complete factorization of $f(x)$, (d) list all real zeros of f, and (e) confirm your results by using a graphing utility to graph the function.

Function	Factors
67. $f(x) = 2x^3 + x^2 - 5x + 2$	$(x + 2), (x - 1)$
68. $f(x) = 3x^3 + 2x^2 - 19x + 6$	$(x + 3), (x - 2)$
69. $f(x) = x^4 - 4x^3 - 15x^2 + 58x - 40$	$(x - 5), (x + 4)$
70. $f(x) = 8x^4 - 14x^3 - 71x^2$ $- 10x + 24$	$(x + 2), (x - 4)$
71. $f(x) = 6x^3 + 41x^2 - 9x - 14$	$(2x + 1), (3x - 2)$
72. $f(x) = 10x^3 - 11x^2 - 72x + 45$	$(2x + 5), (5x - 3)$
73. $f(x) = 2x^3 - x^2 - 10x + 5$	$(2x - 1), (x + \sqrt{5})$
74. $f(x) = x^3 + 3x^2 - 48x - 144$	$(x + 4\sqrt{3}), (x + 3)$

Graphical Analysis In Exercises 75–80, (a) use the *zero* or *root* feature of a graphing utility to approximate the zeros of the function accurate to three decimal places, (b) determine the exact value of one of the zeros, and (c) use synthetic division to verify your result from part (b), and then factor the polynomial completely.

75. $f(x) = x^3 - 2x^2 - 5x + 10$

76. $g(x) = x^3 - 4x^2 - 2x + 8$

77. $h(t) = t^3 - 2t^2 - 7t + 2$

78. $f(s) = s^3 - 12s^2 + 40s - 24$

79. $h(x) = x^5 - 7x^4 + 10x^3 + 14x^2 - 24x$

80. $g(x) = 6x^4 - 11x^3 - 51x^2 + 99x - 27$

Simplifying Rational Expressions In Exercises 81–84, simplify the rational expression by using long division or synthetic division.

81. $\dfrac{4x^3 - 8x^2 + x + 3}{2x - 3}$

82. $\dfrac{x^3 + x^2 - 64x - 64}{x + 8}$

83. $\dfrac{x^4 + 6x^3 + 11x^2 + 6x}{x^2 + 3x + 2}$

84. $\dfrac{x^4 + 9x^3 - 5x^2 - 36x + 4}{x^2 - 4}$

85. Profit A company that produces calculators estimated that the profit P (in dollars) from selling a particular model of calculator was

$$P = -152x^3 + 7545x^2 - 169,625, \quad 0 \le x \le 45$$

where x was the advertising expense (in tens of thousands of dollars). For this model of calculator, the advertising expense was \$400,000 ($x = 40$) and the profit was \$2,174,375.

(a) Use a graphing utility to graph the profit function.

(b) Use the graph from part (a) to estimate another amount the company could have spent on advertising that would have produced the same profit.

(c) Use synthetic division to confirm the result of part (b) algebraically.

• • 86. Data Analysis: Lyme Disease • • • • • • • •

The numbers N of confirmed cases of Lyme disease in Maine from 2003 to 2010 are shown in the table, where t represents the year, with $t = 3$ corresponding to 2003. (*Source: Centers for Disease Control and Prevention*)

DATA	Year, t	Number, N
	3	175
	4	225
	5	247
	6	338
	7	529
	8	780
	9	791
	10	559

Spreadsheet at LarsonPrecalculus.com

(a) Use a graphing utility to create a scatter plot of the data.

(b) Use the *regression* feature of the graphing utility to find a quartic model for the data. Graph the model in the same viewing window as the scatter plot.

(c) Use the model to create a table of estimated values of N. Compare the model with the original data.

(d) Use synthetic division to confirm algebraically your estimated value for the year 2010.

Exploration

True or False? **In Exercises 87–90, determine whether the statement is true or false. Justify your answer.**

87. If $(7x + 4)$ is a factor of some polynomial function $f(x)$, then $\frac{4}{7}$ is a zero of f.

88. $(2x - 1)$ is a factor of the polynomial
$$6x^6 + x^5 - 92x^4 + 45x^3 + 184x^2 + 4x - 48.$$

89. The rational expression
$$\frac{x^3 + 2x^2 - 13x + 10}{x^2 - 4x - 12}$$
is improper.

90. The equation
$$\frac{x^3 - 3x^2 + 4}{x + 1} = x^2 - 4x + 4$$
is true for all values of x.

Think About It **In Exercises 91 and 92, perform the division by assuming that n is a positive integer.**

91. $\dfrac{x^{3n} + 9x^{2n} + 27x^n + 27}{x^n + 3}$

92. $\dfrac{x^{3n} - 3x^{2n} + 5x^n - 6}{x^n - 2}$

93. **Writing** Briefly explain what it means for a divisor to divide evenly into a dividend.

94. **Writing** Briefly explain how to check polynomial division, and justify your reasoning. Give an example.

Exploration **In Exercises 95 and 96, find the constant c such that the denominator will divide evenly into the numerator.**

95. $\dfrac{x^3 + 4x^2 - 3x + c}{x - 5}$ 96. $\dfrac{x^5 - 2x^2 + x + c}{x + 2}$

97. **Think About It** Find the value of k such that $x - 4$ is a factor of $x^3 - kx^2 + 2kx - 8$.

98. **HOW DO YOU SEE IT?** The graph below shows a company's estimated profits for different advertising expenses. The company's actual profit was \$936,660 for an advertising expense of \$300,000.

(a) From the graph, it appears that the company could have obtained the same profit for a lesser advertising expense. Use the graph to estimate this expense.

(b) The company's model is
$$P = -140.75x^3 + 5348.3x^2 - 76,560,$$
$$0 \le x \le 35$$
where P is the profit (in dollars) and x is the advertising expense (in tens of thousands of dollars). Explain how you could verify the lesser expense from part (a) algebraically.

2.4 Complex Numbers

You can use complex numbers to model and solve real-life problems in electronics. For instance, in Exercise 91 on page 153, you will use complex numbers to find the impedance of an electrical circuit.

- Use the imaginary unit *i* to write complex numbers.
- Add, subtract, and multiply complex numbers.
- Use complex conjugates to write the quotient of two complex numbers in standard form.
- Find complex solutions of quadratic equations.

The Imaginary Unit *i*

You have learned that some quadratic equations have no real solutions. For instance, the quadratic equation

$$x^2 + 1 = 0$$

has no real solution because there is no real number x that can be squared to produce -1. To overcome this deficiency, mathematicians created an expanded system of numbers using the **imaginary unit *i*,** defined as

$$i = \sqrt{-1} \qquad \text{Imaginary unit}$$

where $i^2 = -1$. By adding real numbers to real multiples of this imaginary unit, the set of **complex numbers** is obtained. Each complex number can be written in the **standard form $a + bi$.** For instance, the standard form of the complex number $-5 + \sqrt{-9}$ is $-5 + 3i$ because

$$-5 + \sqrt{-9} = -5 + \sqrt{3^2(-1)} = -5 + 3\sqrt{-1} = -5 + 3i.$$

Definition of a Complex Number

Let a and b be real numbers. The number $a + bi$ is called a **complex number,** and it is said to be written in **standard form.** The real number a is called the **real part** and the real number b is called the **imaginary part** of the complex number.

When $b = 0$, the number $a + bi$ is a real number. When $b \neq 0$, the number $a + bi$ is called an **imaginary number.** A number of the form bi, where $b \neq 0$, is called a **pure imaginary number.**

The set of real numbers is a subset of the set of complex numbers, as shown below. This is true because every real number a can be written as a complex number using $b = 0$. That is, for every real number a, you can write $a = a + 0i$.

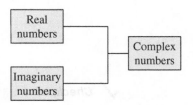

Equality of Complex Numbers

Two complex numbers $a + bi$ and $c + di$, written in standard form, are equal to each other

$$a + bi = c + di \qquad \text{Equality of two complex numbers}$$

if and only if $a = c$ and $b = d$.

Operations with Complex Numbers

To add (or subtract) two complex numbers, you add (or subtract) the real and imaginary parts of the numbers separately.

Addition and Subtraction of Complex Numbers

For two complex numbers $a + bi$ and $c + di$ written in standard form, the sum and difference are defined as follows.

Sum: $(a + bi) + (c + di) = (a + c) + (b + d)i$

Difference: $(a + bi) - (c + di) = (a - c) + (b - d)i$

The **additive identity** in the complex number system is zero (the same as in the real number system). Furthermore, the **additive inverse** of the complex number $a + bi$ is

$$-(a + bi) = -a - bi. \qquad \text{Additive inverse}$$

So, you have

$$(a + bi) + (-a - bi) = 0 + 0i = 0.$$

EXAMPLE 1 **Adding and Subtracting Complex Numbers**

a. $(4 + 7i) + (1 - 6i) = 4 + 7i + 1 - 6i$ Remove parentheses.

$$= (4 + 1) + (7 - 6)i \qquad \text{Group like terms.}$$

$$= 5 + i \qquad \text{Write in standard form.}$$

b. $(1 + 2i) + (3 - 2i) = 1 + 2i + 3 - 2i$ Remove parentheses.

$$= (1 + 3) + (2 - 2)i \qquad \text{Group like terms.}$$

$$= 4 + 0i \qquad \text{Simplify.}$$

$$= 4 \qquad \text{Write in standard form.}$$

> **• • REMARK** Note that the sum of two complex numbers can be a real number.

c. $3i - (-2 + 3i) - (2 + 5i) = 3i + 2 - 3i - 2 - 5i$

$$= (2 - 2) + (3 - 3 - 5)i$$

$$= 0 - 5i$$

$$= -5i$$

d. $(3 + 2i) + (4 - i) - (7 + i) = 3 + 2i + 4 - i - 7 - i$

$$= (3 + 4 - 7) + (2 - 1 - 1)i$$

$$= 0 + 0i$$

$$= 0$$

✓ *Checkpoint* ◄))) *Audio-video solution in English & Spanish at LarsonPrecalculus.com.*

Perform each operation and write the result in standard form.

a. $(7 + 3i) + (5 - 4i)$

b. $(3 + 4i) - (5 - 3i)$

c. $2i + (-3 - 4i) - (-3 - 3i)$

d. $(5 - 3i) + (3 + 5i) - (8 + 2i)$

Many of the properties of real numbers are valid for complex numbers as well. Here are some examples.

Associative Properties of Addition and Multiplication

Commutative Properties of Addition and Multiplication

Distributive Property of Multiplication Over Addition

Notice below how these properties are used when two complex numbers are multiplied.

$$(a + bi)(c + di) = a(c + di) + bi(c + di) \qquad \text{Distributive Property}$$

$$= ac + (ad)i + (bc)i + (bd)i^2 \qquad \text{Distributive Property}$$

$$= ac + (ad)i + (bc)i + (bd)(-1) \qquad i^2 = -1$$

$$= ac - bd + (ad)i + (bc)i \qquad \text{Commutative Property}$$

$$= (ac - bd) + (ad + bc)i \qquad \text{Associative Property}$$

Rather than trying to memorize this multiplication rule, you should simply remember how to use the Distributive Property to multiply two complex numbers.

EXAMPLE 2 **Multiplying Complex Numbers**

a. $4(-2 + 3i) = 4(-2) + 4(3i)$ Distributive Property

$= -8 + 12i$ Simplify.

b. $(2 - i)(4 + 3i) = 2(4 + 3i) - i(4 + 3i)$ Distributive Property

$= 8 + 6i - 4i - 3i^2$ Distributive Property

$= 8 + 6i - 4i - 3(-1)$ $i^2 = -1$

$= (8 + 3) + (6 - 4)i$ Group like terms.

$= 11 + 2i$ Write in standard form.

c. $(3 + 2i)(3 - 2i) = 3(3 - 2i) + 2i(3 - 2i)$ Distributive Property

$= 9 - 6i + 6i - 4i^2$ Distributive Property

$= 9 - 6i + 6i - 4(-1)$ $i^2 = -1$

$= 9 + 4$ Simplify.

$= 13$ Write in standard form.

d. $(3 + 2i)^2 = (3 + 2i)(3 + 2i)$ Square of a binomial

$= 3(3 + 2i) + 2i(3 + 2i)$ Distributive Property

$= 9 + 6i + 6i + 4i^2$ Distributive Property

$= 9 + 6i + 6i + 4(-1)$ $i^2 = -1$

$= 9 + 12i - 4$ Simplify.

$= 5 + 12i$ Write in standard form.

REMARK The procedure described above is similar to multiplying two binomials and combining like terms, as in the FOIL Method shown in Appendix A.3. For instance, you can use the FOIL Method to multiply the two complex numbers from Example 2(b).

$$\overset{\text{F} \quad \text{O} \quad \text{I} \quad \text{L}}{(2 - i)(4 + 3i) = 8 + 6i - 4i - 3i^2}$$

✓ *Checkpoint* ◀))) Audio-video solution in English & Spanish at LarsonPrecalculus.com.

Perform each operation and write the result in standard form.

a. $(2 - 4i)(3 + 3i)$

b. $(4 + 5i)(4 - 5i)$

c. $(4 + 2i)^2$

Complex Conjugates

▷ **ALGEBRA HELP**   You can
compare complex conjugates
with the method for rationalizing
denominators in Appendix A.2.

Notice in Example 2(c) that the product of two complex numbers can be a real number. This occurs with pairs of complex numbers of the form $a + bi$ and $a - bi$, called **complex conjugates.**

$$(a + bi)(a - bi) = a^2 - abi + abi - b^2i^2$$
$$= a^2 - b^2(-1)$$
$$= a^2 + b^2$$

EXAMPLE 3   **Multiplying Conjugates**

Multiply each complex number by its complex conjugate.

a. $1 + i$ **b.** $4 - 3i$

Solution

a. The complex conjugate of $1 + i$ is $1 - i$.

$$(1 + i)(1 - i) = 1^2 - i^2 = 1 - (-1) = 2$$

b. The complex conjugate of $4 - 3i$ is $4 + 3i$.

$$(4 - 3i)(4 + 3i) = 4^2 - (3i)^2 = 16 - 9i^2 = 16 - 9(-1) = 25$$

✓ *Checkpoint* ◀))) *Audio-video solution in English & Spanish at LarsonPrecalculus.com.*

Multiply each complex number by its complex conjugate.

a. $3 + 6i$

b. $2 - 5i$

To write the quotient of $a + bi$ and $c + di$ in standard form, where c and d are not both zero, multiply the numerator and denominator by the complex conjugate of the *denominator* to obtain

$$\frac{a + bi}{c + di} = \frac{a + bi}{c + di}\left(\frac{c - di}{c - di}\right) = \frac{(ac + bd) + (bc - ad)i}{c^2 + d^2}.$$

▷
··REMARK
Note that when you multiply the
numerator and denominator of a
quotient of complex numbers by

$$\frac{c - di}{c - di}$$

you are actually multiplying
the quotient by a form of 1.
You are not changing the
original expression, you are
only creating an expression
that is equivalent to the
original expression.

EXAMPLE 4   **Quotient of Complex Numbers in Standard Form**

$$\frac{2 + 3i}{4 - 2i} = \frac{2 + 3i}{4 - 2i}\left(\frac{4 + 2i}{4 + 2i}\right)$$ Multiply numerator and denominator by complex conjugate of denominator.

$$= \frac{8 + 4i + 12i + 6i^2}{16 - 4i^2}$$ Expand.

$$= \frac{8 - 6 + 16i}{16 + 4}$$ $i^2 = -1$

$$= \frac{2 + 16i}{20}$$ Simplify.

$$= \frac{1}{10} + \frac{4}{5}i$$ Write in standard form.

✓ *Checkpoint* ◀))) *Audio-video solution in English & Spanish at LarsonPrecalculus.com.*

Write $\dfrac{2 + i}{2 - i}$ in standard form.

Complex Solutions of Quadratic Equations

You can write a number such as $\sqrt{-3}$ in standard form by factoring out $i = \sqrt{-1}$.

$$\sqrt{-3} = \sqrt{3(-1)} = \sqrt{3}\sqrt{-1} = \sqrt{3}\,i$$

The number $\sqrt{3}\,i$ is called the *principal square root* of -3.

- - - - - - - - - - - - - - - ▷

·· REMARK
The definition of principal square root uses the rule

$$\sqrt{ab} = \sqrt{a}\sqrt{b}$$

for $a > 0$ and $b < 0$. This rule is not valid if *both* a and b are negative. For example,

$$\sqrt{-5}\sqrt{-5} = \sqrt{5(-1)}\sqrt{5(-1)}$$
$$= \sqrt{5}\,i\sqrt{5}\,i$$
$$= \sqrt{25}\,i^2$$
$$= 5i^2$$
$$= -5$$

whereas

$$\sqrt{(-5)(-5)} = \sqrt{25} = 5.$$

To avoid problems with square roots of negative numbers, be sure to convert complex numbers to standard form *before* multiplying.

▷ **ALGEBRA HELP** You can review the techniques for using the Quadratic Formula in Appendix A.5.

Principal Square Root of a Negative Number

When a is a positive real number, the **principal square root** of $-a$ is defined as

$$\sqrt{-a} = \sqrt{a}\,i.$$

EXAMPLE 5 **Writing Complex Numbers in Standard Form**

a. $\sqrt{-3}\sqrt{-12} = \sqrt{3}\,i\sqrt{12}\,i = \sqrt{36}\,i^2 = 6(-1) = -6$

b. $\sqrt{-48} - \sqrt{-27} = \sqrt{48}\,i - \sqrt{27}\,i = 4\sqrt{3}\,i - 3\sqrt{3}\,i = \sqrt{3}\,i$

c. $\left(-1 + \sqrt{-3}\right)^2 = \left(-1 + \sqrt{3}\,i\right)^2 = (-1)^2 - 2\sqrt{3}\,i + \left(\sqrt{3}\right)^2(i^2)$
$$= 1 - 2\sqrt{3}\,i + 3(-1)$$
$$= -2 - 2\sqrt{3}\,i$$

✓ *Checkpoint* *Audio-video solution in English & Spanish at LarsonPrecalculus.com.*

Write $\sqrt{-14}\sqrt{-2}$ in standard form.

EXAMPLE 6 **Complex Solutions of a Quadratic Equation**

Solve $3x^2 - 2x + 5 = 0$.

Solution

$$x = \frac{-(-2) \pm \sqrt{(-2)^2 - 4(3)(5)}}{2(3)} \qquad \text{Quadratic Formula}$$

$$= \frac{2 \pm \sqrt{-56}}{6} \qquad \text{Simplify.}$$

$$= \frac{2 \pm 2\sqrt{14}\,i}{6} \qquad \text{Write } \sqrt{-56} \text{ in standard form.}$$

$$= \frac{1}{3} \pm \frac{\sqrt{14}}{3}i \qquad \text{Write in standard form.}$$

✓ *Checkpoint*))) *Audio-video solution in English & Spanish at LarsonPrecalculus.com.*

Solve $8x^2 + 14x + 9 = 0$.

Summarize (Section 2.4)

1. Describe how to write complex numbers using the imaginary unit i *(page 147)*.

2. Describe how to add, subtract, and multiply complex numbers *(pages 148 and 149, Examples 1 and 2)*.

3. Describe how to use complex conjugates to write the quotient of two complex numbers in standard form *(page 150, Example 4)*.

4. Describe how to find complex solutions of a quadratic equation *(page 151, Example 6)*.

2.4 Exercises

See **CalcChat.com** for tutorial help and worked-out solutions to odd-numbered exercises.

Vocabulary: **Fill in the blanks.**

1. A _____ number has the form $a + bi$, where $a \neq 0$, $b = 0$.
2. An _____ number has the form $a + bi$, where $a \neq 0$, $b \neq 0$.
3. A _____ _____ number has the form $a + bi$, where $a = 0$, $b \neq 0$.
4. The imaginary unit i is defined as $i =$ _____, where $i^2 =$ _____.
5. When a is a positive real number, the _____ _____ root of $-a$ is defined as $\sqrt{-a} = \sqrt{a}\,i$.
6. The numbers $a + bi$ and $a - bi$ are called _____ _____, and their product is a real number $a^2 + b^2$.

Skills and Applications

Equality of Complex Numbers **In Exercises 7–10, find real numbers a and b such that the equation is true.**

7. $a + bi = -12 + 7i$
8. $a + bi = 13 + 4i$
9. $(a - 1) + (b + 3)i = 5 + 8i$
10. $(a + 6) + 2bi = 6 - 5i$

Writing a Complex Number in Standard Form
In Exercises 11–22, write the complex number in standard form.

11. $8 + \sqrt{-25}$
12. $5 + \sqrt{-36}$
13. $2 - \sqrt{-27}$
14. $1 + \sqrt{-8}$
15. $\sqrt{-80}$
16. $\sqrt{-4}$
17. 14
18. 75
19. $-10i + i^2$
20. $-4i^2 + 2i$
21. $\sqrt{-0.09}$
22. $\sqrt{-0.0049}$

Performing Operations with Complex Numbers
In Exercises 23–42, perform the operation and write the result in standard form.

23. $(7 + i) + (3 - 4i)$
24. $(13 - 2i) + (-5 + 6i)$
25. $(9 - i) - (8 - i)$
26. $(3 + 2i) - (6 + 13i)$
27. $\left(-2 + \sqrt{-8}\right) + \left(5 - \sqrt{-50}\right)$
28. $\left(8 + \sqrt{-18}\right) - \left(4 + 3\sqrt{2}\,i\right)$
29. $13i - (14 - 7i)$
30. $25 + (-10 + 11i) + 15i$
31. $-\left(\frac{3}{2} + \frac{5}{2}i\right) + \left(\frac{5}{3} + \frac{11}{3}i\right)$
32. $(1.6 + 3.2i) + (-5.8 + 4.3i)$
33. $(1 + i)(3 - 2i)$
34. $(7 - 2i)(3 - 5i)$
35. $12i(1 - 9i)$
36. $-8i(9 + 4i)$
37. $\left(\sqrt{14} + \sqrt{10}\,i\right)\left(\sqrt{14} - \sqrt{10}\,i\right)$
38. $\left(\sqrt{3} + \sqrt{15}\,i\right)\left(\sqrt{3} - \sqrt{15}\,i\right)$
39. $(6 + 7i)^2$
40. $(5 - 4i)^2$
41. $(2 + 3i)^2 + (2 - 3i)^2$
42. $(1 - 2i)^2 - (1 + 2i)^2$

Multiplying Conjugates **In Exercises 43–50, write the complex conjugate of the complex number. Then multiply the number by its complex conjugate.**

43. $9 + 2i$
44. $8 - 10i$
45. $-1 - \sqrt{5}\,i$
46. $-3 + \sqrt{2}\,i$
47. $\sqrt{-20}$
48. $\sqrt{-15}$
49. $\sqrt{6}$
50. $1 + \sqrt{8}$

Quotient of Complex Numbers in Standard Form **In Exercises 51–60, write the quotient in standard form.**

51. $\dfrac{3}{i}$
52. $-\dfrac{14}{2i}$
53. $\dfrac{2}{4 - 5i}$
54. $\dfrac{13}{1 - i}$
55. $\dfrac{5 + i}{5 - i}$
56. $\dfrac{6 - 7i}{1 - 2i}$
57. $\dfrac{9 - 4i}{i}$
58. $\dfrac{8 + 16i}{2i}$
59. $\dfrac{3i}{(4 - 5i)^2}$
60. $\dfrac{5i}{(2 + 3i)^2}$

Performing Operations with Complex Numbers
In Exercises 61–64, perform the operation and write the result in standard form.

61. $\dfrac{2}{1 + i} - \dfrac{3}{1 - i}$
62. $\dfrac{2i}{2 + i} + \dfrac{5}{2 - i}$
63. $\dfrac{i}{3 - 2i} + \dfrac{2i}{3 + 8i}$
64. $\dfrac{1 + i}{i} - \dfrac{3}{4 - i}$

Writing a Complex Number in Standard Form
In Exercises 65–70, write the complex number in standard form.

65. $\sqrt{-6} \cdot \sqrt{-2}$
66. $\sqrt{-5} \cdot \sqrt{-10}$
67. $\left(\sqrt{-15}\right)^2$
68. $\left(\sqrt{-75}\right)^2$
69. $\left(3 + \sqrt{-5}\right)\left(7 - \sqrt{-10}\right)$
70. $\left(2 - \sqrt{-6}\right)^2$

Complex Solutions of a Quadratic Equation In Exercises 71–80, use the Quadratic Formula to solve the quadratic equation.

71. $x^2 - 2x + 2 = 0$ 72. $x^2 + 6x + 10 = 0$

73. $4x^2 + 16x + 17 = 0$ 74. $9x^2 - 6x + 37 = 0$

75. $4x^2 + 16x + 15 = 0$ 76. $16t^2 - 4t + 3 = 0$

77. $\frac{3}{2}x^2 - 6x + 9 = 0$ 78. $\frac{7}{8}x^2 - \frac{3}{4}x + \frac{5}{16} = 0$

79. $1.4x^2 - 2x - 10 = 0$ 80. $4.5x^2 - 3x + 12 = 0$

Simplifying a Complex Number In Exercises 81–90, simplify the complex number and write it in standard form.

81. $-6i^3 + i^2$ 82. $4i^2 - 2i^3$

83. $-14i^5$ 84. $(-i)^3$

85. $\left(\sqrt{-72}\right)^3$ 86. $\left(\sqrt{-2}\right)^6$

87. $\dfrac{1}{i^3}$ 88. $\dfrac{1}{(2i)^3}$

89. $(3i)^4$ 90. $(-i)^6$

• • **91. Impedance** • • • • • • • • • • • • • • • • • • •

The opposition to current in an electrical circuit is called its impedance. The impedance z in a parallel circuit with two pathways satisfies the equation

$$\frac{1}{z} = \frac{1}{z_1} + \frac{1}{z_2}$$

where z_1 is the impedance (in ohms) of pathway 1 and z_2 is the impedance of pathway 2.

(a) The impedance of each pathway in a parallel circuit is found by adding the impedances of all components in the pathway. Use the table to find z_1 and z_2.

(b) Find the impedance z.

	Resistor	Inductor	Capacitor
Symbol	─\/\/\─ $a\ \Omega$	─◯◯◯─ $b\ \Omega$	─┤├─ $c\ \Omega$
Impedance	a	bi	$-ci$

92. **Cube of a Complex Number** Cube each complex number.

  (a) $-1 + \sqrt{3}i$ (b) $-1 - \sqrt{3}i$

Exploration

True or False? In Exercises 93–96, determine whether the statement is true or false. Justify your answer.

93. There is no complex number that is equal to its complex conjugate.

94. $-i\sqrt{6}$ is a solution of $x^4 - x^2 + 14 = 56$.

95. $i^{44} + i^{150} - i^{74} - i^{109} + i^{61} = -1$

96. The sum of two complex numbers is always a real number.

97. **Pattern Recognition** Complete the following.

$i^1 = i$ $i^2 = -1$ $i^3 = -i$ $i^4 = 1$

$i^5 = \rule{1cm}{0.15cm}$ $i^6 = \rule{1cm}{0.15cm}$ $i^7 = \rule{1cm}{0.15cm}$ $i^8 = \rule{1cm}{0.15cm}$

$i^9 = \rule{1cm}{0.15cm}$ $i^{10} = \rule{1cm}{0.15cm}$ $i^{11} = \rule{1cm}{0.15cm}$ $i^{12} = \rule{1cm}{0.15cm}$

What pattern do you see? Write a brief description of how you would find i raised to any positive integer power.

 98. **HOW DO YOU SEE IT?** The coordinate system shown below is called the *complex plane*. In the complex plane, the point that corresponds to the complex number $a + bi$ is (a, b).

Match each complex number with its corresponding point.

  (i) 3   (ii) $3i$ (iii) $4 + 2i$

  (iv) $2 - 2i$ (v) $-3 + 3i$ (vi) $-1 - 4i$

99. **Error Analysis** Describe the error.

  $\sqrt{-6}\sqrt{-6} = \sqrt{(-6)(-6)} = \sqrt{36} = 6$

100. **Proof** Prove that the complex conjugate of the product of two complex numbers $a_1 + b_1i$ and $a_2 + b_2i$ is the product of their complex conjugates.

101. **Proof** Prove that the complex conjugate of the sum of two complex numbers $a_1 + b_1i$ and $a_2 + b_2i$ is the sum of their complex conjugates.

2.5 Zeros of Polynomial Functions

■ Use the Fundamental Theorem of Algebra to determine the number of zeros of polynomial functions.
■ Find rational zeros of polynomial functions.
■ Find conjugate pairs of complex zeros.
■ Find zeros of polynomials by factoring.
■ Use Descartes's Rule of Signs and the Upper and Lower Bound Rules to find zeros of polynomials.
■ Find zeros of polynomials in real-life applications.

The Fundamental Theorem of Algebra

In the complex number system, every nth-degree polynomial function has *precisely n* zeros. This important result is derived from the **Fundamental Theorem of Algebra,** first proved by the German mathematician Carl Friedrich Gauss (1777–1855).

> **The Fundamental Theorem of Algebra**
>
> If $f(x)$ is a polynomial of degree n, where $n > 0$, then f has at least one zero in the complex number system.

Finding zeros of polynomial functions is an important part of solving real-life problems. For instance, in Exercise 113 on page 166, the zeros of a polynomial function can help you redesign a storage bin so that it can hold five times as much food.

Using the Fundamental Theorem of Algebra and the equivalence of zeros and factors, you obtain the **Linear Factorization Theorem.**

> **Linear Factorization Theorem**
>
> If $f(x)$ is a polynomial of degree n, where $n > 0$, then $f(x)$ has precisely n linear factors
>
> $$f(x) = a_n(x - c_1)(x - c_2) \cdots (x - c_n)$$
>
> where $c_1, c_2, \ldots, c_n$ are complex numbers.

For a proof of the Linear Factorization Theorem, see Proofs in Mathematics on page 196.

Note that the Fundamental Theorem of Algebra and the Linear Factorization Theorem tell you only that the zeros or factors of a polynomial exist, not how to find them. Such theorems are called **existence theorems.**

•• **REMARK** Recall that in order to find the zeros of a function f, set $f(x)$ equal to 0 and solve the resulting equation for x. For instance, the function in Example 1(a) has a zero at $x = 2$ because

$$x - 2 = 0$$

$$x = 2.$$

EXAMPLE 1 Zeros of Polynomial Functions

a. The first-degree polynomial function $f(x) = x - 2$ has exactly *one* zero: $x = 2$.

b. Counting multiplicity, the second-degree polynomial function

$$f(x) = x^2 - 6x + 9 = (x - 3)(x - 3)$$

has exactly *two* zeros: $x = 3$ and $x = 3$. (This is called a *repeated zero.*)

c. The third-degree polynomial function

$$f(x) = x^3 + 4x = x(x^2 + 4) = x(x - 2i)(x + 2i)$$

has exactly *three* zeros: $x = 0$, $x = 2i$, and $x = -2i$.

▷ **ALGEBRA HELP** Examples 1(b) and 1(c) involve factoring polynomials. You can review the techniques for factoring polynomials in Appendix A.3.

✓ *Checkpoint* ◄))) *Audio-video solution in English & Spanish at LarsonPrecalculus.com.*

Determine the number of zeros of the polynomial function $f(x) = x^4 - 1$.

k45025/Shutterstock.com

The Rational Zero Test

The **Rational Zero Test** relates the possible rational zeros of a polynomial (having integer coefficients) to the leading coefficient and to the constant term of the polynomial.

> **The Rational Zero Test**
>
> If the polynomial $f(x) = a_n x^n + a_{n-1} x^{n-1} + \cdots + a_2 x^2 + a_1 x + a_0$ has *integer* coefficients, then every rational zero of f has the form
>
> $$\text{Rational zero} = \frac{p}{q}$$
>
> where p and q have no common factors other than 1, and
>
> p = a factor of the constant term a_0
>
> q = a factor of the leading coefficient a_n.

To use the Rational Zero Test, you should first list all rational numbers whose numerators are factors of the constant term and whose denominators are factors of the leading coefficient.

$$\text{Possible rational zeros} = \frac{\text{factors of constant term}}{\text{factors of leading coefficient}}$$

Having formed this list of *possible rational zeros,* use a trial-and-error method to determine which, if any, are actual zeros of the polynomial. Note that when the leading coefficient is 1, the possible rational zeros are simply the factors of the constant term.

Although they were not contemporaries, Jean Le Rond d'Alembert (1717–1783) worked independently of Carl Gauss in trying to prove the Fundamental Theorem of Algebra. His efforts were such that, in France, the Fundamental Theorem of Algebra is frequently known as the Theorem of d'Alembert.

EXAMPLE 2   **Rational Zero Test with Leading Coefficient of 1**

Find the rational zeros of

$$f(x) = x^3 + x + 1.$$

Solution   Because the leading coefficient is 1, the possible rational zeros are the factors of the constant term.

Possible rational zeros: 1 and -1

By testing these possible zeros, you can see that neither works.

$$f(1) = (1)^3 + 1 + 1$$
$$= 3$$
$$f(-1) = (-1)^3 + (-1) + 1$$
$$= -1$$

So, you can conclude that the given polynomial has *no* rational zeros. Note from the graph of f in Figure 2.17 that f does have one real zero between -1 and 0. However, by the Rational Zero Test, you know that this real zero is *not* a rational number.

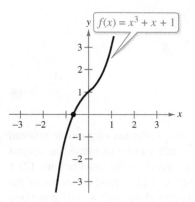

Figure 2.17

✓ *Checkpoint* ◄))) Audio-video solution in English & Spanish at LarsonPrecalculus.com.

Find the rational zeros of each function.

a. $f(x) = x^3 - 5x^2 + 2x + 8$

b. $f(x) = x^3 + 2x^2 + 6x - 4$

c. $f(x) = x^3 - 3x^2 + 2x - 6$

EXAMPLE 3 **Rational Zero Test with Leading Coefficient of 1**

Find the rational zeros of

$$f(x) = x^4 - x^3 + x^2 - 3x - 6.$$

Solution Because the leading coefficient is 1, the possible rational zeros are the factors of the constant term.

Possible rational zeros: $\pm 1, \pm 2, \pm 3, \pm 6$

By applying synthetic division successively, you can determine that $x = -1$ and $x = 2$ are the only two rational zeros.

$$
\begin{array}{r|rrrrr}
-1 & 1 & -1 & 1 & -3 & -6 \\
   &   & -1 & 2 & -3 & 6 \\
\hline
   & 1 & -2 & 3 & -6 & 0 \\
\end{array}
$$
$\longrightarrow$ 0 remainder, so $x = -1$ is a zero.

$$
\begin{array}{r|rrrr}
2 & 1 & -2 & 3 & -6 \\
  &   & 2 & 0 & 6 \\
\hline
  & 1 & 0 & 3 & 0 \\
\end{array}
$$
$\longrightarrow$ 0 remainder, so $x = 2$ is a zero.

So, $f(x)$ factors as

$$f(x) = (x + 1)(x - 2)(x^2 + 3).$$

Because the factor $(x^2 + 3)$ produces no real zeros, you can conclude that $x = -1$ and $x = 2$ are the only *real* zeros of f, which is verified in the figure below.

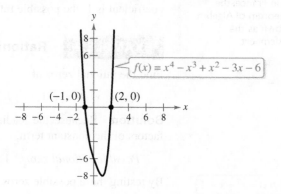

$$f(x) = x^4 - x^3 + x^2 - 3x - 6$$

$(-1, 0)$ $(2, 0)$

✓ *Checkpoint* ◀))) Audio-video solution in English & Spanish at LarsonPrecalculus.com.

Find the rational zeros of

$$f(x) = x^3 - 15x^2 + 75x - 125.$$

When the leading coefficient of a polynomial is not 1, the list of possible rational zeros can increase dramatically. In such cases, the search can be shortened in several ways: (1) a programmable calculator can be used to speed up the calculations; (2) a graph, drawn either by hand or with a graphing utility, can give good estimates of the locations of the zeros; (3) the Intermediate Value Theorem along with a table generated by a graphing utility can give approximations of the zeros; and (4) synthetic division can be used to test the possible rational zeros.

Finding the first zero is often the most difficult part. After that, the search is simplified by working with the lower-degree polynomial obtained in synthetic division, as shown in Example 3.

REMARK When the list of possible rational zeros is small, as in Example 2, it may be quicker to test the zeros by evaluating the function. When the list of possible rational zeros is large, as in Example 3, it may be quicker to use a different approach to test the zeros, such as using synthetic division or sketching a graph.

EXAMPLE 4   **Using the Rational Zero Test**

Find the rational zeros of $f(x) = 2x^3 + 3x^2 - 8x + 3$.

Solution   The leading coefficient is 2 and the constant term is 3.

$$\text{Possible rational zeros: } \frac{\text{Factors of 3}}{\text{Factors of 2}} = \frac{\pm 1, \pm 3}{\pm 1, \pm 2} = \pm 1, \pm 3, \pm\frac{1}{2}, \pm\frac{3}{2}$$

By synthetic division, you can determine that $x = 1$ is a rational zero.

$$
\begin{array}{r|rrrr}
1 & 2 & 3 & -8 & 3 \\
  &   & 2 & 5 & -3 \\
\hline
  & 2 & 5 & -3 & 0
\end{array}
$$

So, $f(x)$ factors as

$$f(x) = (x - 1)(2x^2 + 5x - 3)$$
$$= (x - 1)(2x - 1)(x + 3)$$

and you can conclude that the rational zeros of f are $x = 1$, $x = \frac{1}{2}$, and $x = -3$.

✓ *Checkpoint* *Audio-video solution in English & Spanish at LarsonPrecalculus.com.*

Find the rational zeros of

$$f(x) = 2x^4 - 9x^3 - 18x^2 + 71x - 30.$$

> **REMARK**   Remember that when you try to find the rational zeros of a polynomial function with many possible rational zeros, as in Example 4, you must use trial and error. There is no quick algebraic method to determine which of the possibilities is an actual zero; however, sketching a graph may be helpful.

Recall from Section 2.2 that if $x = a$ is a zero of the polynomial function f, then $x = a$ is a solution of the polynomial equation $f(x) = 0$.

EXAMPLE 5   **Solving a Polynomial Equation**

Find all real solutions of $-10x^3 + 15x^2 + 16x - 12 = 0$.

Solution   The leading coefficient is -10 and the constant term is -12.

$$\text{Possible rational solutions: } \frac{\text{Factors of } -12}{\text{Factors of } -10} = \frac{\pm 1, \pm 2, \pm 3, \pm 4, \pm 6, \pm 12}{\pm 1, \pm 2, \pm 5, \pm 10}$$

With so many possibilities (32, in fact), it is worth your time to stop and sketch a graph. From Figure 2.18, it looks like three reasonable solutions would be $x = -\frac{6}{5}$, $x = \frac{1}{2}$, and $x = 2$. Testing these by synthetic division shows that $x = 2$ is the only rational solution. So, you have

$$(x - 2)(-10x^2 - 5x + 6) = 0.$$

Using the Quadratic Formula for the second factor, you find that the two additional solutions are irrational numbers.

$$x = \frac{-5 - \sqrt{265}}{20} \approx -1.0639$$

and

$$x = \frac{-5 + \sqrt{265}}{20} \approx 0.5639$$

Figure 2.18

$f(x) = -10x^3 + 15x^2 + 16x - 12$

✓ *Checkpoint* 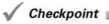 *Audio-video solution in English & Spanish at LarsonPrecalculus.com.*

Find all real solutions of

$$x^3 + 4x^2 - 15x - 18 = 0.$$

> ▷ **ALGEBRA HELP**   You can review the techniques for using the Quadratic Formula in Appendix A.5.

Conjugate Pairs

In Example 1(c), note that the pair of complex zeros are conjugates. That is, they are of the form

$$a + bi$$

and

$$a - bi.$$

Complex Zeros Occur in Conjugate Pairs

Let f be a polynomial function that has *real coefficients*. If $a + bi$, where $b \neq 0$, is a zero of the function, then the conjugate $a - bi$ is also a zero of the function.

Be sure you see that this result is true only when the polynomial function has *real coefficients*. For instance, the result applies to the function

$$f(x) = x^2 + 1$$

but not to the function

$$g(x) = x - i.$$

EXAMPLE 6   **Finding a Polynomial Function with Given Zeros**

Find a fourth-degree polynomial function with real coefficients that has

$$-1, \quad -1, \quad \text{and} \quad 3i$$

as zeros.

Solution   Because $3i$ is a zero *and* the polynomial is stated to have real coefficients, you know that the conjugate $-3i$ must also be a zero. So, the four zeros are

$$-1, \quad -1, \quad 3i, \quad \text{and} \quad -3i.$$

Then, using the Linear Factorization Theorem, $f(x)$ can be written as

$$f(x) = a(x + 1)(x + 1)(x - 3i)(x + 3i).$$

For simplicity, let $a = 1$. Then multiply the factors with real coefficients to obtain

$$(x + 1)(x + 1) = x^2 + 2x + 1$$

and multiply the complex conjugates to obtain

$$(x - 3i)(x + 3i) = x^2 + 9.$$

So, you obtain the following fourth-degree polynomial function.

$$f(x) = (x^2 + 2x + 1)(x^2 + 9)$$

$$= x^4 + 2x^3 + 10x^2 + 18x + 9$$

✓ *Checkpoint* ◄))) *Audio-video solution in English & Spanish at LarsonPrecalculus.com.*

Find a fourth-degree polynomial function with real coefficients that has the given zeros.

a. $2, -2,$ and $-7i$

b. $1, 3,$ and $4 - i$

c. $-1, 2,$ and $3 + i$

Factoring a Polynomial

The Linear Factorization Theorem shows that you can write any nth-degree polynomial as the product of n linear factors.

$$f(x) = a_n(x - c_1)(x - c_2)(x - c_3) \cdots (x - c_n)$$

However, this result includes the possibility that some of the values of c_i are complex. The following theorem says that even if you do not want to get involved with "complex factors," you can still write $f(x)$ as the product of linear and/or quadratic factors. For a proof of this theorem, see Proofs in Mathematics on page 196.

Factors of a Polynomial

Every polynomial of degree $n > 0$ with real coefficients can be written as the product of linear and quadratic factors with real coefficients, where the quadratic factors have no real zeros.

A quadratic factor with no real zeros is said to be *prime* or **irreducible over the reals.** Note that this is not the same as being *irreducible over the rationals.* For example, the quadratic $x^2 + 1 = (x - i)(x + i)$ is irreducible over the reals (and therefore over the rationals). On the other hand, the quadratic $x^2 - 2 = \left(x - \sqrt{2}\right)\left(x + \sqrt{2}\right)$ is irreducible over the rationals but *reducible* over the reals.

▷ **TECHNOLOGY** In Example 7, you can use a graphing utility to graph the function, as shown below.

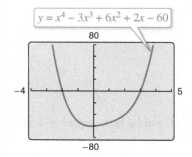

Then you can use the *zero* or *root* feature of the graphing utility to determine that $x = -2$ and $x = 3$ are zeros of the function.

| EXAMPLE 7 | **Finding the Zeros of a Polynomial Function** |

Find all the zeros of $f(x) = x^4 - 3x^3 + 6x^2 + 2x - 60$ given that $1 + 3i$ is a zero of f.

Solution Because complex zeros occur in conjugate pairs, you know that $1 - 3i$ is also a zero of f. This means that both $[x - (1 + 3i)]$ and $[x - (1 - 3i)]$ are factors of $f(x)$. Multiplying these two factors produces

$$[x - (1 + 3i)][x - (1 - 3i)] = [(x - 1) - 3i][(x - 1) + 3i]$$
$$= (x - 1)^2 - 9i^2$$
$$= x^2 - 2x + 10.$$

Using long division, you can divide $x^2 - 2x + 10$ into $f(x)$ to obtain the following.

$$
\begin{array}{r}
x^2 - x - 6 \\
x^2 - 2x + 10 \overline{)\, x^4 - 3x^3 + 6x^2 + 2x - 60} \\
\underline{x^4 - 2x^3 + 10x^2} \\
-x^3 - 4x^2 + 2x \\
\underline{-x^3 + 2x^2 - 10x} \\
-6x^2 + 12x - 60 \\
\underline{-6x^2 + 12x - 60} \\
0
\end{array}
$$

So, you have

$$f(x) = (x^2 - 2x + 10)(x^2 - x - 6) = (x^2 - 2x + 10)(x - 3)(x + 2)$$

and you can conclude that the zeros of f are $x = 1 + 3i$, $x = 1 - 3i$, $x = 3$, and $x = -2$.

✓ **Checkpoint** ◀))) *Audio-video solution in English & Spanish at LarsonPrecalculus.com.*

Find all the zeros of $f(x) = 3x^3 - 2x^2 + 48x - 32$ given that $4i$ is a zero of f. ∎

▷ **ALGEBRA HELP** You can review the techniques for polynomial long division in Section 2.3.

In Example 7, without being told that $1 + 3i$ is a zero of f, you could still find all the zeros of the function by using synthetic division to find the real zeros -2 and 3. Then you could factor the polynomial as

$$(x + 2)(x - 3)(x^2 - 2x + 10).$$

Finally, by using the Quadratic Formula, you could determine that the zeros are

$$x = -2, \quad x = 3, \quad x = 1 + 3i, \quad \text{and} \quad x = 1 - 3i.$$

Example 8 shows how to find all the zeros of a polynomial function, including complex zeros.

▷ TECHNOLOGY In Example 8, the fifth-degree polynomial function has three real zeros. In such cases, you can use the *zoom* and *trace* features or the *zero* or *root* feature of a graphing utility to approximate the real zeros. You can then use these real zeros to determine the complex zeros algebraically.

EXAMPLE 8   **Finding the Zeros of a Polynomial Function**

Write

$$f(x) = x^5 + x^3 + 2x^2 - 12x + 8$$

as the product of linear factors and list all the zeros of the function.

Solution   Because the leading coefficient is 1, the possible rational zeros are the factors of the constant term.

Possible rational zeros: $\pm 1, \pm 2, \pm 4,$ and ± 8

Synthetic division produces the following.

$$
\begin{array}{r|rrrrrr}
1 & 1 & 0 & 1 & 2 & -12 & 8 \\
  &   & 1 & 1 & 2 & 4 & -8 \\
\hline
  & 1 & 1 & 2 & 4 & -8 & 0 \quad \longrightarrow \; 1 \text{ is a zero.}
\end{array}
$$

$$
\begin{array}{r|rrrrr}
-2 & 1 & 1 & 2 & 4 & -8 \\
   &   & -2 & 2 & -8 & 8 \\
\hline
   & 1 & -1 & 4 & -4 & 0 \quad \longrightarrow \; -2 \text{ is a zero.}
\end{array}
$$

So, you have

$$f(x) = x^5 + x^3 + 2x^2 - 12x + 8$$
$$= (x - 1)(x + 2)(x^3 - x^2 + 4x - 4).$$

You can factor $x^3 - x^2 + 4x - 4$ as $(x - 1)(x^2 + 4)$, and by factoring $x^2 + 4$ as

$$x^2 - (-4) = \left(x - \sqrt{-4}\right)\left(x + \sqrt{-4}\right)$$
$$= (x - 2i)(x + 2i)$$

you obtain

$$f(x) = (x - 1)(x - 1)(x + 2)(x - 2i)(x + 2i)$$

which gives the following five zeros of f.

$$x = 1, \quad x = 1, \quad x = -2, \quad x = 2i, \quad \text{and} \quad x = -2i$$

From the graph of f shown in Figure 2.19, you can see that the *real* zeros are the only ones that appear as x-intercepts. Note that $x = 1$ is a repeated zero.

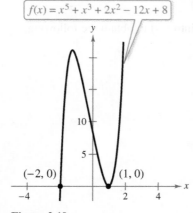

$f(x) = x^5 + x^3 + 2x^2 - 12x + 8$

$(-2, 0)$ $(1, 0)$

Figure 2.19

✓ *Checkpoint* ◀))) *Audio-video solution in English & Spanish at LarsonPrecalculus.com.*

Write each function as the product of linear factors and list all the zeros of the function.

a. $f(x) = x^4 + 8x^2 - 9$
b. $g(x) = x^3 - 3x^2 + 7x - 5$
c. $h(x) = x^3 - 11x^2 + 41x - 51$

Other Tests for Zeros of Polynomials

You know that an nth-degree polynomial function can have *at most* n real zeros. Of course, many nth-degree polynomials do not have that many real zeros. For instance, $f(x) = x^2 + 1$ has no real zeros, and $f(x) = x^3 + 1$ has only one real zero. The following theorem, called **Descartes's Rule of Signs,** sheds more light on the number of real zeros of a polynomial.

Descartes's Rule of Signs

Let $f(x) = a_n x^n + a_{n-1} x^{n-1} + \cdots + a_2 x^2 + a_1 x + a_0$ be a polynomial with real coefficients and $a_0 \neq 0$.

1. The number of *positive real zeros* of f is either equal to the number of variations in sign of $f(x)$ or less than that number by an even integer.

2. The number of *negative real zeros* of f is either equal to the number of variations in sign of $f(-x)$ or less than that number by an even integer.

A **variation in sign** means that two consecutive coefficients have opposite signs.

When using Descartes's Rule of Signs, a zero of multiplicity k should be counted as k zeros. For instance, the polynomial $x^3 - 3x + 2$ has two variations in sign, and so it has either two positive or no positive real zeros. Because

$$x^3 - 3x + 2 = (x - 1)(x - 1)(x + 2)$$

you can see that the two positive real zeros are $x = 1$ of multiplicity 2.

EXAMPLE 9 **Using Descartes's Rule of Signs**

Determine the possible numbers of positive and negative real zeros of

$$f(x) = 3x^3 - 5x^2 + 6x - 4.$$

Solution   The original polynomial has *three* variations in sign.

The polynomial

$$f(-x) = 3(-x)^3 - 5(-x)^2 + 6(-x) - 4$$
$$= -3x^3 - 5x^2 - 6x - 4$$

has no variations in sign. So, from Descartes's Rule of Signs, the polynomial

$$f(x) = 3x^3 - 5x^2 + 6x - 4$$

has either three positive real zeros or one positive real zero, and has no negative real zeros. From the graph in Figure 2.20, you can see that the function has only one real zero, $x = 1$.

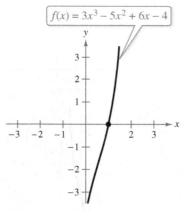

$f(x) = 3x^3 - 5x^2 + 6x - 4$

Figure 2.20

✓ *Checkpoint* Audio-video solution in English & Spanish at LarsonPrecalculus.com.

Determine the possible numbers of positive and negative real zeros of

$$f(x) = -2x^3 + 5x^2 - x + 8.$$

Another test for zeros of a polynomial function is related to the sign pattern in the last row of the synthetic division array. This test can give you an upper or lower bound for the real zeros of f. A real number c is an **upper bound** for the real zeros of f when no zeros are greater than c. Similarly, c is a **lower bound** when no real zeros of f are less than c.

Upper and Lower Bound Rules

Let $f(x)$ be a polynomial with real coefficients and a positive leading coefficient. Suppose $f(x)$ is divided by $x - c$, using synthetic division.

1. If $c > 0$ and each number in the last row is either positive or zero, then c is an **upper bound** for the real zeros of f.

2. If $c < 0$ and the numbers in the last row are alternately positive and negative (zero entries count as positive or negative), then c is a **lower bound** for the real zeros of f.

EXAMPLE 10   **Finding the Zeros of a Polynomial Function**

Find all real zeros of

$$f(x) = 6x^3 - 4x^2 + 3x - 2.$$

Solution   The possible real zeros are as follows.

$$\frac{\text{Factors of } -2}{\text{Factors of } 6} = \frac{\pm 1, \pm 2}{\pm 1, \pm 2, \pm 3, \pm 6} = \pm 1, \pm\frac{1}{2}, \pm\frac{1}{3}, \pm\frac{1}{6}, \pm\frac{2}{3}, \pm 2$$

The original polynomial $f(x)$ has three variations in sign. The polynomial

$$f(-x) = 6(-x)^3 - 4(-x)^2 + 3(-x) - 2$$
$$= -6x^3 - 4x^2 - 3x - 2$$

has no variations in sign. As a result of these two findings, you can apply Descartes's Rule of Signs to conclude that there are three positive real zeros or one positive real zero, and no negative real zeros. Trying $x = 1$ produces the following.

$$
\begin{array}{r|rrrr}
1 & 6 & -4 & 3 & -2 \\
  &   & 6 & 2 & 5 \\
\hline
  & 6 & 2 & 5 & 3
\end{array}
$$

So, $x = 1$ is not a zero, but because the last row has all positive entries, you know that $x = 1$ is an upper bound for the real zeros. So, you can restrict the search to zeros between 0 and 1. By trial and error, you can determine that $x = \frac{2}{3}$ is a zero. So,

$$f(x) = \left(x - \frac{2}{3}\right)(6x^2 + 3).$$

$f(x) = 6x^3 - 4x^2 + 3x - 2$

Because $6x^2 + 3$ has no real zeros, it follows that $x = \frac{2}{3}$ is the only real zero, as shown at the right.

✓ **Checkpoint** ◄))) *Audio-video solution in English & Spanish at LarsonPrecalculus.com.*

Find all real zeros of

$$f(x) = 8x^3 - 4x^2 + 6x - 3.$$

Application

According to the National Candle Association, 7 out of 10 U.S. households use candles.

EXAMPLE 11 **Using a Polynomial Model**

You are designing candle making kits. Each kit contains 25 cubic inches of candle wax and a mold for making a pyramid-shaped candle. You want the height of the candle to be 2 inches less than the length of each side of the candle's square base. What should the dimensions of your candle mold be?

Solution The volume of a pyramid is $V = \frac{1}{3}Bh$, where B is the area of the base and h is the height. The area of the base is x^2 and the height is $(x - 2)$. So, the volume of the pyramid is $V = \frac{1}{3}x^2(x - 2)$. Substituting 25 for the volume yields the following.

$$25 = \tfrac{1}{3}x^2(x - 2) \qquad \text{Substitute 25 for } V.$$

$$75 = x^3 - 2x^2 \qquad \text{Multiply each side by 3, and distribute } x^2.$$

$$0 = x^3 - 2x^2 - 75 \qquad \text{Write in general form.}$$

The possible rational solutions are $x = \pm 1, \pm 3, \pm 5, \pm 15, \pm 25, \pm 75$. Use synthetic division to test some of the possible solutions. Note that in this case it makes sense to test only positive x-values. Using synthetic division, you can determine that $x = 5$ is a solution.

$$
\begin{array}{r|rrrr}
5 & 1 & -2 & 0 & -75 \\
  &   & 5 & 15 & 75 \\
\hline
  & 1 & 3 & 15 & 0
\end{array}
$$

The other two solutions that satisfy $x^2 + 3x + 15 = 0$ are imaginary and can be discarded. You can conclude that the base of the candle mold should be 5 inches by 5 inches and the height should be $5 - 2 = 3$ inches.

✓ *Checkpoint* *Audio-video solution in English & Spanish at LarsonPrecalculus.com.*

Rework Example 11 when each kit contains 147 cubic inches of candle wax and you want the height of the pyramid-shaped candle to be 2 inches more than the length of each side of the candle's square base.

Before concluding this section, here is an additional hint that can help you find the real zeros of a polynomial. When the terms of $f(x)$ have a common monomial factor, it should be factored out before applying the tests in this section. For instance, by writing

$$f(x) = x^4 - 5x^3 + 3x^2 + x = x(x^3 - 5x^2 + 3x + 1)$$

you can see that $x = 0$ is a zero of f and that the remaining zeros can be obtained by analyzing the cubic factor.

Summarize (Section 2.5)

1. State the Fundamental Theorem of Algebra and the Linear Factorization Theorem (*page 154, Example 1*).
2. Describe the Rational Zero Test (*page 155, Examples 2–5*).
3. State the definition of conjugates (*page 158, Example 6*).
4. Describe what it means for a quadratic factor to be irreducible over the reals (*page 159, Examples 7 and 8*).
5. State Descartes's Rule of Signs and the Upper and Lower Bound Rules (*pages 161 and 162, Examples 9 and 10*).
6. Describe a real-life situation involving finding the zeros of a polynomial (*page 163, Example 11*).

2.5 Exercises

See **CalcChat.com** for tutorial help and worked-out solutions to odd-numbered exercises.

Vocabulary: Fill in the blanks.

1. The _____ _____ of _____ states that if $f(x)$ is a polynomial of degree n $(n > 0)$, then f has at least one zero in the complex number system.

2. The _____ _____ _____ states that if $f(x)$ is a polynomial of degree n $(n > 0)$, then $f(x)$ has precisely n linear factors, $f(x) = a_n(x - c_1)(x - c_2) \cdots (x - c_n)$, where $c_1, c_2, \ldots, c_n$ are complex numbers.

3. The test that gives a list of the possible rational zeros of a polynomial function is the _____ _____ Test.

4. If $a + bi$ is a complex zero of a polynomial with real coefficients, then so is its _____, $a - bi$.

5. Every polynomial of degree $n > 0$ with real coefficients can be written as the product of _____ and _____ factors with real coefficients, where the _____ factors have no real zeros.

6. A quadratic factor that cannot be factored further as a product of linear factors containing real numbers is said to be _____ over the _____.

7. The theorem that can be used to determine the possible numbers of positive real zeros and negative real zeros of a function is called _____ _____ of _____.

8. A real number b is a _____ bound for the real zeros of f when no real zeros are less than b, and is a _____ bound when no real zeros are greater than b.

Skills and Applications

Zeros of Polynomial Functions In Exercises 9–14, determine the number of zeros of the polynomial function.

9. $f(x) = x + 3$
10. $f(x) = x^2 + 5x - 6$
11. $g(x) = 1 - x^3$
12. $f(x) = x^6 - x^7$
13. $f(x) = (x + 5)^2$
14. $h(t) = (t - 1)^2 - (t + 1)^2$

Using the Rational Zero Test In Exercises 15–18, use the Rational Zero Test to list the possible rational zeros of f. Verify that the zeros of f shown on the graph are contained in the list.

15. $f(x) = x^3 + 2x^2 - x - 2$

16. $f(x) = x^3 - 4x^2 - 4x + 16$

17. $f(x) = 2x^4 - 17x^3 + 35x^2 + 9x - 45$

18. $f(x) = 4x^5 - 8x^4 - 5x^3 + 10x^2 + x - 2$

Using the Rational Zero Test In Exercises 19–28, find the rational zeros of the function.

19. $f(x) = x^3 - 7x - 6$
20. $f(x) = x^3 - 13x + 12$
21. $g(x) = x^3 - 4x^2 - x + 4$
22. $h(x) = x^3 - 9x^2 + 20x - 12$
23. $h(t) = t^3 + 8t^2 + 13t + 6$
24. $p(x) = x^3 - 9x^2 + 27x - 27$
25. $C(x) = 2x^3 + 3x^2 - 1$
26. $f(x) = 3x^3 - 19x^2 + 33x - 9$
27. $f(x) = 9x^4 - 9x^3 - 58x^2 + 4x + 24$
28. $f(x) = 2x^4 - 15x^3 + 23x^2 + 15x - 25$

Solving a Polynomial Equation In Exercises 29–32, find all real solutions of the polynomial equation.

29. $z^4 + z^3 + z^2 + 3z - 6 = 0$

30. $x^4 - 13x^2 - 12x = 0$

31. $2y^4 + 3y^3 - 16y^2 + 15y - 4 = 0$

32. $x^5 - x^4 - 3x^3 + 5x^2 - 2x = 0$

Using the Rational Zero Test In Exercises 33–36, (a) list the possible rational zeros of f, (b) sketch the graph of f so that some of the possible zeros in part (a) can be disregarded, and then (c) determine all real zeros of f.

33. $f(x) = x^3 + x^2 - 4x - 4$

34. $f(x) = -3x^3 + 20x^2 - 36x + 16$

35. $f(x) = -4x^3 + 15x^2 - 8x - 3$

36. $f(x) = 4x^3 - 12x^2 - x + 15$

Using the Rational Zero Test In Exercises 37–40, (a) list the possible rational zeros of f, (b) use a graphing utility to graph f so that some of the possible zeros in part (a) can be disregarded, and then (c) determine all real zeros of f.

37. $f(x) = -2x^4 + 13x^3 - 21x^2 + 2x + 8$

38. $f(x) = 4x^4 - 17x^2 + 4$

39. $f(x) = 32x^3 - 52x^2 + 17x + 3$

40. $f(x) = 4x^3 + 7x^2 - 11x - 18$

Graphical Analysis In Exercises 41–44, (a) use the *zero* or *root* feature of a graphing utility to approximate the zeros of the function accurate to three decimal places, (b) determine the exact value of one of the zeros (use synthetic division to verify your result), and (c) factor the polynomial completely.

41. $f(x) = x^4 - 3x^2 + 2$

42. $P(t) = t^4 - 7t^2 + 12$

43. $h(x) = x^5 - 7x^4 + 10x^3 + 14x^2 - 24x$

44. $g(x) = 6x^4 - 11x^3 - 51x^2 + 99x - 27$

Finding a Polynomial Function with Given Zeros In Exercises 45–50, find a polynomial function with real coefficients that has the given zeros. (There are many correct answers.)

45. $1, 5i$

46. $4, -3i$

47. $2, 5 + i$

48. $5, 3 - 2i$

49. $\frac{2}{3}, -1, 3 + \sqrt{2}i$

50. $-5, -5, 1 + \sqrt{3}i$

Factoring a Polynomial In Exercises 51–54, write the polynomial (a) as the product of factors that are irreducible over the *rationals*, (b) as the product of linear and quadratic factors that are irreducible over the *reals*, and (c) in completely factored form.

51. $f(x) = x^4 + 6x^2 - 27$

52. $f(x) = x^4 - 2x^3 - 3x^2 + 12x - 18$
   (*Hint:* One factor is $x^2 - 6$.)

53. $f(x) = x^4 - 4x^3 + 5x^2 - 2x - 6$
   (*Hint:* One factor is $x^2 - 2x - 2$.)

54. $f(x) = x^4 - 3x^3 - x^2 - 12x - 20$
   (*Hint:* One factor is $x^2 + 4$.)

Finding the Zeros of a Polynomial Function In Exercises 55–62, use the given zero to find all the zeros of the function.

Function	Zero
55. $f(x) = x^3 - x^2 + 4x - 4$	$2i$
56. $f(x) = 2x^3 + 3x^2 + 18x + 27$	$3i$
57. $f(x) = 2x^4 - x^3 + 49x^2 - 25x - 25$	$5i$
58. $g(x) = x^3 - 7x^2 - x + 87$	$5 + 2i$
59. $g(x) = 4x^3 + 23x^2 + 34x - 10$	$-3 + i$
60. $h(x) = 3x^3 - 4x^2 + 8x + 8$	$1 - \sqrt{3}i$
61. $f(x) = x^4 + 3x^3 - 5x^2 - 21x + 22$	$-3 + \sqrt{2}i$
62. $f(x) = x^3 + 4x^2 + 14x + 20$	$-1 - 3i$

Finding the Zeros of a Polynomial Function In Exercises 63–80, write the polynomial as the product of linear factors and list all the zeros of the function.

63. $f(x) = x^2 + 36$ **64.** $f(x) = x^2 - x + 56$

65. $h(x) = x^2 - 2x + 17$ **66.** $g(x) = x^2 + 10x + 17$

67. $f(x) = x^4 - 16$ **68.** $f(y) = y^4 - 256$

69. $f(z) = z^2 - 2z + 2$ **70.** $h(x) = x^3 - 3x^2 + 4x - 2$

71. $g(x) = x^3 - 3x^2 + x + 5$

72. $f(x) = x^3 - x^2 + x + 39$

73. $h(x) = x^3 - x + 6$

74. $h(x) = x^3 + 9x^2 + 27x + 35$

75. $f(x) = 5x^3 - 9x^2 + 28x + 6$

76. $g(x) = 2x^3 - x^2 + 8x + 21$

77. $g(x) = x^4 - 4x^3 + 8x^2 - 16x + 16$

78. $h(x) = x^4 + 6x^3 + 10x^2 + 6x + 9$

79. $f(x) = x^4 + 10x^2 + 9$ **80.** $f(x) = x^4 + 29x^2 + 100$

Finding the Zeros of a Polynomial Function In Exercises 81–86, find all the zeros of the function. When there is an extended list of possible rational zeros, use a graphing utility to graph the function in order to disregard any of the possible rational zeros that are obviously not zeros of the function.

81. $f(x) = x^3 + 24x^2 + 214x + 740$

82. $f(s) = 2s^3 - 5s^2 + 12s - 5$

83. $f(x) = 16x^3 - 20x^2 - 4x + 15$

84. $f(x) = 9x^3 - 15x^2 + 11x - 5$

85. $f(x) = 2x^4 + 5x^3 + 4x^2 + 5x + 2$

86. $g(x) = x^5 - 8x^4 + 28x^3 - 56x^2 + 64x - 32$

Using Descartes's Rule of Signs   In Exercises 87–94, use Descartes's Rule of Signs to determine the possible numbers of positive and negative real zeros of the function.

87. $g(x) = 2x^3 - 3x^2 - 3$

88. $h(x) = 4x^2 - 8x + 3$

89. $h(x) = 2x^3 + 3x^2 + 1$

90. $h(x) = 2x^4 - 3x + 2$

91. $g(x) = 5x^5 - 10x$

92. $f(x) = 4x^3 - 3x^2 + 2x - 1$

93. $f(x) = -5x^3 + x^2 - x + 5$

94. $f(x) = 3x^3 + 2x^2 + x + 3$

Verifying Upper and Lower Bounds   In Exercises 95–98, use synthetic division to verify the upper and lower bounds of the real zeros of f.

95. $f(x) = x^3 + 3x^2 - 2x + 1$

    (a) Upper: $x = 1$ (b) Lower: $x = -4$

96. $f(x) = x^3 - 4x^2 + 1$

    (a) Upper: $x = 4$ (b) Lower: $x = -1$

97. $f(x) = x^4 - 4x^3 + 16x - 16$

    (a) Upper: $x = 5$ (b) Lower: $x = -3$

98. $f(x) = 2x^4 - 8x + 3$

    (a) Upper: $x = 3$ (b) Lower: $x = -4$

Finding the Zeros of a Polynomial Function   In Exercises 99–102, find all real zeros of the function.

99. $f(x) = 4x^3 - 3x - 1$

100. $f(z) = 12z^3 - 4z^2 - 27z + 9$

101. $f(y) = 4y^3 + 3y^2 + 8y + 6$

102. $g(x) = 3x^3 - 2x^2 + 15x - 10$

Finding the Rational Zeros of a Polynomial   In Exercises 103–106, find the rational zeros of the polynomial function.

103. $P(x) = x^4 - \frac{25}{4}x^2 + 9 = \frac{1}{4}(4x^4 - 25x^2 + 36)$

104. $f(x) = x^3 - \frac{3}{2}x^2 - \frac{23}{2}x + 6 = \frac{1}{2}(2x^3 - 3x^2 - 23x + 12)$

105. $f(x) = x^3 - \frac{1}{4}x^2 - x + \frac{1}{4} = \frac{1}{4}(4x^3 - x^2 - 4x + 1)$

106. $f(z) = z^3 + \frac{11}{6}z^2 - \frac{1}{2}z - \frac{1}{3} = \frac{1}{6}(6z^3 + 11z^2 - 3z - 2)$

Rational and Irrational Zeros   In Exercises 107–110, match the cubic function with the numbers of rational and irrational zeros.

(a) Rational zeros: 0; irrational zeros: 1

(b) Rational zeros: 3; irrational zeros: 0

(c) Rational zeros: 1; irrational zeros: 2

(d) Rational zeros: 1; irrational zeros: 0

107. $f(x) = x^3 - 1$ **108.** $f(x) = x^3 - 2$

109. $f(x) = x^3 - x$ **110.** $f(x) = x^3 - 2x$

111. Geometry   You want to make an open box from a rectangular piece of material, 15 centimeters by 9 centimeters, by cutting equal squares from the corners and turning up the sides.

    (a) Let x represent the side length of each of the squares removed. Draw a diagram showing the squares removed from the original piece of material and the resulting dimensions of the open box.

    (b) Use the diagram to write the volume V of the box as a function of x. Determine the domain of the function.

    (c) Sketch the graph of the function and approximate the dimensions of the box that will yield a maximum volume.

    (d) Find values of x such that $V = 56$. Which of these values is a physical impossibility in the construction of the box? Explain.

112. Geometry   A rectangular package to be sent by a delivery service (see figure) can have a maximum combined length and girth (perimeter of a cross section) of 120 inches.

    (a) Use the diagram to write the volume V of the package as a function of x.

    (b) Use a graphing utility to graph the function and approximate the dimensions of the package that will yield a maximum volume.

    (c) Find values of x such that $V = 13,500$. Which of these values is a physical impossibility in the construction of the package? Explain.

113. Geometry

A bulk food storage bin with dimensions 2 feet by 3 feet by 4 feet needs to be increased in size to hold five times as much food as the current bin. (Assume each dimension is increased by the same amount.)

(a) Write a function that represents the volume V of the new bin.

(b) Find the dimensions of the new bin.

114. Cost The ordering and transportation cost C (in thousands of dollars) for machine parts is

$$C = 100\left(\frac{200}{x^2} + \frac{x}{x + 30}\right), \quad x \geq 1$$

where x is the order size (in hundreds). In calculus, it can be shown that the cost is a minimum when

$$3x^3 - 40x^2 - 2400x - 36,000 = 0.$$

Use a calculator to approximate the optimal order size to the nearest hundred units.

Exploration

True or False?   In Exercises 115 and 116, decide whether the statement is true or false. Justify your answer.

115. It is possible for a third-degree polynomial function with integer coefficients to have no real zeros.

116. If $x = -i$ is a zero of the function

$$f(x) = x^3 + ix^2 + ix - 1$$

then $x = i$ must also be a zero of f.

Think About It   In Exercises 117–122, determine (if possible) the zeros of the function g when the function f has zeros at $x = r_1$, $x = r_2$, and $x = r_3$.

117. $g(x) = -f(x)$ **118.** $g(x) = 3f(x)$

119. $g(x) = f(x - 5)$ **120.** $g(x) = f(2x)$

121. $g(x) = 3 + f(x)$ **122.** $g(x) = f(-x)$

123. Think About It A cubic polynomial function f has real zeros -2, $\frac{1}{2}$, and 3, and its leading coefficient is negative. Write an equation for f and sketch its graph. How many different polynomial functions are possible for f?

124. Think About It Sketch the graph of a fifth-degree polynomial function whose leading coefficient is positive and that has a zero at $x = 3$ of multiplicity 2.

Writing an Equation   In Exercises 125 and 126, the graph of a cubic polynomial function $y = f(x)$ is shown. One of the zeros is $1 + i$. Write an equation for f.

125.   **126.**

127. Think About It Let $y = f(x)$ be a quartic polynomial with leading coefficient $a = 1$ and $f(i) = f(2i) = 0$. Write an equation for f.

128. Think About It Let $y = f(x)$ be a cubic polynomial with leading coefficient $a = -1$ and $f(2) = f(i) = 0$. Write an equation for f.

129. Writing an Equation Write the equation for a quadratic function f (with integer coefficients) that has the given zeros. Assume that b is a positive integer.

(a) $\pm\sqrt{b}i$

(b) $a \pm bi$

130. **HOW DO YOU SEE IT?** Use the information in the table to answer each question.

Interval	Value of $f(x)$
$(-\infty, -2)$	Positive
$(-2, 1)$	Negative
$(1, 4)$	Negative
$(4, \infty)$	Positive

(a) What are the three real zeros of the polynomial function f?

(b) What can be said about the behavior of the graph of f at $x = 1$?

(c) What is the least possible degree of f? Explain. Can the degree of f ever be odd? Explain.

(d) Is the leading coefficient of f positive or negative? Explain.

(e) Sketch a graph of a function that exhibits the behavior described in the table.

131. Graphical Reasoning The graph of one of the following functions is shown below. Identify the function shown in the graph. Explain why each of the others is not the correct function. Use a graphing utility to verify your result.

(a) $f(x) = x^2(x + 2)(x - 3.5)$

(b) $g(x) = (x + 2)(x - 3.5)$

(c) $h(x) = (x + 2)(x - 3.5)(x^2 + 1)$

(d) $k(x) = (x + 1)(x + 2)(x - 3.5)$

2.6 Rational Functions

Rational functions can help you model and solve real-life problems relating to environmental scenarios. For instance, in Exercise 71 on page 178, you will use a rational function to determine the cost of supplying recycling bins to the population of a rural township.

- Find the domains of rational functions.
- Find the vertical and horizontal asymptotes of the graphs of rational functions.
- Sketch the graphs of rational functions.
- Sketch the graphs of rational functions that have slant asymptotes.
- Use rational functions to model and solve real-life problems.

Introduction

A **rational function** is a quotient of polynomial functions. It can be written in the form

$$f(x) = \frac{N(x)}{D(x)}$$

where $N(x)$ and $D(x)$ are polynomials and $D(x)$ is not the zero polynomial.

In general, the *domain* of a rational function of x includes all real numbers except x-values that make the denominator zero. Much of the discussion of rational functions will focus on their graphical behavior near the x-values excluded from the domain.

| EXAMPLE 1 | **Finding the Domain of a Rational Function** |

Find the domain of $f(x) = \dfrac{1}{x}$ and discuss the behavior of f near any excluded x-values.

Solution Because the denominator is zero when $x = 0$, the domain of f is all real numbers except $x = 0$. To determine the behavior of f near this excluded value, evaluate $f(x)$ to the left and right of $x = 0$, as indicated in the following tables.

x	-1	-0.5	-0.1	-0.01	-0.001	$\longrightarrow 0$
$f(x)$	-1	-2	-10	-100	-1000	$\longrightarrow -\infty$

x	$0 \longleftarrow$	0.001	0.01	0.1	0.5	1
$f(x)$	$\infty \longleftarrow$	1000	100	10	2	1

Note that as x approaches 0 *from the left*, $f(x)$ decreases without bound. In contrast, as x approaches 0 *from the right*, $f(x)$ increases without bound. The graph of f is shown below.

✓ *Checkpoint* ◄))) *Audio-video solution in English & Spanish at LarsonPrecalculus.com.*

Find the domain of the rational function $f(x) = \dfrac{3x}{x - 1}$ and discuss the behavior of f near any excluded x-values.

ZQFotography/Shutterstock.com

Vertical and Horizontal Asymptotes

In Example 1, the behavior of f near $x = 0$ is denoted as follows.

Vertical asymptote: $x = 0$

$f(x) = \dfrac{1}{x}$

Horizontal asymptote: $y = 0$

Figure 2.21

$$\underbrace{f(x) \longrightarrow -\infty \text{ as } x \longrightarrow 0^{-}}$$

$f(x)$ decreases without bound as x approaches 0 from the left.

$$\underbrace{f(x) \longrightarrow \infty \text{ as } x \longrightarrow 0^{+}}$$

$f(x)$ increases without bound as x approaches 0 from the right.

The line $x = 0$ is a **vertical asymptote** of the graph of f, as shown in Figure 2.21. From this figure, you can see that the graph of f also has a **horizontal asymptote**—the line $y = 0$. The behavior of f near $y = 0$ is denoted as follows.

$$\underbrace{f(x) \longrightarrow 0 \text{ as } x \longrightarrow -\infty}$$

$f(x)$ approaches 0 as x decreases without bound.

$$\underbrace{f(x) \longrightarrow 0 \text{ as } x \longrightarrow \infty}$$

$f(x)$ approaches 0 as x increases without bound.

Definitions of Vertical and Horizontal Asymptotes

1. The line $x = a$ is a **vertical asymptote** of the graph of f when

$$f(x) \longrightarrow \infty \quad \text{or} \quad f(x) \longrightarrow -\infty$$

as $x \longrightarrow a$, either from the right or from the left.

2. The line $y = b$ is a **horizontal asymptote** of the graph of f when

$$f(x) \longrightarrow b$$

as $x \longrightarrow \infty$ or $x \longrightarrow -\infty$.

Eventually (as $x \longrightarrow \infty$ or $x \longrightarrow -\infty$), the distance between the horizontal asymptote and the points on the graph must approach zero. Figure 2.22 shows the vertical and horizontal asymptotes of the graphs of three rational functions.

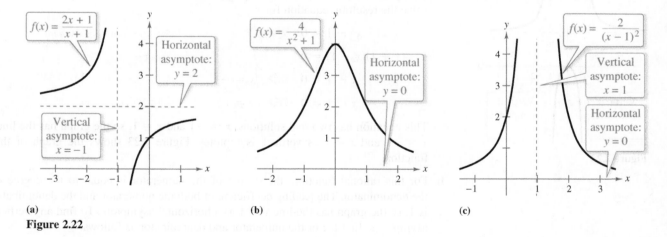

(a)   (b)   (c)

Figure 2.22

The graphs of

$$f(x) = \frac{1}{x}$$

in Figure 2.21 and

$$f(x) = \frac{2x + 1}{x + 1}$$

in Figure 2.22(a) are **hyperbolas.**

Vertical and Horizontal Asymptotes of a Rational Function

Let f be the rational function

$$f(x) = \frac{N(x)}{D(x)} = \frac{a_n x^n + a_{n-1} x^{n-1} + \cdots + a_1 x + a_0}{b_m x^m + b_{m-1} x^{m-1} + \cdots + b_1 x + b_0}$$

where $N(x)$ and $D(x)$ have no common factors.

1. The graph of f has *vertical* asymptotes at the zeros of $D(x)$.

2. The graph of f has one or no *horizontal* asymptote determined by comparing the degrees of $N(x)$ and $D(x)$.

     a. When $n < m$, the graph of f has the line $y = 0$ (the x-axis) as a horizontal asymptote.

     b. When $n = m$, the graph of f has the line $y = a_n/b_m$ (ratio of the leading coefficients) as a horizontal asymptote.

     c. When $n > m$, the graph of f has no horizontal asymptote.

EXAMPLE 2   **Finding Vertical and Horizontal Asymptotes**

Find all vertical and horizontal asymptotes of the graph of each rational function.

a. $f(x) = \dfrac{2x^2}{x^2 - 1}$ **b.** $f(x) = \dfrac{x^2 + x - 2}{x^2 - x - 6}$

Solution

a. For this rational function, the degree of the numerator is *equal* to the degree of the denominator. The leading coefficient of the numerator is 2 and the leading coefficient of the denominator is 1, so the graph has the line $y = 2$ as a horizontal asymptote. To find any vertical asymptotes, set the denominator equal to zero and solve the resulting equation for x.

$$x^2 - 1 = 0 \qquad \text{Set denominator equal to zero.}$$

$$(x + 1)(x - 1) = 0 \qquad \text{Factor.}$$

$$x + 1 = 0 \implies x = -1 \qquad \text{Set 1st factor equal to 0.}$$

$$x - 1 = 0 \implies x = 1 \qquad \text{Set 2nd factor equal to 0.}$$

This equation has two real solutions, $x = -1$ and $x = 1$, so the graph has the lines $x = -1$ and $x = 1$ as vertical asymptotes. Figure 2.23 shows the graph of this function.

b. For this rational function, the degree of the numerator is equal to the degree of the denominator. The leading coefficient of both the numerator and the denominator is 1, so the graph has the line $y = 1$ as a horizontal asymptote. To find any vertical asymptotes, first factor the numerator and denominator as follows.

$$f(x) = \frac{x^2 + x - 2}{x^2 - x - 6} = \frac{(x - 1)(x + 2)}{(x + 2)(x - 3)} = \frac{x - 1}{x - 3}, \quad x \neq -2$$

By setting the denominator $x - 3$ (of the simplified function) equal to zero, you can determine that the graph has the line $x = 3$ as a vertical asymptote.

✓ *Checkpoint* Audio-video solution in English & Spanish at LarsonPrecalculus.com.

Find all vertical and horizontal asymptotes of the graph of $f(x) = \dfrac{3x^2 + 7x - 6}{x^2 + 4x + 3}$. ∎

Horizontal asymptote: $y = 2$

$f(x) = \dfrac{2x^2}{x^2 - 1}$

Vertical asymptote: $x = -1$

Vertical asymptote: $x = 1$

Figure 2.23

▷ **ALGEBRA HELP** You can review the techniques for factoring in Appendix A.3.

Sketching the Graph of a Rational Function

To sketch the graph of a rational function, use the following guidelines.

•••**REMARK** You may also
want to test for symmetry
when graphing rational
functions, especially for simple
rational functions. Recall from
Section 1.6 that the graph of
the reciprocal function

$$f(x) = \frac{1}{x}$$

is symmetric with respect to the
origin.

Guidelines for Graphing Rational Functions

Let $f(x) = \dfrac{N(x)}{D(x)}$, where $N(x)$ and $D(x)$ are polynomials and $D(x)$ is not the zero polynomial.

1. Simplify f, if possible.

2. Find and plot the y-intercept (if any) by evaluating $f(0)$.

3. Find the zeros of the numerator (if any) by solving the equation $N(x) = 0$. Then plot the corresponding x-intercepts.

4. Find the zeros of the denominator (if any) by solving the equation $D(x) = 0$. Then sketch the corresponding vertical asymptotes.

5. Find and sketch the horizontal asymptote (if any) by using the rule for finding the horizontal asymptote of a rational function.

6. Plot at least one point *between* and one point *beyond* each x-intercept and vertical asymptote.

7. Use smooth curves to complete the graph between and beyond the vertical asymptotes.

▷ **TECHNOLOGY** Some graphing utilities have difficulty graphing rational functions that have vertical asymptotes. Often, the graphing utility will connect portions of the graph that are not supposed to be connected. For instance, the screen on the left below shows the graph of $f(x) = 1/(x - 2)$. Notice that the graph should consist of two unconnected portions—one to the left of $x = 2$ and the other to the right of $x = 2$. To eliminate this problem, you can try changing the mode of the graphing utility to *dot* mode. The problem with this is that the graph is then represented as a collection of dots (as shown in the screen on the right) rather than as a smooth curve.

 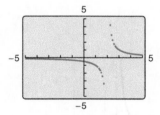

The concept of *test intervals* from Section 2.2 can be extended to graphing of rational functions. To do this, use the fact that a rational function can change signs only at its zeros and its undefined values (the x-values for which its denominator is zero). Between two consecutive zeros of the numerator and the denominator, a rational function must be entirely positive or entirely negative. This means that when put in order, the zeros of the numerator and the denominator of a rational function divide the real number line into test intervals in which the function has no sign changes. Choose a representative x-value to determine whether the value of the rational function is positive (the graph lies above the x-axis) or negative (the graph lies below the x-axis).

EXAMPLE 3 **Sketching the Graph of a Rational Function**

Sketch the graph of $g(x) = \dfrac{3}{x-2}$ and state its domain.

Solution

y-intercept: $\left(0, -\frac{3}{2}\right)$, because $g(0) = -\frac{3}{2}$

x-intercept: none, because $3 \neq 0$

Vertical asymptote: $x = 2$, zero of denominator

Horizontal asymptote: $y = 0$, because degree of $N(x) <$ degree of $D(x)$

Additional points:

Test Interval	Representative x-Value	Value of g	Sign	Point on Graph
$(-\infty, 2)$	-4	$g(-4) = -0.5$	Negative	$(-4, -0.5)$
$(2, \infty)$	3	$g(3) = 3$	Positive	$(3, 3)$

By plotting the intercept, asymptotes, and a few additional points, you can obtain the graph shown in Figure 2.24. The domain of g is all real numbers except $x = 2$.

✓ *Checkpoint* ◄))) Audio-video solution in English & Spanish at LarsonPrecalculus.com.

Sketch the graph of $f(x) = \dfrac{1}{x+3}$ and state its domain.

Horizontal asymptote: $y = 0$

$g(x) = \dfrac{3}{x-2}$

Vertical asymptote: $x = 2$

Figure 2.24

EXAMPLE 4 **Sketching the Graph of a Rational Function**

Sketch the graph of $f(x) = (2x - 1)/x$ and state its domain.

Solution

y-intercept: none, because $x = 0$ is not in the domain

x-intercept: $\left(\frac{1}{2}, 0\right)$, because $f\left(\frac{1}{2}\right) = 0$

Vertical asymptote: $x = 0$, zero of denominator

Horizontal asymptote: $y = 2$, because degree of $N(x) =$ degree of $D(x)$

Additional points:

Test Interval	Representative x-Value	Value of f	Sign	Point on Graph
$(-\infty, 0)$	-1	$f(-1) = 3$	Positive	$(-1, 3)$
$\left(0, \frac{1}{2}\right)$	$\frac{1}{4}$	$f\left(\frac{1}{4}\right) = -2$	Negative	$\left(\frac{1}{4}, -2\right)$
$\left(\frac{1}{2}, \infty\right)$	4	$f(4) = 1.75$	Positive	$(4, 1.75)$

By plotting the intercept, asymptotes, and a few additional points, you can obtain the graph shown in Figure 2.25. The domain of f is all real numbers except $x = 0$.

✓ *Checkpoint* ◄))) Audio-video solution in English & Spanish at LarsonPrecalculus.com.

Sketch the graph of $C(x) = (3 + 2x)/(1 + x)$ and state its domain.

Horizontal asymptote: $y = 2$

Vertical asymptote: $x = 0$

$f(x) = \dfrac{2x - 1}{x}$

Figure 2.25

Figure 2.26

EXAMPLE 5   **Sketching the Graph of a Rational Function**

Sketch the graph of $f(x) = x/(x^2 - x - 2)$.

Solution   Factoring the denominator, you have $f(x) = x/[(x + 1)(x - 2)]$.

Intercept: $(0, 0)$, because $f(0) = 0$

Vertical asymptotes: $x = -1, x = 2$, zeros of denominator

Horizontal asymptote: $y = 0$, because degree of $N(x) <$ degree of $D(x)$

Additional points:

Test Interval	Representative x-Value	Value of f	Sign	Point on Graph
$(-\infty, -1)$	-3	$f(-3) = -0.3$	Negative	$(-3, -0.3)$
$(-1, 0)$	-0.5	$f(-0.5) = 0.4$	Positive	$(-0.5, 0.4)$
$(0, 2)$	1	$f(1) = -0.5$	Negative	$(1, -0.5)$
$(2, \infty)$	3	$f(3) = 0.75$	Positive	$(3, 0.75)$

Figure 2.26 shows the graph of this function.

✓ **Checkpoint** ◄))) Audio-video solution in English & Spanish at LarsonPrecalculus.com.

Sketch the graph of $f(x) = 3x/(x^2 + x - 2)$.

REMARK If you are unsure of the shape of a portion of the graph of a rational function, then plot some additional points. Also note that when the numerator and the denominator of a rational function have a common factor, the graph of the function has a *hole* at the zero of the common factor (see Example 6).

EXAMPLE 6   **A Rational Function with Common Factors**

Sketch the graph of $f(x) = (x^2 - 9)/(x^2 - 2x - 3)$.

Solution   By factoring the numerator and denominator, you have

$$f(x) = \frac{x^2 - 9}{x^2 - 2x - 3} = \frac{(x - 3)(x + 3)}{(x - 3)(x + 1)} = \frac{x + 3}{x + 1}, \quad x \neq 3.$$

y-intercept: $(0, 3)$, because $f(0) = 3$

x-intercept: $(-3, 0)$, because $f(-3) = 0$

Vertical asymptote: $x = -1$, zero of (simplified) denominator

Horizontal asymptote: $y = 1$, because degree of $N(x) =$ degree of $D(x)$

Additional points:

Test Interval	Representative x-Value	Value of f	Sign	Point on Graph
$(-\infty, -3)$	-4	$f(-4) = 0.33$	Positive	$(-4, 0.33)$
$(-3, -1)$	-2	$f(-2) = -1$	Negative	$(-2, -1)$
$(-1, \infty)$	2	$f(2) = 1.67$	Positive	$(2, 1.67)$

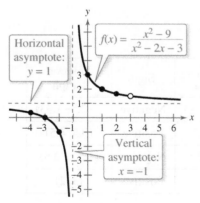

Hole at $x = 3$

Figure 2.27

Figure 2.27 shows the graph of this function. Notice that there is a hole in the graph at $x = 3$, because the function is not defined when $x = 3$.

✓ **Checkpoint** ◄))) Audio-video solution in English & Spanish at LarsonPrecalculus.com.

Sketch the graph of $f(x) = (x^2 - 4)/(x^2 - x - 6)$.

Figure 2.28

Slant Asymptotes

Consider a rational function whose denominator is of degree 1 or greater. If the degree of the numerator is exactly *one more* than the degree of the denominator, then the graph of the function has a **slant** (or **oblique**) **asymptote.** For example, the graph of

$$f(x) = \frac{x^2 - x}{x + 1}$$

has a slant asymptote, as shown in Figure 2.28. To find the equation of a slant asymptote, use long division. For instance, by dividing $x + 1$ into $x^2 - x$, you obtain

$$f(x) = \frac{x^2 - x}{x + 1} = \underbrace{x - 2}_{\substack{\text{Slant asymptote} \\ (y = x - 2)}} + \frac{2}{x + 1}.$$

As x increases or decreases without bound, the remainder term $2/(x + 1)$ approaches 0, so the graph of f approaches the line $y = x - 2$, as shown in Figure 2.28.

EXAMPLE 7 **A Rational Function with a Slant Asymptote**

Sketch the graph of $f(x) = \dfrac{x^2 - x - 2}{x - 1}$.

Solution Factoring the numerator as $(x - 2)(x + 1)$ allows you to recognize the *x*-intercepts. Using long division

$$f(x) = \frac{x^2 - x - 2}{x - 1}$$

$$= x - \frac{2}{x - 1}$$

allows you to recognize that the line $y = x$ is a slant asymptote of the graph.

y-intercept: $\quad$ $(0, 2)$, because $f(0) = 2$

x-intercepts: $\quad$ $(-1, 0)$ and $(2, 0)$

Vertical asymptote: $x = 1$, zero of denominator

Slant asymptote: $\quad$ $y = x$

Additional points:

Test Interval	Representative *x*-Value	Value of f	Sign	Point on Graph
$(-\infty, -1)$	-2	$f(-2) = -1.33$	Negative	$(-2, -1.33)$
$(-1, 1)$	0.5	$f(0.5) = 4.5$	Positive	$(0.5, 4.5)$
$(1, 2)$	1.5	$f(1.5) = -2.5$	Negative	$(1.5, -2.5)$
$(2, \infty)$	3	$f(3) = 2$	Positive	$(3, 2)$

Figure 2.29

Figure 2.29 shows the graph of this function.

✓ *Checkpoint* ◀))) Audio-video solution in English & Spanish at LarsonPrecalculus.com.

Sketch the graph of $f(x) = \dfrac{3x^2 + 1}{x}$.

Applications

There are many examples of asymptotic behavior in real life. For instance, Example 8 shows how a vertical asymptote can help you to analyze the cost of removing pollutants from smokestack emissions.

EXAMPLE 8   **Cost-Benefit Model**

A utility company burns coal to generate electricity. The cost C (in dollars) of removing $p\%$ of the smokestack pollutants is given by

$$C = \frac{80,000p}{100 - p}, \quad 0 \le p < 100.$$

You are a member of a state legislature considering a law that would require utility companies to remove 90% of the pollutants from their smokestack emissions. The current law requires 85% removal. How much additional cost would the utility company incur as a result of the new law?

Algebraic Solution

Because the current law requires 85% removal, the current cost to the utility company is

$$C = \frac{80,000(85)}{100 - 85} \approx \$453,333. \qquad \text{Evaluate } C \text{ when } p = 85.$$

The cost to remove 90% of the pollutants would be

$$C = \frac{80,000(90)}{100 - 90} = \$720,000. \qquad \text{Evaluate } C \text{ when } p = 90.$$

So, the new law would require the utility company to spend an additional

$$720,000 - 453,333 = \$266,667. \qquad \begin{array}{l}\text{Subtract 85\% removal cost}\\\text{from 90\% removal cost.}\end{array}$$

Graphical Solution

Use a graphing utility to graph the function

$$y_1 = \frac{80,000x}{100 - x}$$

as shown below. Note that the graph has a vertical asymptote at

$$x = 100.$$

Then approximate the values of y_1 when $x = 85$ and $x = 90$. You should obtain the following values.

When $x = 85$, $y_1 \approx 453,333$.

When $x = 90$, $y_1 = 720,000$.

So, the new law would require the utility company to spend an additional

$$720,000 - 453,333 = \$266,667.$$

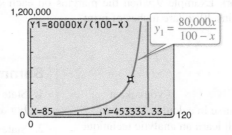

$$Y1 = 80000X/(100-X) \qquad y_1 = \frac{80,000x}{100 - x}$$

X=85   Y=453333.33

 Checkpoint *Audio-video solution in English & Spanish at LarsonPrecalculus.com.*

The cost C (in millions of dollars) of removing $p\%$ of the industrial and municipal pollutants discharged into a river is given by

$$C = \frac{255p}{100 - p}, \quad 0 \le p < 100.$$

a. Find the costs of removing 20%, 45%, and 80% of the pollutants.

b. According to the model, would it be possible to remove 100% of the pollutants? Explain.

EXAMPLE 9 **Finding a Minimum Area**

A rectangular page contains 48 square inches of print. The margins at the top and bottom of the page are each 1 inch deep. The margins on each side are $1\frac{1}{2}$ inches wide. What should the dimensions of the page be so that the least amount of paper is used?

Figure 2.30

Graphical Solution

Let A be the area to be minimized. From Figure 2.30, you can write $A = (x + 3)(y + 2)$. The printed area inside the margins is modeled by $48 = xy$ or $y = 48/x$. To find the minimum area, rewrite the equation for A in terms of just one variable by substituting $48/x$ for y.

$$A = (x + 3)\left(\frac{48}{x} + 2\right) = \frac{(x + 3)(48 + 2x)}{x}, \quad x > 0$$

The graph of this rational function is shown below. Because x represents the width of the printed area, you need to consider only the portion of the graph for which x is positive. Using a graphing utility, you can approximate the minimum value of A to occur when $x \approx 8.5$ inches. The corresponding value of y is $48/8.5 \approx 5.6$ inches. So, the dimensions should be $x + 3 \approx 11.5$ inches by $y + 2 \approx 7.6$ inches.

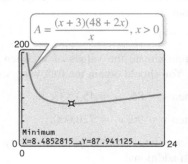

$A = \frac{(x + 3)(48 + 2x)}{x}, x > 0$

Minimum
X=8.4852815 Y=87.941125

Numerical Solution

Let A be the area to be minimized. From Figure 2.30, you can write $A = (x + 3)(y + 2)$. The printed area inside the margins is modeled by $48 = xy$ or $y = 48/x$. To find the minimum area, rewrite the equation for A in terms of just one variable by substituting $48/x$ for y.

$$A = (x + 3)\left(\frac{48}{x} + 2\right) = \frac{(x + 3)(48 + 2x)}{x}, \quad x > 0$$

Use a graphing utility to create a table of values for the function $y_1 = [(x + 3)(48 + 2x)]/x$ beginning at $x = 1$. The minimum value of y_1 occurs when x is somewhere between 8 and 9, as shown in Figure 2.31. To approximate the minimum value of y_1 to one decimal place, change the table so that it starts at $x = 8$ and increases by 0.1. The minimum value of y_1 occurs when $x \approx 8.5$, as shown in Figure 2.32. The corresponding value of y is $48/8.5 \approx 5.6$ inches. So, the dimensions should be $x + 3 \approx 11.5$ inches by $y + 2 \approx 7.6$ inches.

X	Y1	
6	90	
7	88.571	
8	88	
9	88	
10	88.4	
11	89.091	
12	90	
X=8		

Figure 2.31

X	Y1	
8.2	87.961	
8.3	87.949	
8.4	87.943	
8.5	87.941	
8.6	87.944	
8.7	87.952	
8.8	87.964	
X=8.5		

Figure 2.32

✓ *Checkpoint* *Audio-video solution in English & Spanish at LarsonPrecalculus.com.*

Rework Example 9 when the margins on each side are 2 inches wide and the page contains 40 square inches of print.

- - - - - - - - - - - - - - - - ▷

•• **REMARK** If you take a course in calculus, then you will learn an analytic technique for finding the exact value of x that produces a minimum area. In Example 9, that value is $x = 6\sqrt{2} \approx 8.485$.

Summarize (Section 2.6)

1. State the definition and describe the domain of a rational function *(page 168)*. For an example of finding the domain of a rational function, see Example 1.

2. State the definitions of vertical and horizontal asymptotes *(page 169)*. For an example of finding vertical and horizontal asymptotes of the graphs of rational functions, see Example 2.

3. State the guidelines for graphing rational functions *(page 171)*. For examples of sketching the graphs of rational functions, see Examples 3–6.

4. Describe when a rational function has a slant asymptote *(page 174)*. For an example of sketching the graph of a rational function that has a slant asymptote, see Example 7.

5. Describe examples of how to use rational functions to model and solve real-life problems *(pages 175 and 176, Examples 8 and 9)*.

2.6 Exercises

See CalcChat.com for tutorial help and worked-out solutions to odd-numbered exercises.

Vocabulary: Fill in the blanks.

1. Functions of the form $f(x) = N(x)/D(x)$, where $N(x)$ and $D(x)$ are polynomials and $D(x)$ is not the zero polynomial, are called _____ _____.
2. When $f(x) \to \pm\infty$ as $x \to a$ from the left or the right, $x = a$ is a _____ _____ of the graph of f.
3. When $f(x) \to b$ as $x \to \pm\infty$, $y = b$ is a _____ _____ of the graph of f.
4. For the rational function $f(x) = N(x)/D(x)$, if the degree of $N(x)$ is exactly one more than the degree of $D(x)$, then the graph of f has a _____ (or oblique) _____.

Skills and Applications

Finding the Domain of a Rational Function In Exercises 5–8, find the domain of the function and discuss the behavior of f near any excluded x-values.

5. $f(x) = \dfrac{1}{x-1}$

6. $f(x) = \dfrac{5x}{x+2}$

7. $f(x) = \dfrac{3x^2}{x^2-1}$

8. $f(x) = \dfrac{2x}{x^2-4}$

Finding Vertical and Horizontal Asymptotes In Exercises 9–16, find all vertical and horizontal asymptotes of the graph of the function.

9. $f(x) = \dfrac{4}{x^2}$

10. $f(x) = \dfrac{1}{(x-2)^3}$

11. $f(x) = \dfrac{5+x}{5-x}$

12. $f(x) = \dfrac{3-7x}{3+2x}$

13. $f(x) = \dfrac{x^3}{x^2-1}$

14. $f(x) = \dfrac{4x^2}{x+2}$

15. $f(x) = \dfrac{3x^2+1}{x^2+x+9}$

16. $f(x) = \dfrac{3x^2+x-5}{x^2+1}$

Sketching the Graph of a Rational Function In Exercises 17–40, (a) state the domain of the function, (b) identify all intercepts, (c) find any vertical or horizontal asymptotes, and (d) plot additional solution points as needed to sketch the graph of the rational function.

17. $f(x) = \dfrac{1}{x+2}$

18. $f(x) = \dfrac{1}{x-3}$

19. $h(x) = \dfrac{-1}{x+4}$

20. $g(x) = \dfrac{1}{6-x}$

21. $C(x) = \dfrac{7+2x}{2+x}$

22. $P(x) = \dfrac{1-3x}{1-x}$

23. $f(x) = \dfrac{x^2}{x^2+9}$

24. $g(s) = \dfrac{4s}{s^2+4}$

25. $f(t) = \dfrac{1-2t}{t}$

26. $f(x) = -\dfrac{1}{(x-2)^2}$

27. $h(x) = \dfrac{x^2-5x+4}{x^2-4}$

28. $g(x) = \dfrac{x^2-2x-8}{x^2-9}$

29. $f(x) = \dfrac{x-4}{x^2-16}$

30. $f(x) = \dfrac{x+1}{x^2-1}$

31. $f(t) = \dfrac{t^2-1}{t-1}$

32. $f(x) = \dfrac{x^2-36}{x+6}$

33. $f(x) = \dfrac{x^2-25}{x^2-4x-5}$

34. $f(x) = \dfrac{x^2-4}{x^2-3x+2}$

35. $f(x) = \dfrac{x^2+3x}{x^2+x-6}$

36. $f(x) = \dfrac{5(x+4)}{x^2+x-12}$

37. $f(x) = \dfrac{x^2-3x-4}{2x^2+x-1}$

38. $f(x) = \dfrac{6x^2-11x+3}{6x^2-7x-3}$

39. $f(x) = \dfrac{2x^2-5x-3}{x^3-2x^2-x+2}$

40. $f(x) = \dfrac{x^2-x-2}{x^3-2x^2-5x+6}$

Matching a Rational Function with Its Graph In Exercises 41–44, match the rational function with its graph. [The graphs are labeled (a), (b), (c), and (d).]

(a)

(b)

(c)

(d)

41. $f(x) = \dfrac{4}{x+5}$

42. $f(x) = \dfrac{5}{x-2}$

43. $f(x) = \dfrac{2x^2}{x^2-1}$

44. $f(x) = \dfrac{3}{(x-2)^2}$

Analytical and Graphical Analysis In Exercises 45–48, (a) state the domains of f and g, (b) use a graphing utility to graph f and g in the same viewing window, and (c) explain why the graphing utility may not show the difference in the domains of f and g.

45. $f(x) = \dfrac{x^2 - 1}{x + 1}, \quad g(x) = x - 1$

46. $f(x) = \dfrac{x^2(x - 2)}{x^2 - 2x}, \quad g(x) = x$

47. $f(x) = \dfrac{x - 2}{x^2 - 2x}, \quad g(x) = \dfrac{1}{x}$

48. $f(x) = \dfrac{2x - 6}{x^2 - 7x + 12}, \quad g(x) = \dfrac{2}{x - 4}$

A Rational Function with a Slant Asymptote In Exercises 49–62, (a) state the domain of the function, (b) identify all intercepts, (c) find any vertical or slant asymptotes, and (d) plot additional solution points as needed to sketch the graph of the rational function.

49. $h(x) = \dfrac{x^2 - 9}{x}$

50. $g(x) = \dfrac{x^2 + 5}{x}$

51. $f(x) = \dfrac{2x^2 + 1}{x}$

52. $f(x) = \dfrac{1 - x^2}{x}$

53. $g(x) = \dfrac{x^2 + 1}{x}$

54. $h(x) = \dfrac{x^2}{x - 1}$

55. $f(t) = -\dfrac{t^2 + 1}{t + 5}$

56. $f(x) = \dfrac{x^2}{3x + 1}$

57. $f(x) = \dfrac{x^3}{x^2 - 4}$

58. $g(x) = \dfrac{x^3}{2x^2 - 8}$

59. $f(x) = \dfrac{x^2 - x + 1}{x - 1}$

60. $f(x) = \dfrac{2x^2 - 5x + 5}{x - 2}$

61. $f(x) = \dfrac{2x^3 - x^2 - 2x + 1}{x^2 + 3x + 2}$

62. $f(x) = \dfrac{2x^3 + x^2 - 8x - 4}{x^2 - 3x + 2}$

Graphical Analysis In Exercises 63–66, use a graphing utility to graph the rational function. State the domain of the function and find any asymptotes. Then zoom out sufficiently far so that the graph appears as a line. Identify the line.

63. $f(x) = \dfrac{x^2 + 5x + 8}{x + 3}$

64. $f(x) = \dfrac{2x^2 + x}{x + 1}$

65. $g(x) = \dfrac{1 + 3x^2 - x^3}{x^2}$

66. $h(x) = \dfrac{12 - 2x - x^2}{2(4 + x)}$

Graphical Reasoning In Exercises 67–70, (a) use the graph to determine any x-intercepts of the graph of the rational function and (b) set $y = 0$ and solve the resulting equation to confirm your result in part (a).

67. $y = \dfrac{x + 1}{x - 3}$

68. $y = \dfrac{2x}{x - 3}$

69. $y = \dfrac{1}{x} - x$

70. $y = x - 3 + \dfrac{2}{x}$

71. Recycling

The cost C (in dollars) of supplying recycling bins to $p\%$ of the population of a rural township is given by

$$C = \dfrac{25{,}000p}{100 - p}, \quad 0 \le p < 100.$$

(a) Use a graphing utility to graph the cost function.

(b) Find the costs of supplying bins to 15%, 50%, and 90% of the population.

(c) According to the model, would it be possible to supply bins to 100% of the population? Explain.

72. Population Growth The game commission introduces 100 deer into newly acquired state game lands. The population N of the herd is modeled by

$$N = \dfrac{20(5 + 3t)}{1 + 0.04t}, \quad t \ge 0$$

where t is the time in years.

(a) Use a graphing utility to graph the model.

(b) Find the populations when $t = 5$, $t = 10$, and $t = 25$.

(c) What is the limiting size of the herd as time increases?

73. Page Design A page that is x inches wide and y inches high contains 30 square inches of print. The top and bottom margins are each 1 inch deep, and the margins on each side are 2 inches wide (see figure).

(a) Write a function for the total area A of the page in terms of x.

(b) Determine the domain of the function based on the physical constraints of the problem.

(c) Use a graphing utility to graph the area function and approximate the page size for which the least amount of paper is used.

74. Page Design A rectangular page contains 64 square inches of print. The margins at the top and bottom of the page are each 1 inch deep. The margins on each side are $1\frac{1}{2}$ inches wide. What should the dimensions of the page be so that the least amount of paper is used?

75. Average Speed A driver averaged 50 miles per hour on the round trip between two cities 100 miles apart. The average speeds for going and returning were x and y miles per hour, respectively.

(a) Show that $y = (25x)/(x - 25)$.

(b) Determine the vertical and horizontal asymptotes of the graph of the function.

(c) Use a graphing utility to graph the function.

(d) Complete the table.

x	30	35	40	45	50	55	60
y							

(e) Are the results in the table what you expected? Explain.

(f) Is it possible to average 20 miles per hour in one direction and still average 50 miles per hour on the round trip? Explain.

Exploration

76. Writing Is every rational function a polynomial function? Is every polynomial function a rational function? Explain.

True or False? In Exercises 77–79, determine whether the statement is true or false. Justify your answer.

77. The graph of a polynomial function can have infinitely many vertical asymptotes.

78. The graph of a rational function can never cross one of its asymptotes.

79. The graph of a rational function can have a vertical asymptote, a horizontal asymptote, and a slant asymptote.

80. HOW DO YOU SEE IT? The graph of a rational function

$$f(x) = \frac{N(x)}{D(x)}$$

is shown below. Determine which of the statements about the function is false. Justify your answer.

(a) $D(1) = 0$.

(b) The degrees of $N(x)$ and $D(x)$ are equal.

(c) The ratio of the leading coefficients of $N(x)$ and $D(x)$ is 1.

Multiple Choice In Exercises 81 and 82, identify which rational function the graph represents.

81.

(a) $f(x) = \dfrac{x^2 - 9}{x^2 - 4}$

(b) $f(x) = \dfrac{x^2 - 4}{x^2 - 9}$

(c) $f(x) = \dfrac{x - 4}{x^2 - 9}$

(d) $f(x) = \dfrac{x - 9}{x^2 - 4}$

82.

(a) $f(x) = \dfrac{x^2 - 1}{x^2 + 1}$

(b) $f(x) = \dfrac{x^2 + 1}{x^2 - 1}$

(c) $f(x) = \dfrac{x}{x^2 - 1}$

(d) $f(x) = \dfrac{x}{x^2 + 1}$

Project: Department of Defense To work an extended application analyzing the total numbers of military personnel on active duty from 1980 through 2010, visit this text's website at *LarsonPrecalculus.com*. (*Source: U.S. Department of Defense*)

2.7 Nonlinear Inequalities

■ Solve polynomial inequalities.
■ Solve rational inequalities.
■ Use inequalities to model and solve real-life problems.

Polynomial Inequalities

To solve a polynomial inequality such as $x^2 - 2x - 3 < 0$, you can use the fact that a polynomial can change signs only at its zeros (the x-values that make the polynomial equal to zero). Between two consecutive zeros, a polynomial must be entirely positive or entirely negative. This means that when the real zeros of a polynomial are put in order, they divide the real number line into intervals in which the polynomial has no sign changes. These zeros are the **key numbers** of the inequality, and the resulting intervals are the *test intervals* for the inequality. For instance, the polynomial above factors as

$$x^2 - 2x - 3 = (x + 1)(x - 3)$$

and has two zeros,

$$x = -1 \quad \text{and} \quad x = 3.$$

These zeros divide the real number line into three test intervals:

$$(-\infty, -1), \quad (-1, 3), \quad \text{and} \quad (3, \infty). \qquad \text{(See figure.)}$$

So, to solve the inequality $x^2 - 2x - 3 < 0$, you need only test one value from each of these test intervals. When a value from a test interval satisfies the original inequality, you can conclude that the interval is a solution of the inequality.

Three test intervals for $x^2 - 2x - 3$

You can use the same basic approach to determine the test intervals for any polynomial.

> **Finding Test Intervals for a Polynomial**
>
> To determine the intervals on which the values of a polynomial are entirely negative or entirely positive, use the following steps.
>
> 1. Find all real zeros of the polynomial, and arrange the zeros in increasing order (from least to greatest). These zeros are the key numbers of the polynomial.
>
> 2. Use the key numbers of the polynomial to determine its test intervals.
>
> 3. Choose one representative x-value in each test interval and evaluate the polynomial at that value. When the value of the polynomial is negative, the polynomial has negative values for every x-value in the interval. When the value of the polynomial is positive, the polynomial has positive values for every x-value in the interval.

You can use inequalities to model and solve real-life problems. For instance, in Exercises 73 and 74 on page 188, you will use a polynomial inequality to model the height of a projectile.

EXAMPLE 1 **Solving a Polynomial Inequality**

Solve $x^2 - x - 6 < 0$. Then graph the solution set.

▷ **ALGEBRA HELP** You
can review the techniques
for factoring polynomials
in Appendix A.3.

Solution By factoring the polynomial as

$$x^2 - x - 6 = (x + 2)(x - 3)$$

you can see that the key numbers are $x = -2$ and $x = 3$. So, the polynomial's test intervals are

$$(-\infty, -2), \quad (-2, 3), \quad \text{and} \quad (3, \infty). \qquad \text{Test intervals}$$

In each test interval, choose a representative x-value and evaluate the polynomial.

Test Interval	x-Value	Polynomial Value	Conclusion
$(-\infty, -2)$	$x = -3$	$(-3)^2 - (-3) - 6 = 6$	Positive
$(-2, 3)$	$x = 0$	$(0)^2 - (0) - 6 = -6$	Negative
$(3, \infty)$	$x = 4$	$(4)^2 - (4) - 6 = 6$	Positive

From this, you can conclude that the inequality is satisfied for all x-values in $(-2, 3)$. This implies that the solution of the inequality

$$x^2 - x - 6 < 0$$

is the interval $(-2, 3)$, as shown below. Note that the original inequality contains a "less than" symbol. This means that the solution set does not contain the endpoints of the test interval $(-2, 3)$.

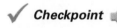

✓ **Checkpoint** ◄))) *Audio-video solution in English & Spanish at LarsonPrecalculus.com.*

Solve $x^2 - x - 20 < 0$. Then graph the solution set. ∎

As with linear inequalities, you can check the reasonableness of a solution by substituting x-values into the original inequality. For instance, to check the solution found in Example 1, try substituting several x-values from the interval $(-2, 3)$ into the inequality

$$x^2 - x - 6 < 0.$$

Regardless of which x-values you choose, the inequality should be satisfied.

You can also use a graph to check the result of Example 1. Sketch the graph of

$$y = x^2 - x - 6$$

as shown in Figure 2.33. Notice that the graph is below the x-axis on the interval $(-2, 3)$.

In Example 1, the polynomial inequality was given in general form (with the polynomial on one side and zero on the other). Whenever this is not the case, you should begin the solution process by writing the inequality in general form.

Figure 2.33

EXAMPLE 2   **Solving a Polynomial Inequality**

Solve $2x^3 - 3x^2 - 32x > -48$. Then graph the solution set.

Solution

$$2x^3 - 3x^2 - 32x + 48 > 0 \qquad \text{Write in general form.}$$

$$(x - 4)(x + 4)(2x - 3) > 0 \qquad \text{Factor.}$$

The key numbers are $x = -4$, $x = \frac{3}{2}$, and $x = 4$, and the test intervals are $(-\infty, -4)$, $\left(-4, \frac{3}{2}\right)$, $\left(\frac{3}{2}, 4\right)$, and $(4, \infty)$.

Test Interval	x-Value	Polynomial Value	Conclusion
$(-\infty, -4)$	$x = -5$	$2(-5)^3 - 3(-5)^2 - 32(-5) + 48 = -117$	Negative
$\left(-4, \frac{3}{2}\right)$	$x = 0$	$2(0)^3 - 3(0)^2 - 32(0) + 48 = 48$	Positive
$\left(\frac{3}{2}, 4\right)$	$x = 2$	$2(2)^3 - 3(2)^2 - 32(2) + 48 = -12$	Negative
$(4, \infty)$	$x = 5$	$2(5)^3 - 3(5)^2 - 32(5) + 48 = 63$	Positive

From this, you can conclude that the inequality is satisfied on the open intervals $\left(-4, \frac{3}{2}\right)$ and $(4, \infty)$. So, the solution set is $\left(-4, \frac{3}{2}\right) \cup (4, \infty)$, as shown below.

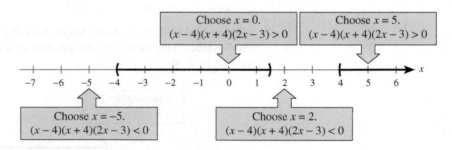

✓ *Checkpoint* ◀))) *Audio-video solution in English & Spanish at LarsonPrecalculus.com.*

Solve $3x^3 - x^2 - 12x > -4$. Then graph the solution set.

EXAMPLE 3   **Solving a Polynomial Inequality**

Solve $4x^2 - 5x > 6$.

Algebraic Solution

$$4x^2 - 5x - 6 > 0 \qquad \text{Write in general form.}$$

$$(x - 2)(4x + 3) > 0 \qquad \text{Factor.}$$

Key Numbers: $x = -\frac{3}{4}$, $x = 2$

Test Intervals: $\left(-\infty, -\frac{3}{4}\right)$, $\left(-\frac{3}{4}, 2\right)$, $(2, \infty)$

Test: Is $(x - 2)(4x + 3) > 0$?

After testing these intervals, you can see that the polynomial $4x^2 - 5x - 6$ is positive on the open intervals $\left(-\infty, -\frac{3}{4}\right)$ and $(2, \infty)$. So, the solution set of the inequality is $\left(-\infty, -\frac{3}{4}\right) \cup (2, \infty)$.

Graphical Solution

First write the polynomial inequality $4x^2 - 5x > 6$ as $4x^2 - 5x - 6 > 0$. Then use a graphing utility to graph $y = 4x^2 - 5x - 6$. In the figure below, you can see that the graph is *above* the x-axis when x is less than $-\frac{3}{4}$ or when x is greater than 2. So, the solution set is $\left(-\infty, -\frac{3}{4}\right) \cup (2, \infty)$.

✓ *Checkpoint* ◀))) *Audio-video solution in English & Spanish at LarsonPrecalculus.com.*

Solve $2x^2 + 3x < 5$ (a) algebraically and (b) graphically.

You may find it easier to determine the sign of a polynomial from its *factored* form. For instance, in Example 3, when you substitute the test value $x = 1$ into the factored form

$$(x - 2)(4x + 3)$$

you can see that the sign pattern of the factors is

$$(-)(+)$$

which yields a negative result. Try using the factored forms of the polynomials to determine the signs of the polynomials in the test intervals of the other examples in this section.

When solving a polynomial inequality, be sure to account for the particular type of inequality symbol given in the inequality. For instance, in Example 3, note that the original inequality contained a "greater than" symbol and the solution consisted of two open intervals. If the original inequality had been

$$4x^2 - 5x \geq 6$$

then the solution set would have been $\left(-\infty, -\frac{3}{4}\right] \cup [2, \infty)$.

Each of the polynomial inequalities in Examples 1, 2, and 3 has a solution set that consists of a single interval or the union of two intervals. When solving the exercises for this section, watch for unusual solution sets, as illustrated in Example 4.

EXAMPLE 4   Unusual Solution Sets

a. The solution set of

$$x^2 + 2x + 4 > 0$$

consists of the entire set of real numbers, $(-\infty, \infty)$. In other words, the value of the quadratic $x^2 + 2x + 4$ is positive for every real value of x.

b. The solution set of

$$x^2 + 2x + 1 \leq 0$$

consists of the single real number $\{-1\}$, because the quadratic $x^2 + 2x + 1$ has only one key number, $x = -1$, and it is the only value that satisfies the inequality.

c. The solution set of

$$x^2 + 3x + 5 < 0$$

is empty. In other words, the quadratic $x^2 + 3x + 5$ is not less than zero for any value of x.

d. The solution set of

$$x^2 - 4x + 4 > 0$$

consists of all real numbers except $x = 2$. In interval notation, this solution set can be written as $(-\infty, 2) \cup (2, \infty)$.

✓ **Checkpoint** 🔊)) *Audio-video solution in English & Spanish at LarsonPrecalculus.com.*

What is unusual about the solution set of each inequality?

a. $x^2 + 6x + 9 < 0$

b. $x^2 + 4x + 4 \leq 0$

c. $x^2 - 6x + 9 > 0$

d. $x^2 - 2x + 1 \geq 0$

Rational Inequalities

The concepts of key numbers and test intervals can be extended to rational inequalities. Use the fact that the value of a rational expression can change sign only at its *zeros* (the *x*-values for which its numerator is zero) and its *undefined values* (the *x*-values for which its denominator is zero). These two types of numbers make up the *key numbers* of a rational inequality. When solving a rational inequality, begin by writing the inequality in general form with the rational expression on the left and zero on the right.

EXAMPLE 5 **Solving a Rational Inequality**

Solve $\dfrac{2x-7}{x-5} \le 3$. Then graph the solution set.

Solution

$$\frac{2x-7}{x-5} \le 3 \qquad \text{Write original inequality.}$$

$$\frac{2x-7}{x-5} - 3 \le 0 \qquad \text{Write in general form.}$$

$$\frac{2x-7-3x+15}{x-5} \le 0 \qquad \text{Find the LCD and subtract fractions.}$$

$$\frac{-x+8}{x-5} \le 0 \qquad \text{Simplify.}$$

Key Numbers: $x = 5, x = 8$ Zeros and undefined values of rational expression

Test Intervals: $(-\infty, 5), (5, 8), (8, \infty)$

Test: Is $\dfrac{-x+8}{x-5} \le 0$?

After testing these intervals, as shown below, you can see that the inequality is satisfied on the open intervals $(-\infty, 5)$ and $(8, \infty)$. Moreover, because

$$\frac{-x+8}{x-5} = 0$$

when $x = 8$, you can conclude that the solution set consists of all real numbers in the intervals $(-\infty, 5) \cup [8, \infty)$. (Be sure to use a bracket to indicate that *x* can equal 8.)

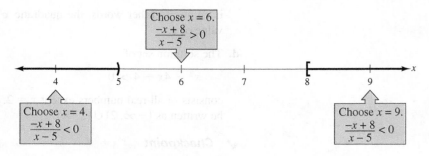

> **• • REMARK** In Example 5, write 3 as $\frac{3}{1}$. You should be able to see that the LCD (least common denominator) is $(x-5)(1) = x-5$. So, you can rewrite the general form as
> $$\frac{2x-7}{x-5} - \frac{3(x-5)}{x-5} \le 0,$$
> which simplifies as shown.

✓ **Checkpoint** ◀))) *Audio-video solution in English & Spanish at LarsonPrecalculus.com.*

Solve each inequality. Then graph the solution set.

a. $\dfrac{x-2}{x-3} \ge -3$

b. $\dfrac{4x-1}{x-6} > 3$

Applications

One common application of inequalities comes from business and involves profit, revenue, and cost. The formula that relates these three quantities is

$$\boxed{\text{Profit}} = \boxed{\text{Revenue}} - \boxed{\text{Cost}}$$

$$P = R - C.$$

EXAMPLE 6 **Increasing the Profit for a Product**

The marketing department of a calculator manufacturer has determined that the demand for a new model of calculator is

$$p = 100 - 0.00001x, \quad 0 \le x \le 10{,}000{,}000 \qquad \text{Demand equation}$$

where p is the price per calculator (in dollars) and x represents the number of calculators sold. (According to this model, no one would be willing to pay \$100 for the calculator. At the other extreme, the company could not *give* away more than 10 million calculators.) The revenue for selling x calculators is

$$R = xp = x(100 - 0.00001x) \qquad \text{Revenue equation}$$

as shown in Figure 2.34. The total cost of producing x calculators is \$10 per calculator plus a one-time development cost of \$2,500,000. So, the total cost is

$$C = 10x + 2{,}500{,}000. \qquad \text{Cost equation}$$

What prices can the company charge per calculator to obtain a profit of at least \$190,000,000?

Calculators

Figure 2.34

Solution

Verbal Model: $\boxed{\text{Profit}} = \boxed{\text{Revenue}} - \boxed{\text{Cost}}$

Equation: $P = R - C$

$$P = 100x - 0.00001x^2 - (10x + 2{,}500{,}000)$$

$$P = -0.00001x^2 + 90x - 2{,}500{,}000$$

To answer the question, solve the inequality

$$P \ge 190{,}000{,}000$$

$$-0.00001x^2 + 90x - 2{,}500{,}000 \ge 190{,}000{,}000.$$

When you write the inequality in general form, find the key numbers and the test intervals, and then test a value in each test interval, you can find the solution to be

$$3{,}500{,}000 \le x \le 5{,}500{,}000$$

as shown in Figure 2.35. Substituting the x-values in the original demand equation shows that prices of

$$\$45.00 \le p \le \$65.00$$

will yield a profit of at least \$190,000,000.

Calculators

Figure 2.35

✓ **Checkpoint** 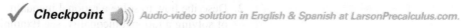 Audio-video solution in English & Spanish at LarsonPrecalculus.com.

The revenue and cost equations for a product are

$$R = x(60 - 0.0001x) \quad \text{and} \quad C = 12x + 1{,}800{,}000$$

where R and C are measured in dollars and x represents the number of units sold. How many units must be sold to obtain a profit of at least \$3,600,000?

Another common application of inequalities is finding the domain of an expression that involves a square root, as shown in Example 7.

EXAMPLE 7   Finding the Domain of an Expression

Find the domain of $\sqrt{64 - 4x^2}$.

Algebraic Solution

Recall that the domain of an expression is the set of all x-values for which the expression is defined. Because $\sqrt{64 - 4x^2}$ is defined (has real values) only if $64 - 4x^2$ is nonnegative, the domain is given by $64 - 4x^2 \geq 0$.

$$64 - 4x^2 \geq 0 \qquad \text{Write in general form.}$$

$$16 - x^2 \geq 0 \qquad \text{Divide each side by 4.}$$

$$(4 - x)(4 + x) \geq 0 \qquad \text{Write in factored form.}$$

So, the inequality has two key numbers: $x = -4$ and $x = 4$. You can use these two numbers to test the inequality, as follows.

Key numbers: $x = -4, x = 4$

Test intervals: $(-\infty, -4), (-4, 4), (4, \infty)$

Test: Is $(4 - x)(4 + x) \geq 0$?

A test shows that the inequality is satisfied in the *closed interval* $[-4, 4]$. So, the domain of the expression $\sqrt{64 - 4x^2}$ is the interval $[-4, 4]$.

Graphical Solution

Begin by sketching the graph of the equation $y = \sqrt{64 - 4x^2}$, as shown below. From the graph, you can determine that the x-values extend from -4 to 4 (including -4 and 4). So, the domain of the expression $\sqrt{64 - 4x^2}$ is the interval $[-4, 4]$.

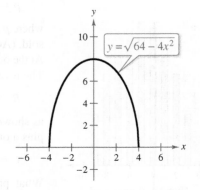

$$y = \sqrt{64 - 4x^2}$$

✓ *Checkpoint* 🔊))) *Audio-video solution in English & Spanish at LarsonPrecalculus.com.*

Find the domain of $\sqrt{x^2 - 7x + 10}$.

To analyze a test interval, choose a representative x-value in the interval and evaluate the expression at that value. For instance, in Example 7, when you substitute any number from the interval $[-4, 4]$ into the expression $\sqrt{64 - 4x^2}$, you obtain a nonnegative number under the radical symbol that simplifies to a real number. When you substitute any number from the intervals $(-\infty, -4)$ and $(4, \infty)$, you obtain a complex number. It might be helpful to draw a visual representation of the intervals, as shown below.

Summarize   (Section 2.7)

1. Describe how to solve a polynomial inequality *(pages 180–183).* For examples of solving polynomial inequalities, see Examples 1–4.

2. Describe how to solve a rational inequality *(page 184).* For an example of solving a rational inequality, see Example 5.

3. Give an example of an application involving a polynomial inequality *(pages 185 and 186, Examples 6 and 7).*

2.7 Exercises

See CalcChat.com for tutorial help and worked-out solutions to odd-numbered exercises.

Vocabulary: Fill in the blanks.

1. Between two consecutive zeros, a polynomial must be entirely _____ or entirely _____.
2. To solve a polynomial inequality, find the _____ numbers of the polynomial, and use these numbers to create _____ _____ for the inequality.
3. The key numbers of a rational expression are its _____ and its _____ _____.
4. The formula that relates cost, revenue, and profit is _____.

Skills and Applications

Checking Solutions In Exercises 5–8, determine whether each value of x is a solution of the inequality.

Inequality	Values
5. $x^2 - 3 < 0$	(a) $x = 3$ (b) $x = 0$
	(c) $x = \frac{3}{2}$ (d) $x = -5$
6. $x^2 - x - 12 \geq 0$	(a) $x = 5$ (b) $x = 0$
	(c) $x = -4$ (d) $x = -3$
7. $\dfrac{x + 2}{x - 4} \geq 3$	(a) $x = 5$ (b) $x = 4$
	(c) $x = -\frac{9}{2}$ (d) $x = \frac{9}{2}$
8. $\dfrac{3x^2}{x^2 + 4} < 1$	(a) $x = -2$ (b) $x = -1$
	(c) $x = 0$ (d) $x = 3$

Finding Key Numbers In Exercises 9–12, find the key numbers of the expression.

9. $3x^2 - x - 2$ **10.** $9x^3 - 25x^2$

11. $\dfrac{1}{x - 5} + 1$ **12.** $\dfrac{x}{x + 2} - \dfrac{2}{x - 1}$

Solving a Polynomial Inequality In Exercises 13–34, solve the inequality. Then graph the solution set.

13. $x^2 < 9$ **14.** $x^2 \leq 16$

15. $(x + 2)^2 \leq 25$ **16.** $(x - 3)^2 \geq 1$

17. $x^2 + 4x + 4 \geq 9$ **18.** $x^2 - 6x + 9 < 16$

19. $x^2 + x < 6$ **20.** $x^2 + 2x > 3$

21. $x^2 + 2x - 3 < 0$ **22.** $x^2 > 2x + 8$

23. $3x^2 - 11x > 20$ **24.** $-2x^2 + 6x \leq -15$

25. $x^2 - 3x - 18 > 0$ **26.** $x^3 + 2x^2 - 4x \leq 8$

27. $x^3 - 3x^2 - x > -3$ **28.** $2x^3 + 13x^2 - 8x \geq 52$

29. $4x^3 - 6x^2 < 0$ **30.** $4x^3 - 12x^2 > 0$

31. $x^3 - 4x \geq 0$ **32.** $2x^3 - x^4 \leq 0$

33. $(x - 1)^2(x + 2)^3 \geq 0$ **34.** $x^4(x - 3) \leq 0$

Unusual Solution Sets In Exercises 35–38, explain what is unusual about the solution set of the inequality.

35. $4x^2 - 4x + 1 \leq 0$ **36.** $x^2 + 3x + 8 > 0$

37. $x^2 - 6x + 12 \leq 0$ **38.** $x^2 - 8x + 16 > 0$

Solving a Rational Inequality In Exercises 39–52, solve the inequality. Then graph the solution set.

39. $\dfrac{4x - 1}{x} > 0$ **40.** $\dfrac{x^2 - 1}{x} < 0$

41. $\dfrac{3x - 5}{x - 5} \geq 0$ **42.** $\dfrac{5 + 7x}{1 + 2x} \leq 4$

43. $\dfrac{x + 6}{x + 1} - 2 < 0$ **44.** $\dfrac{x + 12}{x + 2} - 3 \geq 0$

45. $\dfrac{2}{x + 5} > \dfrac{1}{x - 3}$ **46.** $\dfrac{5}{x - 6} > \dfrac{3}{x + 2}$

47. $\dfrac{1}{x - 3} \leq \dfrac{9}{4x + 3}$ **48.** $\dfrac{1}{x} \geq \dfrac{1}{x + 3}$

49. $\dfrac{x^2 + 2x}{x^2 - 9} \leq 0$ **50.** $\dfrac{x^2 + x - 6}{x} \geq 0$

51. $\dfrac{3}{x - 1} + \dfrac{2x}{x + 1} > -1$ **52.** $\dfrac{3x}{x - 1} \leq \dfrac{x}{x + 4} + 3$

Graphical Analysis In Exercises 53–60, use a graphing utility to graph the equation. Use the graph to approximate the values of x that satisfy each inequality.

Equation	Inequalities
53. $y = -x^2 + 2x + 3$	(a) $y \leq 0$ (b) $y \geq 3$
54. $y = \frac{1}{2}x^2 - 2x + 1$	(a) $y \leq 0$ (b) $y \geq 7$
55. $y = \frac{1}{8}x^3 - \frac{1}{2}x$	(a) $y \geq 0$ (b) $y \leq 6$
56. $y = x^3 - x^2 - 16x + 16$	(a) $y \leq 0$ (b) $y \geq 36$
57. $y = \dfrac{3x}{x - 2}$	(a) $y \leq 0$ (b) $y \geq 6$
58. $y = \dfrac{2(x - 2)}{x + 1}$	(a) $y \leq 0$ (b) $y \geq 8$
59. $y = \dfrac{2x^2}{x^2 + 4}$	(a) $y \geq 1$ (b) $y \leq 2$
60. $y = \dfrac{5x}{x^2 + 4}$	(a) $y \geq 1$ (b) $y \leq 0$

Finding the Domain of an Expression In Exercises 61–66, find the domain of the expression. Use a graphing utility to verify your result.

61. $\sqrt{4 - x^2}$

62. $\sqrt{x^2 - 4}$

63. $\sqrt{x^2 - 9x + 20}$

64. $\sqrt{81 - 4x^2}$

65. $\sqrt{\dfrac{x}{x^2 - 2x - 35}}$

66. $\sqrt{\dfrac{x}{x^2 - 9}}$

Solving an Inequality In Exercises 67–72, solve the inequality. (Round your answers to two decimal places.)

67. $0.4x^2 + 5.26 < 10.2$

68. $-1.3x^2 + 3.78 > 2.12$

69. $-0.5x^2 + 12.5x + 1.6 > 0$

70. $1.2x^2 + 4.8x + 3.1 < 5.3$

71. $\dfrac{1}{2.3x - 5.2} > 3.4$

72. $\dfrac{2}{3.1x - 3.7} > 5.8$

• • **Height of a Projectile** • • • • • • • • • • • • • •

In Exercises 73 and 74, use the position equation

$s = -16t^2 + v_0 t + s_0$

where s represents the height of an object (in feet), v_0 represents the initial velocity of the object (in feet per second), s_0 represents the initial height of the object (in feet), and t represents the time (in seconds).

73. A projectile is fired straight upward from ground level $(s_0 = 0)$ with an initial velocity of 160 feet per second.

  (a) At what instant will it be back at ground level?

  (b) When will the height exceed 384 feet?

74. A projectile is fired straight upward from ground level $(s_0 = 0)$ with an initial velocity of 128 feet per second.

  (a) At what instant will it be back at ground level?

  (b) When will the height be less than 128 feet?

75. Geometry A rectangular playing field with a perimeter of 100 meters is to have an area of at least 500 square meters. Within what bounds must the length of the rectangle lie?

76. Geometry A rectangular parking lot with a perimeter of 440 feet is to have an area of at least 8000 square feet. Within what bounds must the length of the rectangle lie?

77. Cost, Revenue, and Profit The revenue and cost equations for a product are $R = x(75 - 0.0005x)$ and $C = 30x + 250,000$, where R and C are measured in dollars and x represents the number of units sold. How many units must be sold to obtain a profit of at least $750,000? What is the price per unit?

78. Cost, Revenue, and Profit The revenue and cost equations for a product are $R = x(50 - 0.0002x)$ and $C = 12x + 150,000$, where R and C are measured in dollars and x represents the number of units sold. How many units must be sold to obtain a profit of at least $1,650,000? What is the price per unit?

79. School Enrollment The numbers N (in millions) of students enrolled in schools in the United States from 2000 through 2009 are shown in the table. *(Source: U.S. Census Bureau)*

DATA	Year	Number, N
	2000	72.2
	2001	73.1
	2002	74.0
	2003	74.9
	2004	75.5
	2005	75.8
	2006	75.2
	2007	76.0
	2008	76.3
	2009	77.3

Spreadsheet at LarsonPrecalculus.com

  (a) Use a graphing utility to create a scatter plot of the data. Let t represent the year, with $t = 0$ corresponding to 2000.

  (b) Use the *regression* feature of the graphing utility to find a quartic model for the data. (A quartic model has the form $at^4 + bt^3 + ct^2 + dt + e$, where a, b, c, d, and e are constant and t is variable.)

  (c) Graph the model and the scatter plot in the same viewing window. How well does the model fit the data?

  (d) According to the model, when did the number of students enrolled in schools exceed 74 million?

  (e) Is the model valid for long-term predictions of student enrollment? Explain.

80. Safe Load The maximum safe load uniformly distributed over a one-foot section of a two-inch-wide wooden beam can be approximated by the model

Load $= 168.5d^2 - 472.1$

where d is the depth of the beam.

  (a) Evaluate the model for $d = 4$, $d = 6$, $d = 8$, $d = 10$, and $d = 12$. Use the results to create a bar graph.

  (b) Determine the minimum depth of the beam that will safely support a load of 2000 pounds.

81. Resistors When two resistors of resistances R_1 and R_2 are connected in parallel (see figure), the total resistance R satisfies the equation

$$\frac{1}{R} = \frac{1}{R_1} + \frac{1}{R_2}.$$

Find R_1 for a parallel circuit in which $R_2 = 2$ ohms and R must be at least 1 ohm.

82. Teachers' Salaries The mean salaries S (in thousands of dollars) of public school classroom teachers in the United States from 2000 through 2011 are shown in the table.

DATA Year	Salary, S
2000	42.2
2001	43.7
2002	43.8
2003	45.0
2004	45.6
2005	45.9
2006	48.2
2007	49.3
2008	51.3
2009	52.9
2010	54.4
2011	54.2

Spreadsheet at LarsonPrecalculus.com

A model that approximates these data is given by

$$S = \frac{42.16 - 0.236t}{1 - 0.026t}, \quad 0 \le t \le 11$$

where t represents the year, with $t = 0$ corresponding to 2000. (*Source: Educational Research Service, Arlington, VA*)

(a) Use a graphing utility to create a scatter plot of the data. Then graph the model in the same viewing window.

(b) How well does the model fit the data? Explain.

(c) Use the model to predict when the salary for classroom teachers will exceed $60,000.

(d) Is the model valid for long-term predictions of classroom teacher salaries? Explain.

Exploration

True or False? In Exercises 83 and 84, determine whether the statement is true or false. Justify your answer.

83. The zeros of the polynomial $x^3 - 2x^2 - 11x + 12 \ge 0$ divide the real number line into four test intervals.

84. The solution set of the inequality $\frac{3}{2}x^2 + 3x + 6 \ge 0$ is the entire set of real numbers.

Conjecture In Exercises 85–88, (a) find the interval(s) for b such that the equation has at least one real solution and (b) write a conjecture about the interval(s) based on the values of the coefficients.

85. $x^2 + bx + 4 = 0$

86. $x^2 + bx - 4 = 0$

87. $3x^2 + bx + 10 = 0$

88. $2x^2 + bx + 5 = 0$

89. Graphical Analysis You can use a graphing utility to verify the results in Example 4. For instance, the graph of $y = x^2 + 2x + 4$ is shown below. Notice that the y-values are greater than 0 for all values of x, as stated in Example 4(a). Use the graphing utility to graph $y = x^2 + 2x + 1$, $y = x^2 + 3x + 5$, and $y = x^2 - 4x + 4$. Explain how you can use the graphs to verify the results of parts (b), (c), and (d) of Example 4.

90. **HOW DO YOU SEE IT?** Consider the polynomial

$$(x - a)(x - b)$$

and the real number line shown below.

(a) Identify the points on the line at which the polynomial is zero.

(b) In each of the three subintervals of the line, write the sign of each factor and the sign of the product.

(c) At what x-values does the polynomial change signs?

Chapter Summary

	What Did You Learn?	Explanation/Examples	Review Exercises
Section 2.1	Analyze graphs of quadratic functions (p. 114).	Let a, b, and c be real numbers with $a \neq 0$. The function $f(x) = ax^2 + bx + c$ is called a quadratic function. Its graph is a "U"-shaped curve called a parabola.	1, 2
	Write quadratic functions in standard form and use the results to sketch graphs of functions (p. 117).	The quadratic function $f(x) = a(x - h)^2 + k$, $a \neq 0$, is in standard form. The graph of f is a parabola whose axis is the vertical line $x = h$ and whose vertex is (h, k). When $a > 0$, the parabola opens upward. When $a < 0$, the parabola opens downward.	3–8
	Find minimum and maximum values of quadratic functions in real-life applications (p. 119).	Consider $f(x) = ax^2 + bx + c$ with vertex $\left(-\dfrac{b}{2a}, f\left(-\dfrac{b}{2a}\right)\right)$. When $a > 0$, f has a *minimum* at $x = -b/(2a)$. When $a < 0$, f has a *maximum* at $x = -b/(2a)$.	9, 10
Section 2.2	Use transformations to sketch graphs of polynomial functions (p. 124).	The graph of a polynomial function is continuous (no breaks, holes, or gaps) and has only smooth, rounded turns.	11, 12
	Use the Leading Coefficient Test to determine the end behaviors of graphs of polynomial functions (p. 126).	Consider the graph of $f(x) = a_n x^n + \cdots + a_1 x + a_0$. **When n is odd:** If $a_n > 0$, then the graph falls to the left and rises to the right. If $a_n < 0$, then the graph rises to the left and falls to the right. **When n is even:** If $a_n > 0$, then the graph rises to the left and to the right. If $a_n < 0$, then the graph falls to the left and to the right.	13–16
	Find and use the real zeros of polynomial functions as sketching aids (p. 128).	When f is a polynomial function and a is a real number, the following are equivalent: (1) $x = a$ is a *zero* of f, (2) $x = a$ is a *solution* of the equation $f(x) = 0$, (3) $(x - a)$ is a *factor* of $f(x)$, and (4) $(a, 0)$ is an *x-intercept* of the graph of f.	17–20
	Use the Intermediate Value Theorem to help locate the real zeros of polynomial functions (p. 131).	Let a and b be real numbers such that $a < b$. If f is a polynomial function such that $f(a) \neq f(b)$, then, in $[a, b]$, f takes on every value between $f(a)$ and $f(b)$.	21, 22
Section 2.3	Use long division to divide polynomials by other polynomials (p. 138).	Dividend $\longrightarrow$ Quotient $\longrightarrow$ Remainder $$\dfrac{x^2 + 3x + 5}{x + 1} = x + 2 + \dfrac{3}{x + 1}$$ Divisor $\longrightarrow x + 1$; $x + 1 \longleftarrow$ Divisor	23, 24
	Use synthetic division to divide polynomials by binomials of the form $(x - k)$ (p. 141).	Divisor: $x + 3$ Dividend: $x^4 - 10x^2 - 2x + 4$ $$\begin{array}{r|rrrrr} -3 & 1 & 0 & -10 & -2 & 4 \\ & & -3 & 9 & 3 & -3 \\ \hline & 1 & -3 & -1 & 1 & \boxed{1} \end{array}$$ $\longleftarrow$ Remainder: 1 Quotient: $x^3 - 3x^2 - x + 1$	25, 26
	Use the Remainder Theorem and the Factor Theorem (p. 142).	**The Remainder Theorem:** If a polynomial $f(x)$ is divided by $x - k$, then the remainder is $r = f(k)$. **The Factor Theorem:** A polynomial $f(x)$ has a factor $(x - k)$ if and only if $f(k) = 0$.	27, 28

	What Did You Learn?	Explanation/Examples	Review Exercises
Section 2.4	Use the imaginary unit i to write complex numbers (p. 147).	When a and b are real numbers, $a + bi$ is a complex number. Two complex numbers $a + bi$ and $c + di$, written in standard form, are equal to each other if and only if $a = c$ and $b = d$.	29, 30
	Add, subtract, and multiply complex numbers (p. 148).	**Sum:** $(a + bi) + (c + di) = (a + c) + (b + d)i$ **Difference:** $(a + bi) - (c + di) = (a - c) + (b - d)i$	31–34
	Use complex conjugates to write the quotient of two complex numbers in standard form (p. 150).	The numbers $a + bi$ and $a - bi$ are complex conjugates. To write $(a + bi)/(c + di)$ in standard form, where c and d are not both zero, multiply the numerator and denominator by $c - di$.	35, 36
	Find complex solutions of quadratic equations (p. 151).	When a is a positive real number, the principal square root of $-a$ is defined as $\sqrt{-a} = \sqrt{a}i$.	37, 38
Section 2.5	Use the Fundamental Theorem of Algebra to determine the number of zeros of polynomial functions (p. 154).	**The Fundamental Theorem of Algebra** If $f(x)$ is a polynomial of degree n, where $n > 0$, then f has at least one zero in the complex number system.	39, 40
	Find rational zeros of polynomial functions (p. 155), and conjugate pairs of complex zeros (p. 158).	The Rational Zero Test relates the possible rational zeros of a polynomial to the leading coefficient and to the constant term of the polynomial. Let f be a polynomial function that has real coefficients. If $a + bi$ ($b \neq 0$) is a zero of the function, then the conjugate $a - bi$ is also a zero of the function.	41, 42
	Find zeros of polynomials by factoring (p. 159), using Descartes's Rule of Signs (p. 161), and using the Upper and Lower Bound Rules (p. 162).	Every polynomial of degree $n > 0$ with real coefficients can be written as the product of linear and quadratic factors with real coefficients, where the quadratic factors have no real zeros.	43–46
Section 2.6	Find the domains (p. 168), and vertical and horizontal asymptotes (p. 169), of the graphs of rational functions.	The domain of a rational function of x includes all real numbers except x-values that make the denominator zero. The line $x = a$ is a vertical asymptote of the graph of f when $f(x) \to \infty$ or $f(x) \to -\infty$ as $x \to a$, either from the right or from the left. The line $y = b$ is a horizontal asymptote of the graph of f when $f(x) \to b$ as $x \to \infty$ or $x \to -\infty$.	47, 48
	Sketch the graphs of rational functions (p. 171), including functions with slant asymptotes (p. 174).	Consider a rational function whose denominator is of degree 1 or greater. If the degree of the numerator is exactly *one more* than the degree of the denominator, then the graph of the function has a slant asymptote.	49–56
	Use rational functions to model and solve real-life problems (p. 175).	A rational function can help you model the cost of removing a given percent of the smokestack pollutants at a utility company that burns coal. (See Example 8.)	57, 58
Section 2.7	Solve polynomial (p. 180) and rational (p. 184) inequalities.	Use the concepts of key numbers and test intervals to solve both polynomial and rational inequalities.	59–62
	Use inequalities to model and solve real-life problems (p. 185).	A common application of inequalities involves profit P, revenue R, and cost C. (See Example 6.)	63

Review Exercises See CalcChat.com for tutorial help and worked-out solutions to odd-numbered exercises.

2.1 Sketching Graphs of Quadratic Functions
In Exercises 1 and 2, sketch the graph of each quadratic function and compare it with the graph of $y = x^2$.

1. (a) $g(x) = -2x^2$ **2.** (a) $h(x) = (x - 3)^2$
(b) $h(x) = x^2 + 2$ (b) $k(x) = \frac{1}{2}x^2 - 1$

Using Standard Form to Graph a Parabola   In Exercises 3–8, write the quadratic function in standard form and sketch its graph. Identify the vertex, axis of symmetry, and x-intercept(s).

3. $g(x) = x^2 - 2x$ **4.** $f(x) = x^2 + 8x + 10$
5. $h(x) = 3 + 4x - x^2$ **6.** $f(t) = -2t^2 + 4t + 1$
7. $h(x) = 4x^2 + 4x + 13$ **8.** $f(x) = \frac{1}{3}(x^2 + 5x - 4)$

9. Geometry The perimeter of a rectangle is 1000 meters.
   (a) Write the width y as a function of the length x. Use the result to write the area A as a function of x.
   (b) Of all possible rectangles with perimeters of 1000 meters, find the dimensions of the one with the maximum area.

10. Minimum Cost A soft-drink manufacturer has daily production costs of $C = 70{,}000 - 120x + 0.055x^2$, where C is the total cost (in dollars) and x is the number of units produced. How many units should the manufacturer produce each day to yield a minimum cost?

2.2 Sketching a Transformation of a Monomial Function   In Exercises 11 and 12, sketch the graphs of $y = x^n$ and the transformation.

11. $y = x^4$, $f(x) = 6 - x^4$ **12.** $y = x^5$, $f(x) = \frac{1}{2}x^5 + 3$

Applying the Leading Coefficient Test   In Exercises 13–16, describe the right-hand and left-hand behavior of the graph of the polynomial function.

13. $f(x) = -2x^2 - 5x + 12$ **14.** $f(x) = \frac{1}{2}x^3 + 2x$
15. $g(x) = \frac{3}{4}(x^4 + 3x^2 + 2)$ **16.** $h(x) = -x^7 + 8x^2 - 8x$

Sketching the Graph of a Polynomial Function
In Exercises 17–20, sketch the graph of the function by (a) applying the Leading Coefficient Test, (b) finding the real zeros of the polynomial, (c) plotting sufficient solution points, and (d) drawing a continuous curve through the points.

17. $g(x) = 2x^3 + 4x^2$
18. $h(x) = 3x^2 - x^4$
19. $f(x) = -x^3 + x^2 - 2$
20. $f(x) = x(x^3 + x^2 - 5x + 3)$

Using the Intermediate Value Theorem   In Exercises 21 and 22, (a) use the Intermediate Value Theorem and the *table* feature of a graphing utility to find intervals one unit in length in which the polynomial function is guaranteed to have a zero. (b) Adjust the table to approximate the zeros of the function. Use the *zero* or *root* feature of the graphing utility to verify your results.

21. $f(x) = 3x^3 - x^2 + 3$ **22.** $f(x) = x^4 - 5x - 1$

2.3 Long Division of Polynomials   In Exercises 23 and 24, use long division to divide.

23. $\dfrac{30x^2 - 3x + 8}{5x - 3}$ **24.** $\dfrac{5x^3 - 21x^2 - 25x - 4}{x^2 - 5x - 1}$

Using the Factor Theorem   In Exercises 25 and 26, use synthetic division to determine whether the given values of x are zeros of the function.

25. $f(x) = 20x^4 + 9x^3 - 14x^2 - 3x$
   (a) $x = -1$ (b) $x = \frac{3}{4}$ (c) $x = 0$ (d) $x = 1$
26. $f(x) = 3x^3 - 8x^2 - 20x + 16$
   (a) $x = 4$ (b) $x = -4$ (c) $x = \frac{2}{3}$ (d) $x = -1$

Factoring a Polynomial   In Exercises 27 and 28, (a) verify the given factor(s) of $f(x)$, (b) find the remaining factors of $f(x)$, (c) use your results to write the complete factorization of $f(x)$, (d) list all real zeros of f, and (e) confirm your results by using a graphing utility to graph the function.

Function	Factor(s)
27. $f(x) = 2x^3 + 11x^2 - 21x - 90$	$(x + 6)$
28. $f(x) = x^4 - 4x^3 - 7x^2 + 22x + 24$	$(x + 2), (x - 3)$

2.4 Writing a Complex Number in Standard Form
In Exercises 29 and 30, write the complex number in standard form.

29. $8 + \sqrt{-100}$ **30.** $-5i + i^2$

Performing Operations with Complex Numbers
In Exercises 31–34, perform the operation and write the result in standard form.

31. $(7 + 5i) + (-4 + 2i)$
32. $(\sqrt{2} - \sqrt{2}i) - (\sqrt{2} + \sqrt{2}i)$
33. $7i(11 - 9i)$ **34.** $(1 + 6i)(5 - 2i)$

Performing Operations with Complex Numbers
In Exercises 35 and 36, perform the operation and write the result in standard form.

35. $\dfrac{6 + i}{4 - i}$ **36.** $\dfrac{4}{2 - 3i} + \dfrac{2}{1 + i}$

Complex Solutions of a Quadratic Equation **In Exercises 37 and 38, use the Quadratic Formula to solve the quadratic equation.**

37. $x^2 - 2x + 10 = 0$ **38.** $6x^2 + 3x + 27 = 0$

2.5 **Zeros of Polynomial Functions** **In Exercises 39 and 40, determine the number of zeros of the polynomial function.**

39. $g(x) = x^2 - 2x - 8$ **40.** $h(t) = t^2 - t^5$

Finding the Zeros of a Polynomial Function **In Exercises 41 and 42, find all the zeros of the function.**

41. $f(x) = x^3 + 3x^2 - 28x - 60$

42. $f(x) = 4x^4 - 11x^3 + 14x^2 - 6x$

Finding the Zeros of a Polynomial Function **In Exercises 43 and 44, write the polynomial as the product of linear factors and list all the zeros of the function.**

43. $g(x) = x^3 - 7x^2 + 36$

44. $f(x) = x^4 + 8x^3 + 8x^2 - 72x - 153$

45. Using Descartes's Rule of Signs Use Descartes's Rule of Signs to determine the possible numbers of positive and negative real zeros of $h(x) = -2x^5 + 4x^3 - 2x^2 + 5$.

46. Verifying Upper and Lower Bounds Use synthetic division to verify the upper and lower bounds of the real zeros of $f(x) = 4x^3 - 3x^2 + 4x - 3$.

(a) Upper: $x = 1$ (b) Lower: $x = -\frac{1}{4}$

2.6 **Finding Domain and Asymptotes** **In Exercises 47 and 48, find the domain and the vertical and horizontal asymptotes of the graph of the rational function.**

47. $f(x) = \dfrac{3x}{x + 10}$

48. $f(x) = \dfrac{8}{x^2 - 10x + 24}$

Sketching the Graph of a Rational Function **In Exercises 49–56, (a) state the domain of the function, (b) identify all intercepts, (c) find any asymptotes, and (d) plot additional solution points as needed to sketch the graph of the rational function.**

49. $f(x) = \dfrac{4}{x}$ **50.** $h(x) = \dfrac{x - 4}{x - 7}$

51. $f(x) = \dfrac{x}{x^2 + 1}$ **52.** $f(x) = \dfrac{2x^2}{x^2 - 4}$

53. $f(x) = \dfrac{6x^2 - 11x + 3}{3x^2 - x}$ **54.** $f(x) = \dfrac{6x^2 - 7x + 2}{4x^2 - 1}$

55. $f(x) = \dfrac{2x^3}{x^2 + 1}$ **56.** $f(x) = \dfrac{x^2 + 1}{x + 1}$

57. Seizure of Illegal Drugs The cost C (in millions of dollars) for the federal government to seize $p\%$ of an illegal drug as it enters the country is given by

$$C = \frac{528p}{100 - p}, \quad 0 \le p < 100.$$

(a) Use a graphing utility to graph the cost function.

(b) Find the costs of seizing 25%, 50%, and 75% of the drug.

(c) According to the model, would it be possible to seize 100% of the drug?

58. Page Design A page that is x inches wide and y inches high contains 30 square inches of print. The top and bottom margins are each 2 inches deep, and the margins on each side are 2 inches wide.

(a) Write a function for the total area A of the page in terms of x.

(b) Determine the domain of the function based on the physical constraints of the problem.

(c) Use a graphing utility to graph the area function and approximate the page size for which the least amount of paper is used.

2.7 **Solving an Inequality** **In Exercises 59–62, solve the inequality. Then graph the solution set.**

59. $12x^2 + 5x < 2$

60. $x^3 - 16x \ge 0$

61. $\dfrac{2}{x + 1} \ge \dfrac{3}{x - 1}$

62. $\dfrac{x^2 - 9x + 20}{x} < 0$

63. Population of a Species A biologist introduces 200 ladybugs into a crop field. The population P of the ladybugs can be approximated by the model

$$P = \frac{1000(1 + 3t)}{5 + t}$$

where t is the time in days. Find the time required for the population to increase to at least 2000 ladybugs.

Exploration

64. Writing Describe what is meant by an asymptote of a graph.

True or False? **In Exercises 65 and 66, determine whether the statement is true or false. Justify your answer.**

65. A fourth-degree polynomial with real coefficients can have -5, $-8i$, $4i$, and 5 as its zeros.

66. The domain of a rational function can never be the set of all real numbers.

Chapter Test

See CalcChat.com for tutorial help and worked-out solutions to odd-numbered exercises.

Figure for 2

Take this test as you would take a test in class. When you are finished, check your work against the answers given in the back of the book.

1. Sketch the graph of each quadratic function and compare it with the graph of $y = x^2$.

   (a) $g(x) = 2 - x^2$

   (b) $g(x) = \left(x - \frac{3}{2}\right)^2$

2. Write the standard form of the equation of the parabola shown in the figure.

3. The path of a ball is given by the function $f(x) = -\frac{1}{20}x^2 + 3x + 5$, where $f(x)$ is the height (in feet) of the ball and x is the horizontal distance (in feet) from where the ball was thrown.

   (a) What is the maximum height of the ball?

   (b) Which number determines the height at which the ball was thrown? Does changing this value change the coordinates of the maximum height of the ball? Explain.

4. Describe the right-hand and left-hand behavior of the graph of the function $h(t) = -\frac{3}{4}t^5 + 2t^2$. Then sketch its graph.

5. Divide using long division.

$$\frac{3x^3 + 4x - 1}{x^2 + 1}$$

6. Divide using synthetic division.

$$\frac{2x^4 - 5x^2 - 3}{x - 2}$$

7. Use synthetic division to show that $x = \frac{5}{2}$ is a zero of the function

$$f(x) = 2x^3 - 5x^2 - 6x + 15.$$

   Use the result to factor the polynomial function completely and list all the zeros of the function.

8. Perform each operation and write the result in standard form.

   (a) $10i - \left(3 + \sqrt{-25}\right)$

   (b) $\left(2 + \sqrt{3}\,i\right)\left(2 - \sqrt{3}\,i\right)$

9. Write the quotient in standard form: $\dfrac{5}{2 + i}$.

In Exercises 10 and 11, find a polynomial function with real coefficients that has the given zeros. (There are many correct answers.)

10. $0, 3, 2 + i$

11. $1 - \sqrt{3}\,i, 2, 2$

In Exercises 12 and 13, find all the zeros of the function.

12. $f(x) = 3x^3 + 14x^2 - 7x - 10$

13. $f(x) = x^4 - 9x^2 - 22x - 24$

In Exercises 14–16, identify any intercepts and asymptotes of the graph of the function. Then sketch a graph of the function.

14. $h(x) = \dfrac{4}{x^2} - 1$

15. $f(x) = \dfrac{2x^2 - 5x - 12}{x^2 - 16}$

16. $g(x) = \dfrac{x^2 + 2}{x - 1}$

In Exercises 17 and 18, solve the inequality. Then graph the solution set.

17. $2x^2 + 5x > 12$

18. $\dfrac{2}{x} \le \dfrac{1}{x + 6}$

Proofs in Mathematics ■ ■ ■ ■ ■ ■ ■ ■ ■ ■ ■ ■ ■ ■ ■

These two pages contain proofs of four important theorems about polynomial functions. The first two theorems are from Section 2.3, and the second two theorems are from Section 2.5.

The Remainder Theorem *(p. 142)*

If a polynomial $f(x)$ is divided by $x - k$, then the remainder is

$$r = f(k).$$

Proof

From the Division Algorithm, you have

$$f(x) = (x - k)q(x) + r(x)$$

and because either $r(x) = 0$ or the degree of $r(x)$ is less than the degree of $x - k$, you know that $r(x)$ must be a constant. That is, $r(x) = r$. Now, by evaluating $f(x)$ at $x = k$, you have

$$f(k) = (k - k)q(k) + r$$
$$= (0)q(k) + r = r.$$

To be successful in algebra, it is important that you understand the connection among *factors* of a polynomial, *zeros* of a polynomial function, and *solutions* or *roots* of a polynomial equation. The Factor Theorem is the basis for this connection.

The Factor Theorem *(p. 143)*

A polynomial $f(x)$ has a factor $(x - k)$ if and only if $f(k) = 0$.

Proof

Using the Division Algorithm with the factor $(x - k)$, you have

$$f(x) = (x - k)q(x) + r(x).$$

By the Remainder Theorem, $r(x) = r = f(k)$, and you have

$$f(x) = (x - k)q(x) + f(k)$$

where $q(x)$ is a polynomial of lesser degree than $f(x)$. If $f(k) = 0$, then

$$f(x) = (x - k)q(x)$$

and you see that $(x - k)$ is a factor of $f(x)$. Conversely, if $(x - k)$ is a factor of $f(x)$, then division of $f(x)$ by $(x - k)$ yields a remainder of 0. So, by the Remainder Theorem, you have $f(k) = 0$.

Linear Factorization Theorem *(p. 154)*

If $f(x)$ is a polynomial of degree n, where $n > 0$, then $f(x)$ has precisely n linear factors

$$f(x) = a_n(x - c_1)(x - c_2) \cdots (x - c_n)$$

where $c_1, c_2, \ldots, c_n$ are complex numbers.

Proof

Using the Fundamental Theorem of Algebra, you know that f must have at least one zero, c_1. Consequently, $(x - c_1)$ is a factor of $f(x)$, and you have

$$f(x) = (x - c_1)f_1(x).$$

If the degree of $f_1(x)$ is greater than zero, then you again apply the Fundamental Theorem of Algebra to conclude that f_1 must have a zero c_2, which implies that

$$f(x) = (x - c_1)(x - c_2)f_2(x).$$

It is clear that the degree of $f_1(x)$ is $n - 1$, that the degree of $f_2(x)$ is $n - 2$, and that you can repeatedly apply the Fundamental Theorem of Algebra n times until you obtain

$$f(x) = a_n(x - c_1)(x - c_2) \cdots (x - c_n)$$

where a_n is the leading coefficient of the polynomial $f(x)$.

Factors of a Polynomial *(p. 159)*

Every polynomial of degree $n > 0$ with real coefficients can be written as the product of linear and quadratic factors with real coefficients, where the quadratic factors have no real zeros.

Proof

To begin, you use the Linear Factorization Theorem to conclude that $f(x)$ can be *completely* factored in the form

$$f(x) = d(x - c_1)(x - c_2)(x - c_3) \cdots (x - c_n).$$

If each c_i is real, then there is nothing more to prove. If any c_i is complex ($c_i = a + bi$, $b \neq 0$), then, because the coefficients of $f(x)$ are real, you know that the conjugate $c_j = a - bi$ is also a zero. By multiplying the corresponding factors, you obtain

$$(x - c_i)(x - c_j) = [x - (a + bi)][x - (a - bi)]$$
$$= x^2 - 2ax + (a^2 + b^2)$$

where each coefficient is real.

P.S. Problem Solving ▪ ▪ ▪ ▪ ▪ ▪ ▪ ▪ ▪ ▪ ▪ ▪ ▪ ▪

1. **Verifying the Remainder Theorem** Show that if $f(x) = ax^3 + bx^2 + cx + d$, then $f(k) = r$, where $r = ak^3 + bk^2 + ck + d$, using long division. In other words, verify the Remainder Theorem for a third-degree polynomial function.

2. **Babylonian Mathematics** In 2000 B.C., the Babylonians solved polynomial equations by referring to tables of values. One such table gave the values of $y^3 + y^2$. To be able to use this table, the Babylonians sometimes had to manipulate the equation, as shown below.

$$ax^3 + bx^2 = c \qquad \text{Original equation}$$

$$\frac{a^3 x^3}{b^3} + \frac{a^2 x^2}{b^2} = \frac{a^2 c}{b^3} \qquad \text{Multiply each side by } \frac{a^2}{b^3}.$$

$$\left(\frac{ax}{b}\right)^3 + \left(\frac{ax}{b}\right)^2 = \frac{a^2 c}{b^3} \qquad \text{Rewrite.}$$

Then they would find $(a^2c)/b^3$ in the $y^3 + y^2$ column of the table. Because they knew that the corresponding y-value was equal to $(ax)/b$, they could conclude that $x = (by)/a$.

(a) Calculate $y^3 + y^2$ for $y = 1, 2, 3, \ldots , 10$. Record the values in a table.

(b) Use the table from part (a) and the method above to solve each equation.

  (i) $x^3 + x^2 = 252$

  (ii) $x^3 + 2x^2 = 288$

  (iii) $3x^3 + x^2 = 90$

  (iv) $2x^3 + 5x^2 = 2500$

  (v) $7x^3 + 6x^2 = 1728$

  (vi) $10x^3 + 3x^2 = 297$

(c) Using the methods from this chapter, verify your solution of each equation.

3. **Finding Dimensions** At a glassware factory, molten cobalt glass is poured into molds to make paperweights. Each mold is a rectangular prism whose height is 3 inches greater than the length of each side of the square base. A machine pours 20 cubic inches of liquid glass into each mold. What are the dimensions of the mold?

4. **True or False?** Determine whether the statement is true or false. If false, provide one or more reasons why the statement is false and correct the statement. Let $f(x) = ax^3 + bx^2 + cx + d$, $a \neq 0$, and let $f(2) = -1$. Then

$$\frac{f(x)}{x + 1} = q(x) + \frac{2}{x + 1}$$

where $q(x)$ is a second-degree polynomial.

5. **Finding the Equation of a Parabola** The parabola shown in the figure has an equation of the form $y = ax^2 + bx + c$. Find the equation of this parabola using the following methods.

(a) Find the equation analytically.

(b) Use the regression feature of a graphing utility to find the equation.

6. **Finding the Slope of a Tangent Line** One of the fundamental themes of calculus is to find the slope of the tangent line to a curve at a point. To see how this can be done, consider the point $(2, 4)$ on the graph of the quadratic function $f(x) = x^2$, as shown in the figure.

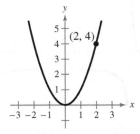

(a) Find the slope m_1 of the line joining $(2, 4)$ and $(3, 9)$. Is the slope of the tangent line at $(2, 4)$ greater than or less than the slope of the line through $(2, 4)$ and $(3, 9)$?

(b) Find the slope m_2 of the line joining $(2, 4)$ and $(1, 1)$. Is the slope of the tangent line at $(2, 4)$ greater than or less than the slope of the line through $(2, 4)$ and $(1, 1)$?

(c) Find the slope m_3 of the line joining $(2, 4)$ and $(2.1, 4.41)$. Is the slope of the tangent line at $(2, 4)$ greater than or less than the slope of the line through $(2, 4)$ and $(2.1, 4.41)$?

(d) Find the slope m_h of the line joining $(2, 4)$ and $(2 + h, f(2 + h))$ in terms of the nonzero number h.

(e) Evaluate the slope formula from part (d) for $h = -1$, 1, and 0.1. Compare these values with those in parts (a)–(c).

(f) What can you conclude the slope m_{tan} of the tangent line at $(2, 4)$ to be? Explain your answer.

7. Writing Cubic Functions Use the form $f(x) = (x - k)q(x) + r$ to write a cubic function that (a) passes through the point $(2, 5)$ and rises to the right and (b) passes through the point $(-3, 1)$ and falls to the right. (There are many correct answers.)

8. Multiplicative Inverse of a Complex Number The multiplicative inverse of z is a complex number z_m such that $z \cdot z_m = 1$. Find the multiplicative inverse of each complex number.

(a) $z = 1 + i$

(b) $z = 3 - i$

(c) $z = -2 + 8i$

9. Proof Prove that the product of a complex number $a + bi$ and its complex conjugate is a real number.

10. Matching Match the graph of the rational function

$$f(x) = \frac{ax + b}{cx + d}$$

with the given conditions.

(a)

(b)

(c)

(d)

(i) $a > 0$ (ii) $a > 0$ (iii) $a < 0$ (iv) $a > 0$
    $b < 0$ $b > 0$ $b > 0$ $b < 0$
    $c > 0$ $c < 0$ $c > 0$ $c > 0$
    $d < 0$ $d < 0$ $d < 0$ $d > 0$

11. Effects of Values on a Graph Consider the function

$$f(x) = \frac{ax}{(x - b)^2}.$$

(a) Determine the effect on the graph of f when $b \neq 0$ and a is varied. Consider cases in which a is positive and a is negative.

(b) Determine the effect on the graph of f when $a \neq 0$ and b is varied.

12. Distinct Vision The endpoints of the interval over which distinct vision is possible are called the *near point* and *far point* of the eye (see figure). With increasing age, these points normally change. The table shows the approximate near points y (in inches) for various ages x (in years).

Object blurry	Object clear	Object blurry

Near point   Far point

Age, x	Near Point, y
16	3.0
32	4.7
44	9.8
50	19.7
60	39.4

(a) Use the *regression* feature of a graphing utility to find a quadratic model for the data. Use the graphing utility to plot the data and graph the model in the same viewing window.

(b) Find a rational model for the data. Take the reciprocals of the near points to generate the points $(x, 1/y)$. Use the *regression* feature of the graphing utility to find a linear model for the data. The resulting line has the form

$$\frac{1}{y} = ax + b.$$

Solve for y. Use the graphing utility to plot the data and graph the model in the same viewing window.

(c) Use the *table* feature of the graphing utility to construct a table showing the predicted near point based on each model for each of the ages in the original table. How well do the models fit the original data?

(d) Use both models to estimate the near point for a person who is 25 years old. Which model is a better fit?

(e) Do you think either model can be used to predict the near point for a person who is 70 years old? Explain.

13. Roots of a Cubic Equation Can a cubic equation with real coefficients have two real zeros and one complex zero? Explain your reasoning.

198

3 Exponential and Logarithmic Functions

3.1 Exponential Functions and Their Graphs
3.2 Logarithmic Functions and Their Graphs
3.3 Properties of Logarithms
3.4 Exponential and Logarithmic Equations
3.5 Exponential and Logarithmic Models

Trees per Acre *(Exercise 83, page 236)*

Sound Intensity *(Exercises 85–88, page 226)*

Nuclear Reactor Accident *(Example 9, page 207)*

Earthquakes
(Example 6, page 244)

Human Memory Model
(Exercise 81, page 220)

3.1 Exponential Functions and Their Graphs

■ Recognize and evaluate exponential functions with base *a*.
■ Graph exponential functions and use the One-to-One Property.
■ Recognize, evaluate, and graph exponential functions with base e.
■ Use exponential functions to model and solve real-life problems.

Exponential Functions

So far, this text has dealt mainly with **algebraic functions,** which include polynomial functions and rational functions. In this chapter, you will study two types of nonalgebraic functions—*exponential functions* and *logarithmic functions*. These functions are examples of **transcendental functions.**

Exponential functions can help you model and solve real-life problems. For instance, Exercise 72 on page 210 uses an exponential function to model the concentration of a drug in the bloodstream.

> ### Definition of Exponential Function
> The **exponential function** *f* **with base** *a* is denoted by
> $$f(x) = a^x$$
> where $a > 0$, $a \neq 1$, and *x* is any real number.

The base $a = 1$ is excluded because it yields $f(x) = 1^x = 1$. This is a constant function, not an exponential function.

You have evaluated a^x for integer and rational values of *x*. For example, you know that $4^3 = 64$ and $4^{1/2} = 2$. However, to evaluate 4^x for any real number *x*, you need to interpret forms with *irrational* exponents. For the purposes of this text, it is sufficient to think of $a^{\sqrt{2}}$ (where $\sqrt{2} \approx 1.41421356$) as the number that has the successively closer approximations

$$a^{1.4}, a^{1.41}, a^{1.414}, a^{1.4142}, a^{1.41421}, \ldots$$

EXAMPLE 1   **Evaluating Exponential Functions**

Use a calculator to evaluate each function at the indicated value of *x*.

	Function	**Value**
a.	$f(x) = 2^x$	$x = -3.1$
b.	$f(x) = 2^{-x}$	$x = \pi$
c.	$f(x) = 0.6^x$	$x = \frac{3}{2}$

Solution

Function Value	**Graphing Calculator Keystrokes**	**Display**
a. $f(-3.1) = 2^{-3.1}$	2 ∧ (−) 3.1 ENTER	0.1166291
b. $f(\pi) = 2^{-\pi}$	2 ∧ (−) π ENTER	0.1133147
c. $f\left(\frac{3}{2}\right) = (0.6)^{3/2}$	.6 ∧ (3 ÷ 2) ENTER	0.4647580

✓ *Checkpoint* ◀))) *Audio-video solution in English & Spanish at LarsonPrecalculus.com.*

Use a calculator to evaluate $f(x) = 8^{-x}$ at $x = \sqrt{2}$. ■

When evaluating exponential functions with a calculator, remember to enclose fractional exponents in parentheses. Because the calculator follows the order of operations, parentheses are crucial in order to obtain the correct result.

Graphs of Exponential Functions

The graphs of all exponential functions have similar characteristics, as shown in Examples 2, 3, and 5.

▷ **ALGEBRA HELP** You can review the techniques for sketching the graph of an equation in Section 1.2.

EXAMPLE 2   **Graphs of $y = a^x$**

In the same coordinate plane, sketch the graph of each function.

a. $f(x) = 2^x$

b. $g(x) = 4^x$

Solution The following table lists some values for each function, and Figure 3.1 shows the graphs of the two functions. Note that both graphs are increasing. Moreover, the graph of $g(x) = 4^x$ is increasing more rapidly than the graph of $f(x) = 2^x$.

x	-3	-2	-1	0	1	2
2^x	$\frac{1}{8}$	$\frac{1}{4}$	$\frac{1}{2}$	1	2	4
4^x	$\frac{1}{64}$	$\frac{1}{16}$	$\frac{1}{4}$	1	4	16

✓ **Checkpoint** ◄))) *Audio-video solution in English & Spanish at LarsonPrecalculus.com.*

In the same coordinate plane, sketch the graph of each function.

a. $f(x) = 3^x$ **b.** $g(x) = 9^x$

Figure 3.1

The table in Example 2 was evaluated by hand. You could, of course, use a graphing utility to construct tables with even more values.

EXAMPLE 3   **Graphs of $y = a^{-x}$**

In the same coordinate plane, sketch the graph of each function.

a. $F(x) = 2^{-x}$

b. $G(x) = 4^{-x}$

Solution The following table lists some values for each function, and Figure 3.2 shows the graphs of the two functions. Note that both graphs are decreasing. Moreover, the graph of $G(x) = 4^{-x}$ is decreasing more rapidly than the graph of $F(x) = 2^{-x}$.

x	-2	-1	0	1	2	3
2^{-x}	4	2	1	$\frac{1}{2}$	$\frac{1}{4}$	$\frac{1}{8}$
4^{-x}	16	4	1	$\frac{1}{4}$	$\frac{1}{16}$	$\frac{1}{64}$

Figure 3.2

✓ **Checkpoint** ◄))) *Audio-video solution in English & Spanish at LarsonPrecalculus.com.*

In the same coordinate plane, sketch the graph of each function.

a. $f(x) = 3^{-x}$ **b.** $g(x) = 9^{-x}$

Note that it is possible to use one of the properties of exponents to rewrite the functions in Example 3 with positive exponents, as follows.

$$F(x) = 2^{-x} = \frac{1}{2^x} = \left(\frac{1}{2}\right)^x \quad \text{and} \quad G(x) = 4^{-x} = \frac{1}{4^x} = \left(\frac{1}{4}\right)^x$$

Comparing the functions in Examples 2 and 3, observe that

$$F(x) = 2^{-x} = f(-x) \quad \text{and} \quad G(x) = 4^{-x} = g(-x).$$

Consequently, the graph of F is a reflection (in the y-axis) of the graph of f. The graphs of G and g have the same relationship. The graphs in Figures 3.1 and 3.2 are typical of the exponential functions $y = a^x$ and $y = a^{-x}$. They have one y-intercept and one horizontal asymptote (the x-axis), and they are continuous. The following summarizes the basic characteristics of these exponential functions.

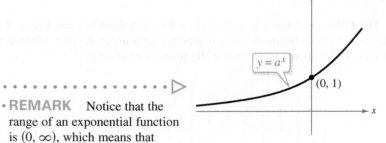

Graph of $y = a^x$, $a > 1$
- Domain: $(-\infty, \infty)$
- Range: $(0, \infty)$
- y-intercept: $(0, 1)$
- Increasing
- x-axis is a horizontal asymptote
  ($a^x \to 0$ as $x \to -\infty$).
- Continuous

REMARK Notice that the range of an exponential function is $(0, \infty)$, which means that $a^x > 0$ for all values of x.

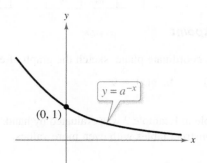

Graph of $y = a^{-x}$, $a > 1$
- Domain: $(-\infty, \infty)$
- Range: $(0, \infty)$
- y-intercept: $(0, 1)$
- Decreasing
- x-axis is a horizontal asymptote
  ($a^{-x} \to 0$ as $x \to \infty$).
- Continuous

Notice that the graph of an exponential function is always increasing or always decreasing. As a result, the graphs pass the Horizontal Line Test, and therefore the functions are one-to-one functions. You can use the following **One-to-One Property** to solve simple exponential equations.

For $a > 0$ and $a \neq 1$, $a^x = a^y$ if and only if $x = y$. One-to-One Property

EXAMPLE 4 **Using the One-to-One Property**

a. $9 = 3^{x+1}$ Original equation

$3^2 = 3^{x+1}$ $9 = 3^2$

$2 = x + 1$ One-to-One Property

$1 = x$ Solve for x.

b. $\left(\frac{1}{2}\right)^x = 8$ Original equation

$2^{-x} = 2^3$ $\left(\frac{1}{2}\right)^x = 2^{-x}, 8 = 2^3$

$x = -3$ One-to-One Property

✓ *Checkpoint* *Audio-video solution in English & Spanish at LarsonPrecalculus.com.*

Use the One-to-One Property to solve the equation for x.

a. $8 = 2^{2x-1}$ **b.** $\left(\frac{1}{3}\right)^{-x} = 27$

In the following example, notice how the graph of $y = a^x$ can be used to sketch the graphs of functions of the form $f(x) = b \pm a^{x+c}$.

▷ **ALGEBRA HELP** You can review the techniques for transforming the graph of a function in Section 1.7.

EXAMPLE 5 **Transformations of Graphs of Exponential Functions**

Each of the following graphs is a transformation of the graph of $f(x) = 3^x$.

a. Because $g(x) = 3^{x+1} = f(x + 1)$, the graph of g can be obtained by shifting the graph of f one unit to the *left*, as shown in Figure 3.3.

b. Because $h(x) = 3^x - 2 = f(x) - 2$, the graph of h can be obtained by shifting the graph of f *down* two units, as shown in Figure 3.4.

c. Because $k(x) = -3^x = -f(x)$, the graph of k can be obtained by *reflecting* the graph of f in the x-axis, as shown in Figure 3.5.

d. Because $j(x) = 3^{-x} = f(-x)$, the graph of j can be obtained by *reflecting* the graph of f in the y-axis, as shown in Figure 3.6.

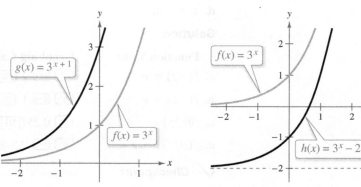

Figure 3.3 Horizontal shift   **Figure 3.4** Vertical shift

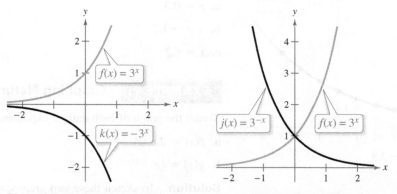

Figure 3.5 Reflection in x-axis   **Figure 3.6** Reflection in y-axis

✓ *Checkpoint* ◀))) *Audio-video solution in English & Spanish at LarsonPrecalculus.com.*

Use the graph of $f(x) = 4^x$ to describe the transformation that yields the graph of each function.

a. $g(x) = 4^{x-2}$ **b.** $h(x) = 4^x + 3$ **c.** $k(x) = 4^{-x} - 3$ ■

Notice that the transformations in Figures 3.3, 3.5, and 3.6 keep the x-axis as a horizontal asymptote, but the transformation in Figure 3.4 yields a new horizontal asymptote of $y = -2$. Also, be sure to note how each transformation affects the y-intercept.

The Natural Base e

In many applications, the most convenient choice for a base is the irrational number

$$e \approx 2.718281828 \ldots.$$

This number is called the **natural base**. The function $f(x) = e^x$ is called the **natural exponential function**. Figure 3.7 shows its graph. Be sure you see that for the exponential function $f(x) = e^x$, e is the constant $2.718281828 \ldots$, whereas x is the variable.

Figure 3.7

EXAMPLE 6　**Evaluating the Natural Exponential Function**

Use a calculator to evaluate the function $f(x) = e^x$ at each value of x.

a. $x = -2$

b. $x = -1$

c. $x = 0.25$

d. $x = -0.3$

Solution

Function Value	Graphing Calculator Keystrokes	Display
a. $f(-2) = e^{-2}$	$\boxed{e^x}$ $\boxed{(-)}$ 2 $\boxed{\text{ENTER}}$	0.1353353
b. $f(-1) = e^{-1}$	$\boxed{e^x}$ $\boxed{(-)}$ 1 $\boxed{\text{ENTER}}$	0.3678794
c. $f(0.25) = e^{0.25}$	$\boxed{e^x}$ 0.25 $\boxed{\text{ENTER}}$	1.2840254
d. $f(-0.3) = e^{-0.3}$	$\boxed{e^x}$ $\boxed{(-)}$ 0.3 $\boxed{\text{ENTER}}$	0.7408182

✓ **Checkpoint** Audio-video solution in English & Spanish at LarsonPrecalculus.com.

Use a calculator to evaluate the function $f(x) = e^x$ at each value of x.

a. $x = 0.3$

b. $x = -1.2$

c. $x = 6.2$

Figure 3.8

EXAMPLE 7　**Graphing Natural Exponential Functions**

Sketch the graph of each natural exponential function.

a. $f(x) = 2e^{0.24x}$

b. $g(x) = \frac{1}{2}e^{-0.58x}$

Solution　To sketch these two graphs, use a graphing utility to construct a table of values, as follows. After constructing the table, plot the points and connect them with smooth curves, as shown in Figures 3.8 and 3.9. Note that the graph in Figure 3.8 is increasing, whereas the graph in Figure 3.9 is decreasing.

x	-3	-2	-1	0	1	2	3
$f(x)$	0.974	1.238	1.573	2.000	2.542	3.232	4.109
$g(x)$	2.849	1.595	0.893	0.500	0.280	0.157	0.088

Figure 3.9

✓ **Checkpoint** Audio-video solution in English & Spanish at LarsonPrecalculus.com.

Sketch the graph of $f(x) = 5e^{0.17x}$.

Applications

One of the most familiar examples of exponential growth is an investment earning *continuously compounded interest*. The formula for *interest compounded n times per year* is

$$A = P\left(1 + \frac{r}{n}\right)^{nt}.$$

In this formula, A is the balance in the account, P is the principal (or original deposit), r is the annual interest rate (in decimal form), n is the number of compoundings per year, and t is the time in years. Using exponential functions, you can *develop* this formula and show how it leads to continuous compounding.

Suppose you invest a principal P at an annual interest rate r, compounded once per year. If the interest is added to the principal at the end of the year, then the new balance P_1 is

$$P_1 = P + Pr$$
$$= P(1 + r).$$

This pattern of multiplying the previous principal by $1 + r$ repeats each successive year, as follows.

Year	Balance After Each Compounding
0	$P = P$
1	$P_1 = P(1 + r)$
2	$P_2 = P_1(1 + r) = P(1 + r)(1 + r) = P(1 + r)^2$
3	$P_3 = P_2(1 + r) = P(1 + r)^2(1 + r) = P(1 + r)^3$
⋮	⋮
t	$P_t = P(1 + r)^t$

To accommodate more frequent (quarterly, monthly, or daily) compounding of interest, let n be the number of compoundings per year and let t be the number of years. Then the rate per compounding is r/n and the account balance after t years is

$$A = P\left(1 + \frac{r}{n}\right)^{nt}. \qquad \text{Amount (balance) with } n \text{ compoundings per year}$$

When you let the number of compoundings n increase without bound, the process approaches what is called **continuous compounding.** In the formula for n compoundings per year, let $m = n/r$. This produces

$$A = P\left(1 + \frac{r}{n}\right)^{nt} \qquad \text{Amount with } n \text{ compoundings per year}$$

$$= P\left(1 + \frac{r}{mr}\right)^{mrt} \qquad \text{Substitute } mr \text{ for } n.$$

$$= P\left(1 + \frac{1}{m}\right)^{mrt} \qquad \text{Simplify.}$$

$$= P\left[\left(1 + \frac{1}{m}\right)^m\right]^{rt}. \qquad \text{Property of exponents}$$

m	$\left(1 + \dfrac{1}{m}\right)^m$
1	2
10	2.59374246
100	2.704813829
1,000	2.716923932
10,000	2.718145927
100,000	2.718268237
1,000,000	2.718280469
10,000,000	2.718281693
↓	↓
∞	e

As m increases without bound (that is, as $m \to \infty$), the table at the left shows that $[1 + (1/m)]^m \to e$. From this, you can conclude that the formula for continuous compounding is

$$A = Pe^{rt}. \qquad \text{Substitute } e \text{ for } (1 + 1/m)^m.$$

•• REMARK   Be sure you see
that, when using the formulas
for compound interest, you must
write the annual interest rate in
decimal form. For instance, you
must write 6% as 0.06.

⋅⋅⋅⋅⋅⋅⋅⋅⋅⋅⋅⋅⋅⋅⋅⋅⋅⋅▷

Formulas for Compound Interest

After t years, the balance A in an account with principal P and annual interest
rate r (in decimal form) is given by the following formulas.

1. For n compoundings per year: $A = P\left(1 + \dfrac{r}{n}\right)^{nt}$

2. For continuous compounding: $A = Pe^{rt}$

EXAMPLE 8   **Compound Interest**

You invest \$12,000 at an annual rate of 3%. Find the balance after 5 years when the
interest is compounded

a. quarterly.

b. monthly.

c. continuously.

Solution

a. For quarterly compounding, you have $n = 4$. So, in 5 years at 3%, the balance is

$$A = P\left(1 + \frac{r}{n}\right)^{nt} \qquad \text{Formula for compound interest}$$

$$= 12{,}000\left(1 + \frac{0.03}{4}\right)^{4(5)} \qquad \text{Substitute for } P, r, n, \text{ and } t.$$

$$\approx \$13{,}934.21. \qquad \text{Use a calculator.}$$

b. For monthly compounding, you have $n = 12$. So, in 5 years at 3%, the balance is

$$A = P\left(1 + \frac{r}{n}\right)^{nt} \qquad \text{Formula for compound interest}$$

$$= 12{,}000\left(1 + \frac{0.03}{12}\right)^{12(5)} \qquad \text{Substitute for } P, r, n, \text{ and } t.$$

$$\approx \$13{,}939.40. \qquad \text{Use a calculator.}$$

c. For continuous compounding, the balance is

$$A = Pe^{rt} \qquad \text{Formula for continuous compounding}$$

$$= 12{,}000e^{0.03(5)} \qquad \text{Substitute for } P, r, \text{ and } t.$$

$$\approx \$13{,}942.01. \qquad \text{Use a calculator.}$$

✓ *Checkpoint* ◀))) *Audio-video solution in English & Spanish at LarsonPrecalculus.com.*

You invest \$6000 at an annual rate of 4%. Find the balance after 7 years when the interest
is compounded

a. quarterly.

b. monthly.

c. continuously.

In Example 8, note that continuous compounding yields more than quarterly and
monthly compounding. This is typical of the two types of compounding. That is, for a
given principal, interest rate, and time, continuous compounding will always yield a
larger balance than compounding n times per year.

EXAMPLE 9   Radioactive Decay

In 1986, a nuclear reactor accident occurred in Chernobyl in what was then the Soviet Union. The explosion spread highly toxic radioactive chemicals, such as plutonium (^{239}Pu), over hundreds of square miles, and the government evacuated the city and the surrounding area. To see why the city is now uninhabited, consider the model

$$P = 10\left(\frac{1}{2}\right)^{t/24,100}$$

which represents the amount of plutonium P that remains (from an initial amount of 10 pounds) after t years. Sketch the graph of this function over the interval from $t = 0$ to $t = 100,000$, where $t = 0$ represents 1986. How much of the 10 pounds will remain in the year 2017? How much of the 10 pounds will remain after 100,000 years?

The International Atomic Energy Authority ranks nuclear incidents and accidents by severity using a scale from 1 to 7 called the International Nuclear and Radiological Event Scale (INES). A level 7 ranking is the most severe. To date, the Chernobyl accident is the only nuclear accident in history to be given an INES level 7 ranking.

Solution The graph of this function is shown in the figure at the right. Note from this graph that plutonium has a *half-life* of about 24,100 years. That is, after 24,100 years, *half* of the original amount will remain. After another 24,100 years, one-quarter of the original amount will remain, and so on. In the year 2017 ($t = 31$), there will still be

$$P = 10\left(\frac{1}{2}\right)^{31/24,100}$$

$$\approx 10\left(\frac{1}{2}\right)^{0.0012863}$$

$$\approx 9.991 \text{ pounds}$$

Radioactive Decay

$P = 10\left(\frac{1}{2}\right)^{t/24,100}$

(24,100, 5)

(100,000, 0.564)

Plutonium (in pounds)

Years of decay

of plutonium remaining. After 100,000 years, there will still be

$$P = 10\left(\frac{1}{2}\right)^{100,000/24,100}$$

$$\approx 0.564 \text{ pound}$$

of plutonium remaining.

 Checkpoint 🔊))) *Audio-video solution in English & Spanish at LarsonPrecalculus.com.*

In Example 9, how much of the 10 pounds will remain in the year 2089? How much of the 10 pounds will remain after 125,000 years?

Summarize   (Section 3.1)

1. State the definition of an exponential function f with base a *(page 200)*. For an example of evaluating exponential functions, see Example 1.

2. Describe the basic characteristics of the exponential functions $y = a^x$ and $y = a^{-x}$, $a > 1$ *(page 202)*. For examples of graphing exponential functions, see Examples 2, 3, and 5.

3. State the definitions of the natural base and the natural exponential function *(page 204)*. For examples of evaluating and graphing natural exponential functions, see Examples 6 and 7.

4. Describe examples of how to use exponential functions to model and solve real-life problems *(pages 206 and 207, Examples 8 and 9)*.

3.1 Exercises

See CalcChat.com for tutorial help and worked-out solutions to odd-numbered exercises.

Vocabulary: Fill in the blanks.

1. Polynomial and rational functions are examples of _____ functions.
2. Exponential and logarithmic functions are examples of nonalgebraic functions, also called _____ functions.
3. You can use the _____ Property to solve simple exponential equations.
4. The exponential function $f(x) = e^x$ is called the _____ _____ function, and the base e is called the _____ base.
5. To find the amount A in an account after t years with principal P and an annual interest rate r compounded n times per year, you can use the formula _____.
6. To find the amount A in an account after t years with principal P and an annual interest rate r compounded continuously, you can use the formula _____.

Skills and Applications

Evaluating an Exponential Function In Exercises 7–12, evaluate the function at the indicated value of x. Round your result to three decimal places.

Function	Value
7. $f(x) = 0.9^x$	$x = 1.4$
8. $f(x) = 2.3^x$	$x = \frac{3}{2}$
9. $f(x) = 5^x$	$x = -\pi$
10. $f(x) = \left(\frac{2}{3}\right)^{5x}$	$x = \frac{3}{10}$
11. $g(x) = 5000(2^x)$	$x = -1.5$
12. $f(x) = 200(1.2)^{12x}$	$x = 24$

Matching an Exponential Function with Its Graph In Exercises 13–16, match the exponential function with its graph. [The graphs are labeled (a), (b), (c), and (d).]

(a)

(b)

(c)

(d)

13. $f(x) = 2^x$
14. $f(x) = 2^x + 1$
15. $f(x) = 2^{-x}$
16. $f(x) = 2^{x-2}$

Graphing an Exponential Function In Exercises 17–22, use a graphing utility to construct a table of values for the function. Then sketch the graph of the function.

17. $f(x) = \left(\frac{1}{2}\right)^x$
18. $f(x) = \left(\frac{1}{2}\right)^{-x}$
19. $f(x) = 6^{-x}$
20. $f(x) = 6^x$
21. $f(x) = 2^{x-1}$
22. $f(x) = 4^{x-3} + 3$

Using the One-to-One Property In Exercises 23–26, use the One-to-One Property to solve the equation for x.

23. $3^{x+1} = 27$
24. $2^{x-3} = 16$
25. $\left(\frac{1}{2}\right)^x = 32$
26. $5^{x-2} = \frac{1}{125}$

Transforming the Graph of an Exponential Function In Exercises 27–30, use the graph of f to describe the transformation that yields the graph of g.

27. $f(x) = 3^x$, $g(x) = 3^x + 1$
28. $f(x) = 10^x$, $g(x) = 10^{-x+3}$
29. $f(x) = \left(\frac{7}{2}\right)^x$, $g(x) = -\left(\frac{7}{2}\right)^{-x}$
30. $f(x) = 0.3^x$, $g(x) = -0.3^x + 5$

Graphing an Exponential Function In Exercises 31–34, use a graphing utility to graph the exponential function.

31. $y = 2^{-x^2}$
32. $y = 3^{-|x|}$
33. $y = 3^{x-2} + 1$
34. $y = 4^{x+1} - 2$

Evaluating a Natural Exponential Function In Exercises 35–38, evaluate the function at the indicated value of x. Round your result to three decimal places.

Function	Value
35. $f(x) = e^x$	$x = 3.2$
36. $f(x) = 1.5e^{x/2}$	$x = 240$
37. $f(x) = 5000e^{0.06x}$	$x = 6$
38. $f(x) = 250e^{0.05x}$	$x = 20$

Graphing a Natural Exponential Function In Exercises 39–44, use a graphing utility to construct a table of values for the function. Then sketch the graph of the function.

39. $f(x) = e^x$

40. $f(x) = e^{-x}$

41. $f(x) = 3e^{x+4}$

42. $f(x) = 2e^{-0.5x}$

43. $f(x) = 2e^{x-2} + 4$

44. $f(x) = 2 + e^{x-5}$

Graphing a Natural Exponential Function In Exercises 45–50, use a graphing utility to graph the exponential function.

45. $y = 1.08e^{-5x}$

46. $y = 1.08e^{5x}$

47. $s(t) = 2e^{0.12t}$

48. $s(t) = 3e^{-0.2t}$

49. $g(x) = 1 + e^{-x}$

50. $h(x) = e^{x-2}$

Using the One-to-One Property In Exercises 51–54, use the One-to-One Property to solve the equation for x.

51. $e^{3x+2} = e^3$

52. $e^{2x-1} = e^4$

53. $e^{x^2-3} = e^{2x}$

54. $e^{x^2+6} = e^{5x}$

Compound Interest In Exercises 55–58, complete the table to determine the balance A for P dollars invested at rate r for t years and compounded n times per year.

n	1	2	4	12	365	Continuous
A						

55. $P = \$1500, r = 2\%, t = 10$ years

56. $P = \$2500, r = 3.5\%, t = 10$ years

57. $P = \$2500, r = 4\%, t = 20$ years

58. $P = \$1000, r = 6\%, t = 40$ years

Compound Interest In Exercises 59–62, complete the table to determine the balance A for \$12,000 invested at rate r for t years, compounded continuously.

t	10	20	30	40	50
A					

59. $r = 4\%$

60. $r = 6\%$

61. $r = 6.5\%$

62. $r = 3.5\%$

63. Trust Fund On the day of a child's birth, a parent deposits \$30,000 in a trust fund that pays 5% interest, compounded continuously. Determine the balance in this account on the child's 25th birthday.

64. Trust Fund A philanthropist deposits \$5000 in a trust fund that pays 7.5% interest, compounded continuously. The balance will be given to the college from which the philanthropist graduated after the money has earned interest for 50 years. How much will the college receive?

65. Inflation Assuming that the annual rate of inflation averages 4% over the next 10 years, the approximate costs C of goods or services during any year in that decade will be modeled by $C(t) = P(1.04)^t$, where t is the time in years and P is the present cost. The price of an oil change for your car is presently \$23.95. Estimate the price 10 years from now.

66. Computer Virus The number V of computers infected by a virus increases according to the model $V(t) = 100e^{4.6052t}$, where t is the time in hours. Find the number of computers infected after (a) 1 hour, (b) 1.5 hours, and (c) 2 hours.

67. Population Growth The projected populations of the United States for the years 2020 through 2050 can be modeled by $P = 290.323e^{0.0083t}$, where P is the population (in millions) and t is the time (in years), with $t = 20$ corresponding to 2020. *(Source: U.S. Census Bureau)*

(a) Use a graphing utility to graph the function for the years 2020 through 2050.

(b) Use the *table* feature of the graphing utility to create a table of values for the same time period as in part (a).

(c) According to the model, during what year will the population of the United States exceed 400 million?

68. Population The populations P (in millions) of Italy from 2000 through 2012 can be approximated by the model $P = 57.563e^{0.0052t}$, where t represents the year, with $t = 0$ corresponding to 2000. *(Source: U.S. Census Bureau, International Data Base)*

(a) According to the model, is the population of Italy increasing or decreasing? Explain.

(b) Find the populations of Italy in 2000 and 2012.

(c) Use the model to predict the populations of Italy in 2020 and 2025.

69. Radioactive Decay Let Q represent a mass of radioactive plutonium (^{239}Pu) (in grams), whose half-life is 24,100 years. The quantity of plutonium present after t years is $Q = 16\left(\frac{1}{2}\right)^{t/24,100}$.

(a) Determine the initial quantity (when $t = 0$).

(b) Determine the quantity present after 75,000 years.

(c) Use a graphing utility to graph the function over the interval $t = 0$ to $t = 150,000$.

70. Radioactive Decay Let Q represent a mass of carbon 14 (^{14}C) (in grams), whose half-life is 5715 years. The quantity of carbon 14 present after t years is $Q = 10\left(\frac{1}{2}\right)^{t/5715}$.

(a) Determine the initial quantity (when $t = 0$).

(b) Determine the quantity present after 2000 years.

(c) Sketch the graph of this function over the interval $t = 0$ to $t = 10,000$.

71. Depreciation   After t years, the value of a wheelchair conversion van that originally cost $49,810 depreciates so that each year it is worth $\frac{7}{8}$ of its value for the previous year.

(a) Find a model for $V(t)$, the value of the van after t years.

(b) Determine the value of the van 4 years after it was purchased.

72. Drug Concentration

Immediately following an injection, the concentration of a drug in the bloodstream is 300 milligrams per milliliter. After t hours, the concentration is 75% of the level of the previous hour.

(a) Find a model for $C(t)$, the concentration of the drug after t hours.

(b) Determine the concentration of the drug after 8 hours.

Exploration

True or False?   In Exercises 73 and 74, determine whether the statement is true or false. Justify your answer.

73. The line $y = -2$ is an asymptote for the graph of $f(x) = 10^x - 2$.

74. $e = \dfrac{271,801}{99,990}$

Think About It   In Exercises 75–78, use properties of exponents to determine which functions (if any) are the same.

75. $f(x) = 3^{x-2}$
$g(x) = 3^x - 9$
$h(x) = \frac{1}{9}(3^x)$

76. $f(x) = 4^x + 12$
$g(x) = 2^{2x+6}$
$h(x) = 64(4^x)$

77. $f(x) = 16(4^{-x})$
$g(x) = \left(\frac{1}{4}\right)^{x-2}$
$h(x) = 16(2^{-2x})$

78. $f(x) = e^{-x} + 3$
$g(x) = e^{3-x}$
$h(x) = -e^{x-3}$

79. Solving Inequalities   Graph the functions $y = 3^x$ and $y = 4^x$ and use the graphs to solve each inequality.

(a) $4^x < 3^x$ (b) $4^x > 3^x$

80. Graphical Analysis   Use a graphing utility to graph each function. Use the graph to find where the function is increasing and decreasing, and approximate any relative maximum or minimum values.

(a) $f(x) = x^2 e^{-x}$ (b) $g(x) = x2^{3-x}$

81. Graphical Analysis   Use a graphing utility to graph $y_1 = (1 + 1/x)^x$ and $y_2 = e$ in the same viewing window. Using the *trace* feature, explain what happens to the graph of y_1 as x increases.

82. Graphical Analysis   Use a graphing utility to graph

$$f(x) = \left(1 + \frac{0.5}{x}\right)^x \quad \text{and} \quad g(x) = e^{0.5}$$

in the same viewing window. What is the relationship between f and g as x increases and decreases without bound?

83. Graphical Analysis   Use a graphing utility to graph each pair of functions in the same viewing window. Describe any similarities and differences in the graphs.

(a) $y_1 = 2^x$, $y_2 = x^2$

(b) $y_1 = 3^x$, $y_2 = x^3$

84.   **HOW DO YOU SEE IT?**   The figure shows the graphs of $y = 2^x$, $y = e^x$, $y = 10^x$, $y = 2^{-x}$, $y = e^{-x}$, and $y = 10^{-x}$. Match each function with its graph. [The graphs are labeled (a) through (f).] Explain your reasoning.

85. Think About It   Which functions are exponential?

(a) $3x$

(b) $3x^2$

(c) 3^x

(d) 2^{-x}

86. Compound Interest   Use the formula

$$A = P\left(1 + \frac{r}{n}\right)^{nt}$$

to calculate the balance of an investment when $P = \$3000$, $r = 6\%$, and $t = 10$ years, and compounding is done (a) by the day, (b) by the hour, (c) by the minute, and (d) by the second. Does increasing the number of compoundings per year result in unlimited growth of the balance? Explain.

Project: Population per Square Mile   To work an extended application analyzing the population per square mile of the United States, visit this text's website at *LarsonPrecalculus.com*.   (*Source: U.S. Census Bureau*)

3.2 Logarithmic Functions and Their Graphs

- Recognize and evaluate logarithmic functions with base *a*.
- Graph logarithmic functions.
- Recognize, evaluate, and graph natural logarithmic functions.
- Use logarithmic functions to model and solve real-life problems.

Logarithmic Functions

Logarithmic functions can often model scientific observations. For instance, Exercise 81 on page 220 uses a logarithmic function to model human memory.

In Section 1.9, you studied the concept of an inverse function. There, you learned that when a function is one-to-one—that is, when the function has the property that no horizontal line intersects the graph of the function more than once—the function must have an inverse function. By looking back at the graphs of the exponential functions introduced in Section 3.1, you will see that every function of the form $f(x) = a^x$ passes the Horizontal Line Test and therefore must have an inverse function. This inverse function is called the **logarithmic function with base *a*.**

Definition of Logarithmic Function with Base *a*

For $x > 0$, $a > 0$, and $a \neq 1$,

$$y = \log_a x \text{ if and only if } x = a^y.$$

The function

$$f(x) = \log_a x \qquad \text{Read as "log base } a \text{ of } x."$$

is called the **logarithmic function with base *a*.**

The equations $y = \log_a x$ and $x = a^y$ are equivalent. The first equation is in logarithmic form and the second is in exponential form. For example, $2 = \log_3 9$ is equivalent to $9 = 3^2$, and $5^3 = 125$ is equivalent to $\log_5 125 = 3$.

When evaluating logarithms, remember that *a logarithm is an exponent.* This means that $\log_a x$ is the exponent to which *a* must be raised to obtain *x*. For instance, $\log_2 8 = 3$ because 2 raised to the third power is 8.

EXAMPLE 1 **Evaluating Logarithms**

Evaluate each logarithm at the indicated value of *x*.

a. $f(x) = \log_2 x, \quad x = 32$ **b.** $f(x) = \log_3 x, \quad x = 1$

c. $f(x) = \log_4 x, \quad x = 2$ **d.** $f(x) = \log_{10} x, \quad x = \frac{1}{100}$

Solution

a. $f(32) = \log_2 32 = 5$ because $2^5 = 32$.

b. $f(1) = \log_3 1 = 0$ because $3^0 = 1$.

c. $f(2) = \log_4 2 = \frac{1}{2}$ because $4^{1/2} = \sqrt{4} = 2$.

d. $f\left(\frac{1}{100}\right) = \log_{10} \frac{1}{100} = -2$ because $10^{-2} = \frac{1}{10^2} = \frac{1}{100}$.

✓ *Checkpoint* ◄))) *Audio-video solution in English & Spanish at LarsonPrecalculus.com.*

Evaluate each logarithm at the indicated value of *x*.

a. $f(x) = \log_6 x, \quad x = 1$ **b.** $f(x) = \log_5 x, \quad x = \frac{1}{125}$ **c.** $f(x) = \log_{10} x, \quad x = 10,000$

The logarithmic function with base 10 is called the **common logarithmic function.** It is denoted by $\log_{10}$ or simply by log. On most calculators, this function is denoted by (LOG). Example 2 shows how to use a calculator to evaluate common logarithmic functions. You will learn how to use a calculator to calculate logarithms to any base in the next section.

EXAMPLE 2 **Evaluating Common Logarithms on a Calculator**

Use a calculator to evaluate the function $f(x) = \log x$ at each value of x.

a. $x = 10$ **b.** $x = \frac{1}{3}$ **c.** $x = 2.5$ **d.** $x = -2$

Solution

Function Value	Graphing Calculator Keystrokes	Display
a. $f(10) = \log 10$	(LOG) 10 (ENTER)	1
b. $f\left(\frac{1}{3}\right) = \log\frac{1}{3}$	(LOG) (( ) 1 (÷) 3 ( )) (ENTER)	-0.4771213
c. $f(2.5) = \log 2.5$	(LOG) 2.5 (ENTER)	0.3979400
d. $f(-2) = \log(-2)$	(LOG) ((−)) 2 (ENTER)	ERROR

Note that the calculator displays an error message (or a complex number) when you try to evaluate $\log(-2)$. The reason for this is that there is no real number power to which 10 can be raised to obtain -2.

✓ **Checkpoint** Audio-video solution in English & Spanish at LarsonPrecalculus.com.

Use a calculator to evaluate the function $f(x) = \log x$ at each value of x.

a. $x = 275$ **b.** $x = 0.275$ **c.** $x = -\frac{1}{2}$ **d.** $x = \frac{1}{2}$

The following properties follow directly from the definition of the logarithmic function with base a.

> **Properties of Logarithms**
>
> **1.** $\log_a 1 = 0$ because $a^0 = 1$.
>
> **2.** $\log_a a = 1$ because $a^1 = a$.
>
> **3.** $\log_a a^x = x$ and $a^{\log_a x} = x$ Inverse Properties
>
> **4.** If $\log_a x = \log_a y$, then $x = y$.   One-to-One Property

EXAMPLE 3 **Using Properties of Logarithms**

a. Simplify $\log_4 1$.   **b.** Simplify $\log_{\sqrt{7}} \sqrt{7}$.   **c.** Simplify $6^{\log_6 20}$.

Solution

a. Using Property 1, $\log_4 1 = 0$.

b. Using Property 2, $\log_{\sqrt{7}} \sqrt{7} = 1$.

c. Using the Inverse Property (Property 3), $6^{\log_6 20} = 20$.

✓ **Checkpoint** Audio-video solution in English & Spanish at LarsonPrecalculus.com.

a. Simplify $\log_9 9$.   **b.** Simplify $20^{\log_{20} 3}$.   **c.** Simplify $\log_{\sqrt{3}} 1$.

You can use the One-to-One Property (Property 4) to solve simple logarithmic equations, as shown in Example 4.

EXAMPLE 4 **Using the One-to-One Property**

a. $\log_3 x = \log_3 12$ Original equation

        $x = 12$ One-to-One Property

b. $\log(2x + 1) = \log 3x$ ⟹ $2x + 1 = 3x$ ⟹ $1 = x$

c. $\log_4(x^2 - 6) = \log_4 10$ ⟹ $x^2 - 6 = 10$ ⟹ $x^2 = 16$ ⟹ $x = \pm 4$

✓ *Checkpoint* *Audio-video solution in English & Spanish at LarsonPrecalculus.com.*

Solve $\log_5(x^2 + 3) = \log_5 12$ for x.

Graphs of Logarithmic Functions

To sketch the graph of $y = \log_a x$, use the fact that the graphs of inverse functions are reflections of each other in the line $y = x$.

EXAMPLE 5 **Graphs of Exponential and Logarithmic Functions**

In the same coordinate plane, sketch the graph of each function.

a. $f(x) = 2^x$ **b.** $g(x) = \log_2 x$

Solution

a. For $f(x) = 2^x$, construct a table of values. By plotting these points and connecting them with a smooth curve, you obtain the graph shown in Figure 3.10.

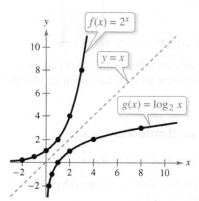

Figure 3.10

x	-2	-1	0	1	2	3
$f(x) = 2^x$	$\frac{1}{4}$	$\frac{1}{2}$	1	2	4	8

b. Because $g(x) = \log_2 x$ is the inverse function of $f(x) = 2^x$, the graph of g is obtained by plotting the points $(f(x), x)$ and connecting them with a smooth curve. The graph of g is a reflection of the graph of f in the line $y = x$, as shown in Figure 3.10.

✓ *Checkpoint* *Audio-video solution in English & Spanish at LarsonPrecalculus.com.*

In the same coordinate plane, sketch the graphs of (a) $f(x) = 8^x$ and (b) $g(x) = \log_8 x$.

EXAMPLE 6 **Sketching the Graph of a Logarithmic Function**

Sketch the graph of $f(x) = \log x$. Identify the vertical asymptote.

Solution Begin by constructing a table of values. Note that some of the values can be obtained without a calculator by using the properties of logarithms. Others require a calculator. Next, plot the points and connect them with a smooth curve, as shown in Figure 3.11. The vertical asymptote is $x = 0$ (y-axis).

Figure 3.11

x	Without calculator				With calculator		
	$\frac{1}{100}$	$\frac{1}{10}$	1	10	2	5	8
$f(x) = \log x$	-2	-1	0	1	0.301	0.699	0.903

✓ *Checkpoint* *Audio-video solution in English & Spanish at LarsonPrecalculus.com.*

Sketch the graph of $f(x) = \log_9 x$. Identify the vertical asymptote.

The nature of the graph in Figure 3.11 is typical of functions of the form $f(x) = \log_a x, a > 1$. They have one x-intercept and one vertical asymptote. Notice how slowly the graph rises for $x > 1$. The following summarizes the basic characteristics of logarithmic graphs.

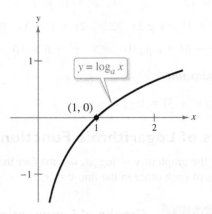

Graph of $y = \log_a x, a > 1$

- Domain: $(0, \infty)$
- Range: $(-\infty, \infty)$
- x-intercept: $(1, 0)$
- Increasing
- One-to-one, therefore has an inverse function
- y-axis is a vertical asymptote
  $(\log_a x \to -\infty \text{ as } x \to 0^+)$.
- Continuous
- Reflection of graph of $y = a^x$ in the line $y = x$

The basic characteristics of the graph of $f(x) = a^x$ are shown below to illustrate the inverse relation between $f(x) = a^x$ and $g(x) = \log_a x$.

- Domain: $(-\infty, \infty)$ • Range: $(0, \infty)$
- y-intercept: $(0, 1)$ • x-axis is a horizontal asymptote $(a^x \to 0 \text{ as } x \to -\infty)$.

The next example uses the graph of $y = \log_a x$ to sketch the graphs of functions of the form $f(x) = b \pm \log_a(x + c)$. Notice how a horizontal shift of the graph results in a horizontal shift of the vertical asymptote.

EXAMPLE 7   **Shifting Graphs of Logarithmic Functions**

The graph of each of the functions is similar to the graph of $f(x) = \log x$.

a. Because $g(x) = \log(x - 1) = f(x - 1)$, the graph of g can be obtained by shifting the graph of f one unit to the right, as shown in Figure 3.12.

b. Because $h(x) = 2 + \log x = 2 + f(x)$, the graph of h can be obtained by shifting the graph of f two units up, as shown in Figure 3.13.

• • REMARK   Use your understanding of transformations to identify vertical asymptotes of logarithmic functions. For instance, in Example 7(a), the graph of $g(x) = f(x - 1)$ shifts the graph of $f(x)$ one unit to the right. So, the vertical asymptote of the graph of $g(x)$ is $x = 1$, one unit to the right of the vertical asymptote of the graph of $f(x)$.

Figure 3.12

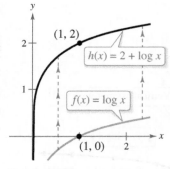

Figure 3.13

✓ *Checkpoint* ◀))) *Audio-video solution in English & Spanish at LarsonPrecalculus.com.*

▷ **ALGEBRA HELP**   You can review the techniques for shifting, reflecting, and stretching graphs in Section 1.7.

Use the graph of $f(x) = \log_3 x$ to sketch the graph of each function.

a. $g(x) = -1 + \log_3 x$

b. $h(x) = \log_3(x + 3)$

The Natural Logarithmic Function

By looking back at the graph of the natural exponential function introduced on page 204 in Section 3.1, you will see that $f(x) = e^x$ is one-to-one and so has an inverse function. This inverse function is called the **natural logarithmic function** and is denoted by the special symbol ln x, read as "the natural log of x" or "el en of x." Note that the natural logarithm is written without a base. The base is understood to be e.

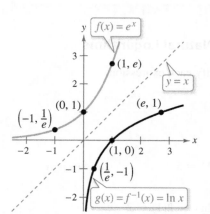

Reflection of graph of $f(x) = e^x$ in the line $y = x$

Figure 3.14

> ### The Natural Logarithmic Function
> The function defined by
> $$f(x) = \log_e x = \ln x, \quad x > 0$$
> is called the **natural logarithmic function.**

The above definition implies that the natural logarithmic function and the natural exponential function are inverse functions of each other. So, every logarithmic equation can be written in an equivalent exponential form, and every exponential equation can be written in an equivalent logarithmic form. That is, $y = \ln x$ and $x = e^y$ are equivalent equations.

Because the functions $f(x) = e^x$ and $g(x) = \ln x$ are inverse functions of each other, their graphs are reflections of each other in the line $y = x$. Figure 3.14 illustrates this reflective property.

On most calculators, $\boxed{\text{LN}}$ denotes the natural logarithm, as illustrated in Example 8.

EXAMPLE 8   **Evaluating the Natural Logarithmic Function**

Use a calculator to evaluate the function $f(x) = \ln x$ at each value of x.

a. $x = 2$

b. $x = 0.3$

c. $x = -1$

d. $x = 1 + \sqrt{2}$

Solution

Function Value	Graphing Calculator Keystrokes	Display
a. $f(2) = \ln 2$	$\boxed{\text{LN}}$ 2 $\boxed{\text{ENTER}}$	0.6931472
b. $f(0.3) = \ln 0.3$	$\boxed{\text{LN}}$ .3 $\boxed{\text{ENTER}}$	−1.2039728
c. $f(-1) = \ln(-1)$	$\boxed{\text{LN}}$ $\boxed{(-)}$ 1 $\boxed{\text{ENTER}}$	ERROR
d. $f(1 + \sqrt{2}) = \ln(1 + \sqrt{2})$	$\boxed{\text{LN}}$ $\boxed{(}$ 1 $\boxed{+}$ $\boxed{\sqrt{}}$ 2 $\boxed{)}$ $\boxed{\text{ENTER}}$	0.8813736

✓ **Checkpoint**))) *Audio-video solution in English & Spanish at LarsonPrecalculus.com.*

Use a calculator to evaluate the function $f(x) = \ln x$ at each value of x.

a. $x = 0.01$ **b.** $x = 4$ **c.** $x = \sqrt{3} + 2$ **d.** $x = \sqrt{3} - 2$

•• **REMARK** Notice that as with every other logarithmic function, the domain of the natural logarithmic function is the set of *positive real numbers*—be sure you see that ln x is not defined for zero or for negative numbers.

In Example 8, be sure you see that $\ln(-1)$ gives an error message on most calculators. (Some calculators may display a complex number.) This occurs because the domain of ln x is the set of positive real numbers (see Figure 3.14). So, $\ln(-1)$ is undefined.

The four properties of logarithms listed on page 212 are also valid for natural logarithms.

Properties of Natural Logarithms

1. $\ln 1 = 0$ because $e^0 = 1$.

2. $\ln e = 1$ because $e^1 = e$.

3. $\ln e^x = x$ and $e^{\ln x} = x$ Inverse Properties

4. If $\ln x = \ln y$, then $x = y$.   One-to-One Property

EXAMPLE 9   **Using Properties of Natural Logarithms**

Use the properties of natural logarithms to simplify each expression.

a. $\ln \dfrac{1}{e}$ **b.** $e^{\ln 5}$ **c.** $\dfrac{\ln 1}{3}$ **d.** $2 \ln e$

Solution

a. $\ln \dfrac{1}{e} = \ln e^{-1} = -1$ Inverse Property   **b.** $e^{\ln 5} = 5$ Inverse Property

c. $\dfrac{\ln 1}{3} = \dfrac{0}{3} = 0$ Property 1   **d.** $2 \ln e = 2(1) = 2$ Property 2

✓ **Checkpoint** ◀))) *Audio-video solution in English & Spanish at LarsonPrecalculus.com.*

Use the properties of natural logarithms to simplify each expression.

a. $\ln e^{1/3}$ **b.** $5 \ln 1$ **c.** $\frac{3}{4} \ln e$ **d.** $e^{\ln 7}$

EXAMPLE 10   **Finding the Domains of Logarithmic Functions**

Find the domain of each function.

a. $f(x) = \ln(x - 2)$ **b.** $g(x) = \ln(2 - x)$ **c.** $h(x) = \ln x^2$

Solution

a. Because $\ln(x - 2)$ is defined only when $x - 2 > 0$, it follows that the domain of f is $(2, \infty)$. Figure 3.15 shows the graph of f.

b. Because $\ln(2 - x)$ is defined only when $2 - x > 0$, it follows that the domain of g is $(-\infty, 2)$. Figure 3.16 shows the graph of g.

c. Because $\ln x^2$ is defined only when $x^2 > 0$, it follows that the domain of h is all real numbers except $x = 0$. Figure 3.17 shows the graph of h.

Figure 3.15

Figure 3.16

Figure 3.17

✓ **Checkpoint** ◀))) *Audio-video solution in English & Spanish at LarsonPrecalculus.com.*

Find the domain of $f(x) = \ln(x + 3)$.

Application

EXAMPLE 11   Human Memory Model

Students participating in a psychology experiment attended several lectures on a subject and took an exam. Every month for a year after the exam, the students took a retest to see how much of the material they remembered. The average scores for the group are given by the *human memory model* $f(t) = 75 - 6 \ln(t + 1), 0 \le t \le 12$, where t is the time in months.

a. What was the average score on the original exam $(t = 0)$?

b. What was the average score at the end of $t = 2$ months?

c. What was the average score at the end of $t = 6$ months?

Algebraic Solution

a. The original average score was

$$f(0) = 75 - 6 \ln(0 + 1) \qquad \text{Substitute 0 for } t.$$

$$= 75 - 6 \ln 1 \qquad \text{Simplify.}$$

$$= 75 - 6(0) \qquad \text{Property of natural logarithms}$$

$$= 75. \qquad \text{Solution}$$

b. After 2 months, the average score was

$$f(2) = 75 - 6 \ln(2 + 1) \qquad \text{Substitute 2 for } t.$$

$$= 75 - 6 \ln 3 \qquad \text{Simplify.}$$

$$\approx 75 - 6(1.0986) \qquad \text{Use a calculator.}$$

$$\approx 68.41. \qquad \text{Solution}$$

c. After 6 months, the average score was

$$f(6) = 75 - 6 \ln(6 + 1) \qquad \text{Substitute 6 for } t.$$

$$= 75 - 6 \ln 7 \qquad \text{Simplify.}$$

$$\approx 75 - 6(1.9459) \qquad \text{Use a calculator.}$$

$$\approx 63.32. \qquad \text{Solution}$$

Graphical Solution

a.
When $t = 0, f(0) = 75.$ So, the original average score was 75.

b.
When $t = 2, f(2) \approx 68.41.$ So, the average score after 2 months was about 68.41.

c.
When $t = 6, f(6) \approx 63.32.$ So, the average score after 6 months was about 63.32.

✓ *Checkpoint* Audio-video solution in English & Spanish at LarsonPrecalculus.com.

In Example 11, find the average score at the end of (a) $t = 1$ month, (b) $t = 9$ months, and (c) $t = 12$ months. ◼

Summarize   (Section 3.2)

1. State the definition of a logarithmic function with base a *(page 211)* and make a list of the properties of logarithms *(page 212)*. For examples of evaluating logarithmic functions and using the properties of logarithms, see Examples 1–4.

2. Explain how to graph a logarithmic function *(pages 213 and 214)*. For examples of graphing logarithmic functions, see Examples 5–7.

3. State the definition of the natural logarithmic function *(page 215)* and make a list of the properties of natural logarithms *(page 216)*. For examples of evaluating natural logarithmic functions and using the properties of natural logarithms, see Examples 8 and 9.

4. Describe an example of how to use a logarithmic function to model and solve a real-life problem *(page 217, Example 11)*.

3.2 Exercises

See CalcChat.com for tutorial help and worked-out solutions to odd-numbered exercises.

Vocabulary: Fill in the blanks.

1. The inverse function of the exponential function $f(x) = a^x$ is called the _____ function with base a.
2. The common logarithmic function has base _____ .
3. The logarithmic function $f(x) = \ln x$ is called the _____ logarithmic function and has base _____ .
4. The Inverse Properties of logarithms state that $\log_a a^x = x$ and _____ .
5. The One-to-One Property of natural logarithms states that if $\ln x = \ln y$, then _____ .
6. The domain of the natural logarithmic function is the set of _____ _____ _____ .

Skills and Applications

Writing an Exponential Equation In Exercises 7–10, write the logarithmic equation in exponential form. For example, the exponential form of $\log_5 25 = 2$ is $5^2 = 25$.

7. $\log_4 16 = 2$
8. $\log_9 \frac{1}{81} = -2$
9. $\log_{32} 4 = \frac{2}{5}$
10. $\log_{64} 8 = \frac{1}{2}$

Writing a Logarithmic Equation In Exercises 11–14, write the exponential equation in logarithmic form. For example, the logarithmic form of $2^3 = 8$ is $\log_2 8 = 3$.

11. $5^3 = 125$
12. $9^{3/2} = 27$
13. $4^{-3} = \frac{1}{64}$
14. $24^0 = 1$

Evaluating a Logarithmic Function In Exercises 15–20, evaluate the function at the indicated value of x without using a calculator.

Function	Value
15. $f(x) = \log_2 x$	$x = 64$
16. $f(x) = \log_{25} x$	$x = 5$
17. $f(x) = \log_8 x$	$x = 1$
18. $f(x) = \log x$	$x = 10$
19. $g(x) = \log_a x$	$x = a^2$
20. $g(x) = \log_b x$	$x = b^{-3}$

Evaluating a Common Logarithm on a Calculator In Exercises 21–24, use a calculator to evaluate $f(x) = \log x$ at the indicated value of x. Round your result to three decimal places.

21. $x = \frac{7}{8}$
22. $x = \frac{1}{500}$
23. $x = 12.5$
24. $x = 96.75$

Using Properties of Logarithms In Exercises 25–28, use the properties of logarithms to simplify the expression.

25. $\log_{11} 11^7$
26. $\log_{3.2} 1$
27. $\log_\pi \pi$
28. $9^{\log_9 15}$

Using the One-to-One Property In Exercises 29–32, use the One-to-One Property to solve the equation for x.

29. $\log_5(x + 1) = \log_5 6$
30. $\log_2(x - 3) = \log_2 9$
31. $\log(2x + 1) = \log 15$
32. $\log(5x + 3) = \log 12$

Graphs of Exponential and Logarithmic Functions In Exercises 33–36, sketch the graphs of f and g in the same coordinate plane.

33. $f(x) = 7^x$, $g(x) = \log_7 x$
34. $f(x) = 5^x$, $g(x) = \log_5 x$
35. $f(x) = 6^x$, $g(x) = \log_6 x$
36. $f(x) = 10^x$, $g(x) = \log x$

Matching a Logarithmic Function with Its Graph In Exercises 37–40, use the graph of $g(x) = \log_3 x$ to match the given function with its graph. Then describe the relationship between the graphs of f and g. [The graphs are labeled (a), (b), (c), and (d).]

(a)

(b)

(c)

(d)

37. $f(x) = -\log_3(x + 2)$
38. $f(x) = \log_3(x - 1)$
39. $f(x) = \log_3(1 - x)$
40. $f(x) = -\log_3(-x)$

Sketching the Graph of a Logarithmic Function
In Exercises 41–48, find the domain, x-intercept, and vertical asymptote of the logarithmic function and sketch its graph.

41. $f(x) = \log_4 x$

42. $g(x) = \log_6 x$

43. $y = -\log_3 x + 2$

44. $h(x) = \log_4(x - 3)$

45. $f(x) = -\log_6(x + 2)$

46. $y = \log_5(x - 1) + 4$

47. $y = \log\left(\dfrac{x}{7}\right)$

48. $y = \log(-x)$

Writing a Natural Exponential Equation In Exercises 49–52, write the logarithmic equation in exponential form.

49. $\ln \frac{1}{2} = -0.693 \ldots$

50. $\ln 7 = 1.945 \ldots$

51. $\ln 250 = 5.521 \ldots$

52. $\ln 1 = 0$

Writing a Natural Logarithmic Equation In Exercises 53–56, write the exponential equation in logarithmic form.

53. $e^2 = 7.3890 \ldots$

54. $e^{1/2} = 1.6487 \ldots$

55. $e^{-0.9} = 0.406 \ldots$

56. $e^{2x} = 3$

Evaluating a Logarithmic Function on a Calculator In Exercises 57–60, use a calculator to evaluate the function at the indicated value of x. Round your result to three decimal places.

Function	Value
57. $f(x) = \ln x$	$x = 18.42$
58. $f(x) = 3 \ln x$	$x = 0.74$
59. $g(x) = 8 \ln x$	$x = 0.05$
60. $g(x) = -\ln x$	$x = \frac{1}{2}$

Evaluating a Natural Logarithm In Exercises 61–64, evaluate $g(x) = \ln x$ at the indicated value of x without using a calculator.

61. $x = e^5$

62. $x = e^{-4}$

63. $x = e^{-5/6}$

64. $x = e^{-5/2}$

Graphing a Natural Logarithmic Function In Exercises 65–68, find the domain, x-intercept, and vertical asymptote of the logarithmic function and sketch its graph.

65. $f(x) = \ln(x - 4)$

66. $h(x) = \ln(x + 5)$

67. $g(x) = \ln(-x)$

68. $f(x) = \ln(3 - x)$

Graphing a Natural Logarithmic Function In Exercises 69–72, use a graphing utility to graph the function. Be sure to use an appropriate viewing window.

69. $f(x) = \ln(x - 1)$

70. $f(x) = \ln(x + 2)$

71. $f(x) = \ln x + 8$

72. $f(x) = 3 \ln x - 1$

Using the One-to-One Property In Exercises 73–76, use the One-to-One Property to solve the equation for x.

73. $\ln(x + 4) = \ln 12$

74. $\ln(x - 7) = \ln 7$

75. $\ln(x^2 - 2) = \ln 23$

76. $\ln(x^2 - x) = \ln 6$

77. Monthly Payment The model

$$t = 16.625 \ln\left(\frac{x}{x - 750}\right), \quad x > 750$$

approximates the length of a home mortgage of $150,000 at 6% in terms of the monthly payment. In the model, t is the length of the mortgage in years and x is the monthly payment in dollars.

(a) Use the model to approximate the lengths of a $150,000 mortgage at 6% when the monthly payment is $897.72 and when the monthly payment is $1659.24.

(b) Approximate the total amounts paid over the term of the mortgage with a monthly payment of $897.72 and with a monthly payment of $1659.24.

(c) Approximate the total interest charges for a monthly payment of $897.72 and for a monthly payment of $1659.24.

(d) What is the vertical asymptote for the model? Interpret its meaning in the context of the problem.

78. Wireless Only The percents P of households in the United States with wireless-only telephone service from 2005 through 2011 can be approximated by the model

$$P = -4.00 + 1.335t \ln t, \quad 5 \le t \le 11$$

where t represents the year, with $t = 5$ corresponding to 2005. (*Source: National Center for Health Statistics*)

(a) Complete the table.

t	5	6	7	8	9	10	11
P							

(b) Use a graphing utility to graph the function.

(c) Can the model be used to predict the percents of households with wireless-only telephone service beyond 2011? Explain.

79. Population The time t (in years) for the world population to double when it is increasing at a continuous rate of r is given by $t = (\ln 2)/r$.

(a) Complete the table and interpret your results.

r	0.005	0.010	0.015	0.020	0.025	0.030
t						

(b) Use a graphing utility to graph the function.

80. Compound Interest A principal P, invested at $5\frac{1}{2}\%$ and compounded continuously, increases to an amount K times the original principal after t years, where $t = (\ln K)/0.055$.

(a) Complete the table and interpret your results.

K	1	2	4	6	8	10	12
t							

(b) Sketch a graph of the function.

• • 81. Human Memory Model • • • • • • • • • • • •

Students in a mathematics class took an exam and then took a retest monthly with an equivalent exam. The average scores for the class are given by the human memory model

$f(t) = 80 - 17 \log(t + 1)$, $0 \le t \le 12$

where t is the time in months.

(a) Use a graphing utility to graph the model over the specified domain.

(b) What was the average score on the original exam ($t = 0$)?

(c) What was the average score after 4 months?

(d) What was the average score after 10 months?

• •

82. Sound Intensity The relationship between the number of decibels β and the intensity of a sound I in watts per square meter is

$$\beta = 10 \log\left(\frac{I}{10^{-12}}\right).$$

(a) Determine the number of decibels of a sound with an intensity of 1 watt per square meter.

(b) Determine the number of decibels of a sound with an intensity of 10^{-2} watt per square meter.

(c) The intensity of the sound in part (a) is 100 times as great as that in part (b). Is the number of decibels 100 times as great? Explain.

Exploration

True or False? **In Exercises 83 and 84, determine whether the statement is true or false. Justify your answer.**

83. The graph of $f(x) = \log_6 x$ is a reflection of the graph of $g(x) = 6^x$ in the x-axis.

84. The graph of $f(x) = \log_3 x$ contains the point $(27, 3)$.

85. Graphical Analysis Use a graphing utility to graph f and g in the same viewing window and determine which is increasing at the greater rate as x approaches $+\infty$. What can you conclude about the rate of growth of the natural logarithmic function?

(a) $f(x) = \ln x$, $g(x) = \sqrt{x}$

(b) $f(x) = \ln x$, $g(x) = \sqrt[4]{x}$

86. Limit of a Function

(a) Complete the table for the function

$f(x) = (\ln x)/x$.

x	1	5	10	10^2	10^4	10^6
$f(x)$						

(b) Use the table in part (a) to determine what value $f(x)$ approaches as x increases without bound.

(c) Use a graphing utility to confirm the result of part (b).

87. Think About It A student obtained the following table of values by evaluating a function. Determine which of the statements may be true and which must be false.

x	1	2	8
y	0	1	3

(a) y is an exponential function of x.

(b) y is a logarithmic function of x.

(c) x is an exponential function of y.

(d) y is a linear function of x.

88. HOW DO YOU SEE IT? The figure shows the graphs of $f(x) = 3^x$ and $g(x) = \log_3 x$. [The graphs are labeled m and n.]

(a) Match each function with its graph.

(b) Given that $f(a) = b$, what is $g(b)$? Explain.

89. Writing Explain why $\log_a x$ is defined only for $0 < a < 1$ and $a > 1$.

3.3 Properties of Logarithms

- Use the change-of-base formula to rewrite and evaluate logarithmic expressions.
- Use properties of logarithms to evaluate or rewrite logarithmic expressions.
- Use properties of logarithms to expand or condense logarithmic expressions.
- Use logarithmic functions to model and solve real-life problems.

Logarithmic functions can help you model and solve real-life problems. For instance, Exercises 85–88 on page 226 use a logarithmic function to model the relationship between the number of decibels and the intensity of a sound.

Change of Base

Most calculators have only two types of log keys, one for common logarithms (base 10) and one for natural logarithms (base e). Although common logarithms and natural logarithms are the most frequently used, you may occasionally need to evaluate logarithms with other bases. To do this, use the following **change-of-base formula.**

Change-of-Base Formula

Let a, b, and x be positive real numbers such that $a \neq 1$ and $b \neq 1$. Then $\log_a x$ can be converted to a different base as follows.

Base b	**Base 10**	**Base e**
$\log_a x = \dfrac{\log_b x}{\log_b a}$	$\log_a x = \dfrac{\log x}{\log a}$	$\log_a x = \dfrac{\ln x}{\ln a}$

One way to look at the change-of-base formula is that logarithms with base a are *constant multiples* of logarithms with base b. The constant multiplier is

$$\frac{1}{\log_b a}.$$

EXAMPLE 1   **Changing Bases Using Common Logarithms**

$$\log_4 25 = \frac{\log 25}{\log 4} \qquad \log_a x = \frac{\log x}{\log a}$$

$$\approx \frac{1.39794}{0.60206} \qquad \text{Use a calculator.}$$

$$\approx 2.3219 \qquad \text{Simplify.}$$

✓ *Checkpoint* 🔊)) *Audio-video solution in English & Spanish at LarsonPrecalculus.com.*

Evaluate $\log_2 12$ using the change-of-base formula and common logarithms.

EXAMPLE 2   **Changing Bases Using Natural Logarithms**

$$\log_4 25 = \frac{\ln 25}{\ln 4} \qquad \log_a x = \frac{\ln x}{\ln a}$$

$$\approx \frac{3.21888}{1.38629} \qquad \text{Use a calculator.}$$

$$\approx 2.3219 \qquad \text{Simplify.}$$

✓ *Checkpoint* 🔊)) *Audio-video solution in English & Spanish at LarsonPrecalculus.com.*

Evaluate $\log_2 12$ using the change-of-base formula and natural logarithms.

Properties of Logarithms

You know from the preceding section that the logarithmic function with base a is the *inverse function* of the exponential function with base a. So, it makes sense that the properties of exponents should have corresponding properties involving logarithms. For instance, the exponential property $a^u a^v = a^{u+v}$ has the corresponding logarithmic property $\log_a(uv) = \log_a u + \log_a v$.

> **REMARK** There is no property that can be used to rewrite $\log_a(u \pm v)$. Specifically, $\log_a(u + v)$ is *not* equal to $\log_a u + \log_a v$.

> **Properties of Logarithms**
>
> Let a be a positive number such that $a \neq 1$, and let n be a real number. If u and v are positive real numbers, then the following properties are true.
>
> | | **Logarithm with Base a** | **Natural Logarithm** |
> |---|---|---|
> | **1.** Product Property: | $\log_a(uv) = \log_a u + \log_a v$ | $\ln(uv) = \ln u + \ln v$ |
> | **2.** Quotient Property: | $\log_a \dfrac{u}{v} = \log_a u - \log_a v$ | $\ln \dfrac{u}{v} = \ln u - \ln v$ |
> | **3.** Power Property: | $\log_a u^n = n \log_a u$ | $\ln u^n = n \ln u$ |

For proofs of the properties listed above, see Proofs in Mathematics on page 258.

EXAMPLE 3 **Using Properties of Logarithms**

Write each logarithm in terms of $\ln 2$ and $\ln 3$.

a. $\ln 6$ **b.** $\ln \dfrac{2}{27}$

Solution

a. $\ln 6 = \ln(2 \cdot 3)$ Rewrite 6 as $2 \cdot 3$.

$\qquad\quad = \ln 2 + \ln 3$ Product Property

b. $\ln \dfrac{2}{27} = \ln 2 - \ln 27$ Quotient Property

$\qquad\quad = \ln 2 - \ln 3^3$ Rewrite 27 as 3^3.

$\qquad\quad = \ln 2 - 3 \ln 3$ Power Property

✓ *Checkpoint* *Audio-video solution in English & Spanish at LarsonPrecalculus.com.*

Write each logarithm in terms of $\log 3$ and $\log 5$.

a. $\log 75$ **b.** $\log \dfrac{9}{125}$

EXAMPLE 4 **Using Properties of Logarithms**

Find the exact value of $\log_5 \sqrt[3]{5}$ without using a calculator.

Solution

$\log_5 \sqrt[3]{5} = \log_5 5^{1/3} = \frac{1}{3} \log_5 5 = \frac{1}{3}(1) = \frac{1}{3}$

✓ *Checkpoint* *Audio-video solution in English & Spanish at LarsonPrecalculus.com.*

Find the exact value of $\ln e^6 - \ln e^2$ without using a calculator.

HISTORICAL NOTE

Rewriting Logarithmic Expressions

The properties of logarithms are useful for rewriting logarithmic expressions in forms that simplify the operations of algebra. This is true because these properties convert complicated products, quotients, and exponential forms into simpler sums, differences, and products, respectively.

EXAMPLE 5 **Expanding Logarithmic Expressions**

Expand each logarithmic expression.

a. $\log_4 5x^3y$ **b.** $\ln \dfrac{\sqrt{3x-5}}{7}$

Solution

a. $\log_4 5x^3y = \log_4 5 + \log_4 x^3 + \log_4 y$ Product Property

$\qquad\qquad\quad = \log_4 5 + 3\log_4 x + \log_4 y$ Power Property

> ▷ **ALGEBRA HELP** You can review rewriting radicals and rational exponents in Appendix A.2.

b. $\ln \dfrac{\sqrt{3x-5}}{7} = \ln \dfrac{(3x-5)^{1/2}}{7}$ Rewrite using rational exponent.

$\qquad\qquad\quad = \ln(3x-5)^{1/2} - \ln 7$ Quotient Property

$\qquad\qquad\quad = \dfrac{1}{2}\ln(3x-5) - \ln 7$ Power Property

✓ **Checkpoint** ◀))) *Audio-video solution in English & Spanish at LarsonPrecalculus.com.*

Expand the expression $\log_3 \dfrac{4x^2}{\sqrt{y}}$.

Example 5 uses the properties of logarithms to *expand* logarithmic expressions. Example 6 reverses this procedure and uses the properties of logarithms to *condense* logarithmic expressions.

EXAMPLE 6 **Condensing Logarithmic Expressions**

Condense each logarithmic expression.

a. $\frac{1}{2}\log x + 3\log(x+1)$ **b.** $2\ln(x+2) - \ln x$ **c.** $\frac{1}{3}[\log_2 x + \log_2(x+1)]$

Solution

a. $\frac{1}{2}\log x + 3\log(x+1) = \log x^{1/2} + \log(x+1)^3$ Power Property

$\qquad\qquad\qquad\qquad = \log\!\left[\sqrt{x}(x+1)^3\right]$ Product Property

b. $2\ln(x+2) - \ln x = \ln(x+2)^2 - \ln x$ Power Property

$\qquad\qquad\qquad\quad = \ln \dfrac{(x+2)^2}{x}$ Quotient Property

c. $\frac{1}{3}[\log_2 x + \log_2(x+1)] = \frac{1}{3}\log_2[x(x+1)]$ Product Property

$\qquad\qquad\qquad\qquad = \log_2[x(x+1)]^{1/3}$ Power Property

$\qquad\qquad\qquad\qquad = \log_2 \sqrt[3]{x(x+1)}$ Rewrite with a radical.

✓ **Checkpoint** ◀))) *Audio-video solution in English & Spanish at LarsonPrecalculus.com.*

Condense the expression $2[\log(x+3) - 2\log(x-2)]$.

Application

One method of determining how the *x*- and *y*-values for a set of nonlinear data are related is to take the natural logarithm of each of the *x*- and *y*-values. If the points, when graphed, fall on a line, then you can determine that the *x*- and *y*-values are related by the equation $\ln y = m \ln x$ where *m* is the slope of the line.

EXAMPLE 7   **Finding a Mathematical Model**

The table shows the mean distance from the sun *x* and the period *y* (the time it takes a planet to orbit the sun) for each of the six planets that are closest to the sun. In the table, the mean distance is given in terms of astronomical units (where Earth's mean distance is defined as 1.0), and the period is given in years. Find an equation that relates *y* and *x*.

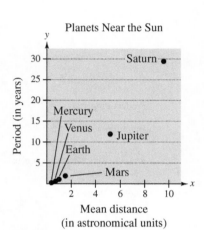

Planets Near the Sun

Period (in years)

Mean distance
(in astronomical units)

Figure 3.18

DATA	Planet	Mean Distance, *x*	Period, *y*
	Mercury	0.387	0.241
	Venus	0.723	0.615
	Earth	1.000	1.000
	Mars	1.524	1.881
	Jupiter	5.203	11.860
	Saturn	9.555	29.420

Spreadsheet at LarsonPrecalculus.com

Solution   Figure 3.18 shows the plots of the points given by the above table. From this figure, it is not clear how to find an equation that relates *y* and *x*. To solve this problem, take the natural logarithm of each of the *x*- and *y*-values, as shown in the table at the left. Now, by plotting the points in the table at the left, you can see that all six of the points appear to lie in a line (see Figure 3.19). Choose any two points to determine the slope of the line. Using the points (0.421, 0.632) and (0, 0), the slope of the line is

Planet	ln *x*	ln *y*
Mercury	−0.949	−1.423
Venus	−0.324	−0.486
Earth	0.000	0.000
Mars	0.421	0.632
Jupiter	1.649	2.473
Saturn	2.257	3.382

$$m = \frac{0.632 - 0}{0.421 - 0} \approx 1.5 = \frac{3}{2}.$$

By the point-slope form, the equation of the line is $Y = \frac{3}{2}X$, where $Y = \ln y$ and $X = \ln x$. So, $\ln y = \frac{3}{2}\ln x$.

✓ **Checkpoint** *Audio-video solution in English & Spanish at LarsonPrecalculus.com.*

Find a logarithmic equation that relates *y* and *x* for the following ordered pairs.

(0.37, 0.51), (1.00, 1.00), (2.72, 1.95) (7.39, 3.79), (20.09, 7.39)

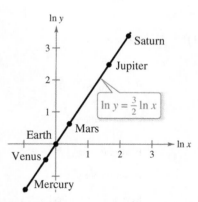

$\ln y = \frac{3}{2}\ln x$

Figure 3.19

Summarize   **(Section 3.3)**

1. State the change-of-base formula *(page 221)*. For examples that use the change-of-base formula to rewrite and evaluate logarithmic expressions, see Examples 1 and 2.

2. Make a list of the properties of logarithms *(page 222)*. For examples that use the properties of logarithms to evaluate or rewrite logarithmic expressions, see Examples 3 and 4.

3. Explain how to use the properties of logarithms to expand or condense logarithmic expressions *(page 223)*. For examples of expanding and condensing logarithmic expressions, see Examples 5 and 6.

4. Describe an example of how to use a logarithmic function to model and solve a real-life problem *(page 224, Example 7)*.

3.3 Exercises

See CalcChat.com for tutorial help and worked-out solutions to odd-numbered exercises.

Vocabulary

In Exercises 1–3, fill in the blanks.

1. To evaluate a logarithm to any base, use the _____ formula.
2. The change-of-base formula for base e is given by $\log_a x =$ _____.
3. You can consider $\log_a x$ to be a constant multiple of $\log_b x$; the constant multiplier is _____.

In Exercises 4–6, match the property of logarithms with its name.

4. $\log_a(uv) = \log_a u + \log_a v$ (a) Power Property
5. $\ln u^n = n \ln u$ (b) Quotient Property
6. $\log_a \dfrac{u}{v} = \log_a u - \log_a v$ (c) Product Property

Skills and Applications

Rewriting a Logarithm In Exercises 7–10, rewrite the logarithm as a ratio of (a) common logarithms and (b) natural logarithms.

7. $\log_5 16$ 8. $\log_{1/5} x$
9. $\log_x \frac{3}{10}$ 10. $\log_{2.6} x$

Using the Change-of-Base Formula In Exercises 11–14, evaluate the logarithm using the change-of-base formula. Round your result to three decimal places.

11. $\log_3 7$ 12. $\log_{1/2} 4$
13. $\log_9 0.1$ 14. $\log_3 0.015$

Using Properties of Logarithms In Exercises 15–20, use the properties of logarithms to rewrite and simplify the logarithmic expression.

15. $\log_4 8$ 16. $\log_2(4^2 \cdot 3^4)$
17. $\log_5 \frac{1}{250}$ 18. $\log \frac{9}{300}$
19. $\ln(5e^6)$ 20. $\ln \dfrac{6}{e^2}$

Using Properties of Logarithms In Exercises 21–36, find the exact value of the logarithmic expression without using a calculator. (If this is not possible, then state the reason.)

21. $\log_3 9$ 22. $\log_5 \frac{1}{125}$
23. $\log_2 \sqrt[4]{8}$ 24. $\log_6 \sqrt[3]{6}$
25. $\log_4 16^2$ 26. $\log_3 81^{-3}$
27. $\log_2(-2)$ 28. $\log_3(-27)$
29. $\ln e^{4.5}$ 30. $3 \ln e^4$
31. $\ln \dfrac{1}{\sqrt{e}}$ 32. $\ln \sqrt[4]{e^3}$
33. $\ln e^2 + \ln e^5$ 34. $2 \ln e^6 - \ln e^5$
35. $\log_5 75 - \log_5 3$ 36. $\log_4 2 + \log_4 32$

Expanding a Logarithmic Expression In Exercises 37–58, use the properties of logarithms to expand the expression as a sum, difference, and/or constant multiple of logarithms. (Assume all variables are positive.)

37. $\ln 4x$ 38. $\log_3 10z$
39. $\log_8 x^4$ 40. $\log_{10} \dfrac{y}{2}$
41. $\log_5 \dfrac{5}{x}$ 42. $\log_6 \dfrac{1}{z^3}$
43. $\ln \sqrt{z}$ 44. $\ln \sqrt[3]{t}$
45. $\ln xyz^2$ 46. $\log 4x^2 y$
47. $\ln z(z-1)^2, \; z > 1$ 48. $\ln\left(\dfrac{x^2 - 1}{x^3}\right), \; x > 1$
49. $\log_2 \dfrac{\sqrt{a-1}}{9}, \; a > 1$ 50. $\ln \dfrac{6}{\sqrt{x^2 + 1}}$
51. $\ln \sqrt[3]{\dfrac{x}{y}}$ 52. $\ln \sqrt{\dfrac{x^2}{y^3}}$
53. $\ln x^2 \sqrt{\dfrac{y}{z}}$ 54. $\log_2 x^4 \sqrt{\dfrac{y}{z^3}}$
55. $\log_5 \dfrac{x^2}{y^2 z^3}$ 56. $\log_{10} \dfrac{xy^4}{z^5}$
57. $\ln \sqrt[4]{x^3(x^2 + 3)}$ 58. $\ln \sqrt{x^2(x + 2)}$

Using Properties of Logarithms In Exercises 59–66, approximate the logarithm using the properties of logarithms, given $\log_b 2 \approx 0.3562$, $\log_b 3 \approx 0.5646$, and $\log_b 5 \approx 0.8271$.

59. $\log_b 10$ 60. $\log_b \frac{2}{3}$
61. $\log_b 8$ 62. $\log_b \sqrt{2}$
63. $\log_b 45$ 64. $\log_b(2b)^{-2}$
65. $\log_b(3b^2)$ 66. $\log_b \sqrt[3]{3b}$

Condensing a Logarithmic Expression In Exercises 67–82, condense the expression to the logarithm of a single quantity.

67. $\ln 2 + \ln x$

68. $\log_5 8 - \log_5 t$

69. $2 \log_2 x + 4 \log_2 y$

70. $\frac{2}{3} \log_7 (z - 2)$

71. $\frac{1}{4} \log_3 5x$

72. $-4 \log_6 2x$

73. $\log x - 2 \log(x + 1)$

74. $2 \ln 8 + 5 \ln(z - 4)$

75. $\log x - 2 \log y + 3 \log z$

76. $3 \log_3 x + 4 \log_3 y - 4 \log_3 z$

77. $\ln x - [\ln(x + 1) + \ln(x - 1)]$

78. $4[\ln z + \ln(z + 5)] - 2 \ln(z - 5)$

79. $\frac{1}{3}[2 \ln(x + 3) + \ln x - \ln(x^2 - 1)]$

80. $2[3 \ln x - \ln(x + 1) - \ln(x - 1)]$

81. $\frac{1}{3}[\log_8 y + 2 \log_8(y + 4)] - \log_8(y - 1)$

82. $\frac{1}{2}[\log_4(x + 1) + 2 \log_4(x - 1)] + 6 \log_4 x$

Comparing Logarithmic Quantities In Exercises 83 and 84, compare the logarithmic quantities. If two are equal, then explain why.

83. $\dfrac{\log_2 32}{\log_2 4}$, $\log_2 \dfrac{32}{4}$, $\log_2 32 - \log_2 4$

84. $\log_7 \sqrt{70}$, $\log_7 35$, $\frac{1}{2} + \log_7 \sqrt{10}$

Sound Intensity

In Exercises 85–88, use the following information. The relationship between the number of decibels β and the intensity of a sound I in watts per square meter is given by

$$\beta = 10 \log\left(\frac{I}{10^{-12}}\right).$$

85. Use the properties of logarithms to write the formula in simpler form, and determine the number of decibels of a sound with an intensity of 10^{-6} watt per square meter.

86. Find the difference in loudness between an average office with an intensity of 1.26×10^{-7} watt per square meter and a broadcast studio with an intensity of 3.16×10^{-10} watt per square meter.

87. Find the difference in loudness between a vacuum cleaner with an intensity of 10^{-4} watt per square meter and rustling leaves with an intensity of 10^{-11} watt per square meter.

88. You and your roommate are playing your stereos at the same time and at the same intensity. How much louder is the music when both stereos are playing compared with just one stereo playing?

Curve Fitting In Exercises 89–92, find a logarithmic equation that relates y and x. Explain the steps used to find the equation.

89.

x	1	2	3	4	5	6
y	1	1.189	1.316	1.414	1.495	1.565

90.

x	1	2	3	4	5	6
y	1	1.587	2.080	2.520	2.924	3.302

91.

x	1	2	3	4	5	6
y	2.5	2.102	1.9	1.768	1.672	1.597

92.

x	1	2	3	4	5	6
y	0.5	2.828	7.794	16	27.951	44.091

93. Galloping Speeds of Animals Four-legged animals run with two different types of motion: trotting and galloping. An animal that is trotting has at least one foot on the ground at all times, whereas an animal that is galloping has all four feet off the ground at some point in its stride. The number of strides per minute at which an animal breaks from a trot to a gallop depends on the weight of the animal. Use the table to find a logarithmic equation that relates an animal's weight x (in pounds) and its lowest galloping speed y (in strides per minute).

DATA	Weight, x	Galloping Speed, y
	25	191.5
	35	182.7
Spreadsheet at LarsonPrecalculus.com	50	173.8
	75	164.2
	500	125.9
	1000	114.2

94. Nail Length The approximate lengths and diameters (in inches) of common nails are shown in the table. Find a logarithmic equation that relates the diameter y of a common nail to its length x.

Length, x	Diameter, y
1	0.072
2	0.120
3	0.148
4	0.203
5	0.238

95. Comparing Models   A cup of water at an initial temperature of 78°C is placed in a room at a constant temperature of 21°C. The temperature of the water is measured every 5 minutes during a half-hour period. The results are recorded as ordered pairs of the form (t, T), where t is the time (in minutes) and T is the temperature (in degrees Celsius).

(0, 78.0°), (5, 66.0°), (10, 57.5°), (15, 51.2°), (20, 46.3°), (25, 42.4°), (30, 39.6°)

(a) The graph of the model for the data should be asymptotic with the graph of the temperature of the room. Subtract the room temperature from each of the temperatures in the ordered pairs. Use a graphing utility to plot the data points (t, T) and $(t, T - 21)$.

(b) An exponential model for the data $(t, T - 21)$ is given by $T - 21 = 54.4(0.964)^t$. Solve for T and graph the model. Compare the result with the plot of the original data.

(c) Take the natural logarithms of the revised temperatures. Use the graphing utility to plot the points $(t, \ln(T - 21))$ and observe that the points appear to be linear. Use the *regression* feature of the graphing utility to fit a line to these data. This resulting line has the form $\ln(T - 21) = at + b$. Solve for T, and verify that the result is equivalent to the model in part (b).

(d) Fit a rational model to the data. Take the reciprocals of the y-coordinates of the revised data points to generate the points

$$\left(t, \frac{1}{T - 21}\right).$$

Use the graphing utility to graph these points and observe that they appear to be linear. Use the *regression* feature of the graphing utility to fit a line to these data. The resulting line has the form

$$\frac{1}{T - 21} = at + b.$$

Solve for T, and use the graphing utility to graph the rational function and the original data points.

(e) Why did taking the logarithms of the temperatures lead to a linear scatter plot? Why did taking the reciprocals of the temperatures lead to a linear scatter plot?

Exploration

96. Graphical Analysis   Use a graphing utility to graph the functions $y_1 = \ln x - \ln(x - 3)$ and $y_2 = \ln \dfrac{x}{x - 3}$ in the same viewing window. Does the graphing utility show the functions with the same domain? If so, should it? Explain your reasoning.

True or False?   In Exercises 97–102, determine whether the statement is true or false given that $f(x) = \ln x$. Justify your answer.

97. $f(0) = 0$

98. $f(ax) = f(a) + f(x), \quad a > 0, \quad x > 0$

99. $f(x - 2) = f(x) - f(2), \quad x > 2$

100. $\sqrt{f(x)} = \frac{1}{2}f(x)$

101. If $f(u) = 2f(v)$, then $v = u^2$.

102. If $f(x) < 0$, then $0 < x < 1$.

Using the Change-of-Base Formula   In Exercises 103–106, use the change-of-base formula to rewrite the logarithm as a ratio of logarithms. Then use a graphing utility to graph the ratio.

103. $f(x) = \log_2 x$

104. $f(x) = \log_{1/2} x$

105. $f(x) = \log_{1/4} x$

106. $f(x) = \log_{11.8} x$

107. Discussion   A classmate claims that the following are true.

(a) $\ln(u + v) = \ln u + \ln v = \ln(uv)$

(b) $\ln(u - v) = \ln u - \ln v = \ln \dfrac{u}{v}$

(c) $(\ln u)^n = n(\ln u) = \ln u^n$

Discuss how you would demonstrate that these claims are not true.

108. **HOW DO YOU SEE IT?**   The figure shows the graphs of $y = \ln x$, $y = \ln x^2$, $y = \ln 2x$, and $y = \ln 2$. Match each function with its graph. (The graphs are labeled A through D.) Explain your reasoning.

109. Think About It   For how many integers between 1 and 20 can you approximate natural logarithms, given the values $\ln 2 \approx 0.6931$, $\ln 3 \approx 1.0986$, and $\ln 5 \approx 1.6094$? Approximate these logarithms (do not use a calculator).

3.4 Exponential and Logarithmic Equations

- ■ Solve simple exponential and logarithmic equations.
- ■ Solve more complicated exponential equations.
- ■ Solve more complicated logarithmic equations.
- ■ Use exponential and logarithmic equations to model and solve real-life problems.

Introduction

Exponential and logarithmic equations can help you model and solve life science applications. For instance, Exercise 83 on page 236 uses an exponential function to model the number of trees per acre given the average diameter of the trees.

So far in this chapter, you have studied the definitions, graphs, and properties of exponential and logarithmic functions. In this section, you will study procedures for *solving equations* involving these exponential and logarithmic functions.

There are two basic strategies for solving exponential or logarithmic equations. The first is based on the One-to-One Properties and was used to solve simple exponential and logarithmic equations in Sections 3.1 and 3.2. The second is based on the Inverse Properties. For $a > 0$ and $a \neq 1$, the following properties are true for all x and y for which $\log_a x$ and $\log_a y$ are defined.

One-to-One Properties	Inverse Properties
$a^x = a^y$ if and only if $x = y$.	$a^{\log_a x} = x$
$\log_a x = \log_a y$ if and only if $x = y$.	$\log_a a^x = x$

EXAMPLE 1   **Solving Simple Equations**

	Original Equation	Rewritten Equation	Solution	Property
a.	$2^x = 32$	$2^x = 2^5$	$x = 5$	One-to-One
b.	$\ln x - \ln 3 = 0$	$\ln x = \ln 3$	$x = 3$	One-to-One
c.	$\left(\frac{1}{3}\right)^x = 9$	$3^{-x} = 3^2$	$x = -2$	One-to-One
d.	$e^x = 7$	$\ln e^x = \ln 7$	$x = \ln 7$	Inverse
e.	$\ln x = -3$	$e^{\ln x} = e^{-3}$	$x = e^{-3}$	Inverse
f.	$\log x = -1$	$10^{\log x} = 10^{-1}$	$x = 10^{-1} = \frac{1}{10}$	Inverse
g.	$\log_3 x = 4$	$3^{\log_3 x} = 3^4$	$x = 81$	Inverse

✓ *Checkpoint*) *Audio-video solution in English & Spanish at LarsonPrecalculus.com.*

Solve each equation for x.

a. $2^x = 512$ **b.** $\log_6 x = 3$ **c.** $5 - e^x = 0$ **d.** $9^x = \frac{1}{3}$

The strategies used in Example 1 are summarized as follows.

Strategies for Solving Exponential and Logarithmic Equations

1. Rewrite the original equation in a form that allows the use of the One-to-One Properties of exponential or logarithmic functions.

2. Rewrite an *exponential* equation in logarithmic form and apply the Inverse Property of logarithmic functions.

3. Rewrite a *logarithmic* equation in exponential form and apply the Inverse Property of exponential functions.

Solving Exponential Equations

EXAMPLE 2 Solving Exponential Equations

Solve each equation and approximate the result to three decimal places, if necessary.

a. $e^{-x^2} = e^{-3x-4}$ **b.** $3(2^x) = 42$

Solution

a.

$$e^{-x^2} = e^{-3x-4}$$ Write original equation.

$$-x^2 = -3x - 4$$ One-to-One Property

$$x^2 - 3x - 4 = 0$$ Write in general form.

$$(x + 1)(x - 4) = 0$$ Factor.

$$(x + 1) = 0 \implies x = -1$$ Set 1st factor equal to 0.

$$(x - 4) = 0 \implies x = 4$$ Set 2nd factor equal to 0.

The solutions are $x = -1$ and $x = 4$. Check these in the original equation.

b.

$$3(2^x) = 42$$ Write original equation.

$$2^x = 14$$ Divide each side by 3.

$$\log_2 2^x = \log_2 14$$ Take log (base 2) of each side.

$$x = \log_2 14$$ Inverse Property

$$x = \frac{\ln 14}{\ln 2} \approx 3.807$$ Change-of-base formula

The solution is $x = \log_2 14 \approx 3.807$. Check this in the original equation.

 Checkpoint Audio-video solution in English & Spanish at LarsonPrecalculus.com.

Solve each equation and approximate the result to three decimal places, if necessary.

a. $e^{2x} = e^{x^2-8}$ **b.** $2(5^x) = 32$

> •• **REMARK**
> Another way to solve
> Example 2(b) is by taking the
> natural log of each side and then
> applying the Power Property,
> as follows.
>
> $$3(2^x) = 42$$
>
> $$2^x = 14$$
>
> $$\ln 2^x = \ln 14$$
>
> $$x \ln 2 = \ln 14$$
>
> $$x = \frac{\ln 14}{\ln 2} \approx 3.807$$
>
> Notice that you obtain the same
> result as in Example 2(b).

In Example 2(b), the exact solution is $x = \log_2 14$, and the approximate solution is $x \approx 3.807$. An exact answer is preferred when the solution is an intermediate step in a larger problem. For a final answer, an approximate solution is easier to comprehend.

EXAMPLE 3 Solving an Exponential Equation

Solve $e^x + 5 = 60$ and approximate the result to three decimal places.

Solution

$$e^x + 5 = 60$$ Write original equation.

$$e^x = 55$$ Subtract 5 from each side.

$$\ln e^x = \ln 55$$ Take natural log of each side.

$$x = \ln 55 \approx 4.007$$ Inverse Property

The solution is $x = \ln 55 \approx 4.007$. Check this in the original equation.

> •• **REMARK** Remember that
> the natural logarithmic function
> has a base of e.

 Checkpoint Audio-video solution in English & Spanish at LarsonPrecalculus.com.

Solve $e^x - 7 = 23$ and approximate the result to three decimal places.

EXAMPLE 4   **Solving an Exponential Equation**

Solve $2(3^{2t-5}) - 4 = 11$ and approximate the result to three decimal places.

Solution

$$2(3^{2t-5}) - 4 = 11 \qquad \text{Write original equation.}$$

$$2(3^{2t-5}) = 15 \qquad \text{Add 4 to each side.}$$

$$3^{2t-5} = \frac{15}{2} \qquad \text{Divide each side by 2.}$$

$$\log_3 3^{2t-5} = \log_3 \frac{15}{2} \qquad \text{Take log (base 3) of each side.}$$

$$2t - 5 = \log_3 \frac{15}{2} \qquad \text{Inverse Property}$$

$$2t = 5 + \log_3 7.5 \qquad \text{Add 5 to each side.}$$

$$t = \frac{5}{2} + \frac{1}{2} \log_3 7.5 \qquad \text{Divide each side by 2.}$$

$$t \approx 3.417 \qquad \text{Use a calculator.}$$

• • REMARK Remember that to evaluate a logarithm such as $\log_3 7.5$, you need to use the change-of-base formula.

$$\log_3 7.5 = \frac{\ln 7.5}{\ln 3} \approx 1.834$$

▷ The solution is $t = \frac{5}{2} + \frac{1}{2} \log_3 7.5 \approx 3.417$. Check this in the original equation.

✔ *Checkpoint* *Audio-video solution in English & Spanish at LarsonPrecalculus.com.*

Solve $6(2^{t+5}) + 4 = 11$ and approximate the result to three decimal places.

When an equation involves two or more exponential expressions, you can still use a procedure similar to that demonstrated in Examples 2, 3, and 4. However, the algebra is a bit more complicated.

EXAMPLE 5   **Solving an Exponential Equation of Quadratic Type**

Solve $e^{2x} - 3e^x + 2 = 0$.

Algebraic Solution

$$e^{2x} - 3e^x + 2 = 0 \qquad \text{Write original equation.}$$

$$(e^x)^2 - 3e^x + 2 = 0 \qquad \text{Write in quadratic form.}$$

$$(e^x - 2)(e^x - 1) = 0 \qquad \text{Factor.}$$

$$e^x - 2 = 0 \qquad \text{Set 1st factor equal to 0.}$$

$$x = \ln 2 \qquad \text{Solution}$$

$$e^x - 1 = 0 \qquad \text{Set 2nd factor equal to 0.}$$

$$x = 0 \qquad \text{Solution}$$

The solutions are $x = \ln 2 \approx 0.693$ and $x = 0$. Check these in the original equation.

Graphical Solution

Use a graphing utility to graph $y = e^{2x} - 3e^x + 2$ and then find the zeros.

So, you can conclude that the solutions are $x = 0$ and $x \approx 0.693$.

✔ *Checkpoint* 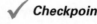 *Audio-video solution in English & Spanish at LarsonPrecalculus.com.*

Solve $e^{2x} - 7e^x + 12 = 0$.

Solving Logarithmic Equations

To solve a logarithmic equation, you can write it in exponential form.

$$\ln x = 3$$ Logarithmic form

$$e^{\ln x} = e^3$$ Exponentiate each side.

$$x = e^3$$ Exponential form

This procedure is called *exponentiating* each side of an equation.

EXAMPLE 6 **Solving Logarithmic Equations**

a. $\ln x = 2$ Original equation

$$e^{\ln x} = e^2$$ Exponentiate each side.

$$x = e^2$$ Inverse Property

b. $\log_3(5x - 1) = \log_3(x + 7)$ Original equation

$$5x - 1 = x + 7$$ One-to-One Property

$$x = 2$$ Solution

c. $\log_6(3x + 14) - \log_6 5 = \log_6 2x$ Original equation

$$\log_6\left(\frac{3x + 14}{5}\right) = \log_6 2x$$ Quotient Property of Logarithms

$$\frac{3x + 14}{5} = 2x$$ One-to-One Property

$$3x + 14 = 10x$$ Multiply each side by 5.

$$x = 2$$ Solution

✓ **Checkpoint** 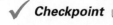 Audio-video solution in English & Spanish at LarsonPrecalculus.com.

Solve each equation.

a. $\ln x = \frac{2}{3}$ **b.** $\log_2(2x - 3) = \log_2(x + 4)$ **c.** $\log 4x - \log(12 + x) = \log 2$

EXAMPLE 7 **Solving a Logarithmic Equation**

Solve $5 + 2 \ln x = 4$ and approximate the result to three decimal places.

Algebraic Solution

$$5 + 2 \ln x = 4$$ Write original equation.

$$2 \ln x = -1$$ Subtract 5 from each side.

$$\ln x = -\frac{1}{2}$$ Divide each side by 2.

$$e^{\ln x} = e^{-1/2}$$ Exponentiate each side.

$$x = e^{-1/2}$$ Inverse Property

$$x \approx 0.607$$ Use a calculator.

Graphical Solution

The intersection point is about $(0.607, 4)$. So, the solution is $x \approx 0.607$.

✓ **Checkpoint** Audio-video solution in English & Spanish at LarsonPrecalculus.com.

Solve $7 + 3 \ln x = 5$ and approximate the result to three decimal places.

EXAMPLE 8 **Solving a Logarithmic Equation**

Solve $2 \log_5 3x = 4$.

Solution

$$2 \log_5 3x = 4 \qquad \text{Write original equation.}$$
$$\log_5 3x = 2 \qquad \text{Divide each side by 2.}$$
$$5^{\log_5 3x} = 5^2 \qquad \text{Exponentiate each side (base 5).}$$
$$3x = 25 \qquad \text{Inverse Property}$$
$$x = \frac{25}{3} \qquad \text{Divide each side by 3.}$$

The solution is $x = \frac{25}{3}$. Check this in the original equation.

✓ **Checkpoint** ◄))) *Audio-video solution in English & Spanish at LarsonPrecalculus.com.*

Solve $3 \log_4 6x = 9$.

Because the domain of a logarithmic function generally does not include all real numbers, you should be sure to check for extraneous solutions of logarithmic equations.

EXAMPLE 9 **Checking for Extraneous Solutions**

Solve $\log 5x + \log(x - 1) = 2$.

Algebraic Solution

$$\log 5x + \log(x - 1) = 2 \qquad \text{Write original equation.}$$
$$\log[5x(x - 1)] = 2 \qquad \text{Product Property of Logarithms}$$
$$10^{\log(5x^2 - 5x)} = 10^2 \qquad \text{Exponentiate each side (base 10).}$$
$$5x^2 - 5x = 100 \qquad \text{Inverse Property}$$
$$x^2 - x - 20 = 0 \qquad \text{Write in general form.}$$
$$(x - 5)(x + 4) = 0 \qquad \text{Factor.}$$
$$x - 5 = 0 \qquad \text{Set 1st factor equal to 0.}$$
$$x = 5 \qquad \text{Solution}$$
$$x + 4 = 0 \qquad \text{Set 2nd factor equal to 0.}$$
$$x = -4 \qquad \text{Solution}$$

The solutions appear to be $x = 5$ and $x = -4$. However, when you check these in the original equation, you can see that $x = 5$ is the only solution.

✓ **Checkpoint** ◄))) *Audio-video solution in English & Spanish at LarsonPrecalculus.com.*

Solve $\log x + \log(x - 9) = 1$.

▷

•• **REMARK** Notice in Example 9 that the logarithmic part of the equation is condensed into a single logarithm before exponentiating each side of the equation.

Graphical Solution

First, rewrite the original equation as
$$\log 5x + \log(x - 1) - 2 = 0.$$
Then use a graphing utility to graph the equation
$$y = \log 5x + \log(x - 1) - 2$$
and find the zero(s).

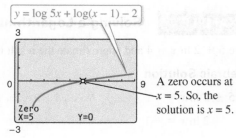

A zero occurs at $x = 5$. So, the solution is $x = 5$.

In Example 9, the domain of $\log 5x$ is $x > 0$ and the domain of $\log(x - 1)$ is $x > 1$, so the domain of the original equation is

$$x > 1.$$

Because the domain is all real numbers greater than 1, the solution $x = -4$ is extraneous. The graphical solution verifies this conclusion.

Applications

EXAMPLE 10 **Doubling an Investment**

You invest \$500 at an annual interest rate of 6.75%, compounded continuously. How long will it take your money to double?

Solution Using the formula for continuous compounding, the balance is

$$A = Pe^{rt}$$

$$A = 500e^{0.0675t}.$$

To find the time required for the balance to double, let $A = 1000$ and solve the resulting equation for t.

$$500e^{0.0675t} = 1000 \qquad \text{Let } A = 1000.$$

$$e^{0.0675t} = 2 \qquad \text{Divide each side by 500.}$$

$$\ln e^{0.0675t} = \ln 2 \qquad \text{Take natural log of each side.}$$

$$0.0675t = \ln 2 \qquad \text{Inverse Property}$$

$$t = \frac{\ln 2}{0.0675} \qquad \text{Divide each side by 0.0675.}$$

$$t \approx 10.27 \qquad \text{Use a calculator.}$$

The balance in the account will double after approximately 10.27 years. This result is demonstrated graphically below.

Doubling an Investment

$A = 500e^{0.0675t}$

(10.27, 1000)

(0, 500)

Balance (in dollars)

Time (in years)

 Checkpoint Audio-video solution in English & Spanish at LarsonPrecalculus.com.

You invest \$500 at an annual interest rate of 5.25%, compounded continuously. How long will it take your money to double? Compare your result with that of Example 10.

In Example 10, an approximate answer of 10.27 years is given. Within the context of the problem, the exact solution

$$t = \frac{\ln 2}{0.0675}$$

does not make sense as an answer.

EXAMPLE 11 **Retail Sales**

The retail sales y (in billions of dollars) of e-commerce companies in the United States from 2002 through 2010 can be modeled by

$$y = -566 + 244.7 \ln t, \quad 12 \leq t \leq 20$$

where t represents the year, with $t = 12$ corresponding to 2002 (see figure). During which year did the sales reach $141 billion? *(Source: U.S. Census Bureau)*

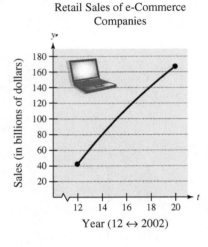

Retail Sales of e-Commerce Companies

Sales (in billions of dollars)

Year (12 ↔ 2002)

Solution

$-566 + 244.7 \ln t = y$	Write original equation.
$-566 + 244.7 \ln t = 141$	Substitute 141 for y.
$244.7 \ln t = 707$	Add 566 to each side.
$\ln t = \dfrac{707}{244.7}$	Divide each side by 244.7.
$e^{\ln t} = e^{707/244.7}$	Exponentiate each side.
$t = e^{707/244.7}$	Inverse Property
$t \approx 18$	Use a calculator.

The solution is $t \approx 18$. Because $t = 12$ represents 2002, it follows that the sales reached $141 billion in 2008.

✓ *Checkpoint* *Audio-video solution in English & Spanish at LarsonPrecalculus.com.*

In Example 11, during which year did the sales reach $80 billion? ■

Summarize (Section 3.4)

1. State the One-to-One Properties and the Inverse Properties that can help you solve simple exponential and logarithmic equations *(page 228)*. For an example of solving simple exponential and logarithmic equations, see Example 1.

2. Describe strategies for solving exponential equations *(pages 229 and 230)*. For examples of solving exponential equations, see Examples 2–5.

3. Describe strategies for solving logarithmic equations *(pages 231 and 232)*. For examples of solving logarithmic equations, see Examples 6–9.

4. Describe examples of how to use exponential and logarithmic equations to model and solve real-life problems *(pages 233 and 234, Examples 10 and 11)*.

3.4 Exercises

See CalcChat.com for tutorial help and worked-out solutions to odd-numbered exercises.

Vocabulary: Fill in the blanks.

1. To solve exponential and logarithmic equations, you can use the following One-to-One and Inverse Properties.

   (a) $a^x = a^y$ if and only if _____.
       (b) $\log_a x = \log_a y$ if and only if _____.

   (c) $a^{\log_a x} =$ _____
       (d) $\log_a a^x =$ _____

2. An _____ solution does not satisfy the original equation.

Skills and Applications

Determining Solutions In Exercises 3–6, determine whether each x-value is a solution (or an approximate solution) of the equation.

3. $4^{2x-7} = 64$
      4. $4e^{x-1} = 60$

   (a) $x = 5$
          (a) $x = 1 + \ln 15$

   (b) $x = 2$
          (b) $x = \ln 16$

5. $\log_2(x + 3) = 10$
    6. $\ln(2x + 3) = 5.8$

   (a) $x = 1021$
        (a) $x = \frac{1}{2}(-3 + \ln 5.8)$

   (b) $x = 17$
         (b) $x = \frac{1}{2}(-3 + e^{5.8})$

   (c) $x = 10^2 - 3$
      (c) $x \approx 163.650$

Solving a Simple Equation In Exercises 7–14, solve for x.

7. $4^x = 16$
        8. $\left(\frac{1}{2}\right)^x = 32$

9. $\ln x - \ln 2 = 0$
   10. $e^x = 2$

11. $\ln x = -1$
      12. $\log x = -2$

13. $\log_4 x = 3$
     14. $\log_5 x = \frac{1}{2}$

Approximating a Point of Intersection In Exercises 15 and 16, approximate the point of intersection of the graphs of f and g. Then solve the equation $f(x) = g(x)$ algebraically to verify your approximation.

15. $f(x) = 2^x$
      16. $f(x) = \log_3 x$

   $g(x) = 8$
        $g(x) = 2$

Solving an Exponential Equation In Exercises 17–44, solve the exponential equation algebraically. Approximate the result to three decimal places.

17. $e^x = e^{x^2 - 2}$
     18. $e^{x^2 - 3} = e^{x-2}$

19. $4(3^x) = 20$
      20. $4e^x = 91$

21. $e^x - 9 = 19$
     22. $6^x + 10 = 47$

23. $3^{2x} = 80$
       24. $4^{-3t} = 0.10$

25. $2^{3-x} = 565$
     26. $8^{-2-x} = 431$

27. $8(10^{3x}) = 12$
    28. $8(3^{6-x}) = 40$

29. $e^{3x} = 12$
       30. $1000e^{-4x} = 75$

31. $7 - 2e^x = 5$
     32. $-14 + 3e^x = 11$

33. $6(2^{3x-1}) - 7 = 9$
  34. $8(4^{6-2x}) + 13 = 41$

35. $2^x = 3^{x+1}$
      36. $2^{x+1} = e^{1-x}$

37. $4^x = 5^{x^2}$
       38. $3^{x^2} = 76 - x$

39. $e^{2x} - 4e^x - 5 = 0$
  40. $e^{2x} - 5e^x + 6 = 0$

41. $\dfrac{500}{100 - e^{x/2}} = 20$
  42. $\dfrac{400}{1 + e^{-x}} = 350$

43. $\left(1 + \dfrac{0.065}{365}\right)^{365t} = 4$
  44. $\left(1 + \dfrac{0.10}{12}\right)^{12t} = 2$

Solving a Logarithmic Equation In Exercises 45–62, solve the logarithmic equation algebraically. Approximate the result to three decimal places.

45. $\ln x = -3$
      46. $\ln x - 7 = 0$

47. $2.1 = \ln 6x$
     48. $\log 3z = 2$

49. $3 \ln 5x = 10$
    50. $\ln \sqrt{x - 8} = 5$

51. $2 - 6 \ln x = 10$

52. $2 + 3 \ln x = 12$

53. $6 \log_3(0.5x) = 11$

54. $4 \log(x - 6) = 11$

55. $\ln x - \ln(x + 1) = 2$

56. $\ln x + \ln(x + 1) = 1$

57. $\ln(x + 5) = \ln(x - 1) - \ln(x + 1)$

58. $\ln(x + 1) - \ln(x - 2) = \ln x$

59. $\log(3x + 4) = \log(x - 10)$

60. $\log_2 x + \log_2(x + 2) = \log_2(x + 6)$

61. $\log_4 x - \log_4(x - 1) = \frac{1}{2}$

62. $\log 8x - \log\left(1 + \sqrt{x}\right) = 2$

Graphing and Solving an Equation In Exercises 63–70, use a graphing utility to graph and solve the equation. Approximate the result to three decimal places. Verify your result algebraically.

63. $5^x = 212$

64. $6e^{1-x} = 25$

65. $8e^{-2x/3} = 11$

66. $e^{0.09t} = 3$

67. $3 - \ln x = 0$

68. $10 - 4\ln(x - 2) = 0$

69. $2\ln(x + 3) = 3$

70. $\ln(x + 1) = 2 - \ln x$

Compound Interest In Exercises 71 and 72, you invest $2500 in an account at interest rate r, compounded continuously. Find the time required for the amount to (a) double and (b) triple.

71. $r = 0.025$

72. $r = 0.0375$

Algebra of Calculus In Exercises 73–80, solve the equation algebraically. Round your result to three decimal places. Verify your answer using a graphing utility.

73. $2x^2 e^{2x} + 2xe^{2x} = 0$

74. $-x^2 e^{-x} + 2xe^{-x} = 0$

75. $-xe^{-x} + e^{-x} = 0$

76. $e^{-2x} - 2xe^{-2x} = 0$

77. $2x\ln x + x = 0$

78. $\dfrac{1 - \ln x}{x^2} = 0$

79. $\dfrac{1 + \ln x}{2} = 0$

80. $2x\ln\left(\dfrac{1}{x}\right) - x = 0$

81. Average Heights The percent m of American males between the ages of 20 and 29 who are under x inches tall is modeled by

$$m(x) = \frac{100}{1 + e^{-0.5536(x - 69.51)}}, \quad 64 \le x \le 78$$

and the percent f of American females between the ages of 20 and 29 who are under x inches tall is modeled by

$$f(x) = \frac{100}{1 + e^{-0.5834(x - 64.49)}}, \quad 60 \le x \le 78.$$

(Source: U.S. National Center for Health Statistics)

(a) Use the graph to determine any horizontal asymptotes of the graphs of the functions. Interpret the meaning in the context of the problem.

(b) What is the average height of each sex?

James Marshall/CORBIS

82. U.S. Currency The values y (in billions of dollars) of U.S. currency in circulation in the years 2000 through 2010 can be modeled by $y = -611 + 507 \ln t$, $10 \le t \le 20$, where t represents the year, with $t = 10$ corresponding to 2000. During which year did the value of U.S. currency in circulation exceed $690 billion? *(Source: Board of Governors of the Federal Reserve System)*

83. Trees per Acre

The number N of trees of a given species per acre is approximated by the model $N = 68(10^{-0.04x})$, $5 \le x \le 40$, where x is the average diameter of the trees (in inches) 3 feet above the ground. Use the model to approximate the average diameter of the trees in a test plot when $N = 21$.

84. Demand The demand equation for a smart phone is

$$p = 5000\left(1 - \frac{4}{4 + e^{-0.002x}}\right).$$

Find the demand x for a price of (a) $p = \$169$ and (b) $p = \$299$.

85. Automobiles Engineers design automobiles with crumple zones that help protect their occupants in crashes. The crumple zones allow the occupants to move short distances when the automobiles come to abrupt stops. The greater the distance moved, the fewer g's the crash victims experience. (One g is equal to the acceleration due to gravity.) In crash tests with vehicles moving at 90 kilometers per hour, analysts measured the numbers of g's experienced during deceleration by crash dummies that were permitted to move x meters during impact. The table shows the data. A model for the data is given by $y = -3.00 + 11.88 \ln x + (36.94/x)$, where y is the number of g's.

x	0.2	0.4	0.6	0.8	1.0
g's	158	80	53	40	32

(a) Complete the table using the model.

x	0.2	0.4	0.6	0.8	1.0
y					

(b) Use a graphing utility to graph the data points and the model in the same viewing window. How do they compare?

(c) Use the model to estimate the distance traveled during impact, assuming that the passenger deceleration must not exceed 30 g's.

(d) Do you think it is practical to lower the number of g's experienced during impact to fewer than 23? Explain your reasoning.

86. Data Analysis An object at a temperature of 160°C was removed from a furnace and placed in a room at 20°C. The temperature T of the object was measured each hour h and recorded in the table. A model for the data is given by $T = 20[1 + 7(2^{-h})]$. The figure shows the graph of this model.

DATA	Hour, h	Temperature, T
	0	160°
	1	90°
	2	56°
	3	38°
	4	29°
	5	24°

Spreadsheet at LarsonPrecalculus.com

(a) Use the graph to identify the horizontal asymptote of the model and interpret the asymptote in the context of the problem.

(b) Use the model to approximate the time when the temperature of the object was 100°C.

Exploration

True or False? **In Exercises 87–90, rewrite each verbal statement as an equation. Then decide whether the statement is true or false. Justify your answer.**

87. The logarithm of the product of two numbers is equal to the sum of the logarithms of the numbers.

88. The logarithm of the sum of two numbers is equal to the product of the logarithms of the numbers.

89. The logarithm of the difference of two numbers is equal to the difference of the logarithms of the numbers.

90. The logarithm of the quotient of two numbers is equal to the difference of the logarithms of the numbers.

91. Think About It Is it possible for a logarithmic equation to have more than one extraneous solution? Explain.

92. HOW DO YOU SEE IT? Solving $\log_3 x + \log_3(x - 8) = 2$ algebraically, the solutions appear to be $x = 9$ and $x = -1$. Use the graph of $y = \log_3 x + \log_3(x - 8) - 2$ to determine whether each value is an actual solution of the equation. Explain your reasoning.

93. Finance You are investing P dollars at an annual interest rate of r, compounded continuously, for t years. Which of the following would result in the highest value of the investment? Explain your reasoning.

(a) Double the amount you invest.

(b) Double your interest rate.

(c) Double the number of years.

94. Think About It Are the times required for the investments in Exercises 71 and 72 to quadruple twice as long as the times for them to double? Give a reason for your answer and verify your answer algebraically.

95. Effective Yield The *effective yield* of an investment plan is the percent increase in the balance after 1 year. Find the effective yield for each investment plan. Which investment plan has the greatest effective yield? Which investment plan will have the highest balance after 5 years?

(a) 7% annual interest rate, compounded annually

(b) 7% annual interest rate, compounded continuously

(c) 7% annual interest rate, compounded quarterly

(d) 7.25% annual interest rate, compounded quarterly

96. Graphical Analysis Let $f(x) = \log_a x$ and $g(x) = a^x$, where $a > 1$.

(a) Let $a = 1.2$ and use a graphing utility to graph the two functions in the same viewing window. What do you observe? Approximate any points of intersection of the two graphs.

(b) Determine the value(s) of a for which the two graphs have one point of intersection.

(c) Determine the value(s) of a for which the two graphs have two points of intersection.

3.5 Exponential and Logarithmic Models

- ■ Recognize the five most common types of models involving exponential and logarithmic functions.
- ■ Use exponential growth and decay functions to model and solve real-life problems.
- ■ Use Gaussian functions to model and solve real-life problems.
- ■ Use logistic growth functions to model and solve real-life problems.
- ■ Use logarithmic functions to model and solve real-life problems.

Introduction

The five most common types of mathematical models involving exponential functions and logarithmic functions are as follows.

1. **Exponential growth model:** $y = ae^{bx}, \quad b > 0$

2. **Exponential decay model:** $y = ae^{-bx}, \quad b > 0$

3. **Gaussian model:** $y = ae^{-(x-b)^2/c}$

4. **Logistic growth model:** $y = \dfrac{a}{1 + be^{-rx}}$

5. **Logarithmic models:** $y = a + b \ln x, \quad y = a + b \log x$

Exponential growth and decay models can often represent the populations of countries. For instance, in Exercise 30 on page 246, you will use exponential growth and decay models to compare the populations of several countries.

The basic shapes of the graphs of these functions are as follows.

Exponential growth model

Exponential decay model

Gaussian model

Logistic growth model

Natural logarithmic model

Common logarithmic model

You often gain insight into a situation modeled by an exponential or logarithmic function by identifying and interpreting the asymptotes of the graph of the function. Identify the asymptote(s) of the graph of each function shown above.

Exponential Growth and Decay

EXAMPLE 1 **Online Advertising**

Estimates of the amounts (in billions of dollars) of U.S. online advertising spending from 2011 through 2015 are shown in the table. A scatter plot of the data is shown at the right. *(Source: eMarketer)*

Year	2011	2012	2013	2014	2015
Advertising Spending	31.3	36.8	41.2	45.5	49.5

An exponential growth model that approximates the data is given by

$$S = 9.30e^{0.1129t}, \quad 11 \le t \le 15$$

where S is the amount of spending (in billions of dollars) and $t = 11$ represents 2011. Compare the values given by the model with the estimates shown in the table. According to this model, when will the amount of U.S. online advertising spending reach \$80 billion?

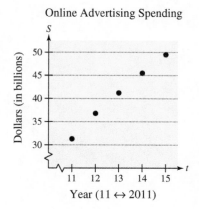
Online Advertising Spending
Year (11 ↔ 2011)

Algebraic Solution

The following table compares the two sets of advertising spending amounts.

Year	2011	2012	2013	2014	2015
Advertising Spending	31.3	36.8	41.2	45.5	49.5
Model	32.2	36.0	40.4	45.2	50.6

To find when the amount of U.S. online advertising spending will reach \$80 billion, let $S = 80$ in the model and solve for t.

$9.30e^{0.1129t} = S$ Write original model.

$9.30e^{0.1129t} = 80$ Substitute 80 for S.

$e^{0.1129t} \approx 8.6022$ Divide each side by 9.30.

$\ln e^{0.1129t} \approx \ln 8.6022$ Take natural log of each side.

$0.1129t \approx 2.1520$ Inverse Property

$t \approx 19.1$ Divide each side by 0.1129.

According to the model, the amount of U.S. online advertising spending will reach \$80 billion in 2019.

Graphical Solution

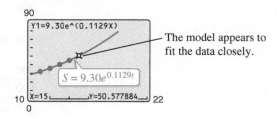

The model appears to fit the data closely.

The intersection point of the model and the line $y = 80$ is about (19.1, 80). So, according to the model, the amount of U.S. online advertising spending will reach \$80 billion in 2019.

✓ **Checkpoint** ◄))) *Audio-video solution in English & Spanish at LarsonPrecalculus.com.*

In Example 1, when will the amount of U.S. online advertising spending reach \$100 billion?

▷ **TECHNOLOGY** Some graphing utilities have an *exponential regression* feature that can help you find exponential models to represent data. If you have such a graphing utility, try using it to find an exponential model for the data given in Example 1. How does your model compare with the model given in Example 1?

In Example 1, the exponential growth model is given. But if this model were not given, then how would you find such a model? Example 2 demonstrates one technique.

EXAMPLE 2 **Modeling Population Growth**

In a research experiment, a population of fruit flies is increasing according to the law of exponential growth. After 2 days there are 100 flies, and after 4 days there are 300 flies. How many flies will there be after 5 days?

Solution Let y be the number of flies at time t. From the given information, you know that $y = 100$ when $t = 2$ and $y = 300$ when $t = 4$. Substituting this information into the model $y = ae^{bt}$ produces

$$100 = ae^{2b} \quad \text{and} \quad 300 = ae^{4b}.$$

To solve for b, solve for a in the first equation.

$$100 = ae^{2b} \qquad \text{Write first equation.}$$

$$\frac{100}{e^{2b}} = a \qquad \text{Solve for } a.$$

Then substitute the result into the second equation.

$$300 = ae^{4b} \qquad \text{Write second equation.}$$

$$300 = \left(\frac{100}{e^{2b}}\right)e^{4b} \qquad \text{Substitute } \frac{100}{e^{2b}} \text{ for } a.$$

$$\frac{300}{100} = e^{2b} \qquad \text{Simplify, and divide each side by 100.}$$

$$\ln 3 = 2b \qquad \text{Take natural log of each side.}$$

$$\frac{1}{2}\ln 3 = b \qquad \text{Solve for } b.$$

Using $b = \frac{1}{2}\ln 3$ and the equation you found for a,

$$a = \frac{100}{e^{2[(1/2)\ln 3]}} \qquad \text{Substitute } \frac{1}{2}\ln 3 \text{ for } b.$$

$$= \frac{100}{e^{\ln 3}} \qquad \text{Simplify.}$$

$$= \frac{100}{3} \qquad \text{Inverse Property}$$

$$\approx 33.33. \qquad \text{Divide.}$$

So, with $a \approx 33.33$ and $b = \frac{1}{2}\ln 3 \approx 0.5493$, the exponential growth model is

$$y = 33.33e^{0.5493t}$$

as shown in Figure 3.20. After 5 days, the population will be

$$y = 33.33e^{0.5493(5)}$$

$$\approx 520 \text{ flies.}$$

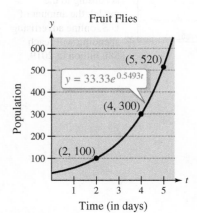

Fruit Flies

$y = 33.33e^{0.5493t}$

(5, 520)

(4, 300)

(2, 100)

Time (in days)

Figure 3.20

✓ **Checkpoint** ◄))) *Audio-video solution in English & Spanish at LarsonPrecalculus.com.*

The number of bacteria in a culture is increasing according to the law of exponential growth. After 1 hour there are 100 bacteria, and after 2 hours there are 200 bacteria. How many bacteria will there be after 3 hours?

In living organic material, the ratio of the number of radioactive carbon isotopes (carbon 14) to the number of nonradioactive carbon isotopes (carbon 12) is about 1 to 10^{12}. When organic material dies, its carbon 12 content remains fixed, whereas its radioactive carbon 14 begins to decay with a half-life of about 5700 years. To estimate the age of dead organic material, scientists use the following formula, which denotes the ratio of carbon 14 to carbon 12 present at any time t (in years).

Carbon Dating

$$R = \frac{1}{10^{12}} e^{-t/8223} \qquad \text{Carbon dating model}$$

The graph of R is shown at the right. Note that R decreases as t increases.

EXAMPLE 3 **Carbon Dating**

Estimate the age of a newly discovered fossil for which the ratio of carbon 14 to carbon 12 is $R = 1/10^{13}$.

Algebraic Solution

In the carbon dating model, substitute the given value of R to obtain the following.

$$\frac{1}{10^{12}} e^{-t/8223} = R \qquad \text{Write original model.}$$

$$\frac{e^{-t/8223}}{10^{12}} = \frac{1}{10^{13}} \qquad \text{Substitute } \tfrac{1}{10^{13}} \text{ for } R.$$

$$e^{-t/8223} = \frac{1}{10} \qquad \text{Multiply each side by } 10^{12}.$$

$$\ln e^{-t/8223} = \ln \frac{1}{10} \qquad \text{Take natural log of each side.}$$

$$-\frac{t}{8223} \approx -2.3026 \qquad \text{Inverse Property}$$

$$t \approx 18{,}934 \qquad \text{Multiply each side by } -8223.$$

So, to the nearest thousand years, the age of the fossil is about 19,000 years.

Graphical Solution

Use a graphing utility to graph the formula for the ratio of carbon 14 to carbon 12 at any time t as

$$y_1 = \frac{1}{10^{12}} e^{-x/8223}.$$

In the same viewing window, graph $y_2 = 1/10^{13}$.

Use the *intersect* feature to estimate that $x \approx 18{,}934$ when $y = 1/10^{13}$.

So, to the nearest thousand years, the age of the fossil is about 19,000 years.

✓ *Checkpoint* 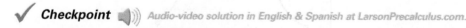 Audio-video solution in English & Spanish at LarsonPrecalculus.com.

Estimate the age of a newly discovered fossil for which the ratio of carbon 14 to carbon 12 is $R = 1/10^{14}$.

The value of b in the exponential decay model $y = ae^{-bt}$ determines the *decay* of radioactive isotopes. For instance, to find how much of an initial 10 grams of ^{226}Ra isotope with a half-life of 1599 years is left after 500 years, substitute this information into the model $y = ae^{-bt}$.

$$\frac{1}{2}(10) = 10e^{-b(1599)} \implies \ln\frac{1}{2} = -1599b \implies b = -\frac{\ln\frac{1}{2}}{1599}$$

Using the value of b found above and $a = 10$, the amount left is

$$y = 10e^{-[-\ln(1/2)/1599](500)} \approx 8.05 \text{ grams.}$$

Gaussian Models

As mentioned at the beginning of this section, Gaussian models are of the form

$$y = ae^{-(x-b)^2/c}.$$

In probability and statistics, this type of model commonly represents populations that are **normally distributed.** The graph of a Gaussian model is called a **bell-shaped curve.** Try graphing the normal distribution with a graphing utility. Can you see why it is called a bell-shaped curve?

For *standard* normal distributions, the model takes the form

$$y = \frac{1}{\sqrt{2\pi}}e^{-x^2/2}.$$

The **average value** of a population can be found from the bell-shaped curve by observing where the maximum y-value of the function occurs. The x-value corresponding to the maximum y-value of the function represents the average value of the independent variable—in this case, x.

EXAMPLE 4   SAT Scores

In 2011, the SAT mathematics scores for high school graduates in the United States roughly followed the normal distribution given by

$$y = 0.0034e^{-(x-514)^2/27,378}, \quad 200 \le x \le 800$$

where x is the SAT score for mathematics. Sketch the graph of this function. From the graph, estimate the average SAT mathematics score.   *(Source: The College Board)*

Solution   The graph of the function is shown below. On this bell-shaped curve, the maximum value of the curve represents the average score. From the graph, you can estimate that the average mathematics score for high school graduates in 2011 was 514.

SAT Scores

Checkpoint ◄))) *Audio-video solution in English & Spanish at LarsonPrecalculus.com.*

In 2011, the SAT critical reading scores for high school graduates in the United States roughly followed the normal distribution given by

$$y = 0.0035e^{-(x-497)^2/25,992}, \quad 200 \le x \le 800$$

where x is the SAT score for critical reading. Sketch the graph of this function. From the graph, estimate the average SAT critical reading score.   *(Source: The College Board)*

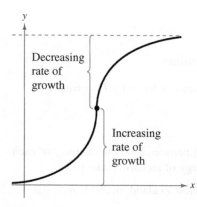

Figure 3.21

Logistic Growth Models

Some populations initially have rapid growth, followed by a declining rate of growth, as indicated by the graph in Figure 3.21. One model for describing this type of growth pattern is the **logistic curve** given by the function

$$y = \frac{a}{1 + be^{-rx}}$$

where y is the population size and x is the time. An example is a bacteria culture that is initially allowed to grow under ideal conditions and then under less favorable conditions that inhibit growth. A logistic growth curve is also called a **sigmoidal curve.**

EXAMPLE 5   **Spread of a Virus**

On a college campus of 5000 students, one student returns from vacation with a contagious and long-lasting flu virus. The spread of the virus is modeled by

$$y = \frac{5000}{1 + 4999e^{-0.8t}}, \quad t \geq 0$$

where y is the total number of students infected after t days. The college will cancel classes when 40% or more of the students are infected.

a. How many students are infected after 5 days?

b. After how many days will the college cancel classes?

Algebraic Solution

a. After 5 days, the number of students infected is

$$y = \frac{5000}{1 + 4999e^{-0.8(5)}} = \frac{5000}{1 + 4999e^{-4}} \approx 54.$$

b. The college will cancel classes when the number of infected students is $(0.40)(5000) = 2000$.

$$2000 = \frac{5000}{1 + 4999e^{-0.8t}}$$

$$1 + 4999e^{-0.8t} = 2.5$$

$$e^{-0.8t} = \frac{1.5}{4999}$$

$$-0.8t = \ln\frac{1.5}{4999}$$

$$t = -\frac{1}{0.8}\ln\frac{1.5}{4999}$$

$$t \approx 10.14$$

So, after about 10 days, at least 40% of the students will be infected, and the college will cancel classes.

Graphical Solution

a.

Use the *value* feature to estimate that $y \approx 54$ when $x = 5$. So, after 5 days, about 54 students are infected.

b. The college will cancel classes when the number of infected students is $(0.40)(5000) = 2000$. Use a graphing utility to graph

$$y_1 = \frac{5000}{1 + 4999e^{-0.8x}} \quad \text{and} \quad y_2 = 2000$$

in the same viewing window. Use the *intersect* feature of the graphing utility to find the point of intersection of the graphs.

The point of intersection occurs near $x \approx 10.14$. So, after about 10 days, at least 40% of the students will be infected, and the college will cancel classes.

 Checkpoint ◀))) *Audio-video solution in English & Spanish at LarsonPrecalculus.com.*

In Example 5, after how many days are 250 students infected?

Logarithmic Models

EXAMPLE 6 **Magnitudes of Earthquakes**

On the Richter scale, the magnitude R of an earthquake of intensity I is given by

$$R = \log \frac{I}{I_0}$$

where $I_0 = 1$ is the minimum intensity used for comparison. Find the intensity of each earthquake. (Intensity is a measure of the wave energy of an earthquake.)

a. Alaska in 2012: $R = 4.0$ **b.** Christchurch, New Zealand, in 2011: $R = 6.3$

Solution

a. Because $I_0 = 1$ and $R = 4.0$, you have

$$4.0 = \log \frac{I}{1}$$ Substitute 1 for I_0 and 4.0 for R.

$$10^{4.0} = 10^{\log I}$$ Exponentiate each side.

$$10^{4.0} = I$$ Inverse Property

$$10,000 = I.$$ Simplify.

b. For $R = 6.3$, you have

$$6.3 = \log \frac{I}{1}$$ Substitute 1 for I_0 and 6.3 for R.

$$10^{6.3} = 10^{\log I}$$ Exponentiate each side.

$$10^{6.3} = I$$ Inverse Property

$$2,000,000 \approx I.$$ Use a calculator.

Note that an increase of 2.3 units on the Richter scale (from 4.0 to 6.3) represents an increase in intensity by a factor of $2,000,000/10,000 = 200$. In other words, the intensity of the earthquake in Christchurch was about 200 times as great as that of the earthquake in Alaska.

On February 22, 2011, an earthquake of magnitude 6.3 struck Christchurch, New Zealand. The total economic loss was estimated at 15.5 billion U.S. dollars.

✓ **Checkpoint** *Audio-video solution in English & Spanish at LarsonPrecalculus.com.*

Find the intensities of earthquakes whose magnitudes are (a) $R = 6.0$ and (b) $R = 7.9$.

Summarize (Section 3.5)

1. State the five most common types of models involving exponential and logarithmic functions *(page 238)*.

2. Describe examples of how to use exponential growth and decay functions to model and solve real-life problems *(pages 239–241, Examples 1–3)*.

3. Describe an example of how to use a Gaussian function to model and solve a real-life problem *(page 242, Example 4)*.

4. Describe an example of how to use a logistic growth function to model and solve a real-life problem *(page 243, Example 5)*.

5. Describe an example of how to use a logarithmic function to model and solve a real-life problem *(page 244, Example 6)*.

3.5 Exercises

Vocabulary: Fill in the blanks.

1. An exponential growth model has the form _____, and an exponential decay model has the form _____.
2. A logarithmic model has the form _____ or _____.
3. In probability and statistics, Gaussian models commonly represent populations that are _____ _____.
4. A logistic growth model has the form _____.

Skills and Applications

Solving for a Variable **In Exercises 5 and 6, (a) solve for P and (b) solve for t.**

5. $A = Pe^{rt}$

6. $A = P\left(1 + \dfrac{r}{n}\right)^{nt}$

Compound Interest **In Exercises 7–12, complete the table assuming continuously compounded interest.**

Initial Investment	Annual % Rate	Time to Double	Amount After 10 Years
7. $1000	3.5%		
8. $750	$10\frac{1}{2}$%		
9. $750		$7\frac{3}{4}$ yr	
10. $500			$1505.00
11.	4.5%		$10,000.00
12.		12 yr	$2000.00

Compound Interest **In Exercises 13 and 14, determine the principal P that must be invested at rate r, compounded monthly, so that $500,000 will be available for retirement in t years.**

13. $r = 5\%, t = 10$ 14. $r = 3\frac{1}{2}\%, t = 15$

Compound Interest **In Exercises 15 and 16, determine the time necessary for P dollars to double when it is invested at interest rate r compounded (a) annually, (b) monthly, (c) daily, and (d) continuously.**

15. $r = 10\%$ 16. $r = 6.5\%$

17. **Compound Interest** Complete the table for the time t (in years) necessary for P dollars to triple when interest is compounded (a) continuously and (b) annually at rate r.

r	2%	4%	6%	8%	10%	12%
t						

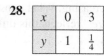
18. **Modeling Data** Draw scatter plots of the data in Exercise 17. Use the *regression* feature of a graphing utility to find models for the data.

19. **Comparing Models** If $1 is invested over a 10-year period, then the balance A, where t represents the time in years, is given by $A = 1 + 0.075[\![t]\!]$ or $A = e^{0.07t}$ depending on whether the interest is simple interest at $7\frac{1}{2}\%$ or continuous compound interest at 7%. Graph each function on the same set of axes. Which grows at a greater rate? (Remember that $[\![t]\!]$ is the greatest integer function discussed in Section 1.6.)

20. **Comparing Models** If $1 is invested over a 10-year period, then the balance A, where t represents the time in years, is given by $A = 1 + 0.06[\![t]\!]$ or $A = [1 + (0.055/365)]^{[\![365t]\!]}$ depending on whether the interest is simple interest at 6% or compound interest at $5\frac{1}{2}\%$ compounded daily. Use a graphing utility to graph each function in the same viewing window. Which grows at a greater rate?

Radioactive Decay **In Exercises 21–24, complete the table for the radioactive isotope.**

Isotope	Half-life (years)	Initial Quantity	Amount After 1000 Years
21. ^{226}Ra	1599	10 g	
22. ^{14}C	5715	6.5 g	
23. ^{14}C	5715		2 g
24. ^{239}Pu	24,100		0.4 g

Finding an Exponential Model **In Exercises 25–28, find the exponential model that fits the points shown in the graph or table.**

25.

26.

27.

x	0	4
y	5	1

28.

x	0	3
y	1	$\frac{1}{4}$

29. Population The populations P (in thousands) of Horry County, South Carolina, from 1980 through 2010 can be modeled by

$$P = 20.6 + 85.5e^{0.0360t}$$

where t represents the year, with $t = 0$ corresponding to 1980. *(Source: U.S. Census Bureau)*

(a) Use the model to complete the table.

Year	1980	1990	2000	2010
Population				

(b) According to the model, when will the population of Horry County reach 350,000?

(c) Do you think the model is valid for long-term predictions of the population? Explain.

30. Population

The table shows the mid-year populations (in millions) of five countries in 2010 and the projected populations (in millions) for the year 2020. *(Source: U.S. Census Bureau)*

Country	2010	2020
Bulgaria	7.1	6.6
Canada	33.8	36.4
China	1330.1	1384.5
United Kingdom	62.3	65.8
United States	310.2	341.4

(a) Find the exponential growth or decay model $y = ae^{bt}$ or $y = ae^{-bt}$ for the population of each country by letting $t = 10$ correspond to 2010. Use the model to predict the population of each country in 2030.

(b) You can see that the populations of the United States and the United Kingdom are growing at different rates. What constant in the equation $y = ae^{bt}$ gives the growth rate? Discuss the relationship between the different growth rates and the magnitude of the constant.

(c) You can see that the population of China is increasing, whereas the population of Bulgaria is decreasing. What constant in the equation $y = ae^{bt}$ reflects this difference? Explain.

31. Website Growth The number y of hits a new website receives each month can be modeled by $y = 4080e^{kt}$, where t represents the number of months the website has been operating. In the website's third month, there were 10,000 hits. Find the value of k, and use this value to predict the number of hits the website will receive after 24 months.

32. Population The populations P (in thousands) of Tallahassee, Florida, from 2005 through 2010 can be modeled by $P = 319.2e^{kt}$, where t represents the year, with $t = 5$ corresponding to 2005. In 2006, the population of Tallahassee was about 347,000. *(Source: U.S. Census Bureau)*

(a) Find the value of k. Is the population increasing or decreasing? Explain.

(b) Use the model to predict the populations of Tallahassee in 2015 and 2020. Are the results reasonable? Explain.

(c) According to the model, during what year will the population reach 410,000?

33. Bacteria Growth The number of bacteria in a culture is increasing according to the law of exponential growth. After 3 hours there are 100 bacteria, and after 5 hours there are 400 bacteria. How many bacteria will there be after 6 hours?

34. Bacteria Growth The number of bacteria in a culture is increasing according to the law of exponential growth. The initial population is 250 bacteria, and the population after 10 hours is double the population after 1 hour. How many bacteria will there be after 6 hours?

35. Depreciation A laptop computer that costs $1150 new has a book value of $550 after 2 years.

(a) Find the linear model $V = mt + b$.

(b) Find the exponential model $V = ae^{kt}$.

(c) Use a graphing utility to graph the two models in the same viewing window. Which model depreciates faster in the first 2 years?

(d) Find the book values of the computer after 1 year and after 3 years using each model.

(e) Explain the advantages and disadvantages of using each model to a buyer and a seller.

36. Learning Curve The management at a plastics factory has found that the maximum number of units a worker can produce in a day is 30. The learning curve for the number N of units produced per day after a new employee has worked t days is modeled by $N = 30(1 - e^{kt})$. After 20 days on the job, a new employee produces 19 units.

(a) Find the learning curve for this employee (first, find the value of k).

(b) How many days should pass before this employee is producing 25 units per day?

37. Carbon Dating

(a) The ratio of carbon 14 to carbon 12 in a piece of wood discovered in a cave is $R = 1/8^{14}$. Estimate the age of the piece of wood.

(b) The ratio of carbon 14 to carbon 12 in a piece of paper buried in a tomb is $R = 1/13^{11}$. Estimate the age of the piece of paper.

38. Radioactive Decay Carbon 14 dating assumes that the carbon dioxide on Earth today has the same radioactive content as it did centuries ago. If this is true, then the amount of ^{14}C absorbed by a tree that grew several centuries ago should be the same as the amount of ^{14}C absorbed by a tree growing today. A piece of ancient charcoal contains only 15% as much radioactive carbon as a piece of modern charcoal. How long ago was the tree burned to make the ancient charcoal, assuming that the half-life of ^{14}C is 5715 years?

39. IQ Scores The IQ scores for a sample of a class of returning adult students at a small northeastern college roughly follow the normal distribution

$$y = 0.0266e^{-(x-100)^2/450}, \quad 70 \le x \le 115$$

where x is the IQ score.

(a) Use a graphing utility to graph the function.

(b) From the graph in part (a), estimate the average IQ score of an adult student.

40. Education The amount of time (in hours per week) a student utilizes a math-tutoring center roughly follows the normal distribution

$$y = 0.7979e^{-(x-5.4)^2/0.5}, \quad 4 \le x \le 7$$

where x is the number of hours.

(a) Use a graphing utility to graph the function.

(b) From the graph in part (a), estimate the average number of hours per week a student uses the tutoring center.

41. Cell Sites A cell site is a site where electronic communications equipment is placed in a cellular network for the use of mobile phones. The numbers y of cell sites from 1985 through 2011 can be modeled by

$$y = \frac{269{,}573}{1 + 985e^{-0.308t}}$$

where t represents the year, with $t = 5$ corresponding to 1985. *(Source: CTIA-The Wireless Association)*

(a) Use the model to find the numbers of cell sites in the years 1998, 2003, and 2006.

(b) Use a graphing utility to graph the function.

(c) Use the graph to determine the year in which the number of cell sites reached 250,000.

(d) Confirm your answer to part (c) algebraically.

42. Population The populations P (in thousands) of a city from 2000 through 2010 can be modeled by

$$P = \frac{2632}{1 + 0.083e^{0.050t}}$$

where t represents the year, with $t = 0$ corresponding to 2000.

(a) Use the model to find the populations of the city in the years 2000, 2005, and 2010.

(b) Use a graphing utility to graph the function.

(c) Use the graph to determine the year in which the population will reach 2.2 million.

(d) Confirm your answer to part (c) algebraically.

43. Population Growth A conservation organization released 100 animals of an endangered species into a game preserve. The preserve has a carrying capacity of 1000 animals. The growth of the pack is modeled by the logistic curve

$$p(t) = \frac{1000}{1 + 9e^{-0.1656t}}$$

where t is measured in months (see figure).

(a) Estimate the population after 5 months.

(b) After how many months is the population 500?

(c) Use a graphing utility to graph the function. Use the graph to determine the horizontal asymptotes, and interpret the meaning of the asymptotes in the context of the problem.

44. Sales After discontinuing all advertising for a tool kit in 2007, the manufacturer noted that sales began to drop according to the model

$$S = \frac{500{,}000}{1 + 0.4e^{kt}}$$

where S represents the number of units sold and $t = 7$ represents 2007. In 2011, 300,000 units were sold.

(a) Complete the model by solving for k.

(b) Estimate sales in 2015.

Geology   **In Exercises 45 and 46, use the Richter scale**

$$R = \log \frac{I}{I_0}$$

for measuring the magnitude R of an earthquake.

45. Find the intensity I of an earthquake measuring R on the Richter scale (let $I_0 = 1$).

  (a) South Shetland Islands in 2012: $R = 6.6$

  (b) Oklahoma in 2011: $R = 5.6$

  (c) Papua New Guinea in 2011: $R = 7.1$

46. Find the magnitude R of each earthquake of intensity I (let $I_0 = 1$).

  (a) $I = 199,500,000$

  (b) $I = 48,275,000$

  (c) $I = 17,000$

Intensity of Sound   **In Exercises 47–50, use the following information for determining sound intensity. The level of sound β, in decibels, with an intensity of I, is given by $\beta = 10 \log(I/I_0)$, where I_0 is an intensity of 10^{-12} watt per square meter, corresponding roughly to the faintest sound that can be heard by the human ear. In Exercises 47 and 48, find the level of sound β.**

47. (a) $I = 10^{-10}$ watt per m^2 (quiet room)

  (b) $I = 10^{-5}$ watt per m^2 (busy street corner)

  (c) $I = 10^{-8}$ watt per m^2 (quiet radio)

  (d) $I = 10^0$ watt per m^2 (threshold of pain)

48. (a) $I = 10^{-11}$ watt per m^2 (rustle of leaves)

  (b) $I = 10^2$ watt per m^2 (jet at 30 meters)

  (c) $I = 10^{-4}$ watt per m^2 (door slamming)

  (d) $I = 10^{-2}$ watt per m^2 (siren at 30 meters)

49. Due to the installation of noise suppression materials, the noise level in an auditorium decreased from 93 to 80 decibels. Find the percent decrease in the intensity level of the noise as a result of the installation of these materials.

50. Due to the installation of a muffler, the noise level of an engine decreased from 88 to 72 decibels. Find the percent decrease in the intensity level of the noise as a result of the installation of the muffler.

pH Levels   **In Exercises 51–56, use the acidity model given by pH $= -\log[\text{H}^+]$, where acidity (pH) is a measure of the hydrogen ion concentration $[\text{H}^+]$ (measured in moles of hydrogen per liter) of a solution.**

51. Find the pH when $[\text{H}^+] = 2.3 \times 10^{-5}$.

52. Find the pH when $[\text{H}^+] = 1.13 \times 10^{-5}$.

53. Compute $[\text{H}^+]$ for a solution in which pH $= 5.8$.

54. Compute $[\text{H}^+]$ for a solution in which pH $= 3.2$.

55. Apple juice has a pH of 2.9 and drinking water has a pH of 8.0. The hydrogen ion concentration of the apple juice is how many times the concentration of drinking water?

56. The pH of a solution decreases by one unit. By what factor does the hydrogen ion concentration increase?

57. **Forensics**   At 8:30 A.M., a coroner went to the home of a person who had died during the night. In order to estimate the time of death, the coroner took the person's temperature twice. At 9:00 A.M. the temperature was 85.7°F, and at 11:00 A.M. the temperature was 82.8°F. From these two temperatures, the coroner was able to determine that the time elapsed since death and the body temperature were related by the formula

$$t = -10 \ln \frac{T - 70}{98.6 - 70}$$

where t is the time in hours elapsed since the person died and T is the temperature (in degrees Fahrenheit) of the person's body. (This formula comes from a general cooling principle called *Newton's Law of Cooling*. It uses the assumptions that the person had a normal body temperature of 98.6°F at death and that the room temperature was a constant 70°F.) Use the formula to estimate the time of death of the person.

58. **Home Mortgage**   A $120,000 home mortgage for 30 years at $7\frac{1}{2}\%$ has a monthly payment of $839.06. Part of the monthly payment covers the interest charge on the unpaid balance, and the remainder of the payment reduces the principal. The amount paid toward the interest is

$$u = M - \left(M - \frac{Pr}{12}\right)\left(1 + \frac{r}{12}\right)^{12t}$$

and the amount paid toward the reduction of the principal is

$$v = \left(M - \frac{Pr}{12}\right)\left(1 + \frac{r}{12}\right)^{12t}.$$

In these formulas, P is the size of the mortgage, r is the interest rate, M is the monthly payment, and t is the time (in years).

  (a) Use a graphing utility to graph each function in the same viewing window. (The viewing window should show all 30 years of mortgage payments.)

  (b) In the early years of the mortgage, is the greater part of the monthly payment paid toward the interest or the principal? Approximate the time when the monthly payment is evenly divided between interest and principal reduction.

  (c) Repeat parts (a) and (b) for a repayment period of 20 years ($M = \$966.71$). What can you conclude?

59. Home Mortgage The total interest u paid on a home mortgage of P dollars at interest rate r for t years is

$$u = P\left[\frac{rt}{1 - \left(\dfrac{1}{1 + r/12}\right)^{12t}} - 1\right].$$

Consider a \$120,000 home mortgage at $7\frac{1}{2}\%$.

(a) Use a graphing utility to graph the total interest function.

(b) Approximate the length of the mortgage for which the total interest paid is the same as the size of the mortgage. Is it possible that some people are paying twice as much in interest charges as the size of the mortgage?

60. Data Analysis The table shows the time t (in seconds) required for a car to attain a speed of s miles per hour from a standing start.

Speed, s	Time, t
30	3.4
40	5.0
50	7.0
60	9.3
70	12.0
80	15.8
90	20.0

Spreadsheet at LarsonPrecalculus.com

Two models for these data are as follows.

$t_1 = 40.757 + 0.556s - 15.817 \ln s$

$t_2 = 1.2259 + 0.0023s^2$

(a) Use the *regression* feature of a graphing utility to find a linear model t_3 and an exponential model t_4 for the data.

(b) Use the graphing utility to graph the data and each model in the same viewing window.

(c) Create a table comparing the data with estimates obtained from each model.

(d) Use the results of part (c) to find the sum of the absolute values of the differences between the data and the estimated values given by each model. Based on the four sums, which model do you think best fits the data? Explain.

Exploration

True or False? **In Exercises 61–64, determine whether the statement is true or false. Justify your answer.**

61. The domain of a logistic growth function cannot be the set of real numbers.

62. A logistic growth function will always have an x-intercept.

63. The graph of $f(x) = \dfrac{4}{1 + 6e^{-2x}} + 5$ is the graph of $g(x) = \dfrac{4}{1 + 6e^{-2x}}$ shifted to the right five units.

64. The graph of a Gaussian model will never have an x-intercept.

65. Writing Use your school's library, the Internet, or some other reference source to write a paper describing John Napier's work with logarithms.

66. HOW DO YOU SEE IT? Identify each model as exponential growth, exponential decay, Gaussian, linear, logarithmic, logistic growth, quadratic, or none of the above. Explain your reasoning.

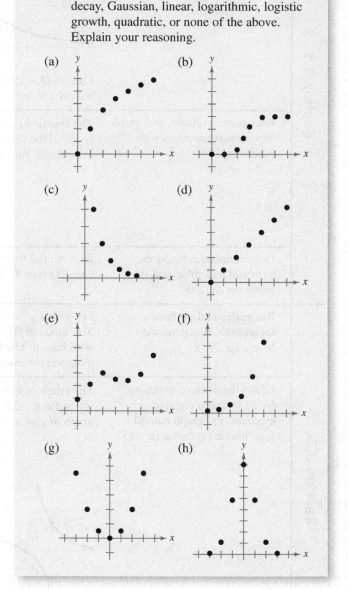

Project: Sales per Share To work an extended application analyzing the sales per share for Kohl's Corporation from 1995 through 2010, visit this text's website at *LarsonPrecalculus.com.* (*Source: Kohl's Corporation*)

Chapter Summary

	What Did You Learn?	Explanation/Examples	Review Exercises
Section 3.1	Recognize and evaluate exponential functions with base a (p. 200).	The exponential function f with base a is denoted by $f(x) = a^x$, where $a > 0$, $a \neq 1$, and x is any real number.	1–6
	Graph exponential functions and use the One-to-One Property (p. 201).	**One-to-One Property:** For $a > 0$ and $a \neq 1$, $a^x = a^y$ if and only if $x = y$.	7–20
	Recognize, evaluate, and graph exponential functions with base e (p. 204).	The function $f(x) = e^x$ is called the natural exponential function.	21–28
	Use exponential functions to model and solve real-life problems (p. 205).	Exponential functions are used in compound interest formulas (see Example 8) and in radioactive decay models (see Example 9).	29–32
Section 3.2	Recognize and evaluate logarithmic functions with base a (p. 211).	For $x > 0$, $a > 0$, and $a \neq 1$, $y = \log_a x$ if and only if $x = a^y$. The function $f(x) = \log_a x$ is called the logarithmic function with base a. The logarithmic function with base 10 is the common logarithmic function. It is denoted by $\log_{10}$ or log.	33–44
	Graph logarithmic functions (p. 213), and recognize, evaluate, and graph natural logarithmic functions (p. 215).	The graph of $y = \log_a x$ is a reflection of the graph of $y = a^x$ in the line $y = x$. The function $f(x) = \ln x$, $x > 0$, is the natural logarithmic function. Its graph is a reflection of the graph of $f(x) = e^x$ in the line $y = x$.	45–56
	Use logarithmic functions to model and solve real-life problems (p. 217).	A logarithmic function can model human memory. (See Example 11.)	57, 58

	What Did You Learn?	**Explanation/Examples**	**Review Exercises**
Section 3.3	Use the change-of-base formula to rewrite and evaluate logarithmic expressions (*p. 221*).	Let a, b, and x be positive real numbers such that $a \neq 1$ and $b \neq 1$. Then $\log_a x$ can be converted to a different base as follows. **Base b** $\log_a x = \dfrac{\log_b x}{\log_b a}$ **Base 10** $\log_a x = \dfrac{\log x}{\log a}$ **Base e** $\log_a x = \dfrac{\ln x}{\ln a}$	59–62

	Use properties of logarithms to evaluate, rewrite, expand, or condense logarithmic expressions (*p. 222*).	Let a be a positive number such that $a \neq 1$, let n be a real number, and let u and v be positive real numbers.
		
		1. Product Property: $\log_a(uv) = \log_a u + \log_a v$
		    $\ln(uv) = \ln u + \ln v$
		
		2. Quotient Property: $\log_a(u/v) = \log_a u - \log_a v$
		    $\ln(u/v) = \ln u - \ln v$
		
		3. Power Property: $\log_a u^n = n \log_a u,\ \ln u^n = n \ln u$
			63–78

	Use logarithmic functions to model and solve real-life problems (*p. 224*).	Logarithmic functions can help you find an equation that relates the periods of several planets and their distances from the sun. (See Example 7.)	79, 80
Section 3.4	Solve simple exponential and logarithmic equations (*p. 228*).	One-to-One Properties and Inverse Properties of exponential or logarithmic functions can help you solve exponential or logarithmic equations.	81–86
	Solve more complicated exponential equations (*p. 229*) and logarithmic equations (*p. 231*).	To solve more complicated equations, rewrite the equations to allow the use of the One-to-One Properties or Inverse Properties of exponential or logarithmic functions. (See Examples 2–9.)	87–104
	Use exponential and logarithmic equations to model and solve real-life problems (*p. 233*).	Exponential and logarithmic equations can help you find how long it will take to double an investment (see Example 10) and find the year in which companies reached a given amount of sales (see Example 11).	105, 106
Section 3.5	Recognize the five most common types of models involving exponential and logarithmic functions (*p. 238*).	**1. Exponential growth model:** $y = ae^{bx},\ b > 0$ **2. Exponential decay model:** $y = ae^{-bx},\ b > 0$ **3. Gaussian model:** $y = ae^{-(x-b)^2/c}$ **4. Logistic growth model:** $y = \dfrac{a}{1 + be^{-rx}}$ **5. Logarithmic models:** $y = a + b \ln x,\ y = a + b \log x$	107–112
	Use exponential growth and decay functions to model and solve real-life problems (*p. 239*).	An exponential growth function can help you model a population of fruit flies (see Example 2), and an exponential decay function can help you estimate the age of a fossil (see Example 3).	113, 114
	Use Gaussian functions (*p. 242*), logistic growth functions (*p. 243*), and logarithmic functions (*p. 244*) to model and solve real-life problems.	A Gaussian function can help you model SAT mathematics scores for high school graduates. (See Example 4.) A logistic growth function can help you model the spread of a flu virus. (See Example 5.) A logarithmic function can help you find the intensity of an earthquake given its magnitude. (See Example 6.)	115–117

Review Exercises
See CalcChat.com for tutorial help and worked-out solutions to odd-numbered exercises.

3.1 **Evaluating an Exponential Function** In Exercises 1–6, evaluate the function at the indicated value of x. Round your result to three decimal places.

1. $f(x) = 0.3^x$, $x = 1.5$ **2.** $f(x) = 30^x$, $x = \sqrt{3}$

3. $f(x) = 2^{-0.5x}$, $x = \pi$ **4.** $f(x) = 1278^{x/5}$, $x = 1$

5. $f(x) = 7(0.2^x)$, $x = -\sqrt{11}$

6. $f(x) = -14(5^x)$, $x = -0.8$

Transforming the Graph of an Exponential Function In Exercises 7–10, use the graph of f to describe the transformation that yields the graph of g.

7. $f(x) = 5^x$, $g(x) = 5^x + 1$

8. $f(x) = 6^x$, $g(x) = 6^{x+1}$

9. $f(x) = 3^x$, $g(x) = 1 - 3^x$

10. $f(x) = \left(\frac{1}{2}\right)^x$, $g(x) = -\left(\frac{1}{2}\right)^{x+2}$

Graphing an Exponential Function In Exercises 11–16, use a graphing utility to construct a table of values for the function. Then sketch the graph of the function.

11. $f(x) = 4^{-x} + 4$ **12.** $f(x) = 2.65^{x-1}$

13. $f(x) = 5^{x-2} + 4$ **14.** $f(x) = 2^{x-6} - 5$

15. $f(x) = \left(\frac{1}{2}\right)^{-x} + 3$ **16.** $f(x) = \left(\frac{1}{8}\right)^{x+2} - 5$

Using the One-to-One Property In Exercises 17–20, use the One-to-One Property to solve the equation for x.

17. $\left(\frac{1}{3}\right)^{x-3} = 9$ **18.** $3^{x+3} = \frac{1}{81}$

19. $e^{3x-5} = e^7$ **20.** $e^{8-2x} = e^{-3}$

Evaluating the Natural Exponential Function In Exercises 21–24, evaluate $f(x) = e^x$ at the indicated value of x. Round your result to three decimal places.

21. $x = 8$ **22.** $x = \frac{5}{8}$

23. $x = -1.7$ **24.** $x = 0.278$

Graphing a Natural Exponential Function In Exercises 25–28, use a graphing utility to construct a table of values for the function. Then sketch the graph of the function.

25. $h(x) = e^{-x/2}$ **26.** $h(x) = 2 - e^{-x/2}$

27. $f(x) = e^{x+2}$ **28.** $s(t) = 4e^{-2/t}$, $t > 0$

29. Waiting Times The average time between incoming calls at a switchboard is 3 minutes. The probability F of waiting less than t minutes until the next incoming call is approximated by the model $F(t) = 1 - e^{-t/3}$. The switchboard has just received a call. Find the probability that the next call will be within

(a) $\frac{1}{2}$ minute.   (b) 2 minutes.   (c) 5 minutes.

30. Depreciation After t years, the value V of a car that originally cost \$23,970 is given by $V(t) = 23,970\left(\frac{3}{4}\right)^t$.

(a) Use a graphing utility to graph the function.

(b) Find the value of the car 2 years after it was purchased.

(c) According to the model, when does the car depreciate most rapidly? Is this realistic? Explain.

(d) According to the model, when will the car have no value?

Compound Interest In Exercises 31 and 32, complete the table to determine the balance A for P dollars invested at rate r for t years and compounded n times per year.

n	1	2	4	12	365	Continuous
A						

31. $P = \$5000$, $r = 3\%$, $t = 10$ years

32. $P = \$4500$, $r = 2.5\%$, $t = 30$ years

3.2 **Writing a Logarithmic Equation** In Exercises 33–36, write the exponential equation in logarithmic form. For example, the logarithmic form of $2^3 = 8$ is $\log_2 8 = 3$.

33. $3^3 = 27$ **34.** $25^{3/2} = 125$

35. $e^{0.8} = 2.2255\ldots$ **36.** $e^0 = 1$

Evaluating a Logarithmic Function In Exercises 37–40, evaluate the function at the indicated value of x without using a calculator.

37. $f(x) = \log x$, $x = 1000$ **38.** $g(x) = \log_9 x$, $x = 3$

39. $g(x) = \log_2 x$, $x = \frac{1}{4}$ **40.** $f(x) = \log_3 x$, $x = \frac{1}{81}$

Using the One-to-One Property In Exercises 41–44, use the One-to-One Property to solve the equation for x.

41. $\log_4(x + 7) = \log_4 14$ **42.** $\log_8(3x - 10) = \log_8 5$

43. $\ln(x + 9) = \ln 4$ **44.** $\ln(2x - 1) = \ln 11$

Sketching the Graph of a Logarithmic Function In Exercises 45–48, find the domain, x-intercept, and vertical asymptote of the logarithmic function and sketch its graph.

45. $g(x) = \log_7 x$

46. $f(x) = \log\left(\frac{x}{3}\right)$

47. $f(x) = 4 - \log(x + 5)$

48. $f(x) = \log(x - 3) + 1$

Evaluating a Logarithmic Function on a Calculator In Exercises 49–52, use a calculator to evaluate the function at the indicated value of x. Round your result to three decimal places, if necessary.

49. $f(x) = \ln x, \quad x = 22.6$ **50.** $f(x) = \ln x, \quad x = e^{-12}$

51. $f(x) = \frac{1}{2} \ln x, \quad x = \sqrt{e}$

52. $f(x) = 5 \ln x, \quad x = 0.98$

Graphing a Natural Logarithmic Function In Exercises 53–56, find the domain, x-intercept, and vertical asymptote of the logarithmic function and sketch its graph.

53. $f(x) = \ln x + 3$ **54.** $f(x) = \ln(x - 3)$

55. $h(x) = \ln(x^2)$ **56.** $f(x) = \frac{1}{4} \ln x$

57. Antler Spread The antler spread a (in inches) and shoulder height h (in inches) of an adult male American elk are related by the model

$$h = 116 \log(a + 40) - 176.$$

Approximate the shoulder height of a male American elk with an antler spread of 55 inches.

58. Snow Removal The number of miles s of roads cleared of snow is approximated by the model

$$s = 25 - \frac{13 \ln(h/12)}{\ln 3}, \quad 2 \le h \le 15$$

where h is the depth of the snow in inches. Use this model to find s when $h = 10$ inches.

3.3 **Using the Change-of-Base Formula** In Exercises 59–62, evaluate the logarithm using the change-of-base formula (a) with common logarithms and (b) with natural logarithms. Round your results to three decimal places.

59. $\log_2 6$ **60.** $\log_{12} 200$

61. $\log_{1/2} 5$ **62.** $\log_3 0.28$

Using Properties of Logarithms In Exercises 63–66, use the properties of logarithms to rewrite and simplify the logarithmic expression.

63. $\log 18$ **64.** $\log_2\left(\frac{1}{12}\right)$

65. $\ln 20$ **66.** $\ln(3e^{-4})$

Expanding a Logarithmic Expression In Exercises 67–72, use the properties of logarithms to expand the expression as a sum, difference, and/or constant multiple of logarithms. (Assume all variables are positive.)

67. $\log_5 5x^2$ **68.** $\log 7x^4$

69. $\log_3 \dfrac{9}{\sqrt{x}}$ **70.** $\log_7 \dfrac{\sqrt[3]{x}}{14}$

71. $\ln x^2 y^2 z$ **72.** $\ln\left(\dfrac{y-1}{4}\right)^2, \quad y > 1$

Condensing a Logarithmic Expression In Exercises 73–78, condense the expression to the logarithm of a single quantity.

73. $\log_2 5 + \log_2 x$

74. $\log_6 y - 2 \log_6 z$

75. $\ln x - \frac{1}{4} \ln y$

76. $3 \ln x + 2 \ln(x + 1)$

77. $\frac{1}{2} \log_3 x - 2 \log_3(y + 8)$

78. $5 \ln(x - 2) - \ln(x + 2) - 3 \ln x$

79. Climb Rate The time t (in minutes) for a small plane to climb to an altitude of h feet is modeled by $t = 50 \log[18{,}000/(18{,}000 - h)]$, where 18,000 feet is the plane's absolute ceiling.

(a) Determine the domain of the function in the context of the problem.

(b) Use a graphing utility to graph the function and identify any asymptotes.

(c) As the plane approaches its absolute ceiling, what can be said about the time required to increase its altitude?

(d) Find the time for the plane to climb to an altitude of 4000 feet.

80. Human Memory Model Students in a learning theory study took an exam and then retested monthly for 6 months with an equivalent exam. The data obtained in the study are given by the ordered pairs (t, s), where t is the time in months after the initial exam and s is the average score for the class. Use the data to find a logarithmic equation that relates t and s.

$(1, 84.2), (2, 78.4), (3, 72.1),$
$(4, 68.5), (5, 67.1), (6, 65.3)$

3.4 **Solving a Simple Equation** In Exercises 81–86, solve for x.

81. $5^x = 125$ **82.** $6^x = \frac{1}{216}$

83. $e^x = 3$ **84.** $\log_6 x = -1$

85. $\ln x = 4$ **86.** $\ln x = -1.6$

Solving an Exponential Equation In Exercises 87–90, solve the exponential equation algebraically. Approximate the result to three decimal places.

87. $e^{4x} = e^{x^2+3}$ **88.** $e^{3x} = 25$

89. $2^x - 3 = 29$ **90.** $e^{2x} - 6e^x + 8 = 0$

Graphing and Solving an Exponential Equation In Exercises 91 and 92, use a graphing utility to graph and solve the equation. Approximate the result to three decimal places. Verify your result algebraically.

91. $25e^{-0.3x} = 12$

92. $2^x = 3 + x - e^x$

Solving a Logarithmic Equation In Exercises 93–100, solve the logarithmic equation algebraically. Approximate the result to three decimal places.

93. $\ln 3x = 8.2$

94. $4 \ln 3x = 15$

95. $\ln x - \ln 3 = 2$

96. $\ln \sqrt{x + 8} = 3$

97. $\log_8(x - 1) = \log_8(x - 2) - \log_8(x + 2)$

98. $\log_6(x + 2) - \log_6 x = \log_6(x + 5)$

99. $\log(1 - x) = -1$

100. $\log(-x - 4) = 2$

Graphing and Solving a Logarithmic Equation In Exercises 101–104, use a graphing utility to graph and solve the equation. Approximate the result to three decimal places. Verify your result algebraically.

101. $2 \ln(x + 3) - 3 = 0$

102. $x - 2 \log(x + 4) = 0$

103. $6 \log(x^2 + 1) - x = 0$

104. $3 \ln x + 2 \log x = e^x - 25$

105. Compound Interest You deposit $8500 in an account that pays 1.5% interest, compounded continuously. How long will it take for the money to triple?

106. Meteorology The speed of the wind S (in miles per hour) near the center of a tornado and the distance d (in miles) the tornado travels are related by the model $S = 93 \log d + 65$. On March 18, 1925, a large tornado struck portions of Missouri, Illinois, and Indiana with a wind speed at the center of about 283 miles per hour. Approximate the distance traveled by this tornado.

3.5 **Matching a Function with Its Graph** In Exercises 107–112, match the function with its graph. [The graphs are labeled (a), (b), (c), (d), (e), and (f).]

(a)

(b)

(c)

(d)

(e)

(f)

107. $y = 3e^{-2x/3}$

108. $y = 4e^{2x/3}$

109. $y = \ln(x + 3)$

110. $y = 7 - \log(x + 3)$

111. $y = 2e^{-(x+4)^2/3}$

112. $y = \dfrac{6}{1 + 2e^{-2x}}$

113. Finding an Exponential Model Find the exponential model $y = ae^{bx}$ that fits the points $(0, 2)$ and $(4, 3)$.

114. Wildlife Population A species of bat is in danger of becoming extinct. Five years ago, the total population of the species was 2000. Two years ago, the total population of the species was 1400. What was the total population of the species one year ago?

115. Test Scores The test scores for a biology test follow a normal distribution modeled by

$$y = 0.0499e^{-(x-71)^2/128}, \quad 40 \le x \le 100$$

where x is the test score. Use a graphing utility to graph the equation and estimate the average test score.

116. Typing Speed In a typing class, the average number N of words per minute typed after t weeks of lessons is

$$N = 157/(1 + 5.4e^{-0.12t}).$$

Find the time necessary to type (a) 50 words per minute and (b) 75 words per minute.

117. Sound Intensity The relationship between the number of decibels β and the intensity of a sound I in watts per square meter is

$$\beta = 10 \log(I/10^{-12}).$$

Find I for each decibel level β.

(a) $\beta = 60$ (b) $\beta = 135$ (c) $\beta = 1$

Exploration

118. Graph of an Exponential Function Consider the graph of $y = e^{kt}$. Describe the characteristics of the graph when k is positive and when k is negative.

True or False? In Exercises 119 and 120, determine whether the equation is true or false. Justify your answer.

119. $\log_b b^{2x} = 2x$

120. $\ln(x + y) = \ln x + \ln y$

Chapter Test

See CalcChat.com for tutorial help and worked-out solutions to odd-numbered exercises.

Take this test as you would take a test in class. When you are finished, check your work against the answers given in the back of the book.

In Exercises 1–4, evaluate the expression. Round your result to three decimal places.

1. $4.2^{0.6}$

2. $4^{3\pi/2}$

3. $e^{-7/10}$

4. $e^{3.1}$

In Exercises 5–7, construct a table of values for the function. Then sketch the graph of the function.

5. $f(x) = 10^{-x}$

6. $f(x) = -6^{x-2}$

7. $f(x) = 1 - e^{2x}$

8. Evaluate (a) $\log_7 7^{-0.89}$ and (b) $4.6 \ln e^2$.

In Exercises 9–11, find the domain, x-intercept, and vertical asymptote of the logarithmic function and sketch its graph.

9. $f(x) = -\log x - 6$

10. $f(x) = \ln(x - 4)$

11. $f(x) = 1 + \ln(x + 6)$

In Exercises 12–14, evaluate the logarithm using the change-of-base formula. Round your result to three decimal places.

12. $\log_7 44$

13. $\log_{16} 0.63$

14. $\log_{3/4} 24$

In Exercises 15–17, use the properties of logarithms to expand the expression as a sum, difference, and/or constant multiple of logarithms. (Assume all variables are positive.)

15. $\log_2 3a^4$

16. $\ln \dfrac{5\sqrt{x}}{6}$

17. $\log \dfrac{(x-1)^3}{y^2 z}$

In Exercises 18–20, condense the expression to the logarithm of a single quantity.

18. $\log_3 13 + \log_3 y$

19. $4 \ln x - 4 \ln y$

20. $3 \ln x - \ln(x + 3) + 2 \ln y$

In Exercises 21–26, solve the equation algebraically. Approximate the result to three decimal places, if necessary.

21. $5^x = \dfrac{1}{25}$

22. $3e^{-5x} = 132$

23. $\dfrac{1025}{8 + e^{4x}} = 5$

24. $\ln x = \dfrac{1}{2}$

25. $18 + 4 \ln x = 7$

26. $\log x + \log(x - 15) = 2$

Exponential Growth

(9, 11,277)

(0, 2745)

Figure for 27

27. Find the exponential growth model that fits the points shown in the graph.

28. The half-life of radioactive actinium (^{227}Ac) is 21.77 years. What percent of a present amount of radioactive actinium will remain after 19 years?

29. A model that can predict the height H (in centimeters) of a child based on his or her age is $H = 70.228 + 5.104x + 9.222 \ln x$, $\frac{1}{4} \le x \le 6$, where x is the age of the child in years. *(Source: Snapshots of Applications in Mathematics)*

   (a) Construct a table of values for the model. Then sketch the graph of the model.

   (b) Use the graph from part (a) to predict the height of a child when he or she is four years old. Then confirm your prediction algebraically.

Cumulative Test for Chapters 1–3

See **CalcChat.com** for tutorial help and worked-out solutions to odd-numbered exercises.

Take this test as you would take a test in class. When you are finished, check your work against the answers given in the back of the book.

1. Plot the points $(-2, 5)$ and $(3, -1)$. Find the coordinates of the midpoint of the line segment joining the points and the distance between the points.

In Exercises 2–4, sketch the graph of the equation.

2. $x - 3y + 12 = 0$ 3. $y = x^2 - 9$ 4. $y = \sqrt{4 - x}$

5. Find an equation of the line passing through $\left(-\frac{1}{2}, 1\right)$ and $(3, 8)$.

6. Explain why the graph at the left does not represent y as a function of x.

7. Evaluate (if possible) the function $f(x) = \dfrac{x}{x - 2}$ at each specified value of the independent variable.

   (a) $f(6)$ (b) $f(2)$ (c) $f(s + 2)$

8. Compare the graph of each function with the graph of $y = \sqrt[3]{x}$. (*Note:* It is not necessary to sketch the graphs.)

   (a) $r(x) = \frac{1}{2}\sqrt[3]{x}$ (b) $h(x) = \sqrt[3]{x} + 2$ (c) $g(x) = \sqrt[3]{x + 2}$

In Exercises 9 and 10, find (a) $(f + g)(x)$, (b) $(f - g)(x)$, (c) $(fg)(x)$, and (d) $(f/g)(x)$. What is the domain of f/g?

9. $f(x) = x - 3$, $g(x) = 4x + 1$

10. $f(x) = \sqrt{x - 1}$, $g(x) = x^2 + 1$

In Exercises 11 and 12, find (a) $f \circ g$ and (b) $g \circ f$. Find the domain of each composite function.

11. $f(x) = 2x^2$, $g(x) = \sqrt{x + 6}$

12. $f(x) = x - 2$, $g(x) = |x|$

13. Determine whether $h(x) = -5x + 3$ has an inverse function. If so, find the inverse function.

14. The power P produced by a wind turbine is proportional to the cube of the wind speed S. A wind speed of 27 miles per hour produces a power output of 750 kilowatts. Find the output for a wind speed of 40 miles per hour.

15. Find the quadratic function whose graph has a vertex at $(-8, 5)$ and passes through the point $(-4, -7)$.

In Exercises 16–18, sketch the graph of the function.

16. $h(x) = -(x^2 + 4x)$

17. $f(t) = \frac{1}{4}t(t - 2)^2$

18. $g(s) = s^2 + 4s + 10$

In Exercises 19–21, find all the zeros of the function and write the function as a product of linear factors.

19. $f(x) = x^3 + 2x^2 + 4x + 8$

20. $f(x) = x^4 + 4x^3 - 21x^2$

21. $f(x) = 2x^4 - 11x^3 + 30x^2 - 62x - 40$

Figure for 6

22. Use long division to divide $6x^3 - 4x^2$ by $2x^2 + 1$.

23. Use synthetic division to divide $3x^4 + 2x^2 - 5x + 3$ by $x - 2$.

 24. Use the Intermediate Value Theorem and the *table* feature of a graphing utility to find intervals one unit in length in which the function $g(x) = x^3 + 3x^2 - 6$ is guaranteed to have a zero. Adjust the table to approximate the real zeros of the function.

In Exercises 25–27, sketch the graph of the rational function. Identify all intercepts and asymptotes.

25. $f(x) = \dfrac{2x}{x^2 + 2x - 3}$

26. $f(x) = \dfrac{x^2 - 4}{x^2 + x - 2}$

27. $f(x) = \dfrac{x^3 - 2x^2 - 9x + 18}{x^2 + 4x + 3}$

In Exercises 28 and 29, solve the inequality. Then graph the solution set.

28. $2x^3 - 18x \le 0$

29. $\dfrac{1}{x + 1} \ge \dfrac{1}{x + 5}$

In Exercises 30 and 31, use the graph of f to describe the transformation that yields the graph of g.

30. $f(x) = \left(\frac{2}{5}\right)^x, \quad g(x) = -\left(\frac{2}{5}\right)^{-x+3}$

31. $f(x) = 2.2^x, \quad g(x) = -2.2^x + 4$

In Exercises 32–35, use a calculator to evaluate the expression. Round your result to three decimal places.

32. $\log 98$

33. $\log \frac{6}{7}$

34. $\ln \sqrt{31}$

35. $\ln\left(\sqrt{40} - 5\right)$

36. Use the properties of logarithms to expand $\ln\left(\dfrac{x^2 - 16}{x^4}\right)$, where $x > 4$.

37. Condense $2 \ln x - \frac{1}{2} \ln(x + 5)$ to the logarithm of a single quantity.

In Exercises 38–40, solve the equation algebraically. Approximate the result to three decimal places.

38. $6e^{2x} = 72$

39. $e^{2x} - 13e^x + 42 = 0$

40. $\ln \sqrt{x + 2} = 3$

Table for 41

 41. The sales S (in billions of dollars) of lottery tickets in the United States from 2000 through 2010 are shown in the table. *(Source: TLF Publications, Inc.)*

(a) Use a graphing utility to create a scatter plot of the data. Let t represent the year, with $t = 0$ corresponding to 2000.

(b) Use the *regression* feature of the graphing utility to find a cubic model for the data.

(c) Use the graphing utility to graph the model in the same viewing window used for the scatter plot. How well does the model fit the data?

(d) Use the model to predict the sales of lottery tickets in 2018. Does your answer seem reasonable? Explain.

42. The number N of bacteria in a culture is given by the model $N = 175e^{kt}$, where t is the time in hours. If $N = 420$ when $t = 8$, then estimate the time required for the population to double in size.

Proofs in Mathematics ■ ■ ■ ■ ■ ■ ■ ■ ■ ■ ■ ■ ■ ■ ■

Each of the following three properties of logarithms can be proved by using properties of exponential functions.

SLIDE RULES

William Oughtred (1574–1660) invented the slide rule in 1625. The slide rule is a computational device with a sliding portion and a fixed portion. A slide rule enables you to perform multiplication by using the Product Property of Logarithms. There are other slide rules that allow for the calculation of roots and trigonometric functions. Mathematicians and engineers used slide rules until the invention of the hand-held calculator in 1972.

Properties of Logarithms *(p. 222)*

Let a be a positive number such that $a \neq 1$, and let n be a real number. If u and v are positive real numbers, then the following properties are true.

	Logarithm with Base a	Natural Logarithm
1. Product Property:	$\log_a(uv) = \log_a u + \log_a v$	$\ln(uv) = \ln u + \ln v$
2. Quotient Property:	$\log_a \dfrac{u}{v} = \log_a u - \log_a v$	$\ln \dfrac{u}{v} = \ln u - \ln v$
3. Power Property:	$\log_a u^n = n \log_a u$	$\ln u^n = n \ln u$

Proof

Let

$$x = \log_a u \quad \text{and} \quad y = \log_a v.$$

The corresponding exponential forms of these two equations are

$$a^x = u \quad \text{and} \quad a^y = v.$$

To prove the Product Property, multiply u and v to obtain

$$uv = a^x a^y$$
$$= a^{x+y}.$$

The corresponding logarithmic form of $uv = a^{x+y}$ is $\log_a(uv) = x + y$. So,

$$\log_a(uv) = \log_a u + \log_a v.$$

To prove the Quotient Property, divide u by v to obtain

$$\frac{u}{v} = \frac{a^x}{a^y}$$
$$= a^{x-y}.$$

The corresponding logarithmic form of $\dfrac{u}{v} = a^{x-y}$ is $\log_a \dfrac{u}{v} = x - y$. So,

$$\log_a \frac{u}{v} = \log_a u - \log_a v.$$

To prove the Power Property, substitute a^x for u in the expression $\log_a u^n$, as follows.

$$\log_a u^n = \log_a(a^x)^n \qquad \text{Substitute } a^x \text{ for } u.$$
$$= \log_a a^{nx} \qquad \text{Property of Exponents}$$
$$= nx \qquad \text{Inverse Property of Logarithms}$$
$$= n \log_a u \qquad \text{Substitute } \log_a u \text{ for } x.$$

So, $\log_a u^n = n \log_a u$.

P.S. Problem Solving

1. Graphical Analysis Graph the exponential function $y = a^x$ for $a = 0.5$, 1.2, and 2.0. Which of these curves intersects the line $y = x$? Determine all positive numbers a for which the curve $y = a^x$ intersects the line $y = x$.

2. Graphical Analysis Use a graphing utility to graph $y_1 = e^x$ and each of the functions $y_2 = x^2$, $y_3 = x^3$, $y_4 = \sqrt{x}$, and $y_5 = |x|$. Which function increases at the greatest rate as x approaches $+\infty$?

3. Conjecture Use the result of Exercise 2 to make a conjecture about the rate of growth of $y_1 = e^x$ and $y = x^n$, where n is a natural number and x approaches $+\infty$.

4. Implication of "Growing Exponentially" Use the results of Exercises 2 and 3 to describe what is implied when it is stated that a quantity is growing exponentially.

5. Exponential Function Given the exponential function

$$f(x) = a^x$$

show that

(a) $f(u + v) = f(u) \cdot f(v)$.   (b) $f(2x) = [f(x)]^2$.

6. Hyperbolic Functions Given that

$$f(x) = \frac{e^x + e^{-x}}{2} \quad \text{and} \quad g(x) = \frac{e^x - e^{-x}}{2}$$

show that

$$[f(x)]^2 - [g(x)]^2 = 1.$$

7. Graphical Analysis Use a graphing utility to compare the graph of the function $y = e^x$ with the graph of each given function. [$n!$ (read "n factorial") is defined as $n! = 1 \cdot 2 \cdot 3 \cdots (n - 1) \cdot n$.]

(a) $y_1 = 1 + \dfrac{x}{1!}$

(b) $y_2 = 1 + \dfrac{x}{1!} + \dfrac{x^2}{2!}$

(c) $y_3 = 1 + \dfrac{x}{1!} + \dfrac{x^2}{2!} + \dfrac{x^3}{3!}$

8. Identifying a Pattern Identify the pattern of successive polynomials given in Exercise 7. Extend the pattern one more term and compare the graph of the resulting polynomial function with the graph of $y = e^x$. What do you think this pattern implies?

9. Finding an Inverse Function Graph the function

$$f(x) = e^x - e^{-x}.$$

From the graph, the function appears to be one-to-one. Assuming that the function has an inverse function, find $f^{-1}(x)$.

10. Finding a Pattern for an Inverse Function Find a pattern for $f^{-1}(x)$ when

$$f(x) = \frac{a^x + 1}{a^x - 1}$$

where $a > 0$, $a \neq 1$.

11. Determining the Equation of a Graph By observation, determine whether equation (a), (b), or (c) corresponds to the graph. Explain your reasoning.

(a) $y = 6e^{-x^2/2}$

(b) $y = \dfrac{6}{1 + e^{-x/2}}$

(c) $y = 6(1 - e^{-x^2/2})$

12. Simple and Compound Interest You have two options for investing $500. The first earns 7% compounded annually, and the second earns 7% simple interest. The figure shows the growth of each investment over a 30-year period.

(a) Identify which graph represents each type of investment. Explain your reasoning.

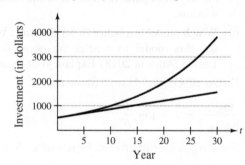

(b) Verify your answer in part (a) by finding the equations that model the investment growth and by graphing the models.

(c) Which option would you choose? Explain your reasoning.

13. Radioactive Decay Two different samples of radioactive isotopes are decaying. The isotopes have initial amounts of c_1 and c_2, as well as half-lives of k_1 and k_2, respectively. Find the time t required for the samples to decay to equal amounts.

14. Bacteria Decay A lab culture initially contains 500 bacteria. Two hours later, the number of bacteria decreases to 200. Find the exponential decay model of the form

$$B = B_0 a^{kt}$$

that approximates the number of bacteria after t hours.

15. Colonial Population The table shows the colonial population estimates of the American colonies from 1700 through 1780. *(Source: U.S. Census Bureau)*

Year	Population
1700	250,900
1710	331,700
1720	466,200
1730	629,400
1740	905,600
1750	1,170,800
1760	1,593,600
1770	2,148,400
1780	2,780,400

Spreadsheet at LarsonPrecalculus.com

In each of the following, let y represent the population in the year t, with $t = 0$ corresponding to 1700.

(a) Use the *regression* feature of a graphing utility to find an exponential model for the data.

(b) Use the *regression* feature of the graphing utility to find a quadratic model for the data.

(c) Use the graphing utility to plot the data and the models from parts (a) and (b) in the same viewing window.

(d) Which model is a better fit for the data? Would you use this model to predict the population of the United States in 2018? Explain your reasoning.

16. Ratio of Logarithms Show that

$$\frac{\log_a x}{\log_{a/b} x} = 1 + \log_a \frac{1}{b}.$$

17. Solving a Logarithmic Equation Solve

$$(\ln x)^2 = \ln x^2.$$

18. Graphical Analysis Use a graphing utility to compare the graph of the function $y = \ln x$ with the graph of each given function.

(a) $y_1 = x - 1$

(b) $y_2 = (x - 1) - \frac{1}{2}(x - 1)^2$

(c) $y_3 = (x - 1) - \frac{1}{2}(x - 1)^2 + \frac{1}{3}(x - 1)^3$

19. Identifying a Pattern Identify the pattern of successive polynomials given in Exercise 18. Extend the pattern one more term and compare the graph of the resulting polynomial function with the graph of $y = \ln x$. What do you think the pattern implies?

20. Finding Slope and y-Intercept Using

$$y = ab^x \quad \text{and} \quad y = ax^b$$

take the natural logarithm of each side of each equation. What are the slope and y-intercept of the line relating x and $\ln y$ for $y = ab^x$? What are the slope and y-intercept of the line relating $\ln x$ and $\ln y$ for $y = ax^b$?

Ventilation Rate In Exercises 21 and 22, use the model

$$y = 80.4 - 11 \ln x, \quad 100 \le x \le 1500$$

which approximates the minimum required ventilation rate in terms of the air space per child in a public school classroom. In the model, x is the air space per child in cubic feet and y is the ventilation rate per child in cubic feet per minute.

21. Use a graphing utility to graph the model and approximate the required ventilation rate when there are 300 cubic feet of air space per child.

22. In a classroom designed for 30 students, the air conditioning system can move 450 cubic feet of air per minute.

(a) Determine the ventilation rate per child in a full classroom.

(b) Estimate the air space required per child.

(c) Determine the minimum number of square feet of floor space required for the room when the ceiling height is 30 feet.

Data Analysis In Exercises 23–26, (a) use a graphing utility to create a scatter plot of the data, (b) decide whether the data could best be modeled by a linear model, an exponential model, or a logarithmic model, (c) explain why you chose the model you did in part (b), (d) use the *regression* feature of the graphing utility to find the model you chose in part (b) for the data and graph the model with the scatter plot, and (e) determine how well the model you chose fits the data.

23. (1, 2.0), (1.5, 3.5), (2, 4.0), (4, 5.8), (6, 7.0), (8, 7.8)

24. (1, 4.4), (1.5, 4.7), (2, 5.5), (4, 9.9), (6, 18.1), (8, 33.0)

25. (1, 7.5), (1.5, 7.0), (2, 6.8), (4, 5.0), (6, 3.5), (8, 2.0)

26. (1, 5.0), (1.5, 6.0), (2, 6.4), (4, 7.8), (6, 8.6), (8, 9.0)

4 Trigonometry

4.1 Radian and Degree Measure
4.2 Trigonometric Functions: The Unit Circle
4.3 Right Triangle Trigonometry
4.4 Trigonometric Functions of Any Angle
4.5 Graphs of Sine and Cosine Functions
4.6 Graphs of Other Trigonometric Functions
4.7 Inverse Trigonometric Functions
4.8 Applications and Models

Television Coverage *(Exercise 84, page 319)*

Waterslide Design
(Exercise 32, page 337)

Respiratory Cycle *(Exercise 88, page 308)*

Meteorology
(Exercise 99, page 298)

Skateboarding *(Example 10, page 285)*

261

4.1 Radian and Degree Measure

- Describe angles.
- Use radian measure.
- Use degree measure.
- Use angles to model and solve real-life problems.

Angles can help you model and solve real-life problems. For instance, in Exercise 68 on page 271, you will use angles to find the speed of a bicycle.

Angles

As derived from the Greek language, the word **trigonometry** means "measurement of triangles." Initially, trigonometry dealt with relationships among the sides and angles of triangles and was used in the development of astronomy, navigation, and surveying. With the development of calculus and the physical sciences in the 17th century, a different perspective arose—one that viewed the classic trigonometric relationships as *functions* with the set of real numbers as their domains. Consequently, the applications of trigonometry expanded to include a vast number of physical phenomena, such as sound waves, planetary orbits, vibrating strings, pendulums, and orbits of atomic particles.

This text incorporates *both* perspectives, starting with angles and their measures.

Angle	Angle in standard position
Figure 4.1	**Figure 4.2**

An **angle** is determined by rotating a ray (half-line) about its endpoint. The starting position of the ray is the **initial side** of the angle, and the position after rotation is the **terminal side,** as shown in Figure 4.1. The endpoint of the ray is the **vertex** of the angle. This perception of an angle fits a coordinate system in which the origin is the vertex and the initial side coincides with the positive *x*-axis. Such an angle is in **standard position,** as shown in Figure 4.2. Counterclockwise rotation generates **positive angles** and clockwise rotation generates **negative angles,** as shown in Figure 4.3. Angles are labeled with Greek letters such as

α (alpha), β (beta),   and θ (theta)

as well as uppercase letters such as

A, B,   and C.

In Figure 4.4, note that angles α and β have the same initial and terminal sides. Such angles are **coterminal.**

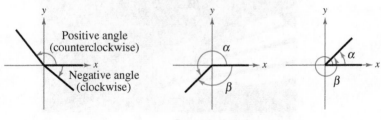

Figure 4.3   Coterminal angles
                        Figure 4.4

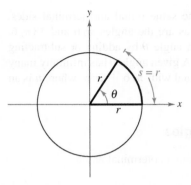

Arc length = radius when $\theta = 1$ radian.
Figure 4.5

Radian Measure

You determine the **measure of an angle** by the amount of rotation from the initial side to the terminal side. One way to measure angles is in *radians*. This type of measure is especially useful in calculus. To define a radian, you can use a **central angle** of a circle, one whose vertex is the center of the circle, as shown in Figure 4.5.

Definition of Radian

One **radian** is the measure of a central angle θ that intercepts an arc s equal in length to the radius r of the circle. See Figure 4.5. Algebraically, this means that

$$\theta = \frac{s}{r}$$

where θ is measured in radians. (Note that $\theta = 1$ when $s = r$.)

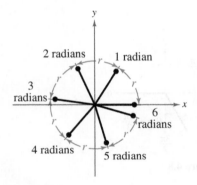

Figure 4.6

Because the circumference of a circle is $2\pi r$ units, it follows that a central angle of one full revolution (counterclockwise) corresponds to an arc length of $s = 2\pi r$. Moreover, because $2\pi \approx 6.28$, there are just over six radius lengths in a full circle, as shown in Figure 4.6. Because the units of measure for s and r are the same, the ratio s/r has no units—it is a real number.

Because the measure of an angle of one full revolution is $s/r = 2\pi r/r = 2\pi$ radians, you can obtain the following.

$$\frac{1}{2} \text{ revolution} = \frac{2\pi}{2} = \pi \text{ radians} \qquad \frac{1}{4} \text{ revolution} = \frac{2\pi}{4} = \frac{\pi}{2} \text{ radians}$$

$$\frac{1}{6} \text{ revolution} = \frac{2\pi}{6} = \frac{\pi}{3} \text{ radians}$$

These and other common angles are shown below.

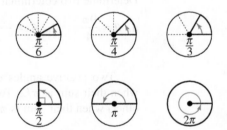

- • **REMARK** The phrase "the terminal side of θ lies in a quadrant" is often abbreviated by the phrase "θ lies in a quadrant." The terminal sides of the "quadrant angles" 0, $\pi/2$, π, and $3\pi/2$ do not lie within quadrants.

▷ Recall that the four quadrants in a coordinate system are numbered I, II, III, and IV. The figure below shows which angles between 0 and 2π lie in each of the four quadrants. Note that angles between 0 and $\pi/2$ are **acute** angles and angles between $\pi/2$ and π are **obtuse** angles.

$$\theta = \frac{\pi}{2}$$

Quadrant II	Quadrant I
$\frac{\pi}{2} < \theta < \pi$	$0 < \theta < \frac{\pi}{2}$

$\theta = \pi$ ——————— $\theta = 0$

Quadrant III	Quadrant IV
$\pi < \theta < \frac{3\pi}{2}$	$\frac{3\pi}{2} < \theta < 2\pi$

$$\theta = \frac{3\pi}{2}$$

Two angles are coterminal when they have the same initial and terminal sides. For instance, the angles 0 and 2π are coterminal, as are the angles $\pi/6$ and $13\pi/6$. You can find an angle that is coterminal to a given angle θ by adding or subtracting 2π (one revolution), as demonstrated in Example 1. A given angle θ has infinitely many coterminal angles. For instance, $\theta = \pi/6$ is coterminal with $\pi/6 + 2n\pi$, where n is an integer.

EXAMPLE 1 Finding Coterminal Angles

▷ **ALGEBRA HELP** You can review operations involving fractions in Appendix A.1.

a. For the positive angle $13\pi/6$, subtract 2π to obtain a coterminal angle

$$\frac{13\pi}{6} - 2\pi = \frac{\pi}{6}. \qquad \text{See Figure 4.7.}$$

b. For the negative angle $-2\pi/3$, add 2π to obtain a coterminal angle

$$-\frac{2\pi}{3} + 2\pi = \frac{4\pi}{3}. \qquad \text{See Figure 4.8.}$$

Figure 4.7   **Figure 4.8**

✓ **Checkpoint** ◀))) *Audio-video solution in English & Spanish at LarsonPrecalculus.com.*

Determine two coterminal angles (one positive and one negative) for each angle.

a. $\theta = \dfrac{9\pi}{4}$ **b.** $\theta = -\dfrac{\pi}{3}$

Complementary angles

Supplementary angles
Figure 4.9

Two positive angles α and β are **complementary** (complements of each other) when their sum is $\pi/2$. Two positive angles are **supplementary** (supplements of each other) when their sum is π. See Figure 4.9.

EXAMPLE 2 Complementary and Supplementary Angles

a. The complement of $\dfrac{2\pi}{5}$ is $\dfrac{\pi}{2} - \dfrac{2\pi}{5} = \dfrac{5\pi}{10} - \dfrac{4\pi}{10} = \dfrac{\pi}{10}$.

The supplement of $\dfrac{2\pi}{5}$ is $\pi - \dfrac{2\pi}{5} = \dfrac{5\pi}{5} - \dfrac{2\pi}{5} = \dfrac{3\pi}{5}$.

b. Because $4\pi/5$ is greater than $\pi/2$, it has no complement. (Remember that complements are *positive* angles.) The supplement of $4\pi/5$ is

$$\pi - \frac{4\pi}{5} = \frac{5\pi}{5} - \frac{4\pi}{5} = \frac{\pi}{5}.$$

✓ **Checkpoint** ◀))) *Audio-video solution in English & Spanish at LarsonPrecalculus.com.*

If possible, find the complement and the supplement of (a) $\pi/6$ and (b) $5\pi/6$.

Figure 4.10

$\frac{\pi}{6}$
30°

$\frac{\pi}{3}$
60°

$\frac{\pi}{4}$
45°

$\frac{\pi}{2}$
90°

π
180°

2π
360°

Figure 4.11

With calculators, it is convenient to use *decimal* degrees to denote fractional parts of degrees. Historically, however, fractional parts of degrees were expressed in *minutes* and *seconds*, using the prime ($'$) and double prime ($''$) notations, respectively. That is,

$1' = $ one minute $= \frac{1}{60}(1°)$

$1'' = $ one second $= \frac{1}{3600}(1°)$.

Consequently, an angle of 64 degrees, 32 minutes, and 47 seconds is represented by $\theta = 64° \, 32' \, 47''$. Many calculators have special keys for converting an angle in degrees, minutes, and seconds (D° M′ S″) to decimal degree form, and vice versa.

Degree Measure

A second way to measure angles is in **degrees,** denoted by the symbol °. A measure of one degree (1°) is equivalent to a rotation of $\frac{1}{360}$ of a complete revolution about the vertex. To measure angles, it is convenient to mark degrees on the circumference of a circle, as shown in Figure 4.10. So, a full revolution (counterclockwise) corresponds to 360°, a half revolution to 180°, a quarter revolution to 90°, and so on.

Because 2π radians corresponds to one complete revolution, degrees and radians are related by the equations

$$360° = 2\pi \text{ rad} \quad \text{and} \quad 180° = \pi \text{ rad}.$$

From the latter equation, you obtain

$$1° = \frac{\pi}{180} \text{ rad} \quad \text{and} \quad 1 \text{ rad} = \left(\frac{180}{\pi}\right)°$$

which lead to the following conversion rules.

Conversions Between Degrees and Radians

1. To convert degrees to radians, multiply degrees by $\dfrac{\pi \text{ rad}}{180°}$.

2. To convert radians to degrees, multiply radians by $\dfrac{180°}{\pi \text{ rad}}$.

To apply these two conversion rules, use the basic relationship π rad = 180°. (See Figure 4.11.)

When no units of angle measure are specified, *radian measure is implied.* For instance, $\theta = 2$ implies that $\theta = 2$ radians.

EXAMPLE 3   **Converting from Degrees to Radians**

a. $135° = (135 \text{ deg})\left(\dfrac{\pi \text{ rad}}{180 \text{ deg}}\right) = \dfrac{3\pi}{4}$ radians   Multiply by $\frac{\pi \text{ rad}}{180°}$.

b. $540° = (540 \text{ deg})\left(\dfrac{\pi \text{ rad}}{180 \text{ deg}}\right) = 3\pi$ radians   Multiply by $\frac{\pi \text{ rad}}{180°}$.

✓ **Checkpoint** ◀))) *Audio-video solution in English & Spanish at LarsonPrecalculus.com.*

Rewrite each angle in radian measure as a multiple of π. (Do not use a calculator.)

a. $\theta = 60°$ **b.** $\theta = 320°$

EXAMPLE 4   **Converting from Radians to Degrees**

a. $-\dfrac{\pi}{2} \text{ rad} = \left(-\dfrac{\pi}{2} \text{ rad}\right)\left(\dfrac{180 \text{ deg}}{\pi \text{ rad}}\right) = -90°$ Multiply by $\frac{180°}{\pi \text{ rad}}$.

b. $2 \text{ rad} = (2 \text{ rad})\left(\dfrac{180 \text{ deg}}{\pi \text{ rad}}\right) = \dfrac{360°}{\pi} \approx 114.59°$ Multiply by $\frac{180°}{\pi \text{ rad}}$.

✓ **Checkpoint** ◀))) *Audio-video solution in English & Spanish at LarsonPrecalculus.com.*

Rewrite each angle in degree measure. (Do not use a calculator.)

a. $\pi/6$ **b.** $5\pi/3$

Applications

The *radian measure* formula, $\theta = s/r$, can be used to measure arc length along a circle.

Arc Length

For a circle of radius r, a central angle θ intercepts an arc of length s given by

$$s = r\theta \qquad \text{Length of circular arc}$$

where θ is measured in radians. Note that if $r = 1$, then $s = \theta$, and the radian measure of θ equals the arc length.

EXAMPLE 5 **Finding Arc Length**

A circle has a radius of 4 inches. Find the length of the arc intercepted by a central angle of 240°, as shown in Figure 4.12.

Solution To use the formula $s = r\theta$, first convert 240° to radian measure.

$$240° = (240 \text{ deg})\left(\frac{\pi \text{ rad}}{180 \text{ deg}}\right)$$

$$= \frac{4\pi}{3} \text{ radians}$$

Then, using a radius of $r = 4$ inches, you can find the arc length to be

$$s = r\theta$$

$$= 4\left(\frac{4\pi}{3}\right)$$

$$\approx 16.76 \text{ inches.}$$

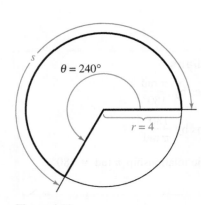

$\theta = 240°$

$r = 4$

Figure 4.12

Note that the units for r determine the units for $r\theta$ because θ is given in radian measure, which has no units.

✓ ***Checkpoint*** 🔊)) *Audio-video solution in English & Spanish at LarsonPrecalculus.com.*

A circle has a radius of 27 inches. Find the length of the arc intercepted by a central angle of 160°. ◼

The formula for the length of a circular arc can help you analyze the motion of a particle moving at a *constant speed* along a circular path.

· · REMARK Linear speed measures how fast the particle moves, and angular speed measures how fast the angle changes. By dividing each side of the formula for arc length by t, you can establish a relationship between linear speed v and angular speed ω, as shown.

$$s = r\theta$$

$$\frac{s}{t} = \frac{r\theta}{t}$$

$$v = r\omega$$

Linear and Angular Speeds

Consider a particle moving at a constant speed along a circular arc of radius r. If s is the length of the arc traveled in time t, then the **linear speed** v of the particle is

$$\text{Linear speed } v = \frac{\text{arc length}}{\text{time}} = \frac{s}{t}.$$

Moreover, if θ is the angle (in radian measure) corresponding to the arc length s, then the **angular speed** ω (the lowercase Greek letter omega) of the particle is

$$\text{Angular speed } \omega = \frac{\text{central angle}}{\text{time}} = \frac{\theta}{t}.$$

Figure 4.13

Figure 4.14

EXAMPLE 6   Finding Linear Speed

The second hand of a clock is 10.2 centimeters long, as shown in Figure 4.13. Find the linear speed of the tip of this second hand as it passes around the clock face.

Solution   In one revolution, the arc length traveled is

$$s = 2\pi r$$

$$= 2\pi(10.2) \qquad \text{Substitute for } r.$$

$$= 20.4\pi \text{ centimeters.}$$

The time required for the second hand to travel this distance is

$$t = 1 \text{ minute}$$

$$= 60 \text{ seconds.}$$

So, the linear speed of the tip of the second hand is

$$\text{Linear speed} = \frac{s}{t}$$

$$= \frac{20.4\pi \text{ centimeters}}{60 \text{ seconds}}$$

$$\approx 1.068 \text{ centimeters per second.}$$

✓ **Checkpoint** 🔊))) *Audio-video solution in English & Spanish at LarsonPrecalculus.com.*

The second hand of a clock is 8 centimeters long. Find the linear speed of the tip of this second hand as it passes around the clock face.

EXAMPLE 7   Finding Angular and Linear Speeds

The blades of a wind turbine are 116 feet long (see Figure 4.14). The propeller rotates at 15 revolutions per minute.

a. Find the angular speed of the propeller in radians per minute.

b. Find the linear speed of the tips of the blades.

Solution

a. Because each revolution generates 2π radians, it follows that the propeller turns

$$(15)(2\pi) = 30\pi \text{ radians per minute.}$$

In other words, the angular speed is

$$\text{Angular speed} = \frac{\theta}{t} = \frac{30\pi \text{ radians}}{1 \text{ minute}} = 30\pi \text{ radians per minute.}$$

b. The linear speed is

$$\text{Linear speed} = \frac{s}{t} = \frac{r\theta}{t} = \frac{(116)(30\pi) \text{ feet}}{1 \text{ minute}} \approx 10{,}933 \text{ feet per minute.}$$

✓ **Checkpoint** 🔊))) *Audio-video solution in English & Spanish at LarsonPrecalculus.com.*

The circular blade on a saw rotates at 2400 revolutions per minute.

a. Find the angular speed of the blade in radians per minute.

b. The blade has a radius of 4 inches. Find the linear speed of a blade tip.

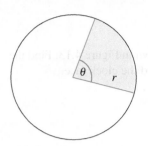

Figure 4.15

A **sector** of a circle is the region bounded by two radii of the circle and their intercepted arc (see Figure 4.15).

Area of a Sector of a Circle

For a circle of radius r, the area A of a sector of the circle with central angle θ is

$$A = \frac{1}{2}r^2\theta$$

where θ is measured in radians.

EXAMPLE 8   **Area of a Sector of a Circle**

Figure 4.16

A sprinkler on a golf course fairway sprays water over a distance of 70 feet and rotates through an angle of 120° (see Figure 4.16). Find the area of the fairway watered by the sprinkler.

Solution

First convert 120° to radian measure as follows.

$$\theta = 120°$$

$$= (120 \text{ deg})\left(\frac{\pi \text{ rad}}{180 \text{ deg}}\right) \qquad \text{Multiply by } \frac{\pi \text{ rad}}{180°}.$$

$$= \frac{2\pi}{3} \text{ radians}$$

Then, using $\theta = 2\pi/3$ and $r = 70$, the area is

$$A = \frac{1}{2}r^2\theta \qquad\qquad \text{Formula for the area of a sector of a circle}$$

$$= \frac{1}{2}(70)^2\left(\frac{2\pi}{3}\right) \qquad \text{Substitute for } r \text{ and } \theta.$$

$$= \frac{4900\pi}{3} \qquad\qquad \text{Multiply.}$$

$$\approx 5131 \text{ square feet.} \qquad \text{Simplify.}$$

✓ *Checkpoint* 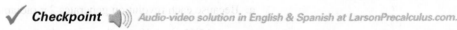 *Audio-video solution in English & Spanish at LarsonPrecalculus.com.*

A sprinkler sprays water over a distance of 40 feet and rotates through an angle of 80°. Find the area watered by the sprinkler.

Summarize   (Section 4.1)

1. Describe an angle *(page 262)*.

2. Describe how to determine the measure of an angle using radians *(page 263)*. For examples involving radian measure, see Examples 1 and 2.

3. Describe how to determine the measure of an angle using degrees *(page 265)*. For examples involving degree measure, see Examples 3 and 4.

4. Describe examples of how to use angles to model and solve real-life problems *(pages 266–268, Examples 5–8)*.

4.1 Exercises

Vocabulary: Fill in the blanks.

1. Two angles that have the same initial and terminal sides are _____.
2. One _____ is the measure of a central angle that intercepts an arc equal to the radius of the circle.
3. Two positive angles that have a sum of $\pi/2$ are _____ angles, whereas two positive angles that have a sum of π are _____ angles.
4. The angle measure that is equivalent to a rotation of $\frac{1}{360}$ of a complete revolution about an angle's vertex is one _____.
5. The _____ speed of a particle is the ratio of the arc length to the time traveled, and the _____ speed of a particle is the ratio of the central angle to the time traveled.
6. The area A of a sector of a circle with radius r and central angle θ, where θ is measured in radians, is given by the formula _____.

Skills and Applications

Estimating an Angle In Exercises 7–10, estimate the angle to the nearest one-half radian.

7.

8.

9.

10.

Determining Quadrants In Exercises 11 and 12, determine the quadrant in which each angle lies.

11. (a) $\dfrac{\pi}{4}$ (b) $\dfrac{5\pi}{4}$ 12. (a) $-\dfrac{\pi}{6}$ (b) $-\dfrac{11\pi}{9}$

Sketching Angles In Exercises 13 and 14, sketch each angle in standard position.

13. (a) $\dfrac{\pi}{3}$ (b) $-\dfrac{2\pi}{3}$ 14. (a) $\dfrac{5\pi}{2}$ (b) 4

Finding Coterminal Angles In Exercises 15 and 16, determine two coterminal angles (one positive and one negative) for each angle. Give your answers in radians.

15. (a) $\dfrac{\pi}{6}$ (b) $\dfrac{7\pi}{6}$ 16. (a) $\dfrac{2\pi}{3}$ (b) $-\dfrac{9\pi}{4}$

Complementary and Supplementary Angles In Exercises 17–20, find (if possible) the complement and the supplement of each angle.

17. (a) $\dfrac{\pi}{3}$ (b) $\dfrac{\pi}{4}$ 18. (a) $\dfrac{\pi}{12}$ (b) $\dfrac{11\pi}{12}$
19. (a) 1   (b) 2   20. (a) 3   (b) 1.5

Estimating an Angle In Exercises 21–24, estimate the number of degrees in the angle.

21.

22.

23.

24.

Determining Quadrants In Exercises 25 and 26, determine the quadrant in which each angle lies.

25. (a) 130°   (b) 8.3°
26. (a) −132° 50′   (b) −3.4°

Sketching Angles In Exercises 27 and 28, sketch each angle in standard position.

27. (a) 270°   (b) 120°
28. (a) −135°   (b) −750°

Finding Coterminal Angles In Exercises 29 and 30, determine two coterminal angles (one positive and one negative) for each angle. Give your answers in degrees.

29. (a) 45°   (b) −36°
30. (a) 120°   (b) −420°

Complementary and Supplementary Angles In Exercises 31–34, find (if possible) the complement and the supplement of each angle.

31. (a) 18°   (b) 85°   32. (a) 46°   (b) 93°
33. (a) 150°   (b) 79°   34. (a) 130°   (b) 170°

Converting from Degrees to Radians In Exercises 35 and 36, rewrite each angle in radian measure as a multiple of π. (Do not use a calculator.)

35. (a) $120°$ (b) $-20°$

36. (a) $-60°$ (b) $144°$

Converting from Radians to Degrees In Exercises 37 and 38, rewrite each angle in degree measure. (Do not use a calculator.)

37. (a) $\dfrac{3\pi}{2}$ (b) $\dfrac{7\pi}{6}$

38. (a) $-\dfrac{7\pi}{12}$ (b) $\dfrac{5\pi}{4}$

Converting from Degrees to Radians In Exercises 39–42, convert the angle measure from degrees to radians. Round to three decimal places.

39. $45°$

40. $-48.27°$

41. $0.54°$

42. $345°$

Converting from Radians to Degrees In Exercises 43–46, convert the angle measure from radians to degrees. Round to three decimal places.

43. $\dfrac{5\pi}{11}$

44. $\dfrac{15\pi}{8}$

45. -4.2π

46. -0.57

Converting to Decimal Degree Form In Exercises 47 and 48, convert each angle measure to decimal degree form without using a calculator. Then check your answers using a calculator.

47. (a) $54° 45'$ (b) $-128° 30'$

48. (a) $-135° 36''$ (b) $-408° 16'20''$

Converting to D°M'S''Form In Exercises 49 and 50, convert each angle measure to degrees, minutes, and seconds without using a calculator. Then check your answers using a calculator.

49. (a) $240.6°$ (b) $-145.8°$

50. (a) $-345.12°$ (b) $-3.58°$

Finding Arc Length In Exercises 51 and 52, find the length of the arc on a circle of radius r intercepted by a central angle θ.

51. $r = 15$ inches, $\theta = 120°$

52. $r = 3$ meters, $\theta = 150°$

Finding the Central Angle In Exercises 53 and 54, find the radian measure of the central angle of a circle of radius r that intercepts an arc of length s.

53. $r = 80$ kilometers, $s = 150$ kilometers

54. $r = 14$ feet, $s = 8$ feet

Finding an Angle In Exercises 55 and 56, use the given arc length and radius to find the angle θ (in radians).

55.

56.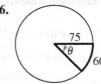

Area of a Sector of a Circle In Exercises 57 and 58, find the area of the sector of a circle of radius r and central angle θ.

57. $r = 12$ millimeters, $\theta = \dfrac{\pi}{4}$

58. $r = 2.5$ feet, $\theta = 225°$

59. Distance Between Cities Find the distance between Dallas, Texas, whose latitude is $32° 47'39''$N, and Omaha, Nebraska, whose latitude is $41° 15'50''$N. Assume that Earth is a sphere of radius 4000 miles and that the cities are on the same longitude (Omaha is due north of Dallas).

60. Difference in Latitudes Assuming that Earth is a sphere of radius 6378 kilometers, what is the difference in the latitudes of Lynchburg, Virginia, and Myrtle Beach, South Carolina, where Lynchburg is about 400 kilometers due north of Myrtle Beach?

61. Instrumentation
The pointer on a voltmeter is 6 centimeters in length (see figure). Find the number of degrees through which the pointer rotates when it moves 2.5 centimeters on the scale.

62. Linear Speed A satellite in a circular orbit 1250 kilometers above Earth makes one complete revolution every 110 minutes. Assuming that Earth is a sphere of radius 6378 kilometers, what is the linear speed (in kilometers per minute) of the satellite?

63. Angular and Linear Speeds The circular blade on a saw rotates at 5000 revolutions per minute.

(a) Find the angular speed of the blade in radians per minute.

(b) The blade has a diameter of $7\frac{1}{4}$ inches. Find the linear speed of a blade tip.

64. Angular and Linear Speeds A carousel with a 50-foot diameter makes 4 revolutions per minute.

(a) Find the angular speed of the carousel in radians per minute.

(b) Find the linear speed (in feet per minute) of the platform rim of the carousel.

65. Angular and Linear Speeds A DVD is approximately 12 centimeters in diameter. The drive motor of the DVD player rotates between 200 and 500 revolutions per minute, depending on what track is being read.

(a) Find an interval for the angular speed of the DVD as it rotates.

(b) Find an interval for the linear speed of a point on the outermost track as the DVD rotates.

66. Angular Speed A car is moving at a rate of 65 miles per hour, and the diameter of its wheels is 2 feet.

(a) Find the number of revolutions per minute the wheels are rotating.

(b) Find the angular speed of the wheels in radians per minute.

67. Linear and Angular Speeds A computerized spin balance machine rotates a 25-inch-diameter tire at 480 revolutions per minute.

(a) Find the road speed (in miles per hour) at which the tire is being balanced.

(b) At what rate should the spin balance machine be set so that the tire is being tested for 55 miles per hour?

• • 68. Speed of a Bicycle • • • • • • • • • • • • • • • •

The radii of the pedal sprocket, the wheel sprocket, and the wheel of the bicycle in the figure are 4 inches, 2 inches, and 14 inches, respectively. A cyclist is pedaling at a rate of 1 revolution per second.

14 in.

2 in.   4 in.

(a) Find the speed of the bicycle in feet per second and miles per hour.

(b) Use your result from part (a) to write a function for the distance d (in miles) a cyclist travels in terms of the number n of revolutions of the pedal sprocket.

(c) Write a function for the distance d (in miles) a cyclist travels in terms of the time t (in seconds). Compare this function with the function from part (b).

69. Area A sprinkler on a golf green sprays water over a distance of 15 meters and rotates through an angle of 140°. Draw a diagram that shows the region that the sprinkler can irrigate. Find the area of the region.

70. Area A car's rear windshield wiper rotates 125°. The total length of the wiper mechanism is 25 inches and wipes the windshield over a distance of 14 inches. Find the area covered by the wiper.

Exploration

True or False? **In Exercises 71–73, determine whether the statement is true or false. Justify your answer.**

71. A measurement of 4 radians corresponds to two complete revolutions from the initial side to the terminal side of an angle.

72. The difference between the measures of two coterminal angles is always a multiple of 360° when expressed in degrees and is always a multiple of 2π radians when expressed in radians.

73. An angle that measures $-1260°$ lies in Quadrant III.

74. HOW DO YOU SEE IT? Determine which angles in the figure are coterminal angles with angle A. Explain your reasoning.

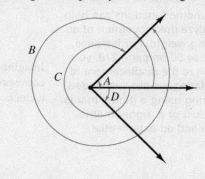

75. Think About It A fan motor turns at a given angular speed. How does the speed of the tips of the blades change when a fan of greater diameter is on the motor? Explain.

76. Think About It Is a degree or a radian the greater unit of measure? Explain.

77. Writing When the radius of a circle increases and the magnitude of a central angle is constant, how does the length of the intercepted arc change? Explain your reasoning.

78. Proof Prove that the area of a circular sector of radius r with central angle θ is

$$A = \frac{1}{2}\theta r^2$$

where θ is measured in radians.

4.2 Trigonometric Functions: The Unit Circle

■ Identify a unit circle and describe its relationship to real numbers.
■ Evaluate trigonometric functions using the unit circle.
■ Use domain and period to evaluate sine and cosine functions, and use a calculator to evaluate trigonometric functions.

Trigonometric functions can help you analyze the movement of an oscillating weight. For instance, in Exercise 50 on page 278, you will analyze the displacement of an oscillating weight suspended by a spring using a model that is the product of a trigonometric function and an exponential function.

The Unit Circle

The two historical perspectives of trigonometry incorporate different methods for introducing the trigonometric functions. One such perspective follows and is based on the unit circle.

Consider the **unit circle** given by

$$x^2 + y^2 = 1 \qquad \text{Unit circle}$$

as shown below.

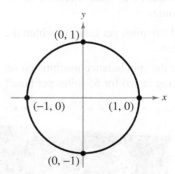

Imagine wrapping the real number line around this circle, with positive numbers corresponding to a counterclockwise wrapping and negative numbers corresponding to a clockwise wrapping, as shown below.

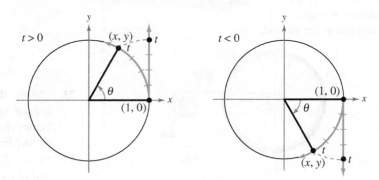

As the real number line wraps around the unit circle, each real number t corresponds to a point (x, y) on the circle. For example, the real number 0 corresponds to the point $(1, 0)$. Moreover, because the unit circle has a circumference of 2π, the real number 2π also corresponds to the point $(1, 0)$.

In general, each real number t also corresponds to a central angle θ (in standard position) whose radian measure is t. With this interpretation of t, the arc length formula

$$s = r\theta \quad (\text{with } r = 1)$$

indicates that the real number t is the (directional) length of the arc intercepted by the angle θ, given in radians.

The Trigonometric Functions

From the preceding discussion, it follows that the coordinates x and y are two functions of the real variable t. You can use these coordinates to define the six trigonometric functions of t.

sine   cosecant   cosine   secant   tangent   cotangent

These six functions are normally abbreviated sin, csc, cos, sec, tan, and cot, respectively.

•• REMARK   Note that the functions in the second row are the *reciprocals* of the corresponding functions in the first row.

Definitions of Trigonometric Functions

Let t be a real number and let (x, y) be the point on the unit circle corresponding to t.

$$\sin t = y \qquad\qquad \cos t = x \qquad\qquad \tan t = \frac{y}{x}, \quad x \neq 0$$

$$\csc t = \frac{1}{y}, \quad y \neq 0 \qquad \sec t = \frac{1}{x}, \quad x \neq 0 \qquad \cot t = \frac{x}{y}, \quad y \neq 0$$

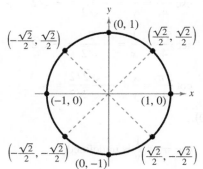

Figure 4.17

In the definitions of the trigonometric functions, note that the tangent and secant are not defined when $x = 0$. For instance, because $t = \pi/2$ corresponds to $(x, y) = (0, 1)$, it follows that $\tan(\pi/2)$ and $\sec(\pi/2)$ are *undefined*. Similarly, the cotangent and cosecant are not defined when $y = 0$. For instance, because $t = 0$ corresponds to $(x, y) = (1, 0)$, cot 0 and csc 0 are *undefined*.

In Figure 4.17, the unit circle is divided into eight equal arcs, corresponding to t-values of

$$0, \frac{\pi}{4}, \frac{\pi}{2}, \frac{3\pi}{4}, \pi, \frac{5\pi}{4}, \frac{3\pi}{2}, \frac{7\pi}{4}, \text{ and } 2\pi.$$

Similarly, in Figure 4.18, the unit circle is divided into 12 equal arcs, corresponding to t-values of

$$0, \frac{\pi}{6}, \frac{\pi}{3}, \frac{\pi}{2}, \frac{2\pi}{3}, \frac{5\pi}{6}, \pi, \frac{7\pi}{6}, \frac{4\pi}{3}, \frac{3\pi}{2}, \frac{5\pi}{3}, \frac{11\pi}{6}, \text{ and } 2\pi.$$

To verify the points on the unit circle in Figure 4.17, note that

$$\left(\frac{\sqrt{2}}{2}, \frac{\sqrt{2}}{2} \right)$$

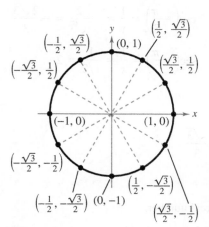

Figure 4.18

also lies on the line $y = x$. So, substituting x for y in the equation of the unit circle produces the following.

$$x^2 + x^2 = 1 \implies 2x^2 = 1 \implies x^2 = \frac{1}{2} \implies x = \pm\frac{\sqrt{2}}{2}$$

Because the point is in the first quadrant and $y = x$, you have

$$x = \frac{\sqrt{2}}{2} \quad \text{and} \quad y = \frac{\sqrt{2}}{2}.$$

You can use similar reasoning to verify the rest of the points in Figure 4.17 and the points in Figure 4.18.

Using the (x, y) coordinates in Figures 4.17 and 4.18, you can evaluate the trigonometric functions for common t-values. Examples 1 and 2 demonstrate this procedure. You should study and learn these exact function values for common t-values because they will help you in later sections to perform calculations.

| EXAMPLE 1 | Evaluating Trigonometric Functions |

▷ **ALGEBRA HELP** You can review dividing fractions and rationalizing denominators in Appendix A.1 and Appendix A.2, respectively.

Evaluate the six trigonometric functions at each real number.

a. $t = \dfrac{\pi}{6}$ **b.** $t = \dfrac{5\pi}{4}$ **c.** $t = \pi$ **d.** $t = -\dfrac{\pi}{3}$

Solution   For each t-value, begin by finding the corresponding point (x, y) on the unit circle. Then use the definitions of trigonometric functions listed on page 273.

a. $t = \pi/6$ corresponds to the point $(x, y) = \left(\sqrt{3}/2,\, 1/2\right)$.

$$\sin\frac{\pi}{6} = y = \frac{1}{2} \qquad\qquad \csc\frac{\pi}{6} = \frac{1}{y} = \frac{1}{1/2} = 2$$

$$\cos\frac{\pi}{6} = x = \frac{\sqrt{3}}{2} \qquad\qquad \sec\frac{\pi}{6} = \frac{1}{x} = \frac{2}{\sqrt{3}} = \frac{2\sqrt{3}}{3}$$

$$\tan\frac{\pi}{6} = \frac{y}{x} = \frac{1/2}{\sqrt{3}/2} = \frac{1}{\sqrt{3}} = \frac{\sqrt{3}}{3} \qquad\qquad \cot\frac{\pi}{6} = \frac{x}{y} = \frac{\sqrt{3}/2}{1/2} = \sqrt{3}$$

b. $t = 5\pi/4$ corresponds to the point $(x, y) = \left(-\sqrt{2}/2,\, -\sqrt{2}/2\right)$.

$$\sin\frac{5\pi}{4} = y = -\frac{\sqrt{2}}{2} \qquad\qquad \csc\frac{5\pi}{4} = \frac{1}{y} = -\frac{2}{\sqrt{2}} = -\sqrt{2}$$

$$\cos\frac{5\pi}{4} = x = -\frac{\sqrt{2}}{2} \qquad\qquad \sec\frac{5\pi}{4} = \frac{1}{x} = -\frac{2}{\sqrt{2}} = -\sqrt{2}$$

$$\tan\frac{5\pi}{4} = \frac{y}{x} = \frac{-\sqrt{2}/2}{-\sqrt{2}/2} = 1 \qquad\qquad \cot\frac{5\pi}{4} = \frac{x}{y} = \frac{-\sqrt{2}/2}{-\sqrt{2}/2} = 1$$

c. $t = \pi$ corresponds to the point $(x, y) = (-1, 0)$.

$$\sin\pi = y = 0 \qquad\qquad \csc\pi = \frac{1}{y} \text{ is undefined.}$$

$$\cos\pi = x = -1 \qquad\qquad \sec\pi = \frac{1}{x} = \frac{1}{-1} = -1$$

$$\tan\pi = \frac{y}{x} = \frac{0}{-1} = 0 \qquad\qquad \cot\pi = \frac{x}{y} \text{ is undefined.}$$

d. Moving *clockwise* around the unit circle, it follows that $t = -\pi/3$ corresponds to the point $(x, y) = \left(1/2,\, -\sqrt{3}/2\right)$.

$$\sin\left(-\frac{\pi}{3}\right) = y = -\frac{\sqrt{3}}{2} \qquad\qquad \csc\left(-\frac{\pi}{3}\right) = \frac{1}{y} = -\frac{2}{\sqrt{3}} = -\frac{2\sqrt{3}}{3}$$

$$\cos\left(-\frac{\pi}{3}\right) = x = \frac{1}{2} \qquad\qquad \sec\left(-\frac{\pi}{3}\right) = \frac{1}{x} = \frac{1}{1/2} = 2$$

$$\tan\left(-\frac{\pi}{3}\right) = \frac{y}{x} = \frac{-\sqrt{3}/2}{1/2} = -\sqrt{3}$$

$$\cot\left(-\frac{\pi}{3}\right) = \frac{x}{y} = \frac{1/2}{-\sqrt{3}/2} = -\frac{1}{\sqrt{3}} = -\frac{\sqrt{3}}{3}$$

✓ *Checkpoint* Audio-video solution in English & Spanish at LarsonPrecalculus.com.

Evaluate the six trigonometric functions at each real number.

a. $t = \pi/2$ **b.** $t = 0$ **c.** $t = -5\pi/6$ **d.** $t = -3\pi/4$

Domain and Period of Sine and Cosine

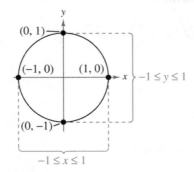

Figure 4.19

The *domain* of the sine and cosine functions is the set of all real numbers. To determine the *range* of these two functions, consider the unit circle shown in Figure 4.19. By definition, $\sin t = y$ and $\cos t = x$. Because (x, y) is on the unit circle, you know that $-1 \le y \le 1$ and $-1 \le x \le 1$. So, the values of sine and cosine also range between -1 and 1.

$$-1 \le y \le 1 \qquad -1 \le x \le 1$$
$$\text{and}$$
$$-1 \le \sin t \le 1 \qquad -1 \le \cos t \le 1$$

Adding 2π to each value of t in the interval $[0, 2\pi]$ results in a revolution around the unit circle, as shown below.

The values of $\sin(t + 2\pi)$ and $\cos(t + 2\pi)$ correspond to those of $\sin t$ and $\cos t$. Similar results can be obtained for repeated revolutions (positive or negative) on the unit circle. This leads to the general result

$$\sin(t + 2\pi n) = \sin t \quad \text{and} \quad \cos(t + 2\pi n) = \cos t$$

for any integer n and real number t. Functions that behave in such a repetitive (or cyclic) manner are called **periodic.**

• • REMARK From this definition, it follows that the sine and cosine functions are periodic and have a period of 2π. The other four trigonometric functions are also periodic and will be discussed further in Section 4.6.

Definition of Periodic Function

A function f is **periodic** when there exists a positive real number c such that

$$f(t + c) = f(t)$$

for all t in the domain of f. The smallest number c for which f is periodic is called the **period** of f.

Recall from Section 1.5 that a function f is *even* when $f(-t) = f(t)$ and is *odd* when $f(-t) = -f(t)$.

Even and Odd Trigonometric Functions

The cosine and secant functions are *even*.

$$\cos(-t) = \cos t \qquad \sec(-t) = \sec t$$

The sine, cosecant, tangent, and cotangent functions are *odd*.

$$\sin(-t) = -\sin t \qquad \csc(-t) = -\csc t$$

$$\tan(-t) = -\tan t \qquad \cot(-t) = -\cot t$$

EXAMPLE 2   Evaluating Sine and Cosine

a. Because $\dfrac{13\pi}{6} = 2\pi + \dfrac{\pi}{6}$, you have $\sin \dfrac{13\pi}{6} = \sin\left(2\pi + \dfrac{\pi}{6}\right) = \sin \dfrac{\pi}{6} = \dfrac{1}{2}$.

b. Because $-\dfrac{7\pi}{2} = -4\pi + \dfrac{\pi}{2}$, you have

$$\cos\left(-\dfrac{7\pi}{2}\right) = \cos\left(-4\pi + \dfrac{\pi}{2}\right) = \cos \dfrac{\pi}{2} = 0.$$

c. For $\sin t = \dfrac{4}{5}$, $\sin(-t) = -\dfrac{4}{5}$ because the sine function is odd.

✓ **Checkpoint** Audio-video solution in English & Spanish at LarsonPrecalculus.com.

a. Use the period of the cosine function to evaluate $\cos(9\pi/2)$.

b. Use the period of the sine function to evaluate $\sin(-7\pi/3)$.

c. Evaluate $\cos t$ given that $\cos(-t) = 0.3$.

▷ **TECHNOLOGY** When evaluating trigonometric functions with a calculator, remember to enclose all fractional angle measures in parentheses. For instance, to evaluate $\sin t$ for $t = \pi/6$, you should enter

⟨SIN⟩⟨(⟩⟨π⟩⟨÷⟩⟨6⟩⟨)⟩⟨ENTER⟩.

These keystrokes yield the correct value of 0.5. Note that some calculators automatically place a left parenthesis after trigonometric functions.

When evaluating a trigonometric function with a calculator, you need to set the calculator to the desired *mode* of measurement (*degree* or *radian*). Most calculators do not have keys for the cosecant, secant, and cotangent functions. To evaluate these functions, you can use the ⟨x⁻¹⟩ key with their respective reciprocal functions: sine, cosine, and tangent. For instance, to evaluate $\csc(\pi/8)$, use the fact that

$$\csc \dfrac{\pi}{8} = \dfrac{1}{\sin(\pi/8)}$$

and enter the following keystroke sequence in *radian* mode.

⟨(⟩⟨SIN⟩⟨(⟩⟨π⟩⟨÷⟩⟨8⟩⟨)⟩⟨)⟩⟨x⁻¹⟩⟨ENTER⟩   Display 2.6131259

EXAMPLE 3   Using a Calculator

Function	Mode	Calculator Keystrokes	Display
a. $\sin \dfrac{2\pi}{3}$	Radian	⟨SIN⟩⟨(⟩⟨2⟩⟨π⟩⟨÷⟩⟨3⟩⟨)⟩⟨ENTER⟩	0.8660254
b. $\cot 1.5$	Radian	⟨(⟩⟨TAN⟩⟨(⟩⟨1.5⟩⟨)⟩⟨)⟩⟨x⁻¹⟩⟨ENTER⟩	0.0709148

✓ **Checkpoint** 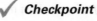 Audio-video solution in English & Spanish at LarsonPrecalculus.com.

Use a calculator to evaluate (a) $\sin(5\pi/7)$ and (b) $\csc 2.0$.

Summarize   (Section 4.2)

1. Explain how to identify a unit circle and describe its relationship to real numbers (*page 272*).

2. State the unit circle definitions of the trigonometric functions (*page 273*). For an example of evaluating trigonometric functions using the unit circle, see Example 1.

3. Explain how to use domain and period to evaluate sine and cosine functions (*page 275*) and describe how to use a calculator to evaluate trigonometric functions (*page 276*). For an example of using period and an odd trigonometric function to evaluate sine and cosine functions, see Example 2. For an example of using a calculator to evaluate trigonometric functions, see Example 3.

4.2 Exercises

See **CalcChat.com** for tutorial help and worked-out solutions to odd-numbered exercises.

Vocabulary: Fill in the blanks.

1. Each real number t corresponds to a point (x, y) on the _____ _____.

2. A function f is _____ when there exists a positive real number c such that $f(t + c) = f(t)$ for all t in the domain of f.

3. The smallest number c for which a function f is periodic is called the _____ of f.

4. A function f is _____ when $f(-t) = -f(t)$ and _____ when $f(-t) = f(t)$.

Skills and Applications

Determining Values of Trigonometric Functions In Exercises 5–8, determine the exact values of the six trigonometric functions of the real number t.

5.

6.

7.

8.

Finding a Point on the Unit Circle In Exercises 9–12, find the point (x, y) on the unit circle that corresponds to the real number t.

9. $t = \pi/2$

10. $t = \pi/4$

11. $t = 5\pi/6$

12. $t = 4\pi/3$

Evaluating Sine, Cosine, and Tangent In Exercises 13–22, evaluate (if possible) the sine, cosine, and tangent at the real number.

13. $t = \dfrac{\pi}{4}$

14. $t = \dfrac{\pi}{3}$

15. $t = -\dfrac{\pi}{6}$

16. $t = -\dfrac{\pi}{4}$

17. $t = -\dfrac{7\pi}{4}$

18. $t = -\dfrac{4\pi}{3}$

19. $t = \dfrac{11\pi}{6}$

20. $t = \dfrac{5\pi}{3}$

21. $t = -\dfrac{3\pi}{2}$

22. $t = -2\pi$

Evaluating Trigonometric Functions In Exercises 23–30, evaluate (if possible) the six trigonometric functions at the real number.

23. $t = 2\pi/3$

24. $t = 5\pi/6$

25. $t = 4\pi/3$

26. $t = 7\pi/4$

27. $t = -5\pi/3$

28. $t = 3\pi/2$

29. $t = -\pi/2$

30. $t = -\pi$

Using Period to Evaluate Sine and Cosine In Exercises 31–36, evaluate the trigonometric function using its period as an aid.

31. $\sin 4\pi$

32. $\cos 3\pi$

33. $\cos \dfrac{7\pi}{3}$

34. $\sin \dfrac{9\pi}{4}$

35. $\sin \dfrac{19\pi}{6}$

36. $\sin\left(-\dfrac{8\pi}{3}\right)$

Using the Value of a Trigonometric Function In Exercises 37–42, use the value of the trigonometric function to evaluate the indicated functions.

37. $\sin t = \frac{1}{2}$
   (a) $\sin(-t)$
   (b) $\csc(-t)$

38. $\sin(-t) = \frac{3}{8}$
   (a) $\sin t$
   (b) $\csc t$

39. $\cos(-t) = -\frac{1}{5}$
   (a) $\cos t$
   (b) $\sec(-t)$

40. $\cos t = -\frac{3}{4}$
   (a) $\cos(-t)$
   (b) $\sec(-t)$

41. $\sin t = \frac{4}{5}$
   (a) $\sin(\pi - t)$
   (b) $\sin(t + \pi)$

42. $\cos t = \frac{4}{5}$
   (a) $\cos(\pi - t)$
   (b) $\cos(t + \pi)$

Using a Calculator In Exercises 43–48, use a calculator to evaluate the trigonometric function. Round your answer to four decimal places. (Be sure the calculator is in the correct mode.)

43. $\tan \pi/3$

44. $\csc 2\pi/3$

45. $\csc 0.8$

46. $\cos(-1.7)$

47. $\sec 1.8$

48. $\cot(-0.9)$

49. Harmonic Motion The displacement from equilibrium of an oscillating weight suspended by a spring is given by

$$y(t) = \frac{1}{4}\cos 6t$$

where y is the displacement (in feet) and t is the time (in seconds). Find the displacement when (a) $t = 0$, (b) $t = \frac{1}{4}$, and (c) $t = \frac{1}{2}$.

50. Harmonic Motion

The displacement from equilibrium of an oscillating weight suspended by a spring and subject to the damping effect of friction is given by $y(t) = \frac{1}{4}e^{-t}\cos 6t$, where y is the displacement (in feet) and t is the time (in seconds).

(a) Complete the table.

t	0	$\frac{1}{4}$	$\frac{1}{2}$	$\frac{3}{4}$	1
y					

(b) Use the *table* feature of a graphing utility to approximate the time when the weight reaches equilibrium.

(c) What appears to happen to the displacement as t increases?

Exploration

True or False? In Exercises 51–54, determine whether the statement is true or false. Justify your answer.

51. Because $\sin(-t) = -\sin t$, the sine of a negative angle is a negative number.

52. The real number 0 corresponds to the point $(0, 1)$ on the unit circle.

53. $\tan a = \tan(a - 6\pi)$

54. $\cos\left(-\frac{7\pi}{2}\right) = \cos\left(\pi + \frac{\pi}{2}\right)$

55. Conjecture Let (x_1, y_1) and (x_2, y_2) be points on the unit circle corresponding to $t = t_1$ and $t = \pi - t_1$, respectively.

(a) Identify the symmetry of the points (x_1, y_1) and (x_2, y_2).

(b) Make a conjecture about any relationship between $\sin t_1$ and $\sin(\pi - t_1)$.

(c) Make a conjecture about any relationship between $\cos t_1$ and $\cos(\pi - t_1)$.

56. Using the Unit Circle Use the unit circle to verify that the cosine and secant functions are even and that the sine, cosecant, tangent, and cotangent functions are odd.

57. Verifying Expressions Are Not Equal Verify that $\cos 2t \neq 2\cos t$ by approximating $\cos 1.5$ and $2\cos 0.75$.

58. Verifying Expressions Are Not Equal Verify that $\sin(t_1 + t_2) \neq \sin t_1 + \sin t_2$ by approximating $\sin 0.25$, $\sin 0.75$, and $\sin 1$.

59. Graphical Analysis With a graphing utility in *radian* and *parametric* modes, enter the equations

$$X_{1T} = \cos T \quad \text{and} \quad Y_{1T} = \sin T$$

and use the following settings.

Tmin = 0, Tmax = 6.3, Tstep = 0.1
Xmin = −1.5, Xmax = 1.5, Xscl = 1
Ymin = −1, Ymax = 1, Yscl = 1

(a) Graph the entered equations and describe the graph.

(b) Use the *trace* feature to move the cursor around the graph. What do the t-values represent? What do the x- and y-values represent?

(c) What are the least and greatest values of x and y?

60. **HOW DO YOU SEE IT?** Use the figure below.

(a) Do all of the trigonometric functions of t exist? Explain your reasoning.

(b) For those trigonometric functions that exist, determine whether the sign of the trigonometric function is positive or negative. Explain your reasoning.

61. Think About It Because $f(t) = \sin t$ is an odd function and $g(t) = \cos t$ is an even function, what can be said about the function $h(t) = f(t)g(t)$?

62. Think About It Because $f(t) = \sin t$ and $g(t) = \tan t$ are odd functions, what can be said about the function $h(t) = f(t)g(t)$?

4.3 Right Triangle Trigonometry

Trigonometric functions can help you analyze real-life situations. For instance, in Exercise 76 on page 289, you will use trigonometric functions to find the height of a helium-filled balloon.

■ Evaluate trigonometric functions of acute angles, and use a calculator to evaluate trigonometric functions.
■ Use the fundamental trigonometric identities.
■ Use trigonometric functions to model and solve real-life problems.

The Six Trigonometric Functions

This section introduces the trigonometric functions from a *right triangle* perspective. Consider a right triangle with one acute angle labeled θ, as shown below. Relative to the angle θ, the three sides of the triangle are the **hypotenuse,** the **opposite side** (the side opposite the angle θ), and the **adjacent side** (the side adjacent to the angle θ).

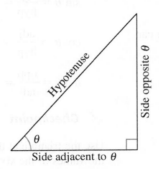

Using the lengths of these three sides, you can form six ratios that define the six trigonometric functions of the acute angle θ.

sine   cosecant   cosine   secant   tangent   cotangent

In the following definitions, it is important to see that

$$0° < \theta < 90°$$

(θ lies in the first quadrant) and that for such angles the value of each trigonometric function is *positive*.

Right Triangle Definitions of Trigonometric Functions

Let θ be an *acute* angle of a right triangle. The six trigonometric functions of the angle θ are defined as follows. (Note that the functions in the second row are the *reciprocals* of the corresponding functions in the first row.)

$$\sin \theta = \frac{\text{opp}}{\text{hyp}} \qquad \cos \theta = \frac{\text{adj}}{\text{hyp}} \qquad \tan \theta = \frac{\text{opp}}{\text{adj}}$$

$$\csc \theta = \frac{\text{hyp}}{\text{opp}} \qquad \sec \theta = \frac{\text{hyp}}{\text{adj}} \qquad \cot \theta = \frac{\text{adj}}{\text{opp}}$$

The abbreviations

opp,   adj,   and   hyp

represent the lengths of the three sides of a right triangle.

opp = the length of the side *opposite* θ

adj = the length of the side *adjacent to* θ

hyp = the length of the *hypotenuse*

Figure 4.20

▷ **ALGEBRA HELP** You can review the Pythagorean Theorem in Section 1.1.

HISTORICAL NOTE

Georg Joachim Rhaeticus (1514–1574) was the leading Teutonic mathematical astronomer of the 16th century. He was the first to define the trigonometric functions as ratios of the sides of a right triangle.

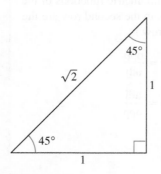

Figure 4.21

EXAMPLE 1 **Evaluating Trigonometric Functions**

Use the triangle in Figure 4.20 to find the values of the six trigonometric functions of θ.

Solution By the Pythagorean Theorem,

$$(\text{hyp})^2 = (\text{opp})^2 + (\text{adj})^2$$

it follows that

$$\text{hyp} = \sqrt{4^2 + 3^2}$$
$$= \sqrt{25}$$
$$= 5.$$

So, the six trigonometric functions of θ are

$$\sin\theta = \frac{\text{opp}}{\text{hyp}} = \frac{4}{5} \qquad \csc\theta = \frac{\text{hyp}}{\text{opp}} = \frac{5}{4}$$

$$\cos\theta = \frac{\text{adj}}{\text{hyp}} = \frac{3}{5} \qquad \sec\theta = \frac{\text{hyp}}{\text{adj}} = \frac{5}{3}$$

$$\tan\theta = \frac{\text{opp}}{\text{adj}} = \frac{4}{3} \qquad \cot\theta = \frac{\text{adj}}{\text{opp}} = \frac{3}{4}.$$

✓ *Checkpoint* ◀))) *Audio-video solution in English & Spanish at LarsonPrecalculus.com.*

Use the triangle at the right to find the values of the six trigonometric functions of θ.

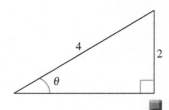

In Example 1, you were given the lengths of two sides of the right triangle, but not the angle θ. Often, you will be asked to find the trigonometric functions of a *given* acute angle θ. To do this, construct a right triangle having θ as one of its angles.

EXAMPLE 2 **Evaluating Trigonometric Functions of 45°**

Find the values of $\sin 45°$, $\cos 45°$, and $\tan 45°$.

Solution Construct a right triangle having 45° as one of its acute angles, as shown in Figure 4.21. Choose 1 as the length of the adjacent side. From geometry, you know that the other acute angle is also 45°. So, the triangle is isosceles and the length of the opposite side is also 1. Using the Pythagorean Theorem, you find the length of the hypotenuse to be $\sqrt{2}$.

$$\sin 45° = \frac{\text{opp}}{\text{hyp}} = \frac{1}{\sqrt{2}} = \frac{\sqrt{2}}{2}$$

$$\cos 45° = \frac{\text{adj}}{\text{hyp}} = \frac{1}{\sqrt{2}} = \frac{\sqrt{2}}{2}$$

$$\tan 45° = \frac{\text{opp}}{\text{adj}} = \frac{1}{1} = 1$$

✓ *Checkpoint* ◀))) *Audio-video solution in English & Spanish at LarsonPrecalculus.com.*

Find the value of $\sec 45°$.

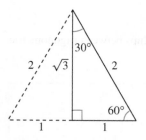

Figure 4.22

▷ **••REMARK** Because the angles 30°, 45°, and 60° ($\pi/6$, $\pi/4$, and $\pi/3$, respectively) occur frequently in trigonometry, you should learn to construct the triangles shown in Figures 4.21 and 4.22.

▷ **••REMARK** Throughout this text, angles are assumed to be measured in radians unless noted otherwise. For example, sin 1 means the sine of 1 radian and sin 1° means the sine of 1 degree.

EXAMPLE 3   **Trigonometric Functions of 30° and 60°**

Use the equilateral triangle shown in Figure 4.22 to find the values of sin 60°, cos 60°, sin 30°, and cos 30°.

Solution For $\theta = 60°$, you have adj $= 1$, opp $= \sqrt{3}$, and hyp $= 2$. So,

$$\sin 60° = \frac{\text{opp}}{\text{hyp}} = \frac{\sqrt{3}}{2} \quad \text{and} \quad \cos 60° = \frac{\text{adj}}{\text{hyp}} = \frac{1}{2}.$$

For $\theta = 30°$, adj $= \sqrt{3}$, opp $= 1$, and hyp $= 2$. So,

$$\sin 30° = \frac{\text{opp}}{\text{hyp}} = \frac{1}{2} \quad \text{and} \quad \cos 30° = \frac{\text{adj}}{\text{hyp}} = \frac{\sqrt{3}}{2}.$$

✓ **Checkpoint** 🔊))) Audio-video solution in English & Spanish at LarsonPrecalculus.com.

Use the equilateral triangle shown in Figure 4.22 to find the values of tan 60° and tan 30°.

Sines, Cosines, and Tangents of Special Angles

$$\sin 30° = \sin \frac{\pi}{6} = \frac{1}{2} \qquad \cos 30° = \cos \frac{\pi}{6} = \frac{\sqrt{3}}{2} \qquad \tan 30° = \tan \frac{\pi}{6} = \frac{\sqrt{3}}{3}$$

$$\sin 45° = \sin \frac{\pi}{4} = \frac{\sqrt{2}}{2} \qquad \cos 45° = \cos \frac{\pi}{4} = \frac{\sqrt{2}}{2} \qquad \tan 45° = \tan \frac{\pi}{4} = 1$$

$$\sin 60° = \sin \frac{\pi}{3} = \frac{\sqrt{3}}{2} \qquad \cos 60° = \cos \frac{\pi}{3} = \frac{1}{2} \qquad \tan 60° = \tan \frac{\pi}{3} = \sqrt{3}$$

In the box, note that $\sin 30° = \frac{1}{2} = \cos 60°$. This occurs because 30° and 60° are complementary angles. In general, it can be shown from the right triangle definitions that *cofunctions of complementary angles are equal*. That is, if θ is an acute angle, then the following relationships are true.

$$\sin(90° - \theta) = \cos \theta \qquad \cos(90° - \theta) = \sin \theta \qquad \tan(90° - \theta) = \cot \theta$$

$$\cot(90° - \theta) = \tan \theta \qquad \sec(90° - \theta) = \csc \theta \qquad \csc(90° - \theta) = \sec \theta$$

To use a calculator to evaluate trigonometric functions of angles measured in degrees, first set the calculator to *degree* mode and then proceed as demonstrated in Section 4.2.

EXAMPLE 4   **Using a Calculator**

Use a calculator to evaluate sec 5° 40′ 12″.

Solution Begin by converting to decimal degree form. $\left[\text{Recall that } 1' = \frac{1}{60}(1°) \text{ and } 1'' = \frac{1}{3600}(1°).\right]$

$$5° \, 40' \, 12'' = 5° + \left(\frac{40}{60}\right)° + \left(\frac{12}{3600}\right)° = 5.67°$$

Then, use a calculator to evaluate sec 5.67°.

Function	Calculator Keystrokes	Display
sec 5° 40′ 12″ = sec 5.67°	(COS (5.67)) x⁻¹ ENTER	1.0049166

✓ **Checkpoint** 🔊))) Audio-video solution in English & Spanish at LarsonPrecalculus.com.

Use a calculator to evaluate csc 34° 30′ 36″.

Trigonometric Identities

In trigonometry, a great deal of time is spent studying relationships between trigonometric functions (identities).

Fundamental Trigonometric Identities

Reciprocal Identities

$$\sin \theta = \frac{1}{\csc \theta} \qquad \cos \theta = \frac{1}{\sec \theta} \qquad \tan \theta = \frac{1}{\cot \theta}$$

$$\csc \theta = \frac{1}{\sin \theta} \qquad \sec \theta = \frac{1}{\cos \theta} \qquad \cot \theta = \frac{1}{\tan \theta}$$

Quotient Identities

$$\tan \theta = \frac{\sin \theta}{\cos \theta} \qquad \cot \theta = \frac{\cos \theta}{\sin \theta}$$

Pythagorean Identities

$$\sin^2 \theta + \cos^2 \theta = 1$$

$$1 + \tan^2 \theta = \sec^2 \theta$$

$$1 + \cot^2 \theta = \csc^2 \theta$$

Note that $\sin^2 \theta$ represents $(\sin \theta)^2$, $\cos^2 \theta$ represents $(\cos \theta)^2$, and so on.

EXAMPLE 5   **Applying Trigonometric Identities**

Let θ be an acute angle such that $\sin \theta = 0.6$. Find the values of (a) $\cos \theta$ and (b) $\tan \theta$ using trigonometric identities.

Solution

a. To find the value of $\cos \theta$, use the Pythagorean identity

$$\sin^2 \theta + \cos^2 \theta = 1.$$

So, you have

$$(0.6)^2 + \cos^2 \theta = 1 \qquad \text{Substitute 0.6 for } \sin \theta.$$

$$\cos^2 \theta = 1 - (0.6)^2 \qquad \text{Subtract } (0.6)^2 \text{ from each side.}$$

$$\cos^2 \theta = 0.64 \qquad \text{Simplify.}$$

$$\cos \theta = \sqrt{0.64} \qquad \text{Extract positive square root.}$$

$$\cos \theta = 0.8. \qquad \text{Simplify.}$$

b. Now, knowing the sine and cosine of θ, you can find the tangent of θ to be

$$\tan \theta = \frac{\sin \theta}{\cos \theta} = \frac{0.6}{0.8} = 0.75.$$

Use the definitions of $\cos \theta$ and $\tan \theta$ and the triangle shown in Figure 4.23 to check these results.

Figure 4.23

 Checkpoint ◀))) *Audio-video solution in English & Spanish at LarsonPrecalculus.com.*

Let θ be an acute angle such that $\cos \theta = 0.25$. Find the values of (a) $\sin \theta$ and (b) $\tan \theta$ using trigonometric identities. ∎

EXAMPLE 6   **Applying Trigonometric Identities**

Let θ be an acute angle such that $\tan \theta = \frac{1}{3}$. Find the values of (a) $\cot \theta$ and (b) $\sec \theta$ using trigonometric identities.

Solution

a. $\cot \theta = \dfrac{1}{\tan \theta}$ Reciprocal identity

$= \dfrac{1}{1/3}$

$= 3$

b. $\sec^2 \theta = 1 + \tan^2 \theta$ Pythagorean identity

$= 1 + (1/3)^2$

$= 10/9$

$\sec \theta = \sqrt{10}/3$

Use the definitions of $\cot \theta$ and $\sec \theta$ and the triangle shown below to check these results.

✓ *Checkpoint* 🔊))) *Audio-video solution in English & Spanish at LarsonPrecalculus.com.*

Let β be an acute angle such that $\tan \beta = 2$. Find the values of (a) $\cot \beta$ and (b) $\sec \beta$ using trigonometric identities.

EXAMPLE 7   **Using Trigonometric Identities**

Use trigonometric identities to transform the left side of the equation into the right side $(0 < \theta < \pi/2)$.

a. $\sin \theta \csc \theta = 1$ **b.** $(\csc \theta + \cot \theta)(\csc \theta - \cot \theta) = 1$

Solution

a. $\sin \theta \csc \theta = \left(\dfrac{1}{\csc \theta}\right)\csc \theta = 1$ Use a reciprocal identity and simplify.

b. $(\csc \theta + \cot \theta)(\csc \theta - \cot \theta)$

$= \csc^2 \theta - \csc \theta \cot \theta + \csc \theta \cot \theta - \cot^2 \theta$ FOIL Method

$= \csc^2 \theta - \cot^2 \theta$ Simplify.

$= 1$ Pythagorean identity

✓ *Checkpoint* 🔊))) *Audio-video solution in English & Spanish at LarsonPrecalculus.com.*

Use trigonometric identities to transform the left side of the equation into the right side $(0 < \theta < \pi/2)$.

a. $\tan \theta \csc \theta = \sec \theta$

b. $(\csc \theta + 1)(\csc \theta - 1) = \cot^2 \theta$

Applications Involving Right Triangles

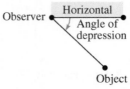

Object

Angle of
elevation

Observer

Horizontal

Observer   Horizontal

Angle of
depression

Object

Figure 4.24

Many applications of trigonometry involve a process called **solving right triangles.** In this type of application, you are usually given one side of a right triangle and one of the acute angles and are asked to find one of the other sides, *or* you are given two sides and are asked to find one of the acute angles.

In Example 8, the angle you are given is the **angle of elevation,** which represents the angle from the horizontal upward to an object. In other applications you may be given the **angle of depression,** which represents the angle from the horizontal downward to an object. (See Figure 4.24.)

EXAMPLE 8   Using Trigonometry to Solve a Right Triangle

A surveyor is standing 115 feet from the base of the Washington Monument, as shown in the figure at the right. The surveyor measures the angle of elevation to the top of the monument as 78.3°. How tall is the Washington Monument?

Angle of
elevation
78.3°

$x = 115$ ft   *Not drawn to scale*

Solution   From the figure, you can see that

$$\tan 78.3° = \frac{\text{opp}}{\text{adj}} = \frac{y}{x}$$

where $x = 115$ and y is the height of the monument. So, the height of the Washington Monument is

$$y = x \tan 78.3°$$
$$\approx 115(4.82882)$$
$$\approx 555 \text{ feet.}$$

✓ **Checkpoint**))) *Audio-video solution in English & Spanish at LarsonPrecalculus.com.*

How tall is the flagpole in Figure 4.25?

y

Angle of
elevation
64.6°

$x = 19$ ft   *Not drawn to scale*

Figure 4.25

EXAMPLE 9   Using Trigonometry to Solve a Right Triangle

A historic lighthouse is 200 yards from a bike path along the edge of a lake. A walkway to the lighthouse is 400 yards long. Find the acute angle θ between the bike path and the walkway, as illustrated in the figure at the right.

θ

200 yd

400 yd

Solution   From the figure, you can see that the sine of the angle θ is

$$\sin \theta = \frac{\text{opp}}{\text{hyp}} = \frac{200}{400} = \frac{1}{2}.$$

Now you should recognize that $\theta = 30°$.

✓ **Checkpoint**))) *Audio-video solution in English & Spanish at LarsonPrecalculus.com.*

Find the acute angle θ between the two paths, as illustrated in Figure 4.26.

3 miles

θ

6 miles

Ranger station

Figure 4.26

In Example 9, you were able to recognize that $\theta = 30°$ is the acute angle that satisfies the equation $\sin \theta = \frac{1}{2}$. Suppose, however, that you were given the equation $\sin \theta = 0.6$ and were asked to find the acute angle θ. Because $\sin 30° = \frac{1}{2} = 0.5000$ and $\sin 45° = 1/\sqrt{2} \approx 0.7071$, you might guess that θ lies somewhere between $30°$ and $45°$. In a later section, you will study a method by which a more precise value of θ can be determined.

Skateboarders can go to a skatepark, which is a recreational environment built with many different types of ramps and rails.

EXAMPLE 10   **Solving a Right Triangle**

Find the length c of the skateboard ramp shown in the figure below. Find the horizontal length a of the ramp.

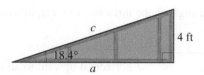

c

4 ft

$18.4°$

a

Solution   From the figure, you can see that

$$\sin 18.4° = \frac{\text{opp}}{\text{hyp}} = \frac{4}{c}.$$

So, the length of the skateboard ramp is

$$c = \frac{4}{\sin 18.4°} \approx \frac{4}{0.3156} \approx 12.7 \text{ feet.}$$

Also from the figure, you can see that

$$\tan 18.4° = \frac{\text{opp}}{\text{adj}} = \frac{4}{a}.$$

So, the horizontal length is

$$a = \frac{4}{\tan 18.4°} \approx 12.0 \text{ feet.}$$

 Checkpoint   Audio-video solution in English & Spanish at LarsonPrecalculus.com.

Find the length c of the loading ramp shown in the figure below. Find the horizontal length a of the ramp.

$11.5°$ c 3.5 ft

a

Summarize   (Section 4.3)

1. State the right triangle definitions of the trigonometric functions *(page 279)* and describe how to use a calculator to evaluate trigonometric functions *(page 281)*. For examples of evaluating trigonometric functions of acute angles, see Examples 1–3. For an example of using a calculator to evaluate a trigonometric function, see Example 4.

2. List the fundamental trigonometric identities *(page 282)*. For examples of using the fundamental trigonometric identities, see Examples 5–7.

3. Describe examples of how to use trigonometric functions to model and solve real-life problems *(pages 284 and 285, Examples 8–10)*.

4.3 Exercises

See CalcChat.com for tutorial help and worked-out solutions to odd-numbered exercises.

Vocabulary

1. Match each trigonometric function with its right triangle definition.

   (a) sine   (b) cosine   (c) tangent   (d) cosecant   (e) secant   (f) cotangent

   (i) $\dfrac{\text{hypotenuse}}{\text{adjacent}}$ (ii) $\dfrac{\text{adjacent}}{\text{opposite}}$ (iii) $\dfrac{\text{hypotenuse}}{\text{opposite}}$ (iv) $\dfrac{\text{adjacent}}{\text{hypotenuse}}$ (v) $\dfrac{\text{opposite}}{\text{hypotenuse}}$ (vi) $\dfrac{\text{opposite}}{\text{adjacent}}$

In Exercises 2–4, fill in the blanks.

2. Relative to the acute angle θ, the three sides of a right triangle are the _____ side, the _____ side, and the _____.

3. Cofunctions of _____ angles are equal.

4. An angle that measures from the horizontal upward to an object is called the angle of _____, whereas an angle that measures from the horizontal downward to an object is called the angle of _____.

Skills and Applications

Evaluating Trigonometric Functions   **In Exercises 5–8, find the exact values of the six trigonometric functions of the angle θ shown in the figure. (Use the Pythagorean Theorem to find the third side of the triangle.)**

5.

6.

7.

8.

Evaluating Trigonometric Functions   **In Exercises 9–12, find the exact values of the six trigonometric functions of the angle θ for each of the two triangles. Explain why the function values are the same.**

9.

10.

11.

12.

Evaluating Trigonometric Functions   **In Exercises 13–20, sketch a right triangle corresponding to the trigonometric function of the acute angle θ. Use the Pythagorean Theorem to determine the third side and then find the other five trigonometric functions of θ.**

13. $\tan \theta = \frac{3}{4}$ 14. $\cos \theta = \frac{5}{6}$

15. $\sec \theta = \frac{3}{2}$ 16. $\tan \theta = \frac{4}{5}$

17. $\sin \theta = \frac{1}{5}$ 18. $\sec \theta = \frac{17}{7}$

19. $\cot \theta = 3$ 20. $\csc \theta = 9$

Evaluating Trigonometric Functions of 30°, 45°, and 60°   **In Exercises 21–30, construct an appropriate triangle to find the missing values. ($0° \leq \theta \leq 90°, 0 \leq \theta \leq \pi/2$)**

Function	θ (deg)	θ (rad)	Function Value
21. sin	30°		
22. cos	45°		
23. sec		$\frac{\pi}{4}$	
24. tan		$\frac{\pi}{3}$	
25. cot			$\frac{\sqrt{3}}{3}$
26. csc			$\sqrt{2}$
27. csc		$\frac{\pi}{6}$	
28. sin		$\frac{\pi}{4}$	
29. cot			1
30. tan			$\frac{\sqrt{3}}{3}$

Using a Calculator In Exercises 31–40, use a calculator to evaluate each function. Round your answers to four decimal places. (Be sure the calculator is in the correct mode.)

31. (a) $\sin 10°$ (b) $\cos 80°$

32. (a) $\tan 23.5°$ (b) $\cot 66.5°$

33. (a) $\sin 16.35°$ (b) $\csc 16.35°$

34. (a) $\cot 79.56°$ (b) $\sec 79.56°$

35. (a) $\cos 4° 50' 15''$ (b) $\sec 4° 50' 15''$

36. (a) $\sec 42° 12'$ (b) $\csc 48° 7'$

37. (a) $\cot 11° 15'$ (b) $\tan 11° 15'$

38. (a) $\sec 56° 8' 10''$ (b) $\cos 56° 8' 10''$

39. (a) $\csc 32° 40' 3''$ (b) $\tan 44° 28' 16''$

40. (a) $\sec\left(\frac{9}{5} \cdot 20 + 32\right)°$ (b) $\cot\left(\frac{9}{5} \cdot 30 + 32\right)°$

Applying Trigonometric Identities In Exercises 41–46, use the given function value(s) and the trigonometric identities to find the indicated trigonometric functions.

41. $\sin 60° = \dfrac{\sqrt{3}}{2}, \quad \cos 60° = \dfrac{1}{2}$

    (a) $\sin 30°$ (b) $\cos 30°$

    (c) $\tan 60°$ (d) $\cot 60°$

42. $\sin 30° = \dfrac{1}{2}, \quad \tan 30° = \dfrac{\sqrt{3}}{3}$

    (a) $\csc 30°$ (b) $\cot 60°$

    (c) $\cos 30°$ (d) $\cot 30°$

43. $\cos \theta = \dfrac{1}{3}$

    (a) $\sin \theta$ (b) $\tan \theta$

    (c) $\sec \theta$ (d) $\csc(90° - \theta)$

44. $\sec \theta = 5$

    (a) $\cos \theta$ (b) $\cot \theta$

    (c) $\cot(90° - \theta)$ (d) $\sin \theta$

45. $\cot \alpha = 5$

    (a) $\tan \alpha$ (b) $\csc \alpha$

    (c) $\cot(90° - \alpha)$ (d) $\cos \alpha$

46. $\cos \beta = \dfrac{\sqrt{7}}{4}$

    (a) $\sec \beta$ (b) $\sin \beta$

    (c) $\cot \beta$ (d) $\sin(90° - \beta)$

Using Trigonometric Identities In Exercises 47–56, use trigonometric identities to transform the left side of the equation into the right side $(0 < \theta < \pi/2)$.

47. $\tan \theta \cot \theta = 1$

48. $\cos \theta \sec \theta = 1$

49. $\tan \alpha \cos \alpha = \sin \alpha$

50. $\cot \alpha \sin \alpha = \cos \alpha$

51. $(1 + \sin \theta)(1 - \sin \theta) = \cos^2 \theta$

52. $(1 + \cos \theta)(1 - \cos \theta) = \sin^2 \theta$

53. $(\sec \theta + \tan \theta)(\sec \theta - \tan \theta) = 1$

54. $\sin^2 \theta - \cos^2 \theta = 2 \sin^2 \theta - 1$

55. $\dfrac{\sin \theta}{\cos \theta} + \dfrac{\cos \theta}{\sin \theta} = \csc \theta \sec \theta$

56. $\dfrac{\tan \beta + \cot \beta}{\tan \beta} = \csc^2 \beta$

Evaluating Trigonometric Functions In Exercises 57–62, find each value of θ in degrees $(0° < \theta < 90°)$ and radians $(0 < \theta < \pi/2)$ without using a calculator.

57. (a) $\sin \theta = \dfrac{1}{2}$ (b) $\csc \theta = 2$

58. (a) $\cos \theta = \dfrac{\sqrt{2}}{2}$ (b) $\tan \theta = 1$

59. (a) $\sec \theta = 2$ (b) $\cot \theta = 1$

60. (a) $\tan \theta = \sqrt{3}$ (b) $\cos \theta = \dfrac{1}{2}$

61. (a) $\csc \theta = \dfrac{2\sqrt{3}}{3}$ (b) $\sin \theta = \dfrac{\sqrt{2}}{2}$

62. (a) $\cot \theta = \dfrac{\sqrt{3}}{3}$ (b) $\sec \theta = \sqrt{2}$

Finding Side Lengths of a Triangle In Exercises 63–66, find the exact values of the indicated variables.

63. Find x and y.   64. Find x and r.

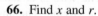

65. Find x and r.   66. Find x and r.

67. **Empire State Building** You are standing 45 meters from the base of the Empire State Building. You estimate that the angle of elevation to the top of the 86th floor (the observatory) is 82°. The total height of the building is another 123 meters above the 86th floor. What is the approximate height of the building? One of your friends is on the 86th floor. What is the distance between you and your friend?

68. Height A six-foot-tall person walks from the base of a broadcasting tower directly toward the tip of the shadow cast by the tower. When the person is 132 feet from the tower and 3 feet from the tip of the shadow, the person's shadow starts to appear beyond the tower's shadow.

(a) Draw a right triangle that gives a visual representation of the problem. Show the known quantities of the triangle and use a variable to indicate the height of the tower.

(b) Use a trigonometric function to write an equation involving the unknown quantity.

(c) What is the height of the tower?

69. Angle of Elevation You are skiing down a mountain with a vertical height of 1500 feet. The distance from the top of the mountain to the base is 3000 feet. What is the angle of elevation from the base to the top of the mountain?

70. Width of a River A biologist wants to know the width w of a river in order to properly set instruments for studying the pollutants in the water. From point A, the biologist walks downstream 100 feet and sights to point C (see figure). From this sighting, the biologist determines that $\theta = 54°$. How wide is the river?

71. Length A guy wire runs from the ground to a cell tower. The wire is attached to the cell tower 150 feet above the ground. The angle formed between the wire and the ground is 43° (see figure).

(a) How long is the guy wire?

(b) How far from the base of the tower is the guy wire anchored to the ground?

72. Height of a Mountain In traveling across flat land, you notice a mountain directly in front of you. Its angle of elevation (to the peak) is 3.5°. After you drive 13 miles closer to the mountain, the angle of elevation is 9° (see figure). Approximate the height of the mountain.

73. Machine Shop Calculations A steel plate has the form of one-fourth of a circle with a radius of 60 centimeters. Two two-centimeter holes are to be drilled in the plate, positioned as shown in the figure. Find the coordinates of the center of each hole.

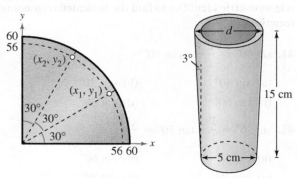

Figure for 73   Figure for 74

74. Machine Shop Calculations A tapered shaft has a diameter of 5 centimeters at the small end and is 15 centimeters long (see figure). The taper is 3°. Find the diameter d of the large end of the shaft.

75. Geometry Use a compass to sketch a quarter of a circle of radius 10 centimeters. Using a protractor, construct an angle of 20° in standard position (see figure). Drop a perpendicular line from the point of intersection of the terminal side of the angle and the arc of the circle. By actual measurement, calculate the coordinates (x, y) of the point of intersection and use these measurements to approximate the six trigonometric functions of a 20° angle.

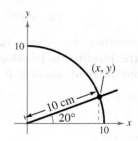

76. Height

A 20-meter line is a tether for a helium-filled balloon. Because of a breeze, the line makes an angle of approximately 85° with the ground.

(a) Draw a right triangle that gives a visual representation of the problem. Show the known quantities of the triangle and use a variable to indicate the height of the balloon.

(b) Use a trigonometric function to write and solve an equation for the height of the balloon.

(c) The breeze becomes stronger and the angle the line makes with the ground decreases. How does this affect the triangle you drew in part (a)?

(d) Complete the table, which shows the heights (in meters) of the balloon for decreasing angle measures θ.

Angle, θ	80°	70°	60°	50°
Height				

Angle, θ	40°	30°	20°	10°
Height				

(e) As θ approaches 0°, how does this affect the height of the balloon? Draw a right triangle to explain your reasoning.

77. Johnstown Inclined Plane The Johnstown Inclined Plane in Pennsylvania is one of the longest and steepest hoists in the world. The railway cars travel a distance of 896.5 feet at an angle of approximately 35.4°, rising to a height of 1693.5 feet above sea level.

896.5 ft

1693.5 feet above sea level

35.4°

Not drawn to scale

(a) Find the vertical rise of the inclined plane.

(b) Find the elevation of the lower end of the inclined plane.

(c) The cars move up the mountain at a rate of 300 feet per minute. Find the rate at which they rise vertically.

Exploration

78. Writing In right triangle trigonometry, explain why $\sin 30° = \frac{1}{2}$ regardless of the size of the triangle.

True or False? In Exercises 79–84, determine whether the statement is true or false. Justify your answer.

79. $\sin 60° \csc 60° = 1$ 80. $\sec 30° = \csc 60°$

81. $\sin 45° + \cos 45° = 1$ 82. $\cot^2 10° - \csc^2 10° = -1$

83. $\dfrac{\sin 60°}{\sin 30°} = \sin 2°$ 84. $\tan[(5°)^2] = \tan^2 5°$

85. Think About It You are given the value of $\tan \theta$. Is it possible to find the value of $\sec \theta$ without finding the measure of θ? Explain.

86. Think About It

(a) Complete the table.

θ	0.1	0.2	0.3	0.4	0.5
$\sin \theta$					

(b) Is θ or $\sin \theta$ greater for θ in the interval $(0, 0.5]$?

(c) As θ approaches 0, how do θ and $\sin \theta$ compare? Explain.

87. Think About It

(a) Complete the table.

θ	0°	18°	36°	54°	72°	90°
$\sin \theta$						
$\cos \theta$						

(b) Discuss the behavior of the sine function for θ in the range from 0° to 90°.

(c) Discuss the behavior of the cosine function for θ in the range from 0° to 90°.

(d) Use the definitions of the sine and cosine functions to explain the results of parts (b) and (c).

88. HOW DO YOU SEE IT? Use the figure below.

$90° - \theta$

r

y

θ

x

(a) Which side is opposite θ?

(b) Which side is adjacent to $90° - \theta$?

(c) Explain why $\sin \theta = \cos(90° - \theta)$.

4.4 Trigonometric Functions of Any Angle

Trigonometric functions can help you model and solve real-life problems. For instance, in Exercise 99 on page 298, you will use trigonometric functions to model the monthly normal temperatures in New York City and Fairbanks, Alaska.

- Evaluate trigonometric functions of any angle.
- Find reference angles.
- Evaluate trigonometric functions of real numbers.

Introduction

In Section 4.3, the definitions of trigonometric functions were restricted to acute angles. In this section, the definitions are extended to cover *any* angle. When θ is an *acute* angle, the definitions here coincide with those given in the preceding section.

Definitions of Trigonometric Functions of Any Angle

Let θ be an angle in standard position with (x, y) a point on the terminal side of θ and $r = \sqrt{x^2 + y^2} \neq 0$.

$$\sin \theta = \frac{y}{r} \qquad\qquad \cos \theta = \frac{x}{r}$$

$$\tan \theta = \frac{y}{x}, \quad x \neq 0 \qquad \cot \theta = \frac{x}{y}, \quad y \neq 0$$

$$\sec \theta = \frac{r}{x}, \quad x \neq 0 \qquad \csc \theta = \frac{r}{y}, \quad y \neq 0$$

Because $r = \sqrt{x^2 + y^2}$ *cannot* be zero, it follows that the sine and cosine functions are defined for any real value of θ. However, when $x = 0$, the tangent and secant of θ are undefined. For example, the tangent of $90°$ is undefined. Similarly, when $y = 0$, the cotangent and cosecant of θ are undefined.

EXAMPLE 1 **Evaluating Trigonometric Functions**

Let $(-3, 4)$ be a point on the terminal side of θ. Find the sine, cosine, and tangent of θ.

Solution Referring to Figure 4.27, you can see that $x = -3$, $y = 4$, and

$$\begin{aligned} r &= \sqrt{x^2 + y^2} \\ &= \sqrt{(-3)^2 + 4^2} \\ &= \sqrt{25} \\ &= 5. \end{aligned}$$

So, you have the following.

$$\sin \theta = \frac{y}{r} = \frac{4}{5}$$

$$\cos \theta = \frac{x}{r} = -\frac{3}{5}$$

$$\tan \theta = \frac{y}{x} = -\frac{4}{3}$$

Figure 4.27

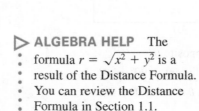

▷ **ALGEBRA HELP** The formula $r = \sqrt{x^2 + y^2}$ is a result of the Distance Formula. You can review the Distance Formula in Section 1.1.

✓ **Checkpoint** ◄))) *Audio-video solution in English & Spanish at LarsonPrecalculus.com.*

Let $(-2, 3)$ be a point on the terminal side of θ. Find the sine, cosine, and tangent of θ.

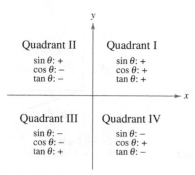

Figure 4.28

The *signs* of the trigonometric functions in the four quadrants can be determined from the definitions of the functions. For instance, because $\cos \theta = x/r$, it follows that $\cos \theta$ is positive wherever $x > 0$, which is in Quadrants I and IV. (Remember, r is always positive.) In a similar manner, you can verify the results shown in Figure 4.28.

EXAMPLE 2 **Evaluating Trigonometric Functions**

Given $\tan \theta = -\frac{5}{4}$ and $\cos \theta > 0$, find $\sin \theta$ and $\sec \theta$.

Solution Note that θ lies in Quadrant IV because that is the only quadrant in which the tangent is negative and the cosine is positive. Moreover, using

$$\tan \theta = \frac{y}{x} = -\frac{5}{4}$$

and the fact that y is negative in Quadrant IV, you can let $y = -5$ and $x = 4$. So, $r = \sqrt{16 + 25} = \sqrt{41}$ and you have the following.

$$\sin \theta = \frac{y}{r}$$

$$= \frac{-5}{\sqrt{41}} \qquad \text{Exact value}$$

$$\approx -0.7809 \qquad \text{Approximate value}$$

$$\sec \theta = \frac{r}{x}$$

$$= \frac{\sqrt{41}}{4} \qquad \text{Exact value}$$

$$\approx 1.6008 \qquad \text{Approximate value}$$

✓ **Checkpoint** Audio-video solution in English & Spanish at LarsonPrecalculus.com.

Given $\sin \theta = \frac{4}{5}$ and $\tan \theta < 0$, find $\cos \theta$.

EXAMPLE 3 **Trigonometric Functions of Quadrant Angles**

Evaluate the cosine and tangent functions at the four quadrant angles 0, $\frac{\pi}{2}$, π, and $\frac{3\pi}{2}$.

Solution To begin, choose a point on the terminal side of each angle, as shown in Figure 4.29. For each of the four points, $r = 1$ and you have the following.

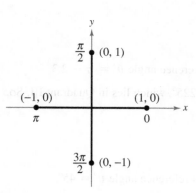

Figure 4.29

$$\cos 0 = \frac{x}{r} = \frac{1}{1} = 1 \qquad \tan 0 = \frac{y}{x} = \frac{0}{1} = 0 \qquad (x, y) = (1, 0)$$

$$\cos \frac{\pi}{2} = \frac{x}{r} = \frac{0}{1} = 0 \qquad \tan \frac{\pi}{2} = \frac{y}{x} = \frac{1}{0} \implies \text{undefined} \qquad (x, y) = (0, 1)$$

$$\cos \pi = \frac{x}{r} = \frac{-1}{1} = -1 \qquad \tan \pi = \frac{y}{x} = \frac{0}{-1} = 0 \qquad (x, y) = (-1, 0)$$

$$\cos \frac{3\pi}{2} = \frac{x}{r} = \frac{0}{1} = 0 \qquad \tan \frac{3\pi}{2} = \frac{y}{x} = \frac{-1}{0} \implies \text{undefined} \qquad (x, y) = (0, -1)$$

✓ **Checkpoint** Audio-video solution in English & Spanish at LarsonPrecalculus.com.

Evaluate the sine and cotangent functions at the quadrant angle $\frac{3\pi}{2}$.

Reference Angles

The values of the trigonometric functions of angles greater than 90° (or less than 0°) can be determined from their values at corresponding acute angles called **reference angles.**

Definition of Reference Angle

Let θ be an angle in standard position. Its **reference angle** is the acute angle θ' formed by the terminal side of θ and the horizontal axis.

The reference angles for θ in Quadrants II, III, and IV are shown below.

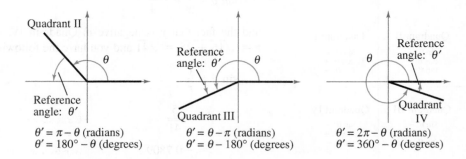

$\theta' = \pi - \theta$ (radians)
$\theta' = 180° - \theta$ (degrees)

$\theta' = \theta - \pi$ (radians)
$\theta' = \theta - 180°$ (degrees)

$\theta' = 2\pi - \theta$ (radians)
$\theta' = 360° - \theta$ (degrees)

EXAMPLE 4 **Finding Reference Angles**

Find the reference angle θ'.

a. $\theta = 300°$ **b.** $\theta = 2.3$ **c.** $\theta = -135°$

Solution

a. Because 300° lies in Quadrant IV, the angle it makes with the x-axis is

$$\theta' = 360° - 300°$$
$$= 60°. \qquad \text{Degrees}$$

Figure 4.30 shows the angle $\theta = 300°$ and its reference angle $\theta' = 60°$.

b. Because 2.3 lies between $\pi/2 \approx 1.5708$ and $\pi \approx 3.1416$, it follows that it is in Quadrant II and its reference angle is

$$\theta' = \pi - 2.3$$
$$\approx 0.8416. \qquad \text{Radians}$$

Figure 4.31 shows the angle $\theta = 2.3$ and its reference angle $\theta' = \pi - 2.3$.

c. First, determine that $-135°$ is coterminal with 225°, which lies in Quadrant III. So, the reference angle is

$$\theta' = 225° - 180°$$
$$= 45°. \qquad \text{Degrees}$$

Figure 4.32 shows the angle $\theta = -135°$ and its reference angle $\theta' = 45°$.

Figure 4.30

Figure 4.31

Figure 4.32

✓ **Checkpoint** ◄))) Audio-video solution in English & Spanish at LarsonPrecalculus.com.

Find the reference angle θ'.

a. $213°$ **b.** $\dfrac{14\pi}{9}$ **c.** $\dfrac{4\pi}{5}$

Trigonometric Functions of Real Numbers

To see how a reference angle is used to evaluate a trigonometric function, consider the point (x, y) on the terminal side of θ, as shown at the right. By definition, you know that

$$\sin \theta = \frac{y}{r}$$

and

$$\tan \theta = \frac{y}{x}.$$

For the right triangle with acute angle θ' and sides of lengths $|x|$ and $|y|$, you have

$$\sin \theta' = \frac{\text{opp}}{\text{hyp}} = \frac{|y|}{r}$$

and

$$\tan \theta' = \frac{\text{opp}}{\text{adj}} = \frac{|y|}{|x|}.$$

$$\text{opp} = |y|, \text{adj} = |x|$$

So, it follows that $\sin \theta$ and $\sin \theta'$ are equal, *except possibly in sign*. The same is true for $\tan \theta$ and $\tan \theta'$ *and* for the other four trigonometric functions. In all cases, the quadrant in which θ lies determines the sign of the function value.

Evaluating Trigonometric Functions of Any Angle

To find the value of a trigonometric function of any angle θ:

1. Determine the function value of the associated reference angle θ'.
2. Depending on the quadrant in which θ lies, affix the appropriate sign to the function value.

• • REMARK Learning the table of values at the right is worth the effort because doing so will increase both your efficiency and your confidence. Here is a pattern for the sine function that may help you remember the values.

θ	0°	30°	45°	60°	90°
$\sin \theta$	$\dfrac{\sqrt{0}}{2}$	$\dfrac{\sqrt{1}}{2}$	$\dfrac{\sqrt{2}}{2}$	$\dfrac{\sqrt{3}}{2}$	$\dfrac{\sqrt{4}}{2}$

Reverse the order to get cosine values of the same angles.

By using reference angles and the special angles discussed in the preceding section, you can greatly extend the scope of *exact* trigonometric values. For instance, knowing the function values of 30° means that you know the function values of all angles for which 30° is a reference angle. For convenience, the table below shows the exact values of the sine, cosine, and tangent functions of special angles and quadrant angles.

Trigonometric Values of Common Angles

θ (degrees)	0°	30°	45°	60°	90°	180°	270°
θ (radians)	0	$\dfrac{\pi}{6}$	$\dfrac{\pi}{4}$	$\dfrac{\pi}{3}$	$\dfrac{\pi}{2}$	π	$\dfrac{3\pi}{2}$
$\sin \theta$	0	$\dfrac{1}{2}$	$\dfrac{\sqrt{2}}{2}$	$\dfrac{\sqrt{3}}{2}$	1	0	-1
$\cos \theta$	1	$\dfrac{\sqrt{3}}{2}$	$\dfrac{\sqrt{2}}{2}$	$\dfrac{1}{2}$	0	-1	0
$\tan \theta$	0	$\dfrac{\sqrt{3}}{3}$	1	$\sqrt{3}$	Undef.	0	Undef.

EXAMPLE 5   **Using Reference Angles**

Evaluate each trigonometric function.

a. $\cos \dfrac{4\pi}{3}$ **b.** $\tan(-210°)$ **c.** $\csc \dfrac{11\pi}{4}$

Solution

a. Because $\theta = 4\pi/3$ lies in Quadrant III, the reference angle is

$$\theta' = \dfrac{4\pi}{3} - \pi = \dfrac{\pi}{3}$$

as shown in Figure 4.33. Moreover, the cosine is negative in Quadrant III, so

$$\cos \dfrac{4\pi}{3} = (-)\cos \dfrac{\pi}{3}$$

$$= -\dfrac{1}{2}.$$

b. Because $-210° + 360° = 150°$, it follows that $-210°$ is coterminal with the second-quadrant angle 150°. So, the reference angle is $\theta' = 180° - 150° = 30°$, as shown in Figure 4.34. Finally, because the tangent is negative in Quadrant II, you have

$$\tan(-210°) = (-)\tan 30°$$

$$= -\dfrac{\sqrt{3}}{3}.$$

c. Because $(11\pi/4) - 2\pi = 3\pi/4$, it follows that $11\pi/4$ is coterminal with the second-quadrant angle $3\pi/4$. So, the reference angle is $\theta' = \pi - (3\pi/4) = \pi/4$, as shown in Figure 4.35. Because the cosecant is positive in Quadrant II, you have

$$\csc \dfrac{11\pi}{4} = (+)\csc \dfrac{\pi}{4}$$

$$= \dfrac{1}{\sin(\pi/4)}$$

$$= \sqrt{2}.$$

Figure 4.33

Figure 4.34

Figure 4.35

✓ *Checkpoint* 🔊))) Audio-video solution in English & Spanish at LarsonPrecalculus.com.

Evaluate each trigonometric function.

a. $\sin \dfrac{7\pi}{4}$ **b.** $\cos(-120°)$ **c.** $\tan \dfrac{11\pi}{6}$

EXAMPLE 6   Using Trigonometric Identities

Let θ be an angle in Quadrant II such that $\sin \theta = \frac{1}{3}$. Find (a) $\cos \theta$ and (b) $\tan \theta$ by using trigonometric identities.

Solution

a. Using the Pythagorean identity $\sin^2 \theta + \cos^2 \theta = 1$, you obtain

$$\left(\tfrac{1}{3}\right)^2 + \cos^2 \theta = 1 \implies \cos^2 \theta = 1 - \tfrac{1}{9} = \tfrac{8}{9}.$$

Because $\cos \theta < 0$ in Quadrant II, use the negative root to obtain

$$\cos \theta = -\frac{\sqrt{8}}{\sqrt{9}} = -\frac{2\sqrt{2}}{3}.$$

b. Using the trigonometric identity $\tan \theta = \dfrac{\sin \theta}{\cos \theta}$, you obtain

$$\tan \theta = \frac{1/3}{-2\sqrt{2}/3} = -\frac{1}{2\sqrt{2}} = -\frac{\sqrt{2}}{4}.$$

✓ **Checkpoint** ◀))) *Audio-video solution in English & Spanish at LarsonPrecalculus.com.*

Let θ be an angle in Quadrant III such that $\sin \theta = -\frac{4}{5}$. Find (a) $\cos \theta$ and (b) $\tan \theta$ by using trigonometric identities.

EXAMPLE 7   Using a Calculator

Use a calculator to evaluate each trigonometric function.

a. $\cot 410°$ **b.** $\sin(-7)$ **c.** $\sec \dfrac{\pi}{9}$

Solution

Function	Mode	Calculator Keystrokes	Display
a. $\cot 410°$	Degree	(TAN (410)) x⁻¹ ENTER	0.8390996
b. $\sin(-7)$	Radian	SIN ((–) 7) ENTER	−0.6569866
c. $\sec(\pi/9)$	Radian	(COS (π ÷ 9)) x⁻¹ ENTER	1.0641778

✓ **Checkpoint** ◀))) *Audio-video solution in English & Spanish at LarsonPrecalculus.com.*

Use a calculator to evaluate each trigonometric function.

a. $\tan 119°$ **b.** $\csc 5$ **c.** $\cos \dfrac{\pi}{5}$

Summarize   (Section 4.4)

1. State the definitions of the trigonometric functions of any angle *(page 290)*. For examples of evaluating trigonometric functions, see Examples 1–3.

2. Explain how to find a reference angle *(page 292)*. For an example of finding reference angles, see Example 4.

3. Explain how to evaluate a trigonometric function of a real number *(page 293)*. For examples of evaluating trigonometric functions of real numbers, see Examples 5–7.

4.4 Exercises

See CalcChat.com for tutorial help and worked-out solutions to odd-numbered exercises.

Vocabulary: Fill in the blanks.

In Exercises 1–6, let θ be an angle in standard position with (x, y) a point on the terminal side of θ and $r = \sqrt{x^2 + y^2} \neq 0$.

1. $\sin \theta =$ _____

2. $\dfrac{r}{y} =$ _____

3. $\tan \theta =$ _____

4. $\sec \theta =$ _____

5. $\dfrac{x}{r} =$ _____

6. $\dfrac{x}{y} =$ _____

7. Because $r = \sqrt{x^2 + y^2}$ cannot be _____, the sine and cosine functions are _____ for any real value of θ.

8. The acute positive angle formed by the terminal side of an angle θ and the horizontal axis is called the _____ angle of θ and is denoted by θ'.

Skills and Applications

Evaluating Trigonometric Functions In Exercises 9–12, determine the exact values of the six trigonometric functions of each angle θ.

9. (a) (b)

10. (a) (b)

11. (a) (b)

12. (a) (b)

Evaluating Trigonometric Functions In Exercises 13–18, the point is on the terminal side of an angle in standard position. Determine the exact values of the six trigonometric functions of the angle.

13. $(5, 12)$

14. $(8, 15)$

15. $(-5, -2)$

16. $(-4, 10)$

17. $(-5.4, 7.2)$

18. $\left(3\frac{1}{2}, -7\frac{3}{4}\right)$

Determining a Quadrant In Exercises 19–22, state the quadrant in which θ lies.

19. $\sin \theta > 0$ and $\cos \theta > 0$

20. $\sin \theta < 0$ and $\cos \theta < 0$

21. $\sin \theta > 0$ and $\cos \theta < 0$

22. $\sec \theta > 0$ and $\cot \theta < 0$

Evaluating Trigonometric Functions In Exercises 23–32, find the values of the six trigonometric functions of θ with the given constraint.

Function Value	Constraint
23. $\tan \theta = -\frac{15}{8}$	$\sin \theta > 0$
24. $\cos \theta = \frac{8}{17}$	$\tan \theta < 0$
25. $\sin \theta = \frac{3}{5}$	θ lies in Quadrant II.
26. $\cos \theta = -\frac{4}{5}$	θ lies in Quadrant III.
27. $\cot \theta = -3$	$\cos \theta > 0$
28. $\csc \theta = 4$	$\cot \theta < 0$
29. $\sec \theta = -2$	$\sin \theta < 0$
30. $\sin \theta = 0$	$\sec \theta = -1$
31. $\cot \theta$ is undefined.	$\pi/2 \leq \theta \leq 3\pi/2$
32. $\tan \theta$ is undefined.	$\pi \leq \theta \leq 2\pi$

An Angle Formed by a Line Through the Origin In Exercises 33–36, the terminal side of θ lies on the given line in the specified quadrant. Find the values of the six trigonometric functions of θ by finding a point on the line.

Line	Quadrant
33. $y = -x$	II
34. $y = \frac{1}{3}x$	III
35. $2x - y = 0$	III
36. $4x + 3y = 0$	IV

Trigonometric Function of a Quadrant Angle In Exercises 37–44, evaluate the trigonometric function of the quadrant angle, if possible.

37. $\sin \pi$

38. $\csc \dfrac{3\pi}{2}$

39. $\sec \dfrac{3\pi}{2}$

40. $\sec \pi$

41. $\sin \dfrac{\pi}{2}$

42. $\cot \pi$

43. $\csc \pi$

44. $\cot \dfrac{\pi}{2}$

Finding a Reference Angle In Exercises 45–52, find the reference angle θ' and sketch θ and θ' in standard position.

45. $\theta = 160°$

46. $\theta = 309°$

47. $\theta = -125°$

48. $\theta = -215°$

49. $\theta = \dfrac{2\pi}{3}$

50. $\theta = \dfrac{7\pi}{6}$

51. $\theta = 4.8$

52. $\theta = 11.6$

Using a Reference Angle In Exercises 53–68, evaluate the sine, cosine, and tangent of the angle without using a calculator.

53. $225°$

54. $300°$

55. $750°$

56. $-405°$

57. $-840°$

58. $510°$

59. $\dfrac{2\pi}{3}$

60. $\dfrac{3\pi}{4}$

61. $\dfrac{5\pi}{4}$

62. $\dfrac{7\pi}{6}$

63. $-\dfrac{\pi}{6}$

64. $-\dfrac{\pi}{2}$

65. $\dfrac{9\pi}{4}$

66. $\dfrac{10\pi}{3}$

67. $-\dfrac{3\pi}{2}$

68. $-\dfrac{23\pi}{4}$

Using Trigonometric Identities In Exercises 69–74, use a trigonometric identity to find the indicated value in the specified quadrant.

Function Value	Quadrant	Value
69. $\sin \theta = -\frac{3}{5}$	IV	$\cos \theta$
70. $\cot \theta = -3$	II	$\sin \theta$
71. $\tan \theta = \frac{3}{2}$	III	$\sec \theta$
72. $\csc \theta = -2$	IV	$\cot \theta$
73. $\cos \theta = \frac{5}{8}$	I	$\sec \theta$
74. $\sec \theta = -\frac{9}{4}$	III	$\tan \theta$

Using a Calculator In Exercises 75–90, use a calculator to evaluate the trigonometric function. Round your answer to four decimal places. (Be sure the calculator is in the correct mode.)

75. $\sin 10°$

76. $\sec 225°$

77. $\cos(-110°)$

78. $\csc(-330°)$

79. $\tan 304°$

80. $\cot 178°$

81. $\sec 72°$

82. $\tan(-188°)$

83. $\tan 4.5$

84. $\cot 1.35$

85. $\tan \dfrac{\pi}{9}$

86. $\tan\left(-\dfrac{\pi}{9}\right)$

87. $\sin(-0.65)$

88. $\sec 0.29$

89. $\cot\left(-\dfrac{11\pi}{8}\right)$

90. $\csc\left(-\dfrac{15\pi}{14}\right)$

Solving for θ In Exercises 91–96, find two solutions of each equation. Give your answers in degrees $(0° \le \theta < 360°)$ and in radians $(0 \le \theta < 2\pi)$. Do not use a calculator.

91. (a) $\sin \theta = \frac{1}{2}$ (b) $\sin \theta = -\frac{1}{2}$

92. (a) $\cos \theta = \dfrac{\sqrt{2}}{2}$ (b) $\cos \theta = -\dfrac{\sqrt{2}}{2}$

93. (a) $\csc \theta = \dfrac{2\sqrt{3}}{3}$ (b) $\cot \theta = -1$

94. (a) $\sec \theta = 2$ (b) $\sec \theta = -2$

95. (a) $\tan \theta = 1$ (b) $\cot \theta = -\sqrt{3}$

96. (a) $\sin \theta = \dfrac{\sqrt{3}}{2}$ (b) $\sin \theta = -\dfrac{\sqrt{3}}{2}$

97. **Distance** An airplane, flying at an altitude of 6 miles, is on a flight path that passes directly over an observer (see figure). Let θ be the angle of elevation from the observer to the plane. Find the distance d from the observer to the plane when (a) $\theta = 30°$, (b) $\theta = 90°$, and (c) $\theta = 120°$.

Not drawn to scale

98. **Harmonic Motion** The displacement from equilibrium of an oscillating weight suspended by a spring is given by $y(t) = 2 \cos 6t$, where y is the displacement (in centimeters) and t is the time (in seconds). Find the displacement when (a) $t = 0$, (b) $t = \frac{1}{4}$, and (c) $t = \frac{1}{2}$.

• • 99. Data Analysis: Meteorology • • • • • • • •

The table shows the monthly normal temperatures (in degrees Fahrenheit) for selected months in New York City (N) and Fairbanks, Alaska (F). *(Source: National Climatic Data Center)*

DATA	Month	New York City, N	Fairbanks, F
	January	33	−10
	April	52	32
	July	77	62
	October	58	24
	December	38	−6

Spreadsheet at LarsonPrecalculus.com

(a) Use the *regression* feature of a graphing utility to find a model of the form $y = a \sin(bt + c) + d$ for each city. Let t represent the month, with $t = 1$ corresponding to January.

(b) Use the models from part (a) to find the monthly normal temperatures for the two cities in February, March, May, June, August, September, and November.

(c) Compare the models for the two cities.

100. Sales A company that produces snowboards forecasts monthly sales over the next 2 years to be

$$S = 23.1 + 0.442t + 4.3 \cos \frac{\pi t}{6}$$

where S is measured in thousands of units and t is the time in months, with $t = 1$ representing January 2014. Predict sales for each of the following months.

(a) February 2014   (b) February 2015

(c) June 2014   (d) June 2015

101. Harmonic Motion The displacement from equilibrium of an oscillating weight suspended by a spring and subject to the damping effect of friction is given by $y(t) = 2e^{-t} \cos 6t$, where y is the displacement (in centimeters) and t is the time (in seconds). Find the displacement when (a) $t = 0$, (b) $t = \frac{1}{4}$, and (c) $t = \frac{1}{2}$.

102. Electric Circuits The current I (in amperes) when 100 volts is applied to a circuit is given by

$$I = 5e^{-2t} \sin t$$

where t is the time (in seconds) after the voltage is applied. Approximate the current at $t = 0.7$ second after the voltage is applied.

Exploration

True or False? **In Exercises 103 and 104, determine whether the statement is true or false. Justify your answer.**

103. In each of the four quadrants, the signs of the secant function and sine function are the same.

104. To find the reference angle for an angle θ (given in degrees), find the integer n such that $0 \le 360°n - \theta \le 360°$. The difference $360°n - \theta$ is the reference angle.

105. Writing Write a short paper explaining to a classmate how to evaluate the six trigonometric functions of any angle θ in standard position. Include an explanation of reference angles and how to use them, the signs of the functions in each of the four quadrants, and the trigonometric values of common angles. Be sure to include figures or diagrams in your paper.

106. **HOW DO YOU SEE IT?** Consider an angle in standard position with $r = 12$ centimeters, as shown in the figure. Describe the changes in the values of x, y, $\sin \theta$, $\cos \theta$, and $\tan \theta$ as θ increases continuously from $0°$ to $90°$.

107. Think About It
The figure shows point $P(x, y)$ on a unit circle and right triangle OAP.

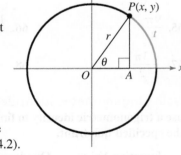

(a) Find $\sin t$ and $\cos t$ using the unit circle definitions of sine and cosine (from Section 4.2).

(b) What is the value of r? Explain.

(c) Use the definitions of sine and cosine given in this section to find $\sin \theta$ and $\cos \theta$. Write your answers in terms of x and y.

(d) Based on your answers to parts (a) and (c), what can you conclude?

4.5   Graphs of Sine and Cosine Functions

- ▪ Sketch the graphs of basic sine and cosine functions.
- ▪ Use amplitude and period to help sketch the graphs of sine and cosine functions.
- ▪ Sketch translations of the graphs of sine and cosine functions.
- ▪ Use sine and cosine functions to model real-life data.

You can use sine and cosine functions in scientific calculations. For instance, in Exercise 88 on page 308, you will use a trigonometric function to model the airflow of your respiratory cycle.

Basic Sine and Cosine Curves

In this section, you will study techniques for sketching the graphs of the sine and cosine functions. The graph of the sine function is a **sine curve.** In Figure 4.36, the black portion of the graph represents one period of the function and is called **one cycle** of the sine curve. The gray portion of the graph indicates that the basic sine curve repeats indefinitely to the left and right. The graph of the cosine function is shown in Figure 4.37.

Recall from Section 4.2 that the domain of the sine and cosine functions is the set of all real numbers. Moreover, the range of each function is the interval $[-1, 1]$, and each function has a period of 2π. Do you see how this information is consistent with the basic graphs shown in Figures 4.36 and 4.37?

Figure 4.36

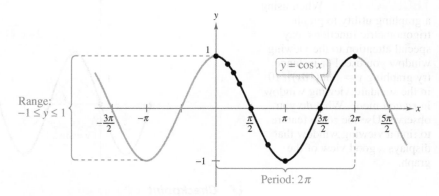

Figure 4.37

Note in Figures 4.36 and 4.37 that the sine curve is symmetric with respect to the *origin,* whereas the cosine curve is symmetric with respect to the *y-axis.* These properties of symmetry follow from the fact that the sine function is odd and the cosine function is even.

To sketch the graphs of the basic sine and cosine functions by hand, it helps to note five **key points** in one period of each graph: the *intercepts, maximum points,* and *minimum points* (see below).

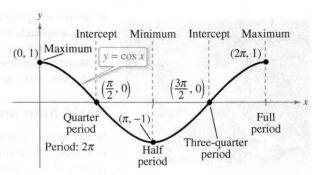

EXAMPLE 1   **EXAMPLE 1   Using Key Points to Sketch a Sine Curve**

Sketch the graph of

$$y = 2 \sin x$$

on the interval $[-\pi, 4\pi]$.

Solution   Note that

$$y = 2 \sin x$$

$$= 2(\sin x)$$

indicates that the y-values for the key points will have twice the magnitude of those on the graph of $y = \sin x$. Divide the period 2π into four equal parts to get the key points

Intercept	Maximum	Intercept	Minimum	Intercept
$(0, 0)$,	$\left(\dfrac{\pi}{2}, 2\right)$,	$(\pi, 0)$,	$\left(\dfrac{3\pi}{2}, -2\right)$, and	$(2\pi, 0)$.

By connecting these key points with a smooth curve and extending the curve in both directions over the interval $[-\pi, 4\pi]$, you obtain the graph shown below.

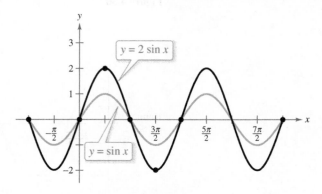

▷ **TECHNOLOGY** When using a graphing utility to graph trigonometric functions, pay special attention to the viewing window you use. For instance, try graphing $y = [\sin(10x)]/10$ in the standard viewing window in *radian* mode. What do you observe? Use the *zoom* feature to find a viewing window that displays a good view of the graph.

✓ **Checkpoint** ◀))) Audio-video solution in English & Spanish at LarsonPrecalculus.com.

Sketch the graph of

$$y = 2 \cos x$$

on the interval $\left[-\dfrac{\pi}{2}, \dfrac{9\pi}{2}\right]$.

Amplitude and Period

In the rest of this section, you will study the graphic effect of each of the constants a, b, c, and d in equations of the forms

$$y = d + a \sin(bx - c)$$

and

$$y = d + a \cos(bx - c).$$

A quick review of the transformations you studied in Section 1.7 should help in this investigation.

The constant factor a in $y = a \sin x$ acts as a *scaling factor*—a *vertical stretch* or *vertical shrink* of the basic sine curve. When $|a| > 1$, the basic sine curve is stretched, and when $|a| < 1$, the basic sine curve is shrunk. The result is that the graph of $y = a \sin x$ ranges between $-a$ and a instead of between -1 and 1. The absolute value of a is the **amplitude** of the function $y = a \sin x$. The range of the function $y = a \sin x$ for $a > 0$ is $-a \leq y \leq a$.

Definition of Amplitude of Sine and Cosine Curves

The **amplitude** of $y = a \sin x$ and $y = a \cos x$ represents half the distance between the maximum and minimum values of the function and is given by

$$\text{Amplitude} = |a|.$$

> **EXAMPLE 2**   Scaling: Vertical Shrinking and Stretching

In the same coordinate plane, sketch the graph of each function.

a. $y = \frac{1}{2} \cos x$

b. $y = 3 \cos x$

Solution

a. Because the amplitude of $y = \frac{1}{2} \cos x$ is $\frac{1}{2}$, the maximum value is $\frac{1}{2}$ and the minimum value is $-\frac{1}{2}$. Divide one cycle, $0 \leq x \leq 2\pi$, into four equal parts to get the key points

Maximum	Intercept	Minimum	Intercept	Maximum
$\left(0, \frac{1}{2}\right)$,	$\left(\frac{\pi}{2}, 0\right)$,	$\left(\pi, -\frac{1}{2}\right)$,	$\left(\frac{3\pi}{2}, 0\right)$, and	$\left(2\pi, \frac{1}{2}\right)$.

b. A similar analysis shows that the amplitude of $y = 3 \cos x$ is 3, and the key points are

Maximum	Intercept	Minimum	Intercept	Maximum
$(0, 3)$,	$\left(\frac{\pi}{2}, 0\right)$,	$(\pi, -3)$,	$\left(\frac{3\pi}{2}, 0\right)$, and	$(2\pi, 3)$.

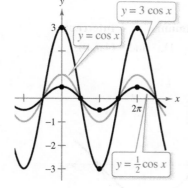

Figure 4.38

The graphs of these two functions are shown in Figure 4.38. Notice that the graph of $y = \frac{1}{2} \cos x$ is a vertical *shrink* of the graph of $y = \cos x$ and the graph of $y = 3 \cos x$ is a vertical *stretch* of the graph of $y = \cos x$.

✓ *Checkpoint* ◄))) *Audio-video solution in English & Spanish at LarsonPrecalculus.com.*

In the same coordinate plane, sketch the graph of each function.

a. $y = \frac{1}{3} \sin x$

b. $y = 3 \sin x$

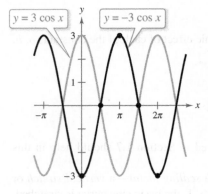

Figure 4.39

You know from Section 1.7 that the graph of $y = -f(x)$ is a **reflection** in the x-axis of the graph of $y = f(x)$. For instance, the graph of $y = -3 \cos x$ is a reflection of the graph of $y = 3 \cos x$, as shown in Figure 4.39.

Because $y = a \sin x$ completes one cycle from $x = 0$ to $x = 2\pi$, it follows that $y = a \sin bx$ completes one cycle from $x = 0$ to $x = 2\pi/b$, where b is a positive real number.

Period of Sine and Cosine Functions

Let b be a positive real number. The **period** of $y = a \sin bx$ and $y = a \cos bx$ is given by

$$\text{Period} = \frac{2\pi}{b}.$$

Note that when $0 < b < 1$, the period of $y = a \sin bx$ is greater than 2π and represents a *horizontal stretching* of the graph of $y = a \sin x$. Similarly, when $b > 1$, the period of $y = a \sin bx$ is less than 2π and represents a *horizontal shrinking* of the graph of $y = a \sin x$. When b is negative, the identities $\sin(-x) = -\sin x$ and $\cos(-x) = \cos x$ are used to rewrite the function.

EXAMPLE 3   **Scaling: Horizontal Stretching**

Sketch the graph of

$$y = \sin \frac{x}{2}.$$

Solution   The amplitude is 1. Moreover, because $b = \frac{1}{2}$, the period is

$$\frac{2\pi}{b} = \frac{2\pi}{\frac{1}{2}} = 4\pi. \qquad \text{Substitute for } b.$$

Now, divide the period-interval $[0, 4\pi]$ into four equal parts using the values $\pi, 2\pi$, and 3π to obtain the key points

Intercept	Maximum	Intercept	Minimum	Intercept
$(0, 0)$,	$(\pi, 1)$,	$(2\pi, 0)$,	$(3\pi, -1)$, and	$(4\pi, 0)$.

The graph is shown below.

Period: 4π

✓ *Checkpoint* ◄))) Audio-video solution in English & Spanish at LarsonPrecalculus.com.

Sketch the graph of

$$y = \cos \frac{x}{3}.$$

REMARK In general, to divide a period-interval into four equal parts, successively add "period/4," starting with the left endpoint of the interval. For instance, for the period-interval $[-\pi/6, \pi/2]$ of length $2\pi/3$, you would successively add

$$\frac{2\pi/3}{4} = \frac{\pi}{6}$$

to get $-\pi/6, 0, \pi/6, \pi/3$, and $\pi/2$ as the x-values for the key points on the graph.

Translations of Sine and Cosine Curves

▷ **ALGEBRA HELP**   You
can review the techniques
for shifting, reflecting,
and stretching graphs in
Section 1.7.

The constant c in the general equations

$$y = a \sin(bx - c) \quad \text{and} \quad y = a \cos(bx - c)$$

creates *horizontal translations* (shifts) of the basic sine and cosine curves. Comparing $y = a \sin bx$ with $y = a \sin(bx - c)$, you find that the graph of $y = a \sin(bx - c)$ completes one cycle from $bx - c = 0$ to $bx - c = 2\pi$. By solving for x, you can find the interval for one cycle to be

Left endpoint   Right endpoint

$$\frac{c}{b} \leq x \leq \frac{c}{b} + \frac{2\pi}{b}.$$

Period

This implies that the period of $y = a \sin(bx - c)$ is $2\pi/b$, and the graph of $y = a \sin bx$ is shifted by an amount c/b. The number c/b is the **phase shift.**

Graphs of Sine and Cosine Functions

The graphs of $y = a \sin(bx - c)$ and $y = a \cos(bx - c)$ have the following characteristics. (Assume $b > 0$.)

$$\text{Amplitude} = |a| \qquad \text{Period} = \frac{2\pi}{b}$$

The left and right endpoints of a one-cycle interval can be determined by solving the equations $bx - c = 0$ and $bx - c = 2\pi$.

EXAMPLE 4   Horizontal Translation

Analyze the graph of $y = \dfrac{1}{2} \sin\left(x - \dfrac{\pi}{3}\right)$.

Algebraic Solution

The amplitude is $\frac{1}{2}$ and the period is 2π. By solving the equations

$$x - \frac{\pi}{3} = 0 \quad \Longrightarrow \quad x = \frac{\pi}{3}$$

and

$$x - \frac{\pi}{3} = 2\pi \quad \Longrightarrow \quad x = \frac{7\pi}{3}$$

you see that the interval $[\pi/3, 7\pi/3]$ corresponds to one cycle of the graph. Dividing this interval into four equal parts produces the key points

Intercept	Maximum	Intercept	Minimum		Intercept
$\left(\dfrac{\pi}{3}, 0\right)$,	$\left(\dfrac{5\pi}{6}, \dfrac{1}{2}\right)$,	$\left(\dfrac{4\pi}{3}, 0\right)$,	$\left(\dfrac{11\pi}{6}, -\dfrac{1}{2}\right)$,	and	$\left(\dfrac{7\pi}{3}, 0\right)$.

Graphical Solution

Use a graphing utility set in *radian* mode to graph $y = (1/2) \sin(x - \pi/3)$, as shown below. Use the *minimum, maximum,* and *zero* or *root* features of the graphing utility to approximate the key points $(1.05, 0)$, $(2.62, 0.5)$, $(4.19, 0)$, $(5.76, -0.5)$, and $(7.33, 0)$.

$$y = \frac{1}{2} \sin\left(x - \frac{\pi}{3}\right)$$

Zero
X=1.0471976   Y=0

✓ **Checkpoint** ◄))) Audio-video solution in English & Spanish at LarsonPrecalculus.com.

Analyze the graph of $y = 2 \cos\left(x - \dfrac{\pi}{2}\right)$.

$y = -3\cos(2\pi x + 4\pi)$

Period 1

Figure 4.40

EXAMPLE 5 **Horizontal Translation**

Sketch the graph of

$$y = -3\cos(2\pi x + 4\pi).$$

Solution The amplitude is 3 and the period is $2\pi/2\pi = 1$. By solving the equations

$$2\pi x + 4\pi = 0$$
$$2\pi x = -4\pi$$
$$x = -2$$

and

$$2\pi x + 4\pi = 2\pi$$
$$2\pi x = -2\pi$$
$$x = -1$$

you see that the interval $[-2, -1]$ corresponds to one cycle of the graph. Dividing this interval into four equal parts produces the key points

Minimum	Intercept	Maximum	Intercept	Minimum
$(-2, -3)$,	$\left(-\dfrac{7}{4}, 0\right)$,	$\left(-\dfrac{3}{2}, 3\right)$,	$\left(-\dfrac{5}{4}, 0\right)$, and	$(-1, -3)$.

The graph is shown in Figure 4.40.

✓ **Checkpoint** ◀))) Audio-video solution in English & Spanish at LarsonPrecalculus.com.

Sketch the graph of

$$y = -\frac{1}{2}\sin(\pi x + \pi).$$

The final type of transformation is the *vertical translation* caused by the constant d in the equations

$$y = d + a\sin(bx - c) \quad \text{and} \quad y = d + a\cos(bx - c).$$

The shift is d units up for $d > 0$ and d units down for $d < 0$. In other words, the graph oscillates about the horizontal line $y = d$ instead of about the x-axis.

EXAMPLE 6 **Vertical Translation**

Sketch the graph of

$$y = 2 + 3\cos 2x.$$

Solution The amplitude is 3 and the period is π. The key points over the interval $[0, \pi]$ are

$$(0, 5), \quad \left(\frac{\pi}{4}, 2\right), \quad \left(\frac{\pi}{2}, -1\right), \quad \left(\frac{3\pi}{4}, 2\right), \quad \text{and} \quad (\pi, 5).$$

The graph is shown in Figure 4.41. Compared with the graph of $f(x) = 3\cos 2x$, the graph of $y = 2 + 3\cos 2x$ is shifted up two units.

✓ **Checkpoint** ◀))) Audio-video solution in English & Spanish at LarsonPrecalculus.com.

Sketch the graph of

$$y = 2\cos x - 5.$$

$y = 2 + 3\cos 2x$

Period π

Figure 4.41

Mathematical Modeling

DATA	Time, t	Depth, y
	0	3.4
	2	8.7
	4	11.3
	6	9.1
	8	3.8
	10	0.1
	12	1.2

Spreadsheet at LarsonPrecalculus.com

Changing Tides

Figure 4.42

Figure 4.43

$y = 5.6\cos(0.524t - 2.094) + 5.7$

EXAMPLE 7   Finding a Trigonometric Model

The table shows the depths (in feet) of the water at the end of a dock at various times during the morning, where $t = 0$ corresponds to midnight.

a. Use a trigonometric function to model the data.

b. Find the depths at 9 A.M. and 3 P.M.

c. A boat needs at least 10 feet of water to moor at the dock. During what times in the afternoon can it safely dock?

Solution

a. Begin by graphing the data, as shown in Figure 4.42. You can use either a sine or cosine model. Suppose you use a cosine model of the form $y = a\cos(bt - c) + d$. The difference between the maximum value and minimum value is twice the amplitude of the function. So, the amplitude is

$$a = \tfrac{1}{2}[(\text{maximum depth}) - (\text{minimum depth})] = \tfrac{1}{2}(11.3 - 0.1) = 5.6.$$

The cosine function completes one half of a cycle between the times at which the maximum and minimum depths occur. So, the period p is

$$p = 2[(\text{time of min. depth}) - (\text{time of max. depth})] = 2(10 - 4) = 12$$

which implies that $b = 2\pi/p \approx 0.524$. Because high tide occurs 4 hours after midnight, consider the left endpoint to be $c/b = 4$, so $c \approx 2.094$. Moreover, because the average depth is $\tfrac{1}{2}(11.3 + 0.1) = 5.7$, it follows that $d = 5.7$. So, you can model the depth with the function $y = 5.6\cos(0.524t - 2.094) + 5.7$.

b. The depths at 9 A.M. and 3 P.M. are as follows.

$$y = 5.6\cos(0.524 \cdot 9 - 2.094) + 5.7 \approx 0.84 \text{ foot}   \qquad \text{9 A.M.}$$

$$y = 5.6\cos(0.524 \cdot 15 - 2.094) + 5.7 \approx 10.57 \text{ feet}   \qquad \text{3 P.M.}$$

c. Using a graphing utility, graph the model with the line $y = 10$. Using the *intersect* feature, you can determine that the depth is at least 10 feet between 2:42 P.M. ($t \approx 14.7$) and 5:18 P.M. ($t \approx 17.3$), as shown in Figure 4.43.

✓ **Checkpoint** ◄))) *Audio-video solution in English & Spanish at LarsonPrecalculus.com.*

Find a sine model for the data in Example 7.

Summarize (Section 4.5)

1. Describe how to sketch the graphs of basic sine and cosine functions (*pages 299 and 300*). For an example of sketching the graph of a sine function, see Example 1.

2. Describe how you can use amplitude and period to help sketch the graphs of sine and cosine functions (*pages 301 and 302*). For examples of using amplitude and period to sketch graphs of sine and cosine functions, see Examples 2 and 3.

3. Describe how to sketch translations of the graphs of sine and cosine functions (*pages 303 and 304*). For examples of translating the graphs of sine and cosine functions, see Examples 4–6.

4. Give an example of how to use sine and cosine functions to model real-life data (*page 305, Example 7*).

4.5 Exercises

See CalcChat.com for tutorial help and worked-out solutions to odd-numbered exercises.

Vocabulary: Fill in the blanks.

1. One period of a sine or cosine function is called one _____ of the sine or cosine curve.

2. The _____ of a sine or cosine curve represents half the distance between the maximum and minimum values of the function.

3. For the function $y = a \sin(bx - c)$, $\dfrac{c}{b}$ represents the _____ _____ of the graph of the function.

4. For the function $y = d + a \cos(bx - c)$, d represents a _____ _____ of the graph of the function.

Skills and Applications

Finding the Period and Amplitude In Exercises 5–18, find the period and amplitude.

5. $y = 2 \sin 5x$

6. $y = 3 \cos 2x$

7. $y = \dfrac{3}{4} \cos \dfrac{x}{2}$

8. $y = -3 \sin \dfrac{x}{3}$

9. $y = \dfrac{1}{2} \sin \dfrac{\pi x}{3}$

10. $y = \dfrac{3}{2} \cos \dfrac{\pi x}{2}$

11. $y = -4 \sin x$

12. $y = -\cos \dfrac{2x}{3}$

13. $y = 3 \sin 10x$

14. $y = \dfrac{1}{5} \sin 6x$

15. $y = \dfrac{5}{3} \cos \dfrac{4x}{5}$

16. $y = \dfrac{5}{2} \cos \dfrac{x}{4}$

17. $y = \dfrac{1}{4} \sin 2\pi x$

18. $y = \dfrac{2}{3} \cos \dfrac{\pi x}{10}$

Describing the Relationship Between Graphs In Exercises 19–30, describe the relationship between the graphs of f and g. Consider amplitude, period, and shifts.

19. $f(x) = \sin x$
    $g(x) = \sin(x - \pi)$

20. $f(x) = \cos x$
    $g(x) = \cos(x + \pi)$

21. $f(x) = \cos 2x$
    $g(x) = -\cos 2x$

22. $f(x) = \sin 3x$
    $g(x) = \sin(-3x)$

23. $f(x) = \cos x$
    $g(x) = \cos 2x$

24. $f(x) = \sin x$
    $g(x) = \sin 3x$

25. $f(x) = \sin 2x$
    $g(x) = 3 + \sin 2x$

26. $f(x) = \cos 4x$
    $g(x) = -2 + \cos 4x$

27.

28.

29.

30.

Sketching Graphs of Sine or Cosine Functions In Exercises 31–38, sketch the graphs of f and g in the same coordinate plane. (Include two full periods.)

31. $f(x) = -2 \sin x$
    $g(x) = 4 \sin x$

32. $f(x) = \sin x$
    $g(x) = \sin \dfrac{x}{3}$

33. $f(x) = \cos x$
    $g(x) = 2 + \cos x$

34. $f(x) = 2 \cos 2x$
    $g(x) = -\cos 4x$

35. $f(x) = -\dfrac{1}{2} \sin \dfrac{x}{2}$
    $g(x) = 3 - \dfrac{1}{2} \sin \dfrac{x}{2}$

36. $f(x) = 4 \sin \pi x$
    $g(x) = 4 \sin \pi x - 3$

37. $f(x) = 2 \cos x$
    $g(x) = 2 \cos(x + \pi)$

38. $f(x) = -\cos x$
    $g(x) = -\cos(x - \pi)$

Sketching the Graph of a Sine or Cosine Function In Exercises 39–60, sketch the graph of the function. (Include two full periods.)

39. $y = 5 \sin x$

40. $y = \dfrac{1}{4} \sin x$

41. $y = \dfrac{1}{3} \cos x$

42. $y = 4 \cos x$

43. $y = \cos \dfrac{x}{2}$

44. $y = \sin 4x$

45. $y = \cos 2\pi x$

46. $y = \sin \dfrac{\pi x}{4}$

47. $y = -\sin \dfrac{2\pi x}{3}$

48. $y = -10 \cos \dfrac{\pi x}{6}$

49. $y = 3 \cos(x + \pi)$

50. $y = \sin(x - 2\pi)$

51. $y = \sin\left(x - \dfrac{\pi}{2}\right)$ **52.** $y = 4\cos\left(x + \dfrac{\pi}{4}\right)$

53. $y = 2 - \sin\dfrac{2\pi x}{3}$ **54.** $y = -3 + 5\cos\dfrac{\pi t}{12}$

55. $y = 2 + \frac{1}{10}\cos 60\pi x$ **56.** $y = 2\cos x - 3$

57. $y = 3\cos(x + \pi) - 3$ **58.** $y = -3\cos(6x + \pi)$

59. $y = \dfrac{2}{3}\cos\left(\dfrac{x}{2} - \dfrac{\pi}{4}\right)$ **60.** $y = 4\cos\left(x + \dfrac{\pi}{4}\right) + 4$

Describing a Transformation In Exercises 61–66, g is related to a parent function $f(x) = \sin(x)$ or $f(x) = \cos(x)$. (a) Describe the sequence of transformations from f to g. (b) Sketch the graph of g. (c) Use function notation to write g in terms of f.

61. $g(x) = \sin(4x - \pi)$ **62.** $g(x) = \sin(2x + \pi)$

63. $g(x) = \cos(x - \pi) + 2$ **64.** $g(x) = 1 + \cos(x + \pi)$

65. $g(x) = 2\sin(4x - \pi) - 3$ **66.** $g(x) = 4 - \sin(2x + \pi)$

Graphing a Sine or Cosine Function In Exercises 67–72, use a graphing utility to graph the function. (Include two full periods.) Be sure to choose an appropriate viewing window.

67. $y = -2\sin(4x + \pi)$ **68.** $y = -4\sin\left(\dfrac{2}{3}x - \dfrac{\pi}{3}\right)$

69. $y = \cos\left(2\pi x - \dfrac{\pi}{2}\right) + 1$

70. $y = 3\cos\left(\dfrac{\pi x}{2} + \dfrac{\pi}{2}\right) - 2$

71. $y = -0.1\sin\left(\dfrac{\pi x}{10} + \pi\right)$ **72.** $y = \dfrac{1}{100}\sin 120\pi t$

Graphical Reasoning In Exercises 73–76, find a and d for the function $f(x) = a\cos x + d$ such that the graph of f matches the figure.

73.

74.

75.

76.

Graphical Reasoning In Exercises 77–80, find a, b, and c for the function $f(x) = a\sin(bx - c)$ such that the graph of f matches the figure.

77.

78.

79.

80.

Graphical Analysis In Exercises 81 and 82, use a graphing utility to graph y_1 and y_2 in the interval $[-2\pi, 2\pi]$. Use the graphs to find real numbers x such that $y_1 = y_2$.

81. $y_1 = \sin x$ **82.** $y_1 = \cos x$

  $y_2 = -\dfrac{1}{2}$ $y_2 = -1$

Writing an Equation In Exercises 83–86, write an equation for the function that is described by the given characteristics.

83. A sine curve with a period of π, an amplitude of 2, a right phase shift of $\pi/2$, and a vertical translation up 1 unit

84. A sine curve with a period of 4π, an amplitude of 3, a left phase shift of $\pi/4$, and a vertical translation down 1 unit

85. A cosine curve with a period of π, an amplitude of 1, a left phase shift of π, and a vertical translation down $\frac{3}{2}$ units

86. A cosine curve with a period of 4π, an amplitude of 3, a right phase shift of $\pi/2$, and a vertical translation up 2 units

87. Respiratory Cycle After exercising for a few minutes, a person has a respiratory cycle for which the velocity of airflow is approximated by

$$v = 1.75\sin\dfrac{\pi t}{2}$$

where t is the time (in seconds). (Inhalation occurs when $v > 0$, and exhalation occurs when $v < 0$.)

(a) Find the time for one full respiratory cycle.

(b) Find the number of cycles per minute.

(c) Sketch the graph of the velocity function.

88. Respiratory Cycle

For a person at rest, the velocity v (in liters per second) of airflow during a respiratory cycle (the time from the beginning of one breath to the beginning of the next) is given by

$$v = 0.85 \sin \frac{\pi t}{3}$$

where t is the time (in seconds).

(a) Find the time for one full respiratory cycle.

(b) Find the number of cycles per minute.

(c) Sketch the graph of the velocity function.

89. Data Analysis: Meteorology The table shows the maximum daily high temperatures in Las Vegas L and International Falls I (in degrees Fahrenheit) for month t, with $t = 1$ corresponding to January. *(Source: National Climatic Data Center)*

Month, t	Las Vegas, L	International Falls, I
1	57.1	13.8
2	63.0	22.4
3	69.5	34.9
4	78.1	51.5
5	87.8	66.6
6	98.9	74.2
7	104.1	78.6
8	101.8	76.3
9	93.8	64.7
10	80.8	51.7
11	66.0	32.5
12	57.3	18.1

Spreadsheet at LarsonPrecalculus.com

(a) A model for the temperatures in Las Vegas is

$$L(t) = 80.60 + 23.50 \cos\left(\frac{\pi t}{6} - 3.67\right).$$

Find a trigonometric model for International Falls.

(b) Use a graphing utility to graph the data points and the model for the temperatures in Las Vegas. How well does the model fit the data?

(c) Use the graphing utility to graph the data points and the model for the temperatures in International Falls. How well does the model fit the data?

(d) Use the models to estimate the average maximum temperature in each city. Which term of the models did you use? Explain.

(e) What is the period of each model? Are the periods what you expected? Explain.

(f) Which city has the greater variability in temperature throughout the year? Which factor of the models determines this variability? Explain.

90. Health The function

$$P = 100 - 20 \cos \frac{5\pi t}{3}$$

approximates the blood pressure P (in millimeters of mercury) at time t (in seconds) for a person at rest.

(a) Find the period of the function.

(b) Find the number of heartbeats per minute.

91. Piano Tuning When tuning a piano, a technician strikes a tuning fork for the A above middle C and sets up a wave motion that can be approximated by $y = 0.001 \sin 880\pi t$, where t is the time (in seconds).

(a) What is the period of the function?

(b) The frequency f is given by $f = 1/p$. What is the frequency of the note?

92. Data Analysis: Astronomy The percent y (in decimal form) of the moon's face illuminated on day x in the year 2014, where $x = 1$ represents January 1, is shown in the table. *(Source: U.S. Naval Observatory)*

x	y
1	0.0
8	0.5
16	1.0
24	0.5
30	0.0
37	0.5

Spreadsheet at LarsonPrecalculus.com

(a) Create a scatter plot of the data.

(b) Find a trigonometric model that fits the data.

(c) Add the graph of your model in part (b) to the scatter plot. How well does the model fit the data?

(d) What is the period of the model?

(e) Estimate the percent of the moon's face illuminated on March 12, 2014.

93. Ferris Wheel A Ferris wheel is built such that the height h (in feet) above ground of a seat on the wheel at time t (in seconds) can be modeled by

$$h(t) = 53 + 50 \sin\left(\frac{\pi}{10}t - \frac{\pi}{2}\right).$$

(a) Find the period of the model. What does the period tell you about the ride?

(b) Find the amplitude of the model. What does the amplitude tell you about the ride?

(c) Use a graphing utility to graph one cycle of the model.

94. Fuel Consumption The daily consumption C (in gallons) of diesel fuel on a farm is modeled by

$$C = 30.3 + 21.6 \sin\left(\frac{2\pi t}{365} + 10.9\right)$$

where t is the time (in days), with $t = 1$ corresponding to January 1.

(a) What is the period of the model? Is it what you expected? Explain.

(b) What is the average daily fuel consumption? Which term of the model did you use? Explain.

(c) Use a graphing utility to graph the model. Use the graph to approximate the time of the year when consumption exceeds 40 gallons per day.

Exploration

True or False? **In Exercises 95 and 96, determine whether the statement is true or false. Justify your answer.**

95. The graph of the function $f(x) = \sin(x + 2\pi)$ translates the graph of $f(x) = \sin x$ exactly one period to the right so that the two graphs look identical.

96. The function $y = \frac{1}{2}\cos 2x$ has an amplitude that is twice that of the function $y = \cos x$.

Conjecture **In Exercises 97 and 98, graph f and g in the same coordinate plane. Include two full periods. Make a conjecture about the functions.**

97. $f(x) = \sin x$, $\quad g(x) = \cos\left(x - \frac{\pi}{2}\right)$

98. $f(x) = \sin x$, $\quad g(x) = -\cos\left(x + \frac{\pi}{2}\right)$

99. Writing Sketch the graph of $y = \cos bx$ for $b = \frac{1}{2}$, 2, and 3. How does the value of b affect the graph? How many complete cycles of the graph of y occur between 0 and 2π for each value of b?

100. Polynomial Approximations Using calculus, it can be shown that the sine and cosine functions can be approximated by the polynomials

$$\sin x \approx x - \frac{x^3}{3!} + \frac{x^5}{5!}$$

and

$$\cos x \approx 1 - \frac{x^2}{2!} + \frac{x^4}{4!}$$

where x is in radians.

(a) Use a graphing utility to graph the sine function and its polynomial approximation in the same viewing window. How do the graphs compare?

(b) Use the graphing utility to graph the cosine function and its polynomial approximation in the same viewing window. How do the graphs compare?

(c) Study the patterns in the polynomial approximations of the sine and cosine functions and predict the next term in each. Then repeat parts (a) and (b). How did the accuracy of the approximations change when an additional term was added?

101. Polynomial Approximations Use the polynomial approximations of the sine and cosine functions in Exercise 100 to approximate the following function values. Compare the results with those given by a calculator. Is the error in the approximation the same in each case? Explain.

(a) $\sin \dfrac{1}{2}$ (b) $\sin 1$ (c) $\sin \dfrac{\pi}{6}$

(d) $\cos(-0.5)$ (e) $\cos 1$ (f) $\cos \dfrac{\pi}{4}$

102. **HOW DO YOU SEE IT?** The figure below shows the graph of $y = \sin(x - c)$ for

$$c = -\frac{\pi}{4}, \quad 0, \quad \text{and} \quad \frac{\pi}{4}.$$

(a) How does the value of c affect the graph?

(b) Which graph is equivalent to that of

$$y = -\cos\left(x + \frac{\pi}{4}\right)?$$

Project: Meteorology To work an extended application analyzing the mean monthly temperature and mean monthly precipitation for Honolulu, Hawaii, visit this text's website at *LarsonPrecalculus.com*. (*Source: National Climatic Data Center*)

4.6 Graphs of Other Trigonometric Functions

You can use graphs of trigonometric functions to model real-life situations such as the distance from a television camera to a unit in a parade, as in Exercise 84 on page 319.

- Sketch the graphs of tangent functions.
- Sketch the graphs of cotangent functions.
- Sketch the graphs of secant and cosecant functions.
- Sketch the graphs of damped trigonometric functions.

Graph of the Tangent Function

Recall that the tangent function is odd. That is, $\tan(-x) = -\tan x$. Consequently, the graph of $y = \tan x$ is symmetric with respect to the origin. You also know from the identity $\tan x = \sin x / \cos x$ that the tangent is undefined for values at which $\cos x = 0$. Two such values are $x = \pm \pi/2 \approx \pm 1.5708$.

x	$-\dfrac{\pi}{2}$	-1.57	-1.5	$-\dfrac{\pi}{4}$	0	$\dfrac{\pi}{4}$	1.5	1.57	$\dfrac{\pi}{2}$
$\tan x$	Undef.	-1255.8	-14.1	-1	0	1	14.1	1255.8	Undef.

As indicated in the table, $\tan x$ increases without bound as x approaches $\pi/2$ from the left and decreases without bound as x approaches $-\pi/2$ from the right. So, the graph of $y = \tan x$ has *vertical asymptotes* at $x = \pi/2$ and $x = -\pi/2$, as shown below. Moreover, because the period of the tangent function is π, vertical asymptotes also occur at $x = \pi/2 + n\pi$, where n is an integer. The domain of the tangent function is the set of all real numbers other than $x = \pi/2 + n\pi$, and the range is the set of all real numbers.

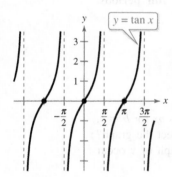

$y = \tan x$

Period: π

Domain: all $x \neq \dfrac{\pi}{2} + n\pi$

Range: $(-\infty, \infty)$

Vertical asymptotes: $x = \dfrac{\pi}{2} + n\pi$

Symmetry: origin

▷ ALGEBRA HELP
- You can review odd and even functions in Section 1.5.
- You can review symmetry of a graph in Section 1.2.
- You can review trigonometric identities in Section 4.3.
- You can review asymptotes in Section 2.6.
- You can review domain and range of a function in Section 1.4.
- You can review intercepts of a graph in Section 1.2.

Sketching the graph of $y = a \tan(bx - c)$ is similar to sketching the graph of $y = a \sin(bx - c)$ in that you locate key points that identify the intercepts and asymptotes. Two consecutive vertical asymptotes can be found by solving the equations

$$bx - c = -\frac{\pi}{2} \quad \text{and} \quad bx - c = \frac{\pi}{2}.$$

The midpoint between two consecutive vertical asymptotes is an x-intercept of the graph. The period of the function $y = a \tan(bx - c)$ is the distance between two consecutive vertical asymptotes. The amplitude of a tangent function is not defined. After plotting the asymptotes and the x-intercept, plot a few additional points between the two asymptotes and sketch one cycle. Finally, sketch one or two additional cycles to the left and right.

Figure 4.44

EXAMPLE 1 **Sketching the Graph of a Tangent Function**

Sketch the graph of $y = \tan \dfrac{x}{2}$.

Solution

By solving the equations

$$\frac{x}{2} = -\frac{\pi}{2} \quad \text{and} \quad \frac{x}{2} = \frac{\pi}{2}$$

$$x = -\pi \qquad\qquad x = \pi$$

you can see that two consecutive vertical asymptotes occur at $x = -\pi$ and $x = \pi$. Between these two asymptotes, plot a few points, including the x-intercept, as shown in the table. Three cycles of the graph are shown in Figure 4.44.

x	$-\pi$	$-\dfrac{\pi}{2}$	0	$\dfrac{\pi}{2}$	π
$\tan\dfrac{x}{2}$	Undef.	-1	0	1	Undef.

✓ *Checkpoint* ◄))) *Audio-video solution in English & Spanish at LarsonPrecalculus.com.*

Sketch the graph of $y = \tan \dfrac{x}{4}$.

EXAMPLE 2 **Sketching the Graph of a Tangent Function**

Sketch the graph of $y = -3 \tan 2x$.

Solution

By solving the equations

$$2x = -\frac{\pi}{2} \quad \text{and} \quad 2x = \frac{\pi}{2}$$

$$x = -\frac{\pi}{4} \qquad\qquad x = \frac{\pi}{4}$$

you can see that two consecutive vertical asymptotes occur at $x = -\pi/4$ and $x = \pi/4$. Between these two asymptotes, plot a few points, including the x-intercept, as shown in the table. Three cycles of the graph are shown in Figure 4.45.

x	$-\dfrac{\pi}{4}$	$-\dfrac{\pi}{8}$	0	$\dfrac{\pi}{8}$	$\dfrac{\pi}{4}$
$-3\tan 2x$	Undef.	3	0	-3	Undef.

By comparing the graphs in Examples 1 and 2, you can see that the graph of $y = a\tan(bx - c)$ increases between consecutive vertical asymptotes when $a > 0$ and decreases between consecutive vertical asymptotes when $a < 0$. In other words, the graph for $a < 0$ is a reflection in the x-axis of the graph for $a > 0$.

✓ *Checkpoint* ◄))) *Audio-video solution in English & Spanish at LarsonPrecalculus.com.*

Sketch the graph of $y = \tan 2x$.

Figure 4.45

Graph of the Cotangent Function

The graph of the cotangent function is similar to the graph of the tangent function. It also has a period of π. However, from the identity

$$y = \cot x = \frac{\cos x}{\sin x}$$

▷ **TECHNOLOGY** Some graphing utilities have difficulty graphing trigonometric functions that have vertical asymptotes. Your graphing utility may connect parts of the graphs of tangent, cotangent, secant, and cosecant functions that are not supposed to be connected. To eliminate this problem, change the mode of the graphing utility to *dot* mode.

you can see that the cotangent function has vertical asymptotes when $\sin x$ is zero, which occurs at $x = n\pi$, where n is an integer. The graph of the cotangent function is shown below. Note that two consecutive vertical asymptotes of the graph of $y = a\cot(bx - c)$ can be found by solving the equations $bx - c = 0$ and $bx - c = \pi$.

Period: π
Domain: all $x \neq n\pi$
Range: $(-\infty, \infty)$
Vertical asymptotes: $x = n\pi$
Symmetry: origin

EXAMPLE 3   **Sketching the Graph of a Cotangent Function**

Sketch the graph of

$$y = 2\cot\frac{x}{3}.$$

Solution

By solving the equations

$$\frac{x}{3} = 0 \quad \text{and} \quad \frac{x}{3} = \pi$$

$$x = 0 \qquad\qquad x = 3\pi$$

you can see that two consecutive vertical asymptotes occur at $x = 0$ and $x = 3\pi$. Between these two asymptotes, plot a few points, including the x-intercept, as shown in the table. Three cycles of the graph are shown in Figure 4.46. Note that the period is 3π, the distance between consecutive asymptotes.

Figure 4.46

x	0	$\dfrac{3\pi}{4}$	$\dfrac{3\pi}{2}$	$\dfrac{9\pi}{4}$	3π
$2\cot\dfrac{x}{3}$	Undef.	2	0	-2	Undef.

 ✓ *Checkpoint* ◀))) Audio-video solution in English & Spanish at LarsonPrecalculus.com.

Sketch the graph of

$$y = \cot\frac{x}{4}.$$

Graphs of the Reciprocal Functions

You can obtain the graphs of the two remaining trigonometric functions from the graphs of the sine and cosine functions using the reciprocal identities

$$\csc x = \frac{1}{\sin x} \quad \text{and} \quad \sec x = \frac{1}{\cos x}.$$

For instance, at a given value of x, the y-coordinate of $\sec x$ is the reciprocal of the y-coordinate of $\cos x$. Of course, when $\cos x = 0$, the reciprocal does not exist. Near such values of x, the behavior of the secant function is similar to that of the tangent function. In other words, the graphs of

$$\tan x = \frac{\sin x}{\cos x} \quad \text{and} \quad \sec x = \frac{1}{\cos x}$$

have vertical asymptotes where $\cos x = 0$—that is, at $x = \pi/2 + n\pi$, where n is an integer. Similarly,

$$\cot x = \frac{\cos x}{\sin x} \quad \text{and} \quad \csc x = \frac{1}{\sin x}$$

have vertical asymptotes where $\sin x = 0$—that is, at $x = n\pi$, where n is an integer.

To sketch the graph of a secant or cosecant function, you should first make a sketch of its reciprocal function. For instance, to sketch the graph of $y = \csc x$, first sketch the graph of $y = \sin x$. Then take reciprocals of the y-coordinates to obtain points on the graph of $y = \csc x$. You can use this procedure to obtain the graphs shown below.

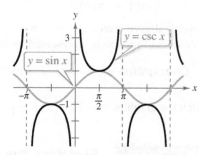

Period: 2π
Domain: all $x \neq n\pi$
Range: $(-\infty, -1] \cup [1, \infty)$
Vertical asymptotes: $x = n\pi$
Symmetry: origin

Period: 2π
Domain: all $x \neq \dfrac{\pi}{2} + n\pi$
Range: $(-\infty, -1] \cup [1, \infty)$
Vertical asymptotes: $x = \dfrac{\pi}{2} + n\pi$
Symmetry: y-axis

In comparing the graphs of the cosecant and secant functions with those of the sine and cosine functions, respectively, note that the "hills" and "valleys" are interchanged. For instance, a hill (or maximum point) on the sine curve corresponds to a valley (a relative minimum) on the cosecant curve, and a valley (or minimum point) on the sine curve corresponds to a hill (a relative maximum) on the cosecant curve, as shown in Figure 4.47. Additionally, x-intercepts of the sine and cosine functions become vertical asymptotes of the cosecant and secant functions, respectively (see Figure 4.47).

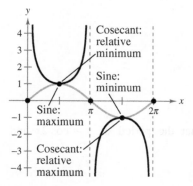

Figure 4.47

EXAMPLE 4 **Sketching the Graph of a Cosecant Function**

Sketch the graph of $y = 2 \csc\left(x + \dfrac{\pi}{4}\right)$.

Solution

Begin by sketching the graph of

$$y = 2 \sin\left(x + \frac{\pi}{4}\right).$$

For this function, the amplitude is 2 and the period is 2π. By solving the equations

$$x + \frac{\pi}{4} = 0 \quad \text{and} \quad x + \frac{\pi}{4} = 2\pi$$

$$x = -\frac{\pi}{4} \qquad\qquad x = \frac{7\pi}{4}$$

you can see that one cycle of the sine function corresponds to the interval from $x = -\pi/4$ to $x = 7\pi/4$. The graph of this sine function is represented by the gray curve in Figure 4.48. Because the sine function is zero at the midpoint and endpoints of this interval, the corresponding cosecant function

$$y = 2 \csc\left(x + \frac{\pi}{4}\right)$$

$$= 2\left(\frac{1}{\sin[x + (\pi/4)]}\right)$$

has vertical asymptotes at $x = -\pi/4$, $x = 3\pi/4$, $x = 7\pi/4$, and so on. The graph of the cosecant function is represented by the black curve in Figure 4.48.

Figure 4.48

✓ *Checkpoint* Audio-video solution in English & Spanish at LarsonPrecalculus.com.

Sketch the graph of $y = 2 \csc\left(x + \dfrac{\pi}{2}\right)$.

EXAMPLE 5 **Sketching the Graph of a Secant Function**

Sketch the graph of $y = \sec 2x$.

Solution

Begin by sketching the graph of $y = \cos 2x$, as indicated by the gray curve in Figure 4.49. Then, form the graph of $y = \sec 2x$ as the black curve in the figure. Note that the x-intercepts of $y = \cos 2x$

$$\left(-\frac{\pi}{4}, 0\right), \quad \left(\frac{\pi}{4}, 0\right), \quad \left(\frac{3\pi}{4}, 0\right), \dots$$

correspond to the vertical asymptotes

$$x = -\frac{\pi}{4}, \quad x = \frac{\pi}{4}, \quad x = \frac{3\pi}{4}, \dots$$

of the graph of $y = \sec 2x$. Moreover, notice that the period of $y = \cos 2x$ and $y = \sec 2x$ is π.

Figure 4.49

✓ *Checkpoint* Audio-video solution in English & Spanish at LarsonPrecalculus.com.

Sketch the graph of $y = \sec \dfrac{x}{2}$.

Damped Trigonometric Graphs

You can graph a *product* of two functions using properties of the individual functions. For instance, consider the function

$$f(x) = x \sin x$$

as the product of the functions $y = x$ and $y = \sin x$. Using properties of absolute value and the fact that $|\sin x| \le 1$, you have

$$0 \le |x||\sin x| \le |x|.$$

Consequently,

$$-|x| \le x \sin x \le |x|$$

which means that the graph of $f(x) = x \sin x$ lies between the lines $y = -x$ and $y = x$. Furthermore, because

$$f(x) = x \sin x = \pm x \quad \text{at} \quad x = \frac{\pi}{2} + n\pi$$

and

$$f(x) = x \sin x = 0 \quad \text{at} \quad x = n\pi$$

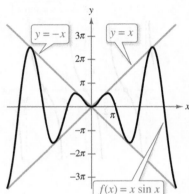

where n is an integer, the graph of f touches the line $y = -x$ or the line $y = x$ at $x = \pi/2 + n\pi$ and has x-intercepts at $x = n\pi$. A sketch of f is shown at the right. In the function $f(x) = x \sin x$, the factor x is called the **damping factor.**

- - - - - - - - - - - - - ▷

REMARK Do you see why the graph of $f(x) = x \sin x$ touches the lines $y = \pm x$ at $x = \pi/2 + n\pi$ and why the graph has x-intercepts at $x = n\pi$? Recall that the sine function is equal to 1 at $\ldots, -3\pi/2, \pi/2, 5\pi/2, \ldots$ $(x = \pi/2 + 2n\pi)$ and -1 at $\ldots, -\pi/2, 3\pi/2, 7\pi/2, \ldots$ $(x = -\pi/2 + 2n\pi)$ and is equal to 0 at $\ldots, -\pi, 0, \pi, 2\pi, 3\pi, \ldots$ $(x = n\pi)$.

| **EXAMPLE 6** | **Damped Sine Wave** |

Sketch the graph of $f(x) = e^{-x} \sin 3x$.

Solution

Consider $f(x)$ as the product of the two functions

$$y = e^{-x} \quad \text{and} \quad y = \sin 3x$$

each of which has the set of real numbers as its domain. For any real number x, you know that $e^{-x} > 0$ and $|\sin 3x| \le 1$. So,

$$e^{-x}|\sin 3x| \le e^{-x}$$

which means that

$$-e^{-x} \le e^{-x} \sin 3x \le e^{-x}.$$

Furthermore, because

$$f(x) = e^{-x} \sin 3x = \pm e^{-x} \quad \text{at} \quad x = \frac{\pi}{6} + \frac{n\pi}{3}$$

and

$$f(x) = e^{-x} \sin 3x = 0 \quad \text{at} \quad x = \frac{n\pi}{3}$$

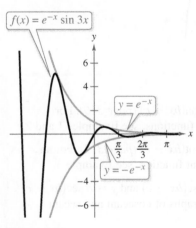

Figure 4.50

the graph of f touches the curve $y = -e^{-x}$ or the curve $y = e^{-x}$ at $x = \pi/6 + n\pi/3$ and has intercepts at $x = n\pi/3$. A sketch of f is shown in Figure 4.50.

✓ *Checkpoint*   *Audio-video solution in English & Spanish at LarsonPrecalculus.com.*

Sketch the graph of $f(x) = e^x \sin 4x$.

Below is a summary of the characteristics of the six basic trigonometric functions.

Domain: $(-\infty, \infty)$
Range: $[-1, 1]$
Period: 2π

Domain: $(-\infty, \infty)$
Range: $[-1, 1]$
Period: 2π

Domain: all $x \neq \dfrac{\pi}{2} + n\pi$
Range: $(-\infty, \infty)$
Period: π

Domain: all $x \neq n\pi$
Range: $(-\infty, \infty)$
Period: π

Domain: all $x \neq n\pi$
Range:
$(-\infty, -1] \cup [1, \infty)$
Period: 2π

Domain: all $x \neq \dfrac{\pi}{2} + n\pi$
Range:
$(-\infty, -1] \cup [1, \infty)$
Period: 2π

Summarize **(Section 4.6)**

1. Describe how to sketch the graph of $y = a\tan(bx - c)$ *(page 310)*. For examples of sketching the graphs of tangent functions, see Examples 1 and 2.

2. Describe how to sketch the graph of $y = a\cot(bx - c)$ *(page 312)*. For an example of sketching the graph of a cotangent function, see Example 3.

3. Describe how to sketch the graphs of $y = a\csc(bx - c)$ and $y = a\sec(bx - c)$ *(page 313)*. For examples of sketching the graphs of cosecant and secant functions, see Examples 4 and 5.

4. Describe how to sketch the graph of a damped trigonometric function *(page 315)*. For an example of sketching the graph of a damped trigonometric function, see Example 6.

4.6 Exercises

See CalcChat.com for tutorial help and worked-out solutions to odd-numbered exercises.

Vocabulary: Fill in the blanks.

1. The tangent, cotangent, and cosecant functions are _____ , so the graphs of these functions have symmetry with respect to the _____.

2. The graphs of the tangent, cotangent, secant, and cosecant functions have _____ asymptotes.

3. To sketch the graph of a secant or cosecant function, first make a sketch of its _____ function.

4. For the function $f(x) = g(x) \cdot \sin x$, $g(x)$ is called the _____ factor of the function $f(x)$.

5. The period of $y = \tan x$ is _____.

6. The domain of $y = \cot x$ is all real numbers such that _____.

7. The range of $y = \sec x$ is _____.

8. The period of $y = \csc x$ is _____.

Skills and Applications

Matching   In Exercises 9–14, match the function with its graph. State the period of the function. [The graphs are labeled (a), (b), (c), (d), (e), and (f).]

(a)

(b)

(c)

(d)

(e)

(f)

9. $y = \sec 2x$

10. $y = \tan \dfrac{x}{2}$

11. $y = \dfrac{1}{2} \cot \pi x$

12. $y = -\csc x$

13. $y = \dfrac{1}{2} \sec \dfrac{\pi x}{2}$

14. $y = -2 \sec \dfrac{\pi x}{2}$

**Sketching the Graph of a Trigonometric Function
In Exercises 15–38, sketch the graph of the function. (Include two full periods.)**

15. $y = \frac{1}{3} \tan x$

16. $y = \tan 4x$

17. $y = -2 \tan 3x$

18. $y = -3 \tan \pi x$

19. $y = -\frac{1}{2} \sec x$

20. $y = \frac{1}{4} \sec x$

21. $y = \csc \pi x$

22. $y = 3 \csc 4x$

23. $y = \frac{1}{2} \sec \pi x$

24. $y = -2 \sec 4x + 2$

25. $y = \csc \dfrac{x}{2}$

26. $y = \csc \dfrac{x}{3}$

27. $y = 3 \cot 2x$

28. $y = 3 \cot \dfrac{\pi x}{2}$

29. $y = 2 \sec 3x$

30. $y = -\frac{1}{2} \tan x$

31. $y = \tan \dfrac{\pi x}{4}$

32. $y = \tan(x + \pi)$

33. $y = 2 \csc(x - \pi)$

34. $y = \csc(2x - \pi)$

35. $y = 2 \sec(x + \pi)$

36. $y = -\sec \pi x + 1$

37. $y = \dfrac{1}{4} \csc\left(x + \dfrac{\pi}{4}\right)$

38. $y = 2 \cot\left(x + \dfrac{\pi}{2}\right)$

 Graphing a Trigonometric Function   In Exercises 39–48, use a graphing utility to graph the function. (Include two full periods.)

39. $y = \tan \dfrac{x}{3}$

40. $y = -\tan 2x$

41. $y = -2 \sec 4x$

42. $y = \sec \pi x$

43. $y = \tan\left(x - \dfrac{\pi}{4}\right)$

44. $y = \dfrac{1}{4} \cot\left(x - \dfrac{\pi}{2}\right)$

45. $y = -\csc(4x - \pi)$

46. $y = 2 \sec(2x - \pi)$

47. $y = 0.1 \tan\left(\dfrac{\pi x}{4} + \dfrac{\pi}{4}\right)$

48. $y = \dfrac{1}{3} \sec\left(\dfrac{\pi x}{2} + \dfrac{\pi}{2}\right)$

Solving a Trigonometric Equation Graphically

In Exercises 49–56, use a graph to solve the equation on the interval $[-2\pi, 2\pi]$.

49. $\tan x = 1$

50. $\tan x = \sqrt{3}$

51. $\cot x = -\dfrac{\sqrt{3}}{3}$

52. $\cot x = 1$

53. $\sec x = -2$

54. $\sec x = 2$

55. $\csc x = \sqrt{2}$

56. $\csc x = -\dfrac{2\sqrt{3}}{3}$

Even and Odd Trigonometric Functions

In Exercises 57–64, use the graph of the function to determine whether the function is even, odd, or neither. Verify your answer algebraically.

57. $f(x) = \sec x$

58. $f(x) = \tan x$

59. $g(x) = \cot x$

60. $g(x) = \csc x$

61. $f(x) = x + \tan x$

62. $f(x) = x^2 - \sec x$

63. $g(x) = x \csc x$

64. $g(x) = x^2 \cot x$

Identifying Damped Trigonometric Functions

In Exercises 65–68, match the function with its graph. Describe the behavior of the function as x approaches zero. [The graphs are labeled (a), (b), (c), and (d).]

(a)

(b)

(c)

(d)

65. $f(x) = |x \cos x|$

66. $f(x) = x \sin x$

67. $g(x) = |x| \sin x$

68. $g(x) = |x| \cos x$

Conjecture

In Exercises 69–72, graph the functions f and g. Use the graphs to make a conjecture about the relationship between the functions.

69. $f(x) = \sin x + \cos\left(x + \dfrac{\pi}{2}\right), \quad g(x) = 0$

70. $f(x) = \sin x - \cos\left(x + \dfrac{\pi}{2}\right), \quad g(x) = 2 \sin x$

71. $f(x) = \sin^2 x, \quad g(x) = \frac{1}{2}(1 - \cos 2x)$

72. $f(x) = \cos^2 \dfrac{\pi x}{2}, \quad g(x) = \dfrac{1}{2}(1 + \cos \pi x)$

Analyzing a Damped Trigonometric Graph

In Exercises 73–76, use a graphing utility to graph the function and the damping factor of the function in the same viewing window. Describe the behavior of the function as x increases without bound.

73. $g(x) = e^{-x^2/2} \sin x$

74. $f(x) = e^{-x} \cos x$

75. $f(x) = 2^{-x/4} \cos \pi x$

76. $h(x) = 2^{-x^2/4} \sin x$

Analyzing a Trigonometric Graph

In Exercises 77–82, use a graphing utility to graph the function. Describe the behavior of the function as x approaches zero.

77. $y = \dfrac{6}{x} + \cos x, \quad x > 0$

78. $y = \dfrac{4}{x} + \sin 2x, \quad x > 0$

79. $g(x) = \dfrac{\sin x}{x}$

80. $f(x) = \dfrac{1 - \cos x}{x}$

81. $f(x) = \sin \dfrac{1}{x}$

82. $h(x) = x \sin \dfrac{1}{x}$

83. Meteorology The normal monthly high temperatures H (in degrees Fahrenheit) in Erie, Pennsylvania, are approximated by

$$H(t) = 56.94 - 20.86 \cos\left(\dfrac{\pi t}{6}\right) - 11.58 \sin\left(\dfrac{\pi t}{6}\right)$$

and the normal monthly low temperatures L are approximated by

$$L(t) = 41.80 - 17.13 \cos\left(\dfrac{\pi t}{6}\right) - 13.39 \sin\left(\dfrac{\pi t}{6}\right)$$

where t is the time (in months), with $t = 1$ corresponding to January (see figure). (*Source: National Climatic Data Center*)

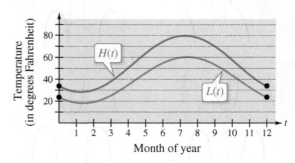

(a) What is the period of each function?

(b) During what part of the year is the difference between the normal high and normal low temperatures greatest? When is it smallest?

(c) The sun is northernmost in the sky around June 21, but the graph shows the warmest temperatures at a later date. Approximate the lag time of the temperatures relative to the position of the sun.

84. Television Coverage

A television camera is on a reviewing platform 27 meters from the street on which a parade will be passing from left to right (see figure). Write the distance d from the camera to a particular unit in the parade as a function of the angle x, and graph the function over the interval $-\pi/2 < x < \pi/2$. Consider x as negative when a unit in the parade approaches from the left.)

Not drawn to scale

27 m

x

Camera

85. Distance A plane flying at an altitude of 7 miles above a radar antenna will pass directly over the radar antenna (see figure). Let d be the ground distance from the antenna to the point directly under the plane and let x be the angle of elevation to the plane from the antenna. (d is positive as the plane approaches the antenna.) Write d as a function of x and graph the function over the interval $0 < x < \pi$.

7 mi

x

d

Not drawn to scale

Exploration

True or False? In Exercises 86 and 87, determine whether the statement is true or false. Justify your answer.

86. You can obtain the graph of $y = \csc x$ on a calculator by graphing the reciprocal of $y = \sin x$.

87. You can obtain the graph of $y = \sec x$ on a calculator by graphing a translation of the reciprocal of $y = \sin x$.

Graphical Analysis In Exercises 88 and 89, use a graphing utility to graph the function. Use the graph to determine the behavior of the function as $x \to c$.

(a) As $x \to 0^+$, the value of $f(x) \to$ ▮.

(b) As $x \to 0^-$, the value of $f(x) \to$ ▮.

(c) As $x \to \pi^+$, the value of $f(x) \to$ ▮.

(d) As $x \to \pi^-$, the value of $f(x) \to$ ▮.

88. $f(x) = \cot x$ **89.** $f(x) = \csc x$

Graphical Analysis In Exercises 90 and 91, use a graphing utility to graph the function. Use the graph to determine the behavior of the function as $x \to c$.

(a) $x \to \left(\dfrac{\pi}{2}\right)^+$ (b) $x \to \left(\dfrac{\pi}{2}\right)^-$

(c) $x \to \left(-\dfrac{\pi}{2}\right)^+$ (d) $x \to \left(-\dfrac{\pi}{2}\right)^-$

90. $f(x) = \tan x$ **91.** $f(x) = \sec x$

92. HOW DO YOU SEE IT? Determine which function is represented by the graph. Do not use a calculator. Explain your reasoning.

(a)

(b)

(i) $f(x) = \tan 2x$ (i) $f(x) = \sec 4x$

(ii) $f(x) = \tan(x/2)$ (ii) $f(x) = \csc 4x$

(iii) $f(x) = 2 \tan x$ (iii) $f(x) = \csc(x/4)$

(iv) $f(x) = -\tan 2x$ (iv) $f(x) = \sec(x/4)$

(v) $f(x) = -\tan(x/2)$ (v) $f(x) = \csc(4x - \pi)$

93. Think About It Consider the function $f(x) = x - \cos x$.

(a) Use a graphing utility to graph the function and verify that there exists a zero between 0 and 1. Use the graph to approximate the zero.

(b) Starting with $x_0 = 1$, generate a sequence $x_1, x_2, x_3, \ldots$, where $x_n = \cos(x_{n-1})$. For example,

$x_0 = 1$

$x_1 = \cos(x_0)$

$x_2 = \cos(x_1)$

$x_3 = \cos(x_2)$

$\vdots$

What value does the sequence approach?

4.7 Inverse Trigonometric Functions

You can use inverse trigonometric functions to model and solve real-life problems. For instance, in Exercise 104 on page 328, you will use an inverse trigonometric function to model the angle of elevation from a television camera to a space shuttle launch.

- Evaluate and graph the inverse sine function.
- Evaluate and graph the other inverse trigonometric functions.
- Evaluate the compositions of trigonometric functions.

Inverse Sine Function

Recall from Section 1.9 that for a function to have an inverse function, it must be one-to-one—that is, it must pass the Horizontal Line Test. From Figure 4.51, you can see that $y = \sin x$ does not pass the test because different values of x yield the same y-value.

sin x has an inverse function on this interval.

Figure 4.51

However, when you restrict the domain to the interval $-\pi/2 \leq x \leq \pi/2$ (corresponding to the black portion of the graph in Figure 4.51), the following properties hold.

1. On the interval $[-\pi/2, \pi/2]$, the function $y = \sin x$ is increasing.
2. On the interval $[-\pi/2, \pi/2]$, $y = \sin x$ takes on its full range of values, $-1 \leq \sin x \leq 1$.
3. On the interval $[-\pi/2, \pi/2]$, $y = \sin x$ is one-to-one.

So, on the restricted domain $-\pi/2 \leq x \leq \pi/2$, $y = \sin x$ has a unique inverse function called the **inverse sine function.** It is denoted by

$$y = \arcsin x \quad \text{or} \quad y = \sin^{-1} x.$$

The notation $\sin^{-1} x$ is consistent with the inverse function notation $f^{-1}(x)$. The arcsin x notation (read as "the arcsine of x") comes from the association of a central angle with its intercepted *arc length* on a unit circle. So, arcsin x means the angle (or arc) whose sine is x. Both notations, arcsin x and $\sin^{-1} x$, are commonly used in mathematics, so remember that $\sin^{-1} x$ denotes the *inverse* sine function rather than $1/\sin x$. The values of arcsin x lie in the interval

$$-\frac{\pi}{2} \leq \arcsin x \leq \frac{\pi}{2}.$$

The graph of $y = \arcsin x$ is shown in Example 2.

REMARK When evaluating the inverse sine function, it helps to remember the phrase "the arcsine of x is the angle (or number) whose sine is x."

Definition of Inverse Sine Function

The **inverse sine function** is defined by

$$y = \arcsin x \quad \text{if and only if} \quad \sin y = x$$

where $-1 \leq x \leq 1$ and $-\pi/2 \leq y \leq \pi/2$. The domain of $y = \arcsin x$ is $[-1, 1]$, and the range is $[-\pi/2, \pi/2]$.

NASA

▷

REMARK As with the trigonometric functions, much of the work with the inverse trigonometric functions can be done by *exact* calculations rather than by calculator approximations. Exact calculations help to increase your understanding of the inverse functions by relating them to the right triangle definitions of the trigonometric functions.

EXAMPLE 1   **Evaluating the Inverse Sine Function**

If possible, find the exact value.

a. $\arcsin\left(-\dfrac{1}{2}\right)$ **b.** $\sin^{-1}\dfrac{\sqrt{3}}{2}$ **c.** $\sin^{-1}2$

Solution

a. Because $\sin\left(-\dfrac{\pi}{6}\right) = -\dfrac{1}{2}$ and $-\dfrac{\pi}{6}$ lies in $\left[-\dfrac{\pi}{2}, \dfrac{\pi}{2}\right]$, it follows that

$$\arcsin\left(-\dfrac{1}{2}\right) = -\dfrac{\pi}{6}. \qquad \text{Angle whose sine is } -\tfrac{1}{2}$$

b. Because $\sin\dfrac{\pi}{3} = \dfrac{\sqrt{3}}{2}$ and $\dfrac{\pi}{3}$ lies in $\left[-\dfrac{\pi}{2}, \dfrac{\pi}{2}\right]$, it follows that

$$\sin^{-1}\dfrac{\sqrt{3}}{2} = \dfrac{\pi}{3}. \qquad \text{Angle whose sine is } \sqrt{3}/2$$

c. It is not possible to evaluate $y = \sin^{-1}x$ when $x = 2$ because there is no angle whose sine is 2. Remember that the domain of the inverse sine function is $[-1, 1]$.

✓ *Checkpoint* Audio-video solution in English & Spanish at LarsonPrecalculus.com.

If possible, find the exact value.

a. $\arcsin 1$ **b.** $\sin^{-1}(-2)$

EXAMPLE 2   **Graphing the Arcsine Function**

Sketch a graph of

$$y = \arcsin x.$$

Solution

By definition, the equations $y = \arcsin x$ and $\sin y = x$ are equivalent for $-\pi/2 \le y \le \pi/2$. So, their graphs are the same. From the interval $[-\pi/2, \pi/2]$, you can assign values to y in the equation $\sin y = x$ to make a table of values. Then plot the points and connect them with a smooth curve.

y	$-\dfrac{\pi}{2}$	$-\dfrac{\pi}{4}$	$-\dfrac{\pi}{6}$	0	$\dfrac{\pi}{6}$	$\dfrac{\pi}{4}$	$\dfrac{\pi}{2}$
$x = \sin y$	-1	$-\dfrac{\sqrt{2}}{2}$	$-\dfrac{1}{2}$	0	$\dfrac{1}{2}$	$\dfrac{\sqrt{2}}{2}$	1

The resulting graph of $y = \arcsin x$ is shown in Figure 4.52. Note that it is the reflection (in the line $y = x$) of the black portion of the graph in Figure 4.51. Be sure you see that Figure 4.52 shows the *entire* graph of the inverse sine function. Remember that the domain of $y = \arcsin x$ is the closed interval $[-1, 1]$ and the range is the closed interval $[-\pi/2, \pi/2]$.

✓ *Checkpoint* Audio-video solution in English & Spanish at LarsonPrecalculus.com.

Use a graphing utility to graph $f(x) = \sin x$, $g(x) = \arcsin x$, and $y = x$ in the same viewing window to verify geometrically that g is the inverse function of f. (Be sure to restrict the domain of f properly.)

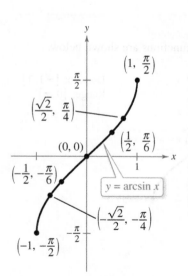

Figure 4.52

Other Inverse Trigonometric Functions

The cosine function is decreasing and one-to-one on the interval $0 \le x \le \pi$, as shown below.

cos x has an inverse function
on this interval.

Consequently, on this interval the cosine function has an inverse function—the **inverse cosine function**—denoted by

$$y = \arccos x \quad \text{or} \quad y = \cos^{-1} x.$$

Similarly, you can define an **inverse tangent function** by restricting the domain of $y = \tan x$ to the interval $(-\pi/2, \pi/2)$. The following list summarizes the definitions of the three most common inverse trigonometric functions. The remaining three are defined in Exercises 115–117.

Definitions of the Inverse Trigonometric Functions

Function	Domain	Range
$y = \arcsin x$ if and only if $\sin y = x$	$-1 \le x \le 1$	$-\dfrac{\pi}{2} \le y \le \dfrac{\pi}{2}$
$y = \arccos x$ if and only if $\cos y = x$	$-1 \le x \le 1$	$0 \le y \le \pi$
$y = \arctan x$ if and only if $\tan y = x$	$-\infty < x < \infty$	$-\dfrac{\pi}{2} < y < \dfrac{\pi}{2}$

The graphs of these three inverse trigonometric functions are shown below.

Domain: $[-1, 1]$
Range: $\left[-\dfrac{\pi}{2}, \dfrac{\pi}{2}\right]$

Domain: $[-1, 1]$
Range: $[0, \pi]$

Domain: $(-\infty, \infty)$
Range: $\left(-\dfrac{\pi}{2}, \dfrac{\pi}{2}\right)$

EXAMPLE 3 **Evaluating Inverse Trigonometric Functions**

Find the exact value.

a. $\arccos \dfrac{\sqrt{2}}{2}$

b. $\arctan 0$

c. $\tan^{-1}(-1)$

Solution

a. Because $\cos(\pi/4) = \sqrt{2}/2$ and $\pi/4$ lies in $[0, \pi]$, it follows that

$$\arccos \dfrac{\sqrt{2}}{2} = \dfrac{\pi}{4}. \qquad \text{Angle whose cosine is } \sqrt{2}/2$$

b. Because $\tan 0 = 0$ and 0 lies in $(-\pi/2, \pi/2)$, it follows that

$$\arctan 0 = 0. \qquad \text{Angle whose tangent is } 0$$

c. Because $\tan(-\pi/4) = -1$ and $-\pi/4$ lies in $(-\pi/2, \pi/2)$, it follows that

$$\tan^{-1}(-1) = -\dfrac{\pi}{4}. \qquad \text{Angle whose tangent is } -1$$

 ✓ *Checkpoint* ◀))) *Audio-video solution in English & Spanish at LarsonPrecalculus.com.*

Find the exact value of $\cos^{-1}(-1)$.

EXAMPLE 4 **Calculators and Inverse Trigonometric Functions**

Use a calculator to approximate the value, if possible.

a. $\arctan(-8.45)$

b. $\sin^{-1} 0.2447$

c. $\arccos 2$

Solution

Function	Mode	Calculator Keystrokes
a. $\arctan(-8.45)$	Radian	(TAN⁻¹) (⃝ (−) 8.45 ⃝) (ENTER)

From the display, it follows that $\arctan(-8.45) \approx -1.453001$.

b. $\sin^{-1} 0.2447$	Radian	(SIN⁻¹) (⃝ 0.2447 ⃝) (ENTER)

From the display, it follows that $\sin^{-1} 0.2447 \approx 0.2472103$.

c. $\arccos 2$	Radian	(COS⁻¹) (⃝ 2 ⃝) (ENTER)

▷ **· ·REMARK** Remember that the domain of the inverse sine function and the inverse cosine function is $[-1, 1]$, as indicated in Example 4(c).

In *radian* mode, the calculator should display an *error message* because the domain of the inverse cosine function is $[-1, 1]$.

✓ *Checkpoint* ◀))) *Audio-video solution in English & Spanish at LarsonPrecalculus.com.*

Use a calculator to approximate the value, if possible.

a. $\arctan 4.84$

b. $\arcsin(-1.1)$

c. $\arccos(-0.349)$

In Example 4, had you set the calculator to *degree* mode, the displays would have been in degrees rather than in radians. This convention is peculiar to calculators. By definition, the values of inverse trigonometric functions are *always in radians*.

Compositions of Functions

▷ **ALGEBRA HELP** You can review the composition of functions in Section 1.8.

Recall from Section 1.9 that for all x in the domains of f and f^{-1}, inverse functions have the properties

$$f(f^{-1}(x)) = x \quad \text{and} \quad f^{-1}(f(x)) = x.$$

Inverse Properties of Trigonometric Functions

If $-1 \le x \le 1$ and $-\pi/2 \le y \le \pi/2$, then

$$\sin(\arcsin x) = x \quad \text{and} \quad \arcsin(\sin y) = y.$$

If $-1 \le x \le 1$ and $0 \le y \le \pi$, then

$$\cos(\arccos x) = x \quad \text{and} \quad \arccos(\cos y) = y.$$

If x is a real number and $-\pi/2 < y < \pi/2$, then

$$\tan(\arctan x) = x \quad \text{and} \quad \arctan(\tan y) = y.$$

Keep in mind that these inverse properties do not apply for arbitrary values of x and y. For instance,

$$\arcsin\left(\sin \frac{3\pi}{2}\right) = \arcsin(-1) = -\frac{\pi}{2} \ne \frac{3\pi}{2}.$$

In other words, the property $\arcsin(\sin y) = y$ is not valid for values of y outside the interval $[-\pi/2, \pi/2]$.

EXAMPLE 5 **Using Inverse Properties**

If possible, find the exact value.

a. $\tan[\arctan(-5)]$ **b.** $\arcsin\left(\sin \dfrac{5\pi}{3}\right)$ **c.** $\cos(\cos^{-1} \pi)$

Solution

a. Because -5 lies in the domain of the arctangent function, the inverse property applies, and you have

$$\tan[\arctan(-5)] = -5.$$

b. In this case, $5\pi/3$ does not lie in the range of the arcsine function, $-\pi/2 \le y \le \pi/2$. However, $5\pi/3$ is coterminal with

$$\frac{5\pi}{3} - 2\pi = -\frac{\pi}{3}$$

which does lie in the range of the arcsine function, and you have

$$\arcsin\left(\sin \frac{5\pi}{3}\right) = \arcsin\left[\sin\left(-\frac{\pi}{3}\right)\right] = -\frac{\pi}{3}.$$

c. The expression $\cos(\cos^{-1} \pi)$ is not defined because $\cos^{-1} \pi$ is not defined. Remember that the domain of the inverse cosine function is $[-1, 1]$.

✓ *Checkpoint* ◄))) Audio-video solution in English & Spanish at LarsonPrecalculus.com.

If possible, find the exact value.

a. $\tan[\tan^{-1}(-14)]$ **b.** $\sin^{-1}\left(\sin \dfrac{7\pi}{4}\right)$ **c.** $\cos(\arccos 0.54)$

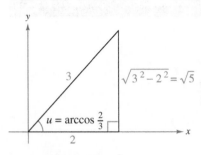

Angle whose cosine is $\frac{2}{3}$
Figure 4.53

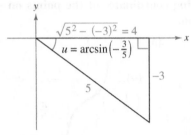

Angle whose sine is $-\frac{3}{5}$
Figure 4.54

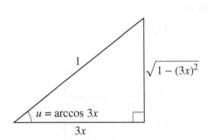

Angle whose cosine is $3x$
Figure 4.55

EXAMPLE 6   **Evaluating Compositions of Functions**

Find the exact value.

a. $\tan\left(\arccos \frac{2}{3}\right)$ **b.** $\cos\left[\arcsin\left(-\frac{3}{5}\right)\right]$

Solution

a. If you let $u = \arccos \frac{2}{3}$, then $\cos u = \frac{2}{3}$. Because the range of the inverse cosine function is the first and second quadrants and $\cos u$ is positive, u is a *first*-quadrant angle. You can sketch and label angle u, as shown in Figure 4.53. Consequently,

$$\tan\left(\arccos \frac{2}{3}\right) = \tan u = \frac{\text{opp}}{\text{adj}} = \frac{\sqrt{5}}{2}.$$

b. If you let $u = \arcsin\left(-\frac{3}{5}\right)$, then $\sin u = -\frac{3}{5}$. Because the range of the inverse sine function is the first and fourth quadrants and $\sin u$ is negative, u is a *fourth*-quadrant angle. You can sketch and label angle u, as shown in Figure 4.54. Consequently,

$$\cos\left[\arcsin\left(-\frac{3}{5}\right)\right] = \cos u = \frac{\text{adj}}{\text{hyp}} = \frac{4}{5}.$$

✓ *Checkpoint*   🔊 *Audio-video solution in English & Spanish at LarsonPrecalculus.com.*

Find the exact value of $\cos\left[\arctan\left(-\frac{3}{4}\right)\right]$.

EXAMPLE 7   **Some Problems from Calculus**

Write each of the following as an algebraic expression in x.

a. $\sin(\arccos 3x), \quad 0 \le x \le \frac{1}{3}$ **b.** $\cot(\arccos 3x), \quad 0 \le x < \frac{1}{3}$

Solution

If you let $u = \arccos 3x$, then $\cos u = 3x$, where $-1 \le 3x \le 1$. Because

$$\cos u = \frac{\text{adj}}{\text{hyp}} = \frac{3x}{1}$$

you can sketch a right triangle with acute angle u, as shown in Figure 4.55. From this triangle, you can easily convert each expression to algebraic form.

a. $\sin(\arccos 3x) = \sin u = \dfrac{\text{opp}}{\text{hyp}} = \sqrt{1 - 9x^2}, \quad 0 \le x \le \dfrac{1}{3}$

b. $\cot(\arccos 3x) = \cot u = \dfrac{\text{adj}}{\text{opp}} = \dfrac{3x}{\sqrt{1 - 9x^2}}, \quad 0 \le x < \dfrac{1}{3}$

✓ *Checkpoint*   🔊 *Audio-video solution in English & Spanish at LarsonPrecalculus.com.*

Write $\sec(\arctan x)$ as an algebraic expression in x. ◼

Summarize   (Section 4.7)

1. State the definition of the inverse sine function *(page 320)*. For examples of evaluating and graphing the inverse sine function, see Examples 1 and 2.

2. State the definitions of the inverse cosine and inverse tangent functions *(page 322)*. For examples of evaluating and graphing inverse trigonometric functions, see Examples 3 and 4.

3. State the inverse properties of trigonometric functions *(page 324)*. For examples involving the compositions of trigonometric functions, see Examples 5–7.

4.7 Exercises

See CalcChat.com for tutorial help and worked-out solutions to odd-numbered exercises.

Vocabulary: Fill in the blanks.

Function	Alternative Notation	Domain	Range
1. $y = \arcsin x$	_____	_____	$-\dfrac{\pi}{2} \le y \le \dfrac{\pi}{2}$
2. _____	$y = \cos^{-1} x$	$-1 \le x \le 1$	_____
3. $y = \arctan x$	_____	_____	_____

4. Without restrictions, no trigonometric function has an _____ function.

Skills and Applications

Evaluating an Inverse Trigonometric Function
In Exercises 5–18, evaluate the expression without using a calculator.

5. $\arcsin \dfrac{1}{2}$ **6.** $\arcsin 0$

7. $\arccos \dfrac{1}{2}$ **8.** $\arccos 0$

9. $\arctan \dfrac{\sqrt{3}}{3}$ **10.** $\arctan 1$

11. $\cos^{-1}\left(-\dfrac{\sqrt{3}}{2}\right)$ **12.** $\sin^{-1}\left(-\dfrac{\sqrt{2}}{2}\right)$

13. $\arctan(-\sqrt{3})$ **14.** $\arctan \sqrt{3}$

15. $\arccos\left(-\dfrac{1}{2}\right)$ **16.** $\arcsin \dfrac{\sqrt{2}}{2}$

17. $\sin^{-1}\left(-\dfrac{\sqrt{3}}{2}\right)$ **18.** $\tan^{-1}\left(-\dfrac{\sqrt{3}}{3}\right)$

Graphing an Inverse Trigonometric Function In Exercises 19 and 20, use a graphing utility to graph f, g, and $y = x$ in the same viewing window to verify geometrically that g is the inverse function of f. (Be sure to restrict the domain of f properly.)

19. $f(x) = \cos x, \quad g(x) = \arccos x$
20. $f(x) = \tan x, \quad g(x) = \arctan x$

Calculators and Inverse Trigonometric Functions
In Exercises 21–38, use a calculator to evaluate the expression. Round your result to two decimal places.

21. $\arccos 0.37$ **22.** $\arcsin 0.65$

23. $\arcsin(-0.75)$ **24.** $\arccos(-0.7)$

25. $\arctan(-3)$ **26.** $\arctan 25$

27. $\sin^{-1} 0.31$ **28.** $\cos^{-1} 0.26$

29. $\arccos(-0.41)$ **30.** $\arcsin(-0.125)$

31. $\arctan 0.92$ **32.** $\arctan 2.8$

33. $\arcsin \dfrac{7}{8}$ **34.** $\arccos\left(-\dfrac{1}{3}\right)$

35. $\tan^{-1} \dfrac{19}{4}$ **36.** $\tan^{-1}\left(-\dfrac{95}{7}\right)$

37. $\tan^{-1}(-\sqrt{372})$ **38.** $\tan^{-1}(-\sqrt{2165})$

Finding Missing Coordinates In Exercises 39 and 40, determine the missing coordinates of the points on the graph of the function.

39.   **40.**

Using an Inverse Trigonometric Function In Exercises 41–46, use an inverse trigonometric function to write θ as a function of x.

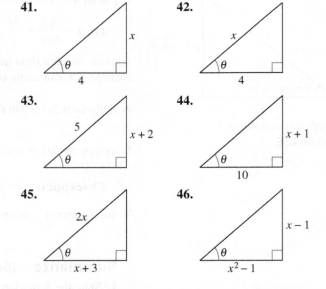

41.   **42.**

43.   **44.**

45.   **46.**

Using Inverse Properties In Exercises 47–52, use the properties of inverse trigonometric functions to evaluate the expression.

47. $\sin(\arcsin 0.3)$ **48.** $\tan(\arctan 45)$

49. $\cos[\arccos(-0.1)]$ **50.** $\sin[\arcsin(-0.2)]$

51. $\arcsin(\sin 3\pi)$ **52.** $\arccos\left(\cos \dfrac{7\pi}{2}\right)$

Evaluating a Composition of Functions In Exercises 53–64, find the exact value of the expression. (*Hint:* Sketch a right triangle.)

53. $\sin\left(\arctan\frac{3}{4}\right)$

54. $\sec\left(\arcsin\frac{4}{5}\right)$

55. $\cos(\tan^{-1} 2)$

56. $\sin\left(\cos^{-1}\frac{\sqrt{5}}{5}\right)$

57. $\cos\left(\arcsin\frac{5}{13}\right)$

58. $\csc\left[\arctan\left(-\frac{5}{12}\right)\right]$

59. $\sec\left[\arctan\left(-\frac{3}{5}\right)\right]$

60. $\tan\left[\arcsin\left(-\frac{3}{4}\right)\right]$

61. $\sin\left[\arccos\left(-\frac{2}{3}\right)\right]$

62. $\cot\left(\arctan\frac{5}{8}\right)$

63. $\csc\left(\cos^{-1}\frac{\sqrt{3}}{2}\right)$

64. $\sec\left[\sin^{-1}\left(-\frac{\sqrt{2}}{2}\right)\right]$

Writing an Expression In Exercises 65–74, write an algebraic expression that is equivalent to the given expression. (*Hint:* Sketch a right triangle, as demonstrated in Example 7.)

65. $\cot(\arctan x)$

66. $\sin(\arctan x)$

67. $\cos(\arcsin 2x)$

68. $\sec(\arctan 3x)$

69. $\sin(\arccos x)$

70. $\sec[\arcsin(x - 1)]$

71. $\tan\left(\arccos\frac{x}{3}\right)$

72. $\cot\left(\arctan\frac{1}{x}\right)$

73. $\csc\left(\arctan\frac{x}{\sqrt{2}}\right)$

74. $\cos\left(\arcsin\frac{x - h}{r}\right)$

Graphical Analysis In Exercises 75 and 76, use a graphing utility to graph f and g in the same viewing window to verify that the two functions are equal. Explain why they are equal. Identify any asymptotes of the graphs.

75. $f(x) = \sin(\arctan 2x)$, $g(x) = \dfrac{2x}{\sqrt{1 + 4x^2}}$

76. $f(x) = \tan\left(\arccos\frac{x}{2}\right)$, $g(x) = \dfrac{\sqrt{4 - x^2}}{x}$

Completing an Equation In Exercises 77–80, complete the equation.

77. $\arctan\dfrac{9}{x} = \arcsin(\quad)$, $x > 0$

78. $\arcsin\dfrac{\sqrt{36 - x^2}}{6} = \arccos(\quad)$, $0 \le x \le 6$

79. $\arccos\dfrac{3}{\sqrt{x^2 - 2x + 10}} = \arcsin(\quad)$

80. $\arccos\dfrac{x - 2}{2} = \arctan(\quad)$, $2 < x < 4$

Comparing Graphs In Exercises 81 and 82, sketch a graph of the function and compare the graph of g with the graph of $f(x) = \arcsin x$.

81. $g(x) = \arcsin(x - 1)$

82. $g(x) = \arcsin\dfrac{x}{2}$

Sketching the Graph of a Function In Exercises 83–88, sketch a graph of the function.

83. $y = 2 \arccos x$

84. $g(t) = \arccos(t + 2)$

85. $f(x) = \arctan 2x$

86. $f(x) = \dfrac{\pi}{2} + \arctan x$

87. $h(v) = \arccos\dfrac{v}{2}$

88. $f(x) = \arccos\dfrac{x}{4}$

Graphing an Inverse Trigonometric Function In Exercises 89–94, use a graphing utility to graph the function.

89. $f(x) = 2 \arccos(2x)$

90. $f(x) = \pi \arcsin(4x)$

91. $f(x) = \arctan(2x - 3)$

92. $f(x) = -3 + \arctan(\pi x)$

93. $f(x) = \pi - \sin^{-1}\left(\frac{2}{3}\right)$

94. $f(x) = \dfrac{\pi}{2} + \cos^{-1}\left(\frac{1}{\pi}\right)$

Using a Trigonometric Identity In Exercises 95 and 96, write the function in terms of the sine function by using the identity

$$A \cos \omega t + B \sin \omega t = \sqrt{A^2 + B^2} \sin\left(\omega t + \arctan\frac{A}{B}\right).$$

Use a graphing utility to graph both forms of the function. What does the graph imply?

95. $f(t) = 3 \cos 2t + 3 \sin 2t$

96. $f(t) = 4 \cos \pi t + 3 \sin \pi t$

Behavior of an Inverse Trigonometric Function In Exercises 97–102, fill in the blank. If not possible, state the reason.

97. As $x \to 1^-$, the value of $\arcsin x \to$ [   ] .

98. As $x \to 1^-$, the value of $\arccos x \to$ [   ] .

99. As $x \to \infty$, the value of $\arctan x \to$ [   ] .

100. As $x \to -1^+$, the value of $\arcsin x \to$ [   ] .

101. As $x \to -1^+$, the value of $\arccos x \to$ [   ] .

102. As $x \to -\infty$, the value of $\arctan x \to$ [   ] .

103. Docking a Boat   A boat is pulled in by means of a winch located on a dock 5 feet above the deck of the boat (see figure). Let θ be the angle of elevation from the boat to the winch and let s be the length of the rope from the winch to the boat.

(a) Write θ as a function of s.

(b) Find θ when $s = 40$ feet and $s = 20$ feet.

104. Photography

A television camera at ground level is filming the lift-off of a space shuttle at a point 750 meters from the launch pad (see figure). Let θ be the angle of elevation to the shuttle and let s be the height of the shuttle.

750 m
Not drawn to scale

(a) Write θ as a function of s.

(b) Find θ when $s = 300$ meters and $s = 1200$ meters.

105. Photography A photographer is taking a picture of a three-foot-tall painting hung in an art gallery. The camera lens is 1 foot below the lower edge of the painting (see figure). The angle β subtended by the camera lens x feet from the painting is given by

$$\beta = \arctan \frac{3x}{x^2 + 4}, \quad x > 0.$$

3 ft

1 ft

x

Not drawn to scale

(a) Use a graphing utility to graph β as a function of x.

(b) Move the cursor along the graph to approximate the distance from the picture when β is maximum.

(c) Identify the asymptote of the graph and discuss its meaning in the context of the problem.

106. Granular Angle of Repose Different types of granular substances naturally settle at different angles when stored in cone-shaped piles. This angle θ is called the *angle of repose* (see figure). When rock salt is stored in a cone-shaped pile 11 feet high, the diameter of the pile's base is about 34 feet. *(Source: Bulk-Store Structures, Inc.)*

11 ft

θ

17 ft

(a) Find the angle of repose for rock salt.

(b) How tall is a pile of rock salt that has a base diameter of 40 feet?

107. Granular Angle of Repose When whole corn is stored in a cone-shaped pile 20 feet high, the diameter of the pile's base is about 82 feet.

(a) Find the angle of repose for whole corn.

(b) How tall is a pile of corn that has a base diameter of 100 feet?

108. Angle of Elevation An airplane flies at an altitude of 6 miles toward a point directly over an observer. Consider θ and x as shown in the figure.

6 mi

θ

x

Not drawn to scale

(a) Write θ as a function of x.

(b) Find θ when $x = 7$ miles and $x = 1$ mile.

109. Security Patrol A security car with its spotlight on is parked 20 meters from a warehouse. Consider θ and x as shown in the figure.

θ

20 m

Not drawn to scale   x

(a) Write θ as a function of x.

(b) Find θ when $x = 5$ meters and $x = 12$ meters.

Exploration

True or False? In Exercises 110–113, determine whether the statement is true or false. Justify your answer.

110. $\sin \dfrac{5\pi}{6} = \dfrac{1}{2}$ ⟹ $\arcsin \dfrac{1}{2} = \dfrac{5\pi}{6}$

111. $\tan \dfrac{5\pi}{4} = 1$ ⟹ $\arctan 1 = \dfrac{5\pi}{4}$

112. $\arctan x = \dfrac{\arcsin x}{\arccos x}$ **113.** $\sin^{-1} x = \dfrac{1}{\sin x}$

114. **HOW DO YOU SEE IT?** Use the figure below to determine the value(s) of x for which each statement is true.

— arcsin(x)   — arccos(x)

(a) $\arcsin x < \arccos x$

(b) $\arcsin x = \arccos x$

(c) $\arcsin x > \arccos x$

115. Inverse Cotangent Function Define the inverse cotangent function by restricting the domain of the cotangent function to the interval $(0, \pi)$, and sketch the graph of the inverse trigonometric function.

116. Inverse Secant Function Define the inverse secant function by restricting the domain of the secant function to the intervals $[0, \pi/2)$ and $(\pi/2, \pi]$, and sketch the graph of the inverse trigonometric function.

117. Inverse Cosecant Function Define the inverse cosecant function by restricting the domain of the cosecant function to the intervals $[-\pi/2, 0)$ and $(0, \pi/2]$, and sketch the graph of the inverse trigonometric function.

118. Writing Use the results of Exercises 115–117 to explain how to graph (a) the inverse cotangent function, (b) the inverse secant function, and (c) the inverse cosecant function on a graphing utility.

Evaluating an Inverse Trigonometric Function In Exercises 119–126, use the results of Exercises 115–117 to evaluate the expression without using a calculator.

119. $\operatorname{arcsec} \sqrt{2}$ **120.** $\operatorname{arcsec} 1$

121. $\operatorname{arccot}(-1)$ **122.** $\operatorname{arccot}\left(-\sqrt{3}\right)$

123. $\operatorname{arccsc} 2$ **124.** $\operatorname{arccsc}(-1)$

125. $\operatorname{arccsc}\left(\dfrac{2\sqrt{3}}{3}\right)$ **126.** $\operatorname{arcsec}\left(-\dfrac{2\sqrt{3}}{3}\right)$

Calculators and Inverse Trigonometric Functions In Exercises 127–134, use the results of Exercises 115–117 and a calculator to approximate the value of the expression. Round your result to two decimal places.

127. $\operatorname{arcsec} 2.54$ **128.** $\operatorname{arcsec}(-1.52)$

129. $\operatorname{arccot} 5.25$ **130.** $\operatorname{arccot}(-10)$

131. $\operatorname{arccot} \dfrac{5}{3}$ **132.** $\operatorname{arccot}\left(-\dfrac{16}{7}\right)$

133. $\operatorname{arccsc}\left(-\dfrac{25}{3}\right)$ **134.** $\operatorname{arccsc}(-12)$

135. Area In calculus, it is shown that the area of the region bounded by the graphs of $y = 0$, $y = 1/(x^2 + 1)$, $x = a$, and $x = b$ is given by

$$\text{Area} = \arctan b - \arctan a$$

(see figure). Find the area for the following values of a and b.

(a) $a = 0, b = 1$ (b) $a = -1, b = 1$

(c) $a = 0, b = 3$ (d) $a = -1, b = 3$

136. Think About It Use a graphing utility to graph the functions $f(x) = \sqrt{x}$ and $g(x) = 6 \arctan x$. For $x > 0$, it appears that $g > f$. Explain why you know that there exists a positive real number a such that $g < f$ for $x > a$. Approximate the number a.

137. Think About It Consider the functions $f(x) = \sin x$ and $f^{-1}(x) = \arcsin x$.

(a) Use a graphing utility to graph the composite functions $f \circ f^{-1}$ and $f^{-1} \circ f$.

(b) Explain why the graphs in part (a) are not the graph of the line $y = x$. Why do the graphs of $f \circ f^{-1}$ and $f^{-1} \circ f$ differ?

138. Proof Prove each identity.

(a) $\arcsin(-x) = -\arcsin x$

(b) $\arctan(-x) = -\arctan x$

(c) $\arctan x + \arctan \dfrac{1}{x} = \dfrac{\pi}{2}, \quad x > 0$

(d) $\arcsin x + \arccos x = \dfrac{\pi}{2}$

(e) $\arcsin x = \arctan \dfrac{x}{\sqrt{1 - x^2}}$

4.8 Applications and Models

- Solve real-life problems involving right triangles.
- Solve real-life problems involving directional bearings.
- Solve real-life problems involving harmonic motion.

Applications Involving Right Triangles

In this section, the three angles of a right triangle are denoted by the letters A, B, and C (where C is the right angle), and the lengths of the sides opposite these angles by the letters a, b, and c, respectively (where c is the hypotenuse).

Right triangles often occur in real-life situations. For instance, in Exercise 32 on page 337, you will use right triangles to analyze the design of a new slide at a water park.

EXAMPLE 1 **Solving a Right Triangle**

Solve the right triangle shown at the right for all unknown sides and angles.

Solution Because $C = 90°$, it follows that

$$A + B = 90° \quad \text{and} \quad B = 90° - 34.2° = 55.8°.$$

To solve for a, use the fact that

$$\tan A = \frac{\text{opp}}{\text{adj}} = \frac{a}{b} \quad \Longrightarrow \quad a = b \tan A.$$

So, $a = 19.4 \tan 34.2° \approx 13.18$. Similarly, to solve for c, use the fact that

$$\cos A = \frac{\text{adj}}{\text{hyp}} = \frac{b}{c} \quad \Longrightarrow \quad c = \frac{b}{\cos A}.$$

So, $c = \dfrac{19.4}{\cos 34.2°} \approx 23.46$.

✓ **Checkpoint** ◀))) *Audio-video solution in English & Spanish at LarsonPrecalculus.com.*

Solve the right triangle shown in Figure 4.56 for all unknown sides and angles.

Figure 4.56

EXAMPLE 2 **Finding a Side of a Right Triangle**

A safety regulation states that the maximum angle of elevation for a rescue ladder is 72°. A fire department's longest ladder is 110 feet. What is the maximum safe rescue height?

Solution A sketch is shown in Figure 4.57. From the equation $\sin A = a/c$, it follows that

$$a = c \sin A$$

$$= 110 \sin 72°$$

$$\approx 104.6.$$

So, the maximum safe rescue height is about 104.6 feet above the height of the fire truck.

✓ **Checkpoint** ◀))) *Audio-video solution in English & Spanish at LarsonPrecalculus.com.*

A ladder that is 16 feet long leans against the side of a house. The angle of elevation of the ladder is 80°. Find the height from the top of the ladder to the ground.

Figure 4.57

Finding a Side of a Right Triangle

At a point 200 feet from the base of a building, the angle of elevation to the *bottom* of a smokestack is 35°, whereas the angle of elevation to the *top* is 53°, as shown in Figure 4.58. Find the height *s* of the smokestack alone.

Solution

Note from Figure 4.58 that this problem involves two right triangles. For the smaller right triangle, use the fact that

$$\tan 35° = \frac{a}{200}$$

to conclude that the height of the building is

$$a = 200 \tan 35°.$$

For the larger right triangle, use the equation

$$\tan 53° = \frac{a + s}{200}$$

to conclude that $a + s = 200 \tan 53°$. So, the height of the smokestack is

$$s = 200 \tan 53° - a$$

$$= 200 \tan 53° - 200 \tan 35°$$

$$\approx 125.4 \text{ feet.}$$

Figure 4.58

✓ *Checkpoint* *Audio-video solution in English & Spanish at LarsonPrecalculus.com.*

At a point 65 feet from the base of a church, the angles of elevation to the bottom of the steeple and the top of the steeple are 35° and 43°, respectively. Find the height of the steeple.

Finding an Acute Angle of a Right Triangle

A swimming pool is 20 meters long and 12 meters wide. The bottom of the pool is slanted so that the water depth is 1.3 meters at the shallow end and 4 meters at the deep end, as shown in Figure 4.59. Find the angle of depression (in degrees) of the bottom of the pool.

Solution Using the tangent function, you can see that

$$\tan A = \frac{\text{opp}}{\text{adj}}$$

$$= \frac{2.7}{20}$$

$$= 0.135.$$

So, the angle of depression is

$$A = \arctan 0.135$$

$$\approx 0.13419 \text{ radian}$$

$$\approx 7.69°.$$

Figure 4.59

✓ *Checkpoint* *Audio-video solution in English & Spanish at LarsonPrecalculus.com.*

From the time a small airplane is 100 feet high and 1600 ground feet from its landing runway, the plane descends in a straight line to the runway. Determine the angle of descent (in degrees) of the plane.

Trigonometry and Bearings

• • • • • • • • • • • • • • • ▷

REMARK In *air navigation*, bearings are measured in degrees *clockwise* from north. Examples of air navigation bearings are shown below.

In surveying and navigation, directions can be given in terms of **bearings.** A bearing measures the acute angle that a path or line of sight makes with a fixed north-south line. For instance, the bearing S 35° E, shown below, means 35 degrees east of south.

S 35° E   N 80° W   N 45° E

EXAMPLE 5   **Finding Directions in Terms of Bearings**

A ship leaves port at noon and heads due west at 20 knots, or 20 nautical miles (nm) per hour. At 2 P.M. the ship changes course to N 54° W, as shown below. Find the ship's bearing and distance from the port of departure at 3 P.M.

Solution

For triangle *BCD*, you have

$$B = 90° - 54° = 36°.$$

The two sides of this triangle can be determined to be

$$b = 20 \sin 36° \quad \text{and} \quad d = 20 \cos 36°.$$

For triangle *ACD*, you can find angle *A* as follows.

$$\tan A = \frac{b}{d + 40} = \frac{20 \sin 36°}{20 \cos 36° + 40} \approx 0.2092494$$

$$A \approx \arctan 0.2092494 \approx 0.2062732 \text{ radian} \approx 11.82°$$

The angle with the north-south line is $90° - 11.82° = 78.18°$. So, the bearing of the ship is N 78.18° W. Finally, from triangle *ACD*, you have $\sin A = b/c$, which yields

$$c = \frac{b}{\sin A}$$

$$= \frac{20 \sin 36°}{\sin 11.82°}$$

$$\approx 57.4 \text{ nautical miles.} \qquad \text{Distance from port}$$

✓ *Checkpoint* ◀))) *Audio-video solution in English & Spanish at LarsonPrecalculus.com.*

A sailboat leaves a pier heading due west at 8 knots. After 15 minutes, the sailboat tacks, changing course to N 16° W at 10 knots. Find the sailboat's distance and bearing from the pier after 12 minutes on this course.

Harmonic Motion

The periodic nature of the trigonometric functions is useful for describing the motion of a point on an object that vibrates, oscillates, rotates, or is moved by wave motion.

For example, consider a ball that is bobbing up and down on the end of a spring, as shown in Figure 4.60. Suppose that 10 centimeters is the maximum distance the ball moves vertically upward or downward from its equilibrium (at rest) position. Suppose further that the time it takes for the ball to move from its maximum displacement above zero to its maximum displacement below zero and back again is $t = 4$ seconds. Assuming the ideal conditions of perfect elasticity and no friction or air resistance, the ball would continue to move up and down in a uniform and regular manner.

| Equilibrium | Maximum negative displacement | Maximum positive displacement |

Figure 4.60

From this spring you can conclude that the period (time for one complete cycle) of the motion is

Period = 4 seconds

its amplitude (maximum displacement from equilibrium) is

Amplitude = 10 centimeters

and its **frequency** (number of cycles per second) is

Frequency = $\frac{1}{4}$ cycle per second.

Motion of this nature can be described by a sine or cosine function and is called **simple harmonic motion.**

Definition of Simple Harmonic Motion

A point that moves on a coordinate line is in **simple harmonic motion** when its distance d from the origin at time t is given by either

$$d = a \sin \omega t \quad \text{or} \quad d = a \cos \omega t$$

where a and ω are real numbers such that $\omega > 0$. The motion has amplitude $|a|$, period $\frac{2\pi}{\omega}$, and frequency $\frac{\omega}{2\pi}$.

EXAMPLE 6   **Simple Harmonic Motion**

Write an equation for the simple harmonic motion of the ball described in Figure 4.60, where the period is 4 seconds. What is the frequency of this harmonic motion?

Solution

Because the spring is at equilibrium ($d = 0$) when $t = 0$, use the equation

$$d = a \sin \omega t.$$

Moreover, because the maximum displacement from zero is 10 and the period is 4, you have the following.

$$\text{Amplitude} = |a|$$
$$= 10$$

$$\text{Period} = \frac{2\pi}{\omega} = 4 \quad \Longrightarrow \quad \omega = \frac{\pi}{2}$$

Consequently, an equation of motion is

$$d = 10 \sin \frac{\pi}{2} t.$$

Note that the choice of

$$a = 10 \quad \text{or} \quad a = -10$$

depends on whether the ball initially moves up or down. The frequency is

$$\text{Frequency} = \frac{\omega}{2\pi}$$

$$= \frac{\pi/2}{2\pi}$$

$$= \frac{1}{4} \text{ cycle per second.}$$

✓ *Checkpoint* Audio-video solution in English & Spanish at LarsonPrecalculus.com.

Find a model for simple harmonic motion that satisfies the following conditions: $d = 0$ when $t = 0$, the amplitude is 6 centimeters, and the period is 3 seconds. Then find the frequency.

One illustration of the relationship between sine waves and harmonic motion is in the wave motion that results when a stone is dropped into a calm pool of water. The waves move outward in roughly the shape of sine (or cosine) waves, as shown in Figure 4.61. As an example, suppose you are fishing and your fishing bobber is attached so that it does not move horizontally. As the waves move outward from the dropped stone, your fishing bobber will move up and down in simple harmonic motion, as shown in Figure 4.62.

Figure 4.61

Figure 4.62

EXAMPLE 7   **Simple Harmonic Motion**

Given the equation for simple harmonic motion $d = 6 \cos \dfrac{3\pi}{4}t$, find (a) the maximum

displacement, (b) the frequency, (c) the value of d when $t = 4$, and (d) the least positive value of t for which $d = 0$.

Algebraic Solution

The given equation has the form $d = a \cos \omega t$, with $a = 6$ and $\omega = 3\pi/4$.

a. The maximum displacement (from the point of equilibrium) is given by the amplitude. So, the maximum displacement is 6.

b. Frequency $= \dfrac{\omega}{2\pi}$

$= \dfrac{3\pi/4}{2\pi}$

$= \dfrac{3}{8}$ cycle per unit of time

c. $d = 6 \cos\left[\dfrac{3\pi}{4}(4)\right] = 6 \cos 3\pi = 6(-1) = -6$

d. To find the least positive value of t for which $d = 0$, solve the equation

$$6 \cos \dfrac{3\pi}{4}t = 0.$$

First divide each side by 6 to obtain

$$\cos \dfrac{3\pi}{4}t = 0.$$

This equation is satisfied when

$$\dfrac{3\pi}{4}t = \dfrac{\pi}{2}, \dfrac{3\pi}{2}, \dfrac{5\pi}{2}, \ldots.$$

Multiply these values by $4/(3\pi)$ to obtain

$$t = \dfrac{2}{3}, 2, \dfrac{10}{3}, \ldots.$$

So, the least positive value of t is $t = \frac{2}{3}$.

Graphical Solution

Use a graphing utility set in *radian* mode.

a.

The maximum displacement from the point of equilibrium ($d = 0$) is 6.

b.

The period is the time for the graph to complete one cycle, which is $t \approx 2.67$. So, the frequency is about $1/2.67 \approx 0.37$ per unit of time.

c.
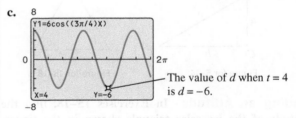
The value of d when $t = 4$ is $d = -6$.

d.   The least positive value of t for which $d = 0$ is $t \approx 0.67$.

✓ **Checkpoint**))) *Audio-video solution in English & Spanish at LarsonPrecalculus.com.*

Rework Example 7 for the equation $d = 4 \cos 6\pi t$.

Summarize   (Section 4.8)

1. Describe real-life problems that can be solved using right triangles (*pages 330 and 331, Examples 1–4*).

2. State the definition of a bearing (*page 332, Example 5*).

3. State the definition of simple harmonic motion (*page 333, Examples 6 and 7*).

4.8 Exercises

See **CalcChat.com** for tutorial help and worked-out solutions to odd-numbered exercises.

Vocabulary: Fill in the blanks.

1. A _____ measures the acute angle that a path or line of sight makes with a fixed north-south line.
2. A point that moves on a coordinate line is said to be in simple _____ _____ when its distance d from the origin at time t is given by either $d = a \sin \omega t$ or $d = a \cos \omega t$.
3. The time for one complete cycle of a point in simple harmonic motion is its _____.
4. The number of cycles per second of a point in simple harmonic motion is its _____.

Skills and Applications

Solving a Right Triangle In Exercises 5–14, solve the right triangle shown in the figure for all unknown sides and angles. Round your answers to two decimal places.

5. $A = 30°, \quad b = 3$
6. $B = 54°, \quad c = 15$
7. $B = 71°, \quad b = 24$
8. $A = 8.4°, \quad a = 40.5$
9. $a = 3, \quad b = 4$
10. $a = 25, \quad c = 35$
11. $b = 16, \quad c = 52$
12. $b = 1.32, \quad c = 9.45$
13. $A = 12°15', \quad c = 430.5$
14. $B = 65°12', \quad a = 14.2$

Figure for 5–14

Figure for 15–18

Finding an Altitude In Exercises 15–18, find the altitude of the isosceles triangle shown in the figure. Round your answers to two decimal places.

15. $\theta = 45°, \quad b = 6$
16. $\theta = 18°, \quad b = 10$
17. $\theta = 32°, \quad b = 8$
18. $\theta = 27°, \quad b = 11$

19. **Length** The sun is 25° above the horizon. Find the length of a shadow cast by a building that is 100 feet tall (see figure).

20. **Length** The sun is 20° above the horizon. Find the length of a shadow cast by a park statue that is 12 feet tall.

21. **Height** A ladder that is 20 feet long leans against the side of a house. The angle of elevation of the ladder is 80°. Find the height from the top of the ladder to the ground.

22. **Height** The length of a shadow of a tree is 125 feet when the angle of elevation of the sun is 33°. Approximate the height of the tree.

23. **Height** At a point 50 feet from the base of a church, the angles of elevation to the bottom of the steeple and the top of the steeple are 35° and 47° 40′, respectively. Find the height of the steeple.

24. **Distance** An observer in a lighthouse 350 feet above sea level observes two ships directly offshore. The angles of depression to the ships are 4° and 6.5° (see figure). How far apart are the ships?

Not drawn to scale

25. **Distance** A passenger in an airplane at an altitude of 10 kilometers sees two towns directly to the east of the plane. The angles of depression to the towns are 28° and 55° (see figure). How far apart are the towns?

Not drawn to scale

26. Altitude You observe a plane approaching overhead and assume that its speed is 550 miles per hour. The angle of elevation of the plane is 16° at one time and 57° one minute later. Approximate the altitude of the plane.

27. Angle of Elevation An engineer erects a 75-foot cellular telephone tower. Find the angle of elevation to the top of the tower at a point on level ground 50 feet from its base.

28. Angle of Elevation The height of an outdoor basketball backboard is $12\frac{1}{2}$ feet, and the backboard casts a shadow $17\frac{1}{3}$ feet long.

(a) Draw a right triangle that gives a visual representation of the problem. Label the known and unknown quantities.

(b) Use a trigonometric function to write an equation involving the unknown angle of elevation.

(c) Find the angle of elevation of the sun.

29. Angle of Depression A cellular telephone tower that is 150 feet tall is placed on top of a mountain that is 1200 feet above sea level. What is the angle of depression from the top of the tower to a cell phone user who is 5 horizontal miles away and 400 feet above sea level?

30. Angle of Depression A Global Positioning System satellite orbits 12,500 miles above Earth's surface (see figure). Find the angle of depression from the satellite to the horizon. Assume the radius of Earth is 4000 miles.

Not drawn to scale

31. Height You are holding one of the tethers attached to the top of a giant character balloon in a parade. Before the start of the parade the balloon is upright and the bottom is floating approximately 20 feet above ground level. You are standing approximately 100 feet ahead of the balloon (see figure).

Not drawn to scale

(a) Find an equation for the length l of the tether you are holding in terms of h, the height of the balloon from top to bottom.

(b) Find an equation for the angle of elevation θ from you to the top of the balloon.

(c) The angle of elevation to the top of the balloon is 35°. Find the height h of the balloon.

32. Waterslide Design

The designers of a water park are creating a new slide and have sketched some preliminary drawings. The length of the ladder is 30 feet, and its angle of elevation is 60° (see figure).

(a) Find the height h of the slide.

(b) Find the angle of depression θ from the top of the slide to the end of the slide at the ground in terms of the horizontal distance d a rider travels.

(c) Safety restrictions require the angle of depression to be no less than 25° and no more than 30°. Find an interval for how far a rider travels horizontally.

33. Speed Enforcement A police department has set up a speed enforcement zone on a straight length of highway. A patrol car is parked parallel to the zone, 200 feet from one end and 150 feet from the other end (see figure).

Not drawn to scale

(a) Find the length l of the zone and the measures of the angles A and B (in degrees).

(b) Find the minimum amount of time (in seconds) it takes for a vehicle to pass through the zone without exceeding the posted speed limit of 35 miles per hour.

34. Airplane Ascent During takeoff, an airplane's angle of ascent is 18° and its speed is 275 feet per second.

(a) Find the plane's altitude after 1 minute.

(b) How long will it take for the plane to climb to an altitude of 10,000 feet?

35. Navigation An airplane flying at 600 miles per hour has a bearing of 52°. After flying for 1.5 hours, how far north and how far east will the plane have traveled from its point of departure?

36. Navigation A jet leaves Reno, Nevada, and is headed toward Miami, Florida, at a bearing of 100°. The distance between the two cities is approximately 2472 miles.

(a) How far north and how far west is Reno relative to Miami?

(b) The jet is to return directly to Reno from Miami. At what bearing should it travel?

37. Navigation A ship leaves port at noon and has a bearing of S 29° W. The ship sails at 20 knots.

(a) How many nautical miles south and how many nautical miles west will the ship have traveled by 6:00 P.M.?

(b) At 6:00 P.M., the ship changes course to due west. Find the ship's bearing and distance from the port of departure at 7:00 P.M.

38. Navigation A privately owned yacht leaves a dock in Myrtle Beach, South Carolina, and heads toward Freeport in the Bahamas at a bearing of S 1.4° E. The yacht averages a speed of 20 knots over the 428-nautical-mile trip.

(a) How long will it take the yacht to make the trip?

(b) How far east and south is the yacht after 12 hours?

(c) A plane leaves Myrtle Beach to fly to Freeport. What bearing should be taken?

39. Navigation A ship is 45 miles east and 30 miles south of port. The captain wants to sail directly to port. What bearing should be taken?

40. Navigation An airplane is 160 miles north and 85 miles east of an airport. The pilot wants to fly directly to the airport. What bearing should be taken?

41. Surveying A surveyor wants to find the distance across a pond (see figure). The bearing from A to B is N 32° W. The surveyor walks 50 meters from A to C, and at the point C the bearing to B is N 68° W.

(a) Find the bearing from A to C.

(b) Find the distance from A to B.

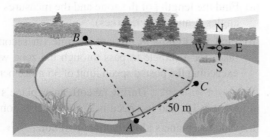

42. Location of a Fire Fire tower A is 30 kilometers due west of fire tower B. A fire is spotted from the towers, and the bearings from A and B are N 76° E and N 56° W, respectively (see figure). Find the distance d of the fire from the line segment AB.

Not drawn to scale

43. Geometry Determine the angle between the diagonal of a cube and the diagonal of its base, as shown in the figure.

44. Geometry Determine the angle between the diagonal of a cube and its edge, as shown in the figure.

45. Geometry Find the length of the sides of a regular pentagon inscribed in a circle of radius 25 inches.

46. Geometry Find the length of the sides of a regular hexagon inscribed in a circle of radius 25 inches.

Harmonic Motion In Exercises 47–50, find a model for simple harmonic motion satisfying the specified conditions.

Displacement ($t = 0$)	Amplitude	Period
47. 0	4 centimeters	2 seconds
48. 0	3 meters	6 seconds
49. 3 inches	3 inches	1.5 seconds
50. 2 feet	2 feet	10 seconds

51. Tuning Fork A point on the end of a tuning fork moves in simple harmonic motion described by $d = a \sin \omega t$. Find ω given that the tuning fork for middle C has a frequency of 264 vibrations per second.

52. Wave Motion   A buoy oscillates in simple harmonic motion as waves go past. The buoy moves a total of 3.5 feet from its low point to its high point (see figure), and it returns to its high point every 10 seconds. Write an equation that describes the motion of the buoy where the high point corresponds to the time $t = 0$.

Harmonic Motion   **In Exercises 53–56, for the simple harmonic motion described by the trigonometric function, find (a) the maximum displacement, (b) the frequency, (c) the value of d when $t = 5$, and (d) the least positive value of t for which $d = 0$. Use a graphing utility to verify your results.**

53. $d = 9 \cos \dfrac{6\pi}{5} t$ **54.** $d = \dfrac{1}{2} \cos 20\pi t$

55. $d = \dfrac{1}{4} \sin 6\pi t$ **56.** $d = \dfrac{1}{64} \sin 792\pi t$

57. Oscillation of a Spring   A ball that is bobbing up and down on the end of a spring has a maximum displacement of 3 inches. Its motion (in ideal conditions) is modeled by $y = \frac{1}{4} \cos 16t$, $t > 0$, where y is measured in feet and t is the time in seconds.

(a) Graph the function.

(b) What is the period of the oscillations?

(c) Determine the first time the weight passes the point of equilibrium ($y = 0$).

58. Data Analysis   The table shows the average sales S (in millions of dollars) of an outerwear manufacturer for each month t, where $t = 1$ represents January.

Time, t	1	2	3	4	5	6
Sales, S	13.46	11.15	8.00	4.85	2.54	1.70

Time, t	7	8	9	10	11	12
Sales, S	2.54	4.85	8.00	11.15	13.46	14.30

(a) Create a scatter plot of the data.

(b) Find a trigonometric model that fits the data. Graph the model with your scatter plot. How well does the model fit the data?

(c) What is the period of the model? Do you think it is reasonable given the context? Explain your reasoning.

(d) Interpret the meaning of the model's amplitude in the context of the problem.

59. Data Analysis   The numbers of hours H of daylight in Denver, Colorado, on the 15th of each month are: 1(9.67), 2(10.72), 3(11.92), 4(13.25), 5(14.37), 6(14.97), 7(14.72), 8(13.77), 9(12.48), 10(11.18), 11(10.00), 12(9.38). The month is represented by t, with $t = 1$ corresponding to January. A model for the data is

$$H(t) = 12.13 + 2.77 \sin\left(\frac{\pi t}{6} - 1.60\right).$$

 (a) Use a graphing utility to graph the data points and the model in the same viewing window.

(b) What is the period of the model? Is it what you expected? Explain.

(c) What is the amplitude of the model? What does it represent in the context of the problem? Explain.

Exploration

60. **HOW DO YOU SEE IT?**   The graph below shows the displacement of an object in simple harmonic motion.

(a) What is the amplitude?

(b) What is the period?

(c) Is the equation of the simple harmonic motion of the form $d = a \sin \omega t$ or $d = a \cos \omega t$?

True or False?   **In Exercises 61 and 62, determine whether the statement is true or false. Justify your answer.**

61. The Leaning Tower of Pisa is not vertical, but when you know the angle of elevation θ to the top of the tower as you stand d feet away from it, you can find its height h using the formula $h = d \tan \theta$.

62. The bearing N 24° E means 24 degrees north of east.

Chapter Summary

	What Did You Learn?	Explanation/Examples	Review Exercises
Section 4.1	Describe angles (p. 262).		1–4
	Convert between degrees and radians (p. 265).	To convert degrees to radians, multiply degrees by $(\pi \, rad)/180°$. To convert radians to degrees, multiply radians by $180°/(\pi \, rad)$.	5–14
	Use angles to model and solve real-life problems (p. 266).	Angles can help you find the length of a circular arc and the area of a sector of a circle. (See Examples 5 and 8.)	15–18
Section 4.2	Identify a unit circle and describe its relationship to real numbers (p. 272).		19–22
	Evaluate trigonometric functions using the unit circle (p. 273).	$t = \dfrac{2\pi}{3}$ corresponds to $(x, y) = \left(-\dfrac{1}{2}, \dfrac{\sqrt{3}}{2}\right)$. So $\cos \dfrac{2\pi}{3} = -\dfrac{1}{2}$, $\sin \dfrac{2\pi}{3} = \dfrac{\sqrt{3}}{2}$, and $\tan \dfrac{2\pi}{3} = -\sqrt{3}$.	23, 24
	Use domain and period to evaluate sine and cosine functions (p. 275), and use a calculator to evaluate trigonometric functions (p. 276).	Because $\dfrac{13\pi}{6} = 2\pi + \dfrac{\pi}{6}$, $\sin \dfrac{13\pi}{6} = \sin \dfrac{\pi}{6} = \dfrac{1}{2}$. $\sin \dfrac{3\pi}{8} \approx 0.9239$, $\cot(-1.2) \approx -0.3888$	25–32
Section 4.3	Evaluate trigonometric functions of acute angles (p. 279), and use a calculator to evaluate trigonometric functions (p. 281).	$\sin \theta = \dfrac{opp}{hyp}$, $\cos \theta = \dfrac{adj}{hyp}$, $\tan \theta = \dfrac{opp}{adj}$ $\csc \theta = \dfrac{hyp}{opp}$, $\sec \theta = \dfrac{hyp}{adj}$, $\cot \theta = \dfrac{adj}{opp}$ $\tan 34.7° \approx 0.6924$, $\csc 29° \, 15' \approx 2.0466$	33–38
	Use the fundamental trigonometric identities (p. 282).	$\sin \theta = \dfrac{1}{\csc \theta}$, $\tan \theta = \dfrac{\sin \theta}{\cos \theta}$, $\sin^2 \theta + \cos^2 \theta = 1$	39, 40
	Use trigonometric functions to model and solve real-life problems (p. 284).	Trigonometric functions can help you find the height of a monument, the angle between two paths, and the length of a ramp. (See Examples 8–10.)	41, 42

What Did You Learn?	Explanation/Examples	Review Exercises
Section 4.4 Evaluate trigonometric functions of any angle (p. 290).	Let $(3, 4)$ be a point on the terminal side of θ. Then $\sin \theta = \frac{4}{5}$, $\cos \theta = \frac{3}{5}$, and $\tan \theta = \frac{4}{3}$.	43–50
Find reference angles (p. 292).	Let θ be an angle in standard position. Its reference angle is the acute angle θ' formed by the terminal side of θ and the horizontal axis.	51–54
Evaluate trigonometric functions of real numbers (p. 293).	$\cos \frac{7\pi}{3} = \frac{1}{2}$ because $\theta' = \frac{7\pi}{3} - 2\pi = \frac{\pi}{3}$ and $\cos \frac{\pi}{3} = \frac{1}{2}$.	55–62
Section 4.5 Sketch the graphs of sine and cosine functions using amplitude and period (p. 299).	$y = 3 \sin 2x$ $\qquad$ $y = 2 \cos 3x$	63, 64
Sketch translations of the graphs of sine and cosine functions (p. 303).	For $y = d + a \sin(bx - c)$ and $y = d + a \cos(bx - c)$, the constant c creates a horizontal translation. The constant d creates a vertical translation. (See Examples 4–6.)	65–68
Use sine and cosine functions to model real-life data (p. 305).	A cosine function can help you model the depth of the water at the end of a dock at various times. (See Example 7.)	69, 70
Section 4.6 Sketch the graphs of tangent (p. 310), cotangent (p. 312), secant (p. 313), and cosecant (p. 313) functions.	$y = \tan x$ $\qquad$ $y = \sec x = \frac{1}{\cos x}$	71–74
Sketch the graphs of damped trigonometric functions (p. 315).	In $f(x) = x \cos 2x$, the factor x is called the damping factor.	75, 76
Section 4.7 Evaluate and graph inverse trigonometric functions (p. 320).	$\sin^{-1} \frac{\sqrt{3}}{2} = \frac{\pi}{3}$, $\quad \cos^{-1}\left(-\frac{\sqrt{2}}{2}\right) = \frac{3\pi}{4}$, $\quad \tan^{-1}(-1) = -\frac{\pi}{4}$	77–86
Evaluate the compositions of trigonometric functions (p. 324).	$\cos\left[\arctan\left(\frac{5}{12}\right)\right] = \frac{12}{13}$, $\quad \sin(\sin^{-1} 0.4) = 0.4$	87–92
Section 4.8 Solve real-life problems involving right triangles (p. 330).	A trigonometric function can help you find the height of a smokestack on top of a building. (See Example 3.)	93, 94
Solve real-life problems involving directional bearings (p. 332).	Trigonometric functions can help you find a ship's bearing and distance from a port at a given time. (See Example 5.)	95
Solve real-life problems involving harmonic motion (p. 333).	Sine or cosine functions can help you describe the motion of an object that vibrates, oscillates, rotates, or is moved by wave motion. (See Examples 6 and 7.)	96

Review Exercises   See CalcChat.com for tutorial help and worked-out solutions to odd-numbered exercises.

4.1 **Using Radian or Degree Measure** In Exercises 1–4, (a) sketch the angle in standard position, (b) determine the quadrant in which the angle lies, and (c) determine one positive and one negative coterminal angle.

1. $\dfrac{15\pi}{4}$

2. $-\dfrac{4\pi}{3}$

3. $-110°$

4. $280°$

Converting from Degrees to Radians In Exercises 5–8, convert the angle measure from degrees to radians. Round to three decimal places.

5. $450°$

6. $-112.5°$

7. $-33°\,45'$

8. $197°\,17'$

Converting from Radians to Degrees In Exercises 9–12, convert the angle measure from radians to degrees. Round to three decimal places.

9. $\dfrac{3\pi}{10}$

10. $-\dfrac{11\pi}{6}$

11. -3.5

12. 5.7

Converting to D° M′ S″ Form In Exercises 13 and 14, convert the angle measure to degrees, minutes, and seconds without using a calculator. Then check your answer using a calculator.

13. $198.4°$

14. $-5.96°$

15. **Arc Length** Find the length of the arc on a circle of radius 20 inches intercepted by a central angle of $138°$.

16. **Phonograph** Phonograph records are vinyl discs that rotate on a turntable. A typical record album is 12 inches in diameter and plays at $33\frac{1}{3}$ revolutions per minute.

    (a) What is the angular speed of a record album?

    (b) What is the linear speed of the outer edge of a record album?

17. **Circular Sector** Find the area of the sector of a circle of radius 18 inches and central angle $\theta = 120°$.

18. **Circular Sector** Find the area of the sector of a circle of radius 6.5 millimeters and central angle $\theta = 5\pi/6$.

4.2 **Finding a Point on the Unit Circle** In Exercises 19–22, find the point (x, y) on the unit circle that corresponds to the real number t.

19. $t = \dfrac{2\pi}{3}$

20. $t = \dfrac{7\pi}{4}$

21. $t = \dfrac{7\pi}{6}$

22. $t = -\dfrac{4\pi}{3}$

Evaluating Trigonometric Functions In Exercises 23 and 24, evaluate (if possible) the six trigonometric functions at the real number.

23. $t = \dfrac{3\pi}{4}$

24. $t = -\dfrac{2\pi}{3}$

Using Period to Evaluate Sine and Cosine In Exercises 25–28, evaluate the trigonometric function using its period as an aid.

25. $\sin \dfrac{11\pi}{4}$

26. $\cos 4\pi$

27. $\sin\left(-\dfrac{17\pi}{6}\right)$

28. $\cos\left(-\dfrac{13\pi}{3}\right)$

Using a Calculator In Exercises 29–32, use a calculator to evaluate the trigonometric function. Round your answer to four decimal places. (Be sure the calculator is in the correct mode.)

29. $\tan 33$

30. $\csc 10.5$

31. $\sec \dfrac{12\pi}{5}$

32. $\sin\left(-\dfrac{\pi}{9}\right)$

4.3 **Evaluating Trigonometric Functions** In Exercises 33 and 34, find the exact values of the six trigonometric functions of the angle θ shown in the figure. (Use the Pythagorean Theorem to find the third side of the triangle.)

33.

34.

Using a Calculator In Exercises 35–38, use a calculator to evaluate the trigonometric function. Round your answer to four decimal places. (Be sure the calculator is in the correct mode.)

35. $\tan 33°$

36. $\sec 79.3°$

37. $\cot 15°\,14'$

38. $\cos 78°\,11'58''$

Applying Trigonometric Identities In Exercises 39 and 40, use the given function value and the trigonometric identities to find the indicated trigonometric functions.

39. $\sin \theta = \frac{1}{3}$ (a) $\csc \theta$ (b) $\cos \theta$
    (c) $\sec \theta$ (d) $\tan \theta$

40. $\csc \theta = 5$ (a) $\sin \theta$ (b) $\cot \theta$
    (c) $\tan \theta$ (d) $\sec(90° - \theta)$

41. Railroad Grade A train travels 3.5 kilometers on a straight track with a grade of $1° \, 10'$ (see figure). What is the vertical rise of the train in that distance?

3.5 km

$1°10'$

Not drawn to scale

42. Guy Wire A guy wire runs from the ground to the top of a 25-foot telephone pole. The angle formed between the wire and the ground is $52°$. How far from the base of the pole is the wire attached to the ground? Assume the pole is perpendicular to the ground.

4.4 Evaluating Trigonometric Functions In Exercises 43–46, the point is on the terminal side of an angle in standard position. Determine the exact values of the six trigonometric functions of the angle.

43. $(12, 16)$ **44.** $(3, -4)$

45. $(0.3, 0.4)$ **46.** $\left(-\frac{10}{3}, -\frac{2}{3}\right)$

Evaluating Trigonometric Functions In Exercises 47–50, find the values of the remaining five trigonometric functions of θ with the given constraint.

Function Value	Constraint
47. $\sec \theta = \frac{6}{5}$	$\tan \theta < 0$
48. $\csc \theta = \frac{3}{2}$	$\cos \theta < 0$
49. $\cos \theta = -\frac{2}{5}$	$\sin \theta > 0$
50. $\sin \theta = -\frac{1}{2}$	$\cos \theta > 0$

Finding a Reference Angle In Exercises 51–54, find the reference angle θ' and sketch θ and θ' in standard position.

51. $\theta = 264°$ **52.** $\theta = 635°$

53. $\theta = -6\pi/5$ **54.** $\theta = 17\pi/3$

Using a Reference Angle In Exercises 55–58, evaluate the sine, cosine, and tangent of the angle without using a calculator.

55. $\pi/3$ **56.** $-5\pi/4$

57. $-150°$ **58.** $495°$

Using a Calculator In Exercises 59–62, use a calculator to evaluate the trigonometric function. Round your answer to four decimal places. (Be sure the calculator is in the correct mode.)

59. $\sin 4$

60. $\cot(-4.8)$

61. $\sin(12\pi/5)$

62. $\tan(-25\pi/7)$

4.5 Sketching the Graph of a Sine or Cosine Function In Exercises 63–68, sketch the graph of the function. (Include two full periods.)

63. $y = \sin 6x$

64. $f(x) = 5 \sin(2x/5)$

65. $y = 5 + \sin x$

66. $y = -4 - \cos \pi x$

67. $g(t) = \frac{5}{2} \sin(t - \pi)$

68. $g(t) = 3 \cos(t + \pi)$

69. Sound Waves Sine functions of the form $y = a \sin bx$, where x is measured in seconds, can model sine waves.

(a) Write an equation of a sound wave whose amplitude is 2 and whose period is $\frac{1}{264}$ second.

(b) What is the frequency of the sound wave described in part (a)?

70. Data Analysis: Meteorology The times S of sunset (Greenwich Mean Time) at $40°$ north latitude on the 15th of each month are: 1(16:59), 2(17:35), 3(18:06), 4(18:38), 5(19:08), 6(19:30), 7(19:28), 8(18:57), 9(18:09), 10(17:21), 11(16:44), 12(16:36). The month is represented by t, with $t = 1$ corresponding to January. A model (in which minutes have been converted to the decimal parts of an hour) for the data is $S(t) = 18.09 + 1.41 \sin[(\pi t/6) + 4.60]$.

(a) Use a graphing utility to graph the data points and the model in the same viewing window.

(b) What is the period of the model? Is it what you expected? Explain.

(c) What is the amplitude of the model? What does it represent in the model? Explain.

4.6 Sketching the Graph of a Trigonometric Function In Exercises 71–74, sketch the graph of the function. (Include two full periods.)

71. $f(t) = \tan\left(t + \dfrac{\pi}{2}\right)$

72. $f(x) = \dfrac{1}{2} \cot x$

73. $f(x) = \dfrac{1}{2} \csc \dfrac{x}{2}$

74. $h(t) = \sec\left(t - \dfrac{\pi}{4}\right)$

Analyzing a Damped Trigonometric Graph In Exercises 75 and 76, use a graphing utility to graph the function and the damping factor of the function in the same viewing window. Describe the behavior of the function as x increases without bound.

75. $f(x) = x \cos x$ **76.** $g(x) = x^4 \cos x$

4.7 Evaluating an Inverse Trigonometric Function In Exercises 77–80, evaluate the expression without using a calculator.

77. $\arcsin(-1)$

78. $\cos^{-1} 1$

79. $\text{arccot } \sqrt{3}$

80. $\text{arcsec}\left(-\sqrt{2}\right)$

Calculators and Inverse Trigonometric Functions In Exercises 81–84, use a calculator to evaluate the expression. Round your result to two decimal places.

81. $\tan^{-1}(-1.5)$

82. $\arccos 0.324$

83. $\text{arccot } 10.5$

84. $\text{arccsc}(-2.01)$

Graphing an Inverse Trigonometric Function In Exercises 85 and 86, use a graphing utility to graph the function.

85. $f(x) = \arctan(x/2)$

86. $f(x) = -\arcsin 2x$

Evaluating a Composition of Functions In Exercises 87–90, find the exact value of the expression. (*Hint:* Sketch a right triangle.)

87. $\cos\left(\arctan \frac{3}{4}\right)$

88. $\sec\left(\tan^{-1} \frac{12}{5}\right)$

89. $\sec\left[\sin^{-1}\left(-\frac{1}{4}\right)\right]$

90. $\cot\left[\arcsin\left(-\frac{12}{13}\right)\right]$

Writing an Expression In Exercises 91 and 92, write an algebraic expression that is equivalent to the given expression. (*Hint:* Sketch a right triangle.)

91. $\tan[\arccos(x/2)]$

92. $\sec(\arcsin x)$

4.8

93. **Angle of Elevation** The height of a radio transmission tower is 70 meters, and it casts a shadow of length 30 meters. Draw a right triangle that gives a visual representation of the problem. Label the known and unknown quantities. Then find the angle of elevation of the sun.

94. **Height** Your football has landed at the edge of the roof of your school building. When you are 25 feet from the base of the building, the angle of elevation to your football is 21°. How high off the ground is your football?

95. **Distance** From city A to city B, a plane flies 650 miles at a bearing of 48°. From city B to city C, the plane flies 810 miles at a bearing of 115°. Find the distance from city A to city C and the bearing from city A to city C.

96. **Wave Motion** Your fishing bobber oscillates in simple harmonic motion from the waves in the lake where you fish. Your bobber moves a total of 1.5 inches from its high point to its low point and returns to its high point every 3 seconds. Write an equation modeling the motion of your bobber, where the high point corresponds to the time $t = 0$.

Exploration

True or False? In Exercises 97 and 98, determine whether the statement is true or false. Justify your answer.

97. $y = \sin \theta$ is not a function because $\sin 30° = \sin 150°$.

98. Because $\tan 3\pi/4 = -1$, $\arctan(-1) = 3\pi/4$.

99. **Writing** Describe the behavior of $f(\theta) = \sec \theta$ at the zeros of $g(\theta) = \cos \theta$. Explain your reasoning.

100. **Conjecture**

(a) Use a graphing utility to complete the table.

θ	0.1	0.4	0.7	1.0	1.3
$\tan\left(\theta - \dfrac{\pi}{2}\right)$					
$-\cot \theta$					

(b) Make a conjecture about the relationship between $\tan[\theta - (\pi/2)]$ and $-\cot \theta$.

101. **Writing** When graphing the sine and cosine functions, determining the amplitude is part of the analysis. Explain why this is not true for the other four trigonometric functions.

102. **Oscillation of a Spring** A weight is suspended from a ceiling by a steel spring. The weight is lifted (positive direction) from the equilibrium position and released. The resulting motion of the weight is modeled by $y = Ae^{-kt} \cos bt = \frac{1}{5}e^{-t/10} \cos 6t$, where y is the distance (in feet) from equilibrium and t is the time (in seconds). The figure shows the graph of the function. For each of the following, describe the change in the system without graphing the resulting function.

(a) A is changed from $\frac{1}{5}$ to $\frac{1}{3}$.

(b) k is changed from $\frac{1}{10}$ to $\frac{1}{3}$.

(c) b is changed from 6 to 9.

Chapter Test

See CalcChat.com for tutorial help and worked-out solutions to odd-numbered exercises.

Take this test as you would take a test in class. When you are finished, check your work against the answers given in the back of the book.

1. Consider an angle that measures $\dfrac{5\pi}{4}$ radians.

    (a) Sketch the angle in standard position.

    (b) Determine two coterminal angles (one positive and one negative).

    (c) Convert the angle to degree measure.

Figure for 4

2. A truck is moving at a rate of 105 kilometers per hour, and the diameter of each of its wheels is 1 meter. Find the angular speed of the wheels in radians per minute.

3. A water sprinkler sprays water on a lawn over a distance of 25 feet and rotates through an angle of 130°. Find the area of the lawn watered by the sprinkler.

4. Find the exact values of the six trigonometric functions of the angle θ shown in the figure.

5. Given that $\tan \theta = \frac{3}{2}$, find the other five trigonometric functions of θ.

6. Determine the reference angle θ' of the angle $\theta = 205°$ and sketch θ and θ' in standard position.

7. Determine the quadrant in which θ lies when $\sec \theta < 0$ and $\tan \theta > 0$.

8. Find two exact values of θ in degrees $(0 \leq \theta < 360°)$ for which $\cos \theta = -\sqrt{3}/2$. (Do not use a calculator.)

9. Use a calculator to approximate two values of θ in radians $(0 \leq \theta < 2\pi)$ for which $\csc \theta = 1.030$. Round the results to two decimal places.

In Exercises 10 and 11, find the values of the remaining five trigonometric functions of θ with the given constraint.

10. $\cos \theta = \frac{3}{5}$, $\tan \theta < 0$

11. $\sec \theta = -\frac{29}{20}$, $\sin \theta > 0$

In Exercises 12 and 13, sketch the graph of the function. (Include two full periods.)

12. $g(x) = -2 \sin\left(x - \dfrac{\pi}{4}\right)$

13. $f(\alpha) = \dfrac{1}{2} \tan 2\alpha$

 In Exercises 14 and 15, use a graphing utility to graph the function. If the function is periodic, then find its period.

14. $y = \sin 2\pi x + 2 \cos \pi x$

15. $y = 6e^{-0.12t} \cos(0.25t)$, $0 \leq t \leq 32$

Figure for 16

16. Find a, b, and c for the function $f(x) = a \sin(bx + c)$ such that the graph of f matches the figure.

17. Find the exact value of $\cot\left(\arcsin \frac{3}{8}\right)$ without using a calculator.

18. Graph the function $f(x) = 2 \arcsin\left(\frac{1}{2}x\right)$.

19. A plane is 90 miles south and 110 miles east of London Heathrow Airport. What bearing should be taken to fly directly to the airport?

20. Write the equation for the simple harmonic motion of a ball on a spring that starts at its lowest point of 6 inches below equilibrium, bounces to its maximum height of 6 inches above equilibrium, and returns to its lowest point in a total of 2 seconds.

Proofs in Mathematics ■ ■ ■ ■ ■ ■ ■ ■ ■ ■ ■ ■ ■ ■ ■

The Pythagorean Theorem

The Pythagorean Theorem is one of the most famous theorems in mathematics. More than 100 different proofs now exist. James A. Garfield, the twentieth president of the United States, developed a proof of the Pythagorean Theorem in 1876. His proof, shown below, involves the fact that a trapezoid can be formed from two congruent right triangles and an isosceles right triangle.

The Pythagorean Theorem

In a right triangle, the sum of the squares of the lengths of the legs is equal to the square of the length of the hypotenuse, where a and b are the legs and c is the hypotenuse.

$$a^2 + b^2 = c^2$$

Proof

$$\text{Area of trapezoid } MNOP = \text{Area of } \triangle MNQ + \text{Area of } \triangle PQO + \text{Area of } \triangle NOQ$$

$$\frac{1}{2}(a + b)(a + b) = \frac{1}{2}ab + \frac{1}{2}ab + \frac{1}{2}c^2$$

$$\frac{1}{2}(a + b)(a + b) = ab + \frac{1}{2}c^2$$

$$(a + b)(a + b) = 2ab + c^2$$

$$a^2 + 2ab + b^2 = 2ab + c^2$$

$$a^2 + b^2 = c^2$$

P.S. Problem Solving ▪ ▪ ▪ ▪ ▪ ▪ ▪ ▪ ▪ ▪ ▪ ▪ ▪ ▪

1. Angle of Rotation The restaurant at the top of the Space Needle in Seattle, Washington, is circular and has a radius of 47.25 feet. The dining part of the restaurant revolves, making about one complete revolution every 48 minutes. A dinner party, seated at the edge of the revolving restaurant at 6:45 P.M., finishes at 8:57 P.M.

(a) Find the angle through which the dinner party rotated.

(b) Find the distance the party traveled during dinner.

2. Bicycle Gears A bicycle's gear ratio is the number of times the freewheel turns for every one turn of the chainwheel (see figure). The table shows the numbers of teeth in the freewheel and chainwheel for the first five gears of an 18-speed touring bicycle. The chainwheel completes one rotation for each gear. Find the angle through which the freewheel turns for each gear. Give your answers in both degrees and radians.

DATA	Gear Number	Number of Teeth in Freewheel	Number of Teeth in Chainwheel
	1	32	24
	2	26	24
	3	22	24
	4	32	40
	5	19	24

Freewheel

Chainwheel

3. Surveying A surveyor in a helicopter is trying to determine the width of an island, as shown in the figure.

3000 ft

Not drawn to scale

(a) What is the shortest distance d the helicopter would have to travel to land on the island?

(b) What is the horizontal distance x the helicopter would have to travel before it would be directly over the nearer end of the island?

(c) Find the width w of the island. Explain how you found your answer.

4. Similar Triangles and Trigonometric Functions Use the figure below.

(a) Explain why $\triangle ABC$, $\triangle ADE$, and $\triangle AFG$ are similar triangles.

(b) What does similarity imply about the ratios

$$\frac{BC}{AB}, \quad \frac{DE}{AD}, \quad \text{and} \quad \frac{FG}{AF}?$$

(c) Does the value of $\sin A$ depend on which triangle from part (a) you use to calculate it? Would using a different right triangle similar to the three given triangles change the value of $\sin A$?

(d) Do your conclusions from part (c) apply to the other five trigonometric functions? Explain.

5. Graphical Analysis Use a graphing utility to graph h, and use the graph to decide whether h is even, odd, or neither.

(a) $h(x) = \cos^2 x$

(b) $h(x) = \sin^2 x$

6. Squares of Even and Odd Functions Given that f is an even function and g is an odd function, use the results of Exercise 5 to make a conjecture about h, where

(a) $h(x) = [f(x)]^2$

(b) $h(x) = [g(x)]^2$.

7. Height of a Ferris Wheel Car The model for the height h (in feet) of a Ferris wheel car is

$$h = 50 + 50 \sin 8\pi t$$

where t is the time (in minutes). (The Ferris wheel has a radius of 50 feet.) This model yields a height of 50 feet when $t = 0$. Alter the model so that the height of the car is 1 foot when $t = 0$.

8. Periodic Function The function f is periodic, with period c. So, $f(t + c) = f(t)$. Are the following statements true? Explain.

(a) $f(t - 2c) = f(t)$

(b) $f\left(t + \frac{1}{2}c\right) = f\left(\frac{1}{2}t\right)$

(c) $f\left(\frac{1}{2}(t + c)\right) = f\left(\frac{1}{2}t\right)$

347

9. **Blood Pressure** The pressure P (in millimeters of mercury) against the walls of the blood vessels of a patient is modeled by

$$P = 100 - 20 \cos\left(\frac{8\pi}{3}t\right)$$

where t is time (in seconds).

(a) Use a graphing utility to graph the model.

(b) What is the period of the model? What does the period tell you about this situation?

(c) What is the amplitude of the model? What does it tell you about this situation?

(d) If one cycle of this model is equivalent to one heartbeat, what is the pulse of this patient?

(e) A physician wants this patient's pulse rate to be 64 beats per minute or less. What should the period be? What should the coefficient of t be?

10. **Biorhythms** A popular theory that attempts to explain the ups and downs of everyday life states that each of us has three cycles, called biorhythms, which begin at birth. These three cycles can be modeled by sine waves.

Physical (23 days): $P = \sin\dfrac{2\pi t}{23}, \quad t \geq 0$

Emotional (28 days): $E = \sin\dfrac{2\pi t}{28}, \quad t \geq 0$

Intellectual (33 days): $I = \sin\dfrac{2\pi t}{33}, \quad t \geq 0$

where t is the number of days since birth. Consider a person who was born on July 20, 1990.

(a) Use a graphing utility to graph the three models in the same viewing window for $7300 \leq t \leq 7380$.

(b) Describe the person's biorhythms during the month of September 2010.

(c) Calculate the person's three energy levels on September 22, 2010.

11. (a) **Graphical Reasoning** Use a graphing utility to graph the functions

$f(x) = 2\cos 2x + 3\sin 3x$ and

$g(x) = 2\cos 2x + 3\sin 4x.$

(b) Use the graphs from part (a) to find the period of each function.

(c) Is the function $h(x) = A\cos \alpha x + B\sin \beta x$, where α and β are positive integers, periodic? Explain your reasoning.

12. **Analyzing Trigonometric Functions** Two trigonometric functions f and g have periods of 2, and their graphs intersect at $x = 5.35$.

(a) Give one positive value of x less than 5.35 and one value of x greater than 5.35 at which the functions have the same value.

(b) Determine one negative value of x at which the graphs intersect.

(c) Is it true that $f(13.35) = g(-4.65)$? Explain your reasoning.

13. **Refraction** When you stand in shallow water and look at an object below the surface of the water, the object will look farther away from you than it really is. This is because when light rays pass between air and water, the water refracts, or bends, the light rays. The index of refraction for water is 1.333. This is the ratio of the sine of θ_1 and the sine of θ_2 (see figure).

(a) While standing in water that is 2 feet deep, you look at a rock at angle $\theta_1 = 60°$ (measured from a line perpendicular to the surface of the water). Find θ_2.

(b) Find the distances x and y.

(c) Find the distance d between where the rock is and where it appears to be.

(d) What happens to d as you move closer to the rock? Explain your reasoning.

14. **Polynomial Approximation** In calculus, it can be shown that the arctangent function can be approximated by the polynomial

$$\arctan x \approx x - \frac{x^3}{3} + \frac{x^5}{5} - \frac{x^7}{7}$$

where x is in radians.

(a) Use a graphing utility to graph the arctangent function and its polynomial approximation in the same viewing window. How do the graphs compare?

(b) Study the pattern in the polynomial approximation of the arctangent function and guess the next term. Then repeat part (a). How does the accuracy of the approximation change when you add additional terms?

5 Analytic Trigonometry

5.1 Using Fundamental Identities
5.2 Verifying Trigonometric Identities
5.3 Solving Trigonometric Equations
5.4 Sum and Difference Formulas
5.5 Multiple-Angle and Product-to-Sum Formulas

Projectile Motion
(Example 10, page 388)

Standing Waves *(page 378)*

Honeycomb Cell *(Example 10, page 370)*

Shadow Length
(Exercise 66, page 363)

Friction *(Exercise 65, page 356)*

5.1 Using Fundamental Identities

■ Recognize and write the fundamental trigonometric identities.
■ Use the fundamental trigonometric identities to evaluate trigonometric functions, simplify trigonometric expressions, and rewrite trigonometric expressions.

Introduction

In Chapter 4, you studied the basic definitions, properties, graphs, and applications of the individual trigonometric functions. In this chapter, you will learn how to use the fundamental identities to do the following.

1. Evaluate trigonometric functions.
2. Simplify trigonometric expressions.
3. Develop additional trigonometric identities.
4. Solve trigonometric equations.

Fundamental trigonometric identities can help you simplify trigonometric expressions. For instance, in Exercise 65 on page 356, you will use trigonometric identities to simplify an expression for the coefficient of friction.

Fundamental Trigonometric Identities

Reciprocal Identities

$$\sin u = \frac{1}{\csc u} \qquad \cos u = \frac{1}{\sec u} \qquad \tan u = \frac{1}{\cot u}$$

$$\csc u = \frac{1}{\sin u} \qquad \sec u = \frac{1}{\cos u} \qquad \cot u = \frac{1}{\tan u}$$

Quotient Identities

$$\tan u = \frac{\sin u}{\cos u} \qquad \cot u = \frac{\cos u}{\sin u}$$

Pythagorean Identities

$$\sin^2 u + \cos^2 u = 1 \qquad 1 + \tan^2 u = \sec^2 u \qquad 1 + \cot^2 u = \csc^2 u$$

Cofunction Identities

$$\sin\left(\frac{\pi}{2} - u\right) = \cos u \qquad \cos\left(\frac{\pi}{2} - u\right) = \sin u$$

$$\tan\left(\frac{\pi}{2} - u\right) = \cot u \qquad \cot\left(\frac{\pi}{2} - u\right) = \tan u$$

$$\sec\left(\frac{\pi}{2} - u\right) = \csc u \qquad \csc\left(\frac{\pi}{2} - u\right) = \sec u$$

Even/Odd Identities

$$\sin(-u) = -\sin u \qquad \cos(-u) = \cos u \qquad \tan(-u) = -\tan u$$

$$\csc(-u) = -\csc u \qquad \sec(-u) = \sec u \qquad \cot(-u) = -\cot u$$

REMARK You should learn the fundamental trigonometric identities well, because you will use them frequently in trigonometry and they will also appear in calculus. Note that u can be an angle, a real number, or a variable.

Pythagorean identities are sometimes used in radical form such as

$$\sin u = \pm\sqrt{1 - \cos^2 u}$$

or

$$\tan u = \pm\sqrt{\sec^2 u - 1}$$

where the sign depends on the choice of u.

Using the Fundamental Identities

One common application of trigonometric identities is to use given values of trigonometric functions to evaluate other trigonometric functions.

EXAMPLE 1 **Using Identities to Evaluate a Function**

Use the values $\sec u = -\frac{3}{2}$ and $\tan u > 0$ to find the values of all six trigonometric functions.

Solution Using a reciprocal identity, you have

$$\cos u = \frac{1}{\sec u} = \frac{1}{-3/2} = -\frac{2}{3}.$$

Using a Pythagorean identity, you have

$$\sin^2 u = 1 - \cos^2 u \qquad \text{Pythagorean identity}$$

$$= 1 - \left(-\tfrac{2}{3}\right)^2 \qquad \text{Substitute } -\tfrac{2}{3} \text{ for } \cos u.$$

$$= \tfrac{5}{9}. \qquad \text{Simplify.}$$

Because $\sec u < 0$ and $\tan u > 0$, it follows that u lies in Quadrant III. Moreover, because $\sin u$ is negative when u is in Quadrant III, choose the negative root and obtain $\sin u = -\sqrt{5}/3$. Knowing the values of the sine and cosine enables you to find the values of all six trigonometric functions.

$$\sin u = -\frac{\sqrt{5}}{3} \qquad\qquad \csc u = \frac{1}{\sin u} = -\frac{3}{\sqrt{5}} = -\frac{3\sqrt{5}}{5}$$

$$\cos u = -\frac{2}{3} \qquad\qquad \sec u = \frac{1}{\cos u} = -\frac{3}{2}$$

$$\tan u = \frac{\sin u}{\cos u} = \frac{-\sqrt{5}/3}{-2/3} = \frac{\sqrt{5}}{2} \qquad \cot u = \frac{1}{\tan u} = \frac{2}{\sqrt{5}} = \frac{2\sqrt{5}}{5}$$

✓ **Checkpoint** *Audio-video solution in English & Spanish at LarsonPrecalculus.com.*

Use the values $\tan x = \frac{1}{3}$ and $\cos x < 0$ to find the values of all six trigonometric functions.

EXAMPLE 2 **Simplifying a Trigonometric Expression**

Simplify

$$\sin x \cos^2 x - \sin x.$$

Solution First factor out a common monomial factor and then use a fundamental identity.

$$\sin x \cos^2 x - \sin x = \sin x(\cos^2 x - 1) \qquad \text{Factor out common monomial factor.}$$

$$= -\sin x(1 - \cos^2 x) \qquad \text{Factor out } -1.$$

$$= -\sin x(\sin^2 x) \qquad \text{Pythagorean identity}$$

$$= -\sin^3 x \qquad \text{Multiply.}$$

✓ **Checkpoint** *Audio-video solution in English & Spanish at LarsonPrecalculus.com.*

Simplify

$$\cos^2 x \csc x - \csc x.$$

▷ **TECHNOLOGY** To use a graphing utility to check the result of Example 2, graph

$$y_1 = \sin x \cos^2 x - \sin x$$

and

$$y_2 = -\sin^3 x$$

in the same viewing window, as shown below. Because Example 2 shows the equivalence algebraically and the two graphs appear to coincide, you can conclude that the expressions are equivalent.

When factoring trigonometric expressions, it is helpful to find a special polynomial factoring form that fits the expression, as shown in Example 3.

EXAMPLE 3   **Factoring Trigonometric Expressions**

Factor each expression.

a. $\sec^2 \theta - 1$ **b.** $4 \tan^2 \theta + \tan \theta - 3$

Solution

a. This expression has the form $u^2 - v^2$, which is the difference of two squares. It factors as

$$\sec^2 \theta - 1 = (\sec \theta + 1)(\sec \theta - 1).$$

b. This expression has the polynomial form $ax^2 + bx + c$, and it factors as

$$4 \tan^2 \theta + \tan \theta - 3 = (4 \tan \theta - 3)(\tan \theta + 1).$$

✓ **Checkpoint** *Audio-video solution in English & Spanish at LarsonPrecalculus.com.*

Factor each expression.

a. $1 - \cos^2 \theta$ **b.** $2 \csc^2 \theta - 7 \csc \theta + 6$

On occasion, factoring or simplifying can best be done by first rewriting the expression in terms of just *one* trigonometric function or in terms of *sine and cosine only*. Examples 4 and 5, respectively, show these strategies.

EXAMPLE 4   **Factoring a Trigonometric Expression**

Factor $\csc^2 x - \cot x - 3$.

Solution   Use the identity $\csc^2 x = 1 + \cot^2 x$ to rewrite the expression.

$$
\begin{aligned}
\csc^2 x - \cot x - 3 &= (1 + \cot^2 x) - \cot x - 3 & &\text{Pythagorean identity} \\
&= \cot^2 x - \cot x - 2 & &\text{Combine like terms.} \\
&= (\cot x - 2)(\cot x + 1) & &\text{Factor.}
\end{aligned}
$$

✓ **Checkpoint** *Audio-video solution in English & Spanish at LarsonPrecalculus.com.*

Factor $\sec^2 x + 3 \tan x + 1$.

EXAMPLE 5   **Simplifying a Trigonometric Expression**

$$
\begin{aligned}
\sin t + \cot t \cos t &= \sin t + \left(\frac{\cos t}{\sin t}\right) \cos t & &\text{Quotient identity} \\
&= \frac{\sin^2 t + \cos^2 t}{\sin t} & &\text{Add fractions.} \\
&= \frac{1}{\sin t} & &\text{Pythagorean identity} \\
&= \csc t & &\text{Reciprocal identity}
\end{aligned}
$$

✓ **Checkpoint** 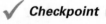 *Audio-video solution in English & Spanish at LarsonPrecalculus.com.*

Simplify $\csc x - \cos x \cot x$.

▷ **ALGEBRA HELP**   In Example 3, you need to be able to factor the difference of two squares and factor a trinomial. You can review the techniques for factoring in Appendix A.3.

•• **REMARK**   Remember that when adding rational expressions, you must first find the least common denominator (LCD). In Example 5, the LCD is $\sin t$.

EXAMPLE 6 **Adding Trigonometric Expressions**

Perform the addition $\dfrac{\sin \theta}{1 + \cos \theta} + \dfrac{\cos \theta}{\sin \theta}$ and simplify.

Solution

$$\dfrac{\sin \theta}{1 + \cos \theta} + \dfrac{\cos \theta}{\sin \theta} = \dfrac{(\sin \theta)(\sin \theta) + (\cos \theta)(1 + \cos \theta)}{(1 + \cos \theta)(\sin \theta)}$$

$$= \dfrac{\sin^2 \theta + \cos^2 \theta + \cos \theta}{(1 + \cos \theta)(\sin \theta)} \qquad \text{Multiply.}$$

$$= \dfrac{1 + \cos \theta}{(1 + \cos \theta)(\sin \theta)} \qquad \begin{array}{l}\text{Pythagorean identity:}\\ \sin^2 \theta + \cos^2 \theta = 1\end{array}$$

$$= \dfrac{1}{\sin \theta} \qquad \text{Divide out common factor.}$$

$$= \csc \theta \qquad \text{Reciprocal identity}$$

✓ **Checkpoint** Audio-video solution in English & Spanish at LarsonPrecalculus.com.

Perform the addition $\dfrac{1}{1 + \sin \theta} + \dfrac{1}{1 - \sin \theta}$ and simplify.

The next two examples involve techniques for rewriting expressions in forms that are used in calculus.

EXAMPLE 7 **Rewriting a Trigonometric Expression**

Rewrite $\dfrac{1}{1 + \sin x}$ so that it is *not* in fractional form.

Solution From the Pythagorean identity

$$\cos^2 x = 1 - \sin^2 x = (1 - \sin x)(1 + \sin x)$$

multiplying both the numerator and the denominator by $(1 - \sin x)$ will produce a monomial denominator.

$$\dfrac{1}{1 + \sin x} = \dfrac{1}{1 + \sin x} \cdot \dfrac{1 - \sin x}{1 - \sin x} \qquad \begin{array}{l}\text{Multiply numerator and}\\ \text{denominator by } (1 - \sin x).\end{array}$$

$$= \dfrac{1 - \sin x}{1 - \sin^2 x} \qquad \text{Multiply.}$$

$$= \dfrac{1 - \sin x}{\cos^2 x} \qquad \text{Pythagorean identity}$$

$$= \dfrac{1}{\cos^2 x} - \dfrac{\sin x}{\cos^2 x} \qquad \text{Write as separate fractions.}$$

$$= \dfrac{1}{\cos^2 x} - \dfrac{\sin x}{\cos x} \cdot \dfrac{1}{\cos x} \qquad \text{Product of fractions}$$

$$= \sec^2 x - \tan x \sec x \qquad \text{Reciprocal and quotient identities}$$

✓ **Checkpoint** 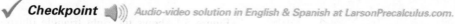 Audio-video solution in English & Spanish at LarsonPrecalculus.com.

Rewrite $\dfrac{\cos^2 \theta}{1 - \sin \theta}$ so that it is *not* in fractional form.

EXAMPLE 8 **Trigonometric Substitution**

Use the substitution $x = 2 \tan \theta$, $0 < \theta < \pi/2$, to write $\sqrt{4 + x^2}$ as a trigonometric function of θ.

Solution Begin by letting $x = 2 \tan \theta$. Then, you obtain

$$\sqrt{4 + x^2} = \sqrt{4 + (2 \tan \theta)^2} \qquad \text{Substitute } 2 \tan \theta \text{ for } x.$$

$$= \sqrt{4 + 4 \tan^2 \theta} \qquad \text{Rule of exponents}$$

$$= \sqrt{4(1 + \tan^2 \theta)} \qquad \text{Factor.}$$

$$= \sqrt{4 \sec^2 \theta} \qquad \text{Pythagorean identity}$$

$$= 2 \sec \theta. \qquad \sec \theta > 0 \text{ for } 0 < \theta < \pi/2$$

✓ **Checkpoint** ◀))) *Audio-video solution in English & Spanish at LarsonPrecalculus.com.*

Use the substitution $x = 3 \sin \theta$, $0 < \theta < \pi/2$, to write $\sqrt{9 - x^2}$ as a trigonometric function of θ.

Angle whose tangent is $x/2$
Figure 5.1

Figure 5.1 shows the right triangle illustration of the trigonometric substitution $x = 2 \tan \theta$ in Example 8. Use this triangle to check the solution of Example 8, as follows. For $0 < \theta < \pi/2$, you have

$$\text{opp} = x, \quad \text{adj} = 2, \quad \text{and} \quad \text{hyp} = \sqrt{4 + x^2}.$$

With these expressions, you can write

$$\sec \theta = \frac{\text{hyp}}{\text{adj}} = \frac{\sqrt{4 + x^2}}{2}.$$

So, $2 \sec \theta = \sqrt{4 + x^2}$, and the solution checks.

EXAMPLE 9 **Rewriting a Logarithmic Expression**

Rewrite $\ln|\csc \theta| + \ln|\tan \theta|$ as a single logarithm and simplify the result.

Solution

$$\ln|\csc \theta| + \ln|\tan \theta| = \ln|\csc \theta \tan \theta| \qquad \text{Product Property of Logarithms}$$

$$= \ln\left|\frac{1}{\sin \theta} \cdot \frac{\sin \theta}{\cos \theta}\right| \qquad \text{Reciprocal and quotient identities}$$

$$= \ln\left|\frac{1}{\cos \theta}\right| \qquad \text{Simplify.}$$

$$= \ln|\sec \theta| \qquad \text{Reciprocal identity}$$

▷ **ALGEBRA HELP** Recall that for positive real numbers u and v,

$$\ln u + \ln v = \ln(uv).$$

You can review the properties of logarithms in Section 3.3.

✓ **Checkpoint** ◀))) *Audio-video solution in English & Spanish at LarsonPrecalculus.com.*

Rewrite $\ln|\sec x| + \ln|\sin x|$ as a single logarithm and simplify the result.

Summarize (Section 5.1)

1. State the fundamental trigonometric identities *(page 350)*.

2. Explain how to use the fundamental trigonometric identities to evaluate trigonometric functions, simplify trigonometric expressions, and rewrite trigonometric expressions *(pages 351–354)*. For examples of these concepts, see Examples 1–9.

5.1 Exercises

See CalcChat.com for tutorial help and worked-out solutions to odd-numbered exercises.

Vocabulary: Fill in the blank to complete the trigonometric identity.

1. $\dfrac{\sin u}{\cos u} = $ _____

2. $\dfrac{1}{\csc u} = $ _____

3. $\dfrac{1}{\tan u} = $ _____

4. $\sec\left(\dfrac{\pi}{2} - u\right) = $ _____

5. $1 + $ _____ $= \csc^2 u$

6. $\cot(-u) = $ _____

Skills and Applications

Using Identities to Evaluate a Function In Exercises 7–14, use the given values to find the values (if possible) of all six trigonometric functions.

7. $\sin x = \dfrac{1}{2}, \quad \cos x = \dfrac{\sqrt{3}}{2}$

8. $\csc \theta = \dfrac{25}{7}, \quad \tan \theta = \dfrac{7}{24}$

9. $\cos\left(\dfrac{\pi}{2} - x\right) = \dfrac{3}{5}, \quad \cos x = \dfrac{4}{5}$

10. $\sin(-x) = -\dfrac{1}{3}, \quad \tan x = -\dfrac{\sqrt{2}}{4}$

11. $\sec x = 4, \quad \sin x > 0$

12. $\csc \theta = -5, \quad \cos \theta < 0$

13. $\sin \theta = -1, \quad \cot \theta = 0$

14. $\tan \theta$ is undefined, $\quad \sin \theta > 0$

Matching Trigonometric Expressions In Exercises 15–20, match the trigonometric expression with one of the following.

(a) $\csc x$ (b) -1 (c) 1

(d) $\sin x \tan x$ (e) $\sec^2 x$ (f) $\sec^2 x + \tan^2 x$

15. $\sec x \cos x$

16. $\cot^2 x - \csc^2 x$

17. $\sec^4 x - \tan^4 x$

18. $\cot x \sec x$

19. $\dfrac{\sec^2 x - 1}{\sin^2 x}$

20. $\dfrac{\cos^2[(\pi/2) - x]}{\cos x}$

Factoring a Trigonometric Expression In Exercises 21–28, factor the expression and use the fundamental identities to simplify. There is more than one correct form of each answer.

21. $\tan^2 x - \tan^2 x \sin^2 x$

22. $\sin^2 x \sec^2 x - \sin^2 x$

23. $\dfrac{\sec^2 x - 1}{\sec x - 1}$

24. $\dfrac{\cos x - 2}{\cos^2 x - 4}$

25. $1 - 2\cos^2 x + \cos^4 x$

26. $\sec^4 x - \tan^4 x$

27. $\cot^3 x + \cot^2 x + \cot x + 1$

28. $\sec^3 x - \sec^2 x - \sec x + 1$

Factoring a Trigonometric Expression In Exercises 29–32, factor the trigonometric expression. There is more than one correct form of each answer.

29. $3\sin^2 x - 5\sin x - 2$

30. $6\cos^2 x + 5\cos x - 6$

31. $\cot^2 x + \csc x - 1$

32. $\sin^2 x + 3\cos x + 3$

Multiplying Trigonometric Expressions In Exercises 33 and 34, perform the multiplication and use the fundamental identities to simplify. There is more than one correct form of each answer.

33. $(\sin x + \cos x)^2$

34. $(2\csc x + 2)(2\csc x - 2)$

Simplifying a Trigonometric Expression In Exercises 35–44, use the fundamental identities to simplify the expression. There is more than one correct form of each answer.

35. $\cot \theta \sec \theta$

36. $\tan(-x)\cos x$

37. $\sin \phi(\csc \phi - \sin \phi)$

38. $\cos t(1 + \tan^2 t)$

39. $\dfrac{1 - \sin^2 x}{\csc^2 x - 1}$

40. $\dfrac{\tan \theta \cot \theta}{\sec \theta}$

41. $\cos\left(\dfrac{\pi}{2} - x\right)\sec x$

42. $\dfrac{\cos^2 y}{1 - \sin y}$

43. $\sin \beta \tan \beta + \cos \beta$

44. $\cot u \sin u + \tan u \cos u$

Adding or Subtracting Trigonometric Expressions In Exercises 45–48, perform the addition or subtraction and use the fundamental identities to simplify. There is more than one correct form of each answer.

45. $\dfrac{1}{1 + \cos x} + \dfrac{1}{1 - \cos x}$

46. $\dfrac{1}{\sec x + 1} - \dfrac{1}{\sec x - 1}$

47. $\tan x - \dfrac{\sec^2 x}{\tan x}$

48. $\dfrac{\cos x}{1 + \sin x} + \dfrac{1 + \sin x}{\cos x}$

Rewriting a Trigonometric Expression In Exercises 49 and 50, rewrite the expression so that it is not in fractional form. There is more than one correct form of each answer.

49. $\dfrac{\sin^2 y}{1 - \cos y}$

50. $\dfrac{5}{\tan x + \sec x}$

Trigonometric Functions and Expressions In Exercises 51 and 52, use a graphing utility to determine which of the six trigonometric functions is equal to the expression. Verify your answer algebraically.

51. $\cos x \cot x + \sin x$ **52.** $\dfrac{1}{\sin x}\left(\dfrac{1}{\cos x} - \cos x\right)$

Trigonometric Substitution In Exercises 53–56, use the trigonometric substitution to write the algebraic expression as a trigonometric function of θ, where $0 < \theta < \pi/2$.

53. $\sqrt{9 - x^2}$, $x = 3\cos\theta$
54. $\sqrt{49 - x^2}$, $x = 7\sin\theta$
55. $\sqrt{x^2 - 4}$, $x = 2\sec\theta$
56. $\sqrt{9x^2 + 25}$, $3x = 5\tan\theta$

Trigonometric Substitution In Exercises 57 and 58, use the trigonometric substitution to write the algebraic equation as a trigonometric equation of θ, where $-\pi/2 < \theta < \pi/2$. Then find $\sin\theta$ and $\cos\theta$.

57. $3 = \sqrt{9 - x^2}$, $x = 3\sin\theta$
58. $-5\sqrt{3} = \sqrt{100 - x^2}$, $x = 10\cos\theta$

Solving a Trigonometric Equation In Exercises 59 and 60, use a graphing utility to solve the equation for θ, where $0 \le \theta < 2\pi$.

59. $\sin\theta = \sqrt{1 - \cos^2\theta}$ **60.** $\sec\theta = \sqrt{1 + \tan^2\theta}$

Rewriting a Logarithmic Expression In Exercises 61–64, rewrite the expression as a single logarithm and simplify the result.

61. $\ln|\sin x| + \ln|\cot x|$ **62.** $\ln|\cos x| - \ln|\sin x|$
63. $\ln|\cot t| + \ln(1 + \tan^2 t)$ **64.** $\ln(\cos^2 t) + \ln(1 + \tan^2 t)$

· · 65. Friction ·

The forces acting on an object weighing W units on an inclined plane positioned at an angle of θ with the horizontal (see figure) are modeled by

$$\mu W \cos\theta = W \sin\theta$$

where μ is the coefficient of friction. Solve the equation for μ and simplify the result.

66. Rate of Change The rate of change of the function $f(x) = \sec x + \cos x$ is given by the expression $\sec x \tan x - \sin x$. Show that this expression can also be written as $\sin x \tan^2 x$.

Exploration

True or False? In Exercises 67 and 68, determine whether the statement is true or false. Justify your answer.

67. The even and odd trigonometric identities are helpful for determining whether the value of a trigonometric function is positive or negative.

68. A cofunction identity can transform a tangent function into a cosecant function.

Finding Limits of Trigonometric Functions In Exercises 69 and 70, fill in the blanks.

69. As $x \to \left(\dfrac{\pi}{2}\right)^{-}$, $\tan x \to$ ▢ and $\cot x \to$ ▢ .

70. As $x \to \pi^{+}$, $\sin x \to$ ▢ and $\csc x \to$ ▢ .

Determining Identities In Exercises 71 and 72, determine whether the equation is an identity, and give a reason for your answer.

71. $\dfrac{(\sin k\theta)}{(\cos k\theta)} = \tan\theta$, k is a constant.

72. $\sin\theta \csc\theta = 1$

73. Trigonometric Substitution Use the trigonometric substitution $u = a\tan\theta$, where $-\pi/2 < \theta < \pi/2$ and $a > 0$, to simplify the expression $\sqrt{a^2 + u^2}$.

74. **HOW DO YOU SEE IT?**
Explain how to use the figure to derive the Pythagorean identities

$$\sin^2\theta + \cos^2\theta = 1,$$
$$1 + \tan^2\theta = \sec^2\theta,$$

and $1 + \cot^2\theta = \csc^2\theta.$

Discuss how to remember these identities and other fundamental trigonometric identities.

75. Writing Trigonometric Functions in Terms of Sine Write each of the other trigonometric functions of θ in terms of $\sin\theta$.

76. Rewriting a Trigonometric Expression Rewrite the following expression in terms of $\sin\theta$ and $\cos\theta$.

$$\frac{\sec\theta\,(1 + \tan\theta)}{\sec\theta + \csc\theta}$$

5.2   Verifying Trigonometric Identities

■ Verify trigonometric identities.

Introduction

In this section, you will study techniques for verifying trigonometric identities. In the next section, you will study techniques for solving trigonometric equations. The key to verifying identities *and* solving equations is the ability to use the fundamental identities and the rules of algebra to rewrite trigonometric expressions.

Remember that a *conditional equation* is an equation that is true for only some of the values in its domain. For example, the conditional equation

$$\sin x = 0 \qquad \text{Conditional equation}$$

is true only for

$$x = n\pi$$

where n is an integer. When you find these values, you are *solving* the equation.

On the other hand, an equation that is true for all real values in the domain of the variable is an *identity*. For example, the familiar equation

$$\sin^2 x = 1 - \cos^2 x \qquad \text{Identity}$$

is true for all real numbers x. So, it is an identity.

Verifying Trigonometric Identities

Although there are similarities, verifying that a trigonometric equation is an identity is quite different from solving an equation. There is no well-defined set of rules to follow in verifying trigonometric identities, and it is best to learn the process by practicing.

Trigonometric identities enable you to rewrite trigonometric equations that model real-life situations. For instance, in Exercise 66 on page 363, trigonometric identities can help you simplify the equation that models the length of a shadow cast by a gnomon (a device used to tell time).

Guidelines for Verifying Trigonometric Identities

1. Work with one side of the equation at a time. It is often better to work with the more complicated side first.

2. Look for opportunities to factor an expression, add fractions, square a binomial, or create a monomial denominator.

3. Look for opportunities to use the fundamental identities. Note which functions are in the final expression you want. Sines and cosines pair up well, as do secants and tangents, and cosecants and cotangents.

4. If the preceding guidelines do not help, then try converting all terms to sines and cosines.

5. Always try *something*. Even making an attempt that leads to a dead end can provide insight.

Verifying trigonometric identities is a useful process when you need to convert a trigonometric expression into a form that is more useful algebraically. When you verify an identity, you cannot *assume* that the two sides of the equation are equal because you are trying to verify that they *are* equal. As a result, when verifying identities, you cannot use operations such as adding the same quantity to each side of the equation or cross multiplication.

EXAMPLE 1 **Verifying a Trigonometric Identity**

Verify the identity $\dfrac{\sec^2 \theta - 1}{\sec^2 \theta} = \sin^2 \theta$.

REMARK Remember that an identity is only true for all real values in the domain of the variable. For instance, in Example 1 the identity is not true when $\theta = \pi/2$ because $\sec^2 \theta$ is not defined when $\theta = \pi/2$.

Solution Start with the left side because it is more complicated.

$$\frac{\sec^2 \theta - 1}{\sec^2 \theta} = \frac{(\tan^2 \theta + 1) - 1}{\sec^2 \theta} \qquad \text{Pythagorean identity}$$

$$= \frac{\tan^2 \theta}{\sec^2 \theta} \qquad \text{Simplify.}$$

$$= \tan^2 \theta (\cos^2 \theta) \qquad \text{Reciprocal identity}$$

$$= \frac{\sin^2 \theta}{(\cos^2 \theta)} (\cos^2 \theta) \qquad \text{Quotient identity}$$

$$= \sin^2 \theta \qquad \text{Simplify.}$$

Notice that you verify the identity by starting with the left side of the equation (the more complicated side) and using the fundamental trigonometric identities to simplify it until you obtain the right side.

✓ **Checkpoint** Audio-video solution in English & Spanish at LarsonPrecalculus.com.

Verify the identity $\dfrac{\sin^2 \theta + \cos^2 \theta}{\cos^2 \theta \sec^2 \theta} = 1$.

There can be more than one way to verify an identity. Here is another way to verify the identity in Example 1.

$$\frac{\sec^2 \theta - 1}{\sec^2 \theta} = \frac{\sec^2 \theta}{\sec^2 \theta} - \frac{1}{\sec^2 \theta} \qquad \text{Write as separate fractions.}$$

$$= 1 - \cos^2 \theta \qquad \text{Reciprocal identity}$$

$$= \sin^2 \theta \qquad \text{Pythagorean identity}$$

EXAMPLE 2 **Verifying a Trigonometric Identity**

Verify the identity $2 \sec^2 \alpha = \dfrac{1}{1 - \sin \alpha} + \dfrac{1}{1 + \sin \alpha}$.

Algebraic Solution

Start with the right side because it is more complicated.

$$\frac{1}{1 - \sin \alpha} + \frac{1}{1 + \sin \alpha} = \frac{1 + \sin \alpha + 1 - \sin \alpha}{(1 - \sin \alpha)(1 + \sin \alpha)} \qquad \text{Add fractions.}$$

$$= \frac{2}{1 - \sin^2 \alpha} \qquad \text{Simplify.}$$

$$= \frac{2}{\cos^2 \alpha} \qquad \text{Pythagorean identity}$$

$$= 2 \sec^2 \alpha \qquad \text{Reciprocal identity}$$

Numerical Solution

Use a graphing utility to create a table that shows the values of $y_1 = 2/\cos^2 x$ and $y_2 = 1/(1 - \sin x) + 1/(1 + \sin x)$ for different values of x.

X	Y1	Y2
-.5	2.5969	2.5969
-.25	2.1304	2.1304
0	2	2
.25	2.1304	2.1304
.5	2.5969	2.5969
.75	3.7357	3.7357
1	6.851	6.851
X=-.5		

The values for y_1 and y_2 appear to be identical, so the equation appears to be an identity.

✓ **Checkpoint** Audio-video solution in English & Spanish at LarsonPrecalculus.com.

Verify the identity $2 \csc^2 \beta = \dfrac{1}{1 - \cos \beta} + \dfrac{1}{1 + \cos \beta}$.

In Example 2, you needed to write the Pythagorean identity $\sin^2 u + \cos^2 u = 1$ in the equivalent form $\cos^2 u = 1 - \sin^2 u$. When verifying identities, you may find it useful to write the Pythagorean identities in one of these equivalent forms.

Pythagorean Identities

$$\sin^2 u + \cos^2 u = 1$$

$$1 + \tan^2 u = \sec^2 u$$

$$1 + \cot^2 u = \csc^2 u$$

Equivalent Forms

$$\sin^2 u = 1 - \cos^2 u$$

$$\cos^2 u = 1 - \sin^2 u$$

$$1 = \sec^2 u - \tan^2 u$$

$$\tan^2 u = \sec^2 u - 1$$

$$1 = \csc^2 u - \cot^2 u$$

$$\cot^2 u = \csc^2 u - 1$$

EXAMPLE 3 **Verifying a Trigonometric Identity**

Verify the identity $(\tan^2 x + 1)(\cos^2 x - 1) = -\tan^2 x$.

Algebraic Solution

By applying identities before multiplying, you obtain the following.

$$(\tan^2 x + 1)(\cos^2 x - 1) = (\sec^2 x)(-\sin^2 x) \quad \text{Pythagorean identities}$$

$$= -\frac{\sin^2 x}{\cos^2 x} \quad \text{Reciprocal identity}$$

$$= -\left(\frac{\sin x}{\cos x}\right)^2 \quad \text{Property of exponents}$$

$$= -\tan^2 x \quad \text{Quotient identity}$$

Graphical Solution

$y_1 = (\tan^2 x + 1)(\cos^2 x - 1)$

$y_2 = -\tan^2 x$

Because the graphs appear to coincide, the given equation appears to be an identity.

✓ **Checkpoint** ◀))) *Audio-video solution in English & Spanish at LarsonPrecalculus.com.*

Verify the identity $(\sec^2 x - 1)(\sin^2 x - 1) = -\sin^2 x$.

REMARK Although a graphing utility can be useful in helping to verify an identity, you must use algebraic techniques to produce a *valid* proof.

EXAMPLE 4 **Converting to Sines and Cosines**

Verify the identity $\tan x + \cot x = \sec x \csc x$.

Solution Convert the left side into sines and cosines.

$$\tan x + \cot x = \frac{\sin x}{\cos x} + \frac{\cos x}{\sin x} \quad \text{Quotient identities}$$

$$= \frac{\sin^2 x + \cos^2 x}{\cos x \sin x} \quad \text{Add fractions.}$$

$$= \frac{1}{\cos x \sin x} \quad \text{Pythagorean identity}$$

$$= \frac{1}{\cos x} \cdot \frac{1}{\sin x} \quad \text{Product of fractions}$$

$$= \sec x \csc x \quad \text{Reciprocal identities}$$

✓ **Checkpoint** ◀))) *Audio-video solution in English & Spanish at LarsonPrecalculus.com.*

Verify the identity $\csc x - \sin x = \cos x \cot x$.

Recall from algebra that *rationalizing the denominator* using conjugates is, on occasion, a powerful simplification technique. A related form of this technique works for simplifying trigonometric expressions as well. For instance, to simplify

$$\frac{1}{1 - \cos x}$$

multiply the numerator and the denominator by $1 + \cos x$.

$$\frac{1}{1 - \cos x} = \frac{1}{1 - \cos x}\left(\frac{1 + \cos x}{1 + \cos x}\right)$$

$$= \frac{1 + \cos x}{1 - \cos^2 x}$$

$$= \frac{1 + \cos x}{\sin^2 x}$$

$$= \csc^2 x(1 + \cos x)$$

The expression $\csc^2 x(1 + \cos x)$ is considered a simplified form of

$$\frac{1}{1 - \cos x}$$

because $\csc^2 x(1 + \cos x)$ does not contain fractions.

EXAMPLE 5   **Verifying a Trigonometric Identity**

Verify the identity $\sec x + \tan x = \dfrac{\cos x}{1 - \sin x}$.

Algebraic Solution

Begin with the *right* side and create a monomial denominator by multiplying the numerator and the denominator by $1 + \sin x$.

$$\frac{\cos x}{1 - \sin x} = \frac{\cos x}{1 - \sin x}\left(\frac{1 + \sin x}{1 + \sin x}\right) \qquad \begin{array}{l}\text{Multiply numerator and}\\ \text{denominator by } 1 + \sin x.\end{array}$$

$$= \frac{\cos x + \cos x \sin x}{1 - \sin^2 x} \qquad \text{Multiply.}$$

$$= \frac{\cos x + \cos x \sin x}{\cos^2 x} \qquad \text{Pythagorean identity}$$

$$= \frac{\cos x}{\cos^2 x} + \frac{\cos x \sin x}{\cos^2 x} \qquad \text{Write as separate fractions.}$$

$$= \frac{1}{\cos x} + \frac{\sin x}{\cos x} \qquad \text{Simplify.}$$

$$= \sec x + \tan x \qquad \text{Identities}$$

Graphical Solution

Because the graphs appear to coincide, the given equation appears to be an identity.

✓ **Checkpoint** ◄))) *Audio-video solution in English & Spanish at LarsonPrecalculus.com.*

Verify the identity $\csc x + \cot x = \dfrac{\sin x}{1 - \cos x}$.

In Examples 1 through 5, you have been verifying trigonometric identities by working with one side of the equation and converting to the form given on the other side. On occasion, it is practical to work with each side *separately*, to obtain one common form that is equivalent to both sides. This is illustrated in Example 6.

EXAMPLE 6 **Working with Each Side Separately**

Verify the identity $\dfrac{\cot^2 \theta}{1 + \csc \theta} = \dfrac{1 - \sin \theta}{\sin \theta}$.

Algebraic Solution

Working with the left side, you have

$$\frac{\cot^2 \theta}{1 + \csc \theta} = \frac{\csc^2 \theta - 1}{1 + \csc \theta} \qquad \text{Pythagorean identity}$$

$$= \frac{(\csc \theta - 1)(\csc \theta + 1)}{1 + \csc \theta} \qquad \text{Factor.}$$

$$= \csc \theta - 1. \qquad \text{Simplify.}$$

Now, simplifying the right side, you have

$$\frac{1 - \sin \theta}{\sin \theta} = \frac{1}{\sin \theta} - \frac{\sin \theta}{\sin \theta} = \csc \theta - 1.$$

This verifies the identity because both sides are equal to $\csc \theta - 1$.

Numerical Solution

Use a graphing utility to create a table that shows the values of

$$y_1 = \frac{\cot^2 x}{1 + \csc x} \quad \text{and} \quad y_2 = \frac{1 - \sin x}{\sin x}$$

for different values of x.

X	Y1	Y2
-.5	-3.086	-3.086
-.25	-5.042	-5.042
0	ERROR	ERROR
.25	3.042	3.042
.5	1.0858	1.0858
.75	.46705	.46705
1	.1884	.1884

X=1

The values for y_1 and y_2 appear to be identical, so the equation appears to be an identity.

✓ **Checkpoint** *Audio-video solution in English & Spanish at LarsonPrecalculus.com.*

Verify the identity $\dfrac{\tan^2 \theta}{1 + \sec \theta} = \dfrac{1 - \cos \theta}{\cos \theta}$.

Example 7 shows powers of trigonometric functions rewritten as more complicated sums of products of trigonometric functions. This is a common procedure used in calculus.

EXAMPLE 7 **Two Examples from Calculus** ∫

Verify each identity.

a. $\tan^4 x = \tan^2 x \sec^2 x - \tan^2 x$ **b.** $\csc^4 x \cot x = \csc^2 x(\cot x + \cot^3 x)$

Solution

a. $\tan^4 x = (\tan^2 x)(\tan^2 x)$ Write as separate factors.

$\qquad = \tan^2 x(\sec^2 x - 1)$ Pythagorean identity

$\qquad = \tan^2 x \sec^2 x - \tan^2 x$ Multiply.

b. $\csc^4 x \cot x = \csc^2 x \csc^2 x \cot x$ Write as separate factors.

$\qquad = \csc^2 x(1 + \cot^2 x) \cot x$ Pythagorean identity

$\qquad = \csc^2 x(\cot x + \cot^3 x)$ Multiply.

✓ **Checkpoint** *Audio-video solution in English & Spanish at LarsonPrecalculus.com.*

Verify each identity.

a. $\tan^3 x = \tan x \sec^2 x - \tan x$ **b.** $\sin^3 x \cos^4 x = (\cos^4 x - \cos^6 x)\sin x$

Summarize (Section 5.2)

1. State the guidelines for verifying trigonometric identities *(page 357)*. For examples of verifying trigonometric identities, see Examples 1–7.

5.2 Exercises

See CalcChat.com for tutorial help and worked-out solutions to odd-numbered exercises.

Vocabulary

In Exercises 1 and 2, fill in the blanks.

1. An equation that is true for all real values in its domain is called an _____.

2. An equation that is true for only some values in its domain is called a _____ _____.

In Exercises 3–8, fill in the blank to complete the fundamental trigonometric identity.

3. $\dfrac{1}{\cot u} =$ _____

4. $\dfrac{\cos u}{\sin u} =$ _____

5. $\sin^2 u +$ _____ $= 1$

6. $\cos\left(\dfrac{\pi}{2} - u\right) =$ _____

7. $\csc(-u) =$ _____

8. $\sec(-u) =$ _____

Skills and Applications

Verifying a Trigonometric Identity   In Exercises 9–50, verify the identity.

9. $\tan t \cot t = 1$

10. $\sec y \cos y = 1$

11. $\cot^2 y(\sec^2 y - 1) = 1$

12. $\cos x + \sin x \tan x = \sec x$

13. $(1 + \sin \alpha)(1 - \sin \alpha) = \cos^2 \alpha$

14. $\cos^2 \beta - \sin^2 \beta = 2\cos^2 \beta - 1$

15. $\cos^2 \beta - \sin^2 \beta = 1 - 2\sin^2 \beta$

16. $\sin^2 \alpha - \sin^4 \alpha = \cos^2 \alpha - \cos^4 \alpha$

17. $\dfrac{\tan^2 \theta}{\sec \theta} = \sin \theta \tan \theta$

18. $\dfrac{\cot^3 t}{\csc t} = \cos t(\csc^2 t - 1)$

19. $\dfrac{\cot^2 t}{\csc t} = \dfrac{1 - \sin^2 t}{\sin t}$

20. $\dfrac{1}{\tan \beta} + \tan \beta = \dfrac{\sec^2 \beta}{\tan \beta}$

21. $\sin^{1/2} x \cos x - \sin^{5/2} x \cos x = \cos^3 x \sqrt{\sin x}$

22. $\sec^6 x(\sec x \tan x) - \sec^4 x(\sec x \tan x) = \sec^5 x \tan^3 x$

23. $\dfrac{\cot x}{\sec x} = \csc x - \sin x$

24. $\dfrac{\sec \theta - 1}{1 - \cos \theta} = \sec \theta$

25. $\sec x - \cos x = \sin x \tan x$

26. $\sec x(\csc x - 2\sin x) = \cot x - \tan x$

27. $\dfrac{1}{\tan x} + \dfrac{1}{\cot x} = \tan x + \cot x$

28. $\dfrac{1}{\sin x} - \dfrac{1}{\csc x} = \csc x - \sin x$

29. $\dfrac{1 + \sin \theta}{\cos \theta} + \dfrac{\cos \theta}{1 + \sin \theta} = 2 \sec \theta$

30. $\dfrac{\cos \theta \cot \theta}{1 - \sin \theta} - 1 = \csc \theta$

31. $\dfrac{1}{\cos x + 1} + \dfrac{1}{\cos x - 1} = -2 \csc x \cot x$

32. $\cos x - \dfrac{\cos x}{1 - \tan x} = \dfrac{\sin x \cos x}{\sin x - \cos x}$

33. $\tan\left(\dfrac{\pi}{2} - \theta\right)\tan \theta = 1$

34. $\dfrac{\cos[(\pi/2) - x]}{\sin[(\pi/2) - x]} = \tan x$

35. $\dfrac{\tan x \cot x}{\cos x} = \sec x$

36. $\dfrac{\csc(-x)}{\sec(-x)} = -\cot x$

37. $(1 + \sin y)[1 + \sin(-y)] = \cos^2 y$

38. $\dfrac{\tan x + \tan y}{1 - \tan x \tan y} = \dfrac{\cot x + \cot y}{\cot x \cot y - 1}$

39. $\dfrac{\tan x + \cot y}{\tan x \cot y} = \tan y + \cot x$

40. $\dfrac{\cos x - \cos y}{\sin x + \sin y} + \dfrac{\sin x - \sin y}{\cos x + \cos y} = 0$

41. $\sqrt{\dfrac{1 + \sin \theta}{1 - \sin \theta}} = \dfrac{1 + \sin \theta}{|\cos \theta|}$

42. $\sqrt{\dfrac{1 - \cos \theta}{1 + \cos \theta}} = \dfrac{1 - \cos \theta}{|\sin \theta|}$

43. $\cos^2 \beta + \cos^2\left(\dfrac{\pi}{2} - \beta\right) = 1$

44. $\sec^2 y - \cot^2\left(\dfrac{\pi}{2} - y\right) = 1$

45. $\sin t \csc\left(\dfrac{\pi}{2} - t\right) = \tan t$

46. $\sec^2\left(\dfrac{\pi}{2} - x\right) - 1 = \cot^2 x$

47. $\tan(\sin^{-1} x) = \dfrac{x}{\sqrt{1 - x^2}}$

48. $\cos(\sin^{-1} x) = \sqrt{1 - x^2}$

49. $\tan\left(\sin^{-1} \dfrac{x - 1}{4}\right) = \dfrac{x - 1}{\sqrt{16 - (x - 1)^2}}$

50. $\tan\left(\cos^{-1} \dfrac{x + 1}{2}\right) = \dfrac{\sqrt{4 - (x + 1)^2}}{x + 1}$

Error Analysis **In Exercises 51 and 52, describe the error(s).**

51. $(1 + \tan x)[1 + \cot(-x)]$

$= (1 + \tan x)(1 + \cot x)$

$= 1 + \cot x + \tan x + \tan x \cot x$

$= 1 + \cot x + \tan x + 1$

$= 2 + \cot x + \tan x$

52. $\dfrac{1 + \sec(-\theta)}{\sin(-\theta) + \tan(-\theta)} = \dfrac{1 - \sec\theta}{\sin\theta - \tan\theta}$

$= \dfrac{1 - \sec\theta}{(\sin\theta)[1 - (1/\cos\theta)]}$

$= \dfrac{1 - \sec\theta}{\sin\theta(1 - \sec\theta)}$

$= \dfrac{1}{\sin\theta} = \csc\theta$

 Determining Trigonometric Identities **In Exercises 53–58, (a) use a graphing utility to graph each side of the equation to determine whether the equation is an identity, (b) use the *table* feature of the graphing utility to determine whether the equation is an identity, and (c) confirm the results of parts (a) and (b) algebraically.**

53. $(1 + \cot^2 x)(\cos^2 x) = \cot^2 x$

54. $\csc x(\csc x - \sin x) + \dfrac{\sin x - \cos x}{\sin x} + \cot x = \csc^2 x$

55. $2 + \cos^2 x - 3\cos^4 x = \sin^2 x(3 + 2\cos^2 x)$

56. $\tan^4 x + \tan^2 x - 3 = \sec^2 x(4\tan^2 x - 3)$

57. $\dfrac{1 + \cos x}{\sin x} = \dfrac{\sin x}{1 - \cos x}$

58. $\dfrac{\cot\alpha}{\csc\alpha + 1} = \dfrac{\csc\alpha + 1}{\cot\alpha}$

Verifying a Trigonometric Identity **In Exercises 59–62, verify the identity.**

59. $\tan^5 x = \tan^3 x \sec^2 x - \tan^3 x$

60. $\sec^4 x \tan^2 x = (\tan^2 x + \tan^4 x)\sec^2 x$

61. $\cos^3 x \sin^2 x = (\sin^2 x - \sin^4 x)\cos x$

62. $\sin^4 x + \cos^4 x = 1 - 2\cos^2 x + 2\cos^4 x$

Using Cofunction Identities **In Exercises 63 and 64, use the cofunction identities to evaluate the expression without using a calculator.**

63. $\sin^2 25° + \sin^2 65°$

64. $\tan^2 63° + \cot^2 16° - \sec^2 74° - \csc^2 27°$

65. Rate of Change The rate of change of the function $f(x) = \sin x + \csc x$ with respect to change in the variable x is given by the expression $\cos x - \csc x \cot x$. Show that the expression for the rate of change can also be written as $-\cos x \cot^2 x$.

• • **66. Shadow Length** • • • • • • • • • • • • • • •

The length s of a shadow cast by a vertical gnomon (a device used to tell time) of height h when the angle of the sun above the horizon is θ can be modeled by the equation

$s = \dfrac{h\sin(90° - \theta)}{\sin\theta}$.

(a) Verify that the expression for s is equal to $h\cot\theta$.

(b) Use a graphing utility to complete the table. Let $h = 5$ feet.

θ	15°	30°	45°	60°	75°	90°
s						

(c) Use your table from part (b) to determine the angles of the sun that result in the maximum and minimum lengths of the shadow.

(d) Based on your results from part (c), what time of day do you think it is when the angle of the sun above the horizon is 90°?

Exploration

True or False? **In Exercises 67–69, determine whether the statement is true or false. Justify your answer.**

67. There can be more than one way to verify a trigonometric identity.

68. The equation $\sin^2\theta + \cos^2\theta = 1 + \tan^2\theta$ is an identity because $\sin^2(0) + \cos^2(0) = 1$ and $1 + \tan^2(0) = 1$.

69. $\sin x^2 = \sin^2 x$

70. **HOW DO YOU SEE IT?** Explain how to use the figure to derive the identity

$\dfrac{\sec^2\theta - 1}{\sec^2\theta} = \sin^2\theta$

given in Example 1.

Think About It **In Exercises 71–74, explain why the equation is not an identity and find one value of the variable for which the equation is not true.**

71. $\sin\theta = \sqrt{1 - \cos^2\theta}$ **72.** $\tan\theta = \sqrt{\sec^2\theta - 1}$

73. $1 - \cos\theta = \sin\theta$ **74.** $1 + \tan\theta = \sec\theta$

5.3   Solving Trigonometric Equations

Trigonometric equations can help you solve a variety of real-life problems. For instance, in Exercise 94 on page 374, you will solve a trigonometric equation to determine the height above ground of a seat on a Ferris wheel.

- Use standard algebraic techniques to solve trigonometric equations.
- Solve trigonometric equations of quadratic type.
- Solve trigonometric equations involving multiple angles.
- Use inverse trigonometric functions to solve trigonometric equations.

Introduction

To solve a trigonometric equation, use standard algebraic techniques (when possible) such as collecting like terms and factoring. Your preliminary goal in solving a trigonometric equation is to *isolate* the trigonometric function on one side of the equation. For example, to solve the equation $2 \sin x = 1$, divide each side by 2 to obtain

$$\sin x = \frac{1}{2}.$$

To solve for x, note in the figure below that the equation $\sin x = \frac{1}{2}$ has solutions $x = \pi/6$ and $x = 5\pi/6$ in the interval $[0, 2\pi)$. Moreover, because $\sin x$ has a period of 2π, there are infinitely many other solutions, which can be written as

$$x = \frac{\pi}{6} + 2n\pi \quad \text{and} \quad x = \frac{5\pi}{6} + 2n\pi \qquad \text{General solution}$$

where n is an integer, as shown below.

The figure below illustrates another way to show that the equation $\sin x = \frac{1}{2}$ has infinitely many solutions. Any angles that are coterminal with $\pi/6$ or $5\pi/6$ will also be solutions of the equation.

When solving trigonometric equations, you should write your answer(s) using exact values, when possible, rather than decimal approximations.

EXAMPLE 1 **Collecting Like Terms**

Solve

$$\sin x + \sqrt{2} = -\sin x.$$

Solution Begin by isolating $\sin x$ on one side of the equation.

$\sin x + \sqrt{2} = -\sin x$	Write original equation.
$\sin x + \sin x + \sqrt{2} = 0$	Add $\sin x$ to each side.
$\sin x + \sin x = -\sqrt{2}$	Subtract $\sqrt{2}$ from each side.
$2 \sin x = -\sqrt{2}$	Combine like terms.
$\sin x = -\dfrac{\sqrt{2}}{2}$	Divide each side by 2.

Because $\sin x$ has a period of 2π, first find all solutions in the interval $[0, 2\pi)$. These solutions are $x = 5\pi/4$ and $x = 7\pi/4$. Finally, add multiples of 2π to each of these solutions to obtain the general form

$$x = \frac{5\pi}{4} + 2n\pi \quad \text{and} \quad x = \frac{7\pi}{4} + 2n\pi \qquad \text{General solution}$$

where n is an integer.

✓ *Checkpoint* Audio-video solution in English & Spanish at LarsonPrecalculus.com.

Solve $\sin x - \sqrt{2} = -\sin x$.

EXAMPLE 2 **Extracting Square Roots**

Solve

$$3 \tan^2 x - 1 = 0.$$

Solution Begin by isolating $\tan x$ on one side of the equation.

$3 \tan^2 x - 1 = 0$	Write original equation.
$3 \tan^2 x = 1$	Add 1 to each side.
$\tan^2 x = \dfrac{1}{3}$	Divide each side by 3.
$\tan x = \pm\dfrac{1}{\sqrt{3}}$	Extract square roots.
$\tan x = \pm\dfrac{\sqrt{3}}{3}$	Rationalize the denominator.

• • **REMARK** When you extract
: square roots, make sure you
• account for both the positive
• and negative solutions.

Because $\tan x$ has a period of π, first find all solutions in the interval $[0, \pi)$. These solutions are $x = \pi/6$ and $x = 5\pi/6$. Finally, add multiples of π to each of these solutions to obtain the general form

$$x = \frac{\pi}{6} + n\pi \quad \text{and} \quad x = \frac{5\pi}{6} + n\pi \qquad \text{General solution}$$

where n is an integer.

✓ *Checkpoint* Audio-video solution in English & Spanish at LarsonPrecalculus.com.

Solve $4 \sin^2 x - 3 = 0$.

The equations in Examples 1 and 2 involved only one trigonometric function. When two or more functions occur in the same equation, collect all terms on one side and try to separate the functions by factoring or by using appropriate identities. This may produce factors that yield no solutions, as illustrated in Example 3.

EXAMPLE 3   **Factoring**

Solve $\cot x \cos^2 x = 2 \cot x$.

Solution   Begin by collecting all terms on one side of the equation and factoring.

$$\cot x \cos^2 x = 2 \cot x \qquad \text{Write original equation.}$$

$$\cot x \cos^2 x - 2 \cot x = 0 \qquad \text{Subtract 2 cot } x \text{ from each side.}$$

$$\cot x(\cos^2 x - 2) = 0 \qquad \text{Factor.}$$

By setting each of these factors equal to zero, you obtain

$$\cot x = 0 \quad \text{and} \quad \cos^2 x - 2 = 0$$

$$\cos^2 x = 2$$

$$\cos x = \pm\sqrt{2}.$$

In the interval $(0, \pi)$, the equation $\cot x = 0$ has the solution

$$x = \frac{\pi}{2}.$$

No solution exists for $\cos x = \pm\sqrt{2}$ because $\pm\sqrt{2}$ are outside the range of the cosine function. Because $\cot x$ has a period of π, you obtain the general form of the solution by adding multiples of π to $x = \pi/2$ to get

$$x = \frac{\pi}{2} + n\pi \qquad \text{General solution}$$

where n is an integer. Confirm this graphically by sketching the graph of $y = \cot x \cos^2 x - 2 \cot x$, as shown below.

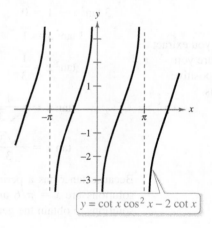

$$y = \cot x \cos^2 x - 2 \cot x$$

Notice that the x-intercepts occur at

$$-\frac{3\pi}{2}, \quad -\frac{\pi}{2}, \quad \frac{\pi}{2}, \quad \frac{3\pi}{2}$$

and so on. These x-intercepts correspond to the solutions of $\cot x \cos^2 x - 2 \cot x = 0$.

✓ **Checkpoint** ◀ᵢ)) *Audio-video solution in English & Spanish at LarsonPrecalculus.com.*

Solve $\sin^2 x = 2 \sin x$.

▷ **ALGEBRA HELP**   You can review the techniques for solving quadratic equations in Appendix A.5.

Equations of Quadratic Type

Many trigonometric equations are of quadratic type $ax^2 + bx + c = 0$, as shown below. To solve equations of this type, factor the quadratic or, when this is not possible, use the Quadratic Formula.

Quadratic in $\sin x$	Quadratic in $\sec x$
$2\sin^2 x - \sin x - 1 = 0$	$\sec^2 x - 3\sec x - 2 = 0$
$2(\sin x)^2 - \sin x - 1 = 0$	$(\sec x)^2 - 3(\sec x) - 2 = 0$

EXAMPLE 4   Factoring an Equation of Quadratic Type

Find all solutions of $2\sin^2 x - \sin x - 1 = 0$ in the interval $[0, 2\pi)$.

Algebraic Solution

Treat the equation as a quadratic in $\sin x$ and factor.

$$2\sin^2 x - \sin x - 1 = 0 \qquad \text{Write original equation.}$$

$$(2\sin x + 1)(\sin x - 1) = 0 \qquad \text{Factor.}$$

Setting each factor equal to zero, you obtain the following solutions in the interval $[0, 2\pi)$.

$$2\sin x + 1 = 0 \qquad \text{and} \quad \sin x - 1 = 0$$

$$\sin x = -\frac{1}{2} \qquad\qquad\qquad \sin x = 1$$

$$x = \frac{7\pi}{6}, \frac{11\pi}{6} \qquad\qquad\qquad x = \frac{\pi}{2}$$

Graphical Solution

$y = 2\sin^2 x - \sin x - 1$

The x-intercepts are $x \approx 1.571$, $x \approx 3.665$, and $x \approx 5.760$.

Zero
X=1.5707957   Y=0

From the above figure, you can conclude that the approximate solutions of $2\sin^2 x - \sin x - 1 = 0$ in the interval $[0, 2\pi)$ are

$$x \approx 1.571 \approx \frac{\pi}{2}, \quad x \approx 3.665 \approx \frac{7\pi}{6}, \quad \text{and} \quad x \approx 5.760 \approx \frac{11\pi}{6}.$$

✓ **Checkpoint** ◀))) *Audio-video solution in English & Spanish at LarsonPrecalculus.com.*

Find all solutions of $2\sin^2 x - 3\sin x + 1 = 0$ in the interval $[0, 2\pi)$.

EXAMPLE 5   Rewriting with a Single Trigonometric Function

Solve $2\sin^2 x + 3\cos x - 3 = 0$.

Solution   This equation contains both sine and cosine functions. You can rewrite the equation so that it has only cosine functions by using the identity $\sin^2 x = 1 - \cos^2 x$.

$$2\sin^2 x + 3\cos x - 3 = 0 \qquad \text{Write original equation.}$$

$$2(1 - \cos^2 x) + 3\cos x - 3 = 0 \qquad \text{Pythagorean identity}$$

$$2\cos^2 x - 3\cos x + 1 = 0 \qquad \text{Multiply each side by } -1.$$

$$(2\cos x - 1)(\cos x - 1) = 0 \qquad \text{Factor.}$$

By setting each factor equal to zero, you can find the solutions in the interval $[0, 2\pi)$ to be $x = 0$, $x = \pi/3$, and $x = 5\pi/3$. Because $\cos x$ has a period of 2π, the general solution is

$$x = 2n\pi, \qquad x = \frac{\pi}{3} + 2n\pi, \qquad x = \frac{5\pi}{3} + 2n\pi \qquad \text{General solution}$$

where n is an integer.

✓ **Checkpoint** ◀))) *Audio-video solution in English & Spanish at LarsonPrecalculus.com.*

Solve $3\sec^2 x - 2\tan^2 x - 4 = 0$.

Sometimes you must square each side of an equation to obtain a quadratic, as demonstrated in the next example. Because this procedure can introduce extraneous solutions, you should check any solutions in the original equation to see whether they are valid or extraneous.

•• **REMARK** You square each side of the equation in Example 6 because the squares of the sine and cosine functions are related by a Pythagorean identity. The same is true for the squares of the secant and tangent functions and for the squares of the cosecant and cotangent functions.

EXAMPLE 6 **Squaring and Converting to Quadratic Type**

Find all solutions of $\cos x + 1 = \sin x$ in the interval $[0, 2\pi)$.

Solution It is not clear how to rewrite this equation in terms of a single trigonometric function. Notice what happens when you square each side of the equation.

$$\cos x + 1 = \sin x \qquad \text{Write original equation.}$$
$$\cos^2 x + 2\cos x + 1 = \sin^2 x \qquad \text{Square each side.}$$
$$\cos^2 x + 2\cos x + 1 = 1 - \cos^2 x \qquad \text{Pythagorean identity}$$
$$\cos^2 x + \cos^2 x + 2\cos x + 1 - 1 = 0 \qquad \text{Rewrite equation.}$$
$$2\cos^2 x + 2\cos x = 0 \qquad \text{Combine like terms.}$$
$$2\cos x(\cos x + 1) = 0 \qquad \text{Factor.}$$

Setting each factor equal to zero produces

$$2\cos x = 0 \qquad \text{and} \qquad \cos x + 1 = 0$$
$$\cos x = 0 \qquad\qquad\qquad \cos x = -1$$
$$x = \frac{\pi}{2}, \frac{3\pi}{2} \qquad\qquad\qquad x = \pi.$$

Because you squared the original equation, check for extraneous solutions.

Check $x = \dfrac{\pi}{2}$

$$\cos\frac{\pi}{2} + 1 \stackrel{?}{=} \sin\frac{\pi}{2} \qquad \text{Substitute } \frac{\pi}{2} \text{ for } x.$$
$$0 + 1 = 1 \qquad \text{Solution checks. } \checkmark$$

Check $x = \dfrac{3\pi}{2}$

$$\cos\frac{3\pi}{2} + 1 \stackrel{?}{=} \sin\frac{3\pi}{2} \qquad \text{Substitute } \frac{3\pi}{2} \text{ for } x.$$
$$0 + 1 \neq -1 \qquad \text{Solution does not check.}$$

Check $x = \pi$

$$\cos\pi + 1 \stackrel{?}{=} \sin\pi \qquad \text{Substitute } \pi \text{ for } x.$$
$$-1 + 1 = 0 \qquad \text{Solution checks. } \checkmark$$

Of the three possible solutions, $x = 3\pi/2$ is extraneous. So, in the interval $[0, 2\pi)$, the only two solutions are

$$x = \frac{\pi}{2} \quad \text{and} \quad x = \pi.$$

✓ **Checkpoint** ◀))) *Audio-video solution in English & Spanish at LarsonPrecalculus.com.*

Find all solutions of $\sin x + 1 = \cos x$ in the interval $[0, 2\pi)$.

Functions Involving Multiple Angles

The next two examples involve trigonometric functions of multiple angles of the forms $\cos ku$ and $\tan ku$. To solve equations of these forms, first solve the equation for ku, and then divide your result by k.

EXAMPLE 7 **Solving a Multiple-Angle Equation**

Solve $2 \cos 3t - 1 = 0$.

Solution

$$2 \cos 3t - 1 = 0 \qquad \text{Write original equation.}$$

$$2 \cos 3t = 1 \qquad \text{Add 1 to each side.}$$

$$\cos 3t = \frac{1}{2} \qquad \text{Divide each side by 2.}$$

In the interval $[0, 2\pi)$, you know that $3t = \pi/3$ and $3t = 5\pi/3$ are the only solutions, so, in general, you have

$$3t = \frac{\pi}{3} + 2n\pi \quad \text{and} \quad 3t = \frac{5\pi}{3} + 2n\pi.$$

Dividing these results by 3, you obtain the general solution

$$t = \frac{\pi}{9} + \frac{2n\pi}{3} \quad \text{and} \quad t = \frac{5\pi}{9} + \frac{2n\pi}{3} \qquad \text{General solution}$$

where n is an integer.

✓ Checkpoint Audio-video solution in English & Spanish at LarsonPrecalculus.com.

Solve $2 \sin 2t - \sqrt{3} = 0$.

EXAMPLE 8 **Solving a Multiple-Angle Equation**

$$3 \tan \frac{x}{2} + 3 = 0 \qquad \text{Original equation}$$

$$3 \tan \frac{x}{2} = -3 \qquad \text{Subtract 3 from each side.}$$

$$\tan \frac{x}{2} = -1 \qquad \text{Divide each side by 3.}$$

In the interval $[0, \pi)$, you know that $x/2 = 3\pi/4$ is the only solution, so, in general, you have

$$\frac{x}{2} = \frac{3\pi}{4} + n\pi.$$

Multiplying this result by 2, you obtain the general solution

$$x = \frac{3\pi}{2} + 2n\pi \qquad \text{General solution}$$

where n is an integer.

✓ Checkpoint Audio-video solution in English & Spanish at LarsonPrecalculus.com.

Solve $2 \tan \frac{x}{2} - 2 = 0$.

Using Inverse Functions

It is possible to find the minimum surface area of a honeycomb cell using a graphing utility or using calculus and the arccosine function.

EXAMPLE 9   **Using Inverse Functions**

$$\sec^2 x - 2 \tan x = 4 \qquad \text{Original equation}$$
$$1 + \tan^2 x - 2 \tan x - 4 = 0 \qquad \text{Pythagorean identity}$$
$$\tan^2 x - 2 \tan x - 3 = 0 \qquad \text{Combine like terms.}$$
$$(\tan x - 3)(\tan x + 1) = 0 \qquad \text{Factor.}$$

Setting each factor equal to zero, you obtain two solutions in the interval $(-\pi/2, \pi/2)$. [Recall that the range of the inverse tangent function is $(-\pi/2, \pi/2)$.]

$$x = \arctan 3 \quad \text{and} \quad x = \arctan(-1) = -\pi/4$$

Finally, because $\tan x$ has a period of π, you add multiples of π to obtain

$$x = \arctan 3 + n\pi \quad \text{and} \quad x = (-\pi/4) + n\pi \qquad \text{General solution}$$

where n is an integer. You can use a calculator to approximate the value of arctan 3.

✓ **Checkpoint** ◄))) *Audio-video solution in English & Spanish at LarsonPrecalculus.com.*

Solve $4 \tan^2 x + 5 \tan x - 6 = 0$.

$h = 2.4$ in.

$s = 0.75$ in.

Figure 5.2

EXAMPLE 10   **Surface Area of a Honeycomb Cell**

The surface area S (in square inches) of a honeycomb cell is given by

$$S = 6hs + 1.5s^2\left[(\sqrt{3} - \cos \theta)/\sin \theta\right], \quad 0 < \theta \le 90°$$

where $h = 2.4$ inches, $s = 0.75$ inch, and θ is the angle shown in Figure 5.2. What value of θ gives the minimum surface area?

Solution   Letting $h = 2.4$ and $s = 0.75$, you obtain

$$S = 10.8 + 0.84375\left[(\sqrt{3} - \cos \theta)/\sin \theta\right].$$

Graph this function using a graphing utility. The minimum point on the graph, which occurs at $\theta \approx 54.7°$, is shown in Figure 5.3. By using calculus, the exact minimum point on the graph can be shown to occur at $\theta = \arccos(1/\sqrt{3}) \approx 0.9553 \approx 54.7356°$.

✓ **Checkpoint** ◄))) *Audio-video solution in English & Spanish at LarsonPrecalculus.com.*

In Example 10, for what value(s) of θ is the surface area 12 square inches?

$$y = 10.8 + 0.84375\left(\frac{\sqrt{3} - \cos x}{\sin x}\right)$$

Minimum
X=54.735623   Y=11.993243

Figure 5.3

Summarize   (Section 5.3)

1. Describe how to use standard algebraic techniques to solve trigonometric equations *(page 364)*. For examples of using standard algebraic techniques to solve trigonometric equations, see Examples 1–3.

2. Explain how to solve a trigonometric equation of quadratic type *(page 367)*. For examples of solving trigonometric equations of quadratic type, see Examples 4–6.

3. Explain how to solve a trigonometric equation involving multiple angles *(page 369)*. For examples of solving trigonometric equations involving multiple angles, see Examples 7 and 8.

4. Explain how to use inverse trigonometric functions to solve trigonometric equations *(page 370)*. For examples of using inverse trigonometric functions to solve trigonometric equations, see Examples 9 and 10.

5.3   Exercises

See CalcChat.com for tutorial help and worked-out solutions to odd-numbered exercises.

Vocabulary: Fill in the blanks.

1. When solving a trigonometric equation, the preliminary goal is to _____ the trigonometric function involved in the equation.

2. The equation $2 \sin \theta + 1 = 0$ has the solutions $\theta = \dfrac{7\pi}{6} + 2n\pi$ and $\theta = \dfrac{11\pi}{6} + 2n\pi$, which are called _____ solutions.

3. The equation $2 \tan^2 x - 3 \tan x + 1 = 0$ is a trigonometric equation that is of _____ type.

4. A solution of an equation that does not satisfy the original equation is called an _____ solution.

Skills and Applications

Verifying Solutions   In Exercises 5–10, verify that the *x*-values are solutions of the equation.

5. $\tan x - \sqrt{3} = 0$

  (a) $x = \dfrac{\pi}{3}$

  (b) $x = \dfrac{4\pi}{3}$

6. $\sec x - 2 = 0$

  (a) $x = \dfrac{\pi}{3}$

  (b) $x = \dfrac{5\pi}{3}$

7. $3 \tan^2 2x - 1 = 0$

  (a) $x = \dfrac{\pi}{12}$

  (b) $x = \dfrac{5\pi}{12}$

8. $2 \cos^2 4x - 1 = 0$

  (a) $x = \dfrac{\pi}{16}$

  (b) $x = \dfrac{3\pi}{16}$

9. $2 \sin^2 x - \sin x - 1 = 0$

  (a) $x = \dfrac{\pi}{2}$

  (b) $x = \dfrac{7\pi}{6}$

10. $\csc^4 x - 4 \csc^2 x = 0$

  (a) $x = \dfrac{\pi}{6}$

  (b) $x = \dfrac{5\pi}{6}$

Solving a Trigonometric Equation   In Exercises 11–24, solve the equation.

11. $\sqrt{3} \csc x - 2 = 0$

12. $\tan x + \sqrt{3} = 0$

13. $\cos x + 1 = -\cos x$

14. $3 \sin x + 1 = \sin x$

15. $3 \sec^2 x - 4 = 0$

16. $3 \cot^2 x - 1 = 0$

17. $4 \cos^2 x - 1 = 0$

18. $\sin^2 x = 3 \cos^2 x$

19. $2 \sin^2 2x = 1$

20. $\tan^2 3x = 3$

21. $\tan 3x(\tan x - 1) = 0$

22. $\cos 2x(2 \cos x + 1) = 0$

23. $\sin x(\sin x + 1) = 0$

24. $(2 \sin^2 x - 1)(\tan^2 x - 3) = 0$

Solving a Trigonometric Equation   In Exercises 25–38, find all solutions of the equation in the interval $[0, 2\pi)$.

25. $\cos^3 x = \cos x$

26. $\sec^2 x - 1 = 0$

27. $3 \tan^3 x = \tan x$

28. $2 \sin^2 x = 2 + \cos x$

29. $\sec^2 x - \sec x = 2$

30. $\sec x \csc x = 2 \csc x$

31. $2 \sin x + \csc x = 0$

32. $\sin x - 2 = \cos x - 2$

33. $2 \cos^2 x + \cos x - 1 = 0$

34. $2 \sin^2 x + 3 \sin x + 1 = 0$

35. $2 \sec^2 x + \tan^2 x - 3 = 0$

36. $\cos x + \sin x \tan x = 2$

37. $\csc x + \cot x = 1$

38. $\sec x + \tan x = 1$

Solving a Multiple-Angle Equation   In Exercises 39–44, solve the multiple-angle equation.

39. $2 \cos 2x - 1 = 0$

40. $2 \sin 2x + \sqrt{3} = 0$

41. $\tan 3x - 1 = 0$

42. $\sec 4x - 2 = 0$

43. $2 \cos \dfrac{x}{2} - \sqrt{2} = 0$

44. $2 \sin \dfrac{x}{2} + \sqrt{3} = 0$

Finding *x*-Intercepts   In Exercises 45–48, find the *x*-intercepts of the graph.

45. $y = \sin \dfrac{\pi x}{2} + 1$

46. $y = \sin \pi x + \cos \pi x$

47. $y = \tan^2\left(\dfrac{\pi x}{6}\right) - 3$

48. $y = \sec^4\left(\dfrac{\pi x}{8}\right) - 4$

Approximating Solutions In Exercises 49–58, use a graphing utility to approximate the solutions (to three decimal places) of the equation in the interval $[0, 2\pi)$.

49. $2 \sin x + \cos x = 0$

50. $4 \sin^3 x + 2 \sin^2 x - 2 \sin x - 1 = 0$

51. $\dfrac{1 + \sin x}{\cos x} + \dfrac{\cos x}{1 + \sin x} = 4$

52. $\dfrac{\cos x \cot x}{1 - \sin x} = 3$

53. $x \tan x - 1 = 0$ **54.** $x \cos x - 1 = 0$

55. $\sec^2 x + 0.5 \tan x - 1 = 0$

56. $\csc^2 x + 0.5 \cot x - 5 = 0$

57. $2 \tan^2 x + 7 \tan x - 15 = 0$

58. $6 \sin^2 x - 7 \sin x + 2 = 0$

Using the Quadratic Formula In Exercises 59–62, use the Quadratic Formula to solve the equation in the interval $[0, 2\pi)$. Then use a graphing utility to approximate the angle x.

59. $12 \sin^2 x - 13 \sin x + 3 = 0$

60. $3 \tan^2 x + 4 \tan x - 4 = 0$

61. $\tan^2 x + 3 \tan x + 1 = 0$

62. $4 \cos^2 x - 4 \cos x - 1 = 0$

Using Inverse Functions In Exercises 63–74, use inverse functions where needed to find all solutions of the equation in the interval $[0, 2\pi)$.

63. $\tan^2 x + \tan x - 12 = 0$

64. $\tan^2 x - \tan x - 2 = 0$

65. $\sec^2 x - 6 \tan x = -4$

66. $\sec^2 x + \tan x - 3 = 0$

67. $2 \sin^2 x + 5 \cos x = 4$ **68.** $2 \cos^2 x + 7 \sin x = 5$

69. $\cot^2 x - 9 = 0$ **70.** $\cot^2 x - 6 \cot x + 5 = 0$

71. $\sec^2 x - 4 \sec x = 0$

72. $\sec^2 x + 2 \sec x - 8 = 0$

73. $\csc^2 x + 3 \csc x - 4 = 0$

74. $\csc^2 x - 5 \csc x = 0$

Approximating Solutions In Exercises 75–78, use a graphing utility to approximate the solutions (to three decimal places) of the equation in the given interval.

75. $3 \tan^2 x + 5 \tan x - 4 = 0$, $\left[-\dfrac{\pi}{2}, \dfrac{\pi}{2}\right]$

76. $\cos^2 x - 2 \cos x - 1 = 0$, $[0, \pi]$

77. $4 \cos^2 x - 2 \sin x + 1 = 0$, $\left[-\dfrac{\pi}{2}, \dfrac{\pi}{2}\right]$

78. $2 \sec^2 x + \tan x - 6 = 0$, $\left[-\dfrac{\pi}{2}, \dfrac{\pi}{2}\right]$

Approximating Maximum and Minimum Points In Exercises 79–84, (a) use a graphing utility to graph the function and approximate the maximum and minimum points on the graph in the interval $[0, 2\pi)$, and (b) solve the trigonometric equation and demonstrate that its solutions are the x-coordinates of the maximum and minimum points of f. (Calculus is required to find the trigonometric equation.)

Function	**Trigonometric Equation**
79. $f(x) = \sin^2 x + \cos x$	$2 \sin x \cos x - \sin x = 0$
80. $f(x) = \cos^2 x - \sin x$	$-2 \sin x \cos x - \cos x = 0$
81. $f(x) = \sin x + \cos x$	$\cos x - \sin x = 0$
82. $f(x) = 2 \sin x + \cos 2x$	$2 \cos x - 4 \sin x \cos x = 0$
83. $f(x) = \sin x \cos x$	$-\sin^2 x + \cos^2 x = 0$
84. $f(x) = \sec x + \tan x - x$	$\sec x \tan x + \sec^2 x = 1$

Number of Points of Intersection In Exercises 85 and 86, use the graph to approximate the number of points of intersection of the graphs of y_1 and y_2.

85. $y_1 = 2 \sin x$

$y_2 = 3x + 1$

86. $y_1 = 2 \sin x$

$y_2 = \frac{1}{2}x + 1$

87. Graphical Reasoning Consider the function $f(x) = (\sin x)/x$ and its graph shown in the figure.

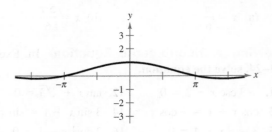

(a) What is the domain of the function?

(b) Identify any symmetry and any asymptotes of the graph.

(c) Describe the behavior of the function as $x \to 0$.

(d) How many solutions does the equation

$$\frac{\sin x}{x} = 0$$

have in the interval $[-8, 8]$? Find the solutions.

88. Graphical Reasoning Consider the function

$$f(x) = \cos \frac{1}{x}$$

and its graph shown in the figure.

(a) What is the domain of the function?

(b) Identify any symmetry and any asymptotes of the graph.

(c) Describe the behavior of the function as $x \to 0$.

(d) How many solutions does the equation

$$\cos \frac{1}{x} = 0$$

have in the interval $[-1, 1]$? Find the solutions.

(e) Does the equation $\cos(1/x) = 0$ have a greatest solution? If so, then approximate the solution. If not, then explain why.

89. Harmonic Motion A weight is oscillating on the end of a spring (see figure). The position of the weight relative to the point of equilibrium is given by

$$y = \tfrac{1}{12}(\cos 8t - 3 \sin 8t)$$

where y is the displacement (in meters) and t is the time (in seconds). Find the times when the weight is at the point of equilibrium $(y = 0)$ for $0 \le t \le 1$.

Equilibrium

90. Damped Harmonic Motion The displacement from equilibrium of a weight oscillating on the end of a spring is given by

$$y = 1.56e^{-0.22t}\cos 4.9t$$

where y is the displacement (in feet) and t is the time (in seconds). Use a graphing utility to graph the displacement function for $0 \le t \le 10$. Find the time beyond which the displacement does not exceed 1 foot from equilibrium.

91. Sales The monthly sales S (in hundreds of units) of skiing equipment at a sports store are approximated by

$$S = 58.3 + 32.5 \cos \frac{\pi t}{6}$$

where t is the time (in months), with $t = 1$ corresponding to January. Determine the months in which sales exceed 7500 units.

92. Projectile Motion A baseball is hit at an angle of θ with the horizontal and with an initial velocity of $v_0 = 100$ feet per second. An outfielder catches the ball 300 feet from home plate (see figure). Find θ when the range r of a projectile is given by

$$r = \frac{1}{32}v_0^2 \sin 2\theta.$$

$r = 300$ ft

Not drawn to scale

93. Data Analysis: Meteorology The table shows the normal daily high temperatures in Houston H (in degrees Fahrenheit) for month t, with $t = 1$ corresponding to January. *(Source: NOAA)*

DATA	Month, t	Houston, H
	1	62.3
	2	66.5
	3	73.3
	4	79.1
	5	85.5
	6	90.7
	7	93.6
	8	93.5
	9	89.3
	10	82.0
	11	72.0
	12	64.6

Spreadsheet at LarsonPrecalculus.com

(a) Create a scatter plot of the data.

(b) Find a cosine model for the temperatures.

(c) Use a graphing utility to graph the data points and the model for the temperatures. How well does the model fit the data?

(d) What is the overall normal daily high temperature?

(e) Use the graphing utility to describe the months during which the normal daily high temperature is above 86°F and below 86°F.

94. Ferris Wheel

The height h (in feet) above ground of a seat on a Ferris wheel at time t (in minutes) can be modeled by

$$h(t) = 53 + 50 \sin\left(\frac{\pi}{16}t - \frac{\pi}{2}\right).$$

The wheel makes one revolution every 32 seconds. The ride begins when $t = 0$.

(a) During the first 32 seconds of the ride, when will a person on the Ferris wheel be 53 feet above ground?

(b) When will a person be at the top of the Ferris wheel for the first time during the ride? If the ride lasts 160 seconds, then how many times will a person be at the top of the ride, and at what times?

95. Geometry The area of a rectangle (see figure) inscribed in one arc of the graph of $y = \cos x$ is given by

$$A = 2x \cos x, \quad 0 < x < \pi/2.$$

(a) Use a graphing utility to graph the area function, and approximate the area of the largest inscribed rectangle.

(b) Determine the values of x for which $A \geq 1$.

96. Quadratic Approximation Consider the function

$$f(x) = 3 \sin(0.6x - 2).$$

(a) Approximate the zero of the function in the interval $[0, 6]$.

(b) A quadratic approximation agreeing with f at $x = 5$ is

$$g(x) = -0.45x^2 + 5.52x - 13.70.$$

Use a graphing utility to graph f and g in the same viewing window. Describe the result.

(c) Use the Quadratic Formula to find the zeros of g. Compare the zero in the interval $[0, 6]$ with the result of part (a).

Fixed Point In Exercises 97 and 98, find the smallest positive fixed point of the function f. [A *fixed point* of a function f is a real number c such that $f(c) = c$.]

97. $f(x) = \tan(\pi x/4)$ **98.** $f(x) = \cos x$

Exploration

True or False? In Exercises 99 and 100, determine whether the statement is true or false. Justify your answer.

99. The equation $2 \sin 4t - 1 = 0$ has four times the number of solutions in the interval $[0, 2\pi)$ as the equation $2 \sin t - 1 = 0$.

100. If you correctly solve a trigonometric equation to the statement $\sin x = 3.4$, then you can finish solving the equation by using an inverse function.

101. Think About It Explain what happens when you divide each side of the equation $\cot x \cos^2 x = 2 \cot x$ by $\cot x$. Is this a correct method to use when solving equations?

102. **HOW DO YOU SEE IT?** Explain how to use the figure to solve the equation $2 \cos x - 1 = 0$.

103. Graphical Reasoning Use a graphing utility to confirm the solutions found in Example 6 in two different ways.

(a) Graph both sides of the equation and find the x-coordinates of the points at which the graphs intersect.

Left side: $y = \cos x + 1$

Right side: $y = \sin x$

(b) Graph the equation $y = \cos x + 1 - \sin x$ and find the x-intercepts of the graph. Do both methods produce the same x-values? Which method do you prefer? Explain.

104. Discussion Explain in your own words how knowledge of algebra is important when solving trigonometric equations.

Project: Meteorology To work an extended application analyzing the normal daily high temperatures in Phoenix and in Seattle, visit this text's website at *LarsonPrecalculus.com. (Source: NOAA)*

5.4 Sum and Difference Formulas

■ Use sum and difference formulas to evaluate trigonometric functions, verify identities, and solve trigonometric equations.

Using Sum and Difference Formulas

In this and the following section, you will study the uses of several trigonometric identities and formulas.

Trigonometric identities enable you to rewrite trigonometric expressions. For instance, in Exercise 79 on page 380, you will use an identity to rewrite a trigonometric expression in a form that helps you analyze a harmonic motion equation.

Sum and Difference Formulas

$$\sin(u + v) = \sin u \cos v + \cos u \sin v$$

$$\sin(u - v) = \sin u \cos v - \cos u \sin v$$

$$\cos(u + v) = \cos u \cos v - \sin u \sin v$$

$$\cos(u - v) = \cos u \cos v + \sin u \sin v$$

$$\tan(u + v) = \frac{\tan u + \tan v}{1 - \tan u \tan v} \qquad \tan(u - v) = \frac{\tan u - \tan v}{1 + \tan u \tan v}$$

For a proof of the sum and difference formulas for $\cos(u \pm v)$ and $\tan(u \pm v)$, see Proofs in Mathematics on page 396.

Examples 1 and 2 show how **sum and difference formulas** can enable you to find exact values of trigonometric functions involving sums or differences of special angles.

EXAMPLE 1   **Evaluating a Trigonometric Function**

Find the exact value of $\sin \dfrac{\pi}{12}$.

Solution   To find the *exact* value of $\sin \pi/12$, use the fact that

$$\frac{\pi}{12} = \frac{\pi}{3} - \frac{\pi}{4}.$$

Consequently, the formula for $\sin(u - v)$ yields

$$\sin \frac{\pi}{12} = \sin\left(\frac{\pi}{3} - \frac{\pi}{4}\right)$$

$$= \sin \frac{\pi}{3} \cos \frac{\pi}{4} - \cos \frac{\pi}{3} \sin \frac{\pi}{4}$$

$$= \frac{\sqrt{3}}{2}\left(\frac{\sqrt{2}}{2}\right) - \frac{1}{2}\left(\frac{\sqrt{2}}{2}\right)$$

$$= \frac{\sqrt{6} - \sqrt{2}}{4}.$$

Try checking this result on your calculator. You will find that $\sin \pi/12 \approx 0.259$.

✓ *Checkpoint* ◄))) *Audio-video solution in English & Spanish at LarsonPrecalculus.com.*

Find the exact value of $\cos \dfrac{\pi}{12}$.

Richard Megna/Fundamental Photographs

•• REMARK Another way to
solve Example 2 is to use the
fact that $75° = 120° - 45°$
together with the formula for
$\cos(u - v)$.

Figure 5.4

Figure 5.5

Figure 5.6

EXAMPLE 2   Evaluating a Trigonometric Function

Find the exact value of cos 75°.

Solution Using the fact that $75° = 30° + 45°$, together with the formula for $\cos(u + v)$, you obtain

$$\cos 75° = \cos(30° + 45°)$$

$$= \cos 30° \cos 45° - \sin 30° \sin 45°$$

$$= \frac{\sqrt{3}}{2}\left(\frac{\sqrt{2}}{2}\right) - \frac{1}{2}\left(\frac{\sqrt{2}}{2}\right)$$

$$= \frac{\sqrt{6} - \sqrt{2}}{4}.$$

✓ **Checkpoint** ◀))) Audio-video solution in English & Spanish at LarsonPrecalculus.com.

Find the exact value of sin 75°.

EXAMPLE 3   Evaluating a Trigonometric Expression

Find the exact value of $\sin(u + v)$ given $\sin u = 4/5$, where $0 < u < \pi/2$, and $\cos v = -12/13$, where $\pi/2 < v < \pi$.

Solution Because $\sin u = 4/5$ and u is in Quadrant I, $\cos u = 3/5$, as shown in Figure 5.4. Because $\cos v = -12/13$ and v is in Quadrant II, $\sin v = 5/13$, as shown in Figure 5.5. You can find $\sin(u + v)$ as follows.

$$\sin(u + v) = \sin u \cos v + \cos u \sin v$$

$$= \frac{4}{5}\left(-\frac{12}{13}\right) + \frac{3}{5}\left(\frac{5}{13}\right)$$

$$= -\frac{33}{65}$$

✓ **Checkpoint** ◀))) Audio-video solution in English & Spanish at LarsonPrecalculus.com.

Find the exact value of $\cos(u + v)$ given $\sin u = 12/13$, where $0 < u < \pi/2$, and $\cos v = -3/5$, where $\pi/2 < v < \pi$.

EXAMPLE 4   An Application of a Sum Formula

Write $\cos(\arctan 1 + \arccos x)$ as an algebraic expression.

Solution This expression fits the formula for $\cos(u + v)$. Figure 5.6 shows angles $u = \arctan 1$ and $v = \arccos x$. So,

$$\cos(u + v) = \cos(\arctan 1) \cos(\arccos x) - \sin(\arctan 1) \sin(\arccos x)$$

$$= \frac{1}{\sqrt{2}} \cdot x - \frac{1}{\sqrt{2}} \cdot \sqrt{1 - x^2}$$

$$= \frac{x - \sqrt{1 - x^2}}{\sqrt{2}}.$$

✓ **Checkpoint** ◀))) Audio-video solution in English & Spanish at LarsonPrecalculus.com.

Write $\sin(\arctan 1 + \arccos x)$ as an algebraic expression.

Hipparchus, considered the most eminent of Greek astronomers, was born about 190 B.C. in Nicaea. He is credited with the invention of trigonometry. He also derived the sum and difference formulas for $\sin(A \pm B)$ and $\cos(A \pm B)$.

 EXAMPLE 5   **Proving a Cofunction Identity**

Use a difference formula to prove the cofunction identity $\cos\left(\dfrac{\pi}{2} - x\right) = \sin x$.

Solution   Using the formula for $\cos(u - v)$, you have

$$\cos\left(\frac{\pi}{2} - x\right) = \cos\frac{\pi}{2}\cos x + \sin\frac{\pi}{2}\sin x$$

$$= (0)(\cos x) + (1)(\sin x)$$

$$= \sin x.$$

✓ *Checkpoint* *Audio-video solution in English & Spanish at LarsonPrecalculus.com.*

Use a difference formula to prove the cofunction identity $\sin\left(x - \dfrac{\pi}{2}\right) = -\cos x$.

Sum and difference formulas can be used to rewrite expressions such as

$$\sin\left(\theta + \frac{n\pi}{2}\right) \quad \text{and} \quad \cos\left(\theta + \frac{n\pi}{2}\right), \quad \text{where } n \text{ is an integer}$$

as expressions involving only $\sin\theta$ or $\cos\theta$. The resulting formulas are called **reduction formulas.**

EXAMPLE 6   **Deriving Reduction Formulas**

Simplify each expression.

a. $\cos\left(\theta - \dfrac{3\pi}{2}\right)$

b. $\tan(\theta + 3\pi)$

Solution

a. Using the formula for $\cos(u - v)$, you have

$$\cos\left(\theta - \frac{3\pi}{2}\right) = \cos\theta\cos\frac{3\pi}{2} + \sin\theta\sin\frac{3\pi}{2}$$

$$= (\cos\theta)(0) + (\sin\theta)(-1)$$

$$= -\sin\theta.$$

b. Using the formula for $\tan(u + v)$, you have

$$\tan(\theta + 3\pi) = \frac{\tan\theta + \tan 3\pi}{1 - \tan\theta\tan 3\pi}$$

$$= \frac{\tan\theta + 0}{1 - (\tan\theta)(0)}$$

$$= \tan\theta.$$

✓ *Checkpoint* *Audio-video solution in English & Spanish at LarsonPrecalculus.com.*

Simplify each expression.

a. $\sin\left(\dfrac{3\pi}{2} - \theta\right)$ **b.** $\tan\left(\theta - \dfrac{\pi}{4}\right)$

EXAMPLE 7   **Solving a Trigonometric Equation**

Find all solutions of $\sin[x + (\pi/4)] + \sin[x - (\pi/4)] = -1$ in the interval $[0, 2\pi)$.

Algebraic Solution

Using sum and difference formulas, rewrite the equation as

$$\sin x \cos \frac{\pi}{4} + \cos x \sin \frac{\pi}{4} + \sin x \cos \frac{\pi}{4} - \cos x \sin \frac{\pi}{4} = -1$$

$$2 \sin x \cos \frac{\pi}{4} = -1$$

$$2(\sin x)\left(\frac{\sqrt{2}}{2}\right) = -1$$

$$\sin x = -\frac{1}{\sqrt{2}}$$

$$\sin x = -\frac{\sqrt{2}}{2}.$$

So, the only solutions in the interval $[0, 2\pi)$ are $x = 5\pi/4$ and $x = 7\pi/4$.

Graphical Solution

The x-intercepts are $x \approx 3.927$ and $x \approx 5.498$.

From the above figure, you can conclude that the approximate solutions in the interval $[0, 2\pi)$ are

$$x \approx 3.927 \approx \frac{5\pi}{4} \quad \text{and} \quad x \approx 5.498 \approx \frac{7\pi}{4}.$$

✓ **Checkpoint** ◄))) *Audio-video solution in English & Spanish at LarsonPrecalculus.com.*

Find all solutions of $\sin[x + (\pi/2)] + \sin[x - (3\pi/2)] = 1$ in the interval $[0, 2\pi)$.

The next example is an application from calculus.

EXAMPLE 8   **An Application from Calculus**

Verify that $\dfrac{\sin(x + h) - \sin x}{h} = (\cos x)\left(\dfrac{\sin h}{h}\right) - (\sin x)\left(\dfrac{1 - \cos h}{h}\right)$, where $h \neq 0$.

Solution   Using the formula for $\sin(u + v)$, you have

$$\frac{\sin(x + h) - \sin x}{h} = \frac{\sin x \cos h + \cos x \sin h - \sin x}{h}$$

$$= \frac{\cos x \sin h - \sin x(1 - \cos h)}{h}$$

$$= (\cos x)\left(\frac{\sin h}{h}\right) - (\sin x)\left(\frac{1 - \cos h}{h}\right).$$

✓ **Checkpoint** ◄))) *Audio-video solution in English & Spanish at LarsonPrecalculus.com.*

Verify that $\dfrac{\cos(x + h) - \cos x}{h} = (\cos x)\left(\dfrac{\cos h - 1}{h}\right) - (\sin x)\left(\dfrac{\sin h}{h}\right)$, where $h \neq 0$.

One application of the sum and difference formulas is in the analysis of standing waves, such as those that can be produced when plucking a guitar string. You will investigate standing waves in Exercise 80.

Summarize   (Section 5.4)

1. State the sum and difference formulas for sine, cosine, and tangent (*page 375*). For examples of using the sum and difference formulas to evaluate trigonometric functions, verify identities, and solve trigonometric equations, see Examples 1–8.

5.4 Exercises

See CalcChat.com for tutorial help and worked-out solutions to odd-numbered exercises.

Vocabulary: Fill in the blank.

1. $\sin(u - v) =$ _____
2. $\cos(u + v) =$ _____
3. $\tan(u + v) =$ _____
4. $\sin(u + v) =$ _____
5. $\cos(u - v) =$ _____
6. $\tan(u - v) =$ _____

Skills and Applications

Evaluating Trigonometric Expressions In Exercises 7–10, find the exact value of each expression.

7. (a) $\cos\left(\dfrac{\pi}{4} + \dfrac{\pi}{3}\right)$ (b) $\cos\dfrac{\pi}{4} + \cos\dfrac{\pi}{3}$

8. (a) $\sin\left(\dfrac{7\pi}{6} - \dfrac{\pi}{3}\right)$ (b) $\sin\dfrac{7\pi}{6} - \sin\dfrac{\pi}{3}$

9. (a) $\sin(135° - 30°)$ (b) $\sin 135° - \cos 30°$

10. (a) $\cos(120° + 45°)$ (b) $\cos 120° + \cos 45°$

Evaluating Trigonometric Functions In Exercises 11–26, find the exact values of the sine, cosine, and tangent of the angle.

11. $\dfrac{11\pi}{12} = \dfrac{3\pi}{4} + \dfrac{\pi}{6}$
12. $\dfrac{7\pi}{12} = \dfrac{\pi}{3} + \dfrac{\pi}{4}$
13. $\dfrac{17\pi}{12} = \dfrac{9\pi}{4} - \dfrac{5\pi}{6}$
14. $-\dfrac{\pi}{12} = \dfrac{\pi}{6} - \dfrac{\pi}{4}$
15. $105° = 60° + 45°$
16. $165° = 135° + 30°$
17. $195° = 225° - 30°$
18. $255° = 300° - 45°$
19. $\dfrac{13\pi}{12}$
20. $-\dfrac{7\pi}{12}$
21. $-\dfrac{13\pi}{12}$
22. $\dfrac{5\pi}{12}$
23. $285°$
24. $-105°$
25. $-165°$
26. $15°$

Rewriting a Trigonometric Expression In Exercises 27–34, write the expression as the sine, cosine, or tangent of an angle.

27. $\sin 3 \cos 1.2 - \cos 3 \sin 1.2$
28. $\cos\dfrac{\pi}{7}\cos\dfrac{\pi}{5} - \sin\dfrac{\pi}{7}\sin\dfrac{\pi}{5}$
29. $\sin 60° \cos 15° + \cos 60° \sin 15°$
30. $\cos 130° \cos 40° - \sin 130° \sin 40°$
31. $\dfrac{\tan 45° - \tan 30°}{1 + \tan 45° \tan 30°}$
32. $\dfrac{\tan 140° - \tan 60°}{1 + \tan 140° \tan 60°}$

33. $\cos 3x \cos 2y + \sin 3x \sin 2y$
34. $\dfrac{\tan 2x + \tan x}{1 - \tan 2x \tan x}$

Evaluating a Trigonometric Expression In Exercises 35–40, find the exact value of the expression.

35. $\sin\dfrac{\pi}{12}\cos\dfrac{\pi}{4} + \cos\dfrac{\pi}{12}\sin\dfrac{\pi}{4}$
36. $\cos\dfrac{\pi}{16}\cos\dfrac{3\pi}{16} - \sin\dfrac{\pi}{16}\sin\dfrac{3\pi}{16}$
37. $\sin 120° \cos 60° - \cos 120° \sin 60°$
38. $\cos 120° \cos 30° + \sin 120° \sin 30°$
39. $\dfrac{\tan(5\pi/6) - \tan(\pi/6)}{1 + \tan(5\pi/6)\tan(\pi/6)}$
40. $\dfrac{\tan 25° + \tan 110°}{1 - \tan 25° \tan 110°}$

Evaluating a Trigonometric Expression In Exercises 41–46, find the exact value of the trigonometric expression given that $\sin u = \dfrac{5}{13}$ and $\cos v = -\dfrac{3}{5}$. (Both u and v are in Quadrant II.)

41. $\sin(u + v)$ 42. $\cos(u - v)$
43. $\tan(u + v)$ 44. $\csc(u - v)$
45. $\sec(v - u)$ 46. $\cot(u + v)$

Evaluating a Trigonometric Expression In Exercises 47–52, find the exact value of the trigonometric expression given that $\sin u = -\dfrac{7}{25}$ and $\cos v = -\dfrac{4}{5}$. (Both u and v are in Quadrant III.)

47. $\cos(u + v)$ 48. $\sin(u + v)$
49. $\tan(u - v)$ 50. $\cot(v - u)$
51. $\csc(u - v)$ 52. $\sec(v - u)$

An Application of a Sum or Difference Formula In Exercises 53–56, write the trigonometric expression as an algebraic expression.

53. $\sin(\arcsin x + \arccos x)$ 54. $\sin(\arctan 2x - \arccos x)$
55. $\cos(\arccos x + \arcsin x)$
56. $\cos(\arccos x - \arctan x)$

Proving a Trigonometric Identity In Exercises 57–64, prove the identity.

57. $\sin\left(\dfrac{\pi}{2} - x\right) = \cos x$

58. $\sin\left(\dfrac{\pi}{2} + x\right) = \cos x$

59. $\sin\left(\dfrac{\pi}{6} + x\right) = \dfrac{1}{2}(\cos x + \sqrt{3}\sin x)$

60. $\cos\left(\dfrac{5\pi}{4} - x\right) = -\dfrac{\sqrt{2}}{2}(\cos x + \sin x)$

61. $\cos(\pi - \theta) + \sin\left(\dfrac{\pi}{2} + \theta\right) = 0$

62. $\tan\left(\dfrac{\pi}{4} - \theta\right) = \dfrac{1 - \tan\theta}{1 + \tan\theta}$

63. $\cos(x + y)\cos(x - y) = \cos^2 x - \sin^2 y$

64. $\sin(x + y) + \sin(x - y) = 2\sin x \cos y$

Deriving a Reduction Formula In Exercises 65–68, simplify the expression algebraically and use a graphing utility to confirm your answer graphically.

65. $\cos\left(\dfrac{3\pi}{2} - x\right)$ **66.** $\cos(\pi + x)$

67. $\sin\left(\dfrac{3\pi}{2} + \theta\right)$ **68.** $\tan(\pi + \theta)$

Solving a Trigonometric Equation In Exercises 69–74, find all solutions of the equation in the interval $[0, 2\pi)$.

69. $\sin(x + \pi) - \sin x + 1 = 0$

70. $\cos(x + \pi) - \cos x - 1 = 0$

71. $\cos\left(x + \dfrac{\pi}{4}\right) - \cos\left(x - \dfrac{\pi}{4}\right) = 1$

72. $\sin\left(x + \dfrac{\pi}{6}\right) - \sin\left(x - \dfrac{7\pi}{6}\right) = \dfrac{\sqrt{3}}{2}$

73. $\tan(x + \pi) + 2\sin(x + \pi) = 0$

74. $\sin\left(x + \dfrac{\pi}{2}\right) - \cos^2 x = 0$

Approximating Solutions In Exercises 75–78, use a graphing utility to approximate the solutions of the equation in the interval $[0, 2\pi)$.

75. $\cos\left(x + \dfrac{\pi}{4}\right) + \cos\left(x - \dfrac{\pi}{4}\right) = 1$

76. $\tan(x + \pi) - \cos\left(x + \dfrac{\pi}{2}\right) = 0$

77. $\sin\left(x + \dfrac{\pi}{2}\right) + \cos^2 x = 0$

78. $\cos\left(x - \dfrac{\pi}{2}\right) - \sin^2 x = 0$

79. Harmonic Motion

A weight is attached to a spring suspended vertically from a ceiling. When a driving force is applied to the system, the weight moves vertically from its equilibrium position, and this motion is modeled by

$$y = \dfrac{1}{3}\sin 2t + \dfrac{1}{4}\cos 2t$$

where y is the distance from equilibrium (in feet) and t is the time (in seconds).

(a) Use the identity

$$a\sin B\theta + b\cos B\theta = \sqrt{a^2 + b^2}\,\sin(B\theta + C)$$

where $C = \arctan(b/a)$, $a > 0$, to write the model in the form

$$y = \sqrt{a^2 + b^2}\,\sin(Bt + C).$$

(b) Find the amplitude of the oscillations of the weight.

(c) Find the frequency of the oscillations of the weight.

80. Standing Waves The equation of a standing wave is obtained by adding the displacements of two waves traveling in opposite directions (see figure). Assume that each of the waves has amplitude A, period T, and wavelength λ. If the models for these waves are

$$y_1 = A\cos 2\pi\left(\dfrac{t}{T} - \dfrac{x}{\lambda}\right) \quad \text{and} \quad y_2 = A\cos 2\pi\left(\dfrac{t}{T} + \dfrac{x}{\lambda}\right)$$

then show that

$$y_1 + y_2 = 2A\cos\dfrac{2\pi t}{T}\cos\dfrac{2\pi x}{\lambda}.$$

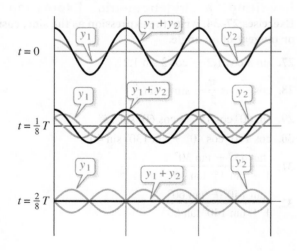

Exploration

True or False?   **In Exercises 81–84, determine whether the statement is true or false. Justify your answer.**

81. $\sin(u \pm v) = \sin u \cos v \pm \cos u \sin v$

82. $\cos(u \pm v) = \cos u \cos v \pm \sin u \sin v$

83. $\tan\left(x - \dfrac{\pi}{4}\right) = \dfrac{\tan x + 1}{1 - \tan x}$

84. $\sin\left(x - \dfrac{\pi}{2}\right) = -\cos x$

85. An Application from Calculus   Let $x = \pi/3$ in the identity in Example 8 and define the functions f and g as follows.

$$f(h) = \dfrac{\sin[(\pi/3) + h] - \sin(\pi/3)}{h}$$

$$g(h) = \cos\dfrac{\pi}{3}\left(\dfrac{\sin h}{h}\right) - \sin\dfrac{\pi}{3}\left(\dfrac{1 - \cos h}{h}\right)$$

(a) What are the domains of the functions f and g?

(b) Use a graphing utility to complete the table.

h	0.5	0.2	0.1	0.05	0.02	0.01
$f(h)$						
$g(h)$						

(c) Use the graphing utility to graph the functions f and g.

(d) Use the table and the graphs to make a conjecture about the values of the functions f and g as $h \to 0^{+}$.

86. **HOW DO YOU SEE IT?**   Explain how to use the figure to justify each statement.

(a) $\sin(u + v) \neq \sin u + \sin v$

(b) $\sin(u - v) \neq \sin u - \sin v$

Verifying an Identity   **In Exercises 87–90, verify the identity.**

87. $\cos(n\pi + \theta) = (-1)^n \cos \theta$, n is an integer

88. $\sin(n\pi + \theta) = (-1)^n \sin \theta$, n is an integer

89. $a \sin B\theta + b \cos B\theta = \sqrt{a^2 + b^2}\, \sin(B\theta + C)$,
where $C = \arctan(b/a)$ and $a > 0$

90. $a \sin B\theta + b \cos B\theta = \sqrt{a^2 + b^2}\, \cos(B\theta - C)$,
where $C = \arctan(a/b)$ and $b > 0$

Rewriting a Trigonometric Expression   **In Exercises 91–94, use the formulas given in Exercises 89 and 90 to write the trigonometric expression in the following forms.**

(a) $\sqrt{a^2 + b^2}\, \sin(B\theta + C)$ (b) $\sqrt{a^2 + b^2}\, \cos(B\theta - C)$

91. $\sin \theta + \cos \theta$ **92.** $3 \sin 2\theta + 4 \cos 2\theta$

93. $12 \sin 3\theta + 5 \cos 3\theta$ **94.** $\sin 2\theta + \cos 2\theta$

Rewriting a Trigonometric Expression   **In Exercises 95 and 96, use the formulas given in Exercises 89 and 90 to write the trigonometric expression in the form $a \sin B\theta + b \cos B\theta$.**

95. $2 \sin\left(\theta + \dfrac{\pi}{4}\right)$ **96.** $5 \cos\left(\theta - \dfrac{\pi}{4}\right)$

Angle Between Two Lines   **In Exercises 97 and 98, use the figure, which shows two lines whose equations are $y_1 = m_1 x + b_1$ and $y_2 = m_2 x + b_2$. Assume that both lines have positive slopes. Derive a formula for the angle between the two lines. Then use your formula to find the angle between the given pair of lines.**

97. $y = x$ and $y = \sqrt{3}x$

98. $y = x$ and $y = \dfrac{1}{\sqrt{3}}x$

Graphical Reasoning   **In Exercises 99 and 100, use a graphing utility to graph y_1 and y_2 in the same viewing window. Use the graphs to determine whether $y_1 = y_2$. Explain your reasoning.**

99. $y_1 = \cos(x + 2)$, $y_2 = \cos x + \cos 2$

100. $y_1 = \sin(x + 4)$, $y_2 = \sin x + \sin 4$

101. Proof

(a) Write a proof of the formula for $\sin(u + v)$.

(b) Write a proof of the formula for $\sin(u - v)$.

5.5 Multiple-Angle and Product-to-Sum Formulas

- Use multiple-angle formulas to rewrite and evaluate trigonometric functions.
- Use power-reducing formulas to rewrite and evaluate trigonometric functions.
- Use half-angle formulas to rewrite and evaluate trigonometric functions.
- Use product-to-sum and sum-to-product formulas to rewrite and evaluate trigonometric functions.
- Use trigonometric formulas to rewrite real-life models.

Multiple-Angle Formulas

In this section, you will study four other categories of trigonometric identities.

1. The first category involves *functions of multiple angles* such as $\sin ku$ and $\cos ku$.

2. The second category involves *squares of trigonometric functions* such as $\sin^2 u$.

3. The third category involves *functions of half-angles* such as $\sin(u/2)$.

4. The fourth category involves *products of trigonometric functions* such as $\sin u \cos v$.

A variety of trigonometric formulas enable you to rewrite trigonometric functions in more convenient forms. For instance, in Exercise 73 on page 390, you will use a half-angle formula to relate the Mach number of a supersonic airplane to the apex angle of the cone formed by the sound waves behind the airplane.

You should learn the **double-angle formulas** because they are used often in trigonometry and calculus. For proofs of these formulas, see Proofs in Mathematics on page 397.

Double-Angle Formulas

$$\sin 2u = 2 \sin u \cos u \qquad \cos 2u = \cos^2 u - \sin^2 u$$

$$\tan 2u = \frac{2 \tan u}{1 - \tan^2 u} \qquad\qquad = 2 \cos^2 u - 1$$

$$\qquad\qquad\qquad\qquad\qquad = 1 - 2 \sin^2 u$$

EXAMPLE 1   **Solving a Multiple-Angle Equation**

Solve $2 \cos x + \sin 2x = 0$.

Solution   Begin by rewriting the equation so that it involves functions of x (rather than $2x$). Then factor and solve.

$2 \cos x + \sin 2x = 0$	Write original equation.
$2 \cos x + 2 \sin x \cos x = 0$	Double-angle formula
$2 \cos x(1 + \sin x) = 0$	Factor.
$2 \cos x = 0 \quad$ and $\quad 1 + \sin x = 0$	Set factors equal to zero.
$x = \dfrac{\pi}{2}, \dfrac{3\pi}{2} \qquad\qquad x = \dfrac{3\pi}{2}$	Solutions in $[0, 2\pi)$

So, the general solution is

$$x = \frac{\pi}{2} + 2n\pi \quad \text{and} \quad x = \frac{3\pi}{2} + 2n\pi$$

where n is an integer. Try verifying these solutions graphically.

✓ *Checkpoint* 🔊)))   *Audio-video solution in English & Spanish at LarsonPrecalculus.com.*

Solve $\cos 2x + \cos x = 0$.

EXAMPLE 2   **Evaluating Functions Involving Double Angles**

Use the following to find $\sin 2\theta$, $\cos 2\theta$, and $\tan 2\theta$.

$$\cos \theta = \frac{5}{13}, \quad \frac{3\pi}{2} < \theta < 2\pi$$

Solution   From Figure 5.7,

$$\sin \theta = \frac{y}{r} = -\frac{12}{13} \quad \text{and} \quad \tan \theta = \frac{y}{x} = -\frac{12}{5}.$$

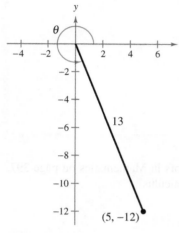

Figure 5.7

Consequently, using each of the double-angle formulas, you can write

$$\sin 2\theta = 2 \sin \theta \cos \theta = 2\left(-\frac{12}{13}\right)\left(\frac{5}{13}\right) = -\frac{120}{169}$$

$$\cos 2\theta = 2 \cos^2 \theta - 1 = 2\left(\frac{25}{169}\right) - 1 = -\frac{119}{169}$$

$$\tan 2\theta = \frac{2 \tan \theta}{1 - \tan^2 \theta} = \frac{2\left(-\dfrac{12}{5}\right)}{1 - \left(-\dfrac{12}{5}\right)^2} = \frac{120}{119}.$$

✓ **Checkpoint** ◀))) *Audio-video solution in English & Spanish at LarsonPrecalculus.com.*

Use the following to find $\sin 2\theta$, $\cos 2\theta$, and $\tan 2\theta$.

$$\sin \theta = \frac{3}{5}, \quad 0 < \theta < \frac{\pi}{2}$$

The double-angle formulas are not restricted to angles 2θ and θ. Other *double* combinations, such as 4θ and 2θ or 6θ and 3θ, are also valid. Here are two examples.

$$\sin 4\theta = 2 \sin 2\theta \cos 2\theta \quad \text{and} \quad \cos 6\theta = \cos^2 3\theta - \sin^2 3\theta$$

By using double-angle formulas together with the sum formulas given in the preceding section, you can form other multiple-angle formulas.

EXAMPLE 3   **Deriving a Triple-Angle Formula**

Rewrite $\sin 3x$ in terms of $\sin x$.

Solution

$\sin 3x = \sin(2x + x)$	Rewrite as a sum.
$= \sin 2x \cos x + \cos 2x \sin x$	Sum formula
$= 2 \sin x \cos x \cos x + (1 - 2 \sin^2 x) \sin x$	Double-angle formulas
$= 2 \sin x \cos^2 x + \sin x - 2 \sin^3 x$	Distributive Property
$= 2 \sin x(1 - \sin^2 x) + \sin x - 2 \sin^3 x$	Pythagorean identity
$= 2 \sin x - 2 \sin^3 x + \sin x - 2 \sin^3 x$	Distributive Property
$= 3 \sin x - 4 \sin^3 x$	Simplify.

✓ **Checkpoint** ◀))) *Audio-video solution in English & Spanish at LarsonPrecalculus.com.*

Rewrite $\cos 3x$ in terms of $\cos x$.

Power-Reducing Formulas

The double-angle formulas can be used to obtain the following **power-reducing formulas.**

Power-Reducing Formulas

$$\sin^2 u = \frac{1 - \cos 2u}{2}$$

$$\cos^2 u = \frac{1 + \cos 2u}{2}$$

$$\tan^2 u = \frac{1 - \cos 2u}{1 + \cos 2u}$$

For a proof of the power-reducing formulas, see Proofs in Mathematics on page 397. Example 4 shows a typical power reduction used in calculus.

EXAMPLE 4 **Reducing a Power**

Rewrite $\sin^4 x$ in terms of first powers of the cosines of multiple angles.

Solution Note the repeated use of power-reducing formulas.

$$\sin^4 x = (\sin^2 x)^2 \qquad \text{Property of exponents}$$

$$= \left(\frac{1 - \cos 2x}{2}\right)^2 \qquad \text{Power-reducing formula}$$

$$= \frac{1}{4}(1 - 2\cos 2x + \cos^2 2x) \qquad \text{Expand.}$$

$$= \frac{1}{4}\left(1 - 2\cos 2x + \frac{1 + \cos 4x}{2}\right) \qquad \text{Power-reducing formula}$$

$$= \frac{1}{4} - \frac{1}{2}\cos 2x + \frac{1}{8} + \frac{1}{8}\cos 4x \qquad \text{Distributive Property}$$

$$= \frac{3}{8} - \frac{1}{2}\cos 2x + \frac{1}{8}\cos 4x \qquad \text{Simplify.}$$

$$= \frac{1}{8}(3 - 4\cos 2x + \cos 4x) \qquad \text{Factor out common factor.}$$

You can use a graphing utility to check this result, as shown below. Notice that the graphs coincide.

$y_1 = \sin^4 x$

$y_2 = \frac{1}{8}(3 - 4\cos 2x + \cos 4x)$

 ✓ *Checkpoint*))) Audio-video solution in English & Spanish at LarsonPrecalculus.com.

Rewrite $\tan^4 x$ in terms of first powers of the cosines of multiple angles.

Half-Angle Formulas

You can derive some useful alternative forms of the power-reducing formulas by replacing u with $u/2$. The results are called **half-angle formulas.**

•• REMARK To find the exact value of a trigonometric function with an angle measure in D°M′S″ form using a half-angle formula, first convert the angle measure to decimal degree form. Then multiply the resulting angle measure by 2.
··················▷

Half-Angle Formulas

$$\sin\frac{u}{2} = \pm\sqrt{\frac{1 - \cos u}{2}} \qquad\qquad \cos\frac{u}{2} = \pm\sqrt{\frac{1 + \cos u}{2}}$$

$$\tan\frac{u}{2} = \frac{1 - \cos u}{\sin u} = \frac{\sin u}{1 + \cos u}$$

The signs of $\sin\dfrac{u}{2}$ and $\cos\dfrac{u}{2}$ depend on the quadrant in which $\dfrac{u}{2}$ lies.

•• REMARK Use your calculator to verify the result obtained in Example 5. That is, evaluate $\sin 105°$ and $\left(\sqrt{2 + \sqrt{3}}\right)/2$. Note that both values are approximately 0.9659258.
··················▷

EXAMPLE 5   **Using a Half-Angle Formula**

Find the exact value of $\sin 105°$.

Solution   Begin by noting that $105°$ is half of $210°$. Then, using the half-angle formula for $\sin(u/2)$ and the fact that $105°$ lies in Quadrant II, you have

$$\sin 105° = \sqrt{\frac{1 - \cos 210°}{2}} = \sqrt{\frac{1 + (\sqrt{3}/2)}{2}} = \frac{\sqrt{2 + \sqrt{3}}}{2}.$$

The positive square root is chosen because $\sin\theta$ is positive in Quadrant II.

✓ **Checkpoint** Audio-video solution in English & Spanish at LarsonPrecalculus.com.

Find the exact value of $\cos 105°$.

EXAMPLE 6   **Solving a Trigonometric Equation**

Find all solutions of $1 + \cos^2 x = 2\cos^2\dfrac{x}{2}$ in the interval $[0, 2\pi)$.

Algebraic Solution

$$1 + \cos^2 x = 2\cos^2\frac{x}{2}$$ Write original equation.

$$1 + \cos^2 x = 2\left(\pm\sqrt{\frac{1 + \cos x}{2}}\right)^2$$ Half-angle formula

$$1 + \cos^2 x = 1 + \cos x$$ Simplify.

$$\cos^2 x - \cos x = 0$$ Simplify.

$$\cos x(\cos x - 1) = 0$$ Factor.

By setting the factors $\cos x$ and $\cos x - 1$ equal to zero, you find that the solutions in the interval $[0, 2\pi)$ are

$$x = \frac{\pi}{2}, \quad x = \frac{3\pi}{2}, \quad\text{and}\quad x = 0.$$

Graphical Solution

The x-intercepts are $x = 0$, $x \approx 1.571$, and $x \approx 4.712$.

From the above figure, you can conclude that the approximate solutions of $1 + \cos^2 x = 2\cos^2 x/2$ in the interval $[0, 2\pi)$ are

$$x = 0, \quad x \approx 1.571 \approx \frac{\pi}{2}, \quad\text{and}\quad x \approx 4.712 \approx \frac{3\pi}{2}.$$

✓ **Checkpoint** Audio-video solution in English & Spanish at LarsonPrecalculus.com.

Find all solutions of $\cos^2 x = \sin^2\dfrac{x}{2}$ in the interval $[0, 2\pi)$.

Product-to-Sum Formulas

Each of the following **product-to-sum formulas** can be verified using the sum and difference formulas discussed in the preceding section.

Product-to-Sum Formulas

$$\sin u \sin v = \frac{1}{2}[\cos(u - v) - \cos(u + v)]$$

$$\cos u \cos v = \frac{1}{2}[\cos(u - v) + \cos(u + v)]$$

$$\sin u \cos v = \frac{1}{2}[\sin(u + v) + \sin(u - v)]$$

$$\cos u \sin v = \frac{1}{2}[\sin(u + v) - \sin(u - v)]$$

Product-to-sum formulas are used in calculus to solve problems involving the products of sines and cosines of two different angles.

EXAMPLE 7   Writing Products as Sums

Rewrite the product $\cos 5x \sin 4x$ as a sum or difference.

Solution   Using the appropriate product-to-sum formula, you obtain

$$\cos 5x \sin 4x = \frac{1}{2}[\sin(5x + 4x) - \sin(5x - 4x)]$$

$$= \frac{1}{2}\sin 9x - \frac{1}{2}\sin x.$$

✓ *Checkpoint* ◄))) *Audio-video solution in English & Spanish at LarsonPrecalculus.com.*

Rewrite the product $\sin 5x \cos 3x$ as a sum or difference.

Occasionally, it is useful to reverse the procedure and write a sum of trigonometric functions as a product. This can be accomplished with the following **sum-to-product formulas.**

Sum-to-Product Formulas

$$\sin u + \sin v = 2 \sin\left(\frac{u + v}{2}\right) \cos\left(\frac{u - v}{2}\right)$$

$$\sin u - \sin v = 2 \cos\left(\frac{u + v}{2}\right) \sin\left(\frac{u - v}{2}\right)$$

$$\cos u + \cos v = 2 \cos\left(\frac{u + v}{2}\right) \cos\left(\frac{u - v}{2}\right)$$

$$\cos u - \cos v = -2 \sin\left(\frac{u + v}{2}\right) \sin\left(\frac{u - v}{2}\right)$$

For a proof of the sum-to-product formulas, see Proofs in Mathematics on page 398.

EXAMPLE 8   **Using a Sum-to-Product Formula**

Find the exact value of $\cos 195° + \cos 105°$.

Solution   Using the appropriate sum-to-product formula, you obtain

$$\cos 195° + \cos 105° = 2 \cos\left(\frac{195° + 105°}{2}\right) \cos\left(\frac{195° - 105°}{2}\right)$$

$$= 2 \cos 150° \cos 45°$$

$$= 2\left(-\frac{\sqrt{3}}{2}\right)\left(\frac{\sqrt{2}}{2}\right)$$

$$= -\frac{\sqrt{6}}{2}.$$

✓ *Checkpoint* Audio-video solution in English & Spanish at LarsonPrecalculus.com.

Find the exact value of $\sin 195° + \sin 105°$.

EXAMPLE 9   **Solving a Trigonometric Equation**

Solve $\sin 5x + \sin 3x = 0$.

Solution

$$\sin 5x + \sin 3x = 0 \qquad \text{Write original equation.}$$

$$2 \sin\left(\frac{5x + 3x}{2}\right) \cos\left(\frac{5x - 3x}{2}\right) = 0 \qquad \text{Sum-to-product formula}$$

$$2 \sin 4x \cos x = 0 \qquad \text{Simplify.}$$

By setting the factor $2 \sin 4x$ equal to zero, you can find that the solutions in the interval $[0, 2\pi)$ are

$$x = 0, \frac{\pi}{4}, \frac{\pi}{2}, \frac{3\pi}{4}, \pi, \frac{5\pi}{4}, \frac{3\pi}{2}, \frac{7\pi}{4}.$$

The equation $\cos x = 0$ yields no additional solutions, so you can conclude that the solutions are of the form $x = n\pi/4$ where n is an integer. To confirm this graphically, sketch the graph of $y = \sin 5x + \sin 3x$, as shown below.

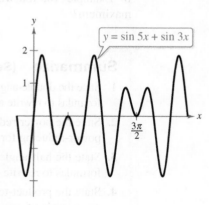

Notice from the graph that the x-intercepts occur at multiples of $\pi/4$.

✓ *Checkpoint* Audio-video solution in English & Spanish at LarsonPrecalculus.com.

Solve $\sin 4x - \sin 2x = 0$.

Application

EXAMPLE 10   **Projectile Motion**

Kicking a football with an initial velocity of 80 feet per second at an angle of 45° with the horizontal results in a distance traveled of 200 feet.

Ignoring air resistance, the range of a projectile fired at an angle θ with the horizontal and with an initial velocity of v_0 feet per second is given by

$$r = \frac{1}{16}v_0^2 \sin \theta \cos \theta$$

where r is the horizontal distance (in feet) that the projectile travels. A football player can kick a football from ground level with an initial velocity of 80 feet per second.

a. Write the projectile motion model in a simpler form.

b. At what angle must the player kick the football so that the football travels 200 feet?

Solution

a. You can use a double-angle formula to rewrite the projectile motion model as

$$r = \frac{1}{32}v_0^2(2 \sin \theta \cos \theta) \qquad \text{Rewrite original projectile motion model.}$$

$$= \frac{1}{32}v_0^2 \sin 2\theta. \qquad \text{Rewrite model using a double-angle formula.}$$

b. $r = \frac{1}{32}v_0^2 \sin 2\theta \qquad \text{Write projectile motion model.}$

$$200 = \frac{1}{32}(80)^2 \sin 2\theta \qquad \text{Substitute 200 for } r \text{ and 80 for } v_0.$$

$$200 = 200 \sin 2\theta \qquad \text{Simplify.}$$

$$1 = \sin 2\theta \qquad \text{Divide each side by 200.}$$

You know that $2\theta = \pi/2$, so dividing this result by 2 produces $\theta = \pi/4$. Because $\pi/4 = 45°$, the player must kick the football at an angle of 45° so that the football travels 200 feet.

✓ *Checkpoint* *Audio-video solution in English & Spanish at LarsonPrecalculus.com.*

In Example 10, for what angle is the horizontal distance the football travels a maximum?

Summarize   **(Section 5.5)**

1. State the double-angle formulas *(page 382)*. For examples of using multiple-angle formulas to rewrite and evaluate trigonometric functions, see Examples 1–3.

2. State the power-reducing formulas *(page 384)*. For an example of using power-reducing formulas to rewrite a trigonometric function, see Example 4.

3. State the half-angle formulas *(page 385)*. For examples of using half-angle formulas to rewrite and evaluate trigonometric functions, see Examples 5 and 6.

4. State the product-to-sum and sum-to-product formulas *(page 386)*. For an example of using a product-to-sum formula to rewrite a trigonometric function, see Example 7. For examples of using sum-to-product formulas to rewrite and evaluate trigonometric functions, see Examples 8 and 9.

5. Describe an example of how to use a trigonometric formula to rewrite a real-life model *(page 388, Example 10)*.

5.5 Exercises

See CalcChat.com for tutorial help and worked-out solutions to odd-numbered exercises.

Vocabulary: Fill in the blank to complete the trigonometric formula.

1. $\sin 2u = $ _____

2. $\cos 2u = $ _____

3. $\dfrac{1 - \cos 2u}{1 + \cos 2u} = $ _____

4. $\sin \dfrac{u}{2} = $ _____

5. $\sin u \cos v = $ _____

6. $\cos u - \cos v = $ _____

Skills and Applications

Solving a Multiple-Angle Equation In Exercises 7–14, find the exact solutions of the equation in the interval $[0, 2\pi)$.

7. $\sin 2x - \sin x = 0$

8. $\sin 2x \sin x = \cos x$

9. $\cos 2x - \cos x = 0$

10. $\cos 2x + \sin x = 0$

11. $\sin 4x = -2 \sin 2x$

12. $(\sin 2x + \cos 2x)^2 = 1$

13. $\tan 2x - \cot x = 0$

14. $\tan 2x - 2 \cos x = 0$

Using a Double-Angle Formula In Exercises 15–20, use a double-angle formula to rewrite the expression.

15. $6 \sin x \cos x$

16. $\sin x \cos x$

17. $6 \cos^2 x - 3$

18. $\cos^2 x - \frac{1}{2}$

19. $4 - 8 \sin^2 x$

20. $10 \sin^2 x - 5$

Evaluating Functions Involving Double Angles In Exercises 21–24, find the exact values of $\sin 2u$, $\cos 2u$, and $\tan 2u$ using the double-angle formulas.

21. $\sin u = -3/5$, $\quad 3\pi/2 < u < 2\pi$

22. $\cos u = -4/5$, $\quad \pi/2 < u < \pi$

23. $\tan u = 3/5$, $\quad 0 < u < \pi/2$

24. $\sec u = -2$, $\quad \pi < u < 3\pi/2$

25. Deriving a Multiple-Angle Formula Rewrite $\cos 4x$ in terms of $\cos x$.

26. Deriving a Multiple-Angle Formula Rewrite $\tan 3x$ in terms of $\tan x$.

Reducing Powers In Exercises 27–32, use the power-reducing formulas to rewrite the expression in terms of the first power of the cosine.

27. $\cos^4 x$

28. $\sin^4 2x$

29. $\tan^4 2x$

30. $\tan^2 2x \cos^4 2x$

31. $\sin^2 2x \cos^2 2x$

32. $\sin^4 x \cos^2 x$

Using Half-Angle Formulas In Exercises 33–36, use the half-angle formulas to determine the exact values of the sine, cosine, and tangent of the angle.

33. $75°$

34. $67° \, 30'$

35. $\pi/8$

36. $7\pi/12$

Using Half-Angle Formulas In Exercises 37–40, (a) determine the quadrant in which $u/2$ lies, and (b) find the exact values of $\sin(u/2)$, $\cos(u/2)$, and $\tan(u/2)$ using the half-angle formulas.

37. $\cos u = 7/25$, $\quad 0 < u < \pi/2$

38. $\sin u = 5/13$, $\quad \pi/2 < u < \pi$

39. $\tan u = -5/12$, $\quad 3\pi/2 < u < 2\pi$

40. $\cot u = 3$, $\quad \pi < u < 3\pi/2$

Using Half-Angle Formulas In Exercises 41–44, use the half-angle formulas to simplify the expression.

41. $\sqrt{\dfrac{1 - \cos 6x}{2}}$

42. $\sqrt{\dfrac{1 + \cos 4x}{2}}$

43. $-\sqrt{\dfrac{1 - \cos 8x}{1 + \cos 8x}}$

44. $-\sqrt{\dfrac{1 - \cos(x - 1)}{2}}$

Solving a Trigonometric Equation In Exercises 45–48, find all solutions of the equation in the interval $[0, 2\pi)$. Use a graphing utility to graph the equation and verify the solutions.

45. $\sin \dfrac{x}{2} + \cos x = 0$

46. $\sin \dfrac{x}{2} + \cos x - 1 = 0$

47. $\cos \dfrac{x}{2} - \sin x = 0$

48. $\tan \dfrac{x}{2} - \sin x = 0$

Using Product-to-Sum Formulas In Exercises 49–52, use the product-to-sum formulas to rewrite the product as a sum or difference.

49. $\sin 5\theta \sin 3\theta$

50. $7 \cos(-5\beta) \sin 3\beta$

51. $\cos 2\theta \cos 4\theta$

52. $\sin(x + y) \cos(x - y)$

Using Sum-to-Product Formulas In Exercises 53–56, use the sum-to-product formulas to rewrite the sum or difference as a product.

53. $\sin 5\theta - \sin 3\theta$

54. $\sin 3\theta + \sin \theta$

55. $\cos 6x + \cos 2x$

56. $\cos\left(\theta + \dfrac{\pi}{2}\right) - \cos\left(\theta - \dfrac{\pi}{2}\right)$

Using Sum-to-Product Formulas **In Exercises 57–60, use the sum-to-product formulas to find the exact value of the expression.**

57. $\sin 75° + \sin 15°$

58. $\cos 120° + \cos 60°$

59. $\cos \dfrac{3\pi}{4} - \cos \dfrac{\pi}{4}$

60. $\sin \dfrac{5\pi}{4} - \sin \dfrac{3\pi}{4}$

Solving a Trigonometric Equation **In Exercises 61–64, find all solutions of the equation in the interval $[0, 2\pi)$. Use a graphing utility to graph the equation and verify the solutions.**

61. $\sin 6x + \sin 2x = 0$

62. $\cos 2x - \cos 6x = 0$

63. $\dfrac{\cos 2x}{\sin 3x - \sin x} - 1 = 0$

64. $\sin^2 3x - \sin^2 x = 0$

Verifying a Trigonometric Identity **In Exercises 65–72, verify the identity.**

65. $\csc 2\theta = \dfrac{\csc \theta}{2 \cos \theta}$

66. $\sin \dfrac{\alpha}{3} \cos \dfrac{\alpha}{3} = \dfrac{1}{2} \sin \dfrac{2\alpha}{3}$

67. $1 + \cos 10y = 2 \cos^2 5y$

68. $\cos^4 x - \sin^4 x = \cos 2x$

69. $(\sin x + \cos x)^2 = 1 + \sin 2x$

70. $\tan \dfrac{u}{2} = \csc u - \cot u$

71. $\dfrac{\sin x \pm \sin y}{\cos x + \cos y} = \tan \dfrac{x \pm y}{2}$

72. $\cos\left(\dfrac{\pi}{3} + x\right) + \cos\left(\dfrac{\pi}{3} - x\right) = \cos x$

73. Mach Number

The Mach number M of a supersonic airplane is the ratio of its speed to the speed of sound. When an airplane travels faster than the speed of sound, the sound waves form a cone behind the airplane. The Mach number is related to the apex angle θ of the cone by $\sin(\theta/2) = 1/M$.

(a) Use a half-angle formula to rewrite the equation in terms of $\cos \theta$.

(b) Find the angle θ that corresponds to a Mach number of 1.

(c) Find the angle θ that corresponds to a Mach number of 4.5.

(d) The speed of sound is about 760 miles per hour. Determine the speed of an object with the Mach numbers from parts (b) and (c).

74. Projectile Motion The range of a projectile fired at an angle θ with the horizontal and with an initial velocity of v_0 feet per second is

$$r = \dfrac{1}{32} v_0^2 \sin 2\theta$$

where r is measured in feet. An athlete throws a javelin at 75 feet per second. At what angle must the athlete throw the javelin so that the javelin travels 130 feet?

75. Railroad Track When two railroad tracks merge, the overlapping portions of the tracks are in the shapes of circular arcs (see figure). The radius of each arc r (in feet) and the angle θ are related by

$$\dfrac{x}{2} = 2r \sin^2 \dfrac{\theta}{2}.$$

Write a formula for x in terms of $\cos \theta$.

Exploration

76. **HOW DO YOU SEE IT?** Explain how to use the figure to verify the double-angle formulas (a) $\sin 2u = 2 \sin u \cos u$ and (b) $\cos 2u = \cos^2 u - \sin^2 u$.

True or False? **In Exercises 77 and 78, determine whether the statement is true or false. Justify your answer.**

77. Because the sine function is an odd function, for a negative number u, $\sin 2u = -2 \sin u \cos u$.

78. $\sin \dfrac{u}{2} = -\sqrt{\dfrac{1 - \cos u}{2}}$ when u is in the second quadrant.

79. Complementary Angles If ϕ and θ are complementary angles, then show that (a) $\sin(\phi - \theta) = \cos 2\theta$ and (b) $\cos(\phi - \theta) = \sin 2\theta$.

Chapter Summary

	What Did You Learn?	Explanation/Examples	Review Exercises
Section 5.1	Recognize and write the fundamental trigonometric identities (*p. 350*).	**Reciprocal Identities** $\sin u = 1/\csc u \qquad \cos u = 1/\sec u \qquad \tan u = 1/\cot u$ $\csc u = 1/\sin u \qquad \sec u = 1/\cos u \qquad \cot u = 1/\tan u$ **Quotient Identities:** $\tan u = \dfrac{\sin u}{\cos u}, \quad \cot u = \dfrac{\cos u}{\sin u}$ **Pythagorean Identities:** $\sin^2 u + \cos^2 u = 1$, $1 + \tan^2 u = \sec^2 u, \quad 1 + \cot^2 u = \csc^2 u$ **Cofunction Identities** $\sin[(\pi/2) - u] = \cos u \qquad \cos[(\pi/2) - u] = \sin u$ $\tan[(\pi/2) - u] = \cot u \qquad \cot[(\pi/2) - u] = \tan u$ $\sec[(\pi/2) - u] = \csc u \qquad \csc[(\pi/2) - u] = \sec u$ **Even/Odd Identities** $\sin(-u) = -\sin u \qquad \cos(-u) = \cos u \qquad \tan(-u) = -\tan u$ $\csc(-u) = -\csc u \qquad \sec(-u) = \sec u \qquad \cot(-u) = -\cot u$	1–4
	Use the fundamental trigonometric identities to evaluate trigonometric functions, simplify trigonometric expressions, and rewrite trigonometric expressions (*p. 351*).	In some cases, when factoring or simplifying trigonometric expressions, it is helpful to rewrite the expression in terms of just *one* trigonometric function or in terms of *sine and cosine only*.	5–18
Section 5.2	Verify trigonometric identities (*p. 357*).	**Guidelines for Verifying Trigonometric Identities** **1.** Work with one side of the equation at a time. **2.** Look to factor an expression, add fractions, square a binomial, or create a monomial denominator. **3.** Look to use the fundamental identities. Note which functions are in the final expression you want. Sines and cosines pair up well, as do secants and tangents, and cosecants and cotangents. **4.** If the preceding guidelines do not help, then try converting all terms to sines and cosines. **5.** Always try *something*.	19–26
Section 5.3	Use standard algebraic techniques to solve trigonometric equations (*p. 364*).	Use standard algebraic techniques (when possible) such as collecting like terms, extracting square roots, and factoring to solve trigonometric equations.	27–32
	Solve trigonometric equations of quadratic type (*p. 367*).	To solve trigonometric equations of quadratic type $ax^2 + bx + c = 0$, factor the quadratic or, when this is not possible, use the Quadratic Formula.	33–36
	Solve trigonometric equations involving multiple angles (*p. 369*).	To solve equations that contain forms such as $\sin ku$ or $\cos ku$, first solve the equation for ku, and then divide your result by k.	37–42
	Use inverse trigonometric functions to solve trigonometric equations (*p. 370*).	After factoring an equation, you may get an equation such as $(\tan x - 3)(\tan x + 1) = 0$. In such cases, use inverse trigonometric functions to solve. (See Example 9.)	43–46

What Did You Learn?	Explanation/Examples	Review Exercises
Section 5.4 Use sum and difference formulas to evaluate trigonometric functions, verify identities, and solve trigonometric equations (p. 375).	**Sum and Difference Formulas** $\sin(u + v) = \sin u \cos v + \cos u \sin v$ $\sin(u - v) = \sin u \cos v - \cos u \sin v$ $\cos(u + v) = \cos u \cos v - \sin u \sin v$ $\cos(u - v) = \cos u \cos v + \sin u \sin v$ $\tan(u + v) = \dfrac{\tan u + \tan v}{1 - \tan u \tan v}$ $\tan(u - v) = \dfrac{\tan u - \tan v}{1 + \tan u \tan v}$	47–62
Section 5.5 Use multiple-angle formulas to rewrite and evaluate trigonometric functions (p. 382).	**Double-Angle Formulas** $\sin 2u = 2 \sin u \cos u \qquad \cos 2u = \cos^2 u - \sin^2 u$ $\tan 2u = \dfrac{2 \tan u}{1 - \tan^2 u} \qquad\quad = 2\cos^2 u - 1$ $\qquad\qquad\qquad\qquad\quad = 1 - 2\sin^2 u$	63–66
Use power-reducing formulas to rewrite and evaluate trigonometric functions (p. 384).	**Power-Reducing Formulas** $\sin^2 u = \dfrac{1 - \cos 2u}{2}, \quad \cos^2 u = \dfrac{1 + \cos 2u}{2}$ $\tan^2 u = \dfrac{1 - \cos 2u}{1 + \cos 2u}$	67, 68
Use half-angle formulas to rewrite and evaluate trigonometric functions (p. 385).	**Half-Angle Formulas** $\sin \dfrac{u}{2} = \pm\sqrt{\dfrac{1 - \cos u}{2}}, \quad \cos \dfrac{u}{2} = \pm\sqrt{\dfrac{1 + \cos u}{2}}$ $\tan \dfrac{u}{2} = \dfrac{1 - \cos u}{\sin u} = \dfrac{\sin u}{1 + \cos u}$ The signs of $\sin(u/2)$ and $\cos(u/2)$ depend on the quadrant in which $u/2$ lies.	69–74
Use product-to-sum and sum-to-product formulas to rewrite and evaluate trigonometric functions (p. 386).	**Product-to-Sum Formulas** $\sin u \sin v = (1/2)[\cos(u - v) - \cos(u + v)]$ $\cos u \cos v = (1/2)[\cos(u - v) + \cos(u + v)]$ $\sin u \cos v = (1/2)[\sin(u + v) + \sin(u - v)]$ $\cos u \sin v = (1/2)[\sin(u + v) - \sin(u - v)]$ **Sum-to-Product Formulas** $\sin u + \sin v = 2 \sin\left(\dfrac{u + v}{2}\right) \cos\left(\dfrac{u - v}{2}\right)$ $\sin u - \sin v = 2 \cos\left(\dfrac{u + v}{2}\right) \sin\left(\dfrac{u - v}{2}\right)$ $\cos u + \cos v = 2 \cos\left(\dfrac{u + v}{2}\right) \cos\left(\dfrac{u - v}{2}\right)$ $\cos u - \cos v = -2 \sin\left(\dfrac{u + v}{2}\right) \sin\left(\dfrac{u - v}{2}\right)$	75–78
Use trigonometric formulas to rewrite real-life models (p. 388).	A trigonometric formula can be used to rewrite the projectile motion model $r = (1/16)v_0^2 \sin \theta \cos \theta$. (See Example 10.)	79, 80

Review Exercises   See CalcChat.com for tutorial help and worked-out solutions to odd-numbered exercises.

5.1 Recognizing a Fundamental Identity In Exercises 1–4, name the trigonometric function that is equivalent to the expression.

1. $\dfrac{\sin x}{\cos x}$ 2. $\dfrac{1}{\sin x}$

3. $\dfrac{1}{\tan x}$ 4. $\sqrt{\cot^2 x + 1}$

Using Identities to Evaluate a Function In Exercises 5 and 6, use the given values and fundamental trigonometric identities to find the values (if possible) of all six trigonometric functions.

5. $\tan \theta = \dfrac{2}{3}, \quad \sec \theta = \dfrac{\sqrt{13}}{3}$

6. $\sin\left(\dfrac{\pi}{2} - x\right) = \dfrac{\sqrt{2}}{2}, \quad \sin x = -\dfrac{\sqrt{2}}{2}$

Simplifying a Trigonometric Expression In Exercises 7–16, use the fundamental trigonometric identities to simplify the expression. There is more than one correct form of each answer.

7. $\dfrac{1}{\cot^2 x + 1}$ 8. $\dfrac{\tan \theta}{1 - \cos^2 \theta}$

9. $\tan^2 x(\csc^2 x - 1)$ 10. $\cot^2 x(\sin^2 x)$

11. $\dfrac{\cot\left(\dfrac{\pi}{2} - u\right)}{\cos u}$ 12. $\dfrac{\sec^2(-\theta)}{\csc^2 \theta}$

13. $\cos^2 x + \cos^2 x \cot^2 x$ 14. $(\tan x + 1)^2 \cos x$

15. $\dfrac{1}{\csc \theta + 1} - \dfrac{1}{\csc \theta - 1}$ 16. $\dfrac{\tan^2 x}{1 + \sec x}$

Trigonometric Substitution In Exercises 17 and 18, use the trigonometric substitution to write the algebraic expression as a trigonometric function of θ, where $0 < \theta < \pi/2$.

17. $\sqrt{25 - x^2}, x = 5 \sin \theta$ 18. $\sqrt{x^2 - 16}, x = 4 \sec \theta$

5.2 Verifying a Trigonometric Identity In Exercises 19–26, verify the identity.

19. $\cos x(\tan^2 x + 1) = \sec x$

20. $\sec^2 x \cot x - \cot x = \tan x$

21. $\sec\left(\dfrac{\pi}{2} - \theta\right) = \csc \theta$ 22. $\cot\left(\dfrac{\pi}{2} - x\right) = \tan x$

23. $\dfrac{1}{\tan \theta \csc \theta} = \cos \theta$ 24. $\dfrac{1}{\tan x \csc x \sin x} = \cot x$

25. $\sin^5 x \cos^2 x = (\cos^2 x - 2 \cos^4 x + \cos^6 x) \sin x$

26. $\cos^3 x \sin^2 x = (\sin^2 x - \sin^4 x) \cos x$

5.3 Solving a Trigonometric Equation In Exercises 27–32, solve the equation.

27. $\sin x = \sqrt{3} - \sin x$ 28. $4 \cos \theta = 1 + 2 \cos \theta$

29. $3\sqrt{3} \tan u = 3$ 30. $\dfrac{1}{2} \sec x - 1 = 0$

31. $3 \csc^2 x = 4$ 32. $4 \tan^2 u - 1 = \tan^2 u$

Solving a Trigonometric Equation In Exercises 33–42, find all solutions of the equation in the interval $[0, 2\pi)$.

33. $2 \cos^2 x - \cos x = 1$ 34. $2 \cos^2 x + 3 \cos x = 0$

35. $\cos^2 x + \sin x = 1$ 36. $\sin^2 x + 2 \cos x = 2$

37. $2 \sin 2x - \sqrt{2} = 0$ 38. $2 \cos \dfrac{x}{2} + 1 = 0$

39. $3 \tan^2\left(\dfrac{x}{3}\right) - 1 = 0$ 40. $\sqrt{3} \tan 3x = 0$

41. $\cos 4x(\cos x - 1) = 0$ 42. $3 \csc^2 5x = -4$

Using Inverse Functions In Exercises 43–46, use inverse functions where needed to find all solutions of the equation in the interval $[0, 2\pi)$.

43. $\tan^2 x - 2 \tan x = 0$

44. $2 \tan^2 x - 3 \tan x = -1$

45. $\tan^2 \theta + \tan \theta - 6 = 0$

46. $\sec^2 x + 6 \tan x + 4 = 0$

5.4 Evaluating Trigonometric Functions In Exercises 47–50, find the exact values of the sine, cosine, and tangent of the angle.

47. $285° = 315° - 30°$ 48. $345° = 300° + 45°$

49. $\dfrac{25\pi}{12} = \dfrac{11\pi}{6} + \dfrac{\pi}{4}$ 50. $\dfrac{19\pi}{12} = \dfrac{11\pi}{6} - \dfrac{\pi}{4}$

Rewriting a Trigonometric Expression In Exercises 51 and 52, write the expression as the sine, cosine, or tangent of an angle.

51. $\sin 60° \cos 45° - \cos 60° \sin 45°$

52. $\dfrac{\tan 68° - \tan 115°}{1 + \tan 68° \tan 115°}$

Evaluating a Trigonometric Expression In Exercises 53–56, find the exact value of the trigonometric expression given that $\tan u = \dfrac{3}{4}$ and $\cos v = -\dfrac{4}{5}$. (u is in Quadrant I and v is in Quadrant III.)

53. $\sin(u + v)$

54. $\tan(u + v)$

55. $\cos(u - v)$

56. $\sin(u - v)$

Proving a Trigonometric Identity   In Exercises 57–60, prove the identity.

57. $\cos\left(x + \dfrac{\pi}{2}\right) = -\sin x$ **58.** $\tan\left(x - \dfrac{\pi}{2}\right) = -\cot x$

59. $\tan(\pi - x) = -\tan x$

60. $\cos 3x = 4\cos^3 x - 3\cos x$

Solving a Trigonometric Equation   In Exercises 61 and 62, find all solutions of the equation in the interval $[0, 2\pi)$.

61. $\sin\left(x + \dfrac{\pi}{4}\right) - \sin\left(x - \dfrac{\pi}{4}\right) = 1$

62. $\cos\left(x + \dfrac{\pi}{6}\right) - \cos\left(x - \dfrac{\pi}{6}\right) = 1$

5.5   Evaluating Functions Involving Double Angles
In Exercises 63 and 64, find the exact values of $\sin 2u$, $\cos 2u$, and $\tan 2u$ using the double-angle formulas.

63. $\sin u = -\dfrac{4}{5}, \quad \pi < u < 3\pi/2$

64. $\cos u = -2/\sqrt{5}, \quad \pi/2 < u < \pi$

Verifying a Trigonometric Identity   In Exercises 65 and 66, use the double-angle formulas to verify the identity algebraically and use a graphing utility to confirm your result graphically.

65. $\sin 4x = 8\cos^3 x \sin x - 4\cos x \sin x$

66. $\tan^2 x = \dfrac{1 - \cos 2x}{1 + \cos 2x}$

Reducing Powers   In Exercises 67 and 68, use the power-reducing formulas to rewrite the expression in terms of the first power of the cosine.

67. $\tan^2 2x$ **68.** $\sin^2 x \tan^2 x$

Using Half-Angle Formulas   In Exercises 69 and 70, use the half-angle formulas to determine the exact values of the sine, cosine, and tangent of the angle.

69. $-75°$ **70.** $\dfrac{19\pi}{12}$

Using Half-Angle Formulas   In Exercises 71 and 72, (a) determine the quadrant in which $u/2$ lies, and (b) find the exact values of $\sin(u/2)$, $\cos(u/2)$, and $\tan(u/2)$ using the half-angle formulas.

71. $\tan u = \dfrac{4}{3}, \quad \pi < u < 3\pi/2$

72. $\cos u = -\dfrac{2}{7}, \quad \pi/2 < u < \pi$

Using Half-Angle Formulas   In Exercises 73 and 74, use the half-angle formulas to simplify the expression.

73. $-\sqrt{\dfrac{1 + \cos 10x}{2}}$ **74.** $\dfrac{\sin 6x}{1 + \cos 6x}$

Using Product-to-Sum Formulas   In Exercises 75 and 76, use the product-to-sum formulas to rewrite the product as a sum or difference.

75. $\cos 4\theta \sin 6\theta$ **76.** $2\sin 7\theta \cos 3\theta$

Using Sum-to-Product Formulas   In Exercises 77 and 78, use the sum-to-product formulas to rewrite the sum or difference as a product.

77. $\cos 6\theta + \cos 5\theta$

78. $\sin\left(x + \dfrac{\pi}{4}\right) - \sin\left(x - \dfrac{\pi}{4}\right)$

79. Projectile Motion   A baseball leaves the hand of a player at first base at an angle of θ with the horizontal and at an initial velocity of $v_0 = 80$ feet per second. A player at second base 100 feet away catches the ball. Find θ when the range r of a projectile is

$$r = \dfrac{1}{32}v_0^2 \sin 2\theta.$$

80. Geometry   A trough for feeding cattle is 4 meters long and its cross sections are isosceles triangles with the two equal sides being $\frac{1}{2}$ meter (see figure). The angle between the two sides is θ.

(a) Write the trough's volume as a function of $\theta/2$.

(b) Write the volume of the trough as a function of θ and determine the value of θ such that the volume is maximum.

Exploration

True or False?   In Exercises 81–84, determine whether the statement is true or false. Justify your answer.

81. If $\dfrac{\pi}{2} < \theta < \pi$, then $\cos\dfrac{\theta}{2} < 0$.

82. $\sin(x + y) = \sin x + \sin y$

83. $4\sin(-x)\cos(-x) = -2\sin 2x$

84. $4\sin 45° \cos 15° = 1 + \sqrt{3}$

85. Think About It   When a trigonometric equation has an infinite number of solutions, is it true that the equation is an identity? Explain.

Take this test as you would take a test in class. When you are finished, check your work against the answers given in the back of the book.

1. When $\tan \theta = \frac{6}{5}$ and $\cos \theta < 0$, evaluate (if possible) all six trigonometric functions of θ.

2. Use the fundamental identities to simplify $\csc^2 \beta(1 - \cos^2 \beta)$.

3. Factor and simplify $\dfrac{\sec^4 x - \tan^4 x}{\sec^2 x + \tan^2 x}$.   4. Add and simplify $\dfrac{\cos \theta}{\sin \theta} + \dfrac{\sin \theta}{\cos \theta}$.

5. Determine the values of $\theta, 0 \le \theta < 2\pi$, for which $\tan \theta = -\sqrt{\sec^2 \theta - 1}$.

6. Use a graphing utility to graph the functions $y_1 = \cos x + \sin x \tan x$ and $y_2 = \sec x$ in the same viewing window. Make a conjecture about y_1 and y_2. Verify the result algebraically.

In Exercises 7–12, verify the identity.

7. $\sin \theta \sec \theta = \tan \theta$ 8. $\sec^2 x \tan^2 x + \sec^2 x = \sec^4 x$

9. $\dfrac{\csc \alpha + \sec \alpha}{\sin \alpha + \cos \alpha} = \cot \alpha + \tan \alpha$ 10. $\tan\left(x + \dfrac{\pi}{2}\right) = -\cot x$

11. $\sin(n\pi + \theta) = (-1)^n \sin \theta$, n is an integer.

12. $(\sin x + \cos x)^2 = 1 + \sin 2x$

13. Rewrite $\sin^4 \dfrac{x}{2}$ in terms of the first power of the cosine.

14. Use a half-angle formula to simplify the expression $(\sin 4\theta)/(1 + \cos 4\theta)$.

15. Rewrite $4 \sin 3\theta \cos 2\theta$ as a sum or difference.

16. Rewrite $\cos 3\theta - \cos \theta$ as a product.

In Exercises 17–20, find all solutions of the equation in the interval $[0, 2\pi)$.

17. $\tan^2 x + \tan x = 0$ 18. $\sin 2\alpha - \cos \alpha = 0$

19. $4 \cos^2 x - 3 = 0$ 20. $\csc^2 x - \csc x - 2 = 0$

21. Use a graphing utility to approximate the solutions (to three decimal places) of $5 \sin x - x = 0$ in the interval $[0, 2\pi)$.

22. Find the exact value of $\cos 105°$ using the fact that $105° = 135° - 30°$.

23. Use the figure to find the exact values of $\sin 2u$, $\cos 2u$, and $\tan 2u$.

24. Cheyenne, Wyoming, has a latitude of 41°N. At this latitude, the position of the sun at sunrise can be modeled by

$$D = 31 \sin\left(\dfrac{2\pi}{365}t - 1.4\right)$$

where t is the time (in days), with $t = 1$ representing January 1. In this model, D represents the number of degrees north or south of due east that the sun rises. Use a graphing utility to determine the days on which the sun is more than 20° north of due east at sunrise.

25. The heights above ground h_1 and h_2 (in feet) of two people in different seats on a Ferris wheel can be modeled by

$$h_1 = 28 \cos 10t + 38 \quad \text{and} \quad h_2 = 28 \cos\left[10\left(t - \dfrac{\pi}{6}\right)\right] + 38, \ 0 \le t \le 2$$

where t is the time (in minutes). When are the two people at the same height?

Figure for 23

Proofs in Mathematics ■ ■ ■ ■ ■ ■ ■ ■ ■ ■ ■ ■ ■ ■ ■

Proof

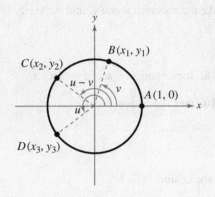

Use the figures at the left for the proofs of the formulas for $\cos(u \pm v)$. In the top figure, let A be the point $(1, 0)$ and then use u and v to locate the points $B(x_1, y_1)$, $C(x_2, y_2)$, and $D(x_3, y_3)$ on the unit circle. So, $x_i^2 + y_i^2 = 1$ for $i = 1, 2,$ and 3. For convenience, assume that $0 < v < u < 2\pi$. In the bottom figure, note that arcs AC and BD have the same length. So, line segments AC and BD are also equal in length, which implies that

$$\sqrt{(x_2 - 1)^2 + (y_2 - 0)^2} = \sqrt{(x_3 - x_1)^2 + (y_3 - y_1)^2}$$

$$x_2^2 - 2x_2 + 1 + y_2^2 = x_3^2 - 2x_1x_3 + x_1^2 + y_3^2 - 2y_1y_3 + y_1^2$$

$$(x_2^2 + y_2^2) + 1 - 2x_2 = (x_3^2 + y_3^2) + (x_1^2 + y_1^2) - 2x_1x_3 - 2y_1y_3$$

$$1 + 1 - 2x_2 = 1 + 1 - 2x_1x_3 - 2y_1y_3$$

$$x_2 = x_3x_1 + y_3y_1.$$

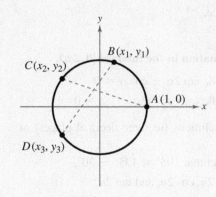

Finally, by substituting the values $x_2 = \cos(u - v)$, $x_3 = \cos u$, $x_1 = \cos v$, $y_3 = \sin u$, and $y_1 = \sin v$, you obtain $\cos(u - v) = \cos u \cos v + \sin u \sin v$. To establish the formula for $\cos(u + v)$, consider $u + v = u - (-v)$ and use the formula just derived to obtain

$$\cos(u + v) = \cos[u - (-v)]$$

$$= \cos u \cos(-v) + \sin u \sin(-v)$$

$$= \cos u \cos v - \sin u \sin v.$$

You can use the sum and difference formulas for sine and cosine to prove the formulas for $\tan(u \pm v)$.

$$\tan(u \pm v) = \frac{\sin(u \pm v)}{\cos(u \pm v)} \qquad \text{Quotient identity}$$

$$= \frac{\sin u \cos v \pm \cos u \sin v}{\cos u \cos v \mp \sin u \sin v} \qquad \text{Sum and difference formulas}$$

$$= \frac{\dfrac{\sin u \cos v \pm \cos u \sin v}{\cos u \cos v}}{\dfrac{\cos u \cos v \mp \sin u \sin v}{\cos u \cos v}} \qquad \begin{array}{l}\text{Divide numerator and denominator}\\ \text{by } \cos u \cos v.\end{array}$$

$$= \dfrac{\dfrac{\sin u \cos v}{\cos u \cos v} \pm \dfrac{\cos u \sin v}{\cos u \cos v}}{\dfrac{\cos u \cos v}{\cos u \cos v} \mp \dfrac{\sin u \sin v}{\cos u \cos v}}$$

Write as separate fractions.

$$= \dfrac{\dfrac{\sin u}{\cos u} \pm \dfrac{\sin v}{\cos v}}{1 \mp \dfrac{\sin u}{\cos u} \cdot \dfrac{\sin v}{\cos v}}$$

Simplify.

$$= \dfrac{\tan u \pm \tan v}{1 \mp \tan u \tan v}$$

Quotient identity

Double-Angle Formulas   *(p. 382)*

$$\sin 2u = 2 \sin u \cos u \qquad \cos 2u = \cos^2 u - \sin^2 u$$

$$\tan 2u = \dfrac{2 \tan u}{1 - \tan^2 u} \qquad\qquad = 2 \cos^2 u - 1$$

$$= 1 - 2 \sin^2 u$$

Proof

To prove all three formulas, let $v = u$ in the corresponding sum formulas.

$$\sin 2u = \sin(u + u) = \sin u \cos u + \cos u \sin u = 2 \sin u \cos u$$

$$\cos 2u = \cos(u + u) = \cos u \cos u - \sin u \sin u = \cos^2 u - \sin^2 u$$

$$\tan 2u = \tan(u + u) = \dfrac{\tan u + \tan u}{1 - \tan u \tan u} = \dfrac{2 \tan u}{1 - \tan^2 u}$$

Power-Reducing Formulas   *(p. 384)*

$$\sin^2 u = \dfrac{1 - \cos 2u}{2} \qquad \cos^2 u = \dfrac{1 + \cos 2u}{2} \qquad \tan^2 u = \dfrac{1 - \cos 2u}{1 + \cos 2u}$$

Proof

To prove the first formula, solve for $\sin^2 u$ in the double-angle formula $\cos 2u = 1 - 2 \sin^2 u$, as follows.

$$\cos 2u = 1 - 2 \sin^2 u$$

Write double-angle formula.

$$2 \sin^2 u = 1 - \cos 2u$$

Subtract $\cos 2u$ from, and add $2 \sin^2 u$ to, each side.

$$\sin^2 u = \dfrac{1 - \cos 2u}{2}$$

Divide each side by 2.

In a similar way, you can prove the second formula by solving for $\cos^2 u$ in the double-angle formula

$$\cos 2u = 2\cos^2 u - 1.$$

To prove the third formula, use a quotient identity, as follows.

$$\tan^2 u = \frac{\sin^2 u}{\cos^2 u}$$

$$= \frac{\dfrac{1 - \cos 2u}{2}}{\dfrac{1 + \cos 2u}{2}}$$

$$= \frac{1 - \cos 2u}{1 + \cos 2u}$$

Sum-to-Product Formulas *(p. 386)*

$$\sin u + \sin v = 2 \sin\left(\frac{u + v}{2}\right) \cos\left(\frac{u - v}{2}\right)$$

$$\sin u - \sin v = 2 \cos\left(\frac{u + v}{2}\right) \sin\left(\frac{u - v}{2}\right)$$

$$\cos u + \cos v = 2 \cos\left(\frac{u + v}{2}\right) \cos\left(\frac{u - v}{2}\right)$$

$$\cos u - \cos v = -2 \sin\left(\frac{u + v}{2}\right) \sin\left(\frac{u - v}{2}\right)$$

Proof

To prove the first formula, let $x = u + v$ and $y = u - v$. Then substitute $u = (x + y)/2$ and $v = (x - y)/2$ in the product-to-sum formula.

$$\sin u \cos v = \frac{1}{2}[\sin(u + v) + \sin(u - v)]$$

$$\sin\left(\frac{x + y}{2}\right) \cos\left(\frac{x - y}{2}\right) = \frac{1}{2}(\sin x + \sin y)$$

$$2 \sin\left(\frac{x + y}{2}\right) \cos\left(\frac{x - y}{2}\right) = \sin x + \sin y$$

The other sum-to-product formulas can be proved in a similar manner.

P.S. Problem Solving ▪ ▪ ▪ ▪ ▪ ▪ ▪ ▪ ▪ ▪ ▪ ▪ ▪ ▪

1. **Writing Trigonometric Functions in Terms of Cosine** Write each of the other trigonometric functions of θ in terms of $\cos \theta$.

2. **Verifying a Trigonometric Identity** Verify that for all integers n,

$$\cos\left[\frac{(2n+1)\pi}{2}\right] = 0.$$

3. **Verifying a Trigonometric Identity** Verify that for all integers n,

$$\sin\left[\frac{(12n+1)\pi}{6}\right] = \frac{1}{2}.$$

4. **Sound Wave** A sound wave is modeled by

$$p(t) = \frac{1}{4\pi}\left[p_1(t) + 30p_2(t) + p_3(t) + p_5(t) + 30p_6(t)\right]$$

where $p_n(t) = \frac{1}{n}\sin(524n\pi t)$, and t is the time (in seconds).

(a) Find the sine components $p_n(t)$ and use a graphing utility to graph the components. Then verify the graph of p shown below.

(b) Find the period of each sine component of p. Is p periodic? If so, then what is its period?

(c) Use the graphing utility to find the t-intercepts of the graph of p over one cycle.

(d) Use the graphing utility to approximate the absolute maximum and absolute minimum values of p over one cycle.

5. **Geometry** Three squares of side s are placed side by side (see figure). Make a conjecture about the relationship between the sum $u + v$ and w. Prove your conjecture by using the identity for the tangent of the sum of two angles.

6. **Projectile Motion** The path traveled by an object (neglecting air resistance) that is projected at an initial height of h_0 feet, an initial velocity of v_0 feet per second, and an initial angle θ is given by

$$y = -\frac{16}{v_0^2 \cos^2 \theta}x^2 + (\tan \theta)x + h_0$$

where x and y are measured in feet. Find a formula for the maximum height of an object projected from ground level at velocity v_0 and angle θ. To do this, find half of the horizontal distance

$$\frac{1}{32}v_0^2 \sin 2\theta$$

and then substitute it for x in the general model for the path of a projectile (where $h_0 = 0$).

7. **Geometry** The length of each of the two equal sides of an isosceles triangle is 10 meters (see figure). The angle between the two sides is θ.

(a) Write the area of the triangle as a function of $\theta/2$.

(b) Write the area of the triangle as a function of θ. Determine the value of θ such that the area is a maximum.

          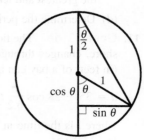

Figure for 7   Figure for 8

8. **Geometry** Use the figure to derive the formulas for

$$\sin \frac{\theta}{2}, \cos \frac{\theta}{2}, \text{ and } \tan \frac{\theta}{2}$$

where θ is an acute angle.

9. **Force** The force F (in pounds) on a person's back when he or she bends over at an angle θ is modeled by

$$F = \frac{0.6W \sin(\theta + 90°)}{\sin 12°}$$

where W is the person's weight (in pounds).

(a) Simplify the model.

(b) Use a graphing utility to graph the model, where $W = 185$ and $0° < \theta < 90°$.

(c) At what angle is the force a maximum? At what angle is the force a minimum?

10. Hours of Daylight The number of hours of daylight that occur at any location on Earth depends on the time of year and the latitude of the location. The following equations model the numbers of hours of daylight in Seward, Alaska (60° latitude), and New Orleans, Louisiana (30° latitude).

$$D = 12.2 - 6.4 \cos\left[\frac{\pi(t + 0.2)}{182.6}\right] \quad \text{Seward}$$

$$D = 12.2 - 1.9 \cos\left[\frac{\pi(t + 0.2)}{182.6}\right] \quad \text{New Orleans}$$

In these models, D represents the number of hours of daylight and t represents the day, with $t = 0$ corresponding to January 1.

(a) Use a graphing utility to graph both models in the same viewing window. Use a viewing window of $0 \le t \le 365$.

(b) Find the days of the year on which both cities receive the same amount of daylight.

(c) Which city has the greater variation in the number of daylight hours? Which constant in each model would you use to determine the difference between the greatest and least numbers of hours of daylight?

(d) Determine the period of each model.

11. Ocean Tide The tide, or depth of the ocean near the shore, changes throughout the day. The water depth d (in feet) of a bay can be modeled by

$$d = 35 - 28 \cos\frac{\pi}{6.2}t$$

where t is the time in hours, with $t = 0$ corresponding to 12:00 A.M.

(a) Algebraically find the times at which the high and low tides occur.

(b) If possible, algebraically find the time(s) at which the water depth is 3.5 feet.

(c) Use a graphing utility to verify your results from parts (a) and (b).

12. Piston Heights The heights h (in inches) of pistons 1 and 2 in an automobile engine can be modeled by

$$h_1 = 3.75 \sin 733t + 7.5$$

and

$$h_2 = 3.75 \sin 733(t + 4\pi/3) + 7.5$$

respectively, where t is measured in seconds.

(a) Use a graphing utility to graph the heights of these pistons in the same viewing window for $0 \le t \le 1$.

(b) How often are the pistons at the same height?

13. Index of Refraction The index of refraction n of a transparent material is the ratio of the speed of light in a vacuum to the speed of light in the material. Some common materials and their indices of refraction are air (1.00), water (1.33), and glass (1.50). Triangular prisms are often used to measure the index of refraction based on the formula

$$n = \frac{\sin\left(\dfrac{\theta}{2} + \dfrac{\alpha}{2}\right)}{\sin\dfrac{\theta}{2}}.$$

For the prism shown in the figure, $\alpha = 60°$.

(a) Write the index of refraction as a function of $\cot(\theta/2)$.

(b) Find θ for a prism made of glass.

14. Sum Formulas

(a) Write a sum formula for $\sin(u + v + w)$.

(b) Write a sum formula for $\tan(u + v + w)$.

15. Solving Trigonometric Inequalities Find the solution of each inequality in the interval $[0, 2\pi)$.

(a) $\sin x \ge 0.5$ (b) $\cos x \le -0.5$

(c) $\tan x < \sin x$ (d) $\cos x \ge \sin x$

16. Sum of Fourth Powers Consider the function $f(x) = \sin^4 x + \cos^4 x$.

(a) Use the power-reducing formulas to write the function in terms of cosine to the first power.

(b) Determine another way of rewriting the function. Use a graphing utility to rule out incorrectly rewritten functions.

(c) Add a trigonometric term to the function so that it becomes a perfect square trinomial. Rewrite the function as a perfect square trinomial minus the term that you added. Use the graphing utility to rule out incorrectly rewritten functions.

(d) Rewrite the result of part (c) in terms of the sine of a double angle. Use the graphing utility to rule out incorrectly rewritten functions.

(e) When you rewrite a trigonometric expression, the result may not be the same as a friend's. Does this mean that one of you is wrong? Explain.

A.1 Real Numbers and Their Properties

Real numbers can represent many real-life quantities. For example, in Exercises 55–58 on page A12, you will use real numbers to represent the federal deficit.

■ Represent and classify real numbers.
■ Order real numbers and use inequalities.
■ Find the absolute values of real numbers and find the distance between two real numbers.
■ Evaluate algebraic expressions.
■ Use the basic rules and properties of algebra.

Real Numbers

Real numbers can describe quantities in everyday life such as age, miles per gallon, and population. Symbols such as

$$-5, 9, 0, \tfrac{4}{3}, 0.666\ldots, 28.21, \sqrt{2}, \pi, \text{ and } \sqrt[3]{-32}$$

represent real numbers. Here are some important **subsets** (each member of a subset B is also a member of a set A) of the real numbers. The three dots, called *ellipsis points*, indicate that the pattern continues indefinitely.

$$\{1, 2, 3, 4, \ldots\} \qquad \text{Set of natural numbers}$$

$$\{0, 1, 2, 3, 4, \ldots\} \qquad \text{Set of whole numbers}$$

$$\{\ldots, -3, -2, -1, 0, 1, 2, 3, \ldots\} \qquad \text{Set of integers}$$

A real number is **rational** when it can be written as the ratio p/q of two integers, where $q \neq 0$. For instance, the numbers

$$\tfrac{1}{3} = 0.3333\ldots = 0.\overline{3}, \tfrac{1}{8} = 0.125, \text{ and } \tfrac{125}{111} = 1.126126\ldots = 1.\overline{126}$$

are rational. The decimal representation of a rational number either repeats $\left(\text{as in } \tfrac{173}{55} = 3.1\overline{45}\right)$ or terminates $\left(\text{as in } \tfrac{1}{2} = 0.5\right)$. A real number that cannot be written as the ratio of two integers is called **irrational.** Irrational numbers have infinite nonrepeating decimal representations. For instance, the numbers

$$\sqrt{2} = 1.4142135\ldots \approx 1.41 \quad \text{and} \quad \pi = 3.1415926\ldots \approx 3.14$$

are irrational. (The symbol $\approx$ means "is approximately equal to.") Figure A.1 shows subsets of real numbers and their relationships to each other.

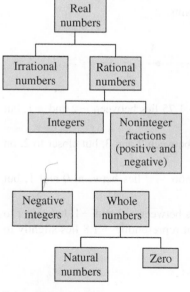

Subsets of real numbers
Figure A.1

EXAMPLE 1   Classifying Real Numbers

Determine which numbers in the set $\left\{-13, -\sqrt{5}, -1, -\tfrac{1}{3}, 0, \tfrac{5}{8}, \sqrt{2}, \pi, 7\right\}$ are (a) natural numbers, (b) whole numbers, (c) integers, (d) rational numbers, and (e) irrational numbers.

Solution

a. Natural numbers: $\{7\}$

b. Whole numbers: $\{0, 7\}$

c. Integers: $\{-13, -1, 0, 7\}$

d. Rational numbers: $\left\{-13, -1, -\dfrac{1}{3}, 0, \dfrac{5}{8}, 7\right\}$

e. Irrational numbers: $\left\{-\sqrt{5}, \sqrt{2}, \pi\right\}$

✓ *Checkpoint* ◀))) *Audio-video solution in English & Spanish at LarsonPrecalculus.com.*

Repeat Example 1 for the set $\left\{-\pi, -\tfrac{1}{4}, \tfrac{6}{3}, \tfrac{1}{2}\sqrt{2}, -7.5, -1, 8, -22\right\}$.

Real numbers are represented graphically on the **real number line.** When you draw a point on the real number line that corresponds to a real number, you are **plotting** the real number. The point 0 on the real number line is the **origin.** Numbers to the right of 0 are positive, and numbers to the left of 0 are negative, as shown below. The term **nonnegative** describes a number that is either positive or zero.

Origin

Negative direction | Positive direction

As illustrated below, there is a *one-to-one correspondence* between real numbers and points on the real number line.

Every real number corresponds to exactly one point on the real number line.

Every point on the real number line corresponds to exactly one real number.

EXAMPLE 2   **Plotting Points on the Real Number Line**

Plot the real numbers on the real number line.

a. $-\dfrac{7}{4}$

b. 2.3

c. $\dfrac{2}{3}$

d. -1.8

Solution   The following figure shows all four points.

a. The point representing the real number $-\dfrac{7}{4} = -1.75$ lies between -2 and -1, but closer to -2, on the real number line.

b. The point representing the real number 2.3 lies between 2 and 3, but closer to 2, on the real number line.

c. The point representing the real number $\dfrac{2}{3} = 0.666 \ldots$ lies between 0 and 1, but closer to 1, on the real number line.

d. The point representing the real number -1.8 lies between -2 and -1, but closer to -2, on the real number line. Note that the point representing -1.8 lies slightly to the left of the point representing $-\dfrac{7}{4}$.

✓ **Checkpoint** ◀))) *Audio-video solution in English & Spanish at LarsonPrecalculus.com.*

Plot the real numbers on the real number line.

a. $\dfrac{5}{2}$ b. -1.6

c. $-\dfrac{3}{4}$ d. 0.7

Ordering Real Numbers

One important property of real numbers is that they are *ordered*.

> ### Definition of Order on the Real Number Line
>
> If a and b are real numbers, then a is *less than* b when $b - a$ is positive. The **inequality** $a < b$ denotes the **order** of a and b. This relationship can also be described by saying that b is *greater than* a and writing $b > a$. The inequality $a \le b$ means that a is *less than or equal to* b, and the inequality $b \ge a$ means that b is *greater than or equal to* a. The symbols $<$, $>$, $\le$, and $\ge$ are *inequality symbols.*

$a < b$ if and only if a lies to the left of b.

Figure A.2

Geometrically, this definition implies that $a < b$ if and only if a lies to the *left* of b on the real number line, as shown in Figure A.2.

EXAMPLE 3   **Ordering Real Numbers**

Place the appropriate inequality symbol ($<$ or $>$) between the pair of real numbers.

a. $-3, 0$ **b.** $-2, -4$ **c.** $\frac{1}{4}, \frac{1}{3}$ **d.** $-\frac{1}{5}, -\frac{1}{2}$

Solution

Figure A.3

a. Because -3 lies to the left of 0 on the real number line, as shown in Figure A.3, you can say that -3 is *less than* 0, and write $-3 < 0$.

Figure A.4

b. Because -2 lies to the right of -4 on the real number line, as shown in Figure A.4, you can say that -2 is *greater than* -4, and write $-2 > -4$.

Figure A.5

c. Because $\frac{1}{4}$ lies to the left of $\frac{1}{3}$ on the real number line, as shown in Figure A.5, you can say that $\frac{1}{4}$ is *less than* $\frac{1}{3}$, and write $\frac{1}{4} < \frac{1}{3}$.

Figure A.6

d. Because $-\frac{1}{5}$ lies to the right of $-\frac{1}{2}$ on the real number line, as shown in Figure A.6, you can say that $-\frac{1}{5}$ is *greater than* $-\frac{1}{2}$, and write $-\frac{1}{5} > -\frac{1}{2}$.

✓ *Checkpoint* ◀))) *Audio-video solution in English & Spanish at LarsonPrecalculus.com.*

Place the appropriate inequality symbol ($<$ or $>$) between the pair of real numbers.

a. $1, -5$ **b.** $\frac{3}{2}, 7$ **c.** $-\frac{2}{3}, -\frac{3}{4}$ **d.** $-3.5, 1$

EXAMPLE 4   **Interpreting Inequalities**

Describe the subset of real numbers that the inequality represents.

a. $x \le 2$ **b.** $-2 \le x < 3$

$x \le 2$

Figure A.7

Solution

a. The inequality $x \le 2$ denotes all real numbers less than or equal to 2, as shown in Figure A.7.

b. The inequality $-2 \le x < 3$ means that $x \ge -2$ *and* $x < 3$. This "double inequality" denotes all real numbers between -2 and 3, including -2 but not including 3, as shown in Figure A.8.

$-2 \le x < 3$

Figure A.8

✓ *Checkpoint* ◀))) *Audio-video solution in English & Spanish at LarsonPrecalculus.com.*

Describe the subset of real numbers that the inequality represents.

a. $x > -3$ **b.** $0 < x \le 4$

Inequalities can describe subsets of real numbers called **intervals.** In the bounded intervals below, the real numbers a and b are the **endpoints** of each interval. The endpoints of a closed interval are included in the interval, whereas the endpoints of an open interval are not included in the interval.

- - - - - - - - - - - - - - - - - ▷

REMARK The reason that the four types of intervals at the right are called *bounded* is that each has a finite length. An interval that does not have a finite length is *unbounded* (see below).

Bounded Intervals on the Real Number Line

Notation	Interval Type	Inequality	Graph
$[a, b]$	Closed	$a \le x \le b$	
(a, b)	Open	$a < x < b$	
$[a, b)$		$a \le x < b$	
$(a, b]$		$a < x \le b$	

The symbols ∞, **positive infinity,** and $-\infty$, **negative infinity,** do not represent real numbers. They are simply convenient symbols used to describe the unboundedness of an interval such as $(1, \infty)$ or $(-\infty, 3]$.

REMARK Whenever you write an interval containing ∞ or $-\infty$, always use a parenthesis and never a bracket next to these symbols. This is because ∞ and $-\infty$ are never an endpoint of an interval and therefore are not included in the interval.

- - - - - - - - - - - - - - - - - ▷

Unbounded Intervals on the Real Number Line

Notation	Interval Type	Inequality	Graph
$[a, \infty)$		$x \ge a$	
(a, ∞)	Open	$x > a$	
$(-\infty, b]$		$x \le b$	
$(-\infty, b)$	Open	$x < b$	
$(-\infty, \infty)$	Entire real line	$-\infty < x < \infty$	

EXAMPLE 5   Interpreting Intervals

a. The interval $(-1, 0)$ consists of all real numbers greater than -1 and less than 0.

b. The interval $[2, \infty)$ consists of all real numbers greater than or equal to 2.

✓ *Checkpoint* ◀))) *Audio-video solution in English & Spanish at LarsonPrecalculus.com.*

Give a verbal description of the interval $[-2, 5)$.

EXAMPLE 6   Using Inequalities to Represent Intervals

a. The inequality $c \le 2$ can represent the statement "c is at most 2."

b. The inequality $-3 < x \le 5$ can represent "all x in the interval $(-3, 5]$."

✓ *Checkpoint* ◀))) *Audio-video solution in English & Spanish at LarsonPrecalculus.com.*

Use inequality notation to represent the statement "x is greater than -2 and at most 4."

Absolute Value and Distance

The **absolute value** of a real number is its *magnitude,* or the distance between the origin and the point representing the real number on the real number line.

Definition of Absolute Value

If a is a real number, then the absolute value of a is

$$|a| = \begin{cases} a, & \text{if } a \geq 0 \\ -a, & \text{if } a < 0 \end{cases}.$$

Notice in this definition that the absolute value of a real number is never negative. For instance, if $a = -5$, then $|-5| = -(-5) = 5$. The absolute value of a real number is either positive or zero. Moreover, 0 is the only real number whose absolute value is 0. So, $|0| = 0$.

EXAMPLE 7 **Finding Absolute Values**

a. $|-15| = 15$ **b.** $\left|\dfrac{2}{3}\right| = \dfrac{2}{3}$

c. $|-4.3| = 4.3$ **d.** $-|-6| = -(6) = -6$

✓ *Checkpoint* Audio-video solution in English & Spanish at LarsonPrecalculus.com.

Evaluate each expression.

a. $|1|$ **b.** $-\left|\dfrac{3}{4}\right|$

c. $\dfrac{2}{|-3|}$ **d.** $-|0.7|$

EXAMPLE 8 **Evaluating the Absolute Value of a Number**

Evaluate $\dfrac{|x|}{x}$ for (a) $x > 0$ and (b) $x < 0$.

Solution

a. If $x > 0$, then $|x| = x$ and $\dfrac{|x|}{x} = \dfrac{x}{x} = 1$.

b. If $x < 0$, then $|x| = -x$ and $\dfrac{|x|}{x} = \dfrac{-x}{x} = -1$.

✓ *Checkpoint* Audio-video solution in English & Spanish at LarsonPrecalculus.com.

Evaluate $\dfrac{|x + 3|}{x + 3}$ for (a) $x > -3$ and (b) $x < -3$.

The **Law of Trichotomy** states that for any two real numbers a and b, *precisely* one of three relationships is possible:

$$a = b, \quad a < b, \quad \text{or} \quad a > b. \qquad \text{Law of Trichotomy}$$

EXAMPLE 9   **Comparing Real Numbers**

Place the appropriate symbol ($<$, $>$, or $=$) between the pair of real numbers.

a. $|-4| \quad |3|$ **b.** $|-10| \quad |10|$ **c.** $-|-7| \quad |-7|$

Solution

a. $|-4| > |3|$ because $|-4| = 4$ and $|3| = 3$, and 4 is greater than 3.

b. $|-10| = |10|$ because $|-10| = 10$ and $|10| = 10$.

c. $-|-7| < |-7|$ because $-|-7| = -7$ and $|-7| = 7$, and -7 is less than 7.

✓ **Checkpoint**))) *Audio-video solution in English & Spanish at LarsonPrecalculus.com.*

Place the appropriate symbol ($<$, $>$, or $=$) between the pair of real numbers.

a. $|-3| \quad |4|$ **b.** $-|-4| \quad -|4|$ **c.** $|-3| \quad -|-3|$ ■

Properties of Absolute Values

1. $|a| \geq 0$ **2.** $|-a| = |a|$

3. $|ab| = |a||b|$ **4.** $\left|\dfrac{a}{b}\right| = \dfrac{|a|}{|b|}, \quad b \neq 0$

Absolute value can be used to define the distance between two points on the real number line. For instance, the distance between -3 and 4 is

$$|-3 - 4| = |-7|$$
$$= 7$$

as shown in Figure A.9.

The distance between -3 and 4 is 7.
Figure A.9

Distance Between Two Points on the Real Number Line

Let a and b be real numbers. The **distance between a and b** is

$$d(a, b) = |b - a| = |a - b|.$$

EXAMPLE 10   **Finding a Distance**

Find the distance between -25 and 13.

Solution

The distance between -25 and 13 is

$$|-25 - 13| = |-38| = 38. \qquad \text{Distance between } -25 \text{ and } 13$$

The distance can also be found as follows.

$$|13 - (-25)| = |38| = 38 \qquad \text{Distance between } -25 \text{ and } 13$$

✓ **Checkpoint**))) *Audio-video solution in English & Spanish at LarsonPrecalculus.com.*

a. Find the distance between 35 and -23.

b. Find the distance between -35 and -23.

c. Find the distance between 35 and 23.

Algebraic Expressions

One characteristic of algebra is the use of letters to represent numbers. The letters are **variables,** and combinations of letters and numbers are **algebraic expressions.** Here are a few examples of algebraic expressions.

$$5x, \quad 2x - 3, \quad \frac{4}{x^2 + 2}, \quad 7x + y$$

Definition of an Algebraic Expression

An **algebraic expression** is a collection of letters (**variables**) and real numbers (**constants**) combined using the operations of addition, subtraction, multiplication, division, and exponentiation.

The **terms** of an algebraic expression are those parts that are separated by *addition.* For example, $x^2 - 5x + 8 = x^2 + (-5x) + 8$ has three terms: x^2 and $-5x$ are the **variable terms** and 8 is the **constant term.** The numerical factor of a term is called the **coefficient.** For instance, the coefficient of $-5x$ is -5, and the coefficient of x^2 is 1.

EXAMPLE 11 **Identifying Terms and Coefficients**

Algebraic Expression	Terms	Coefficients
a. $5x - \dfrac{1}{7}$	$5x, -\dfrac{1}{7}$	$5, -\dfrac{1}{7}$
b. $2x^2 - 6x + 9$	$2x^2, -6x, 9$	$2, -6, 9$
c. $\dfrac{3}{x} + \dfrac{1}{2}x^4 - y$	$\dfrac{3}{x}, \dfrac{1}{2}x^4, -y$	$3, \dfrac{1}{2}, -1$

✓ *Checkpoint* ◄))) *Audio-video solution in English & Spanish at LarsonPrecalculus.com.*

Identify the terms and coefficients of $-2x + 4$. ▪

To **evaluate** an algebraic expression, substitute numerical values for each of the variables in the expression, as shown in the next example.

EXAMPLE 12 **Evaluating Algebraic Expressions**

Expression	Value of Variable	Substitute.	Value of Expression
a. $-3x + 5$	$x = 3$	$-3(3) + 5$	$-9 + 5 = -4$
b. $3x^2 + 2x - 1$	$x = -1$	$3(-1)^2 + 2(-1) - 1$	$3 - 2 - 1 = 0$
c. $\dfrac{2x}{x + 1}$	$x = -3$	$\dfrac{2(-3)}{-3 + 1}$	$\dfrac{-6}{-2} = 3$

Note that you must substitute the value for *each* occurrence of the variable.

✓ *Checkpoint* ◄))) *Audio-video solution in English & Spanish at LarsonPrecalculus.com.*

Evaluate $4x - 5$ when $x = 0$. ▪

Use the **Substitution Principle** to evaluate algebraic expressions. It states that "If $a = b$, then b can replace a in any expression involving a." In Example 12(a), for instance, 3 is *substituted* for x in the expression $-3x + 5$.

Basic Rules of Algebra

There are four arithmetic operations with real numbers: *addition, multiplication, subtraction,* and *division,* denoted by the symbols $+$, $\times$ or $\cdot$, $-$, and $\div$ or $/$, respectively. Of these, addition and multiplication are the two primary operations. Subtraction and division are the inverse operations of addition and multiplication, respectively.

Definitions of Subtraction and Division

Subtraction: Add the opposite.   **Division:** Multiply by the reciprocal.

$$a - b = a + (-b) \qquad\qquad \text{If } b \neq 0, \text{ then } a/b = a\left(\frac{1}{b}\right) = \frac{a}{b}.$$

In these definitions, $-b$ is the **additive inverse** (or opposite) of b, and $1/b$ is the **multiplicative inverse** (or reciprocal) of b. In the fractional form a/b, a is the **numerator** of the fraction and b is the **denominator.**

Because the properties of real numbers below are true for variables and algebraic expressions as well as for real numbers, they are often called the **Basic Rules of Algebra.** Try to formulate a verbal description of each property. For instance, the first property states that *the order in which two real numbers are added does not affect their sum.*

Basic Rules of Algebra

Let a, b, and c be real numbers, variables, or algebraic expressions.

Property		Example
Commutative Property of Addition:	$a + b = b + a$	$4x + x^2 = x^2 + 4x$
Commutative Property of Multiplication:	$ab = ba$	$(4 - x)x^2 = x^2(4 - x)$
Associative Property of Addition:	$(a + b) + c = a + (b + c)$	$(x + 5) + x^2 = x + (5 + x^2)$
Associative Property of Multiplication:	$(ab)c = a(bc)$	$(2x \cdot 3y)(8) = (2x)(3y \cdot 8)$
Distributive Properties:	$a(b + c) = ab + ac$	$3x(5 + 2x) = 3x \cdot 5 + 3x \cdot 2x$
	$(a + b)c = ac + bc$	$(y + 8)y = y \cdot y + 8 \cdot y$
Additive Identity Property:	$a + 0 = a$	$5y^2 + 0 = 5y^2$
Multiplicative Identity Property:	$a \cdot 1 = a$	$(4x^2)(1) = 4x^2$
Additive Inverse Property:	$a + (-a) = 0$	$5x^3 + (-5x^3) = 0$
Multiplicative Inverse Property:	$a \cdot \dfrac{1}{a} = 1, \quad a \neq 0$	$(x^2 + 4)\left(\dfrac{1}{x^2 + 4}\right) = 1$

Because subtraction is defined as "adding the opposite," the Distributive Properties are also true for subtraction. For instance, the "subtraction form" of $a(b + c) = ab + ac$ is $a(b - c) = ab - ac$. Note that the operations of subtraction and division are neither commutative nor associative. The examples

$$7 - 3 \neq 3 - 7 \quad \text{and} \quad 20 \div 4 \neq 4 \div 20$$

show that subtraction and division are not commutative. Similarly

$$5 - (3 - 2) \neq (5 - 3) - 2 \quad \text{and} \quad 16 \div (4 \div 2) \neq (16 \div 4) \div 2$$

demonstrate that subtraction and division are not associative.

EXAMPLE 13   **Identifying Rules of Algebra**

Identify the rule of algebra illustrated by the statement.

a. $(5x^3)2 = 2(5x^3)$ **b.** $(4x + 3) - (4x + 3) = 0$

c. $7x \cdot \dfrac{1}{7x} = 1, \quad x \neq 0$ **d.** $(2 + 5x^2) + x^2 = 2 + (5x^2 + x^2)$

Solution

a. This statement illustrates the Commutative Property of Multiplication. In other words, you obtain the same result whether you multiply $5x^3$ by 2, or 2 by $5x^3$.

b. This statement illustrates the Additive Inverse Property. In terms of subtraction, this property states that when any expression is subtracted from itself the result is 0.

c. This statement illustrates the Multiplicative Inverse Property. Note that x must be a nonzero number. The reciprocal of x is undefined when x is 0.

d. This statement illustrates the Associative Property of Addition. In other words, to form the sum $2 + 5x^2 + x^2$, it does not matter whether 2 and $5x^2$, or $5x^2$ and x^2 are added first.

✔ *Checkpoint*   *Audio-video solution in English & Spanish at LarsonPrecalculus.com.*

Identify the rule of algebra illustrated by the statement.

a. $x + 9 = 9 + x$ **b.** $5(x^3 \cdot 2) = (5x^3)2$ **c.** $(2 + 5x^2)y^2 = 2 \cdot y^2 + 5x^2 \cdot y^2$

> •• **REMARK** Notice the difference between the *opposite of a number* and a *negative number*. If a is negative, then its opposite, $-a$, is positive. For instance, if $a = -5$, then
>
> $-a = -(-5) = 5$.

Properties of Negation and Equality

Let a, b, and c be real numbers, variables, or algebraic expressions.

Property	Example
1. $(-1)a = -a$	$(-1)7 = -7$
2. $-(-a) = a$	$-(-6) = 6$
3. $(-a)b = -(ab) = a(-b)$	$(-5)3 = -(5 \cdot 3) = 5(-3)$
4. $(-a)(-b) = ab$	$(-2)(-x) = 2x$
5. $-(a + b) = (-a) + (-b)$	$-(x + 8) = (-x) + (-8)$
	$\qquad\qquad = -x - 8$
6. If $a = b$, then $a \pm c = b \pm c$.	$\frac{1}{2} + 3 = 0.5 + 3$
7. If $a = b$, then $ac = bc$.	$4^2 \cdot 2 = 16 \cdot 2$
8. If $a \pm c = b \pm c$, then $a = b$.	$1.4 - 1 = \frac{7}{5} - 1 \implies 1.4 = \frac{7}{5}$
9. If $ac = bc$ and $c \neq 0$, then $a = b$.	$3x = 3 \cdot 4 \implies x = 4$

> •• **REMARK** The "or" in the Zero-Factor Property includes the possibility that either or both factors may be zero. This is an *inclusive or*, and it is generally the way the word "or" is used in mathematics.

Properties of Zero

Let a and b be real numbers, variables, or algebraic expressions.

1. $a + 0 = a$ and $a - 0 = a$ **2.** $a \cdot 0 = 0$

3. $\dfrac{0}{a} = 0, \quad a \neq 0$ **4.** $\dfrac{a}{0}$ is undefined.

5. Zero-Factor Property: If $ab = 0$, then $a = 0$ or $b = 0$.

· · · · · · · · · · · · · · · ▷

· · REMARK In Property 1 of fractions, the phrase "if and only if" implies two statements. One statement is: If $a/b = c/d$, then $ad = bc$. The other statement is: If $ad = bc$, where $b \neq 0$ and $d \neq 0$, then $a/b = c/d$.

Properties and Operations of Fractions

Let a, b, c, and d be real numbers, variables, or algebraic expressions such that $b \neq 0$ and $d \neq 0$.

1. **Equivalent Fractions:** $\dfrac{a}{b} = \dfrac{c}{d}$ if and only if $ad = bc$.

2. **Rules of Signs:** $-\dfrac{a}{b} = \dfrac{-a}{b} = \dfrac{a}{-b}$ and $\dfrac{-a}{-b} = \dfrac{a}{b}$

3. **Generate Equivalent Fractions:** $\dfrac{a}{b} = \dfrac{ac}{bc}$, $c \neq 0$

4. **Add or Subtract with Like Denominators:** $\dfrac{a}{b} \pm \dfrac{c}{b} = \dfrac{a \pm c}{b}$

5. **Add or Subtract with Unlike Denominators:** $\dfrac{a}{b} \pm \dfrac{c}{d} = \dfrac{ad \pm bc}{bd}$

6. **Multiply Fractions:** $\dfrac{a}{b} \cdot \dfrac{c}{d} = \dfrac{ac}{bd}$

7. **Divide Fractions:** $\dfrac{a}{b} \div \dfrac{c}{d} = \dfrac{a}{b} \cdot \dfrac{d}{c} = \dfrac{ad}{bc}$, $c \neq 0$

EXAMPLE 14 **Properties and Operations of Fractions**

a. Equivalent fractions: $\dfrac{x}{5} = \dfrac{3 \cdot x}{3 \cdot 5} = \dfrac{3x}{15}$ **b.** Divide fractions: $\dfrac{7}{x} \div \dfrac{3}{2} = \dfrac{7}{x} \cdot \dfrac{2}{3} = \dfrac{14}{3x}$

✓ *Checkpoint* Audio-video solution in English & Spanish at LarsonPrecalculus.com.

a. Multiply fractions: $\dfrac{3}{5} \cdot \dfrac{x}{6}$ **b.** Add fractions: $\dfrac{x}{10} + \dfrac{2x}{5}$

· · REMARK The number 1 is neither prime nor composite.

· · · · · · · · · · · · · · · ▷

If a, b, and c are integers such that $ab = c$, then a and b are **factors** or **divisors** of c. A **prime number** is an integer that has exactly two positive factors—itself and 1—such as 2, 3, 5, 7, and 11. The numbers 4, 6, 8, 9, and 10 are **composite** because each can be written as the product of two or more prime numbers. The **Fundamental Theorem of Arithmetic** states that every positive integer greater than 1 is a prime number or can be written as the product of prime numbers in precisely one way (disregarding order). For instance, the *prime factorization* of 24 is $24 = 2 \cdot 2 \cdot 2 \cdot 3$.

Summarize (Appendix A.1)

1. Describe how to represent and classify real numbers *(pages A1 and A2)*. For examples of representing and classifying real numbers, see Examples 1 and 2.

2. Describe how to order real numbers and use inequalities *(pages A3 and A4)*. For examples of ordering real numbers and using inequalities, see Examples 3–6.

3. State the absolute value of a real number *(page A5)*. For examples of using absolute value, see Examples 7–10.

4. Explain how to evaluate an algebraic expression *(page A7)*. For examples involving algebraic expressions, see Examples 11 and 12.

5. State the basic rules and properties of algebra *(pages A8–A10)*. For examples involving the basic rules and properties of algebra, see Examples 13 and 14.

A.1 Exercises

Vocabulary: Fill in the blanks.

1. _____ numbers have infinite nonrepeating decimal representations.
2. The point 0 on the real number line is called the _____.
3. The distance between the origin and a point representing a real number on the real number line is the _____ _____ of the real number.
4. A number that can be written as the product of two or more prime numbers is called a _____ number.
5. The _____ of an algebraic expression are those parts separated by addition.
6. The _____ _____ states that if $ab = 0$, then $a = 0$ or $b = 0$.

Skills and Applications

Classifying Real Numbers In Exercises 7–10, determine which numbers in the set are (a) natural numbers, (b) whole numbers, (c) integers, (d) rational numbers, and (e) irrational numbers.

7. $\left\{-9, -\frac{7}{2}, 5, \frac{2}{3}, \sqrt{2}, 0, 1, -4, 2, -11\right\}$
8. $\left\{\sqrt{5}, -7, -\frac{7}{3}, 0, 3.12, \frac{5}{4}, -3, 12, 5\right\}$
9. $\{2.01, 0.666\ldots, -13, 0.010110111\ldots, 1, -6\}$
10. $\left\{25, -17, -\frac{12}{5}, \sqrt{9}, 3.12, \frac{1}{2}\pi, 7, -11.1, 13\right\}$

Plotting Points on the Real Number Line In Exercises 11 and 12, plot the real numbers on the real number line.

11. (a) 3   (b) $\frac{7}{2}$ (c) $-\frac{5}{2}$ (d) -5.2
12. (a) 8.5   (b) $\frac{4}{3}$ (c) -4.75 (d) $-\frac{8}{3}$

Plotting and Ordering Real Numbers In Exercises 13–16, plot the two real numbers on the real number line. Then place the appropriate inequality symbol (< or >) between them.

13. $-4, -8$ 14. $1, \frac{16}{3}$ 15. $\frac{5}{6}, \frac{2}{3}$ 16. $-\frac{8}{7}, -\frac{3}{7}$

Interpreting an Inequality or an Interval In Exercises 17–24, (a) give a verbal description of the subset of real numbers represented by the inequality or the interval, (b) sketch the subset on the real number line, and (c) state whether the interval is bounded or unbounded.

17. $x \le 5$
18. $x < 0$
19. $[4, \infty)$
20. $(-\infty, 2)$
21. $-2 < x < 2$
22. $0 < x \le 6$
23. $[-5, 2)$
24. $(-1, 2]$

Using Inequality and Interval Notation In Exercises 25–30, use inequality notation and interval notation to describe the set.

25. y is nonnegative.
26. y is no more than 25.
27. t is at least 10 and at most 22.

28. k is less than 5 but no less than -3.
29. The dog's weight W is more than 65 pounds.
30. The annual rate of inflation r is expected to be at least 2.5% but no more than 5%.

Evaluating an Absolute Value Expression In Exercises 31–40, evaluate the expression.

31. $|-10|$
32. $|0|$
33. $|3 - 8|$
34. $|4 - 1|$
35. $|-1| - |-2|$
36. $-3 - |-3|$
37. $\dfrac{-5}{|-5|}$
38. $-3|-3|$
39. $\dfrac{|x + 2|}{x + 2}$, $x < -2$
40. $\dfrac{|x - 1|}{x - 1}$, $x > 1$

Comparing Real Numbers In Exercises 41–44, place the appropriate symbol (<, >, or =) between the two real numbers.

41. $|-4|$ ▭ $|4|$
42. -5 ▭ $-|5|$
43. $-|-6|$ ▭ $|-6|$
44. $-|-2|$ ▭ $-|2|$

Finding a Distance In Exercises 45–50, find the distance between a and b.

45. $a = 126, b = 75$
46. $a = -126, b = -75$
47. $a = -\frac{5}{2}, b = 0$
48. $a = \frac{1}{4}, b = \frac{11}{4}$
49. $a = \frac{16}{5}, b = \frac{112}{75}$
50. $a = 9.34, b = -5.65$

Using Absolute Value Notation In Exercises 51–54, use absolute value notation to describe the situation.

51. The distance between x and 5 is no more than 3.
52. The distance between x and -10 is at least 6.
53. y is at most two units from a.
54. The temperature in Bismarck, North Dakota, was 60°F at noon, then 23°F at midnight. What was the change in temperature over the 12-hour period?

Federal Deficit

In Exercises 55–58, use the bar graph, which shows the receipts of the federal government (in billions of dollars) for selected years from 2004 through 2010.
In each exercise you are given the expenditures of the federal government. Find the magnitude of the surplus or deficit for the year. *(Source: U.S. Office of Management and Budget)*

Year	Receipts, R	Expenditures, E	$\lvert R - E \rvert$
55. 2004		\$2292.8 billion	
56. 2006		\$2655.1 billion	
57. 2008		\$2982.5 billion	
58. 2010		\$3456.2 billion	

Identifying Terms and Coefficients

In Exercises 59–62, identify the terms. Then identify the coefficients of the variable terms of the expression.

59. $7x + 4$ **60.** $6x^3 - 5x$

61. $4x^3 + 0.5x - 5$ **62.** $3\sqrt{3}x^2 + 1$

Evaluating an Algebraic Expression

In Exercises 63–66, evaluate the expression for each value of x. (If not possible, then state the reason.)

Expression	Values
63. $4x - 6$	(a) $x = -1$ (b) $x = 0$
64. $9 - 7x$	(a) $x = -3$ (b) $x = 3$
65. $-x^2 + 5x - 4$	(a) $x = -1$ (b) $x = 1$
66. $(x + 1)/(x - 1)$	(a) $x = 1$ (b) $x = -1$

Identifying Rules of Algebra

In Exercises 67–72, identify the rule(s) of algebra illustrated by the statement.

67. $\dfrac{1}{h + 6}(h + 6) = 1, \quad h \neq -6$

68. $(x + 3) - (x + 3) = 0$

69. $2(x + 3) = 2 \cdot x + 2 \cdot 3$

70. $(z - 2) + 0 = z - 2$

71. $x(3y) = (x \cdot 3)y = (3x)y$

72. $\frac{1}{7}(7 \cdot 12) = \left(\frac{1}{7} \cdot 7\right)12 = 1 \cdot 12 = 12$

Operations with Fractions   In Exercises 73–76, perform the operation(s). (Write fractional answers in simplest form.)

73. $\frac{5}{8} - \frac{5}{12} + \frac{1}{6}$ **74.** $-\left(6 \cdot \frac{4}{8}\right)$

75. $\frac{2x}{3} - \frac{x}{4}$ **76.** $\frac{5x}{6} \cdot \frac{2}{9}$

Exploration

77. Determining the Sign of an Expression   Use the real numbers A, B, and C shown on the number line to determine the sign of (a) $-A$, (b) $B - A$, (c) $-C$, and (d) $A - C$.

78. **HOW DO YOU SEE IT?**   Match each description with its graph. Which types of real numbers shown in Figure A.1 on page A1 may be included in a range of prices? a range of lengths? Explain.

(i)

(ii)

(a) The price of an item is within \$0.03 of \$1.90.

(b) The distance between the prongs of an electric plug may not differ from 1.9 centimeters by more than 0.03 centimeter.

True or False?   In Exercises 79 and 80, determine whether the statement is true or false. Justify your answer.

79. Every nonnegative number is positive.

80. If $a > 0$ and $b < 0$, then $ab > 0$.

81. Conjecture

(a) Use a calculator to complete the table.

n	0.0001	0.01	1	100	10,000
$5/n$					

(b) Use the result from part (a) to make a conjecture about the value of $5/n$ as n (i) approaches 0, and (ii) increases without bound.

A.2   Exponents and Radicals

Real numbers and algebraic expressions are often written with exponents and radicals. For instance, in Exercise 79 on page A24, you will use an expression involving rational exponents to find the times required for a funnel to empty for different water heights.

- Use properties of exponents.
- Use scientific notation to represent real numbers.
- Use properties of radicals.
- Simplify and combine radicals.
- Rationalize denominators and numerators.
- Use properties of rational exponents.

Integer Exponents

Repeated *multiplication* can be written in **exponential form.**

Repeated Multiplication	Exponential Form
$a \cdot a \cdot a \cdot a \cdot a$	a^5
$(-4)(-4)(-4)$	$(-4)^3$
$(2x)(2x)(2x)(2x)$	$(2x)^4$

Exponential Notation

If a is a real number and n is a positive integer, then

$$a^n = \underbrace{a \cdot a \cdot a \cdots a}_{n \text{ factors}}$$

where n is the **exponent** and a is the **base.** You read a^n as "a to the nth **power.**"

An exponent can also be negative. In Property 3 below, be sure you see how to use a negative exponent.

Properties of Exponents

Let a and b be real numbers, variables, or algebraic expressions, and let m and n be integers. (All denominators and bases are nonzero.)

Property	Example
1. $a^m a^n = a^{m+n}$	$3^2 \cdot 3^4 = 3^{2+4} = 3^6 = 729$
2. $\dfrac{a^m}{a^n} = a^{m-n}$	$\dfrac{x^7}{x^4} = x^{7-4} = x^3$
3. $a^{-n} = \dfrac{1}{a^n} = \left(\dfrac{1}{a}\right)^n$	$y^{-4} = \dfrac{1}{y^4} = \left(\dfrac{1}{y}\right)^4$
4. $a^0 = 1, \quad a \ne 0$	$(x^2 + 1)^0 = 1$
5. $(ab)^m = a^m b^m$	$(5x)^3 = 5^3 x^3 = 125x^3$
6. $(a^m)^n = a^{mn}$	$(y^3)^{-4} = y^{3(-4)} = y^{-12} = \dfrac{1}{y^{12}}$
7. $\left(\dfrac{a}{b}\right)^m = \dfrac{a^m}{b^m}$	$\left(\dfrac{2}{x}\right)^3 = \dfrac{2^3}{x^3} = \dfrac{8}{x^3}$
8. $|a^2| = |a|^2 = a^2$	$|(-2)^2| = |-2|^2 = (2)^2 = 4$

▷ **TECHNOLOGY** You can use a calculator to evaluate exponential expressions. When doing so, it is important to know when to use parentheses because the calculator follows the order of operations. For instance, you would evaluate $(-2)^4$ on a graphing calculator as follows.

⟮(⟯ ⟮(-)⟯ 2 ⟮)⟯ ⟮^⟯ 4 ⟮ENTER⟯

The display will be 16. If you omit the parentheses, then the display will be -16.

It is important to recognize the difference between expressions such as $(-2)^4$ and -2^4. In $(-2)^4$, the parentheses indicate that the exponent applies to the negative sign as well as to the 2, but in $-2^4 = -(2^4)$, the exponent applies only to the 2. So, $(-2)^4 = 16$ and $-2^4 = -16$.

The properties of exponents listed on the preceding page apply to *all* integers m and n, not just to positive integers, as shown in the examples below.

EXAMPLE 1 **Evaluating Exponential Expressions**

a. $(-5)^2 = (-5)(-5) = 25$ Negative sign is part of the base.

b. $-5^2 = -(5)(5) = -25$ Negative sign is *not* part of the base.

c. $2 \cdot 2^4 = 2^{1+4} = 2^5 = 32$ Property 1

d. $\dfrac{4^4}{4^6} = 4^{4-6} = 4^{-2} = \dfrac{1}{4^2} = \dfrac{1}{16}$ Properties 2 and 3

✓ *Checkpoint* ◀))) Audio-video solution in English & Spanish at LarsonPrecalculus.com.

Evaluate each expression.

a. -3^4 **b.** $(-3)^4$

c. $3^2 \cdot 3$ **d.** $\dfrac{3^5}{3^8}$

EXAMPLE 2 **Evaluating Algebraic Expressions**

Evaluate each algebraic expression when $x = 3$.

a. $5x^{-2}$ **b.** $\dfrac{1}{3}(-x)^3$

Solution

a. When $x = 3$, the expression $5x^{-2}$ has a value of

$$5x^{-2} = 5(3)^{-2} = \frac{5}{3^2} = \frac{5}{9}.$$

b. When $x = 3$, the expression $\dfrac{1}{3}(-x)^3$ has a value of

$$\frac{1}{3}(-x)^3 = \frac{1}{3}(-3)^3 = \frac{1}{3}(-27) = -9.$$

✓ *Checkpoint* ◀))) Audio-video solution in English & Spanish at LarsonPrecalculus.com.

Evaluate each algebraic expression when $x = 4$.

a. $-x^{-2}$ **b.** $\dfrac{1}{4}(-x)^4$

EXAMPLE 3   **Using Properties of Exponents**

Use the properties of exponents to simplify each expression.

a. $(-3ab^4)(4ab^{-3})$ b. $(2xy^2)^3$ c. $3a(-4a^2)^0$ d. $\left(\dfrac{5x^3}{y}\right)^2$

Solution

a. $(-3ab^4)(4ab^{-3}) = (-3)(4)(a)(a)(b^4)(b^{-3}) = -12a^2b$

b. $(2xy^2)^3 = 2^3(x)^3(y^2)^3 = 8x^3y^6$

c. $3a(-4a^2)^0 = 3a(1) = 3a, \quad a \neq 0$

d. $\left(\dfrac{5x^3}{y}\right)^2 = \dfrac{5^2(x^3)^2}{y^2} = \dfrac{25x^6}{y^2}$

✓ **Checkpoint**))) *Audio-video solution in English & Spanish at LarsonPrecalculus.com.*

Use the properties of exponents to simplify each expression.

a. $(2x^{-2}y^3)(-x^4y)$ b. $(4a^2b^3)^0$ c. $(-5z)^3(z^2)$ d. $\left(\dfrac{3x^4}{x^2y^2}\right)^2$

EXAMPLE 4   **Rewriting with Positive Exponents**

• • REMARK   Rarely in algebra
is there only one way to solve a
problem. Do not be concerned
when the steps you use to solve
a problem are not exactly the
same as the steps presented in
this text. It is important to use
steps that you understand and,
of course, steps that are justified
by the rules of algebra. For
instance, you might prefer
the following steps for
Example 4(d).

$\left(\dfrac{3x^2}{y}\right)^{-2} = \left(\dfrac{y}{3x^2}\right)^2 = \dfrac{y^2}{9x^4}$

Note how the first step of this
solution uses Property 3. The
fractional form of this property is

$\left(\dfrac{a}{b}\right)^{-m} = \left(\dfrac{b}{a}\right)^m.$

a. $x^{-1} = \dfrac{1}{x}$ Property 3

b. $\dfrac{1}{3x^{-2}} = \dfrac{1(x^2)}{3}$ The exponent -2 does not apply to 3.

    $= \dfrac{x^2}{3}$ Simplify.

c. $\dfrac{12a^3b^{-4}}{4a^{-2}b} = \dfrac{12a^3 \cdot a^2}{4b \cdot b^4}$ Property 3

    $= \dfrac{3a^5}{b^5}$ Property 1

d. $\left(\dfrac{3x^2}{y}\right)^{-2} = \dfrac{3^{-2}(x^2)^{-2}}{y^{-2}}$ Properties 5 and 7

    $= \dfrac{3^{-2}x^{-4}}{y^{-2}}$ Property 6

    $= \dfrac{y^2}{3^2x^4}$ Property 3

    $= \dfrac{y^2}{9x^4}$ Simplify.

✓ **Checkpoint**))) *Audio-video solution in English & Spanish at LarsonPrecalculus.com.*

Rewrite each expression with positive exponents.

a. $2a^{-2}$ b. $\dfrac{3a^{-3}b^4}{15ab^{-1}}$

c. $\left(\dfrac{x}{10}\right)^{-1}$ d. $(-2x^2)^3(4x^3)^{-1}$

Scientific Notation

Exponents provide an efficient way of writing and computing with very large (or very small) numbers. For instance, there are about 359 billion billion gallons of water on Earth—that is, 359 followed by 18 zeros.

$$359,000,000,000,000,000,000,000$$

It is convenient to write such numbers in **scientific notation.** This notation has the form $\pm c \times 10^n$, where $1 \leq c < 10$ and n is an integer. So, the number of gallons of water on Earth, written in scientific notation, is

$$3.59 \times 100,000,000,000,000,000,000 = 3.59 \times 10^{20}.$$

The *positive* exponent 20 indicates that the number is *large* (10 or more) and that the decimal point has been moved 20 places. A *negative* exponent indicates that the number is *small* (less than 1). For instance, the mass (in grams) of one electron is approximately

$$9.0 \times 10^{-28} = 0.\underbrace{0000000000000000000000000009}_{28 \text{ decimal places}}.$$

EXAMPLE 5   Scientific Notation

a. $0.0000782 = 7.82 \times 10^{-5}$

b. $836,100,000 = 8.361 \times 10^8$

✓ *Checkpoint* ◄))) Audio-video solution in English & Spanish at LarsonPrecalculus.com.

Write 45,850 in scientific notation.

EXAMPLE 6   Decimal Notation

a. $-9.36 \times 10^{-6} = -0.00000936$

b. $1.345 \times 10^2 = 134.5$

✓ *Checkpoint* ◄))) Audio-video solution in English & Spanish at LarsonPrecalculus.com.

Write -2.718×10^{-3} in decimal notation.

▷ **TECHNOLOGY** Most calculators automatically switch to scientific notation when they are showing large (or small) numbers that exceed the display range.

To enter numbers in scientific notation, your calculator should have an exponential entry key labeled

    EE   or   EXP.

Consult the user's guide for instructions on keystrokes and how your calculator displays numbers in scientific notation.

EXAMPLE 7   Using Scientific Notation

Evaluate $\dfrac{(2,400,000,000)(0.0000045)}{(0.00003)(1500)}$.

Solution   Begin by rewriting each number in scientific notation and simplifying.

$$\frac{(2,400,000,000)(0.0000045)}{(0.00003)(1500)} = \frac{(2.4 \times 10^9)(4.5 \times 10^{-6})}{(3.0 \times 10^{-5})(1.5 \times 10^3)}$$

$$= \frac{(2.4)(4.5)(10^3)}{(4.5)(10^{-2})}$$

$$= (2.4)(10^5)$$

$$= 240,000$$

✓ *Checkpoint* ◄))) Audio-video solution in English & Spanish at LarsonPrecalculus.com.

Evaluate $(24,000,000,000)(0.00000012)(300,000)$.

Radicals and Their Properties

A **square root** of a number is one of its two equal factors. For example, 5 is a square root of 25 because 5 is one of the two equal factors of 25. In a similar way, a **cube root** of a number is one of its three equal factors, as in $125 = 5^3$.

Definition of *n*th Root of a Number

Let a and b be real numbers and let $n \geq 2$ be a positive integer. If

$$a = b^n$$

then b is an **nth root of a.** When $n = 2$, the root is a **square root.** When $n = 3$, the root is a **cube root.**

Some numbers have more than one *n*th root. For example, both 5 and -5 are square roots of 25. The *principal square* root of 25, written as $\sqrt{25}$, is the positive root, 5. The **principal nth root** of a number is defined as follows.

Principal *n*th Root of a Number

Let a be a real number that has at least one *n*th root. The **principal nth root of a** is the *n*th root that has the same sign as a. It is denoted by a **radical symbol**

$$\sqrt[n]{a}. \qquad \text{Principal } n\text{th root}$$

The positive integer $n \geq 2$ is the **index** of the radical, and the number a is the **radicand.** When $n = 2$, omit the index and write $\sqrt{a}$ rather than $\sqrt[2]{a}$. (The plural of index is *indices*.)

A common misunderstanding is that the square root sign implies both negative and positive roots. This is not correct. The square root sign implies only a positive root. When a negative root is needed, you must use the negative sign with the square root sign.

$$\text{Incorrect: } \cancel{\sqrt{4} = \pm 2} \qquad \text{Correct: } -\sqrt{4} = -2 \quad \text{and} \quad \sqrt{4} = 2$$

EXAMPLE 8   Evaluating Expressions Involving Radicals

a. $\sqrt{36} = 6$ because $6^2 = 36$.

b. $-\sqrt{36} = -6$ because $-\left(\sqrt{36}\right) = -\left(\sqrt{6^2}\right) = -(6) = -6$.

c. $\sqrt[3]{\dfrac{125}{64}} = \dfrac{5}{4}$ because $\left(\dfrac{5}{4}\right)^3 = \dfrac{5^3}{4^3} = \dfrac{125}{64}$.

d. $\sqrt[5]{-32} = -2$ because $(-2)^5 = -32$.

e. $\sqrt[4]{-81}$ is not a real number because no real number raised to the fourth power produces -81.

✓ **Checkpoint** ◀))) *Audio-video solution in English & Spanish at LarsonPrecalculus.com.*

Evaluate each expression (if possible).

a. $-\sqrt{144}$ **b.** $\sqrt{-144}$

c. $\sqrt{\dfrac{25}{64}}$ **d.** $-\sqrt[3]{\dfrac{8}{27}}$

Here are some generalizations about the *n*th roots of real numbers.

Generalizations About *n*th Roots of Real Numbers			
Real Number a	Integer $n > 0$	Root(s) of a	Example
$a > 0$	n is even.	$\sqrt[n]{a}, -\sqrt[n]{a}$	$\sqrt[4]{81} = 3, -\sqrt[4]{81} = -3$
$a > 0$ or $a < 0$	n is odd.	$\sqrt[n]{a}$	$\sqrt[3]{-8} = -2$
$a < 0$	n is even.	No real roots	$\sqrt{-4}$ is not a real number.
$a = 0$	n is even or odd.	$\sqrt[n]{0} = 0$	$\sqrt[5]{0} = 0$

Integers such as 1, 4, 9, 16, 25, and 36 are called **perfect squares** because they have integer square roots. Similarly, integers such as 1, 8, 27, 64, and 125 are called **perfect cubes** because they have integer cube roots.

Properties of Radicals

Let a and b be real numbers, variables, or algebraic expressions such that the indicated roots are real numbers, and let m and n be positive integers.

Property	Example
1. $\sqrt[n]{a^m} = \left(\sqrt[n]{a}\right)^m$	$\sqrt[3]{8^2} = \left(\sqrt[3]{8}\right)^2 = (2)^2 = 4$
2. $\sqrt[n]{a} \cdot \sqrt[n]{b} = \sqrt[n]{ab}$	$\sqrt{5} \cdot \sqrt{7} = \sqrt{5 \cdot 7} = \sqrt{35}$
3. $\dfrac{\sqrt[n]{a}}{\sqrt[n]{b}} = \sqrt[n]{\dfrac{a}{b}}, \quad b \neq 0$	$\dfrac{\sqrt[4]{27}}{\sqrt[4]{9}} = \sqrt[4]{\dfrac{27}{9}} = \sqrt[4]{3}$
4. $\sqrt[m]{\sqrt[n]{a}} = \sqrt[mn]{a}$	$\sqrt[3]{\sqrt{10}} = \sqrt[6]{10}$
5. $\left(\sqrt[n]{a}\right)^n = a$	$\left(\sqrt{3}\right)^2 = 3$
6. For n even, $\sqrt[n]{a^n} = |a|$.	$\sqrt{(-12)^2} = |-12| = 12$
For n odd, $\sqrt[n]{a^n} = a$.	$\sqrt[3]{(-12)^3} = -12$

A common use of Property 6 is $\sqrt{a^2} = |a|$.

EXAMPLE 9 **Using Properties of Radicals**

Use the properties of radicals to simplify each expression.

a. $\sqrt{8} \cdot \sqrt{2}$ b. $\left(\sqrt[3]{5}\right)^3$

c. $\sqrt[3]{x^3}$ d. $\sqrt[6]{y^6}$

Solution

a. $\sqrt{8} \cdot \sqrt{2} = \sqrt{8 \cdot 2} = \sqrt{16} = 4$ b. $\left(\sqrt[3]{5}\right)^3 = 5$

c. $\sqrt[3]{x^3} = x$ d. $\sqrt[6]{y^6} = |y|$

✓ *Checkpoint* *Audio-video solution in English & Spanish at LarsonPrecalculus.com.*

Use the properties of radicals to simplify each expression.

a. $\dfrac{\sqrt{125}}{\sqrt{5}}$ b. $\sqrt[3]{125^2}$ c. $\sqrt[3]{x^2} \cdot \sqrt[3]{x}$ d. $\sqrt{\sqrt{x}}$

Simplifying Radicals

An expression involving radicals is in **simplest form** when the following conditions are satisfied.

1. All possible factors have been removed from the radical.
2. All fractions have radical-free denominators (a process called *rationalizing the denominator* accomplishes this).
3. The index of the radical is reduced.

To simplify a radical, factor the radicand into factors whose exponents are multiples of the index. Write the roots of these factors outside the radical. The "leftover" factors make up the new radicand.

$\cdot\cdot$**REMARK**   When you simplify a radical, it is important that both expressions are defined for the same values of the variable. For instance, in Example 10(c), $\sqrt{75x^3}$ and $5x\sqrt{3x}$ are both defined only for nonnegative values of x. Similarly, in Example 10(e), $\sqrt[4]{(5x)^4}$ and $5|x|$ are both defined for all real values of x.

EXAMPLE 10   **Simplifying Radicals**

$\overset{\text{Perfect cube}}{\downarrow}\quad\overset{\text{Leftover factor}}{\downarrow}$

a. $\sqrt[3]{24} = \sqrt[3]{8 \cdot 3} = \sqrt[3]{2^3 \cdot 3} = 2\sqrt[3]{3}$

$\overset{\text{Perfect}}{\underset{\text{4th power}}{\downarrow}}\quad\overset{\text{Leftover}}{\underset{\text{factor}}{\downarrow}}$

b. $\sqrt[4]{48} = \sqrt[4]{16 \cdot 3} = \sqrt[4]{2^4 \cdot 3} = 2\sqrt[4]{3}$

c. $\sqrt{75x^3} = \sqrt{25x^2 \cdot 3x} = \sqrt{(5x)^2 \cdot 3x} = 5x\sqrt{3x}$

d. $\sqrt[3]{24a^4} = \sqrt[3]{8a^3 \cdot 3a} = \sqrt[3]{(2a)^3 \cdot 3a} = 2a\sqrt[3]{3a}$

e. $\sqrt[4]{(5x)^4} = |5x| = 5|x|$

✓ *Checkpoint* ◀))) *Audio-video solution in English & Spanish at LarsonPrecalculus.com.*

Simplify each radical expression.

a. $\sqrt{32}$ **b.** $\sqrt[3]{250}$ **c.** $\sqrt{24a^5}$ **d.** $\sqrt[3]{-135x^3}$

Radical expressions can be combined (added or subtracted) when they are **like radicals**—that is, when they have the same index and radicand. For instance, $\sqrt{2}, 3\sqrt{2}$, and $\frac{1}{2}\sqrt{2}$ are like radicals, but $\sqrt{3}$ and $\sqrt{2}$ are unlike radicals. To determine whether two radicals can be combined, you should first simplify each radical.

EXAMPLE 11   **Combining Radicals**

a. $2\sqrt{48} - 3\sqrt{27} = 2\sqrt{16 \cdot 3} - 3\sqrt{9 \cdot 3}$ Find square factors.

$= 8\sqrt{3} - 9\sqrt{3}$ Find square roots and multiply by coefficients.

$= (8 - 9)\sqrt{3}$ Combine like radicals.

$= -\sqrt{3}$ Simplify.

b. $\sqrt[3]{16x} - \sqrt[3]{54x^4} = \sqrt[3]{8 \cdot 2x} - \sqrt[3]{27 \cdot x^3 \cdot 2x}$ Find cube factors.

$= 2\sqrt[3]{2x} - 3x\sqrt[3]{2x}$ Find cube roots.

$= (2 - 3x)\sqrt[3]{2x}$ Combine like radicals.

✓ *Checkpoint* ◀))) *Audio-video solution in English & Spanish at LarsonPrecalculus.com.*

Simplify each radical expression.

a. $3\sqrt{8} + \sqrt{18}$ **b.** $\sqrt[3]{81x^5} - \sqrt[3]{24x^2}$

Rationalizing Denominators and Numerators

To rationalize a denominator or numerator of the form $a - b\sqrt{m}$ or $a + b\sqrt{m}$, multiply both numerator and denominator by a **conjugate:** $a + b\sqrt{m}$ and $a - b\sqrt{m}$ are conjugates of each other. If $a = 0$, then the rationalizing factor for $\sqrt{m}$ is itself, $\sqrt{m}$. For cube roots, choose a rationalizing factor that generates a perfect cube.

EXAMPLE 12 **Rationalizing Single-Term Denominators**

Rationalize the denominator of each expression.

a. $\dfrac{5}{2\sqrt{3}}$

b. $\dfrac{2}{\sqrt[3]{5}}$

Solution

a. $\dfrac{5}{2\sqrt{3}} = \dfrac{5}{2\sqrt{3}} \cdot \dfrac{\sqrt{3}}{\sqrt{3}}$ $\sqrt{3}$ is rationalizing factor.

$= \dfrac{5\sqrt{3}}{2(3)}$ Multiply.

$= \dfrac{5\sqrt{3}}{6}$ Simplify.

b. $\dfrac{2}{\sqrt[3]{5}} = \dfrac{2}{\sqrt[3]{5}} \cdot \dfrac{\sqrt[3]{5^2}}{\sqrt[3]{5^2}}$ $\sqrt[3]{5^2}$ is rationalizing factor.

$= \dfrac{2\sqrt[3]{5^2}}{\sqrt[3]{5^3}}$ Multiply.

$= \dfrac{2\sqrt[3]{25}}{5}$ Simplify.

✓ *Checkpoint* ◄))) Audio-video solution in English & Spanish at LarsonPrecalculus.com.

Rationalize the denominator of each expression.

a. $\dfrac{5}{3\sqrt{2}}$ b. $\dfrac{1}{\sqrt[3]{25}}$

EXAMPLE 13 **Rationalizing a Denominator with Two Terms**

$\dfrac{2}{3 + \sqrt{7}} = \dfrac{2}{3 + \sqrt{7}} \cdot \dfrac{3 - \sqrt{7}}{3 - \sqrt{7}}$ Multiply numerator and denominator by conjugate of denominator.

$= \dfrac{2(3 - \sqrt{7})}{3(3) + 3(-\sqrt{7}) + \sqrt{7}(3) - (\sqrt{7})(\sqrt{7})}$ Use Distributive Property.

$= \dfrac{2(3 - \sqrt{7})}{(3)^2 - (\sqrt{7})^2}$ Simplify.

$= \dfrac{2(3 - \sqrt{7})}{2} = 3 - \sqrt{7}$ Simplify.

✓ *Checkpoint* ◄))) Audio-video solution in English & Spanish at LarsonPrecalculus.com.

Rationalize the denominator: $\dfrac{8}{\sqrt{6} - \sqrt{2}}$.

Sometimes it is necessary to rationalize the numerator of an expression. For instance, in Appendix A.4 you will use the technique shown in the next example to rationalize the numerator of an expression from calculus.

EXAMPLE 14 **Rationalizing a Numerator**

$$\frac{\sqrt{5} - \sqrt{7}}{2} = \frac{\sqrt{5} - \sqrt{7}}{2} \cdot \frac{\sqrt{5} + \sqrt{7}}{\sqrt{5} + \sqrt{7}} \qquad \text{Multiply numerator and denominator by conjugate of denominator.}$$

$$= \frac{(\sqrt{5})^2 - (\sqrt{7})^2}{2(\sqrt{5} + \sqrt{7})} \qquad \text{Simplify.}$$

$$= \frac{5 - 7}{2(\sqrt{5} + \sqrt{7})} \qquad \text{Square terms of numerator.}$$

$$= \frac{-2}{2(\sqrt{5} + \sqrt{7})} = \frac{-1}{\sqrt{5} + \sqrt{7}} \qquad \text{Simplify.}$$

> ..**REMARK** Do not confuse the expression $\sqrt{5} + \sqrt{7}$ with the expression $\sqrt{5 + 7}$. In general, $\sqrt{x + y}$ does not equal $\sqrt{x} + \sqrt{y}$. Similarly, $\sqrt{x^2 + y^2}$ does not equal $x + y$.

✓ *Checkpoint* ◀))) *Audio-video solution in English & Spanish at LarsonPrecalculus.com.*

Rationalize the numerator: $\dfrac{2 - \sqrt{2}}{3}$.

Rational Exponents

> **Definition of Rational Exponents**
>
> If a is a real number and n is a positive integer such that the principal nth root of a exists, then $a^{1/n}$ is defined as
>
> $$a^{1/n} = \sqrt[n]{a}, \text{ where } 1/n \text{ is the } \textbf{rational exponent} \text{ of } a.$$
>
> Moreover, if m is a positive integer that has no common factor with n, then
>
> $$a^{m/n} = (a^{1/n})^m = \left(\sqrt[n]{a}\right)^m \quad \text{and} \quad a^{m/n} = (a^m)^{1/n} = \sqrt[n]{a^m}.$$

The numerator of a rational exponent denotes the *power* to which the base is raised, and the denominator denotes the *index* or the *root* to be taken.

$$b^{m/n} = \left(\sqrt[n]{b}\right)^m = \sqrt[n]{b^m}$$

> ..**REMARK** You must remember that the expression $b^{m/n}$ is not defined unless $\sqrt[n]{b}$ is a real number. This restriction produces some unusual results. For instance, the number $(-8)^{1/3}$ is defined because $\sqrt[3]{-8} = -2$, but the number $(-8)^{2/6}$ is undefined because $\sqrt[6]{-8}$ is not a real number.

When you are working with rational exponents, the properties of integer exponents still apply. For instance, $2^{1/2}2^{1/3} = 2^{(1/2)+(1/3)} = 2^{5/6}$.

EXAMPLE 15 **Changing From Radical to Exponential Form**

a. $\sqrt{3} = 3^{1/2}$ **b.** $\sqrt{(3xy)^5} = \sqrt[2]{(3xy)^5} = (3xy)^{5/2}$

c. $2x\sqrt[4]{x^3} = (2x)(x^{3/4}) = 2x^{1+(3/4)} = 2x^{7/4}$

✓ *Checkpoint* ◀))) *Audio-video solution in English & Spanish at LarsonPrecalculus.com.*

Write each expression in exponential form.

a. $\sqrt[3]{27}$ **b.** $\sqrt{x^3y^5z}$ **c.** $3x\sqrt[3]{x^2}$

▷ TECHNOLOGY There are four methods of evaluating radicals on most graphing calculators. For square roots, you can use the *square root key* $\boxed{\sqrt{}}$. For cube roots, you can use the *cube root key* $\boxed{\sqrt[3]{}}$. For other roots, you can first convert the radical to exponential form and then use the *exponential key* $\boxed{\wedge}$, or you can use the *x*th root key $\boxed{\sqrt[x]{}}$ (or menu choice). Consult the user's guide for your calculator for specific keystrokes.

EXAMPLE 16   **Changing From Exponential to Radical Form**

a. $(x^2 + y^2)^{3/2} = \left(\sqrt{x^2 + y^2}\right)^3 = \sqrt{(x^2 + y^2)^3}$

b. $2y^{3/4}z^{1/4} = 2(y^3z)^{1/4} = 2\sqrt[4]{y^3z}$

c. $a^{-3/2} = \dfrac{1}{a^{3/2}} = \dfrac{1}{\sqrt{a^3}}$

d. $x^{0.2} = x^{1/5} = \sqrt[5]{x}$

✓ **Checkpoint** ◀))) Audio-video solution in English & Spanish at LarsonPrecalculus.com.

Write each expression in radical form.

a. $(x^2 - 7)^{-1/2}$ **b.** $-3b^{1/3}c^{2/3}$

c. $a^{0.75}$ **d.** $(x^2)^{2/5}$

Rational exponents are useful for evaluating roots of numbers on a calculator, for reducing the index of a radical, and for simplifying expressions in calculus.

EXAMPLE 17   **Simplifying with Rational Exponents**

a. $(-32)^{-4/5} = \left(\sqrt[5]{-32}\right)^{-4} = (-2)^{-4} = \dfrac{1}{(-2)^4} = \dfrac{1}{16}$

b. $(-5x^{5/3})(3x^{-3/4}) = -15x^{(5/3)-(3/4)} = -15x^{11/12}, \quad x \neq 0$

c. $\sqrt[9]{a^3} = a^{3/9} = a^{1/3} = \sqrt[3]{a}$ Reduce index.

d. $\sqrt[3]{\sqrt{125}} = \sqrt[6]{125} = \sqrt[6]{(5)^3} = 5^{3/6} = 5^{1/2} = \sqrt{5}$

e. $(2x - 1)^{4/3}(2x - 1)^{-1/3} = (2x - 1)^{(4/3)-(1/3)} = 2x - 1, \quad x \neq \frac{1}{2}$

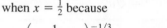

REMARK The expression in Example 17(e) is not defined when $x = \frac{1}{2}$ because

$$\left(2 \cdot \frac{1}{2} - 1\right)^{-1/3} = (0)^{-1/3}$$

is not a real number.

✓ **Checkpoint** ◀))) Audio-video solution in English & Spanish at LarsonPrecalculus.com.

Simplify each expression.

a. $(-125)^{-2/3}$ **b.** $(4x^2y^{3/2})(-3x^{-1/3}y^{-3/5})$

c. $\sqrt[3]{\sqrt[4]{27}}$ **d.** $(3x + 2)^{5/2}(3x + 2)^{-1/2}$

Summarize   (Appendix A.2)

1. Make a list of the properties of exponents *(page A13)*. For examples that use these properties, see Examples 1–4.

2. State the definition of scientific notation *(page A16)*. For examples of scientific notation, see Examples 5–7.

3. Make a list of the properties of radicals *(page A18)*. For an example that uses these properties, see Example 9.

4. Explain how to simplify a radical expression *(page A19)*. For examples of simplifying radical expressions, see Examples 10 and 11.

5. Explain how to rationalize a denominator or a numerator *(page A20)*. For examples of rationalizing denominators and numerators, see Examples 12–14.

6. State the definition of a rational exponent *(page A21)*. For an example of simplifying expressions with rational exponents, see Example 17.

A.2 Exercises

See CalcChat.com for tutorial help and worked-out solutions to odd-numbered exercises.

Vocabulary: **Fill in the blanks.**

1. In the exponential form a^n, n is the _____ and a is the _____.

2. A convenient way of writing very large or very small numbers is called _____ _____.

3. One of the two equal factors of a number is called a _____ _____ of the number.

4. In the radical form $\sqrt[n]{a}$, the positive integer n is the _____ of the radical and the number a is the _____.

5. Radical expressions can be combined (added or subtracted) when they are _____ _____.

6. The expressions $a + b\sqrt{m}$ and $a - b\sqrt{m}$ are _____ of each other.

7. The process used to create a radical-free denominator is known as _____ the denominator.

8. In the expression $b^{m/n}$, m denotes the _____ to which the base is raised and n denotes the _____ or root to be taken.

Skills and Applications

Evaluating Exponential Expressions **In Exercises 9–14, evaluate each expression.**

9. (a) $3 \cdot 3^3$ (b) $\dfrac{3^2}{3^4}$

10. (a) $(3^3)^0$ (b) -3^2

11. (a) $(2^3 \cdot 3^2)^2$ (b) $\left(-\frac{3}{5}\right)^3\left(\frac{5}{3}\right)^2$

12. (a) $\dfrac{3}{3^{-4}}$ (b) $48(-4)^{-3}$

13. (a) $\dfrac{4 \cdot 3^{-2}}{2^{-2} \cdot 3^{-1}}$ (b) $(-2)^0$

14. (a) $3^{-1} + 2^{-2}$ (b) $(3^{-2})^2$

Evaluating an Algebraic Expression **In Exercises 15–20, evaluate the expression for the given value of x.**

15. $-3x^3$, $x = 2$

16. $7x^{-2}$, $x = 4$

17. $6x^0$, $x = 10$

18. $2x^3$, $x = -3$

19. $-3x^4$, $x = -2$

20. $12(-x)^3$, $x = -\frac{1}{3}$

Using Properties of Exponents **In Exercises 21–26, simplify each expression.**

21. (a) $(-5z)^3$ (b) $5x^4(x^2)$

22. (a) $(3x)^2$ (b) $(4x^3)^0$, $x \neq 0$

23. (a) $6y^2(2y^0)^2$ (b) $(-z)^3(3z^4)$

24. (a) $\dfrac{7x^2}{x^3}$ (b) $\dfrac{12(x + y)^3}{9(x + y)}$

25. (a) $\left(\frac{4}{y}\right)^3\left(\frac{3}{y}\right)^4$ (b) $\left(\frac{b^{-2}}{a^{-2}}\right)\left(\frac{b}{a}\right)^2$

26. (a) $[(x^2y^{-2})^{-1}]^{-1}$ (b) $(5x^2z^6)^3(5x^2z^6)^{-3}$

Rewriting with Positive Exponents **In Exercises 27–30, rewrite each expression with positive exponents and simplify.**

27. (a) $(x + 5)^0$, $x \neq -5$ (b) $(2x^2)^{-2}$

28. (a) $(4y^{-2})(8y^4)$ (b) $(z + 2)^{-3}(z + 2)^{-1}$

29. (a) $\left(\frac{x^{-3}y^4}{5}\right)^{-3}$ (b) $\left(\frac{a^{-2}}{b^{-2}}\right)\left(\frac{b}{a}\right)^3$

30. (a) $3^n \cdot 3^{2n}$ (b) $\dfrac{x^2 \cdot x^n}{x^3 \cdot x^n}$

Scientific Notation **In Exercises 31–34, write the number in scientific notation.**

31. $10{,}250.4$

32. -0.000125

33. One micron (millionth of a meter): 0.00003937 inch

34. Land area of Earth: $57{,}300{,}000$ square miles

Decimal Notation **In Exercises 35–38, write the number in decimal notation.**

35. 3.14×10^{-4}

36. -1.801×10^5

37. Light year: 9.46×10^{12} kilometers

38. Width of a human hair: 9.0×10^{-5} meter

Using Scientific Notation **In Exercises 39 and 40, evaluate each expression without using a calculator.**

39. (a) $(2.0 \times 10^9)(3.4 \times 10^{-4})$

  (b) $(1.2 \times 10^7)(5.0 \times 10^{-3})$

40. (a) $\dfrac{6.0 \times 10^8}{3.0 \times 10^{-3}}$ (b) $\dfrac{2.5 \times 10^{-3}}{5.0 \times 10^2}$

Evaluating Expressions Involving Radicals **In Exercises 41 and 42, evaluate each expression without using a calculator.**

41. (a) $\sqrt{9}$ (b) $\sqrt[3]{\frac{27}{8}}$ **42.** (a) $\sqrt[3]{27}$ (b) $\left(\sqrt{36}\right)^3$

Using Properties of Radicals **In Exercises 43 and 44, use the properties of radicals to simplify each expression.**

43. (a) $\left(\sqrt[5]{2}\right)^5$ (b) $\sqrt[5]{32x^5}$

44. (a) $\sqrt{12} \cdot \sqrt{3}$ (b) $\sqrt[4]{(3x^2)^4}$

Simplifying Radical Expressions In Exercises 45–54, simplify each radical expression.

45. (a) $\sqrt{20}$ (b) $\sqrt[3]{128}$

46. (a) $\sqrt[3]{\frac{16}{27}}$ (b) $\sqrt{\frac{75}{4}}$

47. (a) $\sqrt{72x^3}$ (b) $\sqrt{54xy^4}$

48. (a) $\sqrt{\frac{18^2}{z^3}}$ (b) $\sqrt{\frac{32a^4}{b^2}}$

49. (a) $\sqrt[3]{16x^5}$ (b) $\sqrt{75x^2y^{-4}}$

50. (a) $\sqrt[4]{3x^4y^2}$ (b) $\sqrt[5]{160x^8z^4}$

51. (a) $10\sqrt{32} - 6\sqrt{18}$ (b) $\sqrt[3]{16} + 3\sqrt[3]{54}$

52. (a) $5\sqrt{x} - 3\sqrt{x}$ (b) $-2\sqrt{9y} + 10\sqrt{y}$

53. (a) $-3\sqrt{48x^2} + 7\sqrt{75x^2}$
    (b) $7\sqrt{80x} - 2\sqrt{125x}$

54. (a) $-\sqrt{x^3 - 7} + 5\sqrt{x^3 - 7}$
    (b) $11\sqrt{245x^3} - 9\sqrt{45x^3}$

Rationalizing a Denominator In Exercises 55–58, rationalize the denominator of the expression. Then simplify your answer.

55. $\dfrac{1}{\sqrt{3}}$ 56. $\dfrac{8}{\sqrt[3]{2}}$

57. $\dfrac{5}{\sqrt{14} - 2}$ 58. $\dfrac{3}{\sqrt{5} + \sqrt{6}}$

Rationalizing a Numerator In Exercises 59–62, rationalize the numerator of the expression. Then simplify your answer.

59. $\dfrac{\sqrt{8}}{2}$ 60. $\dfrac{\sqrt{2}}{3}$

61. $\dfrac{\sqrt{5} + \sqrt{3}}{3}$ 62. $\dfrac{\sqrt{7} - 3}{4}$

Writing Exponential and Radical Forms In Exercises 63–68, fill in the missing form of the expression.

Radical Form	Rational Exponent Form
63. $\sqrt[3]{64}$	
64.	$(2ab)^{3/4}$
65.	$3x^{-2/3}$
66. $x^2\sqrt{x}$	
67. $x\sqrt{3xy}$	
68.	$a^{0.4}$

Simplifying Expressions In Exercises 69–78, simplify each expression.

69. (a) $32^{-3/5}$ (b) $\left(\frac{16}{81}\right)^{-3/4}$

70. (a) $100^{-3/2}$ (b) $\left(\frac{9}{4}\right)^{-1/2}$

71. (a) $(2x^2)^{3/2} \cdot 2^{-1/2} \cdot x^{-4}$ (b) $(x^4y^2)^{1/3}(xy)^{-1/3}$

72. (a) $x^{-3} \cdot x^{1/2} \cdot x^{-3/2} \cdot x$ (b) $5^{-1/2} \cdot 5x^{5/2}(5x)^{-3/2}$

73. (a) $\sqrt[4]{3^2}$ (b) $\sqrt[6]{(x + 1)^4}$

74. (a) $\sqrt[6]{x^3}$ (b) $\sqrt[4]{(3x^2)^4}$

75. (a) $\sqrt{\sqrt{32}}$ (b) $\sqrt{\sqrt[4]{2x}}$

76. (a) $\sqrt{\sqrt{243(x + 1)}}$ (b) $\sqrt{\sqrt[3]{10a^7b}}$

77. (a) $(x - 1)^{1/3}(x - 1)^{2/3}$
    (b) $(x - 1)^{1/3}(x - 1)^{-4/3}$

78. (a) $(4x + 3)^{5/2}(4x + 3)^{-5/3}$
    (b) $(4x + 3)^{-5/2}(4x + 3)^{1/2}$

79. **Mathematical Modeling**

A funnel is filled with water to a height of h centimeters. The formula

$$t = 0.03[12^{5/2} - (12 - h)^{5/2}], \quad 0 \le h \le 12$$

represents the amount of time t (in seconds) that it will take for the funnel to empty.

(a) Use the *table* feature of a graphing utility to find the times required for the funnel to empty for water heights of $h = 0, h = 1, h = 2, \ldots, h = 12$ centimeters.

(b) What value does t appear to be approaching as the height of the water becomes closer and closer to 12 centimeters?

80. **HOW DO YOU SEE IT?** Package A is a cube with a volume of 500 cubic inches. Package B is a cube with a volume of 250 cubic inches. Is the length x of a side of package A greater than, less than, or equal to twice the length of a side of package B? Explain.

Exploration

True or False? In Exercises 81–84, determine whether the statement is true or false. Justify your answer.

81. $\dfrac{x^{k+1}}{x} = x^k$ 82. $(a^n)^k = a^{n^k}$

83. $(a + b)^2 = a^2 + b^2$ 84. $\dfrac{a}{\sqrt{b}} = \dfrac{a^2}{(\sqrt{b})^2} = \dfrac{a^2}{b}$

A.3 Polynomials and Factoring

Polynomial factoring can help you solve real-life problems. For instance, in Exercise 96 on page A34, you will use factoring to develop an alternative model for the rate of change of an autocatalytic chemical reaction.

- Write polynomials in standard form.
- Add, subtract, and multiply polynomials.
- Use special products to multiply polynomials.
- Remove common factors from polynomials.
- Factor special polynomial forms.
- Factor trinomials as the product of two binomials.
- Factor polynomials by grouping.

Polynomials

One of the most common types of algebraic expressions is the **polynomial.** Some examples are $2x + 5$, $3x^4 - 7x^2 + 2x + 4$, and $5x^2y^2 - xy + 3$. The first two are *polynomials in x* and the third is a *polynomial in x and y*. The terms of a polynomial in x have the form ax^k, where a is the **coefficient** and k is the **degree** of the term. For instance, the polynomial $2x^3 - 5x^2 + 1 = 2x^3 + (-5)x^2 + (0)x + 1$ has coefficients $2, -5, 0$, and 1.

> **Definition of a Polynomial in *x***
>
> Let $a_0, a_1, a_2, \ldots, a_n$ be real numbers and let n be a nonnegative integer. A polynomial in x is an expression of the form
>
> $$a_n x^n + a_{n-1} x^{n-1} + \cdots + a_1 x + a_0$$
>
> where $a_n \neq 0$. The polynomial is of **degree** n, a_n is the **leading coefficient,** and a_0 is the **constant term.**

> · · · · · · · · · · · · · · · · ▷
>
> · **REMARK** Expressions are not polynomials when a variable is underneath a radical or when a polynomial expression (with degree greater than 0) is in the denominator of a term. For example, the expressions $x^3 - \sqrt{3x} = x^3 - (3x)^{1/2}$ and $x^2 + (5/x) = x^2 + 5x^{-1}$ are not polynomials.

Polynomials with one, two, and three terms are called **monomials, binomials,** and **trinomials,** respectively. A polynomial written with descending powers of x is in **standard form.**

EXAMPLE 1 Writing Polynomials in Standard Form

Polynomial	Standard Form	Degree	Leading Coefficient
a. $4x^2 - 5x^7 - 2 + 3x$	$-5x^7 + 4x^2 + 3x - 2$	7	-5
b. $4 - 9x^2$	$-9x^2 + 4$	2	-9
c. 8	$8 \; (8 = 8x^0)$	0	8

✓ *Checkpoint* 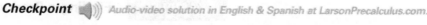 Audio-video solution in English & Spanish at LarsonPrecalculus.com.

Write the polynomial $6 - 7x^3 + 2x$ in standard form. Then identify the degree and leading coefficient of the polynomial. ▪

A polynomial that has all zero coefficients is called the **zero polynomial,** denoted by 0. No degree is assigned to the zero polynomial. For polynomials in more than one variable, the degree of a *term* is the sum of the exponents of the variables in the term. The degree of the *polynomial* is the highest degree of its terms. For instance, the degree of the polynomial $-2x^3y^6 + 4xy - x^7y^4$ is 11 because the sum of the exponents in the last term is the greatest. The leading coefficient of the polynomial is the coefficient of the highest-degree term.

Operations with Polynomials

You can add and subtract polynomials in much the same way you add and subtract real numbers. Add or subtract the *like terms* (terms having the same variables to the same powers) by adding or subtracting their coefficients. For instance, $-3xy^2$ and $5xy^2$ are like terms and their sum is

$$-3xy^2 + 5xy^2 = (-3 + 5)xy^2 = 2xy^2.$$

EXAMPLE 2 **Sums and Differences of Polynomials**

a. $(5x^3 - 7x^2 - 3) + (x^3 + 2x^2 - x + 8)$

$$= (5x^3 + x^3) + (-7x^2 + 2x^2) - x + (-3 + 8) \qquad \text{Group like terms.}$$

$$= 6x^3 - 5x^2 - x + 5 \qquad \text{Combine like terms.}$$

b. $(7x^4 - x^2 - 4x + 2) - (3x^4 - 4x^2 + 3x)$

$$= 7x^4 - x^2 - 4x + 2 - 3x^4 + 4x^2 - 3x \qquad \text{Distributive Property}$$

$$= (7x^4 - 3x^4) + (-x^2 + 4x^2) + (-4x - 3x) + 2 \qquad \text{Group like terms.}$$

$$= 4x^4 + 3x^2 - 7x + 2 \qquad \text{Combine like terms.}$$

✓ *Checkpoint* ◄))) *Audio-video solution in English & Spanish at LarsonPrecalculus.com.*

Find the difference $(2x^3 - x + 3) - (x^2 - 2x - 3)$ and write the resulting polynomial in standard form.

▷ **• • REMARK** When a negative sign precedes an expression inside parentheses, remember to distribute the negative sign to each term inside the parentheses, as shown.

$$-(3x^4 - 4x^2 + 3x)$$

$$= -3x^4 + 4x^2 - 3x$$

To find the *product* of two polynomials, use the left and right Distributive Properties. For example, if you treat $5x + 7$ as a single quantity, then you can multiply $3x - 2$ by $5x + 7$ as follows.

$$(3x - 2)(5x + 7) = 3x(5x + 7) - 2(5x + 7)$$

$$= (3x)(5x) + (3x)(7) - (2)(5x) - (2)(7)$$

$$= 15x^2 + 21x - 10x - 14$$

Product of First terms	Product of Outer terms	Product of Inner terms	Product of Last terms

$$= 15x^2 + 11x - 14$$

Note in this **FOIL Method** (which can only be used to multiply two binomials) that the outer (O) and inner (I) terms are like terms and can be combined.

EXAMPLE 3 **Finding a Product by the FOIL Method**

Use the FOIL Method to find the product of $2x - 4$ and $x + 5$.

Solution

$$\qquad\qquad\qquad\quad \text{F} \quad\ \text{O} \quad\ \text{I} \quad\ \text{L}$$

$$(2x - 4)(x + 5) = 2x^2 + 10x - 4x - 20$$

$$= 2x^2 + 6x - 20$$

✓ *Checkpoint* ◄))) *Audio-video solution in English & Spanish at LarsonPrecalculus.com.*

Use the FOIL Method to find the product of $3x - 1$ and $x - 5$.

Special Products

Some binomial products have special forms that occur frequently in algebra. You do not need to memorize these formulas because you can use the Distributive Property to multiply. However, becoming familiar with these formulas will enable you to manipulate the algebra more quickly.

Special Products

Let u and v be real numbers, variables, or algebraic expressions.

Special Product	Example

Sum and Difference of Same Terms

$$(u + v)(u - v) = u^2 - v^2 \qquad\qquad (x + 4)(x - 4) = x^2 - 4^2$$
$$= x^2 - 16$$

Square of a Binomial

$$(u + v)^2 = u^2 + 2uv + v^2 \qquad (x + 3)^2 = x^2 + 2(x)(3) + 3^2$$
$$= x^2 + 6x + 9$$

$$(u - v)^2 = u^2 - 2uv + v^2 \qquad (3x - 2)^2 = (3x)^2 - 2(3x)(2) + 2^2$$
$$= 9x^2 - 12x + 4$$

Cube of a Binomial

$$(u + v)^3 = u^3 + 3u^2v + 3uv^2 + v^3 \qquad (x + 2)^3 = x^3 + 3x^2(2) + 3x(2^2) + 2^3$$
$$= x^3 + 6x^2 + 12x + 8$$

$$(u - v)^3 = u^3 - 3u^2v + 3uv^2 - v^3 \qquad (x - 1)^3 = x^3 - 3x^2(1) + 3x(1^2) - 1^3$$
$$= x^3 - 3x^2 + 3x - 1$$

EXAMPLE 4   **Sum and Difference of Same Terms**

Find each product.

a. $(5x + 9)(5x - 9)$ **b.** $(x + y - 2)(x + y + 2)$

Solution

a. The product of a sum and a difference of the *same* two terms has no middle term and takes the form $(u + v)(u - v) = u^2 - v^2$.

$$(5x + 9)(5x - 9) = (5x)^2 - 9^2 = 25x^2 - 81$$

b. By grouping $x + y$ in parentheses, you can write the product of the trinomials as a special product.

$$\begin{array}{cc} \text{Difference} & \text{Sum} \\ \downarrow & \downarrow \end{array}$$

$$(x + y - 2)(x + y + 2) = [(x + y) - 2][(x + y) + 2]$$
$$= (x + y)^2 - 2^2 \qquad \text{Sum and difference of same terms}$$
$$= x^2 + 2xy + y^2 - 4$$

✓ **Checkpoint** ◗)) *Audio-video solution in English & Spanish at LarsonPrecalculus.com.*

Find the product: $(x - 2 + 3y)(x - 2 - 3y)$.

Polynomials with Common Factors

The process of writing a polynomial as a product is called **factoring.** It is an important tool for solving equations and for simplifying rational expressions.

Unless noted otherwise, when you are asked to factor a polynomial, assume that you are looking for factors that have integer coefficients. If a polynomial does not factor using integer coefficients, then it is **prime** or **irreducible over the integers.** For instance, the polynomial

$$x^2 - 3$$

is irreducible over the integers. Over the *real numbers,* this polynomial factors as

$$x^2 - 3 = (x + \sqrt{3})(x - \sqrt{3}).$$

A polynomial is **completely factored** when each of its factors is prime. For instance,

$$x^3 - x^2 + 4x - 4 = (x - 1)(x^2 + 4) \qquad\qquad \text{Completely factored}$$

is completely factored, but

$$x^3 - x^2 - 4x + 4 = (x - 1)(x^2 - 4) \qquad\qquad \text{Not completely factored}$$

is not completely factored. Its complete factorization is

$$x^3 - x^2 - 4x + 4 = (x - 1)(x + 2)(x - 2).$$

The simplest type of factoring involves a polynomial that can be written as the product of a monomial and another polynomial. The technique used here is the Distributive Property, $a(b + c) = ab + ac$, in the *reverse* direction.

$$ab + ac = a(b + c) \qquad\qquad a \text{ is a common factor.}$$

Removing (factoring out) any common factors is the first step in completely factoring a polynomial.

EXAMPLE 5   **Removing Common Factors**

Factor each expression.

a. $6x^3 - 4x$
b. $-4x^2 + 12x - 16$
c. $(x - 2)(2x) + (x - 2)(3)$

Solution

a. $6x^3 - 4x = 2x(3x^2) - 2x(2) \qquad\qquad 2x$ is a common factor.

$\qquad\qquad\quad = 2x(3x^2 - 2)$

b. $-4x^2 + 12x - 16 = -4(x^2) + (-4)(-3x) + (-4)4 \qquad -4$ is a common factor.

$\qquad\qquad\qquad\qquad\quad = -4(x^2 - 3x + 4)$

c. $(x - 2)(2x) + (x - 2)(3) = (x - 2)(2x + 3) \qquad\qquad (x - 2)$ is a common factor.

✓ *Checkpoint* ◀))) Audio-video solution in English & Spanish at LarsonPrecalculus.com.

Factor each expression.

a. $5x^3 - 15x^2$
b. $-3 + 6x - 12x^3$
c. $(x + 1)(x^2) - (x + 1)(2)$

Factoring Special Polynomial Forms

Some polynomials have special forms that arise from the special product forms on page A27. You should learn to recognize these forms.

Factoring Special Polynomial Forms

Factored Form	Example
Difference of Two Squares	
$u^2 - v^2 = (u + v)(u - v)$	$9x^2 - 4 = (3x)^2 - 2^2 = (3x + 2)(3x - 2)$
Perfect Square Trinomial	
$u^2 + 2uv + v^2 = (u + v)^2$	$x^2 + 6x + 9 = x^2 + 2(x)(3) + 3^2 = (x + 3)^2$
$u^2 - 2uv + v^2 = (u - v)^2$	$x^2 - 6x + 9 = x^2 - 2(x)(3) + 3^2 = (x - 3)^2$
Sum or Difference of Two Cubes	
$u^3 + v^3 = (u + v)(u^2 - uv + v^2)$	$x^3 + 8 = x^3 + 2^3 = (x + 2)(x^2 - 2x + 4)$
$u^3 - v^3 = (u - v)(u^2 + uv + v^2)$	$27x^3 - 1 = (3x)^3 - 1^3 = (3x - 1)(9x^2 + 3x + 1)$

The factored form of a difference of two squares is always a set of *conjugate pairs*.

$$u^2 - v^2 = (u + v)(u - v)$$ Conjugate pairs

Difference   Opposite signs

To recognize perfect square terms, look for coefficients that are squares of integers and variables raised to *even powers*.

EXAMPLE 6   **Removing a Common Factor First**

> **· · REMARK** In Example 6, note that the first step in factoring a polynomial is to check for any common factors. Once you have removed any common factors, it is often possible to recognize patterns that were not immediately obvious.

$3 - 12x^2 = 3(1 - 4x^2)$ 3 is a common factor.

$\qquad\quad = 3[1^2 - (2x)^2]$

$\qquad\quad = 3(1 + 2x)(1 - 2x)$ Difference of two squares

✓ **Checkpoint**))) Audio-video solution in English & Spanish at LarsonPrecalculus.com.

Factor $100 - 4y^2$.

EXAMPLE 7   **Factoring the Difference of Two Squares**

a. $(x + 2)^2 - y^2 = [(x + 2) + y][(x + 2) - y]$

$\qquad\qquad\qquad = (x + 2 + y)(x + 2 - y)$

b. $16x^4 - 81 = (4x^2)^2 - 9^2$

$\qquad\qquad = (4x^2 + 9)(4x^2 - 9)$ Difference of two squares

$\qquad\qquad = (4x^2 + 9)[(2x)^2 - 3^2]$

$\qquad\qquad = (4x^2 + 9)(2x + 3)(2x - 3)$ Difference of two squares

✓ **Checkpoint**))) Audio-video solution in English & Spanish at LarsonPrecalculus.com.

Factor $(x - 1)^2 - 9y^4$.

A **perfect square trinomial** is the square of a binomial, and it has the form

$$u^2 + 2uv + v^2 = (u + v)^2 \quad \text{or} \quad u^2 - 2uv + v^2 = (u - v)^2.$$

Like signs   Like signs

Note that the first and last terms are squares and the middle term is twice the product of u and v.

EXAMPLE 8   **Factoring Perfect Square Trinomials**

Factor each trinomial.

a. $x^2 - 10x + 25$ **b.** $16x^2 + 24x + 9$

Solution

a. $x^2 - 10x + 25 = x^2 - 2(x)(5) + 5^2 = (x - 5)^2$

b. $16x^2 + 24x + 9 = (4x)^2 + 2(4x)(3) + 3^2 = (4x + 3)^2$

✓ **Checkpoint** ◀))) *Audio-video solution in English & Spanish at LarsonPrecalculus.com.*

Factor $9x^2 - 30x + 25$.

The next two formulas show the sums and differences of cubes. Pay special attention to the signs of the terms.

Like signs   Like signs

$$u^3 + v^3 = (u + v)(u^2 - uv + v^2) \quad u^3 - v^3 = (u - v)(u^2 + uv + v^2)$$

Unlike signs   Unlike signs

EXAMPLE 9   **Factoring the Difference of Cubes**

$x^3 - 27 = x^3 - 3^3$ Rewrite 27 as 3^3.

$\qquad = (x - 3)(x^2 + 3x + 9)$ Factor.

✓ **Checkpoint** ◀))) *Audio-video solution in English & Spanish at LarsonPrecalculus.com.*

Factor $64x^3 - 1$.

EXAMPLE 10   **Factoring the Sum of Cubes**

a. $y^3 + 8 = y^3 + 2^3$ Rewrite 8 as 2^3.

$\qquad = (y + 2)(y^2 - 2y + 4)$ Factor.

b. $3x^3 + 192 = 3(x^3 + 64)$ 3 is a common factor.

$\qquad = 3(x^3 + 4^3)$ Rewrite 64 as 4^3.

$\qquad = 3(x + 4)(x^2 - 4x + 16)$ Factor.

✓ **Checkpoint** ◀))) *Audio-video solution in English & Spanish at LarsonPrecalculus.com.*

Factor each expression.

a. $x^3 + 216$ **b.** $5y^3 + 135$

Trinomials with Binomial Factors

To factor a trinomial of the form $ax^2 + bx + c$, use the following pattern.

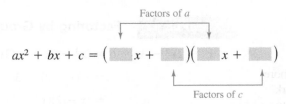

Factors of a

$$ax^2 + bx + c = (\quad x + \quad)(\quad x + \quad)$$

Factors of c

The goal is to find a combination of factors of a and c such that the outer and inner products add up to the middle term bx. For instance, for the trinomial $6x^2 + 17x + 5$, you can write all possible factorizations and determine which one has outer and inner products that add up to $17x$.

$$(6x + 5)(x + 1), (6x + 1)(x + 5), (2x + 1)(3x + 5), (2x + 5)(3x + 1)$$

You can see that $(2x + 5)(3x + 1)$ is the correct factorization because the outer (O) and inner (I) products add up to $17x$.

$$\begin{array}{ccccc} \text{F} & \text{O} & \text{I} & \text{L} & \text{O} + \text{I} \\ \downarrow & \downarrow & \downarrow & \downarrow & \downarrow \end{array}$$

$$(2x + 5)(3x + 1) = 6x^2 + 2x + 15x + 5 = 6x^2 + 17x + 5$$

EXAMPLE 11   Factoring a Trinomial: Leading Coefficient Is 1

Factor $x^2 - 7x + 12$.

Solution   For this trinomial, you have $a = 1$, $b = -7$, and $c = 12$. Because b is negative and c is positive, both factors of 12 must be negative. So, the possible factorizations of $x^2 - 7x + 12$ are

$$(x - 2)(x - 6), \quad (x - 1)(x - 12), \quad \text{and} \quad (x - 3)(x - 4).$$

Testing the middle term, you will find the correct factorization to be

$$x^2 - 7x + 12 = (x - 3)(x - 4).$$

✓ **Checkpoint** ◀))) Audio-video solution in English & Spanish at LarsonPrecalculus.com.

Factor $x^2 + x - 6$.

• • REMARK Factoring a trinomial can involve trial and error. However, once you have produced the factored form, it is relatively easy to check your answer. For instance, verify the factorization in Example 11 by multiplying $(x - 3)$ by $(x - 4)$ to see that you obtain the original trinomial $x^2 - 7x + 12$.

EXAMPLE 12   Factoring a Trinomial: Leading Coefficient Is Not 1

Factor $2x^2 + x - 15$.

Solution   For this trinomial, you have $a = 2$ and $c = -15$, which means that the factors of -15 must have unlike signs. The eight possible factorizations are as follows.

$$(2x - 1)(x + 15) \quad (2x + 1)(x - 15) \quad (2x - 3)(x + 5) \quad (2x + 3)(x - 5)$$

$$(2x - 5)(x + 3) \quad (2x + 5)(x - 3) \quad (2x - 15)(x + 1) \quad (2x + 15)(x - 1)$$

Testing the middle term, you will find the correct factorization to be

$$2x^2 + x - 15 = (2x - 5)(x + 3). \qquad \text{O} + \text{I} = 6x - 5x = x$$

✓ **Checkpoint** ◀))) Audio-video solution in English & Spanish at LarsonPrecalculus.com.

Factor each trinomial.

a. $2x^2 - 5x + 3$ **b.** $12x^2 + 7x + 1$

Factoring by Grouping

Sometimes, polynomials with more than three terms can be **factored by grouping.**

EXAMPLE 13   **Factoring by Grouping**

$$x^3 - 2x^2 - 3x + 6 = (x^3 - 2x^2) - (3x - 6)$$ Group terms.

$$= x^2(x - 2) - 3(x - 2)$$ Factor each group.

$$= (x - 2)(x^2 - 3)$$ Distributive Property

 Checkpoint ◉))) *Audio-video solution in English & Spanish at LarsonPrecalculus.com.*

Factor $x^3 + x^2 - 5x - 5$.

Factoring by grouping can save you some of the trial and error involved in factoring a trinomial. To factor a trinomial of the form $ax^2 + bx + c$ by grouping, rewrite the middle term using the sum of two factors of the product ac that add up to b. Example 14 illustrates this technique.

EXAMPLE 14   **Factoring a Trinomial by Grouping**

In the trinomial $2x^2 + 5x - 3$, $a = 2$ and $c = -3$, so the product ac is -6. Now, -6 factors as $(6)(-1)$ and $6 - 1 = 5 = b$. So, rewrite the middle term as $5x = 6x - x$.

$$2x^2 + 5x - 3 = 2x^2 + 6x - x - 3$$ Rewrite middle term.

$$= (2x^2 + 6x) - (x + 3)$$ Group terms.

$$= 2x(x + 3) - (x + 3)$$ Factor groups.

$$= (x + 3)(2x - 1)$$ Distributive Property

Checkpoint ◉))) *Audio-video solution in English & Spanish at LarsonPrecalculus.com.*

Use factoring by grouping to factor $2x^2 + 5x - 12$.

> **REMARK** Sometimes, more than one grouping will work. For instance, another way to factor the polynomial in Example 13 is as follows.
>
> $$x^3 - 2x^2 - 3x + 6$$
> $$= (x^3 - 3x) - (2x^2 - 6)$$
> $$= x(x^2 - 3) - 2(x^2 - 3)$$
> $$= (x^2 - 3)(x - 2)$$
>
> As you can see, you obtain the same result as in Example 13.

Summarize   (Appendix A.3)

1. State the definition of a polynomial in x and explain what is meant by the standard form of a polynomial *(page A25)*. For an example of writing polynomials in standard form, see Example 1.

2. Describe how to add and subtract polynomials *(page A26)*. For an example of adding and subtracting polynomials, see Example 2.

3. Describe the FOIL Method *(page A26)*. For an example of finding a product using the FOIL Method, see Example 3.

4. Explain how to find binomial products that have special forms *(page A27)*. For an example of binomial products that have special forms, see Example 4.

5. Describe what it means to completely factor a polynomial *(page A28)*. For an example of removing common factors, see Example 5.

6. Make a list of the special polynomial forms of factoring *(page A29)*. For examples of factoring these special forms, see Examples 6–10.

7. Describe how to factor a trinomial of the form $ax^2 + bx + c$ *(page A31)*. For examples of factoring trinomials of this form, see Examples 11 and 12.

8. Explain how to factor a polynomial by grouping *(page A32)*. For examples of factoring by grouping, see Examples 13 and 14.

A.3 Exercises

See CalcChat.com for tutorial help and worked-out solutions to odd-numbered exercises.

Vocabulary: Fill in the blanks.

1. For the polynomial $a_n x^n + a_{n-1} x^{n-1} + \cdots + a_1 x + a_0$, $a_n \neq 0$, the degree is _____, the leading coefficient is _____, and the constant term is _____.

2. A polynomial with one term is called a _____, while a polynomial with two terms is called a _____ and a polynomial with three terms is called a _____.

3. To add or subtract polynomials, add or subtract the _____ _____ by adding their coefficients.

4. The letters in "FOIL" stand for the following. F _____ O _____ I _____ L _____

5. The process of writing a polynomial as a product is called _____.

6. A polynomial is _____ _____ when each of its factors is prime.

7. A _____ _____ _____ is the square of a binomial, and it has the form $u^2 + 2uv + v^2$ or $u^2 - 2uv + v^2$.

8. When a polynomial has more than three terms, a method of factoring called _____ _____ _____ may be used.

Skills and Applications

Polynomials In Exercises 9–18, (a) write the polynomial in standard form, (b) identify the degree and leading coefficient of the polynomial, and (c) state whether the polynomial is a monomial, a binomial, or a trinomial.

9. $14x - \frac{1}{2}x^5$
10. $7x$
11. $3 - x^6$
12. $-y + 25y^2 + 1$
13. 3
14. $-8 + t^2$
15. $1 + 6x^4 - 4x^5$
16. $3 + 2x$
17. $4x^3 y$
18. $-x^5 y + 2x^2 y^2 + xy^4$

Operations with Polynomials In Exercises 19–26, perform the operation and write the result in standard form.

19. $(6x + 5) - (8x + 15)$
20. $(2x^2 + 1) - (x^2 - 2x + 1)$
21. $(15x^2 - 6) - (-8.3x^3 - 14.7x^2 - 17)$
22. $(15.6w^4 - 14w - 17.4) - (16.9w^4 - 9.2w + 13)$
23. $3x(x^2 - 2x + 1)$
24. $y^2(4y^2 + 2y - 3)$
25. $-5z(3z - 1)$
26. $(-3x)(5x + 2)$

Multiplying Polynomials In Exercises 27–40, multiply or find the special product.

27. $(x + 3)(x + 4)$
28. $(x - 5)(x + 10)$
29. $(x^2 - x + 1)(x^2 + x + 1)$
30. $(2x^2 - x + 4)(x^2 + 3x + 2)$
31. $(x + 10)(x - 10)$
32. $(4a + 5b)(4a - 5b)$
33. $(2x + 3)^2$
34. $(8x + 3)^2$
35. $(x + 1)^3$
36. $(3x + 2y)^3$
37. $[(m - 3) + n][(m - 3) - n]$
38. $[(x - 3y) + z][(x - 3y) - z]$
39. $[(x - 3) + y]^2$
40. $[(x + 1) - y]^2$

Factoring Out a Common Factor In Exercises 41–44, factor out the common factor.

41. $2x^3 - 6x$
42. $3z^3 - 6z^2 + 9z$
43. $3x(x - 5) + 8(x - 5)$
44. $(x + 3)^2 - 4(x + 3)$

Greatest Common Factor In Exercises 45–48, find the greatest common factor such that the remaining factors have only integer coefficients.

45. $\frac{1}{2}x^3 + 2x^2 - 5x$
46. $\frac{1}{3}y^4 - 5y^2 + 2y$
47. $\frac{2}{3}x(x - 3) - 4(x - 3)$
48. $\frac{4}{5}y(y + 1) - 2(y + 1)$

Factoring the Difference of Two Squares In Exercises 49–52, completely factor the difference of two squares.

49. $x^2 - 81$
50. $x^2 - 64$
51. $(x - 1)^2 - 4$
52. $25 - (z + 5)^2$

Factoring a Perfect Square Trinomial In Exercises 53–58, factor the perfect square trinomial.

53. $x^2 - 4x + 4$
54. $4t^2 + 4t + 1$
55. $9u^2 + 24uv + 16v^2$
56. $36y^2 - 108y + 81$
57. $z^2 + z + \frac{1}{4}$
58. $9y^2 - \frac{3}{2}y + \frac{1}{16}$

Factoring the Sum or Difference of Cubes In Exercises 59–62, factor the sum or difference of cubes.

59. $x^3 - 8$
60. $27 - x^3$
61. $27x^3 + 8$
62. $u^3 + 27v^3$

Factoring a Trinomial **In Exercises 63–70, factor the trinomial.**

63. $x^2 + x - 2$

64. $s^2 - 5s + 6$

65. $20 - y - y^2$

66. $24 + 5z - z^2$

67. $3x^2 - 5x + 2$

68. $2x^2 - x - 1$

69. $5x^2 + 26x + 5$

70. $-9z^2 + 3z + 2$

Factoring by Grouping **In Exercises 71–76, factor by grouping.**

71. $x^3 - x^2 + 2x - 2$

72. $x^3 + 5x^2 - 5x - 25$

73. $2x^3 - x^2 - 6x + 3$

74. $6 + 2x - 3x^3 - x^4$

75. $x^5 + 2x^3 + x^2 + 2$

76. $8x^5 - 6x^2 + 12x^3 - 9$

Factoring a Trinomial by Grouping **In Exercises 77–80, factor the trinomial by grouping.**

77. $2x^2 + 9x + 9$

78. $6x^2 + x - 2$

79. $6x^2 - x - 15$

80. $12x^2 - 13x + 1$

Factoring Completely **In Exercises 81–94, completely factor the expression.**

81. $6x^2 - 54$

82. $12x^2 - 48$

83. $x^3 - x^2$

84. $x^3 - 16x$

85. $x^2 - 2x + 1$

86. $16 + 6x - x^2$

87. $2x^2 + 4x - 2x^3$

88. $13x + 6 + 5x^2$

89. $5 - x + 5x^2 - x^3$

90. $3u - 2u^2 + 6 - u^3$

91. $5(3 - 4x)^2 - 8(3 - 4x)(5x - 1)$

92. $2(x + 1)(x - 3)^2 - 3(x + 1)^2(x - 3)$

93. $x^4(4)(2x + 1)^3(2x) + (2x + 1)^4(4x^3)$

94. $x^3(3)(x^2 + 1)^2(2x) + (x^2 + 1)^3(3x^2)$

95. **Geometry** The cylindrical shell shown in the figure has a volume of

$$V = \pi R^2 h - \pi r^2 h.$$

(a) Factor the expression for the volume.

(b) From the result of part (a), show that the volume is 2π(average radius)(thickness of the shell)h.

96. **Chemistry**

The rate of change of an autocatalytic chemical reaction is $kQx - kx^2$, where Q is the amount of the original substance, x is the amount of substance formed, and k is a constant of proportionality. Factor the expression.

Exploration

True or False? **In Exercises 97–100, determine whether the statement is true or false. Justify your answer.**

97. The product of two binomials is always a second-degree polynomial.

98. The sum of two binomials is always a binomial.

99. The difference of two perfect squares can be factored as the product of conjugate pairs.

100. The sum of two perfect squares can be factored as the binomial sum squared.

101. **Degree of a Product** Find the degree of the product of two polynomials of degrees m and n.

102. **Degree of a Sum** Find the degree of the sum of two polynomials of degrees m and n, where $m < n$.

103. **Think About It** When the polynomial

$$-x^3 + 3x^2 + 2x - 1$$

is subtracted from an unknown polynomial, the difference is $5x^2 + 8$. If it is possible, then find the unknown polynomial.

104. **Logical Reasoning** Verify that $(x + y)^2$ is not equal to $x^2 + y^2$ by letting $x = 3$ and $y = 4$ and evaluating both expressions. Are there any values of x and y for which $(x + y)^2 = x^2 + y^2$? Explain.

105. **Think About It** Give an example of a polynomial that is prime with respect to the integers.

106. **HOW DO YOU SEE IT?**
The figure shows a large square with an area of a^2 that contains a smaller square with an area of b^2.

(a) Describe the regions that represent $a^2 - b^2$. How can you rearrange these regions to show that $a^2 - b^2 = (a - b)(a + b)$?

(b) How can you use the figure to show that $(a - b)^2 = a^2 - 2ab + b^2$?

(c) Draw another figure to show that $(a + b)^2 = a^2 + 2ab + b^2$. Explain how the figure shows this.

Factoring with Variables in the Exponents **In Exercises 107 and 108, factor the expression as completely as possible.**

107. $x^{2n} - y^{2n}$

108. $x^{3n} + y^{3n}$

A.4 Rational Expressions

Rational expressions can help you solve real-life problems. For instance, in Exercise 73 on page A43, you will use a rational expression to model the temperature of food in a refrigerator.

- Find domains of algebraic expressions.
- Simplify rational expressions.
- Add, subtract, multiply, and divide rational expressions.
- Simplify complex fractions and rewrite difference quotients.

Domain of an Algebraic Expression

The set of real numbers for which an algebraic expression is defined is the **domain** of the expression. Two algebraic expressions are **equivalent** when they have the same domain and yield the same values for all numbers in their domain. For instance,

$$(x + 1) + (x + 2) \quad \text{and} \quad 2x + 3$$

are equivalent because

$$(x + 1) + (x + 2) = x + 1 + x + 2$$
$$= x + x + 1 + 2$$
$$= 2x + 3.$$

EXAMPLE 1   **Finding the Domain of an Algebraic Expression**

a. The domain of the polynomial

$$2x^3 + 3x + 4$$

is the set of all real numbers. In fact, the domain of any polynomial is the set of all real numbers, unless the domain is specifically restricted.

b. The domain of the radical expression

$$\sqrt{x - 2}$$

is the set of real numbers greater than or equal to 2, because the square root of a negative number is not a real number.

c. The domain of the expression

$$\frac{x + 2}{x - 3}$$

is the set of all real numbers except $x = 3$, which would result in division by zero, which is undefined.

✓ *Checkpoint*   Audio-video solution in English & Spanish at LarsonPrecalculus.com.

Find the domain of each expression.

a. $4x^3 + 3, \quad x \geq 0$ **b.** $\sqrt{x + 7}$ **c.** $\dfrac{1 - x}{x}$ ■

The quotient of two algebraic expressions is a *fractional expression*. Moreover, the quotient of two *polynomials* such as

$$\frac{1}{x}, \quad \frac{2x - 1}{x + 1}, \quad \text{or} \quad \frac{x^2 - 1}{x^2 + 1}$$

is a **rational expression.**

Filipe B. Varela/Shutterstock.com

Simplifying Rational Expressions

Recall that a fraction is in simplest form when its numerator and denominator have no factors in common aside from ±1. To write a fraction in simplest form, divide out common factors.

$$\frac{a \cdot c}{b \cdot c} = \frac{a}{b}, \quad c \neq 0$$

The key to success in simplifying rational expressions lies in your ability to *factor* polynomials. When simplifying rational expressions, factor each polynomial completely to determine whether the numerator and denominator have factors in common.

EXAMPLE 2 **Simplifying a Rational Expression**

$$\frac{x^2 + 4x - 12}{3x - 6} = \frac{(x + 6)(x - 2)}{3(x - 2)} \qquad \text{Factor completely.}$$

$$= \frac{x + 6}{3}, \quad x \neq 2 \qquad \text{Divide out common factor.}$$

Note that the original expression is undefined when $x = 2$ (because division by zero is undefined). To make the simplified expression *equivalent* to the original expression, you must list the domain restriction $x \neq 2$ with the simplified expression.

✓ **Checkpoint** Audio-video solution in English & Spanish at LarsonPrecalculus.com.

Write $\dfrac{4x + 12}{x^2 - 3x - 18}$ in simplest form.

> **REMARK** In Example 2, do not make the mistake of trying to simplify further by dividing out terms.
>
> $$\frac{x + 6}{3} = \frac{x + \cancel{6}}{\cancel{3}} = x + 2$$
>
> Remember that to simplify fractions, divide out common *factors,* not terms.

Sometimes it may be necessary to change the sign of a factor by factoring out (-1) to simplify a rational expression, as shown in Example 3.

EXAMPLE 3 **Simplifying a Rational Expression**

$$\frac{12 + x - x^2}{2x^2 - 9x + 4} = \frac{(4 - x)(3 + x)}{(2x - 1)(x - 4)} \qquad \text{Factor completely.}$$

$$= \frac{-(x - 4)(3 + x)}{(2x - 1)(x - 4)} \qquad (4 - x) = -(x - 4)$$

$$= -\frac{3 + x}{2x - 1}, \quad x \neq 4 \qquad \text{Divide out common factor.}$$

✓ **Checkpoint** Audio-video solution in English & Spanish at LarsonPrecalculus.com.

Write $\dfrac{3x^2 - x - 2}{5 - 4x - x^2}$ in simplest form.

In this text, when writing a rational expression, the domain is usually not listed with the expression. It is *implied* that the real numbers that make the denominator zero are excluded from the expression. Also, when performing operations with rational expressions, this text follows the convention of listing *by the simplified expression* all values of x that must be specifically excluded from the domain in order to make the domains of the simplified and original expressions agree. Example 3, for instance, lists the restriction $x \neq 4$ with the simplified expression to make the two domains agree. Note that the value $x = \frac{1}{2}$ is excluded from *both* domains, so it is not necessary to list this value.

Operations with Rational Expressions

To multiply or divide rational expressions, use the properties of fractions discussed in Appendix A.1. Recall that to divide fractions, you invert the divisor and multiply.

EXAMPLE 4 **Multiplying Rational Expressions**

$$\frac{2x^2 + x - 6}{x^2 + 4x - 5} \cdot \frac{x^3 - 3x^2 + 2x}{4x^2 - 6x} = \frac{(2x - 3)(x + 2)}{(x + 5)(x - 1)} \cdot \frac{x(x - 2)(x - 1)}{2x(2x - 3)}$$

$$= \frac{(x + 2)(x - 2)}{2(x + 5)}, \quad x \neq 0, x \neq 1, x \neq \tfrac{3}{2}$$

✓ **Checkpoint** ◀))) *Audio-video solution in English & Spanish at LarsonPrecalculus.com.*

Multiply and simplify: $\dfrac{15x^2 + 5x}{x^3 - 3x^2 - 18x} \cdot \dfrac{x^2 - 2x - 15}{3x^2 - 8x - 3}$.

EXAMPLE 5 **Dividing Rational Expressions**

$$\frac{x^3 - 8}{x^2 - 4} \div \frac{x^2 + 2x + 4}{x^3 + 8} = \frac{x^3 - 8}{x^2 - 4} \cdot \frac{x^3 + 8}{x^2 + 2x + 4} \qquad \text{Invert and multiply.}$$

$$= \frac{(x - 2)(x^2 + 2x + 4)}{(x + 2)(x - 2)} \cdot \frac{(x + 2)(x^2 - 2x + 4)}{(x^2 + 2x + 4)}$$

$$= x^2 - 2x + 4, \quad x \neq \pm 2 \qquad \text{Divide out common factors.}$$

✓ **Checkpoint** ◀))) *Audio-video solution in English & Spanish at LarsonPrecalculus.com.*

Divide and simplify: $\dfrac{x^3 - 1}{x^2 - 1} \div \dfrac{x^2 + x + 1}{x^2 + 2x + 1}$.

To add or subtract rational expressions, use the LCD (least common denominator) method or the *basic definition*

$$\frac{a}{b} \pm \frac{c}{d} = \frac{ad \pm bc}{bd}, \quad b \neq 0, d \neq 0. \qquad \text{Basic definition}$$

This definition provides an efficient way of adding or subtracting *two* fractions that have no common factors in their denominators.

EXAMPLE 6 **Subtracting Rational Expressions**

$$\frac{x}{x - 3} - \frac{2}{3x + 4} = \frac{x(3x + 4) - 2(x - 3)}{(x - 3)(3x + 4)} \qquad \text{Basic definition}$$

$$= \frac{3x^2 + 4x - 2x + 6}{(x - 3)(3x + 4)} \qquad \text{Distributive Property}$$

$$= \frac{3x^2 + 2x + 6}{(x - 3)(3x + 4)} \qquad \text{Combine like terms.}$$

✓ **Checkpoint** ◀))) *Audio-video solution in English & Spanish at LarsonPrecalculus.com.*

Subtract: $\dfrac{x}{2x - 1} - \dfrac{1}{x + 2}$.

▷ **REMARK** Note that Example 4 lists the restrictions $x \neq 0$, $x \neq 1$, and $x \neq \tfrac{3}{2}$ with the simplified expression in order to make the two domains agree. Also note that the value $x = -5$ is excluded from both domains, so it is not necessary to list this value.

▷ **REMARK** When subtracting rational expressions, remember to distribute the negative sign to all the terms in the quantity that is being subtracted.

For three or more fractions, or for fractions with a repeated factor in the denominators, the LCD method works well. Recall that the least common denominator of several fractions consists of the product of all prime factors in the denominators, with each factor given the highest power of its occurrence in any denominator. Here is a numerical example.

$$\frac{1}{6} + \frac{3}{4} - \frac{2}{3} = \frac{1 \cdot 2}{6 \cdot 2} + \frac{3 \cdot 3}{4 \cdot 3} - \frac{2 \cdot 4}{3 \cdot 4} \qquad \text{The LCD is 12.}$$

$$= \frac{2}{12} + \frac{9}{12} - \frac{8}{12}$$

$$= \frac{3}{12}$$

$$= \frac{1}{4}$$

Sometimes, the numerator of the answer has a factor in common with the denominator. In such cases, simplify the answer. For instance, in the example above, $\frac{3}{12}$ simplifies to $\frac{1}{4}$.

EXAMPLE 7 **Combining Rational Expressions: The LCD Method**

Perform the operations and simplify.

$$\frac{3}{x - 1} - \frac{2}{x} + \frac{x + 3}{x^2 - 1}$$

Solution Using the factored denominators

$$(x - 1), \quad x, \quad \text{and} \quad (x + 1)(x - 1)$$

you can see that the LCD is $x(x + 1)(x - 1)$.

$$\frac{3}{x - 1} - \frac{2}{x} + \frac{x + 3}{(x + 1)(x - 1)}$$

$$= \frac{3(x)(x + 1)}{x(x + 1)(x - 1)} - \frac{2(x + 1)(x - 1)}{x(x + 1)(x - 1)} + \frac{(x + 3)(x)}{x(x + 1)(x - 1)}$$

$$= \frac{3(x)(x + 1) - 2(x + 1)(x - 1) + (x + 3)(x)}{x(x + 1)(x - 1)}$$

$$= \frac{3x^2 + 3x - 2x^2 + 2 + x^2 + 3x}{x(x + 1)(x - 1)} \qquad \text{Distributive Property}$$

$$= \frac{3x^2 - 2x^2 + x^2 + 3x + 3x + 2}{x(x + 1)(x - 1)} \qquad \text{Group like terms.}$$

$$= \frac{2x^2 + 6x + 2}{x(x + 1)(x - 1)} \qquad \text{Combine like terms.}$$

$$= \frac{2(x^2 + 3x + 1)}{x(x + 1)(x - 1)} \qquad \text{Factor.}$$

✓ *Checkpoint* ◀))) *Audio-video solution in English & Spanish at LarsonPrecalculus.com.*

Perform the operations and simplify.

$$\frac{4}{x} - \frac{x + 5}{x^2 - 4} + \frac{4}{x + 2}$$

Complex Fractions and the Difference Quotient

Fractional expressions with separate fractions in the numerator, denominator, or both are called **complex fractions.** Here are two examples.

$$\frac{\left(\dfrac{1}{x}\right)}{x^2 + 1} \quad \text{and} \quad \frac{\left(\dfrac{1}{x}\right)}{\left(\dfrac{1}{x^2 + 1}\right)}$$

To simplify a complex fraction, combine the fractions in the numerator into a single fraction and then combine the fractions in the denominator into a single fraction. Then invert the denominator and multiply.

EXAMPLE 8   **Simplifying a Complex Fraction**

$$\frac{\left(\dfrac{2}{x} - 3\right)}{\left(1 - \dfrac{1}{x-1}\right)} = \frac{\left[\dfrac{2 - 3(x)}{x}\right]}{\left[\dfrac{1(x-1) - 1}{x-1}\right]} \qquad \text{Combine fractions.}$$

$$= \frac{\left(\dfrac{2 - 3x}{x}\right)}{\left(\dfrac{x - 2}{x - 1}\right)} \qquad \text{Simplify.}$$

$$= \frac{2 - 3x}{x} \cdot \frac{x - 1}{x - 2} \qquad \text{Invert and multiply.}$$

$$= \frac{(2 - 3x)(x - 1)}{x(x - 2)}, \quad x \neq 1$$

✔ **Checkpoint** ◀))) *Audio-video solution in English & Spanish at LarsonPrecalculus.com.*

Simplify the complex fraction $\dfrac{\left(\dfrac{1}{x + 2} + 1\right)}{\left(\dfrac{x}{3} - 1\right)}$.

Another way to simplify a complex fraction is to multiply its numerator and denominator by the LCD of all fractions in its numerator and denominator. This method is applied to the fraction in Example 8 as follows.

$$\frac{\left(\dfrac{2}{x} - 3\right)}{\left(1 - \dfrac{1}{x-1}\right)} = \frac{\left(\dfrac{2}{x} - 3\right)}{\left(1 - \dfrac{1}{x-1}\right)} \cdot \frac{x(x-1)}{x(x-1)} \qquad \text{LCD is } x(x-1).$$

$$= \frac{\left(\dfrac{2 - 3x}{x}\right) \cdot x(x-1)}{\left(\dfrac{x - 2}{x - 1}\right) \cdot x(x-1)}$$

$$= \frac{(2 - 3x)(x - 1)}{x(x - 2)}, \quad x \neq 1$$

The next three examples illustrate some methods for simplifying rational expressions involving negative exponents and radicals. These types of expressions occur frequently in calculus.

To simplify an expression with negative exponents, one method is to begin by factoring out the common factor with the *lesser* exponent. Remember that when factoring, you *subtract* exponents. For instance, in $3x^{-5/2} + 2x^{-3/2}$, the lesser exponent is $-\frac{5}{2}$ and the common factor is $x^{-5/2}$.

$$3x^{-5/2} + 2x^{-3/2} = x^{-5/2}[3(1) + 2x^{-3/2 - (-5/2)}]$$

$$= x^{-5/2}(3 + 2x^1)$$

$$= \frac{3 + 2x}{x^{5/2}}$$

EXAMPLE 9   **Simplifying an Expression**

Simplify the following expression containing negative exponents.

$$x(1 - 2x)^{-3/2} + (1 - 2x)^{-1/2}$$

Solution   Begin by factoring out the common factor with the *lesser exponent.*

$$x(1 - 2x)^{-3/2} + (1 - 2x)^{-1/2} = (1 - 2x)^{-3/2}[x + (1 - 2x)^{(-1/2) - (-3/2)}]$$

$$= (1 - 2x)^{-3/2}[x + (1 - 2x)^1]$$

$$= \frac{1 - x}{(1 - 2x)^{3/2}}$$

✓ *Checkpoint* Audio-video solution in English & Spanish at LarsonPrecalculus.com.

Simplify $(x - 1)^{-1/3} - x(x - 1)^{-4/3}$.

The next example shows a second method for simplifying an expression with negative exponents.

EXAMPLE 10   **Simplifying an Expression**

$$\frac{(4 - x^2)^{1/2} + x^2(4 - x^2)^{-1/2}}{4 - x^2}$$

$$= \frac{(4 - x^2)^{1/2} + x^2(4 - x^2)^{-1/2}}{4 - x^2} \cdot \frac{(4 - x^2)^{1/2}}{(4 - x^2)^{1/2}}$$

$$= \frac{(4 - x^2)^1 + x^2(4 - x^2)^0}{(4 - x^2)^{3/2}}$$

$$= \frac{4 - x^2 + x^2}{(4 - x^2)^{3/2}}$$

$$= \frac{4}{(4 - x^2)^{3/2}}$$

✓ *Checkpoint* Audio-video solution in English & Spanish at LarsonPrecalculus.com.

Simplify

$$\frac{x^2(x^2 - 2)^{-1/2} + (x^2 - 2)^{1/2}}{x^2 - 2}.$$

EXAMPLE 11   **Rewriting a Difference Quotient**

The following expression from calculus is an example of a *difference quotient*.

$$\frac{\sqrt{x+h}-\sqrt{x}}{h}$$

Rewrite this expression by rationalizing its numerator.

Solution

$$\frac{\sqrt{x+h}-\sqrt{x}}{h} = \frac{\sqrt{x+h}-\sqrt{x}}{h} \cdot \frac{\sqrt{x+h}+\sqrt{x}}{\sqrt{x+h}+\sqrt{x}}$$

$$= \frac{\left(\sqrt{x+h}\right)^2-\left(\sqrt{x}\right)^2}{h\left(\sqrt{x+h}+\sqrt{x}\right)}$$

$$= \frac{x+h-x}{h\left(\sqrt{x+h}+\sqrt{x}\right)}$$

$$= \frac{h}{h\left(\sqrt{x+h}+\sqrt{x}\right)}$$

$$= \frac{1}{\sqrt{x+h}+\sqrt{x}}, \quad h \neq 0$$

> ▷ **ALGEBRA HELP**   You can review the techniques for rationalizing a numerator in Appendix A.2.

Notice that the original expression is undefined when $h = 0$. So, you must exclude $h = 0$ from the domain of the simplified expression so that the expressions are equivalent.

✓ *Checkpoint* 🔊)) *Audio-video solution in English & Spanish at LarsonPrecalculus.com.*

Rewrite the difference quotient

$$\frac{\sqrt{9+h}-3}{h}$$

by rationalizing its numerator.   ▪

Difference quotients, such as that in Example 11, occur frequently in calculus. Often, they need to be rewritten in an equivalent form that can be evaluated when $h = 0$.

Summarize   **(Appendix A.4)**

1. State the definition of the domain of an algebraic expression *(page A35)*. For an example of finding the domains of algebraic expressions, see Example 1.

2. State the definition of a rational expression and describe how to simplify a rational expression *(pages A35 and A36)*. For examples of simplifying rational expressions, see Examples 2 and 3.

3. Describe how to multiply, divide, add, and subtract rational expressions *(page A37)*. For examples of operations with rational expressions, see Examples 4–7.

4. State the definition of a complex fraction *(page A39)*. For an example of simplifying a complex fraction, see Example 8.

5. Describe how to rewrite a difference quotient and why you would want to do so *(page A41)*. For an example of rewriting a difference quotient, see Example 11.

A.4 Exercises

See **CalcChat.com** for tutorial help and worked-out solutions to odd-numbered exercises.

Vocabulary: Fill in the blanks.

1. The set of real numbers for which an algebraic expression is defined is the _____ of the expression.
2. The quotient of two algebraic expressions is a fractional expression, and the quotient of two polynomials is a _____ _____.
3. Fractional expressions with separate fractions in the numerator, denominator, or both are called _____ fractions.
4. Two algebraic expressions that have the same domain and yield the same values for all numbers in their domains are called _____.

Skills and Applications

Finding the Domain of an Algebraic Expression
In Exercises 5–16, find the domain of the expression.

5. $3x^2 - 4x + 7$

6. $6x^2 - 9, \quad x > 0$

7. $\dfrac{1}{3 - x}$

8. $\dfrac{x + 6}{3x + 2}$

9. $\dfrac{x^2 - 1}{x^2 - 2x + 1}$

10. $\dfrac{x^2 - 5x + 6}{x^2 - 4}$

11. $\dfrac{x^2 - 2x - 3}{x^2 - 6x + 9}$

12. $\dfrac{x^2 - x - 12}{x^2 - 8x + 16}$

13. $\sqrt{4 - x}$

14. $\sqrt{2x - 5}$

15. $\dfrac{1}{\sqrt{x - 3}}$

16. $\dfrac{1}{\sqrt{x + 2}}$

Simplifying a Rational Expression In Exercises 17–30, write the rational expression in simplest form.

17. $\dfrac{15x^2}{10x}$

18. $\dfrac{18y^2}{60y^5}$

19. $\dfrac{3xy}{xy + x}$

20. $\dfrac{4y - 8y^2}{10y - 5}$

21. $\dfrac{x - 5}{10 - 2x}$

22. $\dfrac{12 - 4x}{x - 3}$

23. $\dfrac{y^2 - 16}{y + 4}$

24. $\dfrac{x^2 - 25}{5 - x}$

25. $\dfrac{x^3 + 5x^2 + 6x}{x^2 - 4}$

26. $\dfrac{x^2 + 8x - 20}{x^2 + 11x + 10}$

27. $\dfrac{2 - x + 2x^2 - x^3}{x^2 - 4}$

28. $\dfrac{x^2 - 9}{x^3 + x^2 - 9x - 9}$

29. $\dfrac{z^3 - 8}{z^2 + 2z + 4}$

30. $\dfrac{y^3 - 2y^2 - 3y}{y^3 + 1}$

31. **Error Analysis** Describe the error.

$$\dfrac{5x^3}{2x^3 + 4} = \dfrac{5x^3}{2x^3 + 4} = \dfrac{5}{2 + 4} = \dfrac{5}{6}$$

32. **Evaluating a Rational Expression** Complete the table. What can you conclude?

x	0	1	2	3	4	5	6
$\dfrac{x - 3}{x^2 - x - 6}$							
$\dfrac{1}{x + 2}$							

Multiplying or Dividing Rational Expressions In Exercises 33–38, perform the multiplication or division and simplify.

33. $\dfrac{5}{x - 1} \cdot \dfrac{x - 1}{25(x - 2)}$

34. $\dfrac{r}{r - 1} \div \dfrac{r^2}{r^2 - 1}$

35. $\dfrac{4y - 16}{5y + 15} \div \dfrac{4 - y}{2y + 6}$

36. $\dfrac{t^2 - t - 6}{t^2 + 6t + 9} \cdot \dfrac{t + 3}{t^2 - 4}$

37. $\dfrac{x^2 + xy - 2y^2}{x^3 + x^2y} \cdot \dfrac{x}{x^2 + 3xy + 2y^2}$

38. $\dfrac{x^2 - 14x + 49}{x^2 - 49} \div \dfrac{3x - 21}{x + 7}$

Adding or Subtracting Rational Expressions In Exercises 39–46, perform the addition or subtraction and simplify.

39. $6 - \dfrac{5}{x + 3}$

40. $\dfrac{2x - 1}{x + 3} + \dfrac{1 - x}{x + 3}$

41. $\dfrac{3}{x - 2} + \dfrac{5}{2 - x}$

42. $\dfrac{2x}{x - 5} - \dfrac{5}{5 - x}$

43. $\dfrac{4}{2x + 1} - \dfrac{x}{x + 2}$

44. $\dfrac{1}{x^2 - x - 2} - \dfrac{x}{x^2 - 5x + 6}$

45. $-\dfrac{1}{x} + \dfrac{2}{x^2 + 1} + \dfrac{1}{x^3 + x}$

46. $\dfrac{2}{x + 1} + \dfrac{2}{x - 1} + \dfrac{1}{x^2 - 1}$

Error Analysis   **In Exercises 47 and 48, describe the error.**

47. ~~$\dfrac{x+4}{x+2} - \dfrac{3x-8}{x+2} = \dfrac{x+4-3x-8}{x+2}$~~

~~$= \dfrac{-2x-4}{x+2}$~~

~~$= \dfrac{-2(x+2)}{x+2} = -2$~~

48. ~~$\dfrac{6-x}{x(x+2)} + \dfrac{x+2}{x^2} + \dfrac{8}{x^2(x+2)}$~~

~~$= \dfrac{x(6-x) + (x+2)^2 + 8}{x^2(x+2)}$~~

~~$= \dfrac{6x - x^2 + x^2 + 4 + 8}{x^2(x+2)}$~~

~~$= \dfrac{6(x+2)}{x^2(x+2)} = \dfrac{6}{x^2}$~~

Simplifying a Complex Fraction   **In Exercises 49–54, simplify the complex fraction.**

49. $\dfrac{\left(\dfrac{x}{2} - 1\right)}{(x-2)}$

50. $\dfrac{(x-4)}{\left(\dfrac{x}{4} - \dfrac{4}{x}\right)}$

51. $\dfrac{\left[\dfrac{x^2}{(x+1)^2}\right]}{\left[\dfrac{x}{(x+1)^3}\right]}$

52. $\dfrac{\left(\dfrac{x^2-1}{x}\right)}{\left[\dfrac{(x-1)^2}{x}\right]}$

53. $\dfrac{\left(\sqrt{x} - \dfrac{1}{2\sqrt{x}}\right)}{\sqrt{x}}$

54. $\dfrac{\left(\dfrac{t^2}{\sqrt{t^2+1}} - \sqrt{t^2+1}\right)}{t^2}$

Factoring an Expression   **In Exercises 55–60, factor the expression by removing the common factor with the lesser exponent.**

55. $x^5 - 2x^{-2}$

56. $5x^5 + x^{-3}$

57. $x^2(x^2+1)^{-5} - (x^2+1)^{-4}$

58. $2x(x-5)^{-3} - 4x^2(x-5)^{-4}$

59. $2x^2(x-1)^{1/2} - 5(x-1)^{-1/2}$

60. $4x^3(2x-1)^{3/2} - 2x(2x-1)^{-1/2}$

Simplifying an Expression   **In Exercises 61 and 62, simplify the expression.**

61. $\dfrac{3x^{1/3} - x^{-2/3}}{3x^{-2/3}}$

62. $\dfrac{-x^3(1-x^2)^{-1/2} - 2x(1-x^2)^{1/2}}{x^4}$

Simplifying a Difference Quotient   **In Exercises 63–66, simplify the difference quotient.**

63. $\dfrac{\left(\dfrac{1}{x+h} - \dfrac{1}{x}\right)}{h}$

64. $\dfrac{\left[\dfrac{1}{(x+h)^2} - \dfrac{1}{x^2}\right]}{h}$

65. $\dfrac{\left(\dfrac{1}{x+h-4} - \dfrac{1}{x-4}\right)}{h}$

66. $\dfrac{\left(\dfrac{x+h}{x+h+1} - \dfrac{x}{x+1}\right)}{h}$

Rewriting a Difference Quotient   **In Exercises 67–72, rewrite the difference quotient by rationalizing the numerator.**

67. $\dfrac{\sqrt{x+2} - \sqrt{x}}{2}$

68. $\dfrac{\sqrt{z-3} - \sqrt{z}}{3}$

69. $\dfrac{\sqrt{t+3} - \sqrt{3}}{t}$

70. $\dfrac{\sqrt{x+5} - \sqrt{5}}{x}$

71. $\dfrac{\sqrt{x+h+1} - \sqrt{x+1}}{h}$

72. $\dfrac{\sqrt{x+h-2} - \sqrt{x-2}}{h}$

73. Refrigeration

After placing food (at room temperature) in a refrigerator, the time required for the food to cool depends on the amount of food, the air circulation in the refrigerator, the original temperature of the food, and the temperature of the refrigerator. The model that gives the temperature of food that has an original temperature of 75°F and is placed in a 40°F refrigerator is

$$T = 10\left(\dfrac{4t^2 + 16t + 75}{t^2 + 4t + 10}\right)$$

where T is the temperature (in degrees Fahrenheit) and t is the time (in hours).

(a) Complete the table.

t	0	2	4	6	8	10	12
T							

t	14	16	18	20	22
T					

(b) What value of T does the mathematical model appear to be approaching?

74. Rate A digital copier copies in color at a rate of 50 pages per minute.

(a) Find the time required to copy one page.

(b) Find the time required to copy x pages.

(c) Find the time required to copy 120 pages.

Probability **In Exercises 75 and 76, consider an experiment in which a marble is tossed into a box whose base is shown in the figure. The probability that the marble will come to rest in the shaded portion of the box is equal to the ratio of the shaded area to the total area of the figure. Find the probability.**

75.

76.

77. Interactive Money Management The table shows the numbers of U.S. households (in millions) banking online and paying bills online from 2005 through 2010. (*Source: Fiserv, Inc.*)

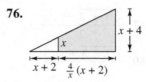

Year	Banking	Paying Bills
2005	46.7	17.9
2006	58.6	26.3
2007	62.8	28.2
2008	67.0	30.0
2009	69.7	32.6
2010	72.5	36.4

Spreadsheet at LarsonPrecalculus.com

Mathematical models for the data are

$$\text{Number banking online} = \frac{-33.74t + 121.8}{-0.40t + 1.0}$$

and

$$\text{Number paying bills online} = \frac{0.307t^2 - 6.54t + 24.6}{0.015t^2 - 0.28t + 1.0}$$

where t represents the year, with $t = 5$ corresponding to 2005.

(a) Using the models, create a table showing the numbers of households banking online and the numbers of households paying bills online for the given years.

(b) Compare the values given by the models with the actual data.

(c) Determine a model for the ratio of the number of households paying bills online to the number of households banking online.

(d) Use the model from part (c) to find the ratios for the given years. Interpret your results.

78. Finance The formula that approximates the annual interest rate r of a monthly installment loan is

$$r = \frac{24(NM - P)}{N} \div \left(P + \frac{NM}{12} \right)$$

where N is the total number of payments, M is the monthly payment, and P is the amount financed.

(a) Approximate the annual interest rate for a five-year car loan of \$28,000 that has monthly payments of \$525.

(b) Simplify the expression for the annual interest rate r, and then rework part (a).

79. Electrical Engineering The total resistance R_T (in ohms) of two resistors connected in parallel is given by

$$R_T = \frac{1}{\dfrac{1}{R_1} + \dfrac{1}{R_2}}$$

where R_1 and R_2 are the resistance values of the first and second resistors, respectively. Simplify the expression for the total resistance R_T.

80. HOW DO YOU SEE IT? The mathematical model

$$P = 100\left(\frac{t^2 - t + 1}{t^2 + 1} \right), \quad t \geq 0$$

gives the percent P of the normal level of oxygen in a pond, where t is the time (in weeks) after organic waste is dumped into the pond. The bar graph shows the situation. What conclusions can you draw from the bar graph?

Exploration

True or False? **In Exercises 81 and 82, determine whether the statement is true or false. Justify your answer.**

81. $\dfrac{x^{2n} - 1^{2n}}{x^n - 1^n} = x^n + 1^n$

82. $\dfrac{x^2 - 3x + 2}{x - 1} = x - 2$, for all values of x

A.5 Solving Equations

You can use linear equations in many real-life applications. For example, you can use linear equations in forensics to determine height from femur length. See Exercises 95 and 96 on page A57.

■ Identify different types of equations.
■ Solve linear equations in one variable and rational equations that lead to linear equations.
■ Solve quadratic equations by factoring, extracting square roots, completing the square, and using the Quadratic Formula.
■ Solve polynomial equations of degree three or greater.
■ Solve radical equations.
■ Solve absolute value equations.
■ Use common formulas to solve real-life problems.

Equations and Solutions of Equations

An **equation** in x is a statement that two algebraic expressions are equal. For example,

$$3x - 5 = 7, \quad x^2 - x - 6 = 0, \quad \text{and} \quad \sqrt{2x} = 4$$

are equations. To **solve** an equation in x means to find all values of x for which the equation is true. Such values are **solutions.** For instance, $x = 4$ is a solution of the equation $3x - 5 = 7$ because $3(4) - 5 = 7$ is a true statement.

The solutions of an equation depend on the kinds of numbers being considered. For instance, in the set of rational numbers, $x^2 = 10$ has no solution because there is no rational number whose square is 10. However, in the set of real numbers, the equation has the two solutions $x = \sqrt{10}$ and $x = -\sqrt{10}$.

An equation that is true for *every* real number in the domain of the variable is called an **identity.** For example,

$$x^2 - 9 = (x + 3)(x - 3) \qquad \text{Identity}$$

is an identity because it is a true statement for any real value of x. The equation

$$\frac{x}{3x^2} = \frac{1}{3x} \qquad \text{Identity}$$

where $x \neq 0$, is an identity because it is true for any nonzero real value of x.

An equation that is true for just *some* (but not all) of the real numbers in the domain of the variable is called a **conditional equation.** For example, the equation

$$x^2 - 9 = 0 \qquad \text{Conditional equation}$$

is conditional because $x = 3$ and $x = -3$ are the only values in the domain that satisfy the equation.

A **contradiction** is an equation that is false for *every* real number in the domain of the variable. For example, the equation

$$2x - 4 = 2x + 1 \qquad \text{Contradiction}$$

is a contradiction because there are no real values of x for which the equation is true.

Linear and Rational Equations

Definition of Linear Equation in One Variable

A **linear equation in one variable** x is an equation that can be written in the standard form

$$ax + b = 0$$

where a and b are real numbers with $a \neq 0$.

A linear equation has exactly one solution. To see this, consider the following steps. (Remember that $a \neq 0$.)

$$ax + b = 0 \qquad \text{Write original equation.}$$

$$ax = -b \qquad \text{Subtract } b \text{ from each side.}$$

$$x = -\frac{b}{a} \qquad \text{Divide each side by } a.$$

To solve a conditional equation in x, isolate x on one side of the equation by a sequence of **equivalent equations,** each having the same solution(s) as the original equation. The operations that yield equivalent equations come from the properties of equality reviewed in Appendix A.1.

Generating Equivalent Equations

An equation can be transformed into an *equivalent equation* by one or more of the following steps.

	Given Equation	Equivalent Equation
1. Remove symbols of grouping, combine like terms, or simplify fractions on one or both sides of the equation.	$2x - x = 4$	$x = 4$
2. Add (or subtract) the same quantity to (from) *each* side of the equation.	$x + 1 = 6$	$x = 5$
3. Multiply (or divide) *each* side of the equation by the same *nonzero* quantity.	$2x = 6$	$x = 3$
4. Interchange the two sides of the equation.	$2 = x$	$x = 2$

The following example shows the steps for solving a linear equation in one variable x.

EXAMPLE 1 **Solving a Linear Equation**

a. $3x - 6 = 0$ Original equation

     $3x = 6$ Add 6 to each side.

     $x = 2$ Divide each side by 3.

b. $5x + 4 = 3x - 8$ Original equation

     $2x + 4 = -8$ Subtract $3x$ from each side.

     $2x = -12$ Subtract 4 from each side.

     $x = -6$ Divide each side by 2.

✓ *Checkpoint* *Audio-video solution in English & Spanish at LarsonPrecalculus.com.*

Solve each equation.

a. $7 - 2x = 15$

b. $7x - 9 = 5x + 7$

• • REMARK After solving an equation, you should check each solution in the original equation. For instance, you can check the solution of Example 1(a) as follows.

$3x - 6 = 0$ Write original equation.

$3(2) - 6 \stackrel{?}{=} 0$ Substitute 2 for x.

$0 = 0$ Solution checks. ✓

Try checking the solution of Example 1(b).

▷

REMARK An equation with a *single fraction* on each side can be cleared of denominators by **cross multiplying**. To do this, multiply the left numerator by the right denominator and the right numerator by the left denominator as follows.

$$\frac{a}{b} = \frac{c}{d} \qquad \text{Original equation}$$

$$ad = cb \qquad \text{Cross multiply.}$$

A **rational equation** is an equation that involves one or more fractional expressions. To solve a rational equation, find the least common denominator (LCD) of all terms and multiply every term by the LCD. This process will clear the original equation of fractions and produce a simpler equation to work with.

EXAMPLE 2 **Solving a Rational Equation**

Solve $\dfrac{x}{3} + \dfrac{3x}{4} = 2$.

Solution

$$\frac{x}{3} + \frac{3x}{4} = 2 \qquad \text{Original equation}$$

$$(12)\frac{x}{3} + (12)\frac{3x}{4} = (12)2 \qquad \text{Multiply each term by the LCD.}$$

$$4x + 9x = 24 \qquad \text{Simplify.}$$

$$13x = 24 \qquad \text{Combine like terms.}$$

$$x = \frac{24}{13} \qquad \text{Divide each side by 13.}$$

The solution is $x = \frac{24}{13}$. Check this in the original equation.

✓ *Checkpoint* ◀))) *Audio-video solution in English & Spanish at LarsonPrecalculus.com.*

Solve $\dfrac{4x}{9} - \dfrac{1}{3} = x + \dfrac{5}{3}$. ■

When multiplying or dividing an equation by a *variable expression,* it is possible to introduce an **extraneous solution** that does not satisfy the original equation.

EXAMPLE 3 **An Equation with an Extraneous Solution**

Solve $\dfrac{1}{x - 2} = \dfrac{3}{x + 2} - \dfrac{6x}{x^2 - 4}$.

▷

REMARK Recall that the least common denominator of two or more fractions consists of the product of all prime factors in the denominators, with each factor given the highest power of its occurrence in any denominator. For instance, in Example 3, by factoring each denominator you can determine that the LCD is $(x + 2)(x - 2)$.

Solution The LCD is $x^2 - 4 = (x + 2)(x - 2)$. Multiply each term by this LCD.

$$\frac{1}{x - 2}(x + 2)(x - 2) = \frac{3}{x + 2}(x + 2)(x - 2) - \frac{6x}{x^2 - 4}(x + 2)(x - 2)$$

$$x + 2 = 3(x - 2) - 6x, \quad x \neq \pm 2$$

$$x + 2 = 3x - 6 - 6x$$

$$x + 2 = -3x - 6$$

$$4x = -8$$

$$x = -2 \qquad \text{Extraneous solution}$$

In the original equation, $x = -2$ yields a denominator of zero. So, $x = -2$ is an extraneous solution, and the original equation has *no solution.*

✓ *Checkpoint* ◀))) *Audio-video solution in English & Spanish at LarsonPrecalculus.com.*

Solve $\dfrac{3x}{x - 4} = 5 + \dfrac{12}{x - 4}$. ■

Quadratic Equations

A **quadratic equation** in x is an equation that can be written in the general form

$$ax^2 + bx + c = 0$$

where a, b, and c are real numbers with $a \neq 0$. A quadratic equation in x is also called a **second-degree polynomial equation** in x.

You should be familiar with the following four methods of solving quadratic equations.

Solving a Quadratic Equation

Factoring

If $ab = 0$, then $a = 0$ or $b = 0$.

Example: $\qquad\qquad x^2 - x - 6 = 0$

$$(x - 3)(x + 2) = 0$$

$$x - 3 = 0 \implies x = 3$$

$$x + 2 = 0 \implies x = -2$$

Square Root Principle

If $u^2 = c$, where $c > 0$, then $u = \pm\sqrt{c}$.

Example: $\qquad (x + 3)^2 = 16$

$$x + 3 = \pm 4$$

$$x = -3 \pm 4$$

$$x = 1 \quad \text{or} \quad x = -7$$

Completing the Square

If $x^2 + bx = c$, then

$$x^2 + bx + \left(\frac{b}{2}\right)^2 = c + \left(\frac{b}{2}\right)^2 \qquad \text{Add } \left(\frac{b}{2}\right)^2 \text{ to each side.}$$

$$\left(x + \frac{b}{2}\right)^2 = c + \frac{b^2}{4}.$$

Example: $\qquad\qquad x^2 + 6x = 5$

$$x^2 + 6x + 3^2 = 5 + 3^2 \qquad \text{Add } \left(\frac{6}{2}\right)^2 \text{ to each side.}$$

$$(x + 3)^2 = 14$$

$$x + 3 = \pm\sqrt{14}$$

$$x = -3 \pm \sqrt{14}$$

Quadratic Formula

If $ax^2 + bx + c = 0$, then $x = \dfrac{-b \pm \sqrt{b^2 - 4ac}}{2a}$.

Example: $\qquad 2x^2 + 3x - 1 = 0$

$$x = \frac{-3 \pm \sqrt{3^2 - 4(2)(-1)}}{2(2)}$$

$$= \frac{-3 \pm \sqrt{17}}{4}$$

▷ **• • REMARK** The Square Root Principle is also referred to as *extracting square roots.*

▷ **• • REMARK** You can solve every quadratic equation by completing the square or using the Quadratic Formula.

EXAMPLE 4   **Solving a Quadratic Equation by Factoring**

a. $2x^2 + 9x + 7 = 3$ Original equation

$\quad 2x^2 + 9x + 4 = 0$ Write in general form.

$\quad (2x + 1)(x + 4) = 0$ Factor.

$\qquad 2x + 1 = 0 \implies x = -\frac{1}{2}$ Set 1st factor equal to 0.

$\qquad x + 4 = 0 \implies x = -4$ Set 2nd factor equal to 0.

The solutions are $x = -\frac{1}{2}$ and $x = -4$. Check these in the original equation.

b. $6x^2 - 3x = 0$ Original equation

$\quad 3x(2x - 1) = 0$ Factor.

$\qquad 3x = 0 \implies x = 0$ Set 1st factor equal to 0.

$\qquad 2x - 1 = 0 \implies x = \frac{1}{2}$ Set 2nd factor equal to 0.

The solutions are $x = 0$ and $x = \frac{1}{2}$. Check these in the original equation.

✓ **Checkpoint** *Audio-video solution in English & Spanish at LarsonPrecalculus.com.*

Solve $2x^2 - 3x + 1 = 6$ by factoring.

Note that the method of solution in Example 4 is based on the Zero-Factor Property from Appendix A.1. This property applies *only* to equations written in general form (in which the right side of the equation is zero). So, all terms must be collected on one side *before* factoring. For instance, in the equation $(x - 5)(x + 2) = 8$, it is *incorrect* to set each factor equal to 8. Try to solve this equation correctly.

EXAMPLE 5   **Extracting Square Roots**

Solve each equation by extracting square roots.

a. $4x^2 = 12$

b. $(x - 3)^2 = 7$

Solution

a. $4x^2 = 12$ Write original equation.

$\quad x^2 = 3$ Divide each side by 4.

$\quad x = \pm\sqrt{3}$ Extract square roots.

The solutions are $x = \sqrt{3}$ and $x = -\sqrt{3}$. Check these in the original equation.

b. $(x - 3)^2 = 7$ Write original equation.

$\quad x - 3 = \pm\sqrt{7}$ Extract square roots.

$\quad x = 3 \pm \sqrt{7}$ Add 3 to each side.

The solutions are $x = 3 \pm \sqrt{7}$. Check these in the original equation.

✓ **Checkpoint** *Audio-video solution in English & Spanish at LarsonPrecalculus.com.*

Solve each equation by extracting square roots.

a. $3x^2 = 36$

b. $(x - 1)^2 = 10$

When solving quadratic equations by completing the square, you must add $(b/2)^2$ to *each side* in order to maintain equality. When the leading coefficient is *not* 1, you must divide each side of the equation by the leading coefficient *before* completing the square, as shown in Example 7.

EXAMPLE 6   **Completing the Square: Leading Coefficient Is 1**

Solve $x^2 + 2x - 6 = 0$ by completing the square.

Solution

$$x^2 + 2x - 6 = 0 \qquad \text{Write original equation.}$$

$$x^2 + 2x = 6 \qquad \text{Add 6 to each side.}$$

$$x^2 + 2x + 1^2 = 6 + 1^2 \qquad \text{Add } 1^2 \text{ to each side.}$$

$$\underset{(\text{half of } 2)^2}{\underline{\qquad\uparrow}}$$

$$(x + 1)^2 = 7 \qquad \text{Simplify.}$$

$$x + 1 = \pm\sqrt{7} \qquad \text{Extract square roots.}$$

$$x = -1 \pm \sqrt{7} \qquad \text{Subtract 1 from each side.}$$

The solutions are

$$x = -1 \pm \sqrt{7}.$$

Check these in the original equation.

✓ **Checkpoint** ◀))) *Audio-video solution in English & Spanish at LarsonPrecalculus.com.*

Solve $x^2 - 4x - 1 = 0$ by completing the square.

EXAMPLE 7   **Completing the Square: Leading Coefficient Is Not 1**

Solve $3x^2 - 4x - 5 = 0$ by completing the square.

Solution

$$3x^2 - 4x - 5 = 0 \qquad \text{Write original equation.}$$

$$3x^2 - 4x = 5 \qquad \text{Add 5 to each side.}$$

$$x^2 - \frac{4}{3}x = \frac{5}{3} \qquad \text{Divide each side by 3.}$$

$$x^2 - \frac{4}{3}x + \left(-\frac{2}{3}\right)^2 = \frac{5}{3} + \left(-\frac{2}{3}\right)^2 \qquad \text{Add } \left(-\frac{2}{3}\right)^2 \text{ to each side.}$$

$$\underset{\left(\text{half of } -\frac{4}{3}\right)^2}{\underline{\qquad\uparrow}}$$

$$\left(x - \frac{2}{3}\right)^2 = \frac{19}{9} \qquad \text{Simplify.}$$

$$x - \frac{2}{3} = \pm\frac{\sqrt{19}}{3} \qquad \text{Extract square roots.}$$

$$x = \frac{2}{3} \pm \frac{\sqrt{19}}{3} \qquad \text{Add } \frac{2}{3} \text{ to each side.}$$

✓ **Checkpoint** ◀))) *Audio-video solution in English & Spanish at LarsonPrecalculus.com.*

Solve $3x^2 - 10x - 2 = 0$ by completing the square.

EXAMPLE 8 **The Quadratic Formula: Two Distinct Solutions**

Use the Quadratic Formula to solve $x^2 + 3x = 9$.

Solution

$x^2 + 3x = 9$	Write original equation.
$x^2 + 3x - 9 = 0$	Write in general form.
$x = \dfrac{-b \pm \sqrt{b^2 - 4ac}}{2a}$	Quadratic Formula
$x = \dfrac{-3 \pm \sqrt{(3)^2 - 4(1)(-9)}}{2(1)}$	Substitute $a = 1$, $b = 3$, and $c = -9$.
$x = \dfrac{-3 \pm \sqrt{45}}{2}$	Simplify.
$x = \dfrac{-3 \pm 3\sqrt{5}}{2}$	Simplify.

REMARK When using the Quadratic Formula, remember that *before* applying the formula, you must first write the quadratic equation in general form.

The two solutions are

$$x = \frac{-3 + 3\sqrt{5}}{2} \quad \text{and} \quad x = \frac{-3 - 3\sqrt{5}}{2}.$$

Check these in the original equation.

✔ *Checkpoint* 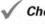 Audio-video solution in English & Spanish at LarsonPrecalculus.com.

Use the Quadratic Formula to solve $3x^2 + 2x - 10 = 0$.

EXAMPLE 9 **The Quadratic Formula: One Solution**

Use the Quadratic Formula to solve $8x^2 - 24x + 18 = 0$.

Solution

$8x^2 - 24x + 18 = 0$	Write original equation.
$4x^2 - 12x + 9 = 0$	Divide out common factor of 2.
$x = \dfrac{-b \pm \sqrt{b^2 - 4ac}}{2a}$	Quadratic Formula
$x = \dfrac{-(-12) \pm \sqrt{(-12)^2 - 4(4)(9)}}{2(4)}$	Substitute $a = 4$, $b = -12$, and $c = 9$.
$x = \dfrac{12 \pm \sqrt{0}}{8} = \dfrac{3}{2}$	Simplify.

This quadratic equation has only one solution:

$$x = \tfrac{3}{2}.$$

Check this in the original equation.

✔ *Checkpoint* 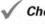 Audio-video solution in English & Spanish at LarsonPrecalculus.com.

Use the Quadratic Formula to solve $18x^2 - 48x + 32 = 0$. ∎

Note that you could have solved Example 9 without first dividing out a common factor of 2. Substituting $a = 8$, $b = -24$, and $c = 18$ into the Quadratic Formula produces the same result.

Polynomial Equations of Higher Degree

The methods used to solve quadratic equations can sometimes be extended to solve polynomial equations of higher degrees.

·······················▷

·· **REMARK** A common mistake in solving an equation such as that in Example 10 is to divide each side of the equation by the variable factor x^2. This loses the solution $x = 0$. When solving an equation, always write the equation in general form, then factor the equation and set each factor equal to zero. Do not divide each side of an equation by a variable factor in an attempt to simplify the equation.

EXAMPLE 10   **Solving a Polynomial Equation by Factoring**

Solve $3x^4 = 48x^2$.

Solution   First write the polynomial equation in general form with zero on one side. Then factor the other side, set each factor equal to zero, and solve.

$3x^4 = 48x^2$	Write original equation.
$3x^4 - 48x^2 = 0$	Write in general form.
$3x^2(x^2 - 16) = 0$	Factor out common factor.
$3x^2(x + 4)(x - 4) = 0$	Write in factored form.
$3x^2 = 0 \implies x = 0$	Set 1st factor equal to 0.
$x + 4 = 0 \implies x = -4$	Set 2nd factor equal to 0.
$x - 4 = 0 \implies x = 4$	Set 3rd factor equal to 0.

You can check these solutions by substituting in the original equation, as follows.

Check

$3(0)^4 = 48(0)^2$	0 checks. ✓
$3(-4)^4 = 48(-4)^2$	-4 checks. ✓
$3(4)^4 = 48(4)^2$	4 checks. ✓

So, the solutions are

$$x = 0, \quad x = -4, \quad \text{and} \quad x = 4.$$

✓ *Checkpoint* ◀))) Audio-video solution in English & Spanish at LarsonPrecalculus.com.

Solve $9x^4 - 12x^2 = 0$.

EXAMPLE 11   **Solving a Polynomial Equation by Factoring**

Solve $x^3 - 3x^2 - 3x + 9 = 0$.

Solution

$x^3 - 3x^2 - 3x + 9 = 0$	Write original equation.
$x^2(x - 3) - 3(x - 3) = 0$	Factor by grouping.
$(x - 3)(x^2 - 3) = 0$	Distributive Property
$x - 3 = 0 \implies x = 3$	Set 1st factor equal to 0.
$x^2 - 3 = 0 \implies x = \pm\sqrt{3}$	Set 2nd factor equal to 0.

The solutions are $x = 3$, $x = \sqrt{3}$, and $x = -\sqrt{3}$. Check these in the original equation.

✓ *Checkpoint* ◀))) Audio-video solution in English & Spanish at LarsonPrecalculus.com.

Solve each equation.

a. $x^3 - 5x^2 - 2x + 10 = 0$

b. $6x^3 - 27x^2 - 54x = 0$

Radical Equations

•• REMARK   When squaring
each side of an equation or
raising each side of an equation
to a rational power, it is possible
to introduce extraneous solutions.
In such cases, checking your
solutions is crucial.
••••••••••••••••••▷

A **radical equation** is an equation that involves one or more radical expressions.

EXAMPLE 12   Solving Radical Equations

a.
$$\sqrt{2x + 7} - x = 2 \qquad \text{Original equation}$$
$$\sqrt{2x + 7} = x + 2 \qquad \text{Isolate radical.}$$
$$2x + 7 = x^2 + 4x + 4 \qquad \text{Square each side.}$$
$$0 = x^2 + 2x - 3 \qquad \text{Write in general form.}$$
$$0 = (x + 3)(x - 1) \qquad \text{Factor.}$$
$$x + 3 = 0 \implies x = -3 \qquad \text{Set 1st factor equal to 0.}$$
$$x - 1 = 0 \implies x = 1 \qquad \text{Set 2nd factor equal to 0.}$$

By checking these values, you can determine that the only solution is $x = 1$.

b.
$$\sqrt{2x - 5} - \sqrt{x - 3} = 1 \qquad \text{Original equation}$$
$$\sqrt{2x - 5} = \sqrt{x - 3} + 1 \qquad \text{Isolate } \sqrt{2x - 5}.$$
$$2x - 5 = x - 3 + 2\sqrt{x - 3} + 1 \qquad \text{Square each side.}$$
$$2x - 5 = x - 2 + 2\sqrt{x - 3} \qquad \text{Combine like terms.}$$
$$x - 3 = 2\sqrt{x - 3} \qquad \text{Isolate } 2\sqrt{x - 3}.$$
$$x^2 - 6x + 9 = 4(x - 3) \qquad \text{Square each side.}$$
$$x^2 - 10x + 21 = 0 \qquad \text{Write in general form.}$$
$$(x - 3)(x - 7) = 0 \qquad \text{Factor.}$$
$$x - 3 = 0 \implies x = 3 \qquad \text{Set 1st factor equal to 0.}$$
$$x - 7 = 0 \implies x = 7 \qquad \text{Set 2nd factor equal to 0.}$$

•• REMARK   When an equation
contains two radicals, it may not
be possible to isolate both. In
such cases, you may have to
raise each side of the equation
to a power at *two* different
stages in the solution, as shown
in Example 12(b).

The solutions are $x = 3$ and $x = 7$. Check these in the original equation.

✓ **Checkpoint** Audio-video solution in English & Spanish at LarsonPrecalculus.com.

Solve $-\sqrt{40 - 9x} + 2 = x$.

EXAMPLE 13   Solving an Equation Involving a Rational Exponent

Solve $(x - 4)^{2/3} = 25$.

Solution

$$(x - 4)^{2/3} = 25 \qquad \text{Write original equation.}$$
$$\sqrt[3]{(x - 4)^2} = 25 \qquad \text{Rewrite in radical form.}$$
$$(x - 4)^2 = 15{,}625 \qquad \text{Cube each side.}$$
$$x - 4 = \pm 125 \qquad \text{Extract square roots.}$$
$$x = 129, \quad x = -121 \qquad \text{Add 4 to each side.}$$

✓ **Checkpoint** Audio-video solution in English & Spanish at LarsonPrecalculus.com.

Solve $(x - 5)^{2/3} = 16$.

Absolute Value Equations

An **absolute value equation** is an equation that involves one or more absolute value expressions. To solve an absolute value equation, remember that the expression inside the absolute value bars can be positive or negative. This results in *two* separate equations, each of which must be solved. For instance, the equation

$$|x - 2| = 3$$

results in the two equations

$$x - 2 = 3 \quad \text{and} \quad -(x - 2) = 3$$

which implies that the equation has two solutions: $x = 5$ and $x = -1$.

EXAMPLE 14 **Solving an Absolute Value Equation**

Solve $|x^2 - 3x| = -4x + 6$.

Solution Because the variable expression inside the absolute value bars can be positive or negative, you must solve the following two equations.

First Equation

$x^2 - 3x = -4x + 6$	Use positive expression.
$x^2 + x - 6 = 0$	Write in general form.
$(x + 3)(x - 2) = 0$	Factor.
$x + 3 = 0 \implies x = -3$	Set 1st factor equal to 0.
$x - 2 = 0 \implies x = 2$	Set 2nd factor equal to 0.

Second Equation

$-(x^2 - 3x) = -4x + 6$	Use negative expression.
$x^2 - 7x + 6 = 0$	Write in general form.
$(x - 1)(x - 6) = 0$	Factor.
$x - 1 = 0 \implies x = 1$	Set 1st factor equal to 0.
$x - 6 = 0 \implies x = 6$	Set 2nd factor equal to 0.

Check

$|(-3)^2 - 3(-3)| \overset{?}{=} -4(-3) + 6$	Substitute -3 for x.
$18 = 18$	-3 checks. ✓
$|(2)^2 - 3(2)| \overset{?}{=} -4(2) + 6$	Substitute 2 for x.
$2 \neq -2$	2 does not check.
$|(1)^2 - 3(1)| \overset{?}{=} -4(1) + 6$	Substitute 1 for x.
$2 = 2$	1 checks. ✓
$|(6)^2 - 3(6)| \overset{?}{=} -4(6) + 6$	Substitute 6 for x.
$18 \neq -18$	6 does not check.

The solutions are $x = -3$ and $x = 1$.

✓ *Checkpoint* ◀))) *Audio-video solution in English & Spanish at LarsonPrecalculus.com.*

Solve $|x^2 + 4x| = 5x + 12$. ◾

Common Formulas

The following geometric formulas are used at various times throughout this course. For your convenience, some of these formulas along with several others are also provided on the inside cover of this text.

Common Formulas for Area *A*, Perimeter *P*, Circumference *C*, and Volume *V*

Rectangle
$A = lw$
$P = 2l + 2w$

Circle
$A = \pi r^2$
$C = 2\pi r$

Rectangular Solid
$V = lwh$

Circular Cylinder
$V = \pi r^2 h$

Sphere
$V = \frac{4}{3}\pi r^3$

|←— 4 cm —→|

Figure A.10

- - - - - - - - - - - - - - - - - - ▷

·· REMARK You can use unit analysis to check that the answer in Example 15 is reasonable.

$$\frac{200 \text{ cm}^3}{16\pi \text{ cm}^2} = \frac{200 \text{ cm} \cdot \text{cm} \cdot \text{cm}}{16\pi \text{ cm} \cdot \text{cm}}$$

$$= \frac{200}{16\pi} \text{ cm}$$

$$\approx 3.98 \text{ cm}$$

EXAMPLE 15   **Using a Geometric Formula**

The cylindrical can shown in Figure A.10 has a volume of 200 cubic centimeters (cm^3). Find the height of the can.

Solution   The formula for the *volume of a cylinder* is $V = \pi r^2 h$. To find the height of the can, solve for h. Then, using $V = 200$ and $r = 4$, find the height.

$$V = \pi r^2 h \implies h = \frac{V}{\pi r^2} = \frac{200}{\pi (4)^2} = \frac{200}{16\pi} \approx 3.98$$

So, the height of the can is about 3.98 centimeters.

✓ **Checkpoint** ◀))) *Audio-video solution in English & Spanish at LarsonPrecalculus.com.*

A cylindrical container has a volume of 84 cubic inches and a radius of 3 inches. Find the height of the container. ▪

Summarize   (Appendix A.5)

1. State the definition of an identity, a conditional equation, and a contradiction *(page A45)*.

2. State the definition of a linear equation *(page A45)*. For examples of solving linear equations and rational equations that lead to linear equations, see Examples 1–3.

3. List the four methods of solving quadratic equations discussed in this section *(page A48)*. For examples of solving quadratic equations, see Examples 4–9.

4. Describe how to solve a polynomial equation by factoring *(page A52)*. For examples of solving polynomial equations by factoring, see Examples 10 and 11.

5. Describe how to solve a radical equation *(page A53)*. For an example of solving radical equations, see Example 12.

6. Describe how to solve an absolute value equation *(page A54)*. For an example of solving an absolute value equation, see Example 14.

7. Describe real-life problems that can be solved using common geometric formulas *(page A55)*. For an example that uses a volume formula, see Example 15.

A.5 Exercises

See **CalcChat.com** for tutorial help and worked-out solutions to odd-numbered exercises.

Vocabulary: Fill in the blanks.

1. An _____ is a statement that equates two algebraic expressions.
2. A linear equation in one variable x is an equation that can be written in the standard form _____.
3. An _____ solution is a solution that does not satisfy the original equation.
4. Four methods that can be used to solve a quadratic equation are _____, extracting _____ _____, _____ the _____, and the _____ _____.

Skills and Applications

Solving a Linear Equation In Exercises 5–12, solve the equation and check your solution. (If not possible, explain why.)

5. $x + 11 = 15$
6. $7 - x = 19$
7. $7 - 2x = 25$
8. $3x - 5 = 2x + 7$
9. $4y + 2 - 5y = 7 - 6y$
10. $0.25x + 0.75(10 - x) = 3$
11. $x - 3(2x + 3) = 8 - 5x$
12. $9x - 10 = 5x + 2(2x - 5)$

Solving a Rational Equation In Exercises 13–24, solve the equation and check your solution. (If not possible, explain why.)

13. $\dfrac{3x}{8} - \dfrac{4x}{3} = 4$
14. $\dfrac{5x}{4} + \dfrac{1}{2} = x - \dfrac{1}{2}$
15. $\dfrac{5x - 4}{5x + 4} = \dfrac{2}{3}$
16. $\dfrac{10x + 3}{5x + 6} = \dfrac{1}{2}$
17. $10 - \dfrac{13}{x} = 4 + \dfrac{5}{x}$
18. $\dfrac{1}{x} + \dfrac{2}{x - 5} = 0$
19. $\dfrac{x}{x + 4} + \dfrac{4}{x + 4} + 2 = 0$
20. $\dfrac{7}{2x + 1} - \dfrac{8x}{2x - 1} = -4$
21. $\dfrac{2}{(x - 4)(x - 2)} = \dfrac{1}{x - 4} + \dfrac{2}{x - 2}$
22. $\dfrac{4}{x - 1} + \dfrac{6}{3x + 1} = \dfrac{15}{3x + 1}$
23. $\dfrac{1}{x - 3} + \dfrac{1}{x + 3} = \dfrac{10}{x^2 - 9}$
24. $\dfrac{1}{x - 2} + \dfrac{3}{x + 3} = \dfrac{4}{x^2 + x - 6}$

Solving a Quadratic Equation by Factoring In Exercises 25–34, solve the quadratic equation by factoring.

25. $6x^2 + 3x = 0$
26. $9x^2 - 1 = 0$
27. $x^2 - 2x - 8 = 0$
28. $x^2 - 10x + 9 = 0$
29. $x^2 + 10x + 25 = 0$
30. $4x^2 + 12x + 9 = 0$
31. $x^2 + 4x = 12$
32. $-x^2 + 8x = 12$
33. $\frac{3}{4}x^2 + 8x + 20 = 0$
34. $\frac{1}{8}x^2 - x - 16 = 0$

Extracting Square Roots In Exercises 35–42, solve the equation by extracting square roots. When a solution is irrational, list both the exact solution *and* its approximation rounded to two decimal places.

35. $x^2 = 49$
36. $x^2 = 32$
37. $3x^2 = 81$
38. $9x^2 = 36$
39. $(x - 12)^2 = 16$
40. $(x + 9)^2 = 24$
41. $(2x - 1)^2 = 18$
42. $(x - 7)^2 = (x + 3)^2$

Completing the Square In Exercises 43–50, solve the quadratic equation by completing the square.

43. $x^2 + 4x - 32 = 0$
44. $x^2 - 2x - 3 = 0$
45. $x^2 + 6x + 2 = 0$
46. $x^2 + 8x + 14 = 0$
47. $9x^2 - 18x = -3$
48. $7 + 2x - x^2 = 0$
49. $2x^2 + 5x - 8 = 0$
50. $3x^2 - 4x - 7 = 0$

Using the Quadratic Formula In Exercises 51–64, use the Quadratic Formula to solve the equation.

51. $2x^2 + x - 1 = 0$
52. $2x^2 - x - 1 = 0$
53. $2 + 2x - x^2 = 0$
54. $x^2 - 10x + 22 = 0$
55. $2x^2 - 3x - 4 = 0$
56. $3x + x^2 - 1 = 0$
57. $12x - 9x^2 = -3$
58. $9x^2 - 37 = 6x$
59. $9x^2 + 30x + 25 = 0$
60. $28x - 49x^2 = 4$
61. $8t = 5 + 2t^2$
62. $25h^2 + 80h + 61 = 0$
63. $(y - 5)^2 = 2y$
64. $(z + 6)^2 = -2z$

Choosing a Method   In Exercises 65–72, solve the equation using any convenient method.

65. $x^2 - 2x - 1 = 0$

66. $11x^2 + 33x = 0$

67. $(x + 3)^2 = 81$

68. $x^2 - 14x + 49 = 0$

69. $x^2 - x - \frac{11}{4} = 0$

70. $x^2 + 3x - \frac{3}{4} = 0$

71. $(x + 1)^2 = x^2$

72. $3x + 4 = 2x^2 - 7$

Solving a Polynomial Equation   In Exercises 73–76, solve the equation. Check your solutions.

73. $6x^4 - 14x^2 = 0$

74. $36x^3 - 100x = 0$

75. $5x^3 + 30x^2 + 45x = 0$

76. $x^3 - 3x^2 - x = -3$

Solving a Radical Equation   In Exercises 77–84, solve the equation. Check your solutions.

77. $\sqrt{3x} - 12 = 0$

78. $\sqrt{x - 10} - 4 = 0$

79. $\sqrt[3]{2x + 5} + 3 = 0$

80. $\sqrt[3]{3x + 1} - 5 = 0$

81. $-\sqrt{26 - 11x} + 4 = x$

82. $x + \sqrt{31 - 9x} = 5$

83. $\sqrt{x} - \sqrt{x - 5} = 1$

84. $2\sqrt{x + 1} - \sqrt{2x + 3} = 1$

Solving an Equation Involving a Rational Exponent   In Exercises 85–88, solve the equation. Check your solutions.

85. $(x - 5)^{3/2} = 8$

86. $(x + 2)^{2/3} = 9$

87. $(x^2 - 5)^{3/2} = 27$

88. $(x^2 - x - 22)^{3/2} = 27$

Solving an Absolute Value Equation   In Exercises 89–92, solve the equation. Check your solutions.

89. $|2x - 5| = 11$ 90. $|3x + 2| = 7$

91. $|x^2 + 6x| = 3x + 18$ 92. $|x - 15| = x^2 - 15x$

93. **Volume of a Billiard Ball**   A billiard ball has a volume of 5.96 cubic inches. Find the radius of a billiard ball.

94. **Length of a Tank**   The diameter of a cylindrical propane gas tank is 4 feet. The total volume of the tank is 603.2 cubic feet. Find the length of the tank.

• • Forensics • • • • • • • • • • • • • • • • •

In Exercises 95 and 96, use the following information. The relationship between the length of an adult's femur (thigh bone) and the height of the adult can be approximated by the linear equations

$y = 0.432x - 10.44$ Female

$y = 0.449x - 12.15$ Male

where y is the length of the femur in inches and x is the height of the adult in inches (see figure).

95. A crime scene investigator discovers a femur belonging to an adult human female. The bone is 18 inches long. Estimate the height of the female.

96. Officials search a forest for a missing man who is 6 feet 2 inches tall. They find an adult male femur that is 21 inches long. Is it possible that the femur belongs to the missing man?

Exploration

True or False?   In Exercises 97–99, determine whether the statement is true or false. Justify your answer.

97. An equation can never have more than one extraneous solution.

98. The equation $2(x - 3) + 1 = 2x - 5$ has no solution.

99. The equation $\sqrt{x + 10} - \sqrt{x - 10} = 0$ has no solution.

100. **HOW DO YOU SEE IT?**   The figure shows a glass cube partially filled with water.

(a) What does the expression $x^2(x - 3)$ represent?

(b) Given $x^2(x - 3) = 320$, explain how you can find the capacity of the cube.

A.6 Linear Inequalities in One Variable

You can use inequalities to model and solve real-life problems. For instance, in Exercise 114 on page A66, you will use an absolute value inequality to analyze the cover layer thickness of a Blu-ray Disc™.

■ Represent solutions of linear inequalities in one variable.
■ Use properties of inequalities to create equivalent inequalities.
■ Solve linear inequalities in one variable.
■ Solve absolute value inequalities.
■ Use inequalities to model and solve real-life problems.

Introduction

Simple inequalities were discussed in Appendix A.1. There, you used the inequality symbols $<$, $\leq$, $>$, and $\geq$ to compare two numbers and to denote subsets of real numbers. For instance, the simple inequality

$$x \geq 3$$

denotes all real numbers x that are greater than or equal to 3.

Now, you will expand your work with inequalities to include more involved statements such as

$$5x - 7 < 3x + 9 \quad \text{and} \quad -3 \leq 6x - 1 < 3.$$

As with an equation, you **solve an inequality** in the variable x by finding all values of x for which the inequality is true. Such values are **solutions** and are said to **satisfy** the inequality. The set of all real numbers that are solutions of an inequality is the **solution set** of the inequality. For instance, the solution set of

$$x + 1 < 4$$

is all real numbers that are less than 3.

The set of all points on the real number line that represents the solution set is the **graph of the inequality.** Graphs of many types of inequalities consist of intervals on the real number line. See Appendix A.1 to review the nine basic types of intervals on the real number line. Note that each type of interval can be classified as *bounded* or *unbounded.*

EXAMPLE 1   **Intervals and Inequalities**

Write an inequality to represent each interval. Then state whether the interval is bounded or unbounded.

a. $(-3, 5]$ **b.** $(-3, \infty)$

c. $[0, 2]$ **d.** $(-\infty, \infty)$

Solution

a. $(-3, 5]$ corresponds to $-3 < x \leq 5$.   Bounded

b. $(-3, \infty)$ corresponds to $x > -3$.   Unbounded

c. $[0, 2]$ corresponds to $0 \leq x \leq 2$.   Bounded

d. $(-\infty, \infty)$ corresponds to $-\infty < x < \infty$.   Unbounded

✓ **Checkpoint** ◀))) *Audio-video solution in English & Spanish at LarsonPrecalculus.com.*

Write an inequality to represent each interval. Then state whether the interval is bounded or unbounded.

a. $[-1, 3]$ **b.** $(-1, 6)$

c. $(-\infty, 4)$ **d.** $[0, \infty)$

Properties of Inequalities

The procedures for solving linear inequalities in one variable are much like those for solving linear equations. To isolate the variable, you can make use of the **properties of inequalities.** These properties are similar to the properties of equality, but there are two important exceptions. When each side of an inequality is multiplied or divided by a negative number, the direction of the inequality symbol must be reversed. Here is an example.

$$-2 < 5 \qquad \text{Original inequality}$$

$$(-3)(-2) > (-3)(5) \qquad \text{Multiply each side by } -3 \text{ and reverse inequality symbol.}$$

$$6 > -15 \qquad \text{Simplify.}$$

Notice that when you do not reverse the inequality symbol in the example above, you obtain the false statement

$$6 < -15. \qquad \text{False statement}$$

Two inequalities that have the same solution set are **equivalent.** For instance, the inequalities

$$x + 2 < 5$$

and

$$x < 3$$

are equivalent. To obtain the second inequality from the first, you can subtract 2 from each side of the inequality. The following list describes the operations that can be used to create equivalent inequalities.

Properties of Inequalities

Let a, b, c, and d be real numbers.

1. Transitive Property

    $$a < b \text{ and } b < c \implies a < c$$

2. Addition of Inequalities

    $$a < b \text{ and } c < d \implies a + c < b + d$$

3. Addition of a Constant

    $$a < b \implies a + c < b + c$$

4. Multiplication by a Constant

    $$\text{For } c > 0, a < b \implies ac < bc$$

    $$\text{For } c < 0, a < b \implies ac > bc \qquad \text{Reverse the inequality symbol.}$$

Each of the properties above is true when the symbol $<$ is replaced by $\leq$ and the symbol $>$ is replaced by $\geq$. For instance, another form of the multiplication property is shown below.

$$\text{For } c > 0, a \leq b \implies ac \leq bc$$

$$\text{For } c < 0, a \leq b \implies ac \geq bc$$

On your own, try to verify each of the properties of inequalities by using several examples with real numbers.

Solving a Linear Inequality in One Variable

The simplest type of inequality is a **linear inequality** in one variable. For instance,

$$2x + 3 > 4$$

is a linear inequality in x.

EXAMPLE 2 **Solving a Linear Inequality**

Solve $5x - 7 > 3x + 9$. Then graph the solution set.

REMARK Checking the solution set of an inequality is not as simple as checking the solutions of an equation. You can, however, get an indication of the validity of a solution set by substituting a few convenient values of x. For instance, in Example 2, try substituting $x = 5$ and $x = 10$ into the original inequality.

Solution

$5x - 7 > 3x + 9$	Write original inequality.
$2x - 7 > 9$	Subtract $3x$ from each side.
$2x > 16$	Add 7 to each side.
$x > 8$	Divide each side by 2.

The solution set is all real numbers that are greater than 8, which is denoted by $(8, \infty)$. The graph of this solution set is shown below. Note that a parenthesis at 8 on the real number line indicates that 8 *is not* part of the solution set.

Solution interval: $(8, \infty)$

✓ **Checkpoint** ◀))) *Audio-video solution in English & Spanish at LarsonPrecalculus.com.*

Solve $7x - 3 \leq 2x + 7$. Then graph the solution set.

EXAMPLE 3 **Solving a Linear Inequality**

Solve $1 - \frac{3}{2}x \geq x - 4$.

Algebraic Solution

$1 - \dfrac{3x}{2} \geq x - 4$	Write original inequality.
$2 - 3x \geq 2x - 8$	Multiply each side by 2.
$2 - 5x \geq -8$	Subtract $2x$ from each side.
$-5x \geq -10$	Subtract 2 from each side.
$x \leq 2$	Divide each side by -5 and reverse the inequality symbol.

The solution set is all real numbers that are less than or equal to 2, which is denoted by $(-\infty, 2]$. The graph of this solution set is shown below. Note that a bracket at 2 on the real number line indicates that 2 *is* part of the solution set.

Solution interval: $(-\infty, 2]$

Graphical Solution

Use a graphing utility to graph $y_1 = 1 - \frac{3}{2}x$ and $y_2 = x - 4$ in the same viewing window, as shown below.

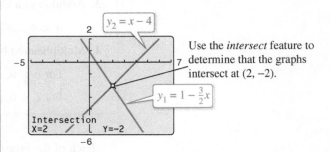

Use the *intersect* feature to determine that the graphs intersect at $(2, -2)$.

The graph of y_1 lies above the graph of y_2 to the left of their point of intersection, which implies that $y_1 \geq y_2$ for all $x \leq 2$.

✓ **Checkpoint** ◀))) *Audio-video solution in English & Spanish at LarsonPrecalculus.com.*

Solve $2 - \frac{5}{3}x > x - 6$ (a) algebraically and (b) graphically. ▪

Sometimes it is possible to write two inequalities as a **double inequality.** For instance, you can write the two inequalities

$$-4 \le 5x - 2$$

and

$$5x - 2 < 7$$

more simply as

$$-4 \le 5x - 2 < 7. \qquad \text{Double inequality}$$

This form allows you to solve the two inequalities together, as demonstrated in Example 4.

EXAMPLE 4   Solving a Double Inequality

Solve $-3 \le 6x - 1 < 3$. Then graph the solution set.

Solution   To solve a double inequality, you can isolate x as the middle term.

$$-3 \le 6x - 1 < 3 \qquad \text{Write original inequality.}$$

$$-3 + 1 \le 6x - 1 + 1 < 3 + 1 \qquad \text{Add 1 to each part.}$$

$$-2 \le 6x < 4 \qquad \text{Simplify.}$$

$$\frac{-2}{6} \le \frac{6x}{6} < \frac{4}{6} \qquad \text{Divide each part by 6.}$$

$$-\frac{1}{3} \le x < \frac{2}{3} \qquad \text{Simplify.}$$

The solution set is all real numbers that are greater than or equal to $-\frac{1}{3}$ and less than $\frac{2}{3}$, which is denoted by $\left[-\frac{1}{3}, \frac{2}{3}\right)$. The graph of this solution set is shown below.

Solution interval: $\left[-\frac{1}{3}, \frac{2}{3}\right)$

✓ **Checkpoint** Audio-video solution in English & Spanish at LarsonPrecalculus.com.

Solve $1 < 2x + 7 < 11$. Then graph the solution set.

You can solve the double inequality in Example 4 in two parts, as follows.

$$-3 \le 6x - 1 \quad \text{and} \quad 6x - 1 < 3$$

$$-2 \le 6x \qquad\qquad\qquad 6x < 4$$

$$-\frac{1}{3} \le x \qquad\qquad\qquad x < \frac{2}{3}$$

The solution set consists of all real numbers that satisfy *both* inequalities. In other words, the solution set is the set of all values of x for which

$$-\frac{1}{3} \le x < \frac{2}{3}.$$

When combining two inequalities to form a double inequality, be sure that the inequalities satisfy the Transitive Property. For instance, it is *incorrect* to combine the inequalities $3 < x$ and $x \le -1$ as $3 < x \le -1$. This "inequality" is wrong because 3 is not less than -1.

Absolute Value Inequalities

▷ **TECHNOLOGY** A graphing
utility can be used to identify
the solution set of an inequality.
For instance, to find the
solution set of $|x - 5| < 2$
(see Example 5a), rewrite the
inequality as $|x - 5| - 2 < 0$,
enter

   Y1 = abs (X − 5) − 2

and press the *graph* key. The
graph should look like the one
shown below.

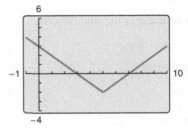

Notice that the graph is below
the *x*-axis on the interval (3, 7).

Solving an Absolute Value Inequality

Let u be an algebraic expression and let a be a real number such that $a > 0$.

1. $|u| < a$ if and only if $-a < u < a$.

2. $|u| \le a$ if and only if $-a \le u \le a$.

3. $|u| > a$ if and only if $u < -a$ or $u > a$.

4. $|u| \ge a$ if and only if $u \le -a$ or $u \ge a$.

EXAMPLE 5   **Solving an Absolute Value Inequality**

Solve each inequality. Then graph the solution set.

a. $|x - 5| < 2$ **b.** $|x + 3| \ge 7$

Solution

a. $|x - 5| < 2$ Write original inequality.

   $-2 < x - 5 < 2$ Write equivalent inequalities.

   $-2 + 5 < x - 5 + 5 < 2 + 5$ Add 5 to each part.

   $3 < x < 7$ Simplify.

The solution set is all real numbers that are greater than 3 and less than 7, which is
denoted by (3, 7). The graph of this solution set is shown below. Note that the graph
of the inequality can be described as all real numbers less than two units from 5.

$|x - 5| < 2$: Solutions lie inside (3, 7).

b. $|x + 3| \ge 7$ Write original inequality.

   $x + 3 \le -7$ or $x + 3 \ge 7$ Write equivalent inequalities.

   $x + 3 - 3 \le -7 - 3$ $x + 3 - 3 \ge 7 - 3$ Subtract 3 from each side.

   $x \le -10$ $x \ge 4$ Simplify.

The solution set is all real numbers that are less than or equal to -10 *or* greater than
or equal to 4, which is denoted by $(-\infty, -10] \cup [4, \infty)$. The symbol $\cup$ is the *union*
symbol, which denotes the combining of two sets. The graph of this solution set
is shown below. Note that the graph of the inequality can be described as all real
numbers at least seven units from -3.

$|x + 3| \ge 7$: Solutions lie outside $(-10, 4)$.

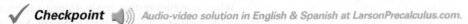

✓ **Checkpoint** ◄))) *Audio-video solution in English & Spanish at LarsonPrecalculus.com.*

Solve $|x - 20| \le 4$. Then graph the solution set.

Applications

 Comparative Shopping

Consider the two cell phone plans shown in Figure A.11. How many *additional* minutes must you use in one month for plan B to cost more than plan A?

Solution   Let m represent your additional minutes in one month. Write and solve an inequality.

$$0.45m + 45.99 > 0.40m + 49.99$$
$$0.05m > 4$$
$$m > 80$$

Plan B costs more when you use more than 80 additional minutes in one month.

Cell Phone Plans
Plan A:
$49.99 per month for 500 minutes plus $0.40 for each additional minute
Plan B:
$45.99 per month for 500 minutes plus $0.45 for each additional minute

Figure A.11

✓ *Checkpoint* *Audio-video solution in English & Spanish at LarsonPrecalculus.com.*

Rework Example 6 when plan A costs $54.99 per month for 500 minutes plus $0.35 for each additional minute.

EXAMPLE 7   **Accuracy of a Measurement**

You buy chocolates that cost $9.89 per pound. The scale used to weigh your bag is accurate to within $\frac{1}{32}$ pound. According to the scale, your bag weighs $\frac{1}{2}$ pound and costs $4.95. How much might you have been undercharged or overcharged?

Solution   Let x represent the actual weight of your bag. The difference of the actual weight and the weight shown on the scale is at most $\frac{1}{32}$ pound. That is, $|x - \frac{1}{2}| \le \frac{1}{32}$. You can solve this inequality as follows.

$$-\frac{1}{32} \le x - \frac{1}{2} \le \frac{1}{32}$$
$$\frac{15}{32} \le x \le \frac{17}{32}$$

The least your bag can weigh is $\frac{15}{32}$ pound, which would have cost $4.64. The most the bag can weigh is $\frac{17}{32}$ pound, which would have cost $5.25. So, you might have been overcharged by as much as $0.31 or undercharged by as much as $0.30.

✓ *Checkpoint* *Audio-video solution in English & Spanish at LarsonPrecalculus.com.*

Rework Example 7 when the scale is accurate to within $\frac{1}{64}$ pound.

Summarize   (Appendix A.6)

1. Describe how to use inequalities to represent intervals *(page A58, Example 1)*.

2. State the properties of inequalities *(page A59)*.

3. Describe how to solve a linear inequality *(pages A60 and A61, Examples 2–4)*.

4. Describe how to solve an absolute value inequality *(page A62, Example 5)*.

5. Describe a real-life example that uses an inequality *(page A63, Examples 6 and 7)*.

A.6 Exercises

Vocabulary: Fill in the blanks.

1. The set of all real numbers that are solutions of an inequality is the _____ _____ of the inequality.
2. The set of all points on the real number line that represents the solution set of an inequality is the _____ of the inequality.
3. It is sometimes possible to write two inequalities as one inequality, called a _____ inequality.
4. The symbol $\cup$ is the _____ symbol, which denotes the combining of two sets.

Skills and Applications

Intervals and Inequalities In Exercises 5–12, write an inequality that represents the interval. Then state whether the interval is bounded or unbounded.

5. $[0, 9)$
6. $(-7, 4)$
7. $[-1, 5]$
8. $(2, 10]$
9. $(11, \infty)$
10. $[-5, \infty)$
11. $(-\infty, -2)$
12. $(-\infty, 7]$

Solving a Linear Inequality In Exercises 13–42, solve the inequality. Then graph the solution set.

13. $4x < 12$
14. $10x < -40$
15. $-2x > -3$
16. $-6x > 15$
17. $x - 5 \geq 7$
18. $x + 7 \leq 12$
19. $2x + 7 < 3 + 4x$
20. $3x + 1 \geq 2 + x$
21. $2x - 1 \geq 1 - 5x$
22. $6x - 4 \leq 2 + 8x$
23. $4 - 2x < 3(3 - x)$
24. $4(x + 1) < 2x + 3$
25. $\frac{3}{4}x - 6 \leq x - 7$
26. $3 + \frac{2}{7}x > x - 2$
27. $\frac{1}{2}(8x + 1) \geq 3x + \frac{5}{2}$
28. $9x - 1 < \frac{3}{4}(16x - 2)$
29. $3.6x + 11 \geq -3.4$
30. $15.6 - 1.3x < -5.2$
31. $1 < 2x + 3 < 9$
32. $-9 \leq -2x - 7 < 5$
33. $0 < 3(x + 7) \leq 20$
34. $-1 \leq -(x - 4) < 7$
35. $-4 < \frac{2x - 3}{3} < 4$
36. $0 \leq \frac{x + 3}{2} < 5$
37. $-1 < \frac{-x - 2}{3} \leq 1$
38. $-1 \leq \frac{-3x + 5}{7} \leq 2$
39. $\frac{3}{4} > x + 1 > \frac{1}{4}$
40. $-1 < 2 - \frac{x}{3} < 1$
41. $3.2 \leq 0.4x - 1 \leq 4.4$
42. $1.6 < 0.3x + 1 < 2.8$

Solving an Absolute Value Inequality In Exercises 43–58, solve the inequality. Then graph the solution set. (Some inequalities have no solution.)

43. $|x| < 5$
44. $|x| \geq 8$
45. $\left|\frac{x}{2}\right| > 1$
46. $\left|\frac{x}{5}\right| > 3$
47. $|x - 5| < -1$
48. $|x - 7| < -5$
49. $|x - 20| \leq 6$
50. $|x - 8| \geq 0$
51. $|3 - 4x| \geq 9$
52. $|1 - 2x| < 5$
53. $\left|\frac{x - 3}{2}\right| \geq 4$
54. $\left|1 - \frac{2x}{3}\right| < 1$
55. $|9 - 2x| - 2 < -1$
56. $|x + 14| + 3 > 17$
57. $2|x + 10| \geq 9$
58. $3|4 - 5x| \leq 9$

Graphical Analysis In Exercises 59–68, use a graphing utility to graph the inequality and identify the solution set.

59. $6x > 12$
60. $3x - 1 \leq 5$
61. $5 - 2x \geq 1$
62. $20 < 6x - 1$
63. $4(x - 3) \leq 8 - x$
64. $3(x + 1) < x + 7$
65. $|x - 8| \leq 14$
66. $|2x + 9| > 13$
67. $2|x + 7| \geq 13$
68. $\frac{1}{2}|x + 1| \leq 3$

Graphical Analysis In Exercises 69–74, use a graphing utility to graph the equation. Use the graph to approximate the values of x that satisfy each inequality.

Equation	Inequalities	
69. $y = 2x - 3$	(a) $y \geq 1$	(b) $y \leq 0$
70. $y = \frac{2}{3}x + 1$	(a) $y \leq 5$	(b) $y \geq 0$
71. $y = -\frac{1}{2}x + 2$	(a) $0 \leq y \leq 3$	(b) $y \geq 0$
72. $y = -3x + 8$	(a) $-1 \leq y \leq 3$	(b) $y \leq 0$
73. $y = |x - 3|$	(a) $y \leq 2$	(b) $y \geq 4$
74. $y = \left|\frac{1}{2}x + 1\right|$	(a) $y \leq 4$	(b) $y \geq 1$

Finding an Interval In Exercises 75–80, find the interval on the real number line for which the radicand is nonnegative.

75. $\sqrt{x - 5}$
76. $\sqrt{x - 10}$
77. $\sqrt{x + 3}$
78. $\sqrt{3 - x}$
79. $\sqrt[4]{7 - 2x}$
80. $\sqrt[4]{6x + 15}$

81. **Think About It** The graph of $|x - 5| < 3$ can be described as all real numbers less than three units from 5. Give a similar description of $|x - 10| < 8$.

82. Think About It The graph of $|x - 2| > 5$ can be described as all real numbers more than five units from 2. Give a similar description of $|x - 8| > 4$.

Using Absolute Value In Exercises 83–90, use absolute value notation to define the interval (or pair of intervals) on the real number line.

83.

84.

85.

86.

87. All real numbers at least 10 units from 12

88. All real numbers at least five units from 8

89. All real numbers more than four units from -3

90. All real numbers no more than seven units from -6

Writing an Inequality In Exercises 91–94, write an inequality to describe the situation.

91. A company expects its earnings per share E for the next quarter to be no less than $4.10 and no more than $4.25.

92. The estimated daily oil production p at a refinery is greater than 2 million barrels but less than 2.4 million barrels.

93. The return r on an investment is expected to be no more than 8%.

94. The net income I of a company is expected to be no less than $239 million.

Physiology The maximum heart rate r (in beats per minute) of a person in normal health is related to the person's age A (in years) by the equation

$$r = 220 - A.$$

In Exercises 95 and 96, determine the interval in which the person's heart rate is from 50% to 85% of the maximum heart rate. (Source: American Heart Association)

95. a 20-year-old   **96.** a 40-year-old

97. Job Offers You are considering two job offers. The first job pays $13.50 per hour. The second job pays $9.00 per hour plus $0.75 per unit produced per hour. How many units must you produce per hour for the second job to pay more per hour than the first job?

98. Job Offers You are considering two job offers. The first job pays $3000 per month. The second job pays $1000 per month plus a commission of 4% of your gross sales. How much must you earn in gross sales for the second job to pay more per month than the first job?

99. Investment For what annual interest rates will an investment of $1000 grow to more than $1062.50 in 2 years? $[A = P(1 + rt)]$

100. Investment For what annual interest rates will an investment of $750 grow to more than $825 in 2 years? $[A = P(1 + rt)]$

101. Cost, Revenue, and Profit The revenue from selling x units of a product is $R = 115.95x$. The cost of producing x units is $C = 95x + 750$. To obtain a profit, the revenue must be greater than the cost. For what values of x will this product return a profit?

102. Cost, Revenue, and Profit The revenue from selling x units of a product is $R = 24.55x$. The cost of producing x units is $C = 15.4x + 150,000$. To obtain a profit, the revenue must be greater than the cost. For what values of x will this product return a profit?

103. Daily Sales A doughnut shop sells a dozen doughnuts for $7.95. Beyond the fixed costs (rent, utilities, and insurance) of $165 per day, it costs $1.45 for enough materials (flour, sugar, and so on) and labor to produce a dozen doughnuts. The daily profit from doughnut sales varies between $400 and $1200. Between what levels (in dozens of doughnuts) do the daily sales vary?

104. Weight Loss Program A person enrolls in a diet and exercise program that guarantees a loss of at least $1\frac{1}{2}$ pounds per week. The person's weight at the beginning of the program is 164 pounds. Find the maximum number of weeks before the person attains a goal weight of 128 pounds.

105. Data Analysis: IQ Scores and GPA The admissions office of a college wants to determine whether there is a relationship between IQ scores x and grade-point averages y after the first year of school. An equation that models the data the admissions office obtained is $y = 0.067x - 5.638$.

(a) Use a graphing utility to graph the model.

(b) Use the graph to estimate the values of x that predict a grade-point average of at least 3.0.

(c) Verify your estimate from part (b) algebraically.

(d) List other factors that may influence GPA.

106. Data Analysis: Weightlifting You want to determine whether there is a relationship between an athlete's weight x (in pounds) and the athlete's maximum bench-press weight y (in pounds). An equation that models the data you obtained is $y = 1.3x - 36$.

(a) Use a graphing utility to graph the model.

(b) Use the graph to estimate the values of x that predict a maximum bench-press weight of at least 200 pounds.

(c) Verify your estimate from part (b) algebraically.

(d) List other factors that might influence an individual's maximum bench-press weight.

107. Teachers' Salaries The average salaries S (in thousands of dollars) for public elementary school teachers in the United States from 2001 through 2011 can be modeled by

$$S = 1.36t + 41.1, \quad 1 \le t \le 11$$

where t represents the year, with $t = 1$ corresponding to 2001. *(Source: National Education Association)*

(a) According to the model, when was the average salary at least $45,000, but no more than $50,000?

(b) Use the model to predict when the average salary will exceed $62,000.

108. Milk Production Milk production M (in billions of pounds) in the United States from 2002 through 2010 can be modeled by

$$M = 3.24t + 161.5, \quad 2 \le t \le 10$$

where t represents the year, with $t = 2$ corresponding to 2002. *(Source: U.S. Department of Agriculture)*

(a) According to the model, when was the annual milk production greater than 178 billion pounds, but no more than 190 billion pounds?

(b) Use the model to predict when milk production will exceed 225 billion pounds.

109. Geometry The side of a square is measured as 10.4 inches with a possible error of $\frac{1}{16}$ inch. Using these measurements, determine the interval containing the possible areas of the square.

110. Geometry The side of a square is measured as 24.2 centimeters with a possible error of 0.25 centimeter. Using these measurements, determine the interval containing the possible areas of the square.

111. Accuracy of Measurement You stop at a self-service gas station to buy 15 gallons of 87-octane gasoline at $3.61 per gallon. The gas pump is accurate to within $\frac{1}{10}$ gallon. How much might you be undercharged or overcharged?

112. Accuracy of Measurement You buy six T-bone steaks that cost $8.99 per pound. The weight that is listed on the package is 5.72 pounds. The scale that weighed the package is accurate to within $\frac{1}{32}$ pound. How much might you be undercharged or overcharged?

113. Time Study A time study was conducted to determine the length of time required to perform a particular task in a manufacturing process. The times required by approximately two-thirds of the workers in the study satisfied the inequality

$$|t - 15.6| \le 1.9$$

where t is time in minutes. Determine the interval in which these times lie.

114. Error Tolerance

The protective cover layer of a Blu-ray Disc™ is 100 micrometers thick with an error tolerance of 3 micrometers. Write an absolute value inequality for the possible thicknesses of the cover layer. Then graph the solution set. *(Source: Blu-ray Disc™ Association)*

Exploration

True or False? In Exercises 115–117, determine whether the statement is true or false. Justify your answer.

115. If a, b, and c are real numbers, and $a < b$, then $a + c < b + c$.

116. If $a, b,$ and c are real numbers, and $a \le b$, then $ac \le bc$.

117. If $-10 \le x \le 8$, then $-10 \ge -x$ and $-x \ge -8$.

118. **HOW DO YOU SEE IT?** Michael Kasha of Florida State University used physics and mathematics to design a new classical guitar. The model he used for the frequency of the vibrations on a circular plate was $v = (2.6t/d^2)\sqrt{E/\rho}$, where v is the frequency (in vibrations per second), t is the plate thickness (in millimeters), d is the diameter of the plate, E is the elasticity of the plate material, and ρ is the density of the plate material. For fixed values of d, E, and ρ, the graph of the equation is a line (see figure).

Plate thickness (in millimeters)

(a) Estimate the frequency when the plate thickness is 2 millimeters.

(b) Approximate the interval for the frequency when the plate thickness is greater than or equal to 0 millimeters and less than 3 millimeters.

A.7 Errors and the Algebra of Calculus

■ Avoid common algebraic errors.
■ Recognize and use algebraic techniques that are common in calculus.

Algebraic Errors to Avoid

This section contains five lists of common algebraic errors: errors involving parentheses, errors involving fractions, errors involving exponents, errors involving radicals, and errors involving dividing out. Many of these errors are made because they seem to be the *easiest* things to do. For instance, the operations of subtraction and division are often believed to be commutative and associative. The following examples illustrate the fact that subtraction and division are neither commutative nor associative.

Not commutative	Not associative
$4 - 3 \neq 3 - 4$	$8 - (6 - 2) \neq (8 - 6) - 2$
$15 \div 5 \neq 5 \div 15$	$20 \div (4 \div 2) \neq (20 \div 4) \div 2$

Errors Involving Parentheses

Potential Error	Correct Form	Comment
$a - (x - b) = a - x - b$	$a - (x - b) = a - x + b$	Distribute to each term in parentheses.
$(a + b)^2 = a^2 + b^2$	$(a + b)^2 = a^2 + 2ab + b^2$	Remember the middle term when squaring binomials.
$\left(\frac{1}{2}a\right)\left(\frac{1}{2}b\right) = \frac{1}{2}(ab)$	$\left(\frac{1}{2}a\right)\left(\frac{1}{2}b\right) = \frac{1}{4}(ab) = \frac{ab}{4}$	$\frac{1}{2}$ occurs twice as a factor.
$(3x + 6)^2 = 3(x + 2)^2$	$(3x + 6)^2 = [3(x + 2)]^2$ $= 3^2(x + 2)^2$	When factoring, raise all factors to the power.

Errors Involving Fractions

Potential Error	Correct Form	Comment
$\dfrac{2}{x + 4} = \dfrac{2}{x} + \dfrac{2}{4}$	Leave as $\dfrac{2}{x + 4}$.	The fraction is already in simplest form.
$= \dfrac{bx}{a}$	$\dfrac{\left(\dfrac{x}{a}\right)}{b} = \left(\dfrac{x}{a}\right)\left(\dfrac{1}{b}\right) = \dfrac{x}{ab}$	Multiply by the reciprocal when dividing fractions.
$\dfrac{1}{a} + \dfrac{1}{b} = \dfrac{1}{a + b}$	$\dfrac{1}{a} + \dfrac{1}{b} = \dfrac{b + a}{ab}$	Use the property for adding fractions.
	$\dfrac{1}{3x} = \dfrac{1}{3} \cdot \dfrac{1}{x}$	Use the property for multiplying fractions.
	$(1/3)x = \dfrac{1}{3} \cdot x = \dfrac{x}{3}$	Be careful when expressing fractions in the form $1/a$.
	$(1/x) + 2 = \dfrac{1}{x} + 2 = \dfrac{1 + 2x}{x}$	Be careful when expressing fractions in the form $1/a$. Be sure to find a common denominator before adding fractions.

Errors Involving Exponents

Potential Error	Correct Form	Comment
$(x^2)^3 = x^5$	$(x^2)^3 = x^{2 \cdot 3} = x^6$	Multiply exponents when raising a power to a power.
$x^2 \cdot x^3 = x^6$	$x^2 \cdot x^3 = x^{2+3} = x^5$	Add exponents when multiplying powers with like bases.
$(2x)^3 = 2x^3$	$(2x)^3 = 2^3 x^3 = 8x^3$	Raise each factor to the power.
$\dfrac{1}{x^2 - x^3} = x^{-2} - x^{-3}$	Leave as $\dfrac{1}{x^2 - x^3}$.	Do not move term-by-term from denominator to numerator.

Errors Involving Radicals

Potential Error	Correct Form	Comment
$\sqrt{5x} = 5\sqrt{x}$	$\sqrt{5x} = \sqrt{5}\sqrt{x}$	Radicals apply to every factor inside the radical.
$\sqrt{x^2 + a^2} = x + a$	Leave as $\sqrt{x^2 + a^2}$.	Do not apply radicals term-by-term when adding or subtracting terms.
$\sqrt{-x + a} = -\sqrt{x - a}$	Leave as $\sqrt{-x + a}$.	Do not factor minus signs out of square roots.

Errors Involving Dividing Out

Potential Error	Correct Form	Comment
$\dfrac{a + bx}{a} = 1 + bx$	$\dfrac{a + bx}{a} = \dfrac{a}{a} + \dfrac{bx}{a} = 1 + \dfrac{b}{a}x$	Divide out common factors, not common terms.
$\dfrac{a + ax}{a} = a + x$	$\dfrac{a + ax}{a} = \dfrac{a(1 + x)}{a} = 1 + x$	Factor before dividing out common factors.
$1 + \dfrac{x}{2x} = 1 + \dfrac{1}{x}$	$1 + \dfrac{x}{2x} = 1 + \dfrac{1}{2} = \dfrac{3}{2}$	Divide out common factors.

A good way to avoid errors is to *work slowly, write neatly,* and *talk to yourself.* Each time you write a step, ask yourself why the step is algebraically legitimate. You can justify the step below because *dividing the numerator and denominator by the same nonzero number produces an equivalent fraction.*

$$\frac{2x}{6} = \frac{2 \cdot x}{2 \cdot 3} = \frac{x}{3}$$

EXAMPLE 1   **Describing and Correcting an Error**

Describe and correct the error. $\dfrac{1}{2x} + \dfrac{1}{3x} = \dfrac{1}{5x}$

Solution   Use the property for adding fractions: $\dfrac{1}{a} + \dfrac{1}{b} = \dfrac{b + a}{ab}$.

$$\frac{1}{2x} + \frac{1}{3x} = \frac{3x + 2x}{6x^2} = \frac{5x}{6x^2} = \frac{5}{6x}$$

✓ *Checkpoint* Audio-video solution in English & Spanish at LarsonPrecalculus.com.

Describe and correct the error. $\sqrt{x^2 + 4} = x + 2$

Some Algebra of Calculus

In calculus it is often necessary to take a simplified algebraic expression and rewrite it. See the following lists, taken from a standard calculus text.

Unusual Factoring

Expression	Useful Calculus Form	Comment
$\dfrac{5x^4}{8}$	$\dfrac{5}{8}x^4$	Write with fractional coefficient.
$\dfrac{x^2 + 3x}{-6}$	$-\dfrac{1}{6}(x^2 + 3x)$	Write with fractional coefficient.
$2x^2 - x - 3$	$2\left(x^2 - \dfrac{x}{2} - \dfrac{3}{2}\right)$	Factor out the leading coefficient.
$\dfrac{x}{2}(x + 1)^{-1/2} + (x + 1)^{1/2}$	$\dfrac{(x + 1)^{-1/2}}{2}[x + 2(x + 1)]$	Factor out the variable expression with the lesser exponent.

Writing with Negative Exponents

Expression	Useful Calculus Form	Comment
$\dfrac{9}{5x^3}$	$\dfrac{9}{5}x^{-3}$	Move the factor to the numerator and change the sign of the exponent.
$\dfrac{7}{\sqrt{2x - 3}}$	$7(2x - 3)^{-1/2}$	Move the factor to the numerator and change the sign of the exponent.

Writing a Fraction as a Sum

Expression	Useful Calculus Form	Comment
$\dfrac{x + 2x^2 + 1}{\sqrt{x}}$	$x^{1/2} + 2x^{3/2} + x^{-1/2}$	Divide each term of the numerator by $x^{1/2}$.
$\dfrac{1 + x}{x^2 + 1}$	$\dfrac{1}{x^2 + 1} + \dfrac{x}{x^2 + 1}$	Rewrite the fraction as a sum of fractions.
$\dfrac{2x}{x^2 + 2x + 1}$	$\dfrac{2x + 2 - 2}{x^2 + 2x + 1}$	Add and subtract the same term.
	$= \dfrac{2x + 2}{x^2 + 2x + 1} - \dfrac{2}{(x + 1)^2}$	Rewrite the fraction as a difference of fractions.
$\dfrac{x^2 - 2}{x + 1}$	$x - 1 - \dfrac{1}{x + 1}$	Use long division. (See Section 2.3.)
$\dfrac{x + 7}{x^2 - x - 6}$	$\dfrac{2}{x - 3} - \dfrac{1}{x + 2}$	Use the method of partial fractions. (See Section 7.4.)

Inserting Factors and Terms

Expression	Useful Calculus Form	Comment
$(2x - 1)^3$	$\dfrac{1}{2}(2x - 1)^3(2)$	Multiply and divide by 2.
$7x^2(4x^3 - 5)^{1/2}$	$\dfrac{7}{12}(4x^3 - 5)^{1/2}(12x^2)$	Multiply and divide by 12.
$\dfrac{4x^2}{9} - 4y^2 = 1$	$\dfrac{x^2}{9/4} - \dfrac{y^2}{1/4} = 1$	Write with fractional denominators.
$\dfrac{x}{x + 1}$	$\dfrac{x + 1 - 1}{x + 1} = 1 - \dfrac{1}{x + 1}$	Add and subtract the same term.

The next five examples demonstrate many of the steps in the preceding lists.

EXAMPLE 2 **Factors Involving Negative Exponents**

Factor $x(x + 1)^{-1/2} + (x + 1)^{1/2}$.

Solution When multiplying powers with like bases, you add exponents. When factoring, you are undoing multiplication, and so you *subtract* exponents.

$$x(x + 1)^{-1/2} + (x + 1)^{1/2} = (x + 1)^{-1/2}[x(x + 1)^0 + (x + 1)^1]$$
$$= (x + 1)^{-1/2}[x + (x + 1)]$$
$$= (x + 1)^{-1/2}(2x + 1)$$

✓ *Checkpoint* Audio-video solution in English & Spanish at LarsonPrecalculus.com.

Factor $x(x - 2)^{-1/2} + 3(x - 2)^{1/2}$.

Another way to simplify the expression in Example 2 is to multiply the expression by a fractional form of 1 and then use the Distributive Property.

$$x(x + 1)^{-1/2} + (x + 1)^{1/2} = [x(x + 1)^{-1/2} + (x + 1)^{1/2}] \cdot \frac{(x + 1)^{1/2}}{(x + 1)^{1/2}}$$
$$= \frac{x(x + 1)^0 + (x + 1)^1}{(x + 1)^{1/2}} = \frac{2x + 1}{\sqrt{x + 1}}$$

EXAMPLE 3 **Inserting Factors in an Expression**

Insert the required factor: $\dfrac{x + 2}{(x^2 + 4x - 3)^2} = (\quad)\dfrac{1}{(x^2 + 4x - 3)^2}(2x + 4)$.

Solution The expression on the right side of the equation is twice the expression on the left side. To make both sides equal, insert a factor of $\frac{1}{2}$.

$$\frac{x + 2}{(x^2 + 4x - 3)^2} = \left(\frac{1}{2}\right)\frac{1}{(x^2 + 4x - 3)^2}(2x + 4) \qquad \begin{array}{l}\text{Right side is multiplied}\\\text{and divided by 2.}\end{array}$$

✓ *Checkpoint* Audio-video solution in English & Spanish at LarsonPrecalculus.com.

Insert the required factor: $\dfrac{6x - 3}{(x^2 - x + 4)^2} = (\quad)\dfrac{1}{(x^2 - x + 4)^2}(2x - 1)$.

EXAMPLE 4 **Rewriting Fractions**

Explain why the two expressions are equivalent.

$$\frac{4x^2}{9} - 4y^2 = \frac{x^2}{9/4} - \frac{y^2}{1/4}$$

Solution To write the expression on the left side of the equation in the form given on the right side, multiply the numerator and denominator of each term by $\frac{1}{4}$.

$$\frac{4x^2}{9} - 4y^2 = \frac{4x^2}{9}\left(\frac{1/4}{1/4}\right) - 4y^2\left(\frac{1/4}{1/4}\right) = \frac{x^2}{9/4} - \frac{y^2}{1/4}$$

✓ **Checkpoint** Audio-video solution in English & Spanish at LarsonPrecalculus.com.

Explain why the two expressions are equivalent.

$$\frac{9x^2}{16} + 25y^2 = \frac{x^2}{16/9} + \frac{y^2}{1/25}$$

EXAMPLE 5 **Rewriting with Negative Exponents**

Rewrite each expression using negative exponents.

a. $\dfrac{-4x}{(1 - 2x^2)^2}$ b. $\dfrac{2}{5x^3} - \dfrac{1}{\sqrt{x}} + \dfrac{3}{5(4x)^2}$

Solution

a. $\dfrac{-4x}{(1 - 2x^2)^2} = -4x(1 - 2x^2)^{-2}$

b. $\dfrac{2}{5x^3} - \dfrac{1}{\sqrt{x}} + \dfrac{3}{5(4x)^2} = \dfrac{2}{5x^3} - \dfrac{1}{x^{1/2}} + \dfrac{3}{5(4x)^2}$

$$= \frac{2}{5}x^{-3} - x^{-1/2} + \frac{3}{5}(4x)^{-2}$$

✓ **Checkpoint** Audio-video solution in English & Spanish at LarsonPrecalculus.com.

Rewrite $\dfrac{-6x}{(1 - 3x^2)^2} + \dfrac{1}{\sqrt[3]{x}}$ using negative exponents.

EXAMPLE 6 **Rewriting a Fraction as a Sum of Terms**

Rewrite each fraction as the sum of three terms.

a. $\dfrac{x^2 - 4x + 8}{2x}$ b. $\dfrac{x + 2x^2 + 1}{\sqrt{x}}$

Solution

a. $\dfrac{x^2 - 4x + 8}{2x} = \dfrac{x^2}{2x} - \dfrac{4x}{2x} + \dfrac{8}{2x}$ b. $\dfrac{x + 2x^2 + 1}{\sqrt{x}} = \dfrac{x}{x^{1/2}} + \dfrac{2x^2}{x^{1/2}} + \dfrac{1}{x^{1/2}}$

$$= \frac{x}{2} - 2 + \frac{4}{x} \qquad\qquad\qquad = x^{1/2} + 2x^{3/2} + x^{-1/2}$$

✓ **Checkpoint** Audio-video solution in English & Spanish at LarsonPrecalculus.com.

Rewrite $\dfrac{x^4 - 2x^3 + 5}{x^3}$ as the sum of three terms.

A.7 Exercises

See CalcChat.com for tutorial help and worked-out solutions to odd-numbered exercises.

Vocabulary: Fill in the blanks.

1. To rewrite the expression $\dfrac{3}{x^5}$ using negative exponents, move x^5 to the _____ and change the sign of the exponent.

2. When dividing fractions, multiply by the _____.

Skills and Applications

Describing and Correcting an Error In Exercises 3–22, describe and correct the error.

3. $2x - (3y + 4) = 2x - 3y + 4$

4. $5z + 3(x - 2) = 5z + 3x - 2$

5. $\dfrac{4}{16x - (2x + 1)} = \dfrac{4}{14x + 1}$

6. $\dfrac{1 - x}{(5 - x)(-x)} = \dfrac{x - 1}{x(x - 5)}$

7. $(5z)(6z) = 30z$

8. $x(yz) = (xy)(xz)$

9. $a\left(\dfrac{x}{y}\right) = \dfrac{ax}{ay}$

10. $(4x)^2 = 4x^2$

11. $\sqrt{x + 9} = \sqrt{x} + 3$

12. $\sqrt{25 - x^2} = 5 - x$

13. $\dfrac{2x^2 + 1}{5x} = \dfrac{2x + 1}{5}$

14. $\dfrac{6x + y}{6x - y} = \dfrac{x + y}{x - y}$

15. $\dfrac{1}{a^{-1} + b^{-1}} = \left(\dfrac{1}{a + b}\right)^{-1}$

16. $\dfrac{1}{x + y^{-1}} = \dfrac{y}{x + 1}$

17. $(x^2 + 5x)^{1/2} = x(x + 5)^{1/2}$

18. $x(2x - 1)^2 = (2x^2 - x)^2$

19. $\dfrac{3}{x} + \dfrac{4}{y} = \dfrac{7}{x + y}$

20. $\dfrac{1}{2y} = (1/2)y$

21. $\dfrac{x}{2y} + \dfrac{y}{3} = \dfrac{x + y}{2y + 3}$

22. $5 + (1/y) = \dfrac{1}{5 + y}$

Inserting Factors in an Expression In Exercises 23–44, insert the required factor in the parentheses.

23. $\dfrac{5x + 3}{4} = \dfrac{1}{4}(\;\boxed{}\;)$

24. $\dfrac{7x^2}{10} = \dfrac{7}{10}(\;\boxed{}\;)$

25. $\dfrac{2}{3}x^2 + \dfrac{1}{3}x + 5 = \dfrac{1}{3}(\;\boxed{}\;)$

26. $\dfrac{3}{4}x + \dfrac{1}{2} = \dfrac{1}{4}(\;\boxed{}\;)$

27. $x^2(x^3 - 1)^4 = (\;\boxed{}\;)(x^3 - 1)^4(3x^2)$

28. $x(1 - 2x^2)^3 = (\;\boxed{}\;)(1 - 2x^2)^3(-4x)$

29. $2(y - 5)^{1/2} + y(y - 5)^{-1/2} = (y - 5)^{-1/2}(\;\boxed{}\;)$

30. $3t(6t + 1)^{-1/2} + (6t + 1)^{1/2} = (6t + 1)^{-1/2}(\;\boxed{}\;)$

31. $\dfrac{4x + 6}{(x^2 + 3x + 7)^3} = (\;\boxed{}\;)\dfrac{1}{(x^2 + 3x + 7)^3}(2x + 3)$

32. $\dfrac{x + 1}{(x^2 + 2x - 3)^2} = (\;\boxed{}\;)\dfrac{1}{(x^2 + 2x - 3)^2}(2x + 2)$

33. $\dfrac{3}{x} + \dfrac{5}{2x^2} - \dfrac{3}{2}x = (\;\boxed{}\;)(6x + 5 - 3x^3)$

34. $\dfrac{(x - 1)^2}{169} + (y + 5)^2 = \dfrac{(x - 1)^3}{169(\;\boxed{}\;)} + (y + 5)^2$

35. $\dfrac{25x^2}{36} + \dfrac{4y^2}{9} = \dfrac{x^2}{(\;\boxed{}\;)} + \dfrac{y^2}{(\;\boxed{}\;)}$

36. $\dfrac{5x^2}{9} - \dfrac{16y^2}{49} = \dfrac{x^2}{(\;\boxed{}\;)} - \dfrac{y^2}{(\;\boxed{}\;)}$

37. $\dfrac{x^2}{3/10} - \dfrac{y^2}{4/5} = \dfrac{10x^2}{(\;\boxed{}\;)} - \dfrac{5y^2}{(\;\boxed{}\;)}$

38. $\dfrac{x^2}{5/8} + \dfrac{y^2}{6/11} = \dfrac{8x^2}{(\;\boxed{}\;)} + \dfrac{11y^2}{(\;\boxed{}\;)}$

39. $x^{1/3} - 5x^{4/3} = x^{1/3}(\;\boxed{}\;)$

40. $3(2x + 1)x^{1/2} + 4x^{3/2} = x^{1/2}(\;\boxed{}\;)$

41. $(1 - 3x)^{4/3} - 4x(1 - 3x)^{1/3} = (1 - 3x)^{1/3}(\;\boxed{}\;)$

42. $\dfrac{1}{2\sqrt{x}} + 5x^{3/2} - 10x^{5/2} = \dfrac{1}{2\sqrt{x}}(\;\boxed{}\;)$

43. $\dfrac{1}{10}(2x + 1)^{5/2} - \dfrac{1}{6}(2x + 1)^{3/2} = \dfrac{(2x + 1)^{3/2}}{15}(\;\boxed{}\;)$

44. $\dfrac{3}{7}(t + 1)^{7/3} - \dfrac{3}{4}(t + 1)^{4/3} = \dfrac{3(t + 1)^{4/3}}{28}(\;\boxed{}\;)$

Rewriting with Negative Exponents In Exercises 45–50, rewrite the expression using negative exponents.

45. $\dfrac{7}{(x + 3)^5}$

46. $\dfrac{2 - x}{(x + 1)^{3/2}}$

47. $\dfrac{2x^5}{(3x + 5)^4}$

48. $\dfrac{x + 1}{x(6 - x)^{1/2}}$

49. $\dfrac{4}{3x} + \dfrac{4}{x^4} - \dfrac{7x}{\sqrt[3]{2x}}$

50. $\dfrac{x}{x - 2} + \dfrac{1}{x^2} + \dfrac{8}{3(9x)^3}$

Rewriting a Fraction as a Sum of Terms In Exercises 51–56, rewrite the fraction as a sum of two or more terms.

51. $\dfrac{x^2 + 6x + 12}{3x}$

52. $\dfrac{x^3 - 5x^2 + 4}{x^2}$

53. $\dfrac{4x^3 - 7x^2 + 1}{x^{1/3}}$

54. $\dfrac{2x^5 - 3x^3 + 5x - 1}{x^{3/2}}$

55. $\dfrac{3 - 5x^2 - x^4}{\sqrt{x}}$

56. $\dfrac{x^3 - 5x^4}{3x^2}$

Simplifying an Expression In Exercises 57–68, simplify the expression.

57. $\dfrac{-2(x^2-3)^{-3}(2x)(x+1)^3-3(x+1)^2(x^2-3)^{-2}}{[(x+1)^3]^2}$

58. $\dfrac{x^5(-3)(x^2+1)^{-4}(2x)-(x^2+1)^{-3}(5)x^4}{(x^5)^2}$

59. $\dfrac{(6x+1)^3(27x^2+2)-(9x^3+2x)(3)(6x+1)^2(6)}{[(6x+1)^3]^2}$

60. $\dfrac{(4x^2+9)^{1/2}(2)-(2x+3)(\frac{1}{2})(4x^2+9)^{-1/2}(8x)}{[(4x^2+9)^{1/2}]^2}$

61. $\dfrac{(x+2)^{3/4}(x+3)^{-2/3}-(x+3)^{1/3}(x+2)^{-1/4}}{[(x+2)^{3/4}]^2}$

62. $(2x-1)^{1/2}-(x+2)(2x-1)^{-1/2}$

63. $\dfrac{2(3x-1)^{1/3}-(2x+1)(\frac{1}{3})(3x-1)^{-2/3}(3)}{(3x-1)^{2/3}}$

64. $\dfrac{(x+1)(\frac{1}{2})(2x-3x^2)^{-1/2}(2-6x)-(2x-3x^2)^{1/2}}{(x+1)^2}$

65. $\dfrac{1}{(x^2+4)^{1/2}}\cdot\dfrac{1}{2}(x^2+4)^{-1/2}(2x)$

66. $\dfrac{1}{x^2-6}(2x)+\dfrac{1}{2x+5}(2)$

67. $(x^2+5)^{1/2}(\frac{3}{2})(3x-2)^{1/2}(3)$
$\qquad +(3x-2)^{3/2}(\frac{1}{2})(x^2+5)^{-1/2}(2x)$

68. $(3x+2)^{-1/2}(3)(x-6)^{1/2}(1)$
$\qquad +(x-6)^3(-\frac{1}{2})(3x+2)^{-3/2}(3)$

69. Athletics An athlete has set up a course for training as part of her regimen in preparation for an upcoming triathlon. She is dropped off by a boat 2 miles from the nearest point on shore. The finish line is 4 miles down the coast and 2 miles inland (see figure). She can swim 2 miles per hour and run 6 miles per hour. The time t (in hours) required for her to reach the finish line can be approximated by the model

$$t=\dfrac{\sqrt{x^2+4}}{2}+\dfrac{\sqrt{(4-x)^2+4}}{6}$$

where x is the distance down the coast (in miles) to the point at which she swims and then leaves the water to start her run.

(a) Find the times required for the triathlete to finish when she swims to the points $x=0.5$, $x=1.0,\ldots,x=3.5$, and $x=4.0$ miles down the coast.

(b) Use your results from part (a) to determine the distance down the coast that will yield the minimum amount of time required for the triathlete to reach the finish line.

(c) The expression below was obtained using calculus. It can be used to find the minimum amount of time required for the triathlete to reach the finish line. Simplify the expression.

$$\tfrac{1}{2}x(x^2+4)^{-1/2}+\tfrac{1}{6}(x-4)(x^2-8x+20)^{-1/2}$$

70. Verifying an Equation

(a) Verify that $y_1=y_2$ analytically.

$$y_1=x^2\left(\dfrac{1}{3}\right)(x^2+1)^{-2/3}(2x)+(x^2+1)^{1/3}(2x)$$

$$y_2=\dfrac{2x(4x^2+3)}{3(x^2+1)^{2/3}}$$

(b) Complete the table and demonstrate the equality in part (a) numerically.

x	-2	-1	$-\frac{1}{2}$	0	1	2	$\frac{5}{2}$
y_1							
y_2							

Exploration

71. Writing Write a paragraph explaining to a classmate why $\dfrac{1}{(x-2)^{1/2}+x^4}\neq(x-2)^{-1/2}+x^{-4}$.

72. Think About It You are taking a course in calculus, and for one of the homework problems you obtain the following answer.

$$\dfrac{1}{10}(2x-1)^{5/2}+\dfrac{1}{6}(2x-1)^{3/2}$$

The answer in the back of the book is

$$\dfrac{1}{15}(2x-1)^{3/2}(3x+1).$$

Show how the second answer can be obtained from the first. Then use the same technique to simplify each of the following expressions.

(a) $\dfrac{2}{3}x(2x-3)^{3/2}-\dfrac{2}{15}(2x-3)^{5/2}$

(b) $\dfrac{2}{3}x(4+x)^{3/2}-\dfrac{2}{15}(4+x)^{5/2}$

Answers to Odd-Numbered Exercises and Tests

Chapter 1

Section 1.1 *(page 8)*

1. Cartesian   **3.** Distance Formula

5.

7. $(-3, 4)$
9. Quadrant IV
11. Quadrant II
13. Quadrant III

15.

17. 13   **19.** $\sqrt{61}$

21. $\dfrac{\sqrt{277}}{6}$ **23.** (a) 5, 12, 13   (b) $5^2 + 12^2 = 13^2$

25. $\left(\sqrt{5}\right)^2 + \left(\sqrt{45}\right)^2 = \left(\sqrt{50}\right)^2$

27. Distances between the points: $\sqrt{29}$, $\sqrt{58}$, $\sqrt{29}$

29. (a)

31. (a)

(b) 8   (c) $(6, 1)$ (b) 10   (c) $(5, 4)$

33. (a)

35. (a)

(b) $2\sqrt{10}$ (c) $(2, 3)$ (b) $\sqrt{556.52}$
(c) $(-5.6, 8.6)$

37. $30\sqrt{41} \approx 192$ km   **39.** \$27,343.5 million

41. $(0, 1), (4, 2), (1, 4)$ **43.** $(-3, 6), (2, 10), (2, 4), (-3, 4)$

45. (a) 2000s   (b) 11.8%; 70.6%   (c) \$12.37

(d) Answers will vary. *Sample answer:* No, the prediction is
too high because it is likely that the percent increase over
a 7-year period (2009–2016) will be less than the percent
increase over a 16-year period (1995–2011).

47. $(2x_m - x_1, 2y_m - y_1)$

49. $\left(\dfrac{3x_1 + x_2}{4}, \dfrac{3y_1 + y_2}{4}\right)$, $\left(\dfrac{x_1 + x_2}{2}, \dfrac{y_1 + y_2}{2}\right)$,

$\left(\dfrac{x_1 + 3x_2}{4}, \dfrac{y_1 + 3y_2}{4}\right)$

51. (a)   (b)

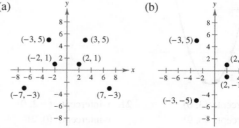

The point is reflected   The point is reflected
through the *y*-axis.   through the *x*-axis.

(c)   The point is reflected through
the origin.

53. No. It depends on the magnitudes of the quantities measured.
55. False. The Midpoint Formula would be used 15 times.
57. False. The polygon could be a rhombus.
59. Use the Midpoint Formula to prove that the diagonals of the
parallelogram bisect each other.

$$\left(\dfrac{b + a}{2}, \dfrac{c + 0}{2}\right) = \left(\dfrac{a + b}{2}, \dfrac{c}{2}\right)$$
$$\left(\dfrac{a + b + 0}{2}, \dfrac{c + 0}{2}\right) = \left(\dfrac{a + b}{2}, \dfrac{c}{2}\right)$$

Section 1.2 *(page 19)*

1. solution or solution point   **3.** intercepts
5. circle; (h, k); r **7.** (a) Yes   (b) Yes
9. (a) Yes   (b) No   **11.** (a) Yes   (b) No
13. (a) No   (b) Yes

15.

x	-1	0	1	2	$\frac{5}{2}$
y	7	5	3	1	0
(x, y)	$(-1, 7)$	$(0, 5)$	$(1, 3)$	$(2, 1)$	$\left(\frac{5}{2}, 0\right)$

17.

x	-1	0	1	2	3
y	4	0	-2	-2	0
(x, y)	$(-1, 4)$	$(0, 0)$	$(1, -2)$	$(2, -2)$	$(3, 0)$

19. x-intercept: $(3, 0)$
y-intercept: $(0, 9)$
21. x-intercept: $(-2, 0)$
y-intercept: $(0, 2)$
23. x-intercept: $\left(\frac{6}{5}, 0\right)$
y-intercept: $(0, -6)$
25. x-intercept: $(-4, 0)$
y-intercept: $(0, 2)$
27. x-intercept: $\left(\frac{7}{3}, 0\right)$
y-intercept: $(0, 7)$
29. x-intercepts: $(0, 0), (2, 0)$
y-intercept: $(0, 0)$
31. x-intercept: $(6, 0)$
y-intercepts: $\left(0, \pm\sqrt{6}\right)$
33. y-axis symmetry
35. Origin symmetry
37. Origin symmetry
39. x-axis symmetry
41.

43.

45. x-intercept: $\left(\frac{1}{3}, 0\right)$
y-intercept: $(0, 1)$
No symmetry

47. x-intercepts: $(0, 0), (2, 0)$
y-intercept: $(0, 0)$
No symmetry

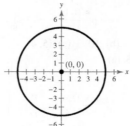

49. x-intercept: $\left(\sqrt[3]{-3}, 0\right)$
y-intercept: $(0, 3)$
No symmetry

51. x-intercept: $(3, 0)$
y-intercept: None
No symmetry

53. x-intercept: $(6, 0)$
y-intercept: $(0, 6)$
No symmetry

55. x-intercept: $(-1, 0)$
y-intercepts: $(0, \pm 1)$
x-axis symmetry

57.

Intercepts: $(6, 0), (0, 3)$

59.

Intercepts:
$(3, 0), (1, 0), (0, 3)$

61.

Intercept: $(0, 0)$

63.

Intercepts: $(-8, 0), (0, 2)$

65.

Intercepts: $(0, 0), (-6, 0)$

67.

Intercepts: $(-3, 0), (0, 3)$

69. $x^2 + y^2 = 16$ **71.** $(x - 2)^2 + (y + 1)^2 = 16$
73. $(x + 1)^2 + (y - 2)^2 = 5$
75. $(x - 3)^2 + (y - 4)^2 = 25$
77. Center: $(0, 0)$; Radius: 5   **79.** Center: $(1, -3)$; Radius: 3

81. Center: $\left(\frac{1}{2}, \frac{1}{2}\right)$; Radius: $\frac{3}{2}$ **83.**

85. (a)

(b) Answers will vary.

(c)

(d) $x = 86\frac{2}{3}, y = 86\frac{2}{3}$

(e) A regulation NFL playing field is 120 yards long and $53\frac{1}{3}$ yards wide. The actual area is 6400 square yards.

87. (a)

The model fits the data very well.

(b) 75.4 yr   (c) 1994

(d) 77.65 yr; The projection given by the model is slightly less.

(e) Answers will vary.

89. (a) $a = 1, b = 0$ (b) $a = 0, b = 1$

Section 1.3   *(page 31)*

1. linear   **3.** point-slope   **5.** perpendicular

7. linear extrapolation   **9.** (a) L_2 (b) L_3 (c) L_1

11.
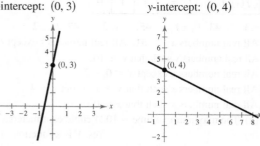

13. $\frac{3}{2}$

15. $m = 5$
y-intercept: $(0, 3)$

17. $m = -\frac{1}{2}$
y-intercept: $(0, 4)$

19. $m = 0$
y-intercept: $(0, 3)$

21. m is undefined.
There is no y-intercept.

23. $m = \frac{7}{6}$; y-intercept: $(0, -5)$ **25.**

$m = -\frac{3}{2}$

27.

$m = 2$

29.

$m = 0$

31.

m is undefined.

33.

$m = 0.15$

35. $(0, 1), (3, 1), (-1, 1)$ **37.** $(-8, 0), (-8, 2), (-8, 3)$

39. $(-4, 6), (-3, 8), (-2, 10)$

41. $(-3, -5), (1, -7), (5, -9)$

43. $y = 3x - 2$

45. $y = -2x$

47. $y = -\frac{1}{3}x + \frac{4}{3}$

49. $y = -\frac{1}{2}x - 2$

51. $x = 6$

53. $y = \frac{5}{2}$

$\left(4, \frac{5}{2}\right)$

55. $y = -\frac{3}{5}x + 2$

$(-5, 5)$

$(5, -1)$

57. $x = -8$

$(-8, 7)$

$(-8, 1)$

59. $y = -\frac{1}{2}x + \frac{3}{2}$

$\left(\frac{1}{2}, \frac{5}{4}\right)$

$\left(2, \frac{1}{2}\right)$

61. $y = 0.4x + 0.2$

$(1, 0.6)$

$(-2, -0.6)$

63. $y = -1$

$\left(\frac{1}{3}, -1\right)$ $(2, -1)$

65. Parallel
67. Neither
69. Perpendicular
71. Parallel

73. (a) $y = 2x - 3$ (b) $y = -\frac{1}{2}x + 2$
75. (a) $y = -\frac{3}{4}x + \frac{3}{8}$ (b) $y = \frac{4}{3}x + \frac{127}{72}$
77. (a) $y = 0$ (b) $x = -1$
79. (a) $y = x + 4.3$ (b) $y = -x + 9.3$
81. $3x + 2y - 6 = 0$ **83.** $12x + 3y + 2 = 0$
85. $x + y - 3 = 0$
87. (a) Sales increasing 135 units/yr   (b) No change in sales
(c) Sales decreasing 40 units/yr
89. 12 ft   **91.** $V(t) = -125t + 4165, \ 13 \le t \le 18$
93. C-intercept: fixed initial cost; Slope: cost of producing an additional laptop bag
95. $V(t) = -175t + 875, \ 0 \le t \le 5$
97. $F = 1.8C + 32$ or $C = \frac{5}{9}F - \frac{160}{9}$
99. (a) $C = 21t + 42,000$ (b) $R = 45t$
(c) $P = 24t - 42,000$ (d) 1750 h
101. False. The slope with the greatest magnitude corresponds to the steepest line.
103. Find the slopes of the lines containing each two points and use the relationship $m_1 = -1/m_2$.

105. No. The slope cannot be determined without knowing the scale on the y-axis. The slopes could be the same.
107. No. The slopes of two perpendicular lines have opposite signs (assume that neither line is vertical or horizontal).
109. The line $y = 4x$ rises most quickly, and the line $y = -4x$ falls most quickly. The greater the magnitude of the slope (the absolute value of the slope), the faster the line rises or falls.
111. $3x - 2y - 1 = 0$ **113.** $80x + 12y + 139 = 0$

Section 1.4   *(page 44)*

1. domain; range; function   **3.** implied domain
5. Yes, each input value has exactly one output value.
7. No, the input values 7 and 10 each have two different output values.
9. (a) Function
(b) Not a function, because the element 1 in A corresponds to two elements, -2 and 1, in B.
(c) Function
(d) Not a function, because not every element in A is matched with an element in B.
11. Not a function   **13.** Function   **15.** Function
17. Function   **19.** Function
21. (a) -1 (b) -9 (c) $2x - 5$
23. (a) 15   (b) $4t^2 - 19t + 27$ (c) $4t^2 - 3t - 10$
25. (a) 1   (b) 2.5   (c) $3 - 2|x|$
27. (a) $-\dfrac{1}{9}$ (b) Undefined   (c) $\dfrac{1}{y^2 + 6y}$
29. (a) 1   (b) -1 (c) $\dfrac{|x - 1|}{x - 1}$
31. (a) -1 (b) 2   (c) 6
33.

x	-2	-1	0	1	2
$f(x)$	1	-2	-3	-2	1

35.

x	-2	-1	0	1	2
$f(x)$	5	$\frac{9}{2}$	4	1	0

37. 5   **39.** $\frac{4}{3}$
41. ± 3 **43.** $0, \pm 1$ **45.** $-1, 2$ **47.** $0, \pm 2$
49. All real numbers x **51.** All real numbers t except $t = 0$
53. All real numbers y such that $y \ge 10$
55. All real numbers x except $x = 0, -2$
57. All real numbers s such that $s \ge 1$ except $s = 4$
59. All real numbers x such that $x > 0$
61. (a) The maximum volume is 1024 cubic centimeters.
(b)

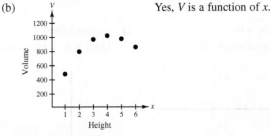

Yes, V is a function of x.

(c) $V = x(24 - 2x)^2, \ 0 < x < 12$
63. $A = \dfrac{P^2}{16}$ **65.** Yes, the ball will be at a height of 6 feet.

67. $A = \dfrac{x^2}{2(x-2)}, \quad x > 2$

69. 2004: 45.58%
2005: 50.15%
2006: 54.72%
2007: 59.29%
2008: 64.40%
2009: 67.75%
2010: 71.10%

71. (a) $C = 12.30x + 98{,}000$ (b) $R = 17.98x$
(c) $P = 5.68x - 98{,}000$

73. (a)   (b) $h = \sqrt{d^2 - 3000^2}$,
$d \geq 3000$

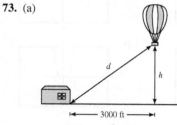

75. (a) $R = \dfrac{240n - n^2}{20}, \quad n \geq 80$

(b)

n	90	100	110	120	130	140	150
$R(n)$	\$675	\$700	\$715	\$720	\$715	\$700	\$675

The revenue is maximum when 120 people take the trip.

77. $3 + h, \; h \neq 0$ **79.** $3x^2 + 3xh + h^2 + 3, \; h \neq 0$

81. $-\dfrac{x+3}{9x^2}, \; x \neq 3$ **83.** $\dfrac{\sqrt{5x} - 5}{x - 5}$

85. $g(x) = cx^2; \; c = -2$ **87.** $r(x) = \dfrac{c}{x}; \; c = 32$

89. False. A function is a special type of relation.

91. False. The range is $[-1, \infty)$.

93. Domain of $f(x)$: all real numbers $x \geq 1$
Domain of $g(x)$: all real numbers $x > 1$
Notice that the domain of $f(x)$ includes $x = 1$ and the domain of $g(x)$ does not because you cannot divide by 0.

95. No; x is the independent variable, f is the name of the function.

97. (a) Yes. The amount you pay in sales tax will increase as the price of the item purchased increases.
(b) No. The length of time that you study will not necessarily determine how well you do on an exam.

Section 1.5 *(page 56)*

1. Vertical Line Test   **3.** decreasing
5. average rate of change; secant
7. Domain: $(-\infty, \infty)$; Range: $[-4, \infty)$
(a) 0 (b) -1 (c) 0 (d) -2
9. Domain: $(-\infty, \infty)$; Range: $(-2, \infty)$
(a) 0 (b) 1 (c) 2 (d) 3
11. Function   **13.** Not a function   **15.** $-\frac{5}{2}, 6$ **17.** 0
19. $0, \pm\sqrt{2}$ **21.** $\pm 3, 4$ **23.** $\frac{1}{2}$
25.   **27.**
$-\frac{5}{3}$ $-\frac{11}{2}$

29.   **31.** Increasing on $(-\infty, \infty)$
$\frac{1}{3}$

33. Increasing on $(-\infty, 0)$ and $(2, \infty)$; Decreasing on $(0, 2)$
35. Increasing on $(1, \infty)$; Decreasing on $(-\infty, -1)$
Constant on $(-1, 1)$
37. Increasing on $(-\infty, 0)$ and $(2, \infty)$; Constant on $(0, 2)$

39.   **41.**
Constant on $(-\infty, \infty)$ Decreasing on $(-\infty, 0)$
Increasing on $(0, \infty)$

43.   **45.**
Decreasing on $(-\infty, 1)$ Increasing on $(0, \infty)$

47.   **49.**
Relative minimum: Relative maximum:
$\left(\frac{1}{3}, -\frac{16}{3}\right)$ $(2.25, 10.125)$

51.   **53.**
Relative maximum: Relative minimum:
$(-0.15, 1.08)$ $(0.33, -0.38)$
Relative minimum:
$(2.15, -5.08)$

55.   **57.**
$(-\infty, 4]$ $[-3, 3]$

59.

$[1, \infty)$

61. The average rate of change from $x_1 = 0$ to $x_2 = 3$ is -2.

63. The average rate of change from $x_1 = 1$ to $x_2 = 3$ is 0.

65. (a)

(b) 484.75 million; The amount the U.S. Department of Energy spent for research and development increased by about \$484.75 million each year from 2005 to 2010.

67. (a) $s = -16t^2 + 64t + 6$

(b)

(e) Secant line: $16t + 6$

(f)

(c) Average rate of change $= 16$

(d) The slope of the secant line is positive.

69. (a) $s = -16t^2 + 120t$

(b)

(e) Secant line: $-8t + 240$

(f)

(c) Average rate of change $= -8$

(d) The slope of the secant line is negative.

71. Even; y-axis symmetry   **73.** Odd; origin symmetry

75. Neither; no symmetry

77.

Even

79.

Neither

81.

Neither

83. $h = 3 - 4x + x^2$ **85.** $L = 2 - \sqrt[3]{2y}$

87. (a)

(b) 30 W

89. (a) Ten thousands   (b) Ten millions   (c) Percents

91. (a)

(b)

(c)

(d)

(e)

(f)

All the graphs pass through the origin. The graphs of the odd powers of x are symmetric with respect to the origin, and the graphs of the even powers are symmetric with respect to the y-axis. As the powers increase, the graphs become flatter in the interval $-1 < x < 1$.

93. False. The function $f(x) = \sqrt{x^2 + 1}$ has a domain of all real numbers.

95. (a) $\left(\frac{5}{3}, -7\right)$ (b) $\left(\frac{5}{3}, 7\right)$

97.

Even

Neither

Odd

Neither

Even

Even

Odd

Equations of odd functions contain only odd powers of x. Equations of even functions contain only even powers of x. Odd functions have all variables raised to odd powers and even functions have all variables raised to even powers. A function that has variables raised to even and odd powers is neither odd nor even.

Section 1.6 (page 65)

1. g   2. i   3. h   4. a   5. b   6. e   7. f
8. c   9. d

11. (a) $f(x) = -2x + 6$
    (b)

13. (a) $f(x) = -1$
    (b)

15.

17.

19.

21.

23.

25.

27. (a) 2   (b) 2   (c) -4 (d) 3
29. (a) 8   (b) 2   (c) 6   (d) 13

31.

33.

35.

37.

39.

41. (a)

(b) Domain: $(-\infty, \infty)$
    Range: $[0, 2)$

43. (a) $W(30) = 420$; $W(40) = 560$;
    $W(45) = 665$; $W(50) = 770$

(b) $W(h) = \begin{cases} 14h, & 0 < h \le 45 \\ 21(h - 45) + 630, & h > 45 \end{cases}$

45.

Interval	Input Pipe	Drain Pipe 1	Drain Pipe 2
$[0, 5]$	Open	Closed	Closed
$[5, 10]$	Open	Open	Closed
$[10, 20]$	Closed	Closed	Closed
$[20, 30]$	Closed	Closed	Open
$[30, 40]$	Open	Open	Open
$[40, 45]$	Open	Closed	Open
$[45, 50]$	Open	Open	Open
$[50, 60]$	Open	Open	Closed

47. $f(t) = \begin{cases} t, & 0 \le t \le 2 \\ 2t - 2, & 2 < t \le 8 \\ \frac{1}{2}t + 10, & 8 < t \le 9 \end{cases}$

Total accumulation $= 14.5$ in.

49. False. A piecewise-defined function is a function that is defined by two or more equations over a specified domain. That domain may or may not include x- and y-intercepts.

Section 1.7 (page 72)

1. rigid   3. vertical stretch; vertical shrink
5. (a)   (b)

CHAPTER 1

7. (a)

(b)

9. (a)

(b)

(c)

(d)

(e)

(f)

(g)

11. (a) $y = x^2 - 1$ (b) $y = 1 - (x + 1)^2$
13. (a) $y = -|x + 3|$ (b) $y = |x - 2| - 4$
15. Horizontal shift of $y = x^3$; $y = (x - 2)^3$
17. Reflection in the x-axis of $y = x^2$; $y = -x^2$
19. Reflection in the x-axis and vertical shift of $y = \sqrt{x}$;
$y = 1 - \sqrt{x}$

21. (a) $f(x) = x^2$
(b) Reflection in the x-axis and vertical shift 12 units up
(c)   (d) $g(x) = 12 - f(x)$

23. (a) $f(x) = x^3$ (b) Vertical shift seven units up
(c)   (d) $g(x) = f(x) + 7$

25. (a) $f(x) = x^2$
(b) Vertical shrink of two-thirds and vertical shift four units up
(c)   (d) $g(x) = \frac{2}{3}f(x) + 4$

27. (a) $f(x) = x^2$
(b) Reflection in the x-axis, horizontal shift five units to the left, and vertical shift two units up
(c)   (d) $g(x) = 2 - f(x + 5)$

29. (a) $f(x) = \sqrt{x}$ (b) Horizontal shrink of one-third
(c)   (d) $g(x) = f(3x)$

31. (a) $f(x) = x^3$
(b) Vertical shift two units up and horizontal shift one unit to the right
(c)
(d) $g(x) = f(x - 1) + 2$

33. (a) $f(x) = x^3$
(b) Vertical stretch of three and horizontal shift two units to the right
(c)
(d) $g(x) = 3f(x - 2)$

35. (a) $f(x) = |x|$
(b) Reflection in the x-axis and vertical shift two units down
(c)
(d) $g(x) = -f(x) - 2$

37. (a) $f(x) = |x|$
(b) Reflection in the x-axis, horizontal shift four units to the left, and vertical shift eight units up
(c)
(d) $g(x) = -f(x + 4) + 8$

39. (a) $f(x) = |x|$
(b) Reflection in the x-axis, vertical stretch of two, horizontal shift one unit to the right, and vertical shift four units down
(c)
(d) $g(x) = -2f(x - 1) - 4$

41. (a) $f(x) = [\![x]\!]$
(b) Reflection in the x-axis and vertical shift three units up
(c)
(d) $g(x) = 3 - f(x)$

43. (a) $f(x) = \sqrt{x}$
(b) Horizontal shift nine units to the right
(c)
(d) $g(x) = f(x - 9)$

45. (a) $f(x) = \sqrt{x}$
(b) Reflection in the y-axis, horizontal shift seven units to the right, and vertical shift two units down
(c)
(d) $g(x) = f(7 - x) - 2$

47. $g(x) = (x - 3)^2 - 7$ **49.** $g(x) = (x - 13)^3$
51. $g(x) = -|x| + 12$ **53.** $g(x) = -\sqrt{-x + 6}$
55. (a) $y = -3x^2$ (b) $y = 4x^2 + 3$
57. (a) $y = -\frac{1}{2}|x|$ (b) $y = 3|x| - 3$
59. Vertical stretch of $y = x^3$; $y = 2x^3$
61. Reflection in the x-axis and vertical shrink of $y = x^2$; $y = -\frac{1}{2}x^2$
63. Reflection in the y-axis and vertical shrink of $y = \sqrt{x}$; $y = \frac{1}{2}\sqrt{-x}$
65. $y = -(x - 2)^3 + 2$ **67.** $y = -\sqrt{x} - 3$
69. (a)

(b) $H\left(\dfrac{x}{1.6}\right) = 0.00078x^2 + 0.003x - 0.029$, $16 \le x \le 160$;
Horizontal stretch
71. False. The graph of $y = f(-x)$ is a reflection of the graph of $f(x)$ in the y-axis.
73. True. $|-x| = |x|$ **75.** $(-2, 0), (-1, 1), (0, 2)$

77. (a)

g is a right shift of four units. h is a right shift of four units and a shift of three units up.

(b)

g is a left shift of one unit. h is a left shift of one unit and a shift of two units down.

(c)

g is a left shift of four units. h is a left shift of four units and a shift of two units up.

79. (a) $g(t) = \frac{3}{4} f(t)$ (b) $g(t) = f(t) + 10,000$
(c) $g(t) = f(t - 2)$

Section 1.8   *(page 81)*

1. addition; subtraction; multiplication; division

3.

5. (a) $2x$ (b) 4 (c) $x^2 - 4$
(d) $\dfrac{x + 2}{x - 2}$; all real numbers x except $x = 2$

7. (a) $x^2 + 4x - 5$ (b) $x^2 - 4x + 5$ (c) $4x^3 - 5x^2$
(d) $\dfrac{x^2}{4x - 5}$; all real numbers x except $x = \dfrac{5}{4}$

9. (a) $x^2 + 6 + \sqrt{1 - x}$ (b) $x^2 + 6 - \sqrt{1 - x}$
(c) $(x^2 + 6)\sqrt{1 - x}$
(d) $\dfrac{(x^2 + 6)\sqrt{1 - x}}{1 - x}$; all real numbers x such that $x < 1$

11. (a) $\dfrac{x + 1}{x^2}$ (b) $\dfrac{x - 1}{x^2}$ (c) $\dfrac{1}{x^3}$
(d) x; all real numbers x except $x = 0$

13. 3   **15.** 5   **17.** $9t^2 - 3t + 5$

19. 74   **21.** 26   **23.** $\frac{3}{5}$

25.

27.

$f(x), g(x)$

29.

$f(x), f(x)$

31. (a) $(x - 1)^2$ (b) $x^2 - 1$ (c) $x - 2$
33. (a) x (b) x (c) $x^9 + 3x^6 + 3x^3 + 2$
35. (a) $\sqrt{x^2 + 4}$ (b) $x + 4$
Domains of f and $g \circ f$: all real numbers x such that $x \geq -4$
Domains of g and $f \circ g$: all real numbers x

37. (a) $x + 1$ (b) $\sqrt{x^2 + 1}$
Domains of f and $g \circ f$: all real numbers x
Domains of g and $f \circ g$: all real numbers x such that $x \geq 0$

39. (a) $|x + 6|$ (b) $|x| + 6$
Domains of f, g, $f \circ g$, and $g \circ f$: all real numbers x

41. (a) $\dfrac{1}{x + 3}$ (b) $\dfrac{1}{x} + 3$
Domains of f and $g \circ f$: all real numbers x except $x = 0$
Domain of g: all real numbers x
Domain of $f \circ g$: all real numbers x except $x = -3$

43. (a) 3   (b) 0   **45.** (a) 0   (b) 4
47. $f(x) = x^2, g(x) = 2x + 1$ **49.** $f(x) = \sqrt[3]{x}, g(x) = x^2 - 4$
51. $f(x) = \dfrac{1}{x}, g(x) = x + 2$ **53.** $f(x) = \dfrac{x + 3}{4 + x}, g(x) = -x^2$
55. (a) $T = \frac{3}{4}x + \frac{1}{15}x^2$

(b)

(c) The braking function $B(x)$. As x increases, $B(x)$ increases at a faster rate than $R(x)$.

57. (a) $p(t) = d(t) + c(t)$
(b) $p(13)$ is the number of dogs and cats in the year 2013.
(c) $h(t) = \dfrac{d(t) + c(t)}{n(t)}$;
The function $h(t)$ represents the number of dogs and cats per capita.

59. (a) $r(x) = \dfrac{x}{2}$ (b) $A(r) = \pi r^2$
(c) $(A \circ r)(x) = \pi\left(\dfrac{x}{2}\right)^2$;
$(A \circ r)(x)$ represents the area of the circular base of the tank on the square foundation with side length x.

61. $g(f(x))$ represents 3 percent of an amount over \$500,000.
63. (a) $O(M(Y)) = 2\left(6 + \frac{1}{2}Y\right) = 12 + Y$
(b) Middle child is 8 years old; youngest child is 4 years old.
65. False. $(f \circ g)(x) = 6x + 1$ and $(g \circ f)(x) = 6x + 6$
67–69. Proofs

Section 1.9   *(page 90)*

1. inverse   **3.** range; domain   **5.** one-to-one
7. $f^{-1}(x) = \dfrac{1}{6}x$ **9.** $f^{-1}(x) = \dfrac{x - 1}{3}$ **11.** $f^{-1}(x) = x^3$

13. $f(g(x)) = f\left(-\dfrac{2x+6}{7}\right) = -\dfrac{7}{2}\left(-\dfrac{2x+6}{7}\right) - 3 = x$

$g(f(x)) = g\left(-\dfrac{7}{2}x - 3\right) = -\dfrac{2\left(-\frac{7}{2}x - 3\right) + 6}{7} = x$

15. $f(g(x)) = f\left(\sqrt[3]{x-5}\right) = \left(\sqrt[3]{x-5}\right)^3 + 5 = x$

$g(f(x)) = g(x^3 + 5) = \sqrt[3]{(x^3+5) - 5} = x$

17.

19.

21. (a) $f(g(x)) = f\left(\dfrac{x}{2}\right) = 2\left(\dfrac{x}{2}\right) = x$

$g(f(x)) = g(2x) = \dfrac{(2x)}{2} = x$

(b)

23. (a) $f(g(x)) = f\left(\dfrac{x-1}{7}\right) = 7\left(\dfrac{x-1}{7}\right) + 1 = x$

$g(f(x)) = g(7x+1) = \dfrac{(7x+1) - 1}{7} = x$

(b)

25. (a) $f(g(x)) = f\left(\sqrt[3]{8x}\right) = \dfrac{\left(\sqrt[3]{8x}\right)^3}{8} = x$

$g(f(x)) = g\left(\dfrac{x^3}{8}\right) = \sqrt[3]{8\left(\dfrac{x^3}{8}\right)} = x$

(b)

27. (a) $f(g(x)) = f(x^2 + 4),\ x \ge 0$

$= \sqrt{(x^2 + 4) - 4} = x$

$g(f(x)) = g\left(\sqrt{x-4}\right)$

$= \left(\sqrt{x-4}\right)^2 + 4 = x$

(b)

29. (a) $f(g(x)) = f\left(\sqrt{9-x}\right),\ x \le 9$

$= 9 - \left(\sqrt{9-x}\right)^2 = x$

$g(f(x)) = g(9 - x^2),\ x \ge 0$

$= \sqrt{9 - (9 - x^2)} = x$

(b)

31. (a) $f(g(x)) = f\left(-\dfrac{5x+1}{x-1}\right) = \dfrac{-\left(\dfrac{5x+1}{x-1}\right) - 1}{-\left(\dfrac{5x+1}{x-1}\right) + 5}$

$= \dfrac{-5x - 1 - x + 1}{-5x - 1 + 5x - 5} = x$

$g(f(x)) = g\left(\dfrac{x-1}{x+5}\right) = \dfrac{-5\left(\dfrac{x-1}{x+5}\right) - 1}{\dfrac{x-1}{x+5} - 1}$

$= \dfrac{-5x + 5 - x - 5}{x - 1 - x - 5} = x$

(b)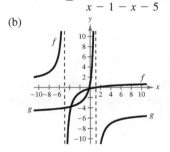

33. No

35.

x	-2	0	2	4	6	8
$f^{-1}(x)$	-2	-1	0	1	2	3

37. Yes   **39.** No

41.

The function has an inverse function.

43.

The function does not have an inverse function.

45. (a) $f^{-1}(x) = \dfrac{x + 3}{2}$

(b)

(c) The graph of f^{-1} is the reflection of the graph of f in the line $y = x$.

(d) The domains and ranges of f and f^{-1} are all real numbers.

47. (a) $f^{-1}(x) = \sqrt[5]{x + 2}$

(b)

(c) The graph of f^{-1} is the reflection of the graph of f in the line $y = x$.

(d) The domains and ranges of f and f^{-1} are all real numbers.

49. (a) $f^{-1}(x) = \sqrt{4 - x^2},\ 0 \le x \le 2$

(b)

(c) The graph of f^{-1} is the same as the graph of f.

(d) The domains and ranges of f and f^{-1} are all real numbers x such that $0 \le x \le 2$.

51. (a) $f^{-1}(x) = \dfrac{4}{x}$

(b)

(c) The graph of f^{-1} is the same as the graph of f.

(d) The domains and ranges of f and f^{-1} are all real numbers x except $x = 0$.

53. (a) $f^{-1}(x) = \dfrac{2x + 1}{x - 1}$

(b)

(c) The graph of f^{-1} is the reflection of the graph of f in the line $y = x$.

(d) The domain of f and the range of f^{-1} are all real numbers x except $x = 2$. The domain of f^{-1} and the range of f are all real numbers x except $x = 1$.

55. (a) $f^{-1}(x) = x^3 + 1$

(b)

(c) The graph of f^{-1} is the reflection of the graph of f in the line $y = x$.

(d) The domains and ranges of f and f^{-1} are all real numbers.

57. No inverse function   **59.** $g^{-1}(x) = 8x$

61. No inverse function   **63.** $f^{-1}(x) = \sqrt{x} - 3$

65. No inverse function   **67.** No inverse function

69. $f^{-1}(x) = \dfrac{x^2 - 3}{2},\ x \ge 0$ **71.** $f^{-1}(x) = \dfrac{5x - 4}{6 - 4x}$

73. $f^{-1}(x) = \sqrt{x} + 2$

The domain of f and the range of f^{-1} are all real numbers x such that $x \ge 2$. The domain of f^{-1} and the range of f are all real numbers x such that $x \ge 0$.

75. $f^{-1}(x) = x - 2$

The domain of f and the range of f^{-1} are all real numbers x such that $x \ge -2$. The domain of f^{-1} and the range of f are all real numbers x such that $x \ge 0$.

77. $f^{-1}(x) = \sqrt{x} - 6$

The domain of f and the range of f^{-1} are all real numbers x such that $x \ge -6$. The domain of f^{-1} and the range of f are all real numbers x such that $x \ge 0$.

79. $f^{-1}(x) = \dfrac{\sqrt{-2(x - 5)}}{2}$

The domain of f and the range of f^{-1} are all real numbers x such that $x \ge 0$. The domain of f^{-1} and the range of f are all real numbers x such that $x \le 5$.

81. $f^{-1}(x) = x + 3$

The domain of f and the range of f^{-1} are all real numbers x such that $x \ge 4$. The domain of f^{-1} and the range of f are all real numbers x such that $x \ge 1$.

83. 32   **85.** 600   **87.** $2\sqrt[3]{x+3}$

89. $\dfrac{x+1}{2}$ **91.** $\dfrac{x+1}{2}$

93. (a) $y = \dfrac{x-10}{0.75}$

x = hourly wage; y = number of units produced

(b) 19 units

95. False. $f(x) = x^2$ has no inverse function.

97.

x	1	3	4	6
y	1	2	6	7

x	1	2	6	7
$f^{-1}(x)$	1	3	4	6

99. Proof   **101.** $k = \frac{1}{4}$

103.

There is an inverse function $f^{-1}(x) = \sqrt{x-1}$ because the domain of f is equal to the range of f^{-1} and the range of f is equal to the domain of f^{-1}.

105. This situation could be represented by a one-to-one function if the runner does not stop to rest. The inverse function would represent the time in hours for a given number of miles completed.

Section 1.10 (page 100)

1. variation; regression   **3.** least squares regression

5. directly proportional

7. directly proportional   **9.** combined

11.

The model fits the data well.

13.

$y = \frac{1}{4}x + 3$

15.

$y = -\frac{1}{2}x + 3$

17. (a) and (b)

$y \approx t + 130$

(c) $y = 1.01t + 130.82$ (d) The models are similar.

19. $y = 7x$ **21.** $y = 205x$ **23.** $y = \frac{1}{5}x$ **25.** $y = 2\pi x$

27.

x	2	4	6	8	10
$y = x^2$	4	16	36	84	100

29.

x	2	4	6	8	10
$y = \frac{1}{2}x^3$	4	32	108	256	500

31.

x	2	4	6	8	10
$y = \dfrac{2}{x}$	1	$\frac{1}{2}$	$\frac{1}{3}$	$\frac{1}{4}$	$\frac{1}{5}$

33.

x	2	4	6	8	10
$y = \dfrac{10}{x^2}$	$\dfrac{5}{2}$	$\dfrac{5}{8}$	$\dfrac{5}{18}$	$\dfrac{5}{32}$	$\dfrac{1}{10}$

35. Inversely   **37.** $y = \dfrac{5}{x}$ **39.** $y = -\dfrac{7}{10}x$ **41.** $A = kr^2$

43. $y = \dfrac{k}{x^2}$ **45.** $F = \dfrac{kg}{r^2}$ **47.** $R = k(T - T_e)$

49. $R = kS(L - S)$

51. The surface area of a sphere varies directly as the square of its radius.

53. The area of a triangle is jointly proportional to its base and height.

55. $A = \pi r^2$ **57.** $y = \dfrac{28}{x}$ **59.** $F = 14rs^3$

61. $z = \dfrac{2x^2}{3y}$ **63.** $I = 0.035P$

65. Model: $y = \frac{33}{13}x$; 25.4 cm, 50.8 cm   **67.** $293\frac{1}{3}$ N

69. 39.47 lb   **71.** About 0.61 mi/h   **73.** 1470 J

75. (a)

(b) Yes. $k_1 = 4200$, $k_2 = 3800$, $k_3 = 4200$,
$k_4 = 4800$, $k_5 = 4500$

(c) $C = \dfrac{4300}{d}$

(d)

(e) About 1433 m

77. False. π is a constant, not a variable.

79. (a) y will change by a factor of four.

(b) y will change by a factor of one-fourth.

Review Exercises   *(page 106)*

1.

3. Quadrant IV

5.

Distance: $3\sqrt{13}$
Midpoint: $\left(1, \frac{3}{2}\right)$

7.

x	-2	-1	0	1	2
y	-11	-8	-5	-2	1

9.

x	-1	0	1	2	3	4
y	4	0	-2	-2	0	4

11. x-intercept: $\left(-\frac{7}{2}, 0\right)$ **13.** x-intercepts: $(1, 0)$, $(5, 0)$
y-intercept: $(0, 7)$ y-intercept: $(0, 5)$

15. x-intercept: $\left(\frac{1}{4}, 0\right)$
y-intercept: $(0, 1)$
No symmetry

17. *x*-intercepts: $(\pm\sqrt{5}, 0)$
y-intercept: $(0, 5)$
y-axis symmetry

19. *x*-intercept: $(\sqrt[3]{-3}, 0)$
y-intercept: $(0, 3)$
No symmetry

37. $y = \frac{2}{7}x + \frac{2}{7}$ **39.** (a) $y = \frac{5}{4}x - \frac{23}{4}$ (b) $y = -\frac{4}{5}x + \frac{2}{5}$
41. $S = 0.80L$ **43.** No   **45.** Yes
47. (a) 5   (b) 17   (c) $t^4 + 1$ (d) $t^2 + 2t + 2$
49. All real numbers *x* such that $-5 \le x \le 5$

21. *x*-intercept: $(-5, 0)$
y-intercept: $(0, \sqrt{5})$
No symmetry

23. Center: $(0, 0)$
Radius: 3

51. 16 ft/sec   **53.** $4x + 2h + 3,\ h \ne 0$
55. Function   **57.** $\frac{7}{3}, 3$ **59.** $-\frac{3}{8}$
61.

Increasing on $(0, \infty)$
Decreasing on $(-\infty, -1)$
Constant on $(-1, 0)$

25. Center: $(-2, 0)$
Radius: 4

27. $(x - 2)^2 + (y + 3)^2 = 13$

63.

65. 4   **67.** Even; *y*-axis symmetry

69. (a) $f(x) = -3x$
(b)

71.

29. slope: 3
y-intercept: 13

31. slope: 0
y-intercept: 6

73.

75. (a) $f(x) = x^2$
(b) Vertical shift nine units down
(c)

(d) $h(x) = f(x) - 9$

33.

$m = \frac{8}{9}$

35. $y = -\frac{1}{2}x + 2$

77. (a) $f(x) = \sqrt{x}$
(b) Reflection in the *x*-axis and vertical shift four units up
(d) $h(x) = -f(x) + 4$
(c)

79. (a) $f(x) = x^2$

(b) Reflection in the x-axis, horizontal shift two units to the left, and vertical shift three units up

(c)   (d) $h(x) = -f(x + 2) + 3$

81. (a) $f(x) = [\![x]\!]$

(b) Reflection in the x-axis and vertical shift six units up

(c)

(d) $h(x) = -f(x) + 6$

83. (a) $f(x) = [\![x]\!]$

(b) Horizontal shift nine units to the right and vertical stretch

(c)

(d) $h(x) = 5f(x - 9)$

85. (a) $x^2 + 2x + 2$

(b) $x^2 - 2x + 4$

(c) $2x^3 - x^2 + 6x - 3$

(d) $\dfrac{x^2 + 3}{2x - 1}$; all real numbers x except $x = \dfrac{1}{2}$

87. (a) $x - \dfrac{8}{3}$

(b) $x - 8$

Domains of f, g, $f \circ g$, and $g \circ f$: all real numbers x

89. $N(T(t)) = 100t^2 + 275$

The composition function $N(T(t))$ represents the number of bacteria in the food as a function of time.

91. $f^{-1}(x) = \dfrac{x - 8}{3}$

$f(f^{-1}(x)) = 3\left(\dfrac{x - 8}{3}\right) + 8 = x$

$f^{-1}(f(x)) = \dfrac{3x + 8 - 8}{3} = x$

93.

The function does not have an inverse function.

95. (a) $f^{-1}(x) = 2x + 6$

(b)

(c) The graphs are reflections of each other in the line $y = x$.

(d) Both f and f^{-1} have domains and ranges that are all real numbers.

97. $x > 4; f^{-1}(x) = \sqrt{\dfrac{x}{2} + 4}, x \neq 0$

99. (a) and (b)

$V = -1.453t + 17.58$

The model is a good fit for the actual data.

101. \$44.80

103. True. If $f(x) = x^3$ and $g(x) = \sqrt[3]{x}$, then the domain of g is all real numbers, which is equal to the range of f, and vice versa.

Chapter Test   *(page 109)*

1.

Midpoint: $\left(2, \frac{5}{2}\right)$; Distance: $\sqrt{89}$

2. $V(h) = 16\pi h$

3. No symmetry

4. y-axis symmetry

5. y-axis symmetry

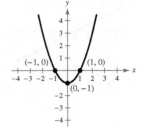

6. $(x - 1)^2 + (y - 3)^2 = 16$

7. $y = -2x + 1$ **8.** $y = -1.7x + 5.9$

9. (a) $5x + 2y - 8 = 0$ (b) $-2x + 5y - 20 = 0$

10. (a) $-\dfrac{1}{8}$ (b) $-\dfrac{1}{28}$ (c) $\dfrac{\sqrt{x}}{x^2 - 18x}$ **11.** $x \le 3$

12. (a) $0, \pm 0.4314$

(b)

(c) Increasing on $(-0.31, 0)$, $(0.31, \infty)$
Decreasing on $(-\infty, -0.31)$, $(0, 0.31)$

(d) Even

13. (a) $0, 3$

(b)

(c) Increasing on $(-\infty, 2)$
Decreasing on $(2, 3)$

(d) Neither

14. (a) -5

(b)

(c) Increasing on $(-5, \infty)$
Decreasing on $(-\infty, -5)$

(d) Neither

15.

16. Reflection in the x-axis of $y = [\![x]\!]$

17. Reflection in the x-axis, horizontal shift, and vertical shift of $y = \sqrt{x}$

18. Reflection in the x-axis, vertical stretch, horizontal shift, and vertical shift of $y = x^3$

19. (a) $2x^2 - 4x - 2$ (b) $4x^2 + 4x - 12$
(c) $-3x^4 - 12x^3 + 22x^2 + 28x - 35$
(d) $\dfrac{3x^2 - 7}{-x^2 - 4x + 5}$, $x \ne -5, 1$
(e) $3x^4 + 24x^3 + 18x^2 - 120x + 68$
(f) $-9x^4 + 30x^2 - 16$

20. (a) $\dfrac{1 + 2x^{3/2}}{x}$, $x > 0$ (b) $\dfrac{1 - 2x^{3/2}}{x}$, $x > 0$
(c) $\dfrac{2\sqrt{x}}{x}$, $x > 0$ (d) $\dfrac{1}{2x^{3/2}}$, $x > 0$
(e) $\dfrac{\sqrt{x}}{2x}$, $x > 0$ (f) $\dfrac{2\sqrt{x}}{x}$, $x > 0$

21. $f^{-1}(x) = \sqrt[3]{x - 8}$ **22.** No inverse
23. $f^{-1}(x) = \left(\tfrac{1}{3}x\right)^{2/3}$, $x \ge 0$ **24.** $v = 6\sqrt{s}$
25. $A = \dfrac{25}{6}xy$ **26.** $b = \dfrac{48}{a}$

Problem Solving (page 111)

1. (a) $W_1 = 2000 + 0.07S$ (b) $W_2 = 2300 + 0.05S$
(c)

Both jobs pay the same monthly salary when sales equal $15,000.

(d) No. Job 1 would pay $3400 and job 2 would pay $3300.

3. (a) The function will be even.
(b) The function will be odd.
(c) The function will be neither even nor odd.

5. $f(x) = a_{2n}x^{2n} + a_{2n-2}x^{2n-2} + \cdots + a_2x^2 + a_0$
$f(-x) = a_{2n}(-x)^{2n} + a_{2n-2}(-x)^{2n-2}$
$\qquad\qquad + \cdots + a_2(-x)^2 + a_0$
$\qquad = f(x)$

7. (a) $81\tfrac{2}{3}$ h
(b) $25\tfrac{5}{7}$ mi/h
(c) $y = \dfrac{-180}{7}x + 3400$

Domain: $0 \le x \le \dfrac{1190}{9}$

Range: $0 \le y \le 3400$

(d)

9. (a) $(f \circ g)(x) = 4x + 24$ (b) $(f \circ g)^{-1}(x) = \tfrac{1}{4}x - 6$
(c) $f^{-1}(x) = \tfrac{1}{4}x$; $g^{-1}(x) = x - 6$
(d) $(g^{-1} \circ f^{-1})(x) = \tfrac{1}{4}x - 6$; They are the same.
(e) $(f \circ g)(x) = 8x^3 + 1$; $(f \circ g)^{-1}(x) = \tfrac{1}{2}\sqrt[3]{x - 1}$;
$f^{-1}(x) = \sqrt[3]{x - 1}$; $g^{-1}(x) = \tfrac{1}{2}x$;
$(g^{-1} \circ f^{-1})(x) = \tfrac{1}{2}\sqrt[3]{x - 1}$
(f) Answers will vary.
(g) $(f \circ g)^{-1}(x) = (g^{-1} \circ f^{-1})(x)$

11. (a)   (b)

(c)   (d)

(e)   (f)

13. Proof

15. (a)

x	-4	-2	0	4
$f(f^{-1}(x))$	-4	-2	0	4

(b)

x	-3	-2	0	1
$(f+f^{-1})(x)$	5	1	-3	-5

(c)

x	-3	-2	0	1
$(f \cdot f^{-1})(x)$	4	0	2	6

(d)

x	-4	-3	0	4
$|f^{-1}(x)|$	2	1	1	3

Chapter 2

Section 2.1 (page 120)

1. polynomial   **3.** quadratic; parabola
5. positive; minimum   **7.** e   **8.** c   **9.** b
10. a   **11.** f   **12.** d

13. (a)   (b)

Vertical shrink   Vertical shrink and
                          reflection in the x-axis

(c)   (d)

Vertical stretch   Vertical stretch and
                          reflection in the x-axis

15. (a)   (b)

Horizontal shift one unit   Horizontal shrink and
to the right   vertical shift one unit up

(c)   (d)

Horizontal stretch and   Horizontal shift three units
vertical shift three units   to the left
down

17. $f(x) = (x-3)^2 - 9$ **19.** $h(x) = (x-4)^2$

Vertex: $(3, -9)$ Vertex: $(4, 0)$
Axis of symmetry: $x = 3$ Axis of symmetry: $x = 4$
x-intercepts: $(0, 0), (6, 0)$ x-intercept: $(4, 0)$

21. $f(x) = (x + 4)^2 - 3$

Vertex: $(-4, -3)$
Axis of symmetry: $x = -4$
x-intercepts: $(-4 \pm \sqrt{3}, 0)$

23. $f(x) = (x - 7)^2 + 5$

Vertex: $(7, 5)$
Axis of symmetry: $x = 7$
No x-intercept

25. $f(x) = (x + 17)^2$

Vertex: $(-17, 0)$
Axis of symmetry: $x = -17$
x-intercept: $(-17, 0)$

27. $f(x) = \left(x - \frac{1}{2}\right)^2 + 1$

Vertex: $\left(\frac{1}{2}, 1\right)$
Axis of symmetry: $x = \frac{1}{2}$
No x-intercept

29. $f(x) = -(x - 1)^2 + 6$

Vertex: $(1, 6)$
Axis of symmetry: $x = 1$
x-intercepts: $\left(1 \pm \sqrt{6}, 0\right)$

31. $h(x) = 4\left(x - \frac{1}{2}\right)^2 + 20$

Vertex: $\left(\frac{1}{2}, 20\right)$
Axis of symmetry: $x = \frac{1}{2}$
No x-intercept

33. $f(x) = \frac{1}{4}(x - 4)^2 - 16$

Vertex: $(4, -16)$
Axis of symmetry: $x = 4$
x-intercepts: $(-4, 0), (12, 0)$

35.

Vertex: $(-1, 4)$
Axis of symmetry: $x = -1$
x-intercepts: $(1, 0), (-3, 0)$

37.

Vertex: $(-4, -5)$
Axis of symmetry: $x = -4$
x-intercepts: $\left(-4 \pm \sqrt{5}, 0\right)$

39.

Vertex: $(4, 0)$
Axis of symmetry: $x = 4$
x-intercept: $(4, 0)$

41.

Vertex: $(-2, -3)$
Axis of symmetry: $x = -2$
x-intercepts: $\left(-2 \pm \sqrt{6}, 0\right)$

43. $y = -(x + 1)^2 + 4$
45. $y = -2(x + 2)^2 + 2$
47. $f(x) = (x + 2)^2 + 5$
49. $f(x) = 4(x - 1)^2 - 2$
51. $f(x) = \frac{3}{4}(x - 5)^2 + 12$
53. $f(x) = -\frac{24}{49}\left(x + \frac{1}{4}\right)^2 + \frac{3}{2}$
55. $f(x) = -\frac{16}{3}\left(x + \frac{5}{2}\right)^2$
57. $(5, 0), (-1, 0)$

59.

$(0, 0), (4, 0)$

61.

$(3, 0), (6, 0)$

63.

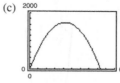

$\left(-\frac{5}{2}, 0\right), (6, 0)$

65. $f(x) = x^2 - 2x - 3$
$g(x) = -x^2 + 2x + 3$

67. $f(x) = x^2 - 10x$
$g(x) = -x^2 + 10x$

69. $f(x) = 2x^2 + 7x + 3$
$g(x) = -2x^2 - 7x - 3$

71. 55, 55   **73.** 12, 6   **75.** 16 ft   **77.** 20 fixtures
79. (a) \$14,000,000; \$14,375,000; \$13,500,000
(b) \$24; \$14,400,000; Answers will vary.
81. (a) $A = \dfrac{8x(50 - x)}{3}$

(b)

x	5	10	15	20	25	30
a	600	$1066\frac{2}{3}$	1400	1600	$1666\frac{2}{3}$	1600

$x = 25$ ft, $y = 33\frac{1}{3}$ ft

(c)

(d) $A = -\frac{8}{3}(x - 25)^2 + \frac{5000}{3}$
(e) They are identical.

$x = 25$ ft, $y = 33\frac{1}{3}$ ft

CHAPTER 2

83. (a) $R = -100x^2 + 3500x, \quad 15 \le x \le 20$
    (b) \$17.50; \$30,625

85. (a)

    (b) 4075 cigarettes; Yes, the warning had an effect because the maximum consumption occurred in 1966.
    (c) 7366 cigarettes per year; 20 cigarettes per day

87. True. The equation has no real solutions, so the graph has no x-intercepts.

89. $b = \pm 20$ **91.** $b = \pm 8$

93. $f(x) = a\left(x + \dfrac{b}{2a}\right)^2 + \dfrac{4ac - b^2}{4a}$ **95.** Proof

Section 2.2   (page 133)

1. continuous   **3.** $n; n - 1$ **5.** touches; crosses

7. standard   **9.** c   **10.** f   **11.** a   **12.** e

13. d   **14.** b

15. (a)   (b)

17. (a)   (b)

    (c)   (d)

(e)   (f)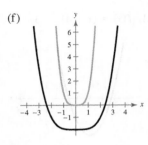

19. Falls to the left, rises to the right
21. Falls to the left, falls to the right
23. Rises to the left, falls to the right
25. Rises to the left, falls to the right
27. Rises to the left, falls to the right
29. Falls to the left, falls to the right

31.   **33.**

35. (a) ± 6
    (b) Odd multiplicity
    (c) 1
    (d)

37. (a) 3
    (b) Even multiplicity
    (c) 1
    (d)

39. (a) $-2, 1$
    (b) Odd multiplicity
    (c) 1
    (d)

41. (a) $0, 2 \pm \sqrt{3}$
    (b) Odd multiplicity
    (c) 2
    (d)

43. (a) $0, 4$
    (b) 0, odd multiplicity; 4, even multiplicity
    (c) 2
    (d)

45. (a) $0, \pm\sqrt{3}$
    (b) 0, odd multiplicity; $\pm\sqrt{3}$, even multiplicity
    (c) 4
    (d)

47. (a) No real zero
    (b) No multiplicity
    (c) 1
    (d)

49. (a) $\pm 2, -3$
    (b) Odd multiplicity
    (c) 2
    (d)

51. (a)

(b) x-intercepts: $(0, 0), \left(\frac{5}{2}, 0\right)$
(c) $x = 0, \frac{5}{2}$
(d) The answers in part (c) match the x-intercepts.

53. (a)

(b) x-intercepts: $(0, 0), (\pm 1, 0), (\pm 2, 0)$
(c) $x = 0, 1, -1, 2, -2$
(d) The answers in part (c) match the x-intercepts.

55. $f(x) = x^2 - 8x$ **57.** $f(x) = x^2 + 4x - 12$
59. $f(x) = x^3 + 9x^2 + 20x$
61. $f(x) = x^4 - 4x^3 - 9x^2 + 36x$ **63.** $f(x) = x^2 - 2x - 2$
65. $f(x) = x^2 + 6x + 9$ **67.** $f(x) = x^3 + 4x^2 - 5x$
69. $f(x) = x^3 - 3x$ **71.** $f(x) = x^4 + x^3 - 15x^2 + 23x - 10$
73. $f(x) = x^5 + 16x^4 + 96x^3 + 256x^2 + 256x$

75. (a) Falls to the left, rises to the right
(b) $0, 5, -5$
(c) Answers will vary.
(d)

77. (a) Rises to the left, rises to the right
(b) No zeros
(c) Answers will vary.
(d)

79. (a) Falls to the left, rises to the right
(b) $0, 2$
(c) Answers will vary.
(d)

81. (a) Falls to the left, rises to the right
(b) $0, 2, 3$
(c) Answers will vary.
(d)

83. (a) Rises to the left, falls to the right
(b) $-5, 0$
(c) Answers will vary.
(d)

85. (a) Falls to the left, rises to the right
(b) $0, 4$
(c) Answers will vary.
(d)

87. (a) Falls to the left, falls to the right
(b) ± 2 (c) Answers will vary.
(d)

89.

Zeros: $0, \pm 4$, odd multiplicity

91.

Zeros: -1, even multiplicity $3, \frac{9}{2}$, odd multiplicity

93. (a) $[-1, 0], [1, 2], [2, 3]$
(b) About $-0.879, 1.347, 2.532$
95. (a) $[-2, -1], [0, 1]$ (b) About $-1.585, 0.779$
97. (a) $V(x) = x(36 - 2x)^2$ (b) Domain: $0 < x < 18$
(c)

(d)

6 in. $\times$ 24 in. $\times$ 24 in.

$x = 6$; The results are the same.

99. (a) $A = -2x^2 + 12x$ (b) $V = -384x^2 + 2304x$
(c) 0 in. $< x < 6$ in.
(d)

When $x = 3$, the volume is maximum at $V = 3456$; dimensions of gutter are 3 in. $\times$ 6 in. $\times$ 3 in.
(e)

The maximum value is the same.
(f) No. Answers will vary.

101. (a) Relative maximum: $(5.01, 655.75)$
Relative minimum: $(9.25, 417.42)$
(b) Increasing: $(3, 5.01), (9.25, 10)$
Decreasing: $(5.01, 9.25)$
(c) Answers will vary.

103. $x \approx 200$

105. False. A fifth-degree polynomial can have at most four turning points.

107. False. The function $f(x) = (x - 2)^2$ has one turning point and two real (repeated) zeros.

109. False. $f(x) = -x^3$ rises to the left.

CHAPTER 2

111. True. The leading coefficient is negative and the degree is odd.

113. Answers will vary. *Sample answers:*

$a_4 < 0$

$a_4 > 0$

115.

(a) Vertical shift of two units; Even
(b) Horizontal shift of two units; Neither
(c) Reflection in the y-axis; Even
(d) Reflection in the x-axis; Even
(e) Horizontal stretch; Even
(f) Vertical shrink; Even
(g) $g(x) = x^3, x \geq 0$; Neither
(h) $g(x) = x^{16}$; Even

117. (a)

Zeros: 3
Relative minimum: 1
Relative maximum: 1
The number of zeros is the same as the degree, and the number of extrema is one less than the degree.

(b)

Zeros: 4
Relative minima: 2
Relative maximum: 1
The number of zeros is the same as the degree, and the number of extrema is one less than the degree.

(c)

Zeros: 3
Relative minimum: 1
Relative maximum: 1
The number of zeros and the number of extrema are both less than the degree.

Section 2.3 *(page 144)*

1. $f(x)$: dividend; $d(x)$: divisor; $q(x)$: quotient; $r(x)$: remainder

3. improper   **5.** Factor   **7.** Answers will vary.

9. (a) and (b)

(c) Answers will vary.

11. $2x + 4, \quad x \neq -3$

13. $x^2 - 3x + 1, \quad x \neq -\frac{5}{4}$ **15.** $x^3 + 3x^2 - 1, \quad x \neq -2$

17. $x^2 + 3x + 9, \quad x \neq 3$ **19.** $7 - \dfrac{11}{x + 2}$

21. $x - \dfrac{x + 9}{x^2 + 1}$ **23.** $2x - 8 + \dfrac{x - 1}{x^2 + 1}$

25. $x + 3 + \dfrac{6x^2 - 8x + 3}{(x - 1)^3}$ **27.** $3x^2 - 2x + 5, \quad x \neq 5$

29. $6x^2 + 25x + 74 + \dfrac{248}{x - 3}$ **31.** $4x^2 - 9, \quad x \neq -2$

33. $-x^2 + 10x - 25, \quad x \neq -10$

35. $5x^2 + 14x + 56 + \dfrac{232}{x - 4}$

37. $10x^3 + 10x^2 + 60x + 360 + \dfrac{1360}{x - 6}$

39. $x^2 - 8x + 64, \quad x \neq -8$

41. $-3x^3 - 6x^2 - 12x - 24 - \dfrac{48}{x - 2}$

43. $-x^3 - 6x^2 - 36x - 36 - \dfrac{216}{x - 6}$

45. $4x^2 + 14x - 30, \quad x \neq -\frac{1}{2}$

47. $f(x) = (x - 4)(x^2 + 3x - 2) + 3, \quad f(4) = 3$

49. $f(x) = \left(x + \frac{2}{3}\right)(15x^3 - 6x + 4) + \frac{34}{3}, \quad f\left(-\frac{2}{3}\right) = \frac{34}{3}$

51. $f(x) = \left(x - \sqrt{2}\right)\left[x^2 + \left(3 + \sqrt{2}\right)x + 3\sqrt{2}\right] - 8, \quad f\left(\sqrt{2}\right) = -8$

53. $f(x) = \left(x - 1 + \sqrt{3}\right)\left[-4x^2 + \left(2 + 4\sqrt{3}\right)x + \left(2 + 2\sqrt{3}\right)\right], \quad f\left(1 - \sqrt{3}\right) = 0$

55. (a) -2 (b) 1 (c) $-\frac{1}{4}$ (d) 5

57. (a) -35 (b) -22 (c) -10 (d) -211

59. $(x - 2)(x + 3)(x - 1)$; Solutions: $2, -3, 1$

61. $(2x - 1)(x - 5)(x - 2)$; Solutions: $\frac{1}{2}, 5, 2$

63. $\left(x + \sqrt{3}\right)\left(x - \sqrt{3}\right)(x + 2)$; Solutions: $-\sqrt{3}, \sqrt{3}, -2$

65. $(x - 1)\left(x - 1 - \sqrt{3}\right)\left(x - 1 + \sqrt{3}\right)$; Solutions: $1, 1 + \sqrt{3}, 1 - \sqrt{3}$

67. (a) Answers will vary.   (b) $2x - 1$
(c) $f(x) = (2x - 1)(x + 2)(x - 1)$ (d) $\frac{1}{2}, -2, 1$
(e)

69. (a) Answers will vary.   (b) $(x - 1), (x - 2)$
(c) $f(x) = (x - 1)(x - 2)(x - 5)(x + 4)$ (d) $1, 2, 5, -4$
(e)

71. (a) Answers will vary.   (b) $x + 7$

(c) $f(x) = (x + 7)(2x + 1)(3x - 2)$ (d) $-7, -\frac{1}{2}, \frac{2}{3}$
(e)

73. (a) Answers will vary.   (b) $x - \sqrt{5}$
(c) $f(x) = \left(x - \sqrt{5}\right)\left(x + \sqrt{5}\right)(2x - 1)$ (d) $\pm\sqrt{5}, \frac{1}{2}$
(e)

75. (a) Zeros are 2 and about ± 2.236.
(b) $x = 2$ (c) $f(x) = (x - 2)\left(x - \sqrt{5}\right)\left(x + \sqrt{5}\right)$
77. (a) Zeros are -2, about 0.268, and about 3.732.
(b) $t = -2$
(c) $h(t) = (t + 2)\left[t - \left(2 + \sqrt{3}\right)\right]\left[t - \left(2 - \sqrt{3}\right)\right]$
79. (a) Zeros are 0, 3, 4, and about ± 1.414.   (b) $x = 0$
(c) $h(x) = x(x - 4)(x - 3)\left(x + \sqrt{2}\right)\left(x - \sqrt{2}\right)$
81. $2x^2 - x - 1$, $x \neq \frac{3}{2}$ **83.** $x^2 + 3x$, $x \neq -2, -1$
85. (a)

(b) $\$250{,}366$
(c) Answers will vary.

87. False. $-\frac{4}{7}$ is a zero of f.
89. True. The degree of the numerator is greater than the degree of the denominator.
91. $x^{2n} + 6x^n + 9$, $x^n \neq -3$ **93.** The remainder is 0.
95. $c = -210$ **97.** $k = 7$

Section 2.4   *(page 152)*

1. real   **3.** pure imaginary   **5.** principal square
7. $a = -12$, $b = 7$ **9.** $a = 6$, $b = 5$ **11.** $8 + 5i$
13. $2 - 3\sqrt{3}i$ **15.** $4\sqrt{5}i$ **17.** 14   **19.** $-1 - 10i$
21. $0.3i$ **23.** $10 - 3i$ **25.** 1   **27.** $3 - 3\sqrt{2}i$
29. $-14 + 20i$ **31.** $\frac{1}{6} + \frac{7}{6}i$ **33.** $5 + i$
35. $108 + 12i$ **37.** 24   **39.** $-13 + 84i$ **41.** -10
43. $9 - 2i$, 85   **45.** $-1 + \sqrt{5}i$, 6   **47.** $-2\sqrt{5}i$, 20
49. $\sqrt{6}$, 6   **51.** $-3i$ **53.** $\frac{8}{41} + \frac{10}{41}i$ **55.** $\frac{12}{13} + \frac{5}{13}i$
57. $-4 - 9i$ **59.** $-\frac{120}{1681} - \frac{27}{1681}i$ **61.** $-\frac{1}{2} - \frac{5}{2}i$
63. $\frac{62}{949} + \frac{297}{949}i$ **65.** $-2\sqrt{3}$ **67.** -15
69. $\left(21 + 5\sqrt{2}\right) + \left(7\sqrt{5} - 3\sqrt{10}\right)i$ **71.** $1 \pm i$
73. $-2 \pm \frac{1}{2}i$ **75.** $-\frac{5}{2}, -\frac{3}{2}$ **77.** $2 \pm \sqrt{2}i$
79. $\frac{5}{7} \pm \frac{5\sqrt{15}}{7}$ **81.** $-1 + 6i$ **83.** $-14i$
85. $-432\sqrt{2}i$ **87.** i **89.** 81
91. (a) $z_1 = 9 + 16i$, $z_2 = 20 - 10i$
(b) $z = \dfrac{11{,}240}{877} + \dfrac{4630}{877}i$
93. False. When the complex number is real, the number equals its conjugate.
95. False.
$i^{44} + i^{150} - i^{74} - i^{109} + i^{61} = 1 - 1 + 1 - i + i = 1$

97. $i, -1, -i, 1, i, -1, -i, 1$; The pattern repeats the first four results. Divide the exponent by 4.
When the remainder is 1, the result is i.
When the remainder is 2, the result is -1.
When the remainder is 3, the result is $-i$.
When the remainder is 0, the result is 1.
99. $\sqrt{-6}\sqrt{-6} = \sqrt{6}i\sqrt{6}i = 6i^2 = -6$
101. Proof

Section 2.5   *(page 164)*

1. Fundamental Theorem of Algebra   **3.** Rational Zero
5. linear; quadratic; quadratic   **7.** Descartes's Rule of Signs
9. 1   **11.** 3   **13.** 2   **15.** $\pm 1, \pm 2$
17. $\pm 1, \pm 3, \pm 5, \pm 9, \pm 15, \pm 45, \pm\frac{1}{2}, \pm\frac{3}{2}, \pm\frac{5}{2}, \pm\frac{9}{2}, \pm\frac{15}{2}, \pm\frac{45}{2}$
19. $-2, -1, 3$ **21.** $1, -1, 4$ **23.** $-6, -1$
25. $\frac{1}{2}, -1$ **27.** $-2, 3, \pm\frac{2}{3}$ **29.** $-2, 1$ **31.** $-4, \frac{1}{2}, 1, 1$
33. (a) $\pm 1, \pm 2, \pm 4$ **35.** (a) $\pm 1, \pm 3, \pm\frac{1}{2}, \pm\frac{3}{2}, \pm\frac{1}{4}, \pm\frac{3}{4}$
(b)   (b)

(c) $-2, -1, 2$ (c) $-\frac{1}{4}, 1, 3$
37. (a) $\pm 1, \pm 2, \pm 4, \pm 8, \pm\frac{1}{2}$
(b)   (c) $-\frac{1}{2}, 1, 2, 4$

39. (a) $\pm 1, \pm 3, \pm\frac{1}{2}, \pm\frac{3}{2}, \pm\frac{1}{4}, \pm\frac{3}{4}, \pm\frac{1}{8}, \pm\frac{3}{8}, \pm\frac{1}{16}, \pm\frac{3}{16}, \pm\frac{1}{32}, \pm\frac{3}{32}$
(b)   (c) $1, \frac{3}{4}, -\frac{1}{8}$

41. (a) ± 1, about ± 1.414 (b) $\pm 1, \pm\sqrt{2}$
(c) $f(x) = (x + 1)(x - 1)\left(x + \sqrt{2}\right)\left(x - \sqrt{2}\right)$
43. (a) 0, 3, 4, about ± 1.414 (b) $0, 3, 4, \pm\sqrt{2}$
(c) $h(x) = x(x - 3)(x - 4)\left(x + \sqrt{2}\right)\left(x - \sqrt{2}\right)$
45. $x^3 - x^2 + 25x - 25$ **47.** $x^3 - 12x^2 + 46x - 52$
49. $3x^4 - 17x^3 + 25x^2 + 23x - 22$
51. (a) $(x^2 + 9)(x^2 - 3)$ (b) $(x^2 + 9)\left(x + \sqrt{3}\right)\left(x - \sqrt{3}\right)$
(c) $(x + 3i)(x - 3i)\left(x + \sqrt{3}\right)\left(x - \sqrt{3}\right)$
53. (a) $(x^2 - 2x - 2)(x^2 - 2x + 3)$
(b) $\left(x - 1 + \sqrt{3}\right)\left(x - 1 - \sqrt{3}\right)(x^2 - 2x + 3)$
(c) $\left(x - 1 + \sqrt{3}\right)\left(x - 1 - \sqrt{3}\right)\left(x - 1 + \sqrt{2}i\right)$
    $\left(x - 1 - \sqrt{2}i\right)$
55. $\pm 2i, 1$ **57.** $\pm 5i, -\frac{1}{2}, 1$ **59.** $-3 \pm i, \frac{1}{4}$
61. $2, -3 \pm \sqrt{2}i, 1$ **63.** $(x + 6i)(x - 6i)$; $\pm 6i$
65. $(x - 1 - 4i)(x - 1 + 4i)$; $1 \pm 4i$
67. $(x - 2)(x + 2)(x - 2i)(x + 2i)$; $\pm 2, \pm 2i$

69. $(z - 1 + i)(z - 1 - i); 1 \pm i$
71. $(x + 1)(x - 2 + i)(x - 2 - i); -1, 2 \pm i$
73. $(x + 2)(x - 1 + \sqrt{2}i)(x - 1 - \sqrt{2}i); -2, 1 \pm \sqrt{2}i$
75. $(5x + 1)(x - 1 + \sqrt{5}i)(x - 1 - \sqrt{5}i); -\frac{1}{5}, 1 \pm \sqrt{5}i$
77. $(x - 2)^2(x + 2i)(x - 2i); 2, \pm 2i$
79. $(x + i)(x - i)(x + 3i)(x - 3i); \pm i, \pm 3i$
81. $-10, -7 \pm 5i$ **83.** $-\frac{3}{4}, 1 \pm \frac{1}{2}i$ **85.** $-2, -\frac{1}{2}, \pm i$
87. One positive zero   **89.** One negative zero
91. One positive zero, one negative zero
93. One or three positive zeros   **95–97.** Answers will vary.
99. $1, -\frac{1}{2}$ **101.** $-\frac{3}{4}$ **103.** $\pm 2, \pm \frac{3}{2}$ **105.** $\pm 1, \frac{1}{4}$
107. d   **108.** a   **109.** b   **110.** c
111. (a)

(b) $V(x) = x(9 - 2x)(15 - 2x)$
Domain: $0 < x < \frac{9}{2}$
(c)

Length of sides of squares removed

$1.82 \text{ cm} \times 5.36 \text{ cm} \times 11.36 \text{ cm}$
(d) $\frac{1}{2}, \frac{7}{2}, 8; 8$ is not in the domain of V.
113. (a) $V(x) = x^3 + 9x^2 + 26x + 24 = 120$ (b) $4 \text{ ft} \times 5 \text{ ft} \times 6 \text{ ft}$
115. False. The most complex zeros it can have is two, and the Linear Factorization Theorem guarantees that there are three linear factors, so one zero must be real.
117. r_1, r_2, r_3 **119.** $5 + r_1, 5 + r_2, 5 + r_3$
121. The zeros cannot be determined.
123. Answers will vary. There are infinitely many possible functions for f. *Sample equation and graph:*
$f(x) = -2x^3 + 3x^2 + 11x - 6$

125. $f(x) = x^3 - 3x^2 + 4x - 2$ **127.** $f(x) = x^4 + 5x^2 + 4$
129. (a) $x^2 + b$ (b) $x^2 - 2ax + a^2 + b^2$
131. (a) Not correct because f has $(0, 0)$ as an intercept.
(b) Not correct because the function must be at least a fourth-degree polynomial.
(c) Correct function
(d) Not correct because k has $(-1, 0)$ as an intercept.

Section 2.6   *(page 177)*

1. rational functions   **3.** horizontal asymptote
5. Domain: all real numbers x except $x = 1$
$f(x) \to -\infty$ as $x \to 1^-$, $f(x) \to \infty$ as $x \to 1^+$
7. Domain: all real numbers x except $x = \pm 1$
$f(x) \to \infty$ as $x \to -1^-$ and as $x \to 1^+$,
$f(x) \to -\infty$ as $x \to -1^+$ and as $x \to 1^-$
9. Vertical asymptote: $x = 0$
Horizontal asymptote: $y = 0$
11. Vertical asymptote: $x = 5$
Horizontal asymptote: $y = -1$
13. Vertical asymptotes: $x = \pm 1$
15. Horizontal asymptote: $y = 3$
17. (a) Domain: all real numbers x except $x = -2$
(b) y-intercept: $\left(0, \frac{1}{2}\right)$
(c) Vertical asymptote: $x = -2$
Horizontal asymptote: $y = 0$
(d)

19. (a) Domain: all real numbers x except $x = -4$
(b) y-intercept: $\left(0, -\frac{1}{4}\right)$
(c) Vertical asymptote: $x = -4$
Horizontal asymptote: $y = 0$
(d)

21. (a) Domain: all real numbers x except $x = -2$
(b) x-intercept: $\left(-\frac{7}{2}, 0\right)$
y-intercept: $\left(0, \frac{7}{2}\right)$
(c) Vertical asymptote: $x = -2$
Horizontal asymptote: $y = 2$
(d)

23. (a) Domain: all real numbers x (b) Intercept: $(0, 0)$
   (c) Horizontal asymptote: $y = 1$
   (d)

25. (a) Domain: all real numbers t except $t = 0$
   (b) t-intercept: $\left(\frac{1}{2}, 0\right)$
   (c) Vertical asymptote: $t = 0$
       Horizontal asymptote: $y = -2$
   (d)

27. (a) Domain: all real numbers x except $x = \pm 2$
   (b) x-intercepts: $(1, 0)$ and $(4, 0)$
       y-intercept: $(0, -1)$
   (c) Vertical asymptotes: $x = \pm 2$
       Horizontal asymptote: $y = 1$
   (d)

29. (a) Domain: all real numbers x except $x = \pm 4$
   (b) y-intercept: $\left(0, \frac{1}{4}\right)$
   (c) Vertical asymptote: $x = -4$
       Horizontal asymptote: $y = 0$
   (d)

31. (a) Domain: all real numbers t except $t = 1$
   (b) t-intercept: $(-1, 0)$
       y-intercept: $(0, 1)$
   (c) Vertical asymptote: None
       Horizontal asymptote: None

(d)

33. (a) Domain: all real numbers x except $x = -1, 5$
   (b) x-intercept: $(-5, 0)$
       y-intercept: $(0, 5)$
   (c) Vertical asymptote: $x = -1$
       Horizontal asymptote: $y = 1$
   (d)

35. (a) Domain: all real numbers x except $x = 2, -3$
   (b) Intercept: $(0, 0)$
   (c) Vertical asymptote: $x = 2$
       Horizontal asymptote: $y = 1$
   (d)

37. (a) Domain: all real numbers x except $x = -1, \frac{1}{2}$
   (b) x-intercept: $(4, 0)$
       y-intercept: $(0, 4)$
   (c) Vertical asymptote: $x = \frac{1}{2}$
       Horizontal asymptote: $y = \frac{1}{2}$
   (d)

39. (a) Domain: all real numbers x except $x = \pm 1, 2$
   (b) x-intercepts: $(3, 0)$, $\left(-\frac{1}{2}, 0\right)$
       y-intercept: $\left(0, -\frac{3}{2}\right)$
   (c) Vertical asymptotes: $x = 2, x = \pm 1$
       Horizontal asymptote: $y = 0$

(d)

41. d   **42.** a   **43.** c   **44.** b

45. (a) Domain of f: all real numbers x except $x = -1$
Domain of g: all real numbers x

(b)   (c) Because there are only a finite number of pixels, the graphing utility may not attempt to evaluate the function where it does not exist.

47. (a) Domain of f: all real numbers x except $x = 0, 2$
Domain of g: all real numbers x except $x = 0$

(b)   (c) Because there are only a finite number of pixels, the graphing utility may not attempt to evaluate the function where it does not exist.

49. (a) Domain: all real numbers x except $x = 0$
(b) x-intercepts: $(-3, 0), (3, 0)$
(c) Vertical asymptote: $x = 0$
Slant asymptote: $y = x$
(d)

51. (a) Domain: all real numbers x except $x = 0$
(b) No intercepts
(c) Vertical asymptote: $x = 0$
Slant asymptote: $y = 2x$
(d)

53. (a) Domain: all real numbers x except $x = 0$
(b) No intercepts
(c) Vertical asymptote: $x = 0$
Slant asymptote: $y = x$

(d)

55. (a) Domain: all real numbers t except $t = -5$
(b) y-intercept: $\left(0, -\frac{1}{5}\right)$
(c) Vertical asymptote: $t = -5$
Slant asymptote: $y = -t + 5$
(d)

57. (a) Domain: all real numbers x except $x = \pm 2$
(b) Intercept: $(0, 0)$
(c) Vertical asymptotes: $x = \pm 2$
Slant asymptote: $y = x$
(d)

59. (a) Domain: all real numbers x except $x = 1$
(b) y-intercept: $(0, -1)$
(c) Vertical asymptote: $x = 1$
Slant asymptote: $y = x$
(d)

61. (a) Domain: all real numbers x except $x = -1, -2$
(b) y-intercept: $\left(0, \frac{1}{2}\right)$
x-intercepts: $\left(\frac{1}{2}, 0\right), (1, 0)$
(c) Vertical asymptote: $x = -2$
Slant asymptote: $y = 2x - 7$

(d)

63.

Domain: all real numbers
x except $x = -3$
Vertical asymptote: $x = -3$
Slant asymptote: $y = x + 2$
$y = x + 2$

65.

Domain: all real numbers
x except $x = 0$
Vertical asymptote: $x = 0$
Slant asymptote: $y = -x + 3$
$y = -x + 3$

67. (a) $(-1, 0)$ (b) -1

69. (a) $(1, 0), (-1, 0)$ (b) ± 1

71. (a)

(b) $4411.76; \$25,000;$
$\$225,000$

(c) No. The function is
undefined at $p = 100$.

73. (a) $A = \dfrac{2x(x + 11)}{x - 4}$ (b) $(4, \infty)$

(c)

11.75 in. $\times$ 5.87 in.

75. (a) Answers will vary.

(b) Vertical asymptote: $x = 25$
Horizontal asymptote: $y = 25$

(c)

x	30	35	40	45	50	55	60
y	150	87.5	66.7	56.3	50	45.8	42.9

(e) *Sample answer:* No. You might expect the average speed
for the round trip to be the average of the average speeds
for the two parts of the trip.

(f) No. At 20 miles per hour you would use more time in one
direction than is required for the round trip at an average
speed of 50 miles per hour.

77. False. Polynomials do not have vertical asymptotes.

79. False. If the degree of the numerator is greater than the degree
of the denominator, then no horizontal asymptote exists.
However, a slant asymptote exists only if the degree of the
numerator is one greater than the degree of the denominator.

81. b

Section 2.7   *(page 187)*

1. positive; negative   **3.** zeros; undefined values

5. (a) No   (b) Yes   (c) Yes   (d) No

7. (a) Yes   (b) No   (c) No   (d) Yes

9. $-\frac{2}{3}, 1$ **11.** 4, 5

13. $(-3, 3)$

15. $[-7, 3]$

17. $(-\infty, -5] \cup [1, \infty)$

19. $(-3, 2)$

21. $(-3, 1)$

23. $\left(-\infty, -\frac{4}{3}\right) \cup (5, \infty)$

25. $(-\infty, -3) \cup (6, \infty)$

27. $(-1, 1) \cup (3, \infty)$

29. $(-\infty, 0) \cup \left(0, \frac{3}{2}\right)$

31. $[-2, 0] \cup [2, \infty)$

33. $[-2, \infty)$

35. The solution set consists of the single real number $\frac{1}{2}$.

37. The solution set is empty.

39. $(-\infty, 0) \cup \left(\frac{1}{4}, \infty\right)$

41. $\left(-\infty, \frac{5}{3}\right] \cup (5, \infty)$

43. $(-\infty, -1) \cup (4, \infty)$

45. $(-5, 3) \cup (11, \infty)$

47. $\left(-\frac{3}{4}, 3\right) \cup [6, \infty)$

49. $(-3, -2] \cup [0, 3)$

51. $(-\infty, -1) \cup (1, \infty)$

53.

(a) $x \le -1, x \ge 3$
(b) $0 \le x \le 2$

55.

(a) $-2 \le x \le 0,$
$2 \le x < \infty$
(b) $x \le 4$

57.
59.

(a) $0 \leq x < 2$
(b) $2 < x \leq 4$

(a) $|x| \geq 2$
(b) $-\infty < x < \infty$

61. $[-2, 2]$ **63.** $(-\infty, 4] \cup [5, \infty)$ **65.** $(-5, 0] \cup (7, \infty)$
67. $(-3.51, 3.51)$ **69.** $(-0.13, 25.13)$ **71.** $(2.26, 2.39)$
73. (a) $t = 10$ sec   (b) 4 sec $< t < 6$ sec
75. 13.8 m $\leq L \leq 36.2$ m
77. $40,000 \leq x \leq 50,000$; $\$50.00 \leq p \leq \$55.00$
79. (a) and (c)

The model fits the data well.

(b) $N = 0.00406t^4 - 0.0564t^3 + 0.147t^2 + 0.86t + 72.2$
(d) 2001
(e) No. The model can be used to predict enrollments for years close to those in its domain but when you project too far into the future, the numbers predicted by the model increase too rapidly to be considered reasonable.

81. $R_1 \geq 2$ ohms
83. True. The test intervals are $(-\infty, -3)$, $(-3, 1)$, $(1, 4)$, and $(4, \infty)$.
85. (a) $(-\infty, -4] \cup [4, \infty)$
(b) When $a > 0$ and $c > 0$, $b \leq -2\sqrt{ac}$ or $b \geq 2\sqrt{ac}$.
87. (a) $(-\infty, -2\sqrt{30}] \cup [2\sqrt{30}, \infty)$
(b) When $a > 0$ and $c > 0$, $b \leq -2\sqrt{ac}$ or $b \geq 2\sqrt{ac}$.
89.

For part (b), the y-values that are less than or equal to 0 occur only at $x = -1$.

For part (c), there are no y-values that are less than 0.

For part (d), the y-values that are greater than 0 occur for all values of x except 2.

Review Exercises   (page 192)

1. (a)   (b)

Vertical stretch and reflection in the x-axis

Vertical shift two units up

3. $g(x) = (x - 1)^2 - 1$

Vertex: $(1, -1)$
Axis of symmetry: $x = 1$
x-intercepts: $(0, 0)$, $(2, 0)$

5. $h(x) = -(x - 2)^2 + 7$

Vertex: $(2, 7)$
Axis of symmetry: $x = 2$
x-intercepts: $(2 \pm \sqrt{7}, 0)$

7. $h(x) = 4\left(x + \frac{1}{2}\right)^2 + 12$

Vertex: $\left(-\frac{1}{2}, 12\right)$
Axis of symmetry: $x = -\frac{1}{2}$
No x-intercept

9. (a) $y = 500 - x$
    $A(x) = 500x - x^2$
(b) $x = 250$, $y = 250$

11.

13. Falls to the left, falls to the right
15. Rises to the left, rises to the right
17. (a) Falls to the left, rises to the right
(b) $-2, 0$ (c) Answers will vary.
(d)

19. (a) Rises to the left, falls to the right
(b) -1 (c) Answers will vary.
(d)

21. (a) $[-1, 0]$ (b) About -0.900

23. $6x + 3 + \dfrac{17}{5x - 3}$

25. (a) Yes   (b) Yes   (c) Yes   (d) No

27. (a) Answers will vary.   (b) $(2x + 5), (x - 3)$
(c) $f(x) = (2x + 5)(x - 3)(x + 6)$ (d) $-\frac{5}{2}, 3, -6$
(e)

29. $8 + 10i$ **31.** $3 + 7i$ **33.** $63 + 77i$ **35.** $\frac{23}{17} + \frac{10}{17}i$

37. $1 \pm 3i$ **39.** 2 **41.** $-6, -2, 5$

43. $g(x) = (x + 2)(x - 3)(x - 6); -2, 3, 6$

45. One or three positive zeros, two or no negative zeros

47. Domain: all real numbers x except $x = -10$
Vertical asymptote: $x = -10$
Horizontal asymptote: $y = 3$

49. (a) Domain: all real numbers x except $x = 0$
(b) No intercepts
(c) Vertical asymptote: $x = 0$
Horizontal asymptote: $y = 0$
(d)

51. (a) Domain: all real numbers x (b) Intercept: $(0, 0)$
(c) Horizontal asymptote: $y = 0$
(d)

53. (a) Domain: all real numbers x except $x = 0, \frac{1}{3}$
(b) x-intercept: $\left(\frac{3}{2}, 0\right)$
(c) Vertical asymptote: $x = 0$
Horizontal asymptote: $y = 2$
(d)

55. (a) Domain: all real numbers x
(b) Intercept: $(0, 0)$ (c) Slant asymptote: $y = 2x$
(d)

57. (a)

(b) \$176 million;
\$528 million;
\$1584 million
(or \$1.584 billion)
(c) No

59. $\left(-\frac{2}{3}, \frac{1}{4}\right)$ **61.** $[-5, -1) \cup (1, \infty)$

63. 9 days

65. False. A fourth-degree polynomial can have at most four zeros, and complex zeros occur in conjugate pairs.

Chapter Test   *(page 194)*

1. (a) Reflection in the x-axis followed by a vertical shift two units up
(b) Horizontal shift $\frac{3}{2}$ units to the right

2. $y = (x - 3)^2 - 6$

3. (a) 50 ft
(b) 5. Yes, changing the constant term results in a vertical translation of the graph and therefore changes the maximum height.

4. Rises to the left, falls to the right

5. $3x + \dfrac{x - 1}{x^2 + 1}$ **6.** $2x^3 + 4x^2 + 3x + 6 + \dfrac{9}{x - 2}$

7. $(2x - 5)\left(x + \sqrt{3}\right)\left(x - \sqrt{3}\right)$;
Zeros: $\frac{5}{2}, \pm\sqrt{3}$

8. (a) $-3 + 5i$ (b) 7
9. $2 - i$ **10.** $f(x) = x^4 - 7x^3 + 17x^2 - 15x$
11. $f(x) = 4x^2 - 16x + 16$ **12.** $-5, -\frac{2}{3}, 1$
13. $-2, 4, -1 \pm \sqrt{2}i$
14. x-intercepts: $(-2, 0), (2, 0)$
   Vertical asymptote: $x = 0$
   Horizontal asymptote: $y = -1$

15. x-intercept: $\left(-\frac{3}{2}, 0\right)$ **16.** y-intercept: $(0, -2)$
   y-intercept: $\left(0, \frac{3}{4}\right)$ Vertical asymptote: $x = 1$
   Vertical asymptote: $x = -4$ Slant asymptote: $y = x + 1$
   Horizontal asymptote: $y = 2$

17. $x < -4$ or $x > \frac{3}{2}$ **18.** $x \le -12$ or $-6 < x < 0$

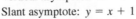

Problem Solving   *(page 197)*

1. Answers will vary.   **3.** 2 in. $\times$ 2 in. $\times$ 5 in.
5. (a) and (b) $y = -x^2 + 5x - 4$
7. (a) $f(x) = (x - 2)x^2 + 5 = x^3 - 2x^2 + 5$
   (b) $f(x) = -(x + 3)x^2 + 1 = -x^3 - 3x^2 + 1$
9. $(a + bi)(a - bi) = a^2 + abi - abi - b^2i^2$
                              $= a^2 + b^2$
11. (a) As $|a|$ increases, the graph stretches vertically. For $a < 0$,
       the graph is reflected in the x-axis.
   (b) As $|b|$ increases, the vertical asymptote is translated. For
       $b > 0$, the graph is translated to the right. For $b < 0$, the
       graph is reflected in the x-axis and is translated to the left.
13. No. Complex zeros always occur in conjugate pairs.

Chapter 3

Section 3.1   *(page 208)*

1. algebraic   **3.** One-to-One   **5.** $A = P\left(1 + \dfrac{r}{n}\right)^{nt}$

7. 0.863   **9.** 0.006   **11.** 1767.767
13. d   **14.** c   **15.** a   **16.** b

17.

x	-2	-1	0	1	2
$f(x)$	4	2	1	0.5	0.25

19.

x	-2	-1	0	1	2
$f(x)$	36	6	1	0.167	0.028

21.

x	-2	-1	0	1	2
$f(x)$	0.125	0.25	0.5	1	2

23. $x = 2$ **25.** $x = -5$ **27.** Shift the graph of f one unit up.
29. Reflect the graph of f in the origin.

31.   **33.**

35. 24.533   **37.** 7166.647
39.

x	-2	-1	0	1	2
$f(x)$	0.135	0.368	1	2.718	7.389

41.

x	−8	−7	−6	−5	−4
f(x)	0.055	0.149	0.406	1.104	3

43.

x	−2	−1	0	1	2
f(x)	4.037	4.100	4.271	4.736	6

45.   **47.**

49.   **51.** $x = \frac{1}{3}$ **53.** $x = 3, -1$

55.

n	1	2	4	12
A	$1828.49	$1830.29	$1831.19	$1831.80

n	365	Continuous
A	$1832.09	$1832.10

57.

n	1	2	4	12
A	$5477.81	$5520.10	$5541.79	$5556.46

n	365	Continuous
A	$5563.61	$5563.85

59.

t	10	20	30
A	$17,901.90	$26,706.49	$39,841.40

t	40	50
A	$59,436.39	$88,668.67

61.

t	10	20	30
A	$22,986.49	$44,031.56	$84,344.25

t	40	50
A	$161,564.86	$309,484.08

63. $104,710.29   **65.** $35.45

67. (a)

(b)

t	20	21	22	23
P (in millions)	342.748	345.604	348.485	351.389

t	24	25	26	27
P (in millions)	354.318	357.271	360.249	363.251

t	28	29	30	31
P (in millions)	366.279	369.331	372.410	375.513

t	32	33	34	35
P (in millions)	378.643	381.799	384.981	388.190

t	36	37	38	39
P (in millions)	391.425	394.687	397.977	401.294

t	40	41	42	43
P (in millions)	404.639	408.011	411.412	414.840

t	44	45	46	47
P (in millions)	418.298	421.784	425.300	428.844

t	48	49	50
P (in millions)	432.419	436.023	439.657

(c) 2038

69. (a) 16 g   (b) 1.85 g   (c)

71. (a) $V(t) = 49,810\left(\frac{7}{8}\right)^t$ (b) $29,197.71

73. True. As $x \to -\infty$, $f(x) \to -2$ but never reaches -2.

75. $f(x) = h(x)$ **77.** $f(x) = g(x) = h(x)$

79.

81.

As the x-value increases, y_1 approaches the value of e.

(a) $x < 0$ (b) $x > 0$

83. (a)   (b)

In both viewing windows, the constant raised to a variable power increases more rapidly than the variable raised to a constant power.

85. c, d

Section 3.2   (page 218)

1. logarithmic   **3.** natural; e **5.** $x = y$ **7.** $4^2 = 16$

9. $32^{2/5} = 4$ **11.** $\log_5 125 = 3$ **13.** $\log_4 \frac{1}{64} = -3$

15. 6   **17.** 0   **19.** 2   **21.** -0.058 **23.** 1.097

25. 7   **27.** 1   **29.** $x = 5$ **31.** $x = 7$

33.   **35.**

37. c   **38.** d   **39.** b   **40.** a

41.

Domain: $(0, \infty)$
x-intercept: $(1, 0)$
Vertical asymptote: $x = 0$

43.

Domain: $(0, \infty)$
x-intercept: $(9, 0)$
Vertical asymptote: $x = 0$

45.

Domain: $(-2, \infty)$
x-intercept: $(-1, 0)$
Vertical asymptote: $x = -2$

47.

Domain: $(0, \infty)$
x-intercept: $(7, 0)$
Vertical asymptote: $x = 0$

49. $e^{-0.693\ldots} = \frac{1}{2}$ **51.** $e^{5.521\ldots} = 250$

53. $\ln 7.3890 \ldots = 2$ **55.** $\ln 0.406 \ldots = -0.9$

57. 2.913   **59.** -23.966 **61.** 5   **63.** $-\frac{5}{6}$

65.

Domain: $(4, \infty)$
x-intercept: $(5, 0)$
Vertical asymptote: $x = 4$

67.

Domain: $(-\infty, 0)$
x-intercept: $(-1, 0)$
Vertical asymptote: $x = 0$

69.   **71.**

73. $x = 8$ **75.** $x = -5, 5$

77. (a) 30 yr; 10 yr   (b) $323,179; $199,109
(c) $173,179; $49,109
(d) $x = 750$; The monthly payment must be greater than $750.

79. (a)

r	0.005	0.010	0.015	0.020	0.025	0.030
t	138.6	69.3	46.2	34.7	27.7	23.1

As the rate of increase r increases, the time t in years for the population to double decreases.

(b)

81. (a)   (b) 80   (c) 68.1   (d) 62.3

83. False. Reflecting $g(x)$ in the line $y = x$ will determine the graph of $f(x)$.

85. (a)

$g(x)$; The natural log function grows at a slower rate than the square root function.

(b)

$g(x)$; The natural log function grows at a slower rate than the fourth root function.

87. (a) False   (b) True   (c) True   (d) False
89. Answers will vary.

Section 3.3   (page 225)

1. change-of-base   **3.** $\dfrac{1}{\log_b a}$ **4.** c

5. a   **6.** b   **7.** (a) $\dfrac{\log 16}{\log 5}$ (b) $\dfrac{\ln 16}{\ln 5}$

9. (a) $\dfrac{\log \frac{3}{10}}{\log x}$ (b) $\dfrac{\ln \frac{3}{10}}{\ln x}$ **11.** 1.771   **13.** -1.048

15. $\frac{3}{2}$ **17.** $-3 - \log_5 2$ **19.** $6 + \ln 5$ **21.** 2   **23.** $\frac{3}{4}$
25. 4   **27.** -2 is not in the domain of $\log_2 x$.   **29.** 4.5
31. $-\frac{1}{2}$ **33.** 7   **35.** 2   **37.** $\ln 4 + \ln x$ **39.** $4 \log_8 x$
41. $1 - \log_5 x$ **43.** $\frac{1}{2} \ln z$ **45.** $\ln x + \ln y + 2 \ln z$
47. $\ln z + 2 \ln(z - 1)$ **49.** $\frac{1}{2} \log_2(a - 1) - 2 \log_2 3$
51. $\frac{1}{3} \ln x - \frac{1}{3} \ln y$ **53.** $2 \ln x + \frac{1}{2} \ln y - \frac{1}{2} \ln z$
55. $2 \log_5 x - 2 \log_5 y - 3 \log_5 z$ **57.** $\frac{3}{4} \ln x + \frac{1}{4} \ln(x^2 + 3)$
59. 1.1833   **61.** 1.0686   **63.** 1.9563   **65.** 2.5646
67. $\ln 2x$ **69.** $\log_2 x^2 y^4$ **71.** $\log_3 \sqrt[4]{5x}$
73. $\log \dfrac{x}{(x + 1)^2}$ **75.** $\log \dfrac{xz^3}{y^2}$ **77.** $\ln \dfrac{x}{(x + 1)(x - 1)}$
79. $\ln \sqrt[3]{\dfrac{x(x + 3)^2}{x^2 - 1}}$ **81.** $\log_8 \dfrac{\sqrt[3]{y(y + 4)^2}}{y - 1}$
83. $\log_2 \frac{32}{4} = \log_2 32 - \log_2 4$; Property 2
85. $\beta = 10(\log I + 12)$; 60 dB   **87.** 70 dB
89. $\ln y = \frac{1}{4} \ln x$ **91.** $\ln y = -\frac{1}{4} \ln x + \ln \frac{5}{2}$
93. $y = 256.24 - 20.8 \ln x$

95. (a) and (b)   (c)

$T = 21 + e^{-0.037t + 3.997}$
The results are similar.

(d)   (e) Answers will vary.

$$T = 21 + \dfrac{1}{0.001t + 0.016}$$

97. False; $\ln 1 = 0$ **99.** False; $\ln(x - 2) \neq \ln x - \ln 2$
101. False; $u = v^2$

103. $f(x) = \dfrac{\log x}{\log 2} = \dfrac{\ln x}{\ln 2}$ **105.** $f(x) = \dfrac{\log x}{\log \frac{1}{4}} = \dfrac{\ln x}{\ln \frac{1}{4}}$

107. *Sample answers:*

(a) $\ln(1 + 3) \overset{?}{=} \ln(1) + \ln(3)$
$1.39 \neq 0 + 1.10$
$\ln u + \ln v = \ln(uv)$, but $\ln(u + v) \neq \ln u + \ln v$

(b) $\ln(3 - 1) \overset{?}{=} \ln(3) - \ln(1)$
$0.69 \neq 1.10 - 0$
$\ln u - \ln v = \ln \dfrac{u}{v}$, but $\ln(u - v) \neq \ln u - \ln v$

(c) $(\ln 2)^3 \overset{?}{=} 3 \ln 2$
$0.33 \neq 2.08$
$n(\ln u) = \ln u^n$, but $(\ln u)^n \neq n(\ln u)$

109. $\ln 1 = 0$ $\ln 9 \approx 2.1972$
$\ln 2 \approx 0.6931$ $\ln 10 \approx 2.3025$
$\ln 3 \approx 1.0986$ $\ln 12 \approx 2.4848$
$\ln 4 \approx 1.3862$ $\ln 15 \approx 2.7080$
$\ln 5 \approx 1.6094$ $\ln 16 \approx 2.7724$
$\ln 6 \approx 1.7917$ $\ln 18 \approx 2.8903$
$\ln 8 \approx 2.0793$ $\ln 20 \approx 2.9956$

Section 3.4   (page 235)

1. (a) $x = y$ (b) $x = y$ (c) x (d) x
3. (a) Yes   (b) No   **5.** (a) Yes   (b) No   (c) No
7. 2   **9.** 2   **11.** $e^{-1} \approx 0.368$ **13.** 64   **15.** $(3, 8)$

17. $2, -1$ **19.** $\dfrac{\ln 5}{\ln 3} \approx 1.465$ **21.** $\ln 28 \approx 3.332$

23. $\dfrac{\ln 80}{2 \ln 3} \approx 1.994$ **25.** $3 - \dfrac{\ln 565}{\ln 2} \approx -6.142$

27. $\dfrac{1}{3} \log\left(\dfrac{3}{2}\right) \approx 0.059$ **29.** $\dfrac{\ln 12}{3} \approx 0.828$

CHAPTER 3

31. 0   **33.** $\dfrac{\ln \frac{8}{3}}{3 \ln 2} + \dfrac{1}{3} \approx 0.805$

35. $\dfrac{\ln 3}{\ln 2 - \ln 3} \approx -2.710$ **37.** $0, \dfrac{\ln 4}{\ln 5} \approx 0.861$

39. $\ln 5 \approx 1.609$ **41.** $2 \ln 75 \approx 8.635$

43. $\dfrac{\ln 4}{365 \ln\left(1 + \dfrac{0.065}{365}\right)} \approx 21.330$ **45.** $e^{-3} \approx 0.050$

47. $\dfrac{e^{2.1}}{6} \approx 1.361$ **49.** $\dfrac{e^{10/3}}{5} \approx 5.606$ **51.** $e^{-4/3} \approx 0.264$

53. $2(3^{11/6}) \approx 14.988$ **55.** No solution

57. No solution   **59.** No solution   **61.** 2

63.

3.328

65.

-0.478

67.

20.086

69.

1.482

71. (a) 27.73 yr   (b) 43.94 yr   **73.** $-1, 0$ **75.** 1

77. $e^{-1/2} \approx 0.607$ **79.** $e^{-1} \approx 0.368$

81. (a) $y = 100$ and $y = 0$; The range falls between 0% and 100%.
(b) Males: 69.51 in.   Females: 64.49 in.

83. 12.76 in.

85. (a)

x	0.2	0.4	0.6	0.8	1.0
y	162.6	78.5	52.5	40.5	33.9

(b)

The model appears to fit the data well.

(c) 1.2 m

(d) No. According to the model, when the number of g's is less than 23, x is between 2.276 meters and 4.404 meters, which isn't realistic in most vehicles.

87. $\log_b uv = \log_b u + \log_b v$
True by Property 1 in Section 3.3.

89. $\log_b(u - v) = \log_b u - \log_b v$
False.
$1.95 \approx \log(100 - 10) \neq \log 100 - \log 10 = 1$

91. Yes. See Exercise 57.

93. For $rt < \ln 2$ years, double the amount you invest. For $rt > \ln 2$ years, double your interest rate or double the number of years, because either of these will double the exponent in the exponential function.

95. (a) 7%   (b) 7.25%   (c) 7.19%   (d) 7.45%
The investment plan with the greatest effective yield and the highest balance after 5 years is plan (d).

Section 3.5   (page 245)

1. $y = ae^{bx}$; $y = ae^{-bx}$ **3.** normally distributed

5. (a) $P = \dfrac{A}{e^{rt}}$ (b) $t = \dfrac{\ln\left(\dfrac{A}{P}\right)}{r}$

Initial Investment	Annual % Rate	Time to Double	Amount After 10 years
7. $1000	3.5%	19.8 yr	$1419.07
9. $750	8.9438%	7.75 yr	$1834.37
11. $6376.28	4.5%	15.4 yr	$10,000.00

13. $303,580.52

15. (a) 7.27 yr   (b) 6.96 yr   (c) 6.93 yr   (d) 6.93 yr

17. (a)

r	2%	4%	6%	8%	10%	12%
t	54.93	27.47	18.31	13.73	10.99	9.16

(b)

r	2%	4%	6%	8%	10%	12%
t	55.48	28.01	18.85	14.27	11.53	9.69

19.

Continuous compounding

Half-life (years)	Initial Quantity	Amount After 1000 Years
21. 1599	10 g	6.48 g
23. 5715	2.26 g	2 g

25. $y = e^{0.7675x}$ **27.** $y = 5e^{-0.4024x}$

29. (a)

Year	1980	1990	2000	2010
Population	106.1	143.15	196.25	272.37

(b) 2017
(c) No; The population will not continue to grow at such a quick rate.

31. $k = 0.2988$; About 5,309,734 hits   **33.** About 800 bacteria

35. (a) $V = -300t + 1150$ (b) $V = 1150e^{-0.368799t}$

(c)

The exponential model depreciates faster.

(d)

t	1 yr	3 yr
$V = -300t + 1150$	850	250
$V = 1150e^{-0.368799t}$	795	380

(e) Answers will vary.

37. (a) About 12,180 yr old   (b) About 4797 yr old

39. (a)   (b) 100

41. (a) 1998: 55,557 sites
    2003: 147,644 sites
    2006: 203,023 sites
    (c) and (d) 2010

43. (a) 203 animals
    (b) 13 mo
    (c)

Horizontal asymptotes: $p = 0, p = 1000$. The population size will approach 1000 as time increases.

45. (a) $10^{6.6} \approx 3,981,072$ (b) $10^{5.6} \approx 398,107$
    (c) $10^{7.1} \approx 12,589,254$
47. (a) 20 dB   (b) 70 dB   (c) 40 dB   (d) 120 dB
49. 95%   **51.** 4.64   **53.** 1.58×10^{-6} moles/L
55. $10^{5.1}$ **57.** 3:00 A.M.
59. (a)   (b) $t \approx 21$ yr; Yes

61. False. The domain can be the set of real numbers for a logistic growth function.
63. False. The graph of $f(x)$ is the graph of $g(x)$ shifted five units up.
65. Answers will vary.

Review Exercises *(page 252)*

1. 0.164   **3.** 0.337   **5.** 1456.529
7. Shift the graph of f one unit up.
9. Reflect f in the x-axis and shift one unit up.
11.

x	-1	0	1	2	3
$f(x)$	8	5	4.25	4.063	4.016

13.

x	-1	0	1	2	3
$f(x)$	4.008	4.04	4.2	5	9

15.

x	-2	-1	0	1	2
$f(x)$	3.25	3.5	4	5	7

17. $x = 1$ **19.** $x = 4$ **21.** 2980.958   **23.** 0.183
25.

x	-2	-1	0	1	2
$h(x)$	2.72	1.65	1	0.61	0.37

27.

x	-3	-2	-1	0	1
$f(x)$	0.37	1	2.72	7.39	20.09

29. (a) 0.154   (b) 0.487   (c) 0.811

CHAPTER 3

31.

n	1	2	4	12
A	\$6719.58	\$6734.28	\$6741.74	\$6746.77

n	365	Continuous
A	\$6749.21	\$6749.29

33. $\log_3 27 = 3$ **35.** $\ln 2.2255\ldots = 0.8$ **37.** 3
39. -2 **41.** $x = 7$ **43.** $x = -5$
45. Domain: $(0, \infty)$ **47.** Domain: $(-5, \infty)$
x-intercept: $(1, 0)$ x-intercept: $(9995, 0)$
Vertical asymptote: $x = 0$ Vertical asymptote: $x = -5$

49. 3.118   **51.** 0.25
53. Domain: $(0, \infty)$ **55.** Domain: $(-\infty, 0), (0, \infty)$
x-intercept: $(e^{-3}, 0)$ x-intercepts: $(\pm 1, 0)$
Vertical asymptote: $x = 0$ Vertical asymptote: $x = 0$

57. 53.4 in.   **59.** (a) and (b) 2.585   **61.** (a) and (b) -2.322
63. $\log 2 + 2 \log 3 \approx 1.255$ **65.** $2 \ln 2 + \ln 5 \approx 2.996$
67. $1 + 2 \log_5 x$ **69.** $2 - \frac{1}{2} \log_3 x$ **71.** $2 \ln x + 2 \ln y + \ln z$
73. $\log_2 5x$ **75.** $\ln \dfrac{x}{\sqrt[4]{y}}$ **77.** $\log_3 \dfrac{\sqrt{x}}{(y + 8)^2}$
79. (a) $0 \le h < 18{,}000$
(b)   Vertical asymptote:
                                    $h = 18{,}000$

(c) The plane is climbing at a slower rate, so the time required
increases.
(d) 5.46 min
81. 3   **83.** $\ln 3 \approx 1.099$ **85.** $e^4 \approx 54.598$ **87.** 1, 3
89. $\dfrac{\ln 32}{\ln 2} = 5$
91.
              93. $\frac{1}{3}e^{8.2} \approx 1213.650$

2.447

95. $3e^2 \approx 22.167$ **97.** No solution   **99.** 0.900
101.   **103.**

1.482   0, 0.416, 13.627
105. 73.2 yr   **107.** e   **108.** b   **109.** f
110. d   **111.** a   **112.** c   **113.** $y = 2e^{0.1014x}$
115.   **117.** (a) 10^{-6} W/m^2
                                                (b) $10\sqrt{10}$ W/m^2
                        (c) 1.259×10^{-12} W/m^2

71
119. True by the inverse properties.

Chapter Test   *(page 255)*

1. 2.366   **2.** 687.291   **3.** 0.497   **4.** 22.198
5.

x	-1	$-\frac{1}{2}$	0	$\frac{1}{2}$	1
$f(x)$	10	3.162	1	0.316	0.1

6.

x	-1	0	1	2	3
$f(x)$	-0.005	-0.028	-0.167	-1	-6

7.

x	-1	$-\frac{1}{2}$	0	$\frac{1}{2}$	1
$f(x)$	0.865	0.632	0	-1.718	-6.389

8. (a) -0.89 (b) 9.2

9. Domain: $(0, \infty)$
x-intercept: $(10^{-6}, 0)$
Vertical asymptote: $x = 0$

10. Domain: $(4, \infty)$
x-intercept: $(5, 0)$
Vertical asymptote: $x = 4$

11. Domain: $(-6, \infty)$
x-intercept: $(e^{-1} - 6, 0)$
Vertical asymptote: $x = -6$

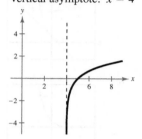

12. 1.945 **13.** -0.167 **14.** -11.047

15. $\log_2 3 + 4 \log_2 a$ **16.** $\ln 5 + \frac{1}{2} \ln x - \ln 6$

17. $3 \log(x - 1) - 2 \log y - \log z$ **18.** $\log_3 13y$

19. $\ln \dfrac{x^4}{y^4}$ **20.** $\ln \dfrac{x^3 y^2}{x + 3}$ **21.** -2 **22.** $\dfrac{\ln 44}{-5} \approx -0.757$

23. $\dfrac{\ln 197}{4} \approx 1.321$ **24.** $e^{1/2} \approx 1.649$ **25.** $e^{-11/4} \approx 0.0639$

26. 20 **27.** $y = 2745 e^{0.1570t}$ **28.** 55%

29. (a)

x	$\frac{1}{4}$	1	2	4	5	6
H	58.720	75.332	86.828	103.43	110.59	117.38

(b) 103 cm; 103.43 cm

Cumulative Test for Chapters 1–3   *(page 256)*

1.

Midpoint: $\left(\frac{1}{2}, 2\right)$
Distance: $\sqrt{61}$

2.

3.

4.

5. $y = 2x + 2$

6. For some values of x there correspond two values of y.

7. (a) $\dfrac{3}{2}$ (b) Division by 0 is undefined.   (c) $\dfrac{s + 2}{s}$

8. (a) Vertical shrink by $\frac{1}{2}$ (b) Vertical shift two units up
(c) Horizontal shift two units to the left

9. (a) $5x - 2$ (b) $-3x - 4$ (c) $4x^2 - 11x - 3$
(d) $\dfrac{x - 3}{4x + 1}$; Domain: all real numbers x except $x = -\dfrac{1}{4}$

10. (a) $\sqrt{x - 1} + x^2 + 1$ (b) $\sqrt{x - 1} - x^2 - 1$
(c) $x^2 \sqrt{x - 1} + \sqrt{x - 1}$
(d) $\dfrac{\sqrt{x - 1}}{x^2 + 1}$; Domain: all real numbers x such that $x \geq 1$

11. (a) $2x + 12$ (b) $\sqrt{2x^2 + 6}$
Domain of $f \circ g$: all real numbers x such that $x \geq -6$
Domain of $g \circ f$: all real numbers

12. (a) $|x| - 2$ (b) $|x - 2|$
Domain of $f \circ g$ and $g \circ f$: all real numbers

13. Yes; $h^{-1}(x) = -\frac{1}{5}(x - 3)$ **14.** 2438.65 kW

15. $y = -\frac{3}{4}(x + 8)^2 + 5$

16.

17.

18.

19. $-2, \pm 2i$; $(x + 2)(x + 2i)(x - 2i)$

20. $-7, 0, 3$; $x(x)(x - 3)(x + 7)$

21. $4, -\frac{1}{2}, 1 \pm 3i$; $(x - 4)(2x + 1)(x - 1 + 3i)(x - 1 - 3i)$

22. $3x - 2 - \dfrac{3x - 2}{2x^2 + 1}$ **23.** $3x^3 + 6x^2 + 14x + 23 + \dfrac{49}{x - 2}$

24.

Interval: $[1, 2]$; 1.20

25. Intercept: $(0, 0)$
Vertical asymptotes:
$x = -3, x = 1$
Horizontal asymptote: $y = 0$

26. y-intercept: $(0, 2)$
x-intercept: $(2, 0)$
Vertical asymptote: $x = 1$
Horizontal asymptote:
$y = 1$

27. y-intercept: $(0, 6)$
x-intercepts: $(2, 0), (3, 0)$
Vertical asymptote: $x = -1$
Slant asymptote:
$y = x - 6$

28. $x \le -3$ or $0 \le x \le 3$

29. All real numbers x such that
$x < -5$ or $x > -1$

30. Reflect f in the x-axis and y-axis, and shift three units to the right.

31. Reflect f in the x-axis, and shift four units up.

32. 1.991   **33.** -0.067 **34.** 1.717   **35.** 0.281

36. $\ln(x + 4) + \ln(x - 4) - 4 \ln x, x > 4$

37. $\ln \dfrac{x^2}{\sqrt{x + 5}}, x > 0$ **38.** $x = \dfrac{\ln 12}{2} \approx 1.242$

39. $\ln 6 \approx 1.792$ or $\ln 7 \approx 1.946$ **40.** $e^6 - 2 \approx 401.429$

41. (a) and (c)

The model is a good fit for the data.
(b) $S = -0.0172t^3 + 0.119t^2 + 2.22t + 36.8$
(d) \$15.0 billion; No; The trend appears to show sales increasing.

42. 6.3 h

Problem Solving   *(page 259)*

1.

$y = 0.5^x$ and $y = 1.2^x$
$0 < a \le e^{1/e}$

3. As $x \to \infty$, the graph of e^x increases at a greater rate than the graph of x^n.

5. Answers will vary.

7. (a)

(b)

(c)

9.

$f^{-1}(x) = \ln\left(\dfrac{x + \sqrt{x^2 + 4}}{2}\right)$

11. c   **13.** $t = \dfrac{\ln c_1 - \ln c_2}{\left(\dfrac{1}{k_2} - \dfrac{1}{k_1}\right)\ln \dfrac{1}{2}}$

15. (a) $y_1 = 252{,}606(1.0310)^t$
(b) $y_2 = 400.88t^2 - 1464.6t + 291{,}782$
(c)

(d) The exponential model is a better fit. No, because the model is rapidly approaching infinity.

17. $1, e^2$

19. $y_4 = (x - 1) - \frac{1}{2}(x - 1)^2 + \frac{1}{3}(x - 1)^3 - \frac{1}{4}(x - 1)^4$

The pattern implies that
$\ln x = (x - 1) - \frac{1}{2}(x - 1)^2 + \frac{1}{3}(x - 1)^3 - \cdots$.

21.

17.7 ft³/min

23. (a)

25. (a)

(b)–(e) Answers will vary.   (b)–(e) Answers will vary.

Chapter 4

Section 4.1 *(page 269)*

1. coterminal   3. complementary; supplementary
5. linear; angular   7. 1 rad   9. −3 rad
11. (a) Quadrant I   (b) Quadrant III
13. (a)   (b)

15. *Sample answers:* (a) $\dfrac{13\pi}{6}, -\dfrac{11\pi}{6}$ (b) $\dfrac{19\pi}{6}, -\dfrac{5\pi}{6}$

17. (a) Complement: $\dfrac{\pi}{6}$; Supplement: $\dfrac{2\pi}{3}$

   (b) Complement: $\dfrac{\pi}{4}$; Supplement: $\dfrac{3\pi}{4}$

19. (a) Complement: $\dfrac{\pi}{2} - 1 \approx 0.57$;

   Supplement: $\pi - 1 \approx 2.14$

   (b) Complement: none; Supplement: $\pi - 2 \approx 1.14$

21. $210°$ 23. $-60°$ 25. (a) Quadrant II   (b) Quadrant I
27. (a)   (b)

29. *Sample answers:* (a) $405°, -315°$ (b) $324°, -396°$
31. (a) Complement: $72°$; Supplement: $162°$
   (b) Complement: $5°$; Supplement: $95°$
33. (a) Complement: none; Supplement: $30°$
   (b) Complement: $11°$; Supplement: $101°$
35. (a) $\dfrac{2\pi}{3}$ (b) $-\dfrac{\pi}{9}$ 37. (a) $270°$ (b) $210°$
39. 0.785 41. 0.009 43. $81.818°$ 45. $-756.000°$
47. (a) $54.75°$ (b) $-128.5°$
49. (a) $240°36'$ (b) $-145°48'$
51. 10π in. ≈ 31.42 in.   53. $\dfrac{15}{8}$ rad   55. 4 rad
57. $18\pi\,\text{mm}^2 \approx 56.55\,\text{mm}^2$ 59. 591.3 mi   61. $23.87°$
63. (a) $10{,}000\pi$ rad/min $\approx 31{,}415.93$ rad/min
   (b) 9490.23 ft/min
65. (a) $[400\pi, 1000\pi]$ rad/min   (b) $[2400\pi, 6000\pi]$ cm/min
67. (a) 35.70 mi/h   (b) 739.50 revolutions/min
69. $A = 87.5\pi\,\text{m}^2 \approx 274.89\,\text{m}^2$

71. False. A measurement of 4π radians corresponds to two complete revolutions from the initial side to the terminal side of an angle.
73. False. The terminal side of the angle lies on the *x*-axis.
75. The speed increases. The linear velocity is proportional to the radius.
77. The arc length is increasing. If θ is constant, the length of the arc is proportional to the radius $(s = r\theta)$.

Section 4.2 *(page 277)*

1. unit circle   3. period
5. $\sin t = \dfrac{5}{13}$ $\csc t = \dfrac{13}{5}$ 7. $\sin t = -\dfrac{3}{5}$ $\csc t = -\dfrac{5}{3}$
   $\cos t = \dfrac{12}{13}$ $\sec t = \dfrac{13}{12}$ $\cos t = -\dfrac{4}{5}$ $\sec t = -\dfrac{5}{4}$
   $\tan t = \dfrac{5}{12}$ $\cot t = \dfrac{12}{5}$ $\tan t = \dfrac{3}{4}$ $\cot t = \dfrac{4}{3}$

9. $(0, 1)$ 11. $\left(-\dfrac{\sqrt{3}}{2}, \dfrac{1}{2}\right)$

13. $\sin\dfrac{\pi}{4} = \dfrac{\sqrt{2}}{2}$ 15. $\sin\left(-\dfrac{\pi}{6}\right) = -\dfrac{1}{2}$

   $\cos\dfrac{\pi}{4} = \dfrac{\sqrt{2}}{2}$ $\cos\left(-\dfrac{\pi}{6}\right) = \dfrac{\sqrt{3}}{2}$

   $\tan\dfrac{\pi}{4} = 1$ $\tan\left(-\dfrac{\pi}{6}\right) = -\dfrac{\sqrt{3}}{3}$

17. $\sin\left(-\dfrac{7\pi}{4}\right) = \dfrac{\sqrt{2}}{2}$ 19. $\sin\dfrac{11\pi}{6} = -\dfrac{1}{2}$

   $\cos\left(-\dfrac{7\pi}{4}\right) = \dfrac{\sqrt{2}}{2}$ $\cos\dfrac{11\pi}{6} = \dfrac{\sqrt{3}}{2}$

   $\tan\left(-\dfrac{7\pi}{4}\right) = 1$ $\tan\dfrac{11\pi}{6} = -\dfrac{\sqrt{3}}{3}$

21. $\sin\left(-\dfrac{3\pi}{2}\right) = 1$

   $\cos\left(-\dfrac{3\pi}{2}\right) = 0$

   $\tan\left(-\dfrac{3\pi}{2}\right)$ is undefined.

23. $\sin\dfrac{2\pi}{3} = \dfrac{\sqrt{3}}{2}$ $\csc\dfrac{2\pi}{3} = \dfrac{2\sqrt{3}}{3}$

   $\cos\dfrac{2\pi}{3} = -\dfrac{1}{2}$ $\sec\dfrac{2\pi}{3} = -2$

   $\tan\dfrac{2\pi}{3} = -\sqrt{3}$ $\cot\dfrac{2\pi}{3} = -\dfrac{\sqrt{3}}{3}$

25. $\sin\dfrac{4\pi}{3} = -\dfrac{\sqrt{3}}{2}$ $\csc\dfrac{4\pi}{3} = -\dfrac{2\sqrt{3}}{3}$

   $\cos\dfrac{4\pi}{3} = -\dfrac{1}{2}$ $\sec\dfrac{4\pi}{3} = -2$

   $\tan\dfrac{4\pi}{3} = \sqrt{3}$ $\cot\dfrac{4\pi}{3} = \dfrac{\sqrt{3}}{3}$

27. $\sin\left(-\dfrac{5\pi}{3}\right) = \dfrac{\sqrt{3}}{2}$ $\csc\left(-\dfrac{5\pi}{3}\right) = \dfrac{2\sqrt{3}}{3}$

   $\cos\left(-\dfrac{5\pi}{3}\right) = \dfrac{1}{2}$ $\sec\left(-\dfrac{5\pi}{3}\right) = 2$

   $\tan\left(-\dfrac{5\pi}{3}\right) = \sqrt{3}$ $\cot\left(-\dfrac{5\pi}{3}\right) = \dfrac{\sqrt{3}}{3}$

29. $\sin\left(-\dfrac{\pi}{2}\right) = -1$ $\csc\left(-\dfrac{\pi}{2}\right) = -1$

   $\cos\left(-\dfrac{\pi}{2}\right) = 0$ $\sec\left(-\dfrac{\pi}{2}\right)$ is undefined.

   $\tan\left(-\dfrac{\pi}{2}\right)$ is undefined. $\cot\left(-\dfrac{\pi}{2}\right) = 0$

CHAPTER 4

31. $\sin 4\pi = \sin 0 = 0$ **33.** $\cos \dfrac{7\pi}{3} = \cos \dfrac{\pi}{3} = \dfrac{1}{2}$

35. $\sin \dfrac{19\pi}{6} = \sin \dfrac{7\pi}{6} = -\dfrac{1}{2}$ **37.** (a) $-\dfrac{1}{2}$ (b) -2

39. (a) $-\dfrac{1}{5}$ (b) -5 **41.** (a) $\dfrac{4}{5}$ (b) $-\dfrac{4}{5}$ **43.** 1.7321

45. 1.3940   **47.** -4.4014

49. (a) 0.25 ft   (b) 0.02 ft   (c) -0.25 ft

51. False. $\sin(-t) = -\sin(t)$ means that the function is odd, not that the sine of a negative angle is a negative number.

53. True. The tangent function has a period of π.

55. (a) y-axis symmetry   (b) $\sin t_1 = \sin(\pi - t_1)$
   (c) $\cos(\pi - t_1) = -\cos t_1$

57. Answers will vary.

59. (a)

Circle of radius 1 centered at $(0, 0)$

(b) The t-values represent the central angle in radians. The x- and y-values represent the location in the coordinate plane.
(c) $-1 \le x \le 1, -1 \le y \le 1$

61. It is an odd function.

Section 4.3   *(page 286)*

1. (a) v   (b) iv   (c) vi   (d) iii   (e) i   (f) ii

3. complementary

5. $\sin \theta = \dfrac{3}{5}$ $\csc \theta = \dfrac{5}{3}$ **7.** $\sin \theta = \dfrac{9}{41}$ $\csc \theta = \dfrac{41}{9}$
$\cos \theta = \dfrac{4}{5}$ $\sec \theta = \dfrac{5}{4}$ $\cos \theta = \dfrac{40}{41}$ $\sec \theta = \dfrac{41}{40}$
$\tan \theta = \dfrac{3}{4}$ $\cot \theta = \dfrac{4}{3}$ $\tan \theta = \dfrac{9}{40}$ $\cot \theta = \dfrac{40}{9}$

9. $\sin \theta = \dfrac{8}{17}$ $\csc \theta = \dfrac{17}{8}$
$\cos \theta = \dfrac{15}{17}$ $\sec \theta = \dfrac{17}{15}$
$\tan \theta = \dfrac{8}{15}$ $\cot \theta = \dfrac{15}{8}$

The triangles are similar, and corresponding sides are proportional.

11. $\sin \theta = \dfrac{1}{3}$ $\csc \theta = 3$

$\cos \theta = \dfrac{2\sqrt{2}}{3}$ $\sec \theta = \dfrac{3\sqrt{2}}{4}$

$\tan \theta = \dfrac{\sqrt{2}}{4}$ $\cot \theta = 2\sqrt{2}$

The triangles are similar, and corresponding sides are proportional.

13.

$\sin \theta = \dfrac{3}{5}$ $\csc \theta = \dfrac{5}{3}$
$\cos \theta = \dfrac{4}{5}$ $\sec \theta = \dfrac{5}{4}$
              $\cot \theta = \dfrac{4}{3}$

15.

$\sin \theta = \dfrac{\sqrt{5}}{3}$ $\csc \theta = \dfrac{3\sqrt{5}}{5}$

$\cos \theta = \dfrac{2}{3}$

$\tan \theta = \dfrac{\sqrt{5}}{2}$ $\cot \theta = \dfrac{2\sqrt{5}}{5}$

17.

$\cos \theta = \dfrac{2\sqrt{6}}{5}$ $\csc \theta = 5$
                   $\sec \theta = \dfrac{5\sqrt{6}}{12}$
$\tan \theta = \dfrac{\sqrt{6}}{12}$ $\cot \theta = 2\sqrt{6}$

19.

$\sin \theta = \dfrac{\sqrt{10}}{10}$ $\csc \theta = \sqrt{10}$

$\cos \theta = \dfrac{3\sqrt{10}}{10}$ $\sec \theta = \dfrac{\sqrt{10}}{3}$

$\tan \theta = \dfrac{1}{3}$

21. $\dfrac{\pi}{6}; \dfrac{1}{2}$ **23.** $45°; \sqrt{2}$ **25.** $60°; \dfrac{\pi}{3}$ **27.** $30°; 2$

29. $45°; \dfrac{\pi}{4}$ **31.** (a) 0.1736   (b) 0.1736

33. (a) 0.2815   (b) 3.5523   **35.** (a) 0.9964   (b) 1.0036

37. (a) 5.0273   (b) 0.1989   **39.** (a) 1.8527   (b) 0.9817

41. (a) $\dfrac{1}{2}$ (b) $\dfrac{\sqrt{3}}{2}$ (c) $\sqrt{3}$ (d) $\dfrac{\sqrt{3}}{3}$

43. (a) $\dfrac{2\sqrt{2}}{3}$ (b) $2\sqrt{2}$ (c) 3   (d) 3

45. (a) $\dfrac{1}{5}$ (b) $\sqrt{26}$ (c) $\dfrac{1}{5}$ (d) $\dfrac{5\sqrt{26}}{26}$

47–55. Answers will vary.   **57.** (a) $30° = \dfrac{\pi}{6}$ (b) $30° = \dfrac{\pi}{6}$

59. (a) $60° = \dfrac{\pi}{3}$ (b) $45° = \dfrac{\pi}{4}$

61. (a) $60° = \dfrac{\pi}{3}$ (b) $45° = \dfrac{\pi}{4}$ **63.** $x = 9, y = 9\sqrt{3}$

65. $x = \dfrac{32\sqrt{3}}{3}, r = \dfrac{64\sqrt{3}}{3}$ **67.** 443.2 m; 323.3 m

69. $30° = \dfrac{\pi}{6}$ **71.** (a) 219.9 ft   (b) 160.9 ft

73. $(x_1, y_1) = \left(28\sqrt{3}, 28\right)$
     $(x_2, y_2) = \left(28, 28\sqrt{3}\right)$

75. $\sin 20° \approx 0.34, \cos 20° \approx 0.94, \tan 20° \approx 0.36,$
     $\csc 20° \approx 2.92, \sec 20° \approx 1.06, \cot 20° \approx 2.75$

77. (a) 519.33 ft   (b) 1174.17 ft   (c) 173.11 ft/min

79. True, $\csc x = \dfrac{1}{\sin x}$.   **81.** False, $\dfrac{\sqrt{2}}{2} + \dfrac{\sqrt{2}}{2} \ne 1$.

83. False, $1.7321 \ne 0.0349$.

85. Yes, $\tan \theta$ is equal to opp/adj. You can find the value of the hypotenuse by the Pythagorean Theorem. Then you can find $\sec \theta$, which is equal to hyp/adj.

87. (a)

θ	0°	18°	36°	54°	72°	90°
$\sin \theta$	0	0.3090	0.5878	0.8090	0.9511	1
$\cos \theta$	1	0.9511	0.8090	0.5878	0.3090	0

(b) Increasing function   (c) Decreasing function
(d) As the angle increases, the length of the side opposite the angle increases relative to the length of the hypotenuse and the length of the side adjacent to the angle decreases relative to the length of the hypotenuse. Thus, the sine increases and the cosine decreases.

Section 4.4   *(page 296)*

1. $\dfrac{y}{r}$ **3.** $\dfrac{y}{x}$ **5.** $\cos \theta$ **7.** zero; defined

9. (a) $\sin \theta = \dfrac{3}{5}$ $\csc \theta = \dfrac{5}{3}$

  $\cos \theta = \dfrac{4}{5}$ $\sec \theta = \dfrac{5}{4}$

  $\tan \theta = \dfrac{3}{4}$ $\cot \theta = \dfrac{4}{3}$

  (b) $\sin \theta = \dfrac{15}{17}$ $\csc \theta = \dfrac{17}{15}$

  $\cos \theta = -\dfrac{8}{17}$ $\sec \theta = -\dfrac{17}{8}$

  $\tan \theta = -\dfrac{15}{8}$ $\cot \theta = -\dfrac{8}{15}$

11. (a) $\sin \theta = -\dfrac{1}{2}$ $\csc \theta = -2$

  $\cos \theta = -\dfrac{\sqrt{3}}{2}$ $\sec \theta = -\dfrac{2\sqrt{3}}{3}$

  $\tan \theta = \dfrac{\sqrt{3}}{3}$ $\cot \theta = \sqrt{3}$

  (b) $\sin \theta = -\dfrac{\sqrt{17}}{17}$ $\csc \theta = -\sqrt{17}$

  $\cos \theta = \dfrac{4\sqrt{17}}{17}$ $\sec \theta = \dfrac{\sqrt{17}}{4}$

  $\tan \theta = -\dfrac{1}{4}$ $\cot \theta = -4$

13. $\sin \theta = \dfrac{12}{13}$ $\csc \theta = \dfrac{13}{12}$

  $\cos \theta = \dfrac{5}{13}$ $\sec \theta = \dfrac{13}{5}$

  $\tan \theta = \dfrac{12}{5}$ $\cot \theta = \dfrac{5}{12}$

15. $\sin \theta = -\dfrac{2\sqrt{29}}{29}$ $\csc \theta = -\dfrac{\sqrt{29}}{2}$

  $\cos \theta = -\dfrac{5\sqrt{29}}{29}$ $\sec \theta = -\dfrac{\sqrt{29}}{5}$

  $\tan \theta = \dfrac{2}{5}$ $\cot \theta = \dfrac{5}{2}$

17. $\sin \theta = \dfrac{4}{5}$ $\csc \theta = \dfrac{5}{4}$

  $\cos \theta = -\dfrac{3}{5}$ $\sec \theta = -\dfrac{5}{3}$

  $\tan \theta = -\dfrac{4}{3}$ $\cot \theta = -\dfrac{3}{4}$

19. Quadrant I   **21.** Quadrant II

23. $\sin \theta = \dfrac{15}{17}$ $\csc \theta = \dfrac{17}{15}$

  $\cos \theta = -\dfrac{8}{17}$ $\sec \theta = -\dfrac{17}{8}$

  $\tan \theta = -\dfrac{15}{8}$ $\cot \theta = -\dfrac{8}{15}$

25. $\sin \theta = \dfrac{3}{5}$ $\csc \theta = \dfrac{5}{3}$

  $\cos \theta = -\dfrac{4}{5}$ $\sec \theta = -\dfrac{5}{4}$

  $\tan \theta = -\dfrac{3}{4}$ $\cot \theta = -\dfrac{4}{3}$

27. $\sin \theta = -\dfrac{\sqrt{10}}{10}$ $\csc \theta = -\sqrt{10}$

  $\cos \theta = \dfrac{3\sqrt{10}}{10}$ $\sec \theta = \dfrac{\sqrt{10}}{3}$

  $\tan \theta = -\dfrac{1}{3}$ $\cot \theta = -3$

29. $\sin \theta = -\dfrac{\sqrt{3}}{2}$ $\csc \theta = -\dfrac{2\sqrt{3}}{3}$

  $\cos \theta = -\dfrac{1}{2}$ $\sec \theta = -2$

  $\tan \theta = \sqrt{3}$ $\cot \theta = \dfrac{\sqrt{3}}{3}$

31. $\sin \theta = 0$ $\csc \theta$ is undefined.

  $\cos \theta = -1$ $\sec \theta = -1$

  $\tan \theta = 0$ $\cot \theta$ is undefined.

33. $\sin \theta = \dfrac{\sqrt{2}}{2}$ $\csc \theta = \sqrt{2}$

  $\cos \theta = -\dfrac{\sqrt{2}}{2}$ $\sec \theta = -\sqrt{2}$

  $\tan \theta = -1$ $\cot \theta = -1$

35. $\sin \theta = -\dfrac{2\sqrt{5}}{5}$ $\csc \theta = -\dfrac{\sqrt{5}}{2}$

  $\cos \theta = -\dfrac{\sqrt{5}}{5}$ $\sec \theta = -\sqrt{5}$

  $\tan \theta = 2$ $\cot \theta = \dfrac{1}{2}$

37. 0   **39.** Undefined   **41.** 1   **43.** Undefined

45. $\theta' = 20°$ **47.** $\theta' = 55°$

49. $\theta' = \dfrac{\pi}{3}$ **51.** $\theta' = 2\pi - 4.8$

53. $\sin 225° = -\dfrac{\sqrt{2}}{2}$ **55.** $\sin 750° = \dfrac{1}{2}$

  $\cos 225° = -\dfrac{\sqrt{2}}{2}$ $\cos 750° = \dfrac{\sqrt{3}}{2}$

  $\tan 225° = 1$ $\tan 750° = \dfrac{\sqrt{3}}{3}$

57. $\sin(-840°) = -\dfrac{\sqrt{3}}{2}$ **59.** $\sin \dfrac{2\pi}{3} = \dfrac{\sqrt{3}}{2}$

  $\cos(-840°) = -\dfrac{1}{2}$ $\cos \dfrac{2\pi}{3} = -\dfrac{1}{2}$

  $\tan(-840°) = \sqrt{3}$ $\tan \dfrac{2\pi}{3} = -\sqrt{3}$

61. $\sin \dfrac{5\pi}{4} = -\dfrac{\sqrt{2}}{2}$ **63.** $\sin\left(-\dfrac{\pi}{6}\right) = -\dfrac{1}{2}$

  $\cos \dfrac{5\pi}{4} = -\dfrac{\sqrt{2}}{2}$ $\cos\left(-\dfrac{\pi}{6}\right) = \dfrac{\sqrt{3}}{2}$

  $\tan \dfrac{5\pi}{4} = 1$ $\tan\left(-\dfrac{\pi}{6}\right) = -\dfrac{\sqrt{3}}{3}$

65. $\sin \dfrac{9\pi}{4} = \dfrac{\sqrt{2}}{2}$ **67.** $\sin\left(-\dfrac{3\pi}{2}\right) = 1$

  $\cos \dfrac{9\pi}{4} = \dfrac{\sqrt{2}}{2}$ $\cos\left(-\dfrac{3\pi}{2}\right) = 0$

  $\tan \dfrac{9\pi}{4} = 1$ $\tan\left(-\dfrac{3\pi}{2}\right)$ is undefined.

69. $\dfrac{4}{5}$ **71.** $-\dfrac{\sqrt{13}}{2}$ **73.** $\dfrac{8}{5}$ **75.** 0.1736

77. -0.3420 **79.** -1.4826 **81.** 3.2361   **83.** 4.6373

85. 0.3640   **87.** -0.6052 **89.** -0.4142

91. (a) $30° = \dfrac{\pi}{6}, 150° = \dfrac{5\pi}{6}$ (b) $210° = \dfrac{7\pi}{6}, 330° = \dfrac{11\pi}{6}$

93. (a) $60° = \dfrac{\pi}{3}, 120° = \dfrac{2\pi}{3}$ (b) $135° = \dfrac{3\pi}{4}, 315° = \dfrac{7\pi}{4}$

95. (a) $45° = \dfrac{\pi}{4}, 225° = \dfrac{5\pi}{4}$ (b) $150° = \dfrac{5\pi}{6}, 330° = \dfrac{11\pi}{6}$

97. (a) 12 mi   (b) 6 mi   (c) 6.9 mi

99. (a) $N = 22.099 \sin(0.522t - 2.219) + 55.008$
   $F = 36.641 \sin(0.502t - 1.831) + 25.610$
   (b) February: $N = 34.6°, F = -1.4°$
   March: $N = 41.6°, F = 13.9°$
   May: $N = 63.4°, F = 48.6°$
   June: $N = 72.5°, F = 59.5°$
   August: $N = 75.5°, F = 55.6°$
   September: $N = 68.6°, F = 41.7°$
   November: $N = 46.8°, F = 6.5°$
   (c) Answers will vary.

101. (a) 2 cm   (b) 0.11 cm   (c) -1.2 cm

103. False. In each of the four quadrants, the signs of the secant function and the cosine function are the same because these functions are reciprocals of each other.

105. Answers will vary.

107. (a) $\sin t = y$ (b) $r = 1$ because it is a unit circle.
   $\cos t = x$
   (c) $\sin \theta = y$ (d) $\sin t = \sin \theta$ and $\cos t = \cos \theta$
   $\cos \theta = x$

Section 4.5   *(page 306)*

1. cycle   **3.** phase shift   **5.** Period: $\dfrac{2\pi}{5}$; Amplitude: 2

7. Period: 4π; Amplitude: $\dfrac{3}{4}$ **9.** Period: 6; Amplitude: $\dfrac{1}{2}$

11. Period: 2π; Amplitude: 4   **13.** Period: $\dfrac{\pi}{5}$; Amplitude: 3

15. Period: $\dfrac{5\pi}{2}$; Amplitude: $\dfrac{5}{3}$ **17.** Period: 1; Amplitude: $\dfrac{1}{4}$

19. g is a shift of f π units to the right.

21. g is a reflection of f in the x-axis.

23. The period of f is twice the period of g.

25. g is a shift of f three units up.

27. The graph of g has twice the amplitude of the graph of f.

29. The graph of g is a horizontal shift of the graph of f π units to the right.

31.

33.

35.

37.

39.

41.

43.

45.

47.

49.

51.

53.

55.

57.

59.

61. (a) $g(x)$ is obtained by a horizontal shrink of four, and one cycle of $g(x)$ corresponds to the interval $[\pi/4, 3\pi/4]$.

(b)   (c) $g(x) = f(4x - \pi)$

63. (a) One cycle of $g(x)$ corresponds to the interval $[\pi, 3\pi]$, and $g(x)$ is obtained by shifting $f(x)$ up two units.

(b)   (c) $g(x) = f(x - \pi) + 2$

65. (a) One cycle of $g(x)$ is $[\pi/4, 3\pi/4]$. $g(x)$ is also shifted down three units and has an amplitude of two.

(b)   (c) $g(x) = 2f(4x - \pi) - 3$

67.   **69.**

71.   **73.** $a = 2, d = 1$

75. $a = -4, d = 4$ **77.** $a = -3, b = 2, c = 0$

79. $a = 2, b = 1, c = -\dfrac{\pi}{4}$

81. $x = -\dfrac{\pi}{6}, -\dfrac{5\pi}{6}, \dfrac{7\pi}{6}, \dfrac{11\pi}{6}$

83. $y = 1 + 2\sin(2x - \pi)$ **85.** $y = \cos(2x + 2\pi) - \dfrac{3}{2}$

87. (a) 4 sec   (b) 15 cycles/min

(c)

89. (a) $I(t) = 46.2 + 32.4\cos\left(\dfrac{\pi t}{6} - 3.67\right)$

(b)   (c)

The model fits the data well.   The model fits the data well.

(d) Las Vegas: 80.6°; International Falls: 46.2°
The constant term gives the annual average temperature.

(e) 12; yes; One full period is one year.

(f) International Falls; amplitude; The greater the amplitude, the greater the variability in temperature.

91. (a) $\dfrac{1}{440}$ sec   (b) 440 cycles/sec

93. (a) 20 sec; It takes 20 seconds to complete one revolution on the Ferris wheel.

(b) 50 ft; The diameter of the Ferris wheel is 100 feet.

(c)

95. False. The graph of $f(x) = \sin(x + 2\pi)$ translates the graph of $f(x) = \sin x$ exactly one period to the left so that the two graphs look identical.

97.

Conjecture: $\sin x = \cos\left(x - \dfrac{\pi}{2}\right)$

99.

The value of b affects the period of the graph.

$b = \frac{1}{2} \rightarrow \frac{1}{2}$ cycle

$b = 2 \rightarrow 2$ cycles

$b = 3 \rightarrow 3$ cycles

101. (a) 0.4794, 0.4794   (b) 0.8417, 0.8415   (c) 0.5, 0.5

(d) 0.8776, 0.8776   (e) 0.5417, 0.5403

(f) 0.7074, 0.7071

The error increases as x moves farther away from 0.

Section 4.6   *(page 317)*

1. odd; origin   **3.** reciprocal   **5.** π

7. $(-\infty, -1] \cup [1, \infty)$ **9.** e, π **10.** c, 2π **11.** a, 1

12. d, 2π **13.** f, 4   **14.** b, 4

15.   **17.**

19.   **21.**

23.   **25.**

27.   **29.**

31.   **33.**

35.   **37.**

39.   **41.**

43.   **45.**

47.   **49.** $-\dfrac{7\pi}{4}, -\dfrac{3\pi}{4}, \dfrac{\pi}{4}, \dfrac{5\pi}{4}$

51. $-\dfrac{4\pi}{3}, -\dfrac{\pi}{3}, \dfrac{2\pi}{3}, \dfrac{5\pi}{3}$ **53.** $-\dfrac{4\pi}{3}, -\dfrac{2\pi}{3}, \dfrac{2\pi}{3}, \dfrac{4\pi}{3}$

55. $-\dfrac{7\pi}{4}, -\dfrac{5\pi}{4}, \dfrac{\pi}{4}, \dfrac{3\pi}{4}$ **57.** Even   **59.** Odd   **61.** Odd

63. Even   **65.** d, $f \rightarrow 0$ as $x \rightarrow 0$.   **66.** a, $f \rightarrow 0$ as $x \rightarrow 0$.

67. b, $g \rightarrow 0$ as $x \rightarrow 0$.   **68.** c, $g \rightarrow 0$ as $x \rightarrow 0$.

69.   **71.**

The functions are equal.   The functions are equal.

73.   **75.**

As $x \rightarrow \infty$, $g(x) \rightarrow 0$.   As $x \rightarrow \infty$, $f(x) \rightarrow 0$.

77.

As $x \to 0$, $y \to \infty$.

79.

As $x \to 0$, $g(x) \to 1$.

81.

As $x \to 0$, $f(x)$ oscillates between 1 and -1.

83. (a) Period of $H(t)$: 12 mo
Period of $L(t)$: 12 mo
(b) Summer; winter
(c) About 0.5 mo

85. $d = 7 \cot x$

87. True. $y = \sec x$ is equal to $y = 1/\cos x$, and if the reciprocal of $y = \sin x$ is translated $\pi/2$ units to the left, then

$$\frac{1}{\sin\left(x + \dfrac{\pi}{2}\right)} = \frac{1}{\cos x} = \sec x.$$

89. (a) As $x \to 0^+$, $f(x) \to \infty$. (b) As $x \to 0^-$, $f(x) \to -\infty$.
(c) As $x \to \pi^+$, $f(x) \to -\infty$. (d) As $x \to \pi^-$, $f(x) \to \infty$.

91. (a) As $x \to \left(\dfrac{\pi}{2}\right)^+$, $f(x) \to -\infty$.

(b) As $x \to \left(\dfrac{\pi}{2}\right)^-$, $f(x) \to \infty$.

(c) As $x \to \left(-\dfrac{\pi}{2}\right)^+$, $f(x) \to \infty$.

(d) As $x \to \left(-\dfrac{\pi}{2}\right)^-$, $f(x) \to -\infty$.

93. (a)

0.7391

(b) 1, 0.5403, 0.8576, 0.6543, 0.7935, 0.7014, 0.7640, 0.7221, 0.7504, 0.7314, . . . ; 0.7391

Section 4.7 (page 326)

1. $y = \sin^{-1} x$; $-1 \le x \le 1$

3. $y = \tan^{-1} x$; $-\infty < x < \infty$; $-\dfrac{\pi}{2} < y < \dfrac{\pi}{2}$

5. $\dfrac{\pi}{6}$ **7.** $\dfrac{\pi}{3}$ **9.** $\dfrac{\pi}{6}$ **11.** $\dfrac{5\pi}{6}$ **13.** $-\dfrac{\pi}{3}$

15. $\dfrac{2\pi}{3}$ **17.** $-\dfrac{\pi}{3}$

19.

21. 1.19 **23.** -0.85 **25.** -1.25 **27.** 0.32

29. 1.99 **31.** 0.74 **33.** 1.07 **35.** 1.36 **37.** -1.52

39. $-\dfrac{\pi}{3}, -\dfrac{\sqrt{3}}{3}, 1$ **41.** $\theta = \arctan \dfrac{x}{4}$ **43.** $\theta = \arcsin \dfrac{x+2}{5}$

45. $\theta = \arccos \dfrac{x+3}{2x}$ **47.** 0.3 **49.** -0.1 **51.** 0

53. $\dfrac{3}{5}$ **55.** $\dfrac{\sqrt{5}}{5}$ **57.** $\dfrac{12}{13}$ **59.** $\dfrac{\sqrt{34}}{5}$ **61.** $\dfrac{\sqrt{5}}{3}$

63. 2 **65.** $\dfrac{1}{x}$ **67.** $\sqrt{1 - 4x^2}$ **69.** $\sqrt{1 - x^2}$

71. $\dfrac{\sqrt{9 - x^2}}{x}$ **73.** $\dfrac{\sqrt{x^2 + 2}}{x}$

75.

77. $\dfrac{9}{\sqrt{x^2 + 81}}$

79. $\dfrac{|x - 1|}{\sqrt{x^2 - 2x + 10}}$

Asymptotes: $y = \pm 1$

81.

83.

The graph of g is a horizontal shift one unit to the right of f.

85.

87.

89.

91.

93.

CHAPTER 4

95. $3\sqrt{2}\sin\left(2t + \dfrac{\pi}{4}\right)$

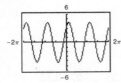

The graph implies that the identity is true.

97. $\dfrac{\pi}{2}$ **99.** $\dfrac{\pi}{2}$ **101.** π

103. (a) $\theta = \arcsin\dfrac{5}{s}$ (b) $0.13, 0.25$

105. (a)

(b) 2 ft   (c) $\beta = 0$; As x increases, β approaches 0.

107. (a) $\theta \approx 26.0°$ (b) 24.4 ft

109. (a) $\theta = \arctan\dfrac{x}{20}$ (b) $14.0°, 31.0°$

111. False. $\dfrac{5\pi}{4}$ is not in the range of the arctangent.

113. False. $\sin^{-1} x$ is the inverse of $\sin x$, not the reciprocal.

115. Domain: **117.** Domain:
   $(-\infty, \infty)$ $(-\infty, -1] \cup [1, \infty)$
   Range: Range:
   $(0, \pi)$ $[-\pi/2, 0) \cup (0, \pi/2]$

119. $\dfrac{\pi}{4}$ **121.** $\dfrac{3\pi}{4}$ **123.** $\dfrac{\pi}{6}$ **125.** $\dfrac{\pi}{3}$ **127.** 1.17

129. 0.19   **131.** 0.54   **133.** -0.12

135. (a) $\dfrac{\pi}{4}$ (b) $\dfrac{\pi}{2}$ (c) 1.25   (d) 2.03

137. (a) $f \circ f^{-1}$ $f^{-1} \circ f$

(b) The domains and ranges of the functions are restricted. The graphs of $f \circ f^{-1}$ and $f^{-1} \circ f$ differ because of the domains and ranges of f and f^{-1}.

Section 4.8   *(page 336)*

1. bearing   **3.** period

5. $a \approx 1.73$ **7.** $a \approx 8.26$ **9.** $c = 5$
   $c \approx 3.46$ $c \approx 25.38$ $A \approx 36.87°$
   $B = 60°$ $A = 19°$ $B \approx 53.13°$

11. $a \approx 49.48$ **13.** $a \approx 91.34$ **15.** 3.00
   $A \approx 72.08°$ $b \approx 420.70$
   $B \approx 17.92°$ $B = 77°45'$

17. 2.50   **19.** 214.45 ft   **21.** 19.7 ft

23. 19.9 ft   **25.** 11.8 km   **27.** 56.3°   **29.** 2.06°

31. (a) $\sqrt{h^2 + 34h + 10{,}289}$ (b) $\theta = \arccos\dfrac{100}{l}$

   (c) 53.02 ft

33. (a) $l = 250$ ft, $A \approx 36.87°$, $B \approx 53.13°$ (b) 4.87 sec

35. 554 mi north; 709 mi east

37. (a) 104.95 nm south; 58.18 nm west
   (b) S 36.7° W; distance $\approx$ 130.9 nm

39. N 56.31° W   **41.** (a) N 58° E   (b) 68.82 m

43. 35.3°   **45.** 29.4 in.   **47.** $d = 4\sin \pi t$

49. $d = 3\cos\dfrac{4\pi t}{3}$ **51.** $\omega = 528\pi$

53. (a) 9   (b) $\dfrac{3}{5}$ (c) 9   (d) $\dfrac{5}{12}$

55. (a) $\dfrac{1}{4}$ (b) 3   (c) 0   (d) $\dfrac{1}{6}$

57. (a)   (b) $\dfrac{\pi}{8}$ (c) $\dfrac{\pi}{32}$

59. (a)   (b) 12; Yes, there are 12 months in a year.

(c) 2.77; The maximum change in the number of hours of daylight

61. False. The scenario does not create a right triangle because the tower is not vertical.

Review Exercises   *(page 342)*

1. (a)

(b) Quadrant IV   (c) $\dfrac{23\pi}{4}, -\dfrac{\pi}{4}$

3. (a)

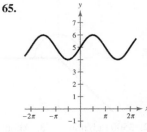

    (b) Quadrant III   (c) $250°, -470°$

5. 7.854   **7.** -0.589 **9.** $54.000°$ **11.** $-200.535°$

13. $198° \, 24'$ **15.** 48.17 in.   **17.** Area ≈ 339.29 in.^{2}

19. $\left(-\dfrac{1}{2}, \dfrac{\sqrt{3}}{2}\right)$ **21.** $\left(-\dfrac{\sqrt{3}}{2}, -\dfrac{1}{2}\right)$

23. $\sin\dfrac{3\pi}{4} = \dfrac{\sqrt{2}}{2}$ $\csc\dfrac{3\pi}{4} = \sqrt{2}$

    $\cos\dfrac{3\pi}{4} = -\dfrac{\sqrt{2}}{2}$ $\sec\dfrac{3\pi}{4} = -\sqrt{2}$

    $\tan\dfrac{3\pi}{4} = -1$ $\cot\dfrac{3\pi}{4} = -1$

25. $\sin\dfrac{11\pi}{4} = \sin\dfrac{3\pi}{4} = \dfrac{\sqrt{2}}{2}$

27. $\sin\left(-\dfrac{17\pi}{6}\right) = \sin\dfrac{7\pi}{6} = -\dfrac{1}{2}$ **29.** -75.3130 **31.** 3.2361

33. $\sin\theta = \dfrac{4\sqrt{41}}{41}$ $\csc\theta = \dfrac{\sqrt{41}}{4}$

    $\cos\theta = \dfrac{5\sqrt{41}}{41}$ $\sec\theta = \dfrac{\sqrt{41}}{5}$

    $\tan\theta = \dfrac{4}{5}$ $\cot\theta = \dfrac{5}{4}$

35. 0.6494   **37.** 3.6722

39. (a) 3 (b) $\dfrac{2\sqrt{2}}{3}$ (c) $\dfrac{3\sqrt{2}}{4}$ (d) $\dfrac{\sqrt{2}}{4}$ **41.** 71.3 m

43. $\sin\theta = \dfrac{4}{5}$ $\csc\theta = \dfrac{5}{4}$ **45.** $\sin\theta = \dfrac{4}{5}$ $\csc\theta = \dfrac{5}{4}$

    $\cos\theta = \dfrac{3}{5}$ $\sec\theta = \dfrac{5}{3}$ $\cos\theta = \dfrac{3}{5}$ $\sec\theta = \dfrac{5}{3}$

    $\tan\theta = \dfrac{4}{3}$ $\cot\theta = \dfrac{3}{4}$ $\tan\theta = \dfrac{4}{3}$ $\cot\theta = \dfrac{3}{4}$

47. $\sin\theta = -\dfrac{\sqrt{11}}{6}$ **49.** $\sin\theta = \dfrac{\sqrt{21}}{5}$

    $\cos\theta = \dfrac{5}{6}$ $\tan\theta = -\dfrac{\sqrt{21}}{2}$

    $\tan\theta = -\dfrac{\sqrt{11}}{5}$ $\csc\theta = \dfrac{5\sqrt{21}}{21}$

    $\csc\theta = -\dfrac{6\sqrt{11}}{11}$ $\sec\theta = -\dfrac{5}{2}$

    $\cot\theta = -\dfrac{5\sqrt{11}}{11}$ $\cot\theta = -\dfrac{2\sqrt{21}}{21}$

51. $\theta' = 84°$ **53.** $\theta' = \dfrac{\pi}{5}$

55. $\sin\dfrac{\pi}{3} = \dfrac{\sqrt{3}}{2}$; $\cos\dfrac{\pi}{3} = \dfrac{1}{2}$; $\tan\dfrac{\pi}{3} = \sqrt{3}$

57. $\sin(-150°) = -\dfrac{1}{2}$; $\cos(-150°) = -\dfrac{\sqrt{3}}{2}$;

    $\tan(-150°) = \dfrac{\sqrt{3}}{3}$

59. -0.7568 **61.** 0.9511

63.

65.

67.

69. (a) $y = 2\sin 528\pi x$

    (b) 264 cycles/sec

71.   **73.**

75.

As $x \to +\infty$, $f(x)$ oscillates.

77. $-\dfrac{\pi}{2}$ **79.** $\dfrac{\pi}{6}$ **81.** -0.98 **83.** 0.09

85.   **87.** $\dfrac{4}{5}$ **89.** $\dfrac{4\sqrt{15}}{15}$

91. $\dfrac{\sqrt{4 - x^2}}{x}$ **93.**   **95.** 1221 mi, 85.6°

$\theta \approx 66.8°$

70 m

θ

30 m

97. False. For each θ there corresponds exactly one value of y.

99. The function is undefined because $\sec \theta = 1/\cos \theta$.

101. The ranges of the other four trigonometric functions are $(-\infty, \infty)$ or $(-\infty, -1] \cup [1, \infty)$.

Chapter Test (page 345)

1. (a)   (b) $\dfrac{13\pi}{4}, -\dfrac{3\pi}{4}$ (c) $225°$

2. 3500 rad/min   **3.** About 709.04 ft²

4. $\sin \theta = \dfrac{3\sqrt{10}}{10}$ $\csc \theta = \dfrac{\sqrt{10}}{3}$

$\cos \theta = -\dfrac{\sqrt{10}}{10}$ $\sec \theta = -\sqrt{10}$

$\tan \theta = -3$ $\cot \theta = -\dfrac{1}{3}$

5. For $0 \le \theta < \dfrac{\pi}{2}$:   For $\pi \le \theta < \dfrac{3\pi}{2}$:

$\sin \theta = \dfrac{3\sqrt{13}}{13}$ $\sin \theta = -\dfrac{3\sqrt{13}}{13}$

$\cos \theta = \dfrac{2\sqrt{13}}{13}$ $\cos \theta = -\dfrac{2\sqrt{13}}{13}$

$\csc \theta = \dfrac{\sqrt{13}}{3}$ $\csc \theta = -\dfrac{\sqrt{13}}{3}$

$\sec \theta = \dfrac{\sqrt{13}}{2}$ $\sec \theta = -\dfrac{\sqrt{13}}{2}$

$\cot \theta = \dfrac{2}{3}$ $\cot \theta = \dfrac{2}{3}$

6. $\theta' = 25°$ **7.** Quadrant III

8. $150°, 210°$

9. $1.33, 1.81$

10. $\sin \theta = -\dfrac{4}{5}$ **11.** $\sin \theta = \dfrac{21}{29}$

$\tan \theta = -\dfrac{4}{3}$ $\cos \theta = -\dfrac{20}{29}$

$\csc \theta = -\dfrac{5}{4}$ $\tan \theta = -\dfrac{21}{20}$

$\sec \theta = \dfrac{5}{3}$ $\csc \theta = \dfrac{29}{21}$

$\cot \theta = -\dfrac{3}{4}$ $\cot \theta = -\dfrac{20}{21}$

12.   **13.**

14.   **15.**

Period: 2   Not periodic

16. $a = -2, b = \dfrac{1}{2}, c = -\dfrac{\pi}{4}$ **17.** $\dfrac{\sqrt{55}}{3}$

18.

19. $309.3°$ **20.** $d = -6 \cos \pi t$

Problem Solving (page 347)

1. (a) $\dfrac{11\pi}{2}$ rad or $990°$ (b) About 816.42 ft

3. (a) 4767 ft   (b) 3705 ft

(c) $w \approx 2183$ ft, $\tan 63° = \dfrac{w + 3705}{3000}$

5. (a)   (b)

Even   Even

7. $h = 51 - 50 \sin\left(8\pi t + \dfrac{\pi}{2}\right)$

9. (a)

(b) Period $= \dfrac{3}{4}$ sec; Answers will vary.

(c) 20 mm; Answers will vary.   (d) 80 beats/min

(e) Period $= \dfrac{15}{16}$ sec; $\dfrac{32\pi}{15}$

11. (a)

(b) Period of f: 2π; Period of g: π

(c) Yes, because the sine and cosine functions are periodic.

13. (a) $40.5°$ (b) $x \approx 1.71$ ft; $y \approx 3.46$ ft   (c) About 1.75 ft

(d) As you move closer to the rock, d must get smaller and smaller. The angles θ_1 and θ_2 will decrease along with the distance y, so d will decrease.

Chapter 5

Section 5.1   (page 355)

1. $\tan u$ **3.** $\cot u$ **5.** $\cot^2 u$

7. $\sin x = \dfrac{1}{2}$

$\cos x = \dfrac{\sqrt{3}}{2}$

$\tan x = \dfrac{\sqrt{3}}{3}$

$\csc x = 2$

$\sec x = \dfrac{2\sqrt{3}}{3}$

$\cot x = \sqrt{3}$

9. $\sin x = \dfrac{3}{5}$

$\cos x = \dfrac{4}{5}$

$\tan x = \dfrac{3}{4}$

$\csc x = \dfrac{5}{3}$

$\sec x = \dfrac{5}{4}$

$\cot x = \dfrac{4}{3}$

11. $\sin x = \dfrac{\sqrt{15}}{4}$

$\cos x = \dfrac{1}{4}$

$\tan x = \sqrt{15}$

$\csc x = \dfrac{4\sqrt{15}}{15}$

$\sec x = 4$

$\cot x = \dfrac{\sqrt{15}}{15}$

13. $\sin \theta = -1$

$\cos \theta = 0$

$\tan \theta$ is undefined.

$\csc \theta = -1$

$\sec \theta$ is undefined.

$\cot \theta = 0$

15. c   **16.** b   **17.** f   **18.** a   **19.** e   **20.** d

21. $\sin^2 x$ **23.** $\sec x + 1$ **25.** $\sin^4 x$

27. $\csc^2 x(\cot x + 1)$ **29.** $(3\sin x + 1)(\sin x - 2)$

31. $(\csc x - 1)(\csc x + 2)$ **33.** $1 + 2\sin x \cos x$

35. $\csc \theta$ **37.** $\cos^2 \phi$ **39.** $\sin^2 x$ **41.** $\tan x$

43. $\sec \beta$ **45.** $2\csc^2 x$ **47.** $-\cot x$ **49.** $1 + \cos y$

51. $\csc x$ **53.** $3\sin \theta$ **55.** $2\tan \theta$

57. $3\cos \theta = 3$; $\sin \theta = 0$; $\cos \theta = 1$ **59.** $0 \le \theta \le \pi$

61. $\ln|\cos x|$ **63.** $\ln|\csc t \sec t|$ **65.** $\mu = \tan \theta$

67. True. For example, $\sin(-x) = -\sin x$.   **69.** $\infty, 0$

71. Not an identity because $\dfrac{\sin k\theta}{\cos k\theta} = \tan k\theta$ **73.** $a\sec \theta$

75. $\cos \theta = \pm\sqrt{1 - \sin^2 \theta}$

$\tan \theta = \pm\dfrac{\sin \theta}{\sqrt{1 - \sin^2 \theta}}$

$\cot \theta = \pm\dfrac{\sqrt{1 - \sin^2 \theta}}{\sin \theta}$

$\sec \theta = \pm\dfrac{1}{\sqrt{1 - \sin^2 \theta}}$

$\csc \theta = \dfrac{1}{\sin \theta}$

Section 5.2   (page 362)

1. identity   **3.** $\tan u$ **5.** $\cos^2 u$ **7.** $-\csc u$

9–49. Answers will vary.

51. In the first line, $\cot(x)$ is substituted for $\cot(-x)$, which is incorrect; $\cot(-x) = -\cot(x)$.

53. (a)

(b)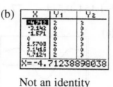

Identity

(c) Answers will vary.

55. (a)

(b)

Not an identity

(c) Answers will vary.

57. (a)

(b)

Identity

(c) Answers will vary.

59–61. Answers will vary.   **63.** 1

65. Answers will vary.

67. True. Many different techniques can be used to verify identities.

69. False. $\sin x^2 = \sin(x \cdot x) \ne \sin^2 x = (\sin x)(\sin x)$

71. The equation is not an identity because $\sin \theta = \pm\sqrt{1 - \cos^2 \theta}$.

Possible answer: $\dfrac{7\pi}{4}$

73. The equation is not an identity because $1 - \cos^2 \theta = \sin^2 \theta$.

Possible answer: $-\dfrac{\pi}{2}$

Section 5.3   (page 371)

1. isolate   **3.** quadratic   **5–9.** Answers will vary.

11. $\dfrac{\pi}{3} + 2n\pi, \dfrac{2\pi}{3} + 2n\pi$ **13.** $\dfrac{2\pi}{3} + 2n\pi, \dfrac{4\pi}{3} + 2n\pi$

15. $\dfrac{\pi}{6} + n\pi, \dfrac{5\pi}{6} + n\pi$ **17.** $\dfrac{\pi}{3} + n\pi, \dfrac{2\pi}{3} + n\pi$

19. $\dfrac{\pi}{8} + \dfrac{n\pi}{2}, \dfrac{3\pi}{8} + \dfrac{n\pi}{2}$ **21.** $\dfrac{n\pi}{3}, \dfrac{\pi}{4} + n\pi$

23. $n\pi, \dfrac{3\pi}{2} + 2n\pi$ **25.** $0, \dfrac{\pi}{2}, \pi, \dfrac{3\pi}{2}$

27. $0, \pi, \dfrac{\pi}{6}, \dfrac{5\pi}{6}, \dfrac{7\pi}{6}, \dfrac{11\pi}{6}$ **29.** $\dfrac{\pi}{3}, \dfrac{5\pi}{3}, \pi$ **31.** No solution

33. $\pi, \dfrac{\pi}{3}, \dfrac{5\pi}{3}$ **35.** $\dfrac{\pi}{6}, \dfrac{5\pi}{6}, \dfrac{7\pi}{6}, \dfrac{11\pi}{6}$ **37.** $\dfrac{\pi}{2}$

39. $\dfrac{\pi}{6} + n\pi, \dfrac{5\pi}{6} + n\pi$ **41.** $\dfrac{\pi}{12} + \dfrac{n\pi}{3}$

43. $\dfrac{\pi}{2} + 4n\pi, \dfrac{7\pi}{2} + 4n\pi$ **45.** $3 + 4n$

47. $-2 + 6n, 2 + 6n$ **49.** $2.678, 5.820$ **51.** $1.047, 5.236$

53. $0.860, 3.426$ **55.** $0, 2.678, 3.142, 5.820$

57. $0.983, 1.768, 4.124, 4.910$

59. $0.3398, 0.8481, 2.2935, 2.8018$

61. $1.9357, 2.7767, 5.0773, 5.9183$

63. $\arctan(-4) + \pi, \arctan(-4) + 2\pi, \arctan 3, \arctan 3 + \pi$

CHAPTER 5

65. $\dfrac{\pi}{4}, \dfrac{5\pi}{4}$, arctan 5, arctan $5 + \pi$ **67.** $\dfrac{\pi}{3}, \dfrac{5\pi}{3}$

69. $\arctan\left(\frac{1}{3}\right)$, $\arctan\left(\frac{1}{3}\right) + \pi$, $\arctan\left(-\frac{1}{3}\right) + \pi$, $\arctan\left(-\frac{1}{3}\right) + 2\pi$

71. $\arccos\left(\frac{1}{4}\right)$, $2\pi - \arccos\left(\frac{1}{4}\right)$

73. $\dfrac{\pi}{2}$, $\arcsin\left(-\frac{1}{4}\right) + 2\pi$, $\arcsin\left(\frac{1}{4}\right) + \pi$

75. $-1.154, 0.534$ **77.** 1.110

79. (a)

(b) $\dfrac{\pi}{3} \approx 1.0472$

$\dfrac{5\pi}{3} \approx 5.2360$

0

$\pi \approx 3.1416$

Maximum: $(1.0472, 1.25)$
Maximum: $(5.2360, 1.25)$
Minimum: $(0, 1)$
Minimum: $(3.1416, -1)$

81. (a)

(b) $\dfrac{\pi}{4} \approx 0.7854$

$\dfrac{5\pi}{4} \approx 3.9270$

Maximum: $(0.7854, 1.4142)$
Minimum: $(3.9270, -1.4142)$

83. (a)

(b) $\dfrac{\pi}{4} \approx 0.7854$

$\dfrac{5\pi}{4} \approx 3.9270$

$\dfrac{3\pi}{4} \approx 2.3562$

$\dfrac{7\pi}{4} \approx 5.4978$

Maximum: $(0.7854, 0.5)$
Maximum: $(3.9270, 0.5)$
Minimum: $(2.3562, -0.5)$
Minimum: $(5.4978, -0.5)$

85. 1

87. (a) All real numbers x except $x = 0$
(b) y-axis symmetry   (c) y approaches 1.
(d) Four solutions: $\pm\pi, \pm 2\pi$

89. 0.04 sec, 0.43 sec, 0.83 sec

91. January, November, December

93. (a) and (c)

The model fits the data well.

(b) $H = 15.65 \cos\left(\dfrac{\pi}{6}t - \dfrac{7\pi}{6}\right) + 77.95$ (d) $77.95°$F

(e) Above 86°: June through September
Below 86°: October through May

95. (a)

$A \approx 1.12$

(b) $0.6 < x < 1.1$

97. 1

99. True. The first equation has a smaller period than the second equation, so it will have more solutions in the interval $[0, 2\pi)$.

101. The equation would become $\cos^2 x = 2$; this is not the correct method to use when solving equations.

103. (a)

Graphs intersect when $x = \dfrac{\pi}{2}$ and $x = \pi$.

(b)

x-intercepts: $\left(\dfrac{\pi}{2}, 0\right)$, $(\pi, 0)$

Both methods produce the same x-values.

Section 5.4   (page 379)

1. $\sin u \cos v - \cos u \sin v$ **3.** $\dfrac{\tan u + \tan v}{1 - \tan u \tan v}$

5. $\cos u \cos v + \sin u \sin v$

7. (a) $\dfrac{\sqrt{2} - \sqrt{6}}{4}$ (b) $\dfrac{\sqrt{2} + 1}{2}$

9. (a) $\dfrac{\sqrt{6} + \sqrt{2}}{4}$ (b) $\dfrac{\sqrt{2} - \sqrt{3}}{2}$

11. $\sin \dfrac{11\pi}{12} = \dfrac{\sqrt{2}}{4}\left(\sqrt{3} - 1\right)$ **13.** $\sin \dfrac{17\pi}{12} = -\dfrac{\sqrt{2}}{4}\left(\sqrt{3} + 1\right)$

$\cos \dfrac{11\pi}{12} = -\dfrac{\sqrt{2}}{4}\left(\sqrt{3} + 1\right)$ $\cos \dfrac{17\pi}{12} = \dfrac{\sqrt{2}}{4}\left(1 - \sqrt{3}\right)$

$\tan \dfrac{11\pi}{12} = -2 + \sqrt{3}$ $\tan \dfrac{17\pi}{12} = 2 + \sqrt{3}$

15. $\sin 105° = \dfrac{\sqrt{2}}{4}\left(\sqrt{3} + 1\right)$ **17.** $\sin 195° = \dfrac{\sqrt{2}}{4}\left(1 - \sqrt{3}\right)$

$\cos 105° = \dfrac{\sqrt{2}}{4}\left(1 - \sqrt{3}\right)$ $\cos 195° = -\dfrac{\sqrt{2}}{4}\left(\sqrt{3} + 1\right)$

$\tan 105° = -2 - \sqrt{3}$ $\tan 195° = 2 - \sqrt{3}$

19. $\sin \dfrac{13\pi}{12} = \dfrac{\sqrt{2}}{4}\left(1 - \sqrt{3}\right)$

$\cos \dfrac{13\pi}{12} = -\dfrac{\sqrt{2}}{4}\left(1 + \sqrt{3}\right)$

$\tan \dfrac{13\pi}{12} = 2 - \sqrt{3}$

21. $\sin\left(-\dfrac{13\pi}{12}\right) = \dfrac{\sqrt{2}}{4}(\sqrt{3} - 1)$

$\cos\left(-\dfrac{13\pi}{12}\right) = -\dfrac{\sqrt{2}}{4}(\sqrt{3} + 1)$

$\tan\left(-\dfrac{13\pi}{12}\right) = -2 + \sqrt{3}$

23. $\sin 285° = -\dfrac{\sqrt{2}}{4}(\sqrt{3} + 1)$

$\cos 285° = \dfrac{\sqrt{2}}{4}(\sqrt{3} - 1)$

$\tan 285° = -(2 + \sqrt{3})$

25. $\sin(-165°) = -\dfrac{\sqrt{2}}{4}(\sqrt{3} - 1)$

$\cos(-165°) = -\dfrac{\sqrt{2}}{4}(1 + \sqrt{3})$

$\tan(-165°) = 2 - \sqrt{3}$

27. $\sin 1.8$ **29.** $\sin 75°$ **31.** $\tan 15°$ **33.** $\cos(3x - 2y)$

35. $\dfrac{\sqrt{3}}{2}$ **37.** $\dfrac{\sqrt{3}}{2}$ **39.** $-\sqrt{3}$ **41.** $-\dfrac{63}{65}$ **43.** $-\dfrac{63}{16}$

45. $\dfrac{65}{56}$ **47.** $\dfrac{3}{5}$ **49.** $-\dfrac{44}{117}$ **51.** $-\dfrac{125}{44}$ **53.** 1 **55.** 0

57–63. Proofs   **65.** $-\sin x$ **67.** $-\cos\theta$ **69.** $\dfrac{\pi}{6}, \dfrac{5\pi}{6}$

71. $\dfrac{5\pi}{4}, \dfrac{7\pi}{4}$ **73.** $0, \dfrac{\pi}{3}, \pi, \dfrac{5\pi}{3}$ **75.** $\dfrac{\pi}{4}, \dfrac{7\pi}{4}$ **77.** $\dfrac{\pi}{2}, \pi, \dfrac{3\pi}{2}$

79. (a) $y = \dfrac{5}{12}\sin(2t + 0.6435)$ (b) $\dfrac{5}{12}$ ft   (c) $\dfrac{1}{\pi}$ cycle/sec

81. True. $\sin(u \pm v) = \sin u \cos v \pm \cos u \sin v$

83. False. $\tan\left(x - \dfrac{\pi}{4}\right) = \dfrac{\tan x - 1}{1 + \tan x}$

85. (a) All real numbers h except $h = 0$

(b)

h	0.5	0.2	0.1
$f(h)$	0.267	0.410	0.456
$g(h)$	0.267	0.410	0.456

h	0.05	0.02	0.01
$f(h)$	0.478	0.491	0.496
$g(h)$	0.478	0.491	0.496

(c)

(d) As $h \to 0^+$, $f \to 0.5$ and $g \to 0.5$.

87–89. Answers will vary.

91. (a) $\sqrt{2}\sin\left(\theta + \dfrac{\pi}{4}\right)$ (b) $\sqrt{2}\cos\left(\theta - \dfrac{\pi}{4}\right)$

93. (a) $13\sin(3\theta + 0.3948)$ (b) $13\cos(3\theta - 1.1760)$

95. $\sqrt{2}\sin\theta + \sqrt{2}\cos\theta$ **97.** $15°$

99.

No, $y_1 \neq y_2$ because their graphs are different.

101. (a) and (b) Proofs

Section 5.5   *(page 389)*

1. $2\sin u \cos u$ **3.** $\tan^2 u$

5. $\dfrac{1}{2}[\sin(u + v) + \sin(u - v)]$ **7.** $0, \dfrac{\pi}{3}, \pi, \dfrac{5\pi}{3}$

9. $0, \dfrac{2\pi}{3}, \dfrac{4\pi}{3}$ **11.** $0, \dfrac{\pi}{2}, \pi, \dfrac{3\pi}{2}$

13. $\dfrac{\pi}{2}, \dfrac{\pi}{6}, \dfrac{5\pi}{6}, \dfrac{7\pi}{6}, \dfrac{3\pi}{2}, \dfrac{11\pi}{6}$ **15.** $3\sin 2x$ **17.** $3\cos 2x$

19. $4\cos 2x$ **21.** $\sin 2u = -\dfrac{24}{25}$, $\cos 2u = \dfrac{7}{25}$, $\tan 2u = -\dfrac{24}{7}$

23. $\sin 2u = \dfrac{15}{17}$, $\cos 2u = \dfrac{8}{17}$, $\tan 2u = \dfrac{15}{8}$

25. $8\cos^4 x - 8\cos^2 x + 1$ **27.** $\dfrac{1}{8}(3 + 4\cos 2x + \cos 4x)$

29. $\dfrac{(3 - 4\cos 4x + \cos 8x)}{(3 + 4\cos 4x + \cos 8x)}$ **31.** $\dfrac{1}{8}(1 - \cos 8x)$

33. $\sin 75° = \dfrac{1}{2}\sqrt{2 + \sqrt{3}}$ **35.** $\sin\dfrac{\pi}{8} = \dfrac{1}{2}\sqrt{2 - \sqrt{2}}$

$\cos 75° = \dfrac{1}{2}\sqrt{2 - \sqrt{3}}$ $\cos\dfrac{\pi}{8} = \dfrac{1}{2}\sqrt{2 + \sqrt{2}}$

$\tan 75° = 2 + \sqrt{3}$ $\tan\dfrac{\pi}{8} = \sqrt{2} - 1$

37. (a) Quadrant I

(b) $\sin\dfrac{u}{2} = \dfrac{3}{5}$, $\cos\dfrac{u}{2} = \dfrac{4}{5}$, $\tan\dfrac{u}{2} = \dfrac{3}{4}$

39. (a) Quadrant II

(b) $\sin\dfrac{u}{2} = \dfrac{\sqrt{26}}{26}$, $\cos\dfrac{u}{2} = -\dfrac{5\sqrt{26}}{26}$, $\tan\dfrac{u}{2} = -\dfrac{1}{5}$

41. $|\sin 3x|$ **43.** $-|\tan 4x|$

45. π **47.** $\dfrac{\pi}{3}, \pi, \dfrac{5\pi}{3}$

49. $\dfrac{1}{2}(\cos 2\theta - \cos 8\theta)$ **51.** $\dfrac{1}{2}(\cos(-2\theta) + \cos 6\theta)$

53. $2\cos 4\theta \sin\theta$ **55.** $2\cos 4x \cos 2x$ **57.** $\dfrac{\sqrt{6}}{2}$

59. $-\sqrt{2}$

61. $0, \dfrac{\pi}{4}, \dfrac{\pi}{2}, \dfrac{3\pi}{4}, \pi, \dfrac{5\pi}{4}, \dfrac{3\pi}{2}, \dfrac{7\pi}{4}$ **63.** $\dfrac{\pi}{6}, \dfrac{5\pi}{6}$

65–71. Answers will vary.

73. (a) $\cos\theta = \dfrac{M^2 - 2}{M^2}$ (b) π (c) 0.4482

(d) 760 mi/h; 3420 mi/h

75. $x = 2r(1 - \cos\theta)$

77. False. For $u < 0$,   **79.** Answers will vary.

$\sin 2u = -\sin(-2u)$

$\qquad = -2\sin(-u)\cos(-u)$

$\qquad = -2(-\sin u)\cos u$

$\qquad = 2\sin u \cos u.$

Review Exercises   (page 393)

1. $\tan x$ **3.** $\cot x$

5. $\sin \theta = \dfrac{2\sqrt{13}}{13}$ $\cos \theta = \dfrac{3\sqrt{13}}{13}$

$\csc \theta = \dfrac{\sqrt{13}}{2}$ $\cot \theta = \dfrac{3}{2}$

7. $\sin^2 x$ **9.** 1   **11.** $\tan u \sec u$ **13.** $\cot^2 x$

15. $-2 \tan^2 \theta$ **17.** $5 \cos \theta$ **19–25.** Answers will vary.

27. $\dfrac{\pi}{3} + 2n\pi, \dfrac{2\pi}{3} + 2n\pi$ **29.** $\dfrac{\pi}{6} + n\pi$

31. $\dfrac{\pi}{3} + n\pi, \dfrac{2\pi}{3} + n\pi$ **33.** $0, \dfrac{2\pi}{3}, \dfrac{4\pi}{3}$ **35.** $0, \dfrac{\pi}{2}, \pi$

37. $\dfrac{\pi}{8}, \dfrac{3\pi}{8}, \dfrac{9\pi}{8}, \dfrac{11\pi}{8}$ **39.** $\dfrac{\pi}{2}$

41. $0, \dfrac{\pi}{8}, \dfrac{3\pi}{8}, \dfrac{5\pi}{8}, \dfrac{7\pi}{8}, \dfrac{9\pi}{8}, \dfrac{11\pi}{8}, \dfrac{13\pi}{8}, \dfrac{15\pi}{8}$

43. $0, \pi, \arctan 2, \arctan 2 + \pi$

45. $\arctan(-3) + \pi, \arctan(-3) + 2\pi, \arctan 2, \arctan 2 + \pi$

47. $\sin 285° = -\dfrac{\sqrt{2}}{4}(\sqrt{3} + 1)$ **49.** $\sin \dfrac{25\pi}{12} = \dfrac{\sqrt{2}}{4}(\sqrt{3} - 1)$

$\cos 285° = \dfrac{\sqrt{2}}{4}(\sqrt{3} - 1)$ $\cos \dfrac{25\pi}{12} = \dfrac{\sqrt{2}}{4}(\sqrt{3} + 1)$

$\tan 285° = -2 - \sqrt{3}$ $\tan \dfrac{25\pi}{12} = 2 - \sqrt{3}$

51. $\sin 15°$ **53.** $-\dfrac{24}{25}$ **55.** -1

57–59. Answers will vary.   **61.** $\dfrac{\pi}{4}, \dfrac{7\pi}{4}$ **63.** $\sin 2u = \dfrac{24}{25}$

$\cos 2u = -\dfrac{7}{25}$

$\tan 2u = -\dfrac{24}{7}$

65.   **67.** $\dfrac{1 - \cos 4x}{1 + \cos 4x}$

69. $\sin(-75°) = -\dfrac{1}{2}\sqrt{2 + \sqrt{3}}$

$\cos(-75°) = \dfrac{1}{2}\sqrt{2 - \sqrt{3}}$

$\tan(-75°) = -2 - \sqrt{3}$

71. (a) Quadrant II

(b) $\sin \dfrac{u}{2} = \dfrac{2\sqrt{5}}{5}, \cos \dfrac{u}{2} = -\dfrac{\sqrt{5}}{5}, \tan \dfrac{u}{2} = -2$

73. $-|\cos 5x|$ **75.** $\dfrac{1}{2}[\sin 10\theta - \sin(-2\theta)]$

77. $2 \cos \dfrac{11\theta}{2} \cos \dfrac{\theta}{2}$ **79.** $\theta = 15°$ or $\dfrac{\pi}{12}$

81. False. If $(\pi/2) < \theta < \pi$, then $\cos(\theta/2) > 0$. The sign of $\cos(\theta/2)$ depends on the quadrant in which $\theta/2$ lies.

83. True. $4 \sin(-x) \cos(-x) = 4(-\sin x) \cos x$

$= -4 \sin x \cos x$

$= -2(2 \sin x \cos x)$

$= -2 \sin 2x$

85. No. For an equation to be an identity, the equation must be true for all real numbers x. $\sin \theta = \frac{1}{2}$ has an infinite number of solutions but is not an identity.

Chapter Test   (page 395)

1. $\sin \theta = -\dfrac{6\sqrt{61}}{61}$ $\csc \theta = -\dfrac{\sqrt{61}}{6}$

$\cos \theta = -\dfrac{5\sqrt{61}}{61}$ $\sec \theta = -\dfrac{\sqrt{61}}{5}$

$\tan \theta = \dfrac{6}{5}$ $\cot \theta = \dfrac{5}{6}$

2. 1   **3.** 1   **4.** $\csc \theta \sec \theta$

5. $\theta = 0, \pi/2 < \theta \le \pi, 3\pi/2 < \theta < 2\pi$

6.

$y_1 = y_2$

7–12. Answers will vary.   **13.** $\frac{1}{8}(3 - 4 \cos x + \cos 2x)$

14. $\tan 2\theta$ **15.** $2(\sin 5\theta + \sin \theta)$ **16.** $-2 \sin 2\theta \sin \theta$

17. $0, \dfrac{3\pi}{4}, \pi, \dfrac{7\pi}{4}$ **18.** $\dfrac{\pi}{6}, \dfrac{\pi}{2}, \dfrac{5\pi}{6}, \dfrac{3\pi}{2}$ **19.** $\dfrac{\pi}{6}, \dfrac{5\pi}{6}, \dfrac{7\pi}{6}, \dfrac{11\pi}{6}$

20. $\dfrac{\pi}{6}, \dfrac{5\pi}{6}, \dfrac{3\pi}{2}$ **21.** $0, 2.596$ **22.** $\dfrac{\sqrt{2} - \sqrt{6}}{4}$

23. $\sin 2u = -\frac{20}{29}, \cos 2u = -\frac{21}{29}, \tan 2u = \frac{20}{21}$

24. Day 123 to day 223

25. $t = 0.26, 0.58, 0.89, 1.20, 1.52, 1.83$

Problem Solving   (page 399)

1. $\sin \theta = \pm\sqrt{1 - \cos^2 \theta}$

$\csc \theta = \pm\dfrac{1}{\sqrt{1 - \cos^2 \theta}}$ $\sec \theta = \dfrac{1}{\cos \theta}$

$\tan \theta = \pm\dfrac{\sqrt{1 - \cos^2 \theta}}{\cos \theta}$ $\cot \theta = \pm\dfrac{\cos \theta}{\sqrt{1 - \cos^2 \theta}}$

3. Answers will vary.   **5.** $u + v = w$

7. (a) $A = 100 \sin \dfrac{\theta}{2} \cos \dfrac{\theta}{2}$ (b) $A = 50 \sin \theta; \theta = \dfrac{\pi}{2}$

9. (a) $F = \dfrac{0.6W \cos \theta}{\sin 12°}$ (b)

(c) Maximum: $\theta = 0°$

Minimum: $\theta = 90°$

11. (a) High tides: 6:12 A.M., 6:36 P.M.

Low tides: 12:00 A.M., 12:24 P.M.

(b) The water depth never   (c)

falls below 7 feet.

13. (a) $n = \dfrac{1}{2}\left(\cot \dfrac{\theta}{2} + \sqrt{3}\right)$ (b) $\theta \approx 76.5°$

15. (a) $\dfrac{\pi}{6} \le x \le \dfrac{5\pi}{6}$ (b) $\dfrac{2\pi}{3} \le x \le \dfrac{4\pi}{3}$

(c) $\dfrac{\pi}{2} < x < \pi, \dfrac{3\pi}{2} < x < 2\pi$

(d) $0 \le x \le \dfrac{\pi}{4}, \dfrac{5\pi}{4} \le x < 2\pi$

Appendix A

Appendix A.1 *(page A11)*

1. irrational **3.** absolute value **5.** terms
7. (a) 5, 1, 2 (b) 0, 5, 1, 2 (c) $-9, 5, 0, 1, -4, 2, -11$
  (d) $-\frac{7}{2}, \frac{2}{3}, -9, 5, 0, 1, -4, 2, -11$ (e) $\sqrt{2}$
9. (a) 1 (b) 1 (c) $-13, 1, -6$
  (d) $2.01, -13, 1, -6, 0.666\ldots$ (e) $0.010110111\ldots$
11. (a) [number line with point at 3.5, marks $-2\ -1\ 0\ 1\ 2\ 3\ 4$] (b) [number line with point at $\frac{7}{2}$, marks $-1\ 0\ 1\ 2\ 3\ 4\ 5$]

  (c) [number line with point at $-\frac{5}{2}$, marks $-5\ -4\ -3\ -2\ -1\ 0\ 1$] (d) [number line with point at -5.2, marks $-7\ -6\ -5\ -4\ -3\ -2\ -1$]

13. [number line with points at -8 and -4, marks $-8\ -7\ -6\ -5\ -4$] **15.** [number line with points at $\frac{2}{3}$ and $\frac{5}{6}$, marks $0\ 1$]
  $-4 > -8$
  $\frac{5}{6} > \frac{2}{3}$

17. (a) $x \le 5$ denotes the set of all real numbers less than or equal to 5.
  (b) [number line, ray from 5 to left, marks $0\ 1\ 2\ 3\ 4\ 5\ 6$] (c) Unbounded
19. (a) $[4, \infty)$ denotes the set of all real numbers greater than or equal to 4.
  (b) [number line, ray from 4 to right, marks $1\ 2\ 3\ 4\ 5\ 6\ 7$] (c) Unbounded
21. (a) $-2 < x < 2$ denotes the set of all real numbers greater than -2 and less than 2.
  (b) [number line, open interval -2 to 2, marks $-2\ -1\ 0\ 1\ 2$] (c) Bounded
23. (a) $[-5, 2)$ denotes the set of all real numbers greater than or equal to -5 and less than 2.
  (b) [number line, interval -5 to 2, marks $-5\ -3\ -1\ 1\ 3$] (c) Bounded

Inequality	Interval
25. $y \ge 0$	$[0, \infty)$
27. $10 \le t \le 22$	$[10, 22]$
29. $W > 65$	$(65, \infty)$

31. 10 **33.** 5 **35.** -1 **37.** -1 **39.** -1
41. $|-4| = |4|$ **43.** $-|-6| < |-6|$ **45.** 51 **47.** $\frac{5}{2}$
49. $\frac{128}{75}$ **51.** $|x - 5| \le 3$ **53.** $|y - a| \le 2$
55. \$1880.1 billion; \$412.7 billion
57. \$2524.0 billion; \$458.5 billion
59. $7x$ and 4 are the terms; 7 is the coefficient.
61. $4x^3, 0.5x$, and -5 are the terms; 4 and 0.5 are the coefficients.
63. (a) -10 (b) -6 **65.** (a) -10 (b) 0
67. Multiplicative Inverse Property
69. Distributive Property
71. Associative and Commutative Properties of Multiplication
73. $\frac{3}{8}$ **75.** $\frac{5x}{12}$
77. (a) Negative (b) Negative (c) Positive (d) Positive
79. False. Zero is nonnegative, but not positive.
81. (a)

n	0.0001	0.01	1	100	10,000
$\dfrac{5}{n}$	50,000	500	5	0.05	0.0005

(b) (i) The value of $5/n$ approaches infinity as n approaches 0.
  (ii) The value of $5/n$ approaches 0 as n increases without bound.

Appendix A.2 *(page A23)*

1. exponent; base **3.** square root **5.** like radicals
7. rationalizing **9.** (a) 81 (b) $\frac{1}{9}$
11. (a) 5184 (b) $-\frac{3}{5}$ **13.** (a) $\frac{16}{3}$ (b) 1
15. -24 **17.** 6 **19.** -48 **21.** (a) $-125z^3$ (b) $5x^6$
23. (a) $24y^2$ (b) $-3z^7$ **25.** (a) $\dfrac{5184}{y^7}$ (b) 1
27. (a) 1 (b) $\dfrac{1}{4x^4}$ **29.** (a) $\dfrac{125x^9}{y^{12}}$ (b) $\dfrac{b^5}{a^5}$
31. 1.02504×10^4 **33.** 3.937×10^{-5} in. **35.** 0.000314
37. 9,460,000,000,000 km
39. (a) 6.8×10^5 (b) 6.0×10^4 **41.** (a) 3 (b) $\frac{3}{2}$
43. (a) 2 (b) $2x$ **45.** (a) $2\sqrt{5}$ (b) $4\sqrt[3]{2}$
47. (a) $6x\sqrt{2x}$ (b) $3y^2\sqrt{6x}$
49. (a) $2x\sqrt[3]{2x^2}$ (b) $\dfrac{5|x|\sqrt{3}}{y^2}$ **51.** (a) $22\sqrt{2}$ (b) $11\sqrt[3]{2}$
53. (a) $23|x|\sqrt{3}$ (b) $18\sqrt{5x}$ **55.** $\dfrac{\sqrt{3}}{3}$
57. $\dfrac{\sqrt{14}+2}{2}$ **59.** $\dfrac{2}{\sqrt{2}}$ **61.** $\dfrac{2}{3(\sqrt{5}-\sqrt{3})}$ **63.** $64^{1/3}$
65. $\dfrac{3}{\sqrt[3]{x^2}}$ **67.** $(3x^3y)^{1/2}$ **69.** (a) $\frac{1}{8}$ (b) $\frac{27}{8}$
71. (a) $\dfrac{2}{|x|}$ (b) $xy^{1/3}$ **73.** (a) $\sqrt{3}$ (b) $\sqrt[3]{(x+1)^2}$
75. (a) $2\sqrt[4]{2}$ (b) $\sqrt[8]{2x}$ **77.** (a) $x - 1$ (b) $\dfrac{1}{x-1}$
79. (a)

h	0	1	2	3	4	5	6
t	0	2.93	5.48	7.67	9.53	11.08	12.32

h	7	8	9	10	11	12
t	13.29	14.00	14.50	14.80	14.93	14.96

(b) $t \to 8.64\sqrt{3} \approx 14.96$
81. False. When $x = 0$, the expressions are not equal.
83. False. For instance, $(3 + 5)^2 = 8^2 = 64 \ne 34 = 3^2 + 5^2$.

Appendix A.3 *(page A33)*

1. $n; a_n; a_0$ **3.** like terms **5.** factoring
7. perfect square trinomial
9. (a) $-\frac{1}{2}x^5 + 14x$ (b) Degree: 5; Leading coefficient: $-\frac{1}{2}$
  (c) Binomial
11. (a) $-x^6 + 3$ (b) Degree: 6; Leading coefficient: -1
  (c) Binomial
13. (a) 3 (b) Degree: 0; Leading coefficient: 3
  (c) Monomial
15. (a) $-4x^5 + 6x^4 + 1$
  (b) Degree: 5; Leading coefficient: -4 (c) Trinomial
17. (a) $4x^3y$ (b) Degree: 4; Leading coefficient: 4
  (c) Monomial
19. $-2x - 10$ **21.** $8.3x^3 + 29.7x^2 + 11$
23. $3x^3 - 6x^2 + 3x$ **25.** $-15z^2 + 5z$

27. $x^2 + 7x + 12$ 29. $x^4 + x^2 + 1$ 31. $x^2 - 100$

33. $4x^2 + 12x + 9$ 35. $x^3 + 3x^2 + 3x + 1$

37. $m^2 - n^2 - 6m + 9$ 39. $x^2 + 2xy + y^2 - 6x - 6y + 9$

41. $2x(x^2 - 3)$ 43. $(x - 5)(3x + 8)$

45. $\frac{1}{2}x(x^2 + 4x - 10)$ 47. $\frac{2}{3}(x - 6)(x - 3)$

49. $(x + 9)(x - 9)$ 51. $(x + 1)(x - 3)$ 53. $(x - 2)^2$

55. $(3u + 4v)^2$ 57. $\left(z + \frac{1}{2}\right)^2$ 59. $(x - 2)(x^2 + 2x + 4)$

61. $(3x + 2)(9x^2 - 6x + 4)$ 63. $(x + 2)(x - 1)$

65. $-(y + 5)(y - 4)$ 67. $(3x - 2)(x - 1)$

69. $(5x + 1)(x + 5)$ 71. $(x - 1)(x^2 + 2)$

73. $(2x - 1)(x^2 - 3)$ 75. $(x^2 + 2)(x + 1)(x^2 - x + 1)$

77. $(x + 3)(2x + 3)$ 79. $(2x + 3)(3x - 5)$

81. $6(x + 3)(x - 3)$ 83. $x^2(x - 1)$ 85. $(x - 1)^2$

87. $-2x(x + 1)(x - 2)$ 89. $(5 - x)(1 + x^2)$

91. $(3 - 4x)(23 - 60x)$ 93. $4x^3(2x + 1)^3(2x^2 + 2x + 1)$

95. (a) $\pi h(R + r)(R - r)$ (b) $V = 2\pi\left[\left(\dfrac{R + r}{2}\right)(R - r)\right]h$

97. False. $(4x^2 + 1)(3x + 1) = 12x^3 + 4x^2 + 3x + 1$

99. True. $a^2 - b^2 = (a + b)(a - b)$

101. $m + n$ 103. $-x^3 + 8x^2 + 2x + 7$

105. Answers will vary. *Sample answer:* $x^2 - 3$

107. $(x^n + y^n)(x^n - y^n)$

Appendix A.4   *(page A42)*

1. domain   3. complex   5. All real numbers x

7. All real numbers x such that $x \neq 3$

9. All real numbers x such that $x \neq 1$

11. All real numbers x such that $x \neq 3$

13. All real numbers x such that $x \leq 4$

15. All real numbers x such that $x > 3$

17. $\dfrac{3x}{2}$, $x \neq 0$ 19. $\dfrac{3y}{y + 1}$, $x \neq 0$ 21. $-\dfrac{1}{2}$, $x \neq 5$

23. $y - 4$, $y \neq -4$ 25. $\dfrac{x(x + 3)}{x - 2}$, $x \neq -2$

27. $\dfrac{-(x^2 + 1)}{x + 2}$, $x \neq 2$ 29. $z - 2$

31. When simplifying fractions, you can only divide out common factors, not terms.

33. $\dfrac{1}{5(x - 2)}$, $x \neq 1$ 35. $-\dfrac{8}{5}$, $y \neq -3, 4$

37. $\dfrac{x - y}{x(x + y)^2}$, $x \neq -2y$ 39. $\dfrac{6x + 13}{x + 3}$ 41. $-\dfrac{2}{x - 2}$

43. $\dfrac{-2x^2 + 3x + 8}{(2x + 1)(x + 2)}$ 45. $\dfrac{2 - x}{x^2 + 1}$, $x \neq 0$

47. The error is incorrect subtraction in the numerator.

49. $\dfrac{1}{2}$, $x \neq 2$ 51. $x(x + 1)$, $x \neq -1, 0$

53. $\dfrac{2x - 1}{2x}$, $x > 0$ 55. $\dfrac{x^7 - 2}{x^2}$ 57. $\dfrac{-1}{(x^2 + 1)^5}$

59. $\dfrac{2x^3 - 2x^2 - 5}{(x - 1)^{1/2}}$ 61. $\dfrac{3x - 1}{3}$, $x \neq 0$

63. $\dfrac{-1}{x(x + h)}$, $h \neq 0$ 65. $\dfrac{-1}{(x - 4)(x + h - 4)}$, $h \neq 0$

67. $\dfrac{1}{\sqrt{x + 2} + \sqrt{x}}$ 69. $\dfrac{1}{\sqrt{t + 3} + \sqrt{3}}$, $t \neq 0$

71. $\dfrac{1}{\sqrt{x + h + 1} + \sqrt{x + 1}}$, $h \neq 0$

73. (a)

t	0	2	4	6	8	10	12
T	75	55.9	48.3	45	43.3	42.3	41.7

t	14	16	18	20	22
T	41.3	41.1	40.9	40.7	40.6

(b) The model is approaching a T-value of 40.

75. $\dfrac{x}{2(2x + 1)}$, $x \neq 0$

77. (a)

Year, t	Banking (millions)	Paying Bills (millions)
5	46.9	17
6	57.6	25.6
7	63.5	27.3
8	67.3	28.8
9	69.9	30.8
10	71.9	33.7

(b) The estimates are fairly close to the actual numbers of households.

(c) Ratio $= \dfrac{-0.1228t^3 + 2.923t^2 - 16.38t + 24.6}{-0.5061t^3 + 11.2742t^2 - 67.844t + 121.8}$

(d)

Year	Ratio
2005	0.3625
2006	0.4449
2007	0.4292
2008	0.4282
2009	0.4403
2010	0.4685

Answers will vary.

79. $\dfrac{R_1 R_2}{R_2 + R_1}$

81. False. In order for the simplified expression to be equivalent to the original expression, the domain of the simplified expression needs to be restricted. If n is even, $x \neq -1, 1$. If n is odd, $x \neq 1$.

Appendix A.5   *(page A56)*

1. equation   3. extraneous   5. 4   7. -9 9. 1

11. No solution   13. $-\frac{96}{23}$ 15. 4   17. 3

19. No solution. The variable is divided out.

21. No solution. The solution is extraneous.

23. 5   25. $0, -\frac{1}{2}$ 27. $4, -2$ 29. -5 31. $2, -6$

33. $-\frac{20}{3}, -4$ 35. ± 7 37. $\pm 3\sqrt{3} = \pm 5.20$

39. 8, 16   41. $\dfrac{1 \pm 3\sqrt{2}}{2} \approx 2.62, -1.62$ 43. $4, -8$

45. $-3 \pm \sqrt{7}$ 47. $1 \pm \dfrac{\sqrt{6}}{3}$ 49. $\dfrac{-5 \pm \sqrt{89}}{4}$

51. $\frac{1}{2}, -1$ **53.** $1 \pm \sqrt{3}$ **55.** $\frac{3}{4} \pm \frac{\sqrt{41}}{4}$ **57.** $\frac{2}{3} \pm \frac{\sqrt{7}}{3}$

59. $-\frac{5}{3}$ **61.** $2 \pm \frac{\sqrt{6}}{2}$ **63.** $6 \pm \sqrt{11}$ **65.** $1 \pm \sqrt{2}$

67. $6, -12$ **69.** $\frac{1}{2} \pm \sqrt{3}$ **71.** $-\frac{1}{2}$ **73.** $0, \pm\frac{\sqrt{21}}{3}$

75. $-3, 0$ **77.** 48 **79.** -16 **81.** $2, -5$ **83.** 9

85. 9 **87.** $\pm\sqrt{14}$ **89.** $8, -3$ **91.** $-6, -3, 3$

93. $\sqrt[3]{\frac{4.47}{\pi}} \approx 1.12$ in.   **95.** 65.8 in.

97. False. See Example 14 on page A54.

99. True. There is no value that satisfies this equation.

Appendix A.6   *(page A64)*

1. solution set   **3.** double

5. $0 \le x < 9$; Bounded   **7.** $-1 \le x \le 5$; Bounded

9. $x > 11$; Unbounded   **11.** $x < -2$; Unbounded

13. $x < 3$ **15.** $x < \frac{3}{2}$

17. $x \ge 12$ **19.** $x > 2$

21. $x \ge \frac{2}{7}$ **23.** $x < 5$

25. $x \ge 4$ **27.** $x \ge 2$

29. $x \ge -4$ **31.** $-1 < x < 3$

33. $-7 < x \le -\frac{1}{3}$ **35.** $-\frac{9}{2} < x < \frac{15}{2}$

37. $-5 \le x < 1$ **39.** $-\frac{3}{4} < x < -\frac{1}{4}$

41. $10.5 \le x \le 13.5$ **43.** $-5 < x < 5$

45. $x < -2, x > 2$ **47.** No solution

49. $14 \le x \le 26$ **51.** $x \le -\frac{3}{2}, x \ge 3$

53. $x \le -5, x \ge 11$ **55.** $4 < x < 5$

57. $x \le -\frac{29}{2}, x \ge -\frac{11}{2}$

59.   **61.**

$x > 2$ $x \le 2$

63.   **65.**

$x \le 4$ $-6 \le x \le 22$

67.   **69.**

$x \le -\frac{27}{2}, x \ge -\frac{1}{2}$ (a) $x \ge 2$ (b) $x \le \frac{3}{2}$

71.   **73.**

(a) $-2 \le x \le 4$ (a) $1 \le x \le 5$

(b) $x \le 4$ (b) $x \le -1, x \ge 7$

75. $[5, \infty)$ **77.** $[-3, \infty)$ **79.** $\left(-\infty, \frac{7}{2}\right]$

81. All real numbers less than eight units from 10

83. $|x| \le 3$ **85.** $|x - 7| \ge 3$ **87.** $|x - 12| \ge 10$

89. $|x + 3| > 4$ **91.** $4.10 \le E \le 4.25$ **93.** $r < 0.08$

95. $100 \le r \le 170$ **97.** More than 6 units per hour

99. Greater than 3.125%   **101.** $x \ge 36$

103. $87 \le x \le 210$

105. (a)

(b) $x \ge 129$ (c) $x \ge 128.93$ (d) Answers will vary.

107. (a) $2.87 \le t \le 6.54$ (Between 2002 and 2006)

(b) $t > 15.37$ (2015)

109. 106.864 in.^{2} $\le$ area ≤ 109.464 in.^{2}

111. $\$0.36$ **113.** $13.7 < t < 17.5$

115. True by the Addition of a Constant Property of Inequalities.

117. False. If $-10 \le x \le 8$, then $10 \ge -x$ and $-x \ge -8$.

Appendix A.7   *(page A72)*

1. numerator

3. Change all signs when distributing the minus sign.

$2x - (3y + 4) = 2x - 3y - 4$

5. Change all signs when distributing the minus sign.

$$\frac{4}{16x - (2x + 1)} = \frac{4}{14x - 1}$$

7. z occurs twice as a factor. $(5z)(6z) = 30z^2$

9. The fraction as a whole is multiplied by a, not the numerator and denominator separately.

$$a\!\left(\frac{x}{y}\right) = \frac{ax}{y}$$

11. $\sqrt{x + 9}$ cannot be simplified.

13. Divide out common factors, not common terms.

$$\frac{2x^2 + 1}{5x} \text{ cannot be simplified.}$$

15. To get rid of negative exponents:

$$\frac{1}{a^{-1} + b^{-1}} = \frac{1}{a^{-1} + b^{-1}} \cdot \frac{ab}{ab} = \frac{ab}{b + a}.$$

17. Factor within grouping symbols before applying exponent to each factor.

$$(x^2 + 5x)^{1/2} = [x(x + 5)]^{1/2} = x^{1/2}(x + 5)^{1/2}$$

19. To add fractions, first find a common denominator.

$$\frac{3}{x} + \frac{4}{y} = \frac{3y + 4x}{xy}$$

21. To add fractions, first find a common denominator.

$$\frac{x}{2y} + \frac{y}{3} = \frac{3x + 2y^2}{6y}$$

23. $5x + 3$ **25.** $2x^2 + x + 15$ **27.** $\frac{1}{3}$ **29.** $3y - 10$

31. 2 **33.** $\dfrac{1}{2x^2}$ **35.** $\dfrac{36}{25}, \dfrac{9}{4}$ **37.** $3, 4$ **39.** $1 - 5x$

41. $1 - 7x$ **43.** $3x - 1$ **45.** $7(x + 3)^{-5}$

47. $2x^5(3x + 5)^{-4}$ **49.** $\frac{4}{3}x^{-1} + 4x^{-4} - 7x(2x)^{-1/3}$

51. $\dfrac{x}{3} + 2 + \dfrac{4}{x}$ **53.** $4x^{8/3} - 7x^{5/3} + \dfrac{1}{x^{1/3}}$

55. $\dfrac{3}{x^{1/2}} - 5x^{3/2} - x^{7/2}$ **57.** $\dfrac{-7x^2 - 4x + 9}{(x^2 - 3)^3(x + 1)^4}$

59. $\dfrac{27x^2 - 24x + 2}{(6x + 1)^4}$ **61.** $\dfrac{-1}{(x + 3)^{2/3}(x + 2)^{7/4}}$

63. $\dfrac{4x - 3}{(3x - 1)^{4/3}}$ **65.** $\dfrac{x}{x^2 + 4}$

67. $\dfrac{(3x - 2)^{1/2}(15x^2 - 4x + 45)}{2(x^2 + 5)^{1/2}}$

69. (a)

x	0.50	1.0	1.5	2.0
t	1.70	1.72	1.78	1.89

x	2.5	3.0	3.5	4.0
t	2.02	2.18	2.36	2.57

(b) $x = 0.5$ mi

(c) $\dfrac{3x\sqrt{x^2 - 8x + 20} + (x - 4)\sqrt{x^2 + 4}}{6\sqrt{x^2 + 4}\sqrt{x^2 - 8x + 20}}$

71. You cannot move term-by-term from the denominator to the numerator.

Index

A

Absolute value
    of a complex number, 440
    equation, A54
    inequality, A62
        solution of, A62
    properties of, A6
    of a real number, A5
Acute angle, 263
Addition
    of complex numbers, 148
    of fractions
        with like denominators, A10
        with unlike denominators, A10
    of matrices, 552
        properties of, 554
    vector, 420
        parallelogram law for, 420
        properties of, 421
        resultant of, 420
Additive identity
    for a complex number, 148
    for a matrix, 555
    for a real number, A8
Additive inverse, A8
    for a complex number, 148
    for a real number, A8
Adjacent side of a right triangle, 279
Adjoining matrices, 559, 567
Algebraic expression, A7
    domain of, A35
    equivalent, A35
    evaluate, A7
    term of, A7
Algebraic function, 200
Algebraic tests for symmetry, 15
Alternative definition of conic, 755
Alternative form
    of dot product, 433
    of Law of Cosines, 411, 460
Ambiguous case (SSA), 404
Amplitude of sine and cosine curves, 301
Angle(s), 262
    acute, 263
    between two lines, 689
    between two vectors, 432, 462
    central, 263
    complementary, 264
    conversions between degrees and
        radians, 265
    coterminal, 262
    degree measure of, 265
    of depression, 284
    direction, of a vector, 424
    of elevation, 284
    initial side of, 262
    measure of, 263
    negative, 262
    obtuse, 263

positive, 262
    radian measure of, 263
    reference, 292
    of repose, 328
    standard position, 262
    supplementary, 264
    terminal side of, 262
    vertex of, 262
Angular speed, 266
Annuity, increasing, 630
Aphelion distance, 708, 760
Apogee, 708
"Approximately equal to" symbol, A1
Arc length, 266
Arccosine function, 322
Arcsine function, 320, 322
Arctangent function, 322
Area
    common formulas for, A55
    of an oblique triangle, 406
    of a sector of a circle, 268
    of a triangle
        using a determinant, 585
        Heron's Area Formula, 414, 461
Argument of a complex number, 441
Arithmetic combination of functions, 76
Arithmetic mean, 615
Arithmetic sequence, 616
    common difference of, 616
    nth partial sum of, 620
    nth term of, 617
    recursion formula, 618
    sum of a finite, 619, 683
Associative Property of Addition
    for complex numbers, 149
    for matrices, 554
    for real numbers, A8
Associative Property of Multiplication
    for complex numbers, 149
    for matrices, 558
    for real numbers, A8
Associative Property of Scalar
        Multiplication for matrices, 554,
        558
Astronomical unit, 758
Asymptote(s)
    horizontal, 169
    of a hyperbola, 715
    oblique, 174
    of a rational function, 170
    slant, 174
    vertical, 169
Augmented matrix, 539
Average rate of change, 54
Average value of a population, 242
Axis (axes)
    conjugate, of a hyperbola, 715
    imaginary, 440
    major, of an ellipse, 704

minor, of an ellipse, 704
    of a parabola, 115, 696
    polar, 741
    real, 440
    rotation of, 723
    of symmetry, 115
    transverse, of a hyperbola, 713

B

Back-substitution, 467
Base, A13
    natural, 204
Basic conics, 695
    circle, 695
    ellipse, 695
    hyperbola, 695
    parabola, 695
Basic equation of a partial fraction
        decomposition, 501
    guidelines for solving, 505
Basic Rules of Algebra, A8
Bearings, 332
Bell-shaped curve, 242
Binomial, 644, A25
    coefficient, 644
    cube of, A27
    expanding, 647
    square of, A27
    sum and difference of same terms,
        A27
Binomial Theorem, 644, 684
Book value, 29
Bound
    lower, 162
    upper, 162
Bounded intervals, A4
Boyle's Law, 102
Branches of a hyperbola, 713
Break-even point, 471
Butterfly curve, 772

C

Cardioid, 751
Cartesian plane, 2
Center
    of a circle, 17
    an ellipse, 704
    of a hyperbola, 713
Central angle of a circle, 263
Certain event, 663
Change-of-base formula, 221
Characteristics of a function from set A
        to set B, 35
Circle, 17, 751
    arc length of, 266
    center of, 17
    central angle of, 263

classifying
    by discriminant, 727
    by general equation, 719
involute of, 771
radius of, 17
sector of, 268
    area of, 268
standard form of the equation of, 17
unit, 272
Circular arc, length of, 266
Circumference, formula for, A55
Classification of conics
    by discriminant, 727
    by general equation, 719
Coded row matrices, 588
Coefficient(s)
    binomial, 644
    correlation, 94
    equating, 503
    leading, A25
    of a term, A25
    of a variable term, A7
Coefficient matrix, 539, 559
Cofactor(s)
    expanding by, 577
    of a matrix, 576
Cofunction identities, 350
Cofunctions of complementary angles,
    281
Collinear points, 10, 586
    test for, 586
Column matrix, 538
Combinations of functions, 76
Combinations of n elements taken r at a
    time, 657
Combined variation, 98
Common difference of an arithmetic
    sequence, 616
Common formulas, A55
    area, A55
    circumference, A55
    perimeter, A55
    volume, A55
Common logarithmic function, 212
Common ratio of a geometric sequence,
    625
Commutative Property of Addition
    for complex numbers, 149
    for matrices, 554
    for real numbers, A8
Commutative Property of Multiplication
    for complex numbers, 149
    for real numbers, A8
Complement of an event, 669
    probability of, 669
Complementary angles, 264
    cofunctions of, 281
Completely factored, A28
Completing the square, A48
Complex conjugates, 150
Complex fraction, A39
Complex number(s), 147

absolute value of, 440
addition of, 148
additive identity, 148
additive inverse, 148
argument of, 441
Associative Property of Addition, 149
Associative Property of
    Multiplication, 149
Commutative Property of Addition, 149
Commutative Property of
    Multiplication, 149
conjugate of, 150
difference of, 148
Distributive Property, 149
division of, 442
equality of, 147
imaginary part of, 147
modulus of, 441
multiplication of, 442
nth root of, 445, 446
nth roots of unity, 446
polar form of, 441
powers of, 444
product of two, 442
quotient of two, 442
real part of, 147
standard form of, 147
subtraction of, 148
sum of, 148
trigonometric form of, 441
Complex plane, 153, 440
    imaginary axis, 440
    real axis, 440
Complex solutions of quadratic
    equations, 151
Complex zeros occur in conjugate pairs,
    158
Component form of a vector $\mathbf{v}$, 419
Components, vector, 419, 434
    horizontal, 422
    vertical, 422
Composite number, A10
Composition of functions, 78
Compound interest
    compounded n times per year, 205
    continuously compounded, 205
    formulas for, 206
Condensing logarithmic expressions, 223
Conditional equation, 357, A45
Conic(s) or conic section(s), 695, 755
    alternative definition, 755
    basic, 695
        circle, 695
        ellipse, 695
        hyperbola, 695
        parabola, 695
    classifying
        by discriminant, 727
        by general equation, 719
    degenerate, 695
        line, 695
        point, 695

two intersecting lines, 695
    eccentricity of, 755
    locus of, 695
    polar equations of, 755, 770
    rotation of axes, 723
Conjecture, 639
Conjugate, 158, A20
    of a complex number, 150, 158
Conjugate axis of a hyperbola, 715
Conjugate pairs, 158, A29
    complex zeros occur in, 158
Consistent system of linear equations,
    480
Constant, A7
    function, 36, 52, 61
    matrix, 559
    of proportionality, 95
    term, A7, A25
    of variation, 95
Constraints, 518
Consumer surplus, 513
Continuous compounding, 205
Continuous function, 124, 731
Contradiction, A45
    proof by, 534
Conversions between degrees and
    radians, 265
Convex limaçon, 751
Coordinate(s), 2
    polar, 741
Coordinate axes, reflection in, 69
Coordinate conversion, 743
    polar to rectangular, 743
    rectangular to polar, 743
Coordinate system
    polar, 741
    rectangular, 2
Correlation coefficient, 94
Correspondence, one-to-one, A2
Cosecant function, 273, 279
    of any angle, 290
    graph of, 313, 316
Cosine curve, amplitude of, 301
Cosine function, 273, 279
    of any angle, 290
    common angles, 293
    domain of, 275
    graph of, 303, 316
    inverse, 322
    period of, 302
    range of, 275
    special angles, 281
Cotangent function, 273, 279
    of any angle, 290
    graph of, 312, 316
Coterminal angles, 262
Counting Principle, Fundamental, 653
Cramer's Rule, 582, 583
Cross multiplying, A47
Cryptogram, 588
Cube of a binomial, A27
Cube root, A17

Cubic function, 62
Curtate cycloid, 740
Curve
    bell-shaped, 242
    butterfly, 772
    logistic, 243
    orientation of, 732
    plane, 731
    rose, 750, 751
    sigmoidal, 243
    sine, 299
Cycle of a sine curve, 299
Cycloid, 736
    curtate, 740

D
Damping factor, 315
Decomposition of $N(x)/D(x)$ into partial
        fractions, 500
Decreasing function, 52
Defined, 43
Degenerate conic, 695
    line, 695
    point, 695
    two intersecting lines, 695
Degree
    conversion to radians, 265
    fractional part of, 265
    measure of angles, 265
    of a polynomial, A25
    of a term, A25
DeMoivre's Theorem, 444
Denominator, A8
    rationalizing, 360, A19, A20
Dependent system of linear equations,
        480
Dependent variable, 37, 43
Depreciation
    linear, 29
    straight-line, 29
Descartes's Rule of Signs, 161
Determinant
    area of a triangle using, 585
    of a square matrix, 574, 577
    of a 2×2 matrix, 569, 574
Diagonal matrix, 564, 581
Diagonal of a polygon, 661
Difference
    common, of an arithmetic sequence,
            616
    of complex numbers, 148
    of functions, 76
    quotient, 42, 649, A41
    of two cubes, A29
    of two squares, A29
    of vectors, 420
Differences
    first, 641
    second, 641
Diminishing returns, point of, 136
Dimpled limaçon, 751

Direct variation, 95
    as an nth power, 96
Directed line segment, 418
    initial point of, 418
    length of, 418
    magnitude of, 418
    terminal point of, 418
Direction angle of a vector, 424
Directly proportional, 95
    to the nth power, 96
Directrix of a parabola, 696
Discrete mathematics, 37
Discriminant, 727
    classification of conics by, 727
Distance
    between a point and a line, 690, 768
    between two points
        in the plane, 4
        on the real number line, A6
Distance Formula, 4
    in space, 775
Distinguishable permutations, 656
Distributive Property
    for complex numbers, 149
    for matrices, 554, 558
    for real numbers, A8
Dividing out
    errors involving, A68
Division
    of complex numbers, 442
    of fractions, A10
    long, of polynomials, 138
    of real numbers, A8
    synthetic, 141
Division Algorithm, 139
Divisors, A10
Domain
    of an algebraic expression, A35
    of the cosine function, 275
    of a function, 35, 43
    implied, 40, 43
    of a rational function, 168
    of the sine function, 275
Dot product, 431
    alternative form, 433
    properties of, 431, 462
Double inequality, A3, A61
Double subscript notation, 538
Double-angle formulas, 382, 397
Doyle Log Rule, 474
Drag, 464

E
e, the number, 204
Eccentricity
    of a conic, 755
    of an ellipse, 709, 755
    of a hyperbola, 717, 755
    of a parabola, 755
Effective yield, 237
Elementary row operations, 540

Eliminating the parameter, 733
Elimination
    Gaussian, 489, 490
        with back-substitution, 544
    Gauss-Jordan, 545
    method of, 476, 477
Ellipse, 704, 755
    center of, 704
    classifying
        by discriminant, 727
        by general equation, 719
    eccentricity of, 709, 755
    foci of, 704
    latus rectum of, 712
    major axis of, 704
    minor axis of, 704
    standard form of the equation of, 705
    vertices of, 704
Ellipsis points, A1
Encryption, 588
Endpoints of an interval, A4
Entry of a matrix, 538
    main diagonal, 538
Epicycloid, 740
Equal
    matrices, 551
    vectors, 419
Equality
    of complex numbers, 147
    properties of, A9
Equating the coefficients, 503
Equation(s), 11, A45
    absolute value, A54
    basic, of a partial fraction
            decomposition, 501
    circle, standard form, 17
    conditional, 357, A45
    of conics, polar, 755, 770
    contradiction, A45
    ellipse, standard form, 705
    equivalent, A46
        generating, A46
    exponential, solving, 228
    graph of, 11
    hyperbola, standard form, 714
    identity, A45
    of a line, 22
        general form, 30
        graph of, 22
        intercept form, 32
        point-slope form, 26, 30
        slope-intercept form, 22, 30
        summary of, 30
        two-point form, 26, 30, 587
    linear, 13
        in one variable, A46
        in two variables, 22
    logarithmic, solving, 228
    parabola, standard form, 696, 769
    parametric, 731
    polar, graph of, 747
    polynomial, solution of, 128

position, 494
quadratic, 13, A48
quadratic type, 367
radical, A53
rational, A47
second-degree polynomial, A48
solution of, 11, A45
solution point, 11
solving, A45
system of, 466
trigonometric, solving, 364
in two variables, 11
Equilibrium point, 483, 513
Equivalent
algebraic expressions, A35
equations, A46
generating, A46
fractions, A10
generate, A10
inequalities, A59
systems, 478, 489
operations that produce, 489
Errors
involving dividing out, A68
involving exponents, A68
involving fractions, A67
involving parentheses, A67
involving radicals, A68
Evaluate an algebraic expression, A7
Evaluating trigonometric functions of any
angle, 293
Even function, 55
trigonometric, 276
Even/odd identities, 350
Event(s), 662
certain, 663
complement of, 669
probability of, 669
impossible, 663
independent, 668
probability of, 668
mutually exclusive, 666
probability of, 663
the union of two, 666
Existence theorems, 154
Expanding
a binomial, 647
by cofactors, 577
logarithmic expressions, 223
Expected value, 686
Experiment, 662
outcomes of, 662
sample space of, 662
Exponent(s), A13
errors involving, A68
negative, writing with, A69
properties of, A13
rational, A21
Exponential decay model, 238
Exponential equations, solving, 228
Exponential form, A13
Exponential function, 200

f with base a, 200
graph of, 201
natural, 204
one-to-one property, 202
Exponential growth model, 238
Exponential notation, A13
Exponentiating, 231
Expression
algebraic, A7
fractional, A35
rational, A35
Extended Principle of Mathematical
Induction, 636
Extracting square roots, A48
Extraneous solution, A47, A53
Extrapolation, linear, 30

F

Factor(s)
damping, 315
of an integer, A10
of a polynomial, 128, 159, 196
prime, 159
quadratic, 159
repeated
linear, 502
quadratic, 504
scaling, 301
and terms, inserting, A70
Factor Theorem, 143, 195
Factorial, 609
Factoring, A28
completely, A28
by grouping, A32
solving a quadratic equation by, A48
special polynomial forms, A29
unusual, A69
Family of functions, 67
Far point, 198
Feasible solutions, 518
Fibonacci sequence, 608
Finding
a formula for the nth term of a
sequence, 639
intercepts, 14
an inverse function, 88
an inverse matrix, 567
nth roots of a complex number, 446
test intervals for a polynomial, 180
vertical and horizontal asymptotes of
a rational function, 170
Finite sequence, 606
Finite series, 611
First differences, 641
Fixed cost, 28
Fixed point, 374
Focal chord
latus rectum, 698
of a parabola, 698
Focus (foci)
of an ellipse, 704

of a hyperbola, 713
of a parabola, 696
FOIL Method, A26
Formula(s)
change-of-base, 221
common, A55
for area, perimeter, circumference,
and volume, A55
for compound interest, 206
Distance, 4
double-angle, 382, 397
half-angle, 385
Heron's Area, 414, 461
Midpoint, 5, 110
for the nth term of a sequence, 639
power-reducing, 384, 397
product-to-sum, 386
Quadratic, A48
radian measure, 266
recursion, 618
reduction, 377
sum and difference, 375, 396
sum-to-product, 386, 398
Four ways to represent a function, 36
Fractal, 686
Fraction(s)
addition of
with like denominators, A10
with unlike denominators, A10
complex, A39
division of, A10
equivalent, A10
generate, A10
errors involving, A67
multiplication of, A10
operations of, A10
partial, 500
decomposition, 500
properties of, A10
rules of signs for, A10
subtraction of
with like denominators, A10
with unlike denominators, A10
writing as a sum, A69
Fractional expression, A35
Fractional parts of degrees
minute, 265
second, 265
Frequency, 333
Function(s), 35, 43
algebraic, 200
arccosine, 322
arcsine, 320, 322
arctangent, 322
arithmetic combinations of, 76
characteristics of, 35
combinations of, 76
common logarithmic, 212
composition of, 78
constant, 36, 52, 61
continuous, 124, 731
cosecant, 273, 279, 290

cosine, 273, 279, 290
cotangent, 273, 279, 290
cubic, 62
decreasing, 52
defined, 43
difference of, 76
domain of, 35, 43
even, 55
exponential, 200
family of, 67
four ways to represent, 36
graph of, 49
greatest integer, 63
of half-angles, 382
Heaviside, 112
identity, 61
implied domain of, 40, 43
increasing, 52
inverse, 84, 85
    cosine, 322
    finding, 88
    sine, 320, 322
    tangent, 322
    trigonometric, 322
linear, 60
logarithmic, 211
of multiple angles, 382
name of, 37, 43
natural exponential, 204
natural logarithmic, 215
notation, 37, 43
objective, 518
odd, 55
one-to-one, 87
parent, 64
period of, 275
periodic, 275
piecewise-defined, 38
polynomial, 114
product of, 76
quadratic, 114
quotient of, 76
range of, 35, 43
rational, 168
reciprocal, 62
representation, 36
secant, 273, 279, 290
sine, 273, 279, 290
square root, 62
squaring, 61
step, 63
sum of, 76
summary of terminology, 43
tangent, 273, 279, 290
transcendental, 200
transformations of, 67
    nonrigid, 71
    rigid, 71
trigonometric, 273, 279, 290
undefined, 43
value of, 37, 43
Vertical Line Test, 50

zeros of, 51
Fundamental Counting Principle, 653
Fundamental Theorem
    of Algebra, 154
    of Arithmetic, A10
Fundamental trigonometric identities,
    282, 350

G

Gaussian elimination, 489, 490
    with back-substitution, 544
Gaussian model, 238
Gauss-Jordan elimination, 545
General form
    of the equation of a line, 30
    of a quadratic equation, A49
Generalizations about nth roots of real
    numbers, A18
Generate equivalent fractions, A10
Generating equivalent equations, A46
Geometric sequence, 625
    common ratio of, 625
    nth term of, 626
    sum of a finite, 628, 683
Geometric series, 629
    sum of an infinite, 629
Graph, 11
    of cosecant function, 313, 316
    of cosine function, 303, 316
    of cotangent function, 312, 316
    of an equation, 11
    of an exponential function, 201
    of a function, 49
    of an inequality, 508, A58
        in two variables, 508
    intercepts of, 14
    of inverse cosine function, 322
    of an inverse function, 86
    of inverse sine function, 322
    of inverse tangent function, 322
    of a line, 22
    of a logarithmic function, 213
    of a polar equation, 747
    point-plotting method, 11
    of a polynomial function, x-intercept
        of, 128
    reflecting, 69
    of secant function, 313, 316
    shifting, 67
    of sine function, 303, 316
    special polar, 751
    symmetry of a, 15
    of tangent function, 310, 316
Graphical interpretations of solutions,
    480
Graphical method, for solving a system
    of equations, 470
Graphical tests for symmetry, 15
Graphing rational functions, 171
    guidelines, 171
Greatest integer function, 63

Guidelines
    for graphing rational functions, 171
    for solving the basic equation of a
        partial fraction decomposition,
        505
    for verifying trigonometric identities,
        357

H

Half-angle formulas, 385
Half-angles, functions of, 382
Half-life, 207
Harmonic motion, simple, 333
Heaviside function, 112
Heron's Area Formula, 414, 461
Hole, in the graph of a rational function,
    173
Hooke's Law, 102
Horizontal asymptote, 169
    of a rational function, 170
Horizontal component of $\mathbf{v}$, 422
Horizontal line, 30
Horizontal Line Test, 87
Horizontal shifts, 67
Horizontal shrink, 71
    of a trigonometric function, 302
Horizontal stretch, 71
    of a trigonometric function, 302
Horizontal translation of a trigonometric
    function, 303
Human memory model, 217
Hyperbola, 169, 713, 755
    asymptotes of, 715
    branches of, 713
    center of, 713
    classifying
        by discriminant, 727
        by general equation, 719
    conjugate axis of, 715
    eccentricity of, 717, 755
    foci of, 713
    standard form of the equation of, 714
    transverse axis of, 713
    vertices of, 713
Hypocycloid, 772
Hypotenuse of a right triangle, 279
Hypothesis, 639

I

i, imaginary unit, 147
Idempotent square matrix, 603
Identities
    cofunction, 350
    even/odd, 350
    Pythagorean, 282, 350
    quotient, 282, 350
    reciprocal, 282, 350
    trigonometric
        fundamental, 282, 350
        guidelines for verifying, 357

Identity, 357, A45
    function, 61
    matrix of order $n \times n$, 558
Imaginary axis of the complex plane, 440
Imaginary number, 147
    pure, 147
Imaginary part of a complex number, 147
Imaginary unit i, 147
Implied domain, 40, 43
Impossible event, 663
Improper rational expression, 139
Inclination of a line, 688
    and slope, 688, 768
Inclusive or, A9
Inconsistent system of linear equations,
    480, 544
Increasing annuity, 630
Increasing function, 52
Independent events, 668
    probability of, 668
Independent system of linear equations,
    480
Independent variable, 37, 43
Index
    of a radical, A17
    of summation, 610
Indirect proof, 534
Induction, mathematical, 634
Inductive, 577
Inequality (inequalities), A3
    absolute value, A62
        solution of, A62
    double, A3, A61
    equivalent, A59
    graph of, 508, A58
    linear, 509, A60
    nonlinear, 180
    polynomial, 180
    properties of, A59
    rational, 184
    satisfy, A58
    solution of, 508, A58
    solution set of, A58
    solution of a system of, 510
        solution set, 510
    solving, A58
    symbol, A3
Infinite geometric series, 629
    sum of, 629
Infinite sequence, 606
Infinite series, 611
Infinite wedge, 512
Infinitely many solutions, A46
    negative, A4
    positive, A4
Initial point, 418
Initial side of an angle, 262
Inserting factors and terms, A70
Integer(s), A1
    divisors of, A10
    factors of, A10
    irreducible over, A28

sums of powers of, 640
Intercept form of the equation of a line,
    32
Intercepts, 14
    finding, 14
Interest
    compound, formulas for, 206
    compounded n times per year, 205
    continuously compounded, 205
Intermediate Value Theorem, 131
Interpolation, linear, 30
Intersection, points of, 470
Interval(s), A4
    bounded, A4
    endpoints of, A4
    using inequalities to represent, A4
    on the real number line, A4
    unbounded, A4
Invariant under rotation, 727
Inverse
    additive, A8
    multiplicative, A8
    of a matrix, 565
Inverse function, 84, 85
    cosine, 322
    finding, 88
    graph of, 86
    Horizontal Line Test, 87
    sine, 320, 322
    tangent, 322
Inverse of a matrix, 565
    finding, 567
Inverse properties
    of logarithms, 212
    of natural logarithms, 216
    of trigonometric functions, 324
Inverse trigonometric functions, 322
Inverse variation, 97
Inversely proportional, 97
Invertible matrix, 566
Involute of a circle, 771
Irrational number, A1
Irreducible
    over the integers, A28
    over the rationals, 159
    over the reals, 159

J

Joint variation, 99
Jointly proportional, 99

K

Kepler's Laws, 758
Key numbers
    of a polynomial inequality, 180
    of a rational inequality, 184
Key points of the graph of a
        trigonometric function, 300
    intercepts, 300
    maximum points, 300
    minimum points, 300

L

Latus rectum
    of an ellipse, 712
    of a parabola, 698
Law of Cosines, 411, 460
    alternative form, 411, 460
    standard form, 411, 460
Law of Sines, 402, 459
Law of Tangents, 459
Law of Trichotomy, A5
Leading coefficient of a polynomial, A25
Leading Coefficient Test, 126
Leading 1, 542
Least squares regression
    line, 94, 486
    parabola, 498
Lemniscate, 751
Length
    of a circular arc, 266
    of a directed line segment, 418
    of a vector, 419
Lift, 464
Like radicals, A19
Like terms of a polynomial, A26
Limaçon, 748, 751
    convex, 751
    dimpled, 751
    with inner loop, 751
Limit of summation
    lower, 610
    upper, 610
Line(s) in the plane
    angle between two, 689
    general form of the equation of, 30
    graph of, 22
    horizontal, 30
    inclination of, 688
    intercept form of the equation of, 32
    least squares regression, 94, 486
    parallel, 27
    perpendicular, 27
    point-slope form of the equation of,
        26, 30
    secant, 54
    segment, directed, 418
    slope of, 22, 24
    slope-intercept form of the equation
        of, 22, 30
    summary of equations, 30
    tangent, to a parabola, 698
    two-point form of the equation of, 26,
        30, 587
    vertical, 22, 30
Linear combination of vectors, 422
Linear depreciation, 29
Linear equation, 13
    general form, 30
    graph of, 22
    intercept form, 32
    in one variable, A46
    point-slope form, 26, 30
    slope-intercept form, 22, 30

summary of, 30
in two variables, 22
two-point form, 26, 30, 587
Linear extrapolation, 30
Linear factor, repeated, 502
Linear Factorization Theorem, 154, 196
Linear function, 60
Linear inequality, 509, A60
Linear interpolation, 30
Linear programming, 518
    problem
        optimal solution, 518
        solving, 518
Linear speed, 266
Linear system
    consistent, 480
    dependent, 480
    inconsistent, 480, 544
    independent, 480
    nonsquare, 493
    number of solutions, 491
    row operations, 489
    row-echelon form, 488
    square, 493, 570
Local maximum, 53
Local minimum, 53
Locus, 695
Logarithm(s)
    change-of-base formula, 221
    natural, properties of, 216, 222, 258
        inverse, 216
        one-to-one, 216
        power, 222, 258
        product, 222, 258
        quotient, 222, 258
    properties of, 212, 222, 258
        inverse, 212
        one-to-one, 212
        power, 222, 258
        product, 222, 258
        quotient, 222, 258
Logarithmic equations, solving, 228
Logarithmic expressions
    condensing, 223
    expanding, 223
Logarithmic function, 211
    with base a, 211
    common, 212
    graph of, 213
    natural, 215
Logarithmic model, 238
Logistic
    curve, 243
    growth model, 102, 238
Long division of polynomials, 138
Lower bound, 162
Lower limit of summation, 610

M

Magnitude, A5
    of a directed line segment, 418
    of a vector, 419

Main diagonal entries of a square matrix, 538
Major axis of an ellipse, 704
Marginal cost, 28
Mathematical induction, 634
    Extended Principle of, 636
    Principle of, 635
Matrix (matrices), 538
    addition, 552
        properties of, 554
    additive identity, 555
    adjoining, 559, 567
    augmented, 539
    coded row, 588
    coefficient, 539, 559
    cofactor of, 576
    column, 538
    constant, 559
    determinant of, 569, 574, 577
    diagonal, 564, 581
    elementary row operations, 540
    entry of a, 538
    equal, 551
    idempotent, 603
    identity, 558
    inverse of, 565
        finding, 567
    invertible, 566
    main diagonal entries of a, 538
    minor of, 576
    multiplication, 556
        properties of, 558
    nonsingular, 566
    order of a, 538
    reduced row-echelon form, 542
    representation of, 551
    row, 538
    row-echelon form, 542
    row-equivalent, 540
    scalar identity, 554
    scalar multiplication, 552
        properties of, 554
    singular, 566
    square, 538
    stochastic, 564
    subtraction, 553
    transpose of, 603
    uncoded row, 588
    zero, 555
Maximum
    local, 53
    relative, 53
    value of a quadratic function, 119
Mean, arithmetic, 615
Measure of an angle, 263
    degree, 265
    radian, 263
Method
    of elimination, 476, 477
    of substitution, 466
Midpoint Formula, 5, 110
Midpoint of a line segment, 5

Minimum
    local, 53
    relative, 53
    value of a quadratic function, 119
Minor axis of an ellipse, 704
Minor of a matrix, 576
Minors and cofactors of a square matrix, 576
Minute, fractional part of a degree, 265
Modulus of a complex number, 441
Monomial, A25
Multiple angles, functions of, 382
Multiplication
    of complex numbers, 442
    of fractions, A10
    of matrices, 556
        properties of, 558
    scalar
        of matrices, 552
        of vectors, 420
Multiplicative identity of a real number, A8
Multiplicative inverse, A8
    of a matrix, 565
    of a real number, A8
Multiplicity, 128
Multiplier effect, 633
Mutually exclusive events, 666

N

n factorial, 609
Name of a function, 37, 43
Natural base, 204
Natural exponential function, 204
Natural logarithm
    properties of, 216, 222, 258
        inverse, 216
        one-to-one, 216
        power, 222, 258
        product, 222, 258
        quotient, 222, 258
Natural logarithmic function, 215
Natural numbers, A1
Near point, 198
Negation, properties of, A9
Negative
    angle, 262
    exponents, writing with, A69
    infinity, A4
    number, principal square root of, 151
    of a vector, 420
Newton's Law of Cooling, 102, 248
Newton's Law of Universal Gravitation, 102
No solution, A46
Nonlinear inequalities, 180
Nonnegative number, A2
Nonrigid transformations, 71
Nonsingular matrix, 566
Nonsquare system of linear equations, 493

Normally distributed, 242
Notation
  double subscript, 538
  exponential, A13
  function, 37, 43
  scientific, A16
  sigma, 610
  summation, 610
nth partial sum, 611, 620
  of an arithmetic sequence, 620
nth root(s)
  of a, A17
  of a complex number, 445, 446
  generalizations about, A18
  principal, A17
  of unity, 446
nth term
  of an arithmetic sequence, 617
  of a geometric sequence, 626
  of a sequence, finding a formula for,
    639
Number(s)
  complex, 147
  composite, A10
  imaginary, 147
    pure, 147
  irrational, A1
  key, 180, 184
  natural, A1
  negative, principal square root of, 151
  nonnegative, A2
  of outcomes, 663
  pentagonal, 686
  prime, A10
  rational, A1
  real, A1
  whole, A1
Number of permutations of n elements,
  654
  taken r at a time, 655
Number of solutions of a linear system,
  491
Numerator, A8
  rationalizing, A21

O

Objective function, 518
Oblique asymptote, 174
Oblique triangle, 402
  area of, 406
Obtuse angle, 263
Odd/even identities, 350
Odd function, 55
  trigonometric, 276
Odds, 686
One cycle of a sine curve, 299
One-to-one correspondence, A2
One-to-one function, 87
One-to-one property
  of exponential functions, 202
  of logarithms, 212
  of natural logarithms, 216

Operations
  of fractions, A10
  that produce equivalent systems, 489
Opposite side of a right triangle, 279
Optimal solution of a linear programming
    problem, 518
Optimization, 518
Order
  of a matrix, 538
  on the real number line, A3
Ordered pair, 2
Ordered triple, 488
Orientation of a curve, 732
Origin, 2, A2
  of polar coordinate system, 741
  of the real number line, A2
  of the rectangular coordinate system, 2
  symmetric with respect to, 15
Orthogonal vectors, 433
Outcomes, 662
  number of, 663

P

Parabola, 114, 696, 755
  axis of, 115, 696
  classifying
    by discriminant, 727
    by general equation, 719
  directrix of, 696
  eccentricity of, 755
  focal chord of, 698
  focus of, 696
  latus rectum of, 698
  least squares regression, 498
  reflective property of, 698
  standard form of the equation of, 696,
    769
  tangent line to, 698
  vertex of, 115, 696
Parallel lines, 27
Parallelogram law for vector addition,
    420
Parameter, 731
  eliminating, 733
Parametric equations, 731
Parent functions, 64
Parentheses, errors involving, A67
Partial fraction, 500
  decomposition, 500
Partial sum, nth, 611, 620
Pascal's Triangle, 646
Pentagonal numbers, 686
Perfect
  cube, A18
  square, A18
  square trinomial, A29, A30
Perigee, 708
Perihelion distance, 708, 760
Perimeter, common formulas for, A55
Period
  of a function, 275

of sine and cosine functions, 302
Periodic function, 275
Permutation(s), 654
  distinguishable, 656
  of n elements, 654
    taken r at a time, 655
Perpendicular
  lines, 27
  vectors, 433
Petal of a rose curve, 750
Phase shift, 303
Piecewise-defined function, 38
Plane curve, 731
  orientation of, 732
Plotting, on the real number line, A2
Point(s)
  break-even, 471
  collinear, 10, 586
    test for, 586
  of diminishing returns, 136
  equilibrium, 483, 513
  fixed, 374
  initial, 418
  of intersection, 470
  solution, 11
  terminal, 418
Point-plotting method of graphing, 11
Point-slope form of the equation of a
    line, 26, 30
Polar axis, 741
Polar coordinate system, 741
  pole (origin) of, 741
Polar coordinates, 741
  conversion to rectangular, 743
  tests for symmetry in, 748, 749
Polar equation, graph of, 747
Polar equations of conics, 755, 770
Polar form of a complex number, 441
Pole, 741
Polygon, diagonal of, 661
Polynomial(s), A25
  completely factored, A28
  constant term of, A25
  degree of, A25
  equation
    second-degree, A48
    solution of, 128
  factoring special forms, A29
  factors of, 128, 159, 196
  finding test intervals for, 180
  inequality, 180
  irreducible, A28
  leading coefficient of, A25
  like terms, A26
  long division of, 138
  operations with, A26
  prime, A28
  prime quadratic factor, 159
  standard form of, A25
  synthetic division, 141
  test intervals for, 129
Polynomial function, 114

Leading Coefficient Test, 126
real zeros of, 128
standard form, 129
of x with degree n, 114
x-intercept of the graph of, 128
zeros of, 128
Position equation, 494
Positive
angle, 262
infinity, A4
Power, A13
of a complex number, 444
Power property
of logarithms, 222, 258
of natural logarithms, 222, 258
Power-reducing formulas, 384, 397
Powers of integers, sums of, 640
Prime
factor of a polynomial, 159
factorization, A10
number, A10
polynomial, A28
quadratic factor, 159
Principal nth root
of a, A17
of a number, A17
Principal square root of a negative
number, 151
Principle of Mathematical Induction, 635
Extended, 636
Probability
of a complement, 669
of an event, 663
of independent events, 668
of the union of two events, 666
Producer surplus, 513
Product
of functions, 76
of trigonometric functions, 382
triple scalar, 792
of two complex numbers, 442
Product property
of logarithms, 222, 258
of natural logarithms, 222, 258
Product-to-sum formulas, 386
Projection of a vector, 434
Proof, 110
by contradiction, 534
indirect, 534
without words, 602
Proper rational expression, 139
Properties
of absolute value, A6
of the dot product, 431, 462
of equality, A9
of exponents, A13
of fractions, A10
of inequalities, A59
inverse, of trigonometric functions, 324
of limits, 819
of logarithms, 212, 222, 258
inverse, 212

one-to-one, 212
power, 222, 258
product, 222, 258
quotient, 222, 258
of matrix addition and scalar
multiplication, 554
of matrix multiplication, 558
of natural logarithms, 216, 222, 258
inverse, 216
one-to-one, 216
power, 222, 258
product, 222, 258
quotient, 222, 258
of negation, A9
one-to-one, exponential functions, 202
of radicals, A18
reflective, of a parabola, 698
of sums, 610, 682
of vector addition and scalar
multiplication, 421
of zero, A9
Proportional
directly, 95
to the nth power, 96
inversely, 97
jointly, 99
Proportionality, constant of, 95
Pure imaginary number, 147
Pythagorean identities, 282, 350
Pythagorean Theorem, 4, 346

Q
Quadrants, 2
Quadratic equation, 13, A48
complex solutions of, 151
general form of, A49
solving
by completing the square, A48
by extracting square roots, A48
by factoring, A48
using the Quadratic Formula, A48
using the Square Root Principle,
A48
Quadratic factor
prime, 159
repeated, 504
Quadratic Formula, A48
Quadratic function, 114
maximum value, 119
minimum value, 119
standard form of, 117
Quadratic type equations, 367
Quick tests for symmetry in polar
coordinates, 749
Quotient
difference, 42, 649, A41
of functions, 76
of two complex numbers, 442
Quotient identities, 282, 350
Quotient property
of logarithms, 222, 258
of natural logarithms, 222, 258

R
Radian, 263
conversion to degrees, 265
Radian measure formula, 266
Radical(s)
equation, A53
errors involving, A68
index of, A17
like, A19
properties of, A18
simplest form, A19
symbol, A17
Radicand, A17
Radius of a circle, 17
Random selection
with replacement, 652
without replacement, 652
Range
of the cosine function, 275
of a function, 35, 43
of the sine function, 275
Rate, 28
Rate of change, 28
average, 54
Ratio, 28
Rational equation, A47
Rational exponent, A21
Rational expression(s), A35
improper, 139
proper, 139
Rational function, 168
asymptotes of, 170
domain of, 168
graphing, guidelines, 171
hole in the graph, 173
test intervals for, 171
Rational inequality, 184
test intervals, 184
Rational number, A1
Rational Zero Test, 155
Rationalizing
a denominator, 360, A19, A20
a numerator, A21
Real axis of the complex plane, 440
Real number(s), A1
absolute value of, A5
classifying, A1
division of, A8
subset of, A1
subtraction of, A8
Real number line, A2
bounded intervals on, A4
distance between two points, A6
interval on, A4
order on, A3
origin of, A2
plotting on, A2
unbounded intervals on, A4
Real part of a complex number, 147
Real zeros of a polynomial function, 128
Reciprocal function, 62
Reciprocal identities, 282, 350

Rectangular coordinate system, 2
Rectangular coordinates, conversion to
    polar, 743
Recursion formula, 618
Recursive sequence, 608
Reduced row-echelon form of a matrix,
    542
Reducible over the reals, 159
Reduction formulas, 377
Reference angle, 292
Reflection, 69
    of a trigonometric function, 302
Reflective property of a parabola, 698
Regression, least squares
    line, 94, 486
    parabola, 498
Relation, 35
Relative maximum, 53
Relative minimum, 53
Remainder Theorem, 142, 195
Repeated linear factor, 502
Repeated quadratic factor, 504
Repeated zero, 128
Representation
    of functions, 36
    of matrices, 551
Resultant of vector addition, 420
Right triangle
    adjacent side of, 279
    definitions of trigonometric functions,
        279
    hypotenuse of, 279
    opposite side of, 279
    solving, 284
Rigid transformations, 71
Root(s)
    of a complex number, 445, 446
    cube, A17
    nth, A17
    principal nth, A17
    square, A17
Rose curve, 750, 751
    petal of, 750
Rotation
    of axes, 723
        to eliminate an xy-term, 723
    invariants, 727
Row matrix, 538
    coded, 588
    uncoded, 588
Row operations, 489
    elementary, 540
Row-echelon form, 488
    of a matrix, 542
        reduced, 542
Row-equivalent matrices, 540
Rules of signs for fractions, A10

S

Sample space, 662
Satisfy the inequality, A58

Scalar, 420, 552
    multiple, 552
Scalar Identity Property for matrices, 554
Scalar multiplication
    of matrices, 552
        properties of, 554
    of a vector, 420
        properties of, 421
Scaling factor, 301
Scatter plot, 3
Scientific notation, A16
Scribner Log Rule, 474
Secant function, 273, 279
    of any angle, 290
    graph of, 313, 316
Secant line, 54
Second, fractional part of a degree, 265
Second differences, 641
Second-degree polynomial equation, A48
Sector of a circle, 268
    area of, 268
Sequence, 606
    arithmetic, 616
    Fibonacci, 608
    finite, 606
    first differences of, 641
    geometric, 625
    infinite, 606
    nth partial sum of, 611
    recursive, 608
    second differences of, 641
    terms of, 606
Series, 611
    finite, 611
    geometric, 629
    infinite, 611
        geometric, 629
Shifting graphs, 67
Shrink
    horizontal, 71
    vertical, 71
Sierpinski Triangle, 686
Sigma notation, 610
Sigmoidal curve, 243
Simple harmonic motion, 333
    frequency, 333
Simplest form, of an expression involving
    radicals, A19
Sine curve, 299
    amplitude of, 301
    one cycle of, 299
Sine function, 273, 279
    of any angle, 290
    common angles, 293
    domain of, 275
    graph of, 303, 316
    inverse, 320, 322
    period of, 302
    range of, 275
    special angles, 281
Sines, cosines, and tangents of special
    angles, 281

Singular matrix, 566
Sketching the graph of an inequality in
    two variables, 508
Slant asymptote, 174
Slope
    and inclination, 688, 768
    of a line, 22, 24
Slope-intercept form of the equation of a
    line, 22, 30
Solution(s), 11
    of an absolute value inequality, A62
    of an equation, 11, A45
    extraneous, A47, A53
    feasible, 518
    of an inequality, 508, A58
    infinitely many, A46
    of a linear programming problem,
        optimal, 518
    of a linear system, number of, 491
    no, A46
    of a polynomial equation, 128
    of a quadratic equation, complex, 151
    of a system of equations, 466
        graphical interpretations, 480
    of a system of inequalities, 510
        solution set, 510
Solution point, 11
Solution set
    of an inequality, A58
    of a system of inequalities, 510
Solving
    an absolute value inequality, A62
    the basic equation of a partial fraction
        decomposition, 505
    an equation, A45
    exponential and logarithmic equations,
        228
    an inequality, A58
    a linear programming problem, 518
    a polynomial inequality, 181
    a quadratic equation
        by completing the square, A48
        by extracting square roots, A48
        by factoring, A48
        using the Quadratic Formula, A48
        using the Square Root Principle, A48
    a rational inequality, 184
    right triangles, 284
    a system of equations, 466
        Cramer's Rule, 582, 583
        Gaussian elimination, 489, 490
            with back-substitution, 544
        Gauss-Jordan elimination, 545
        graphical method, 470
        method of elimination, 476, 477
        method of substitution, 466
    a trigonometric equation, 364
Special angles
    cosines of, 281
    sines of, 281
    tangents of, 281
Special products, A27

Speed
   angular, 266
   linear, 266
Square
   of a binomial, A27
   of trigonometric functions, 382
Square matrix, 538
   determinant of, 574, 577
   diagonal, 581
   idempotent, 603
   main diagonal entries of, 538
   minors and cofactors of, 576
Square root(s), A17
   extracting, A48
   function, 62
   of a negative number, 151
   principal, of a negative number, 151
Square Root Principle, A48
Square system of linear equations, 493,
      570
Squaring function, 61
Standard form
   of a complex number, 147
   of the equation
      of a circle, 17
      of an ellipse, 705
      of a hyperbola, 714
      of a parabola, 696, 769
   of Law of Cosines, 411, 460
   of a polynomial, A25
   of a polynomial function, 129
   of a quadratic function, 117
Standard position
   of an angle, 262
   of a vector, 419
Standard unit vector, 422
Step function, 63
Stochastic matrix, 564
Straight-line depreciation, 29
Strategies for solving exponential and
      logarithmic equations, 228
Stretch
   horizontal, 71
   vertical, 71
Strophoid, 772
Subsets, A1
Substitution, method of, 466
Substitution Principle, A7
Subtraction
   of complex numbers, 148
   of fractions
      with like denominators, A10
      with unlike denominators, A10
   of matrices, 553
   of real numbers, A8
Sum(s)
   of complex numbers, 148
   of a finite arithmetic sequence, 619, 683
   of a finite geometric sequence, 628, 683
      of functions, 76
   of an infinite geometric series, 629
   nth partial, 611, 620

   of powers of integers, 640
   properties of, 610, 682
   of square differences, 94
   of two cubes, A29
   of vectors, 420
Sum and difference formulas, 375, 396
Sum and difference of same terms, A27
Summary
   of equations of lines, 30
   of function terminology, 43
Summation
   index of, 610
   lower limit of, 610
   notation, 610
   upper limit of, 610
Sum-to-product formulas, 386, 398
Supplementary angles, 264
Surplus
   consumer, 513
   producer, 513
Symbol
   "approximately equal to," A1
   inequality, A3
   radical, A17
   union, A62
Symmetry, 15
   algebraic tests for, 15
   axis of, of a parabola, 115
   graphical tests for, 15
   in polar coordinates, tests for, 748, 749
   with respect to the origin, 15
   with respect to the x-axis, 15
   with respect to the y-axis, 15
Synthetic division, 141
System of equations, 466
   equivalent, 478, 489
   solution of, 466
   solving, 466
   with a unique solution, 570
System of inequalities, solution of, 510
   solution set, 510
System of linear equations
   consistent, 480
   dependent, 480
   inconsistent, 480, 544
   independent, 480
   nonsquare, 493
   number of solutions, 491
   row operations, 489
   row-echelon form, 488
   square, 493, 570

T

Tangent function, 273, 279
   of any angle, 290
   common angles, 293
   graph of, 310, 316
   inverse, 322
   special angles, 281
Tangent line to a parabola, 698
Term

   of an algebraic expression, A7
   coefficient of, A25
   constant, A7, A25
   degree of, A25
   of a sequence, 606
   variable, A7
Terminal point, 418
Terminal side of an angle, 262
Terms, inserting factors and, A70
Test(s)
   for collinear points, 586
   Horizontal Line, 87
   Leading Coefficient, 126
   Rational Zero, 155
   for symmetry
      algebraic, 15
      graphical, 15
      in polar coordinates, 748, 749
   Vertical Line, 50
Test intervals
   polynomial, 129
   polynomial inequality, 180
   rational function, 171
   rational inequality, 184
Theorem
   of Algebra, Fundamental, 154
   of Arithmetic, Fundamental, A10
   Binomial, 644, 684
   DeMoivre's, 444
   Descartes's Rule of Signs, 161
   existence, 154
   Factor, 143, 195
   Intermediate Value, 131
   Linear Factorization, 154, 196
   Pythagorean, 4, 346
   Remainder, 142, 195
Thrust, 464
Transcendental function, 200
Transformations of functions, 67
   nonrigid, 71
   rigid, 71
Transpose of a matrix, 603
Transverse axis of a hyperbola, 713
Triangle
   area of
      using a determinant, 585
      Heron's Area Formula, 414, 461
   oblique, 402
      area of, 406
Trigonometric equations, solving, 364
Trigonometric form of a complex
      number, 441
   argument of, 441
   modulus of, 441
Trigonometric functions, 273, 279, 290
   of any angle, 290
      evaluating, 293
   cosecant, 273, 279, 290
   cosine, 273, 279, 290
   cotangent, 273, 279, 290
   even, 276
   horizontal shrink of, 302

horizontal stretch of, 302
horizontal translation of, 303
inverse, 322
inverse properties of, 324
key points, 300
    intercepts, 300
    maximum points, 300
    minimum points, 300
odd, 276
product of, 382
reflection of, 302
right triangle definitions of, 279
secant, 273, 279, 290
sine, 273, 279, 290
square of, 382
tangent, 273, 279, 290
unit circle definitions of, 273
vertical shrink of, 301
vertical stretch of, 301
vertical translation of, 304
Trigonometric identities
cofunction, 350
even/odd, 350
fundamental, 282, 350
guidelines for verifying, 357
Pythagorean, 282, 350
quotient, 282, 350
reciprocal, 282, 350
Trigonometric values of common angles, 293
Trigonometry, 262
Trinomial, A25
perfect square, A29, A30
Two-point form of the equation of a line, 26, 30, 587

U

Unbounded intervals, A4
Uncoded row matrices, 588
Undefined, 43
Union symbol, A62
Union of two events, probability of, 666
Unit circle, 272
definitions of trigonometric functions, 273
Unit vector, 419
in the direction of **v**, 422
standard, 422
Unity, nth roots of, 446
Unusual factoring, A69
Upper bound, 162
Upper limit of summation, 610
Upper and Lower Bound Rules, 162

V

Value of a function, 37, 43
Variable, A7
dependent, 37, 43
independent, 37, 43
term, A7
Variation
combined, 98
constant of, 95
direct, 95
    as an nth power, 96
inverse, 97
joint, 99
in sign, 161
Vary directly, 95
    as nth power, 96
Vary inversely, 97
Vary jointly, 99
Vector(s), 418
addition of, 420
    properties of, 421
    resultant of, 420
angle between two, 432, 462
component form of, 419
components of, 419, 434
difference of, 420
directed line segment representation, 418
direction angle of, 424
dot product of, 431
    properties of, 431, 462
equal, 419
horizontal component of, 422
length of, 419
linear combination of, 422
magnitude of, 419
negative of, 420
orthogonal, 433
parallelogram law, 420
perpendicular, 433
in the plane, 418
projection of, 434
resultant of, 420
scalar multiplication of, 420
    properties of, 421
standard position of, 419
sum of, 420
unit, 419
    in the direction of **v**, 422
    standard, 422
v in the plane, 418
vertical component of, 422
zero, 419
Vertex (vertices)
of an angle, 262

of an ellipse, 704
    of a hyperbola, 713
    of a parabola, 115, 696
Vertical asymptote, 169
    of a rational function, 170
Vertical component of **v**, 422
Vertical line, 22, 30
Vertical Line Test, 50
Vertical shifts, 67
Vertical shrink, 71
    of a trigonometric function, 301
Vertical stretch, 71
    of a trigonometric function, 301
Vertical translation of a trigonometric function, 304
Volume, common formulas for, A55

W

Wedge, infinite, 512
Whole numbers, A1
With replacement, 652
Without replacement, 652
Work, 437
Writing
a fraction as a sum, A69
with negative exponents, A69

X

x-axis, 2
symmetric with respect to, 15
x-coordinate, 2
x-intercepts
finding, 14
of the graph of a polynomial function, 128

Y

y-axis, 2
symmetric with respect to, 15
y-coordinate, 2
y-intercepts, finding, 14

Z

Zero(s)
of a function, 51
matrix, 555
multiplicity of, 128
of a polynomial function, 128
    bounds for, 162
    real, 128
properties of, A9
repeated, 128
vector, 419
Zero polynomial, A25
Zero-Factor Property, A9

WebAssign Student Quick Start Guide

You can use WebAssign to access your homework, quizzes, and tests — whatever your instructor chooses — at any time of day or night, from any computer with a connection to the Internet and a Web browser. Your instructor creates your assignments, schedules them, and decides how many submissions you get. Your instructor also determines if you can have an extension, if you can save your work without submitting it at the time, and how much feedback you get after you submit an assignment.

The WebAssign support staff cannot change your username or password, give extensions, change your score, give you extra submissions, or help you with the content of your assignments.

Logging In
You can log in to WebAssign using any Web browser connected to the Internet. There are two different ways to log in to WebAssign. Each requires information from your teacher. If you are unsure about how to log in, please check with your teacher or another student in your class.

Go to the login page at http://webassign.net/login.html or the web address provided by your teacher. The way you log in depends on how your instructor set up the class:

- If your teacher created a WebAssign account for you, they will provide you with a **Username**, an **Institution** code and a **Password**. Simply enter this information in the boxes provided and click the **Log In** button.

Web**Assign**.

- If your teacher wants you to **Self-Enroll** in the WebAssign course they will provide you with a **Class Key**. You will create your own username and password. It is important that you remember this information so you can log in for the remainder of the class. In this case, just click the **I have a Class Key** button. You don't need to enter any other information on this page.

  Then, enter the **Class Key** your instructor provided and click **Submit**. Verify you are enrolling in the correct class on the next page.

Class Key

Enter the Class Key that you received from your instructor. You will only need to complete this once. After you have created your account, you can log in on the main page.

Class Key

[_____] [_____] [_____]

Class Keys generally start with an institution code, followed by two sets of four digits.

[Submit]

- Enter your preferred Login and Student information.

- Click the **Create My Account** button to complete the enrollment process.

- A review screen will display, showing your username, institution code, and password. **Retain a copy of this information.** You will need it to log into WebAssign.

Log In Information

Required fields are marked with an asterisk (*).

Preferred Username	* [_____]	[Check Availability]
	Your username may contain letters, numbers, and the following characters: underscore (_), hyphen (-), period (.)	
Institution Code	**webassign**	
Password	* [_____]	
Re-Enter Password	* [_____]	
	Passwords are case-sensitive.	

Student Information

Required fields are marked with an asterisk (*).

First Name	* [_____]
Last Name	* [_____]
Email Address	* [_____]
Student ID Number	[_____]

[Create My Account]

Access Codes

Once you log in, you may see a WebAssign Notice about entering an access code for your class. You can get an Access Code from any of the following places if you need to use one:

- A new textbook you purchased for the class.
- Your bookstore, which may sell Access Code cards.
- Online, where you can purchase an access code with a credit card.

You have a 14 day grace period to use WebAssign, starting with the WebAssign class start date. During this time you can work on and view your WebAssign assignments without registering a code.

After the grace period is over you will only see the code registration message until you submit or purchase a code.

There are two types of WebAssign access code cards. The small card requires you to scratch off the silver surface in order to reveal the complete access code.

Web**Assign**.

The larger security envelope card requires you to open the card to reveal the access code number.

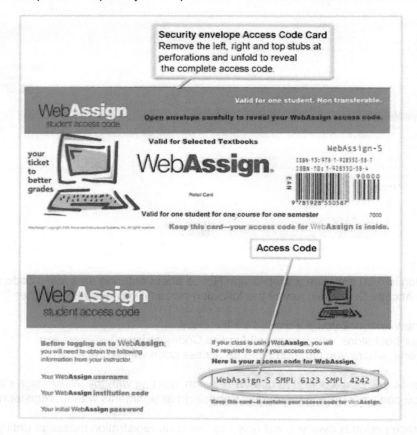

If you would like to purchase an access code directly from WebAssign online, you may do so with a credit card. Your code will be automatically registered to your WebAssign account as soon as the transaction is complete. You will receive an email confirmation. Please keep a copy for your records.

WebAssign

Your WebAssign Home Page

Once you have successfully logged in you will see your WebAssign homepage. If you are taking more than one WebAssign class, you will need to select which class you wish to view first.

The upper right corner features links to a complete Student **Guide**, as well as a link to WebAssign Technical Support under **Help**. If you want to change your password or add or update your email address, simply click **My Options** in the upper right hand corner.

You will see your assignments and due dates listed, as well as any Communications, Grades, and Announcements posted by your teacher.

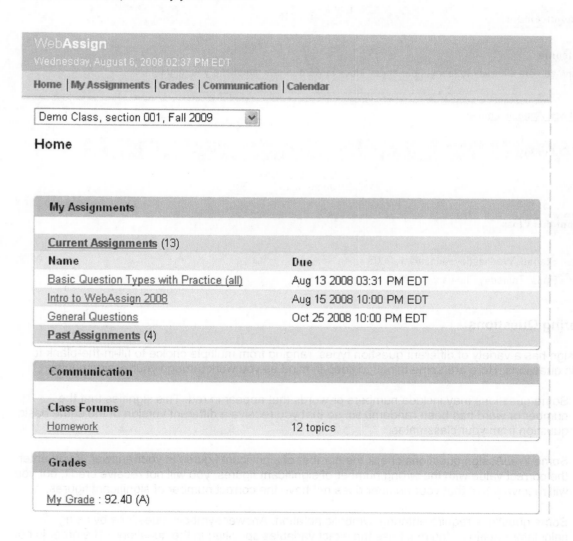

WebAssign.

David Thomson
Instructor: John Smith
Demo school

Announcements

Welcome
I hope you are all ready to learn in our class. I look forward to any questions you might have.

Archived Announcements

My Calendar

Jump to...

About this Class

Class Started: Wednesday, January 1, 2003

Class Ends: Thursday, January 14, 2010

Answering Questions

WebAssign has a variety of different question types, ranging from multiple choice to fill-in-the-blank to symbolic questions. Here are some things to keep in mind as you work through your assignments:

- Some questions may include numbers or words that appear in red. This signifies that the number or word has been randomized, so that you receive a different version of the same basic question from your classmates.

- Some WebAssign questions check the number of significant figures in your answer. If you enter the correct value with the wrong number of significant figures, you will not receive credit, but you will receive a hint that your number does not have the correct number of significant figures.

- Some questions require entering symbolic notation. Answer symbolic questions by using calculator notation. You must use the exact variables specified in the questions. The order is not important as long as it is mathematically correct. Clicking on the eye button previews the expression you enter in proper mathematical notation. Clicking on the symbolic formatting help button provides tips for using the correct keystrokes.

WebAssign.

- When you click on some WebAssign chemistry or math questions an input palette will open. These palettes, called chemPad and mathPad, will help you enter your answer in proper notation.

- Some questions may require the use of an Active Figure simulation. Active Figures require the free Macromedia Flash Player plug-in, downloadable from www.macromedia.com.

- If your instructor allows it, you can save your work without grading by selecting the Save Work button at the end of the question. After you save your work, it will be available to you the next time you click the assignment.

- Please note that WebAssign will **not** automatically submit your answers for scoring if you only **Save** your work. Your teacher will not be able to see your submissions. Please be sure to **Submit** prior to the due date and time.

- If your instructor allows it, you can submit answers by question part or for the entire assignment. To submit an individual question answer for grading, click the **Submit New Answers to Question __** button at the bottom of each question. To submit the entire assignment for grading, click the **Submit All New Answers** button at the end of the assignment.

Technical Support

If you are having difficulty logging in, please be sure to check with your teacher and verify whether an account has been created for you or whether you need to self-enroll. In either case your teacher needs to provide the appropriate information (username, institution code and password OR Class Key).

To email WebAssign Support go to http://www.webassign.net/info/support/report.html. This page also lists answers to **Common Problems**, and provides links to the **Student Guide**.

August 7, 2008